81st CONGRESS, 2D SESSION

HOUSE DOCUMENT No. 691

THE YEARBOOK OF AGRICULTURE

1950-1951

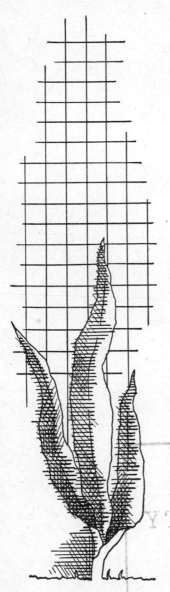

Crops
in Peace
and War

THE YEARBOOK OF
AGRICULTURE
1950–1951

United States
Department of Agriculture
Washington, D. C.

UNITED STATES GOVERNMENT PRINTING OFFICE

EVERY AMERICAN can be proud of the accomplishments described in this book. Proud, yes, but more than that in this challenging age. Thankful, as well, for the benefits they bring in time of peace and for the contributions they make as we mobilize for defense. They exemplify how and why free men work in a free society.

For these accomplishments sprang from vision and dedication to the public welfare. They developed through the cooperation of many persons—Congressmen, who vote the necessary authority and recognize that farmers and farming are as much a part of this age of science as the rest of our economy; scientists in State, Federal, and industrial laboratories; processors, consumers, manufacturers, and taxpayers. These achievements are helping greatly to strengthen the foundations of our agriculture, a fact of importance in these days when expanded production is needed for national defense. They point a way to steadier incomes for farmers. They have led to the establishment of new industries and the enlargement of others. They have added to everyone's comfort and health. They have shown ways to make wiser use of our abundance and to utilize what once was wasted.

They have saved or earned millions of dollars; they have contributed to national well-being to an extent that cannot be measured in money. Yet they cost comparatively little—much less than one might think.

They did not just happen. They were born of planning and hard work. Many of them look like miracles, but actually they are the expected outcome of basic and applied research and steady progress toward a foreseen goal. They are not static; they and the sciences that produced them move forward always, sometimes at measured pace, sometimes (as in the fast tempo of wartime) at great acceleration. To be of utmost value, research must reflect the kaleidoscopic changes in new opportunities presented by new tools of science.

We can use the vision and cooperation behind

research to achieve our immediate goals of national mobilization and the ultimate goals of improved living in a long-envisioned era of international amity and peace. As research moves forward, we will need to apply the advances to changing national and international patterns. Our agriculture will use them to produce abundant supplies of specified foods and fibers to supply our Armed Forces and civilians and to provide food for hungry people elsewhere. Our processors and distributors of food will be alert to apply the advances to serve better the growing population.

As we strengthen the free-world pattern of preparedness by these findings, we open the way to still further accomplishments for all men in the years to come. What we already have achieved is truly a matter both for pride and thankfulness, but what we may achieve on today's foundation holds even greater promise for tomorrow.

CHARLES F. BRANNAN.

THE EDITOR

TO THE READER

FOR NEARLY a hundred years the Yearbooks and annual reports of the Department of Agriculture have offered farmers information on how to produce more—how to grow two blades of grass where one grew before.

This Yearbook extends that purpose and group of readers. It deals with that second blade, and so reflects the changes in the scope of American farming. Now, ranking almost alongside production as the main function of agriculture are such factors as the marketing of farm goods, finding industrial uses for some, the interplay of price and demand, our changing preferences in foods, the care of the farm plant, and international forces of conflict and diplomacy, which can make dried eggs (for example) a vital need one year and a surplus the next year.

This book touches the phases of those factors that pertain to our central theme, the uses of farm products in peace and war. We tell all we could get between two covers about what happens to agricultural goods after they leave the farm. We set forth the possibilities of using surplus products in new ways, for this is largely a report of work in four laboratories whose establishment Congress authorized in 1938 to study such possibilities.

Modern farmers, who are as aware of happenings in Washington and Beltsville and Oak Ridge as their grandfathers were aware of happenings in the nearest crossroads trading center, are interested in our subject. They will find here practical information that they can use in planning their operations to take advantage of shifts in demand and need for their products.

But we have had something else in mind, too. We seek to help farmers by indicating to nonfarmers the extent and limitations of present and possible uses of farm products. Thus we address ourselves also to processors and consumers: Makers and users of plastics, cloth, drugs, insecticides, ice cream, and a thousand other items; housewives, restaurateurs, and others who prepare and sell food; sellers and users of oils, fats, and animal products; businessmen and brokers, students of applied sciences. We give something of a background for the products of the laboratory that are being announced every day. So fast does science move these days that we could not give it all; a key to a door, not the whole house, is presented here.

This book was originally intended to be issued in 1950, but a second edition of *Grass,* the 1948 Yearbook, was requested by the Congress to take the place of a new volume in 1950. Consequently this book is dated 1950–1951.

During the time we were working on this book, many aspects of the work changed and changed again—problems of printing, the emphasis given this or that project, the prices and stocks of commodities, crop programs. Almost overnight we all but stopped using a very common word—surplus.

But the premise we started with survived the changes pretty well: Come what may, it is wise to give attention to the better use of the products of the soil. With only secondary thoughts in 1949 of world events, we found ourselves turning to developments in the Second World War to stress the importance of a crop or a process at any time, in war or peace. The word *war* in our title refers to that war.

In a few months, also, figures of production changed considerably, but we thought that average or "normal" figures would present a truer long-range picture, although they might seem outdated, than would later figures that reflect the strains of 1951.

Because of the different types of interest and groups of readers to whom we address ourselves, we have tried to make every chapter self-contained and self-explanatory, even at the cost of much duplication and repetitions of facts and definitions in the various parts of the book.

Our drawings were made by Elmo White, of the Office of Information, or under his direction.

ALFRED STEFFERUD.

CONTENTS

This Is the Challenge

These Are the Tools

Nature Has a Part

Food or Feed or Fabric

Starch Has Many Uses

Potatoes

Vegetables and Some Fruit

CONTENTS

continued

Sugar, Honey, and Maple

Crops of the Field

Fibers From Cotton

Natural and Man-Made Fibers

Oilseeds, Oils, and Fats

CONTENTS

continued

Proteins Are Basic

Meat, Poultry, Eggs

Milk: Food for All

Hides, Skins, Leather

To Keep Us Well

Crops From the Forest

CONTENTS

continued

Waste Not, Want Not

THIS IS THE CHALLENGE

Science in the Agriculture of Tomorrow

R. W. Trullinger

Let us recognize that our agricultural industry is gradually becoming a big food- and fiber-production business. American farming has become more than just a way of life. Agriculture is operating on a gradually shrinking number of farm units. Against a drop of nearly a million farm units since 1935 is a considerable rise in the average size of the individual farm. Several factors and conditions can account for the change. The major impelling factor appears to be the need for greater efficiency in the production of larger yields of food and fiber of higher quality—this despite the further fact that fewer and fewer people are engaged in farming. In 1945 one farm worker produced enough food and fiber to clothe and feed himself and 14 other persons. He produced twice as much as did one farm worker 50 years ago.

The upsurge of efforts to develop better procedures of marketing and distribution during the past few years seems to accept the fact that large-volume production is here to stay. Everything is geared for mass production on a big-business scale, and it would be difficult to believe that the agricultural industry of today will voluntarily revert to last-generation methods and practices. Efficiency is of paramount importance in farming now. We can expect that future years will intensify it.

In wartime, when technology moves faster, efficiency becomes even more vital. The fruits of many previous years of research and a stepped-up program of research to meet the farmers' wartime needs helped produce the record crops that helped us to victory in the Second World War. Since then, agricultural research and its application have advanced even more rapidly. As a result, the Nation has reasonable assurance that its farm plant can meet the needs of a population that has grown by 18 million in the past decade and at the same time satisfy our greater international obligations.

Agriculture is not only a mechanical industry. It is one in which biology plays a major part. It is so dynamic biologically as to permit of relatively little human control. When we recognize that fact, we begin to appreciate the importance of science in our agricultural operations. Scientific research and its counterpart, the application of the findings of research to farming, are the core of our agricultural technology. This technology has brought rapid changes. Daily the numbers of mechanized farm units have increased. With the help of soil science, plant breeding, and the other scientific services made available by their agricultural institutions, American farmers have made astounding progress. But with new technologies come new problems. New practices constantly force adjustments in customs and ways of life.

The symptoms are recognized as we move along. Farmers expect their research institutions to find the answers, both for the everyday, lesser problems and for the big ones that have no chance of being solved by the single, isolated research approach.

WE HAVE only so much land on which to produce crops and livestock. Improved varieties of crops have been developed, the yields from which are far beyond yields of the same crops in previous years. Soils have been put under terrific strain in the process, and lands have gone out of production for one crop and gone into production for another. Some lands have been abandoned altogether through misuse.

Others not previously used have come into production, either wisely or unwisely. But the fact remains that we have only a certain acreage of agricultural or potentially agricultural land available in the United States. This, in the face of a steadily increasing population, makes one thing sure: Future research must, above all, keep in mind the need to feed and clothe more and more people from a limited over-all acreage. The problems of land use, therefore, become paramount. They call for the best of scientific approaches.

Surpluses and how to dispose of them with a minimum of loss will probably always constitute a problem. History indicates that George Washington and Thomas Jefferson and other prominent farmers of this country had to struggle with surpluses. Adequate distribution and marketing mechanisms always have been and probably always will be a foremost need. Certainly a reasonable part of our research effort will have to be devoted to this need, now and in the future. Such research not only helps prevent loss for farmer-producers, but it serves to get adequate amounts of food and fiber to the places where they are needed and where they can be used most effectively. As a people we would much rather see surpluses of food and fiber than to be confronted with terrible shortages of these necessities of life. Many people on this earth, even some within the limits of our continent, frequently go undernourished and ill-

clad. I well remember that when I was a farm boy, big crops meant that we were comfortable and well-fed, even though the prices of corn, hogs, and beef cattle went down. But crop failures were usually accompanied on a wide front by hunger and misery. Research appears the best way out of either a surplus or an undersupply situation.

WITHOUT INTELLIGENTLY planned research and more efficient production, people in the United States could be faced by widespread crop failures in the not too distant future. We are feeding and clothing more people than ever. Fewer people are working at the job of farming. Our productive resources have been overworked and strained. We are taking all kinds of risks with our resources so as to attain big production. It would be a new and harrowing experience for this great country to be filled with hordes of hungry people struggling for existence. That should never happen. It can be prevented if our powers of deductive reasoning, as they relate to the maintenance and constant development and improvement of our productive resources, are supported and encouraged.

That means that we must utilize the best and most modern scientific principles and techniques. We must devise ways and means to conserve our existing and potential resources of soil, water, plants, and animals, and to conserve and maintain our facilities and resources for future production.

WE KNOW A LOT about the soil. We know that it is a dynamic substance, alive and constantly changing. Our research scientists have identified the ultimate particle size of soil that is considered to be the nucleus of soil energy.

Only slow, natural processes have been able in the past to release this energy in amounts and at rates dictated by Nature. Probably this has been a good thing when one considers what might happen as a result of heavy fertilization and cultural treatments or other practices if Nature did not put on the brakes. One predominantly agricultural State, for example, produced immense crops during the war by use of improved crop varieties and excessively heavy fertilization. After a few years, however, the productive level of the soils of that State began to go down, despite continued heavy fertilization and cultural treatment. What happened? No one knows—except that Nature rebelled. But the soil scientists of the experiment station in the State are starting from scratch to get the answer.

That is not an unusual occurrence. It is being met in many areas and apparently for a multitude of reasons. In my own experience, I learned that a tractor with one bad spark plug can play havoc with the productive level of certain soils. Some of our advanced technologies also have created new and difficult problems. We thought we knew all about the soil, how to maintain its fertility and level of productivity for crops. We know enough now to recognize that under normal conditions soil accumulates and stores energy and releases it in crop production through some strange mechanism, the exact nature of which we apparently do not yet know nor do we know how to control it. The phenomenon of photosynthesis, which involves the manufacture of a still strange substance named chlorophyll, apparently essential to plant prosperity, is largely a scientific secret.

All those points are factors involved in assuring greater precision in the production of the right kinds of food and fiber from the soil, if we can only learn their basic mechanisms and how we can manipulate them constructively without destroying them or the basic resources on which they depend. The future of agriculture presents the need to find out about all these factors and how to assemble them with all the new technologies into a workable whole.

WE TALK glibly about the sun's rays in relation to the total energy needed to grow a food crop. Yet what do we actually know about the basic mechanism involved in utilization of the sun's energy? And how might we improve on such use and thereby possibly conserve our more tangible resources of energy? What do we know about the possible influence of the sun on the ability of rain water to expedite plant growth? We have many laboratory techniques that use elements of the solar spectrum. But what have we accomplished with the sun beyond that? What do we know about cosmic rays? What do we know about many things affecting the relationship between the natural elements and their ways of expression and the sustained productive capacity of the soil for food crops of both plant and animal form? We have developed improved crops that increase yields. What have these increases in yield done to the total supply of available productive energy and how may we balance income and outgo of energy when we grow a bigger and better crop on the same area of land?

Crops include livestock forage and feeds and food consumed directly by human beings. In the face of the growing need for more food by a growing population to be produced from the same over-all land area, the unit nutritive value of that food must always be kept in mind. We have learned much in recent years about the nutritive value of foods and feeds. We know that through some strange mechanism their nutritive properties can be influenced by soil management and treatment and by development of the crops themselves through the application of the principles of fertilization, genetics, and breeding. There is much that we do not know about these phenomena, but research scientists are finding out a little more every day.

EVERY FOOD and feed crop is subject to vicious attack by diseases and insects, which seem to be increasing in number and destructiveness.

Virus diseases of food crops are one of the most baffling types of research problems. For a long time research scientists have had to be satisfied with what amounted to circumstantial evidence as to the character and activity of the diseases. Much progress has been made through the development and use of new and improved techniques. These include, particularly, better aids to vision; among them is the electron microscope. So far, however, virus diseases have been overcome mainly through breeding resistant varieties of crops. This takes a long time.

How long will it be before some scientist will develop ways and means of treating infected plants, or of preventing disease infection by treating the plants with vaccines or by some other effective method? Probably not until a lot more is learned about these things through a type of research not now written in the books. Years ago some farsighted scientist dreamed of this possibility and some still are working at it. They or their successors will undoubtedly sometime accomplish the objective. Give them encouragement.

In the 41 years since I joined the staff of the Office of Experiment Stations, I have sat many a time in conferences and hearings that took up the pros and cons of fundamental research.

Some people raise questions about what they choose to term the proper relationship between fundamental or basic research and applied research. I take the stand, disputed by many, that all research is basic—or else it is not true research. I do firmly believe that future agricultural research will bear this out. Perhaps in the earlier years of agricultural research too much effort was devoted to superficial experimentation that did not always result in the establishment of permanent scientifically sound facts. But in more recent years, and particularly since agriculture has become a big business, operating with business methods, agricultural research agencies have had of necessity to employ the best of scientifically trained minds and the most modern of the scientific principles and techniques.

That has been in full recognition of the need for doing in research everything possible to solve the problems of agriculture as they are encountered. It will be intensified as the agricultural situation in this country becomes more acute under increased population pressure.

I agree that research should be of the kind that can be applied to get some desirable result. But research is a constant pushing forward of the frontiers of knowledge. Our scope of information today must constantly shrink in the light of developments tomorrow. To do their best work, therefore, research workers must have freedom.

As far back as 1937, a young geneticist at the Iowa Agricultural Experiment Station undertook, with a Federal grant, a project on radiation effects on biological substances. Questions were raised as to whether the information he would derive from the project might eventually be of practical value to agriculture. The young man showed that the information he was after might lead to man's ability to modify or control the behavior or transmission of genes or virus in a way that would lead to the improvement of plants and animals or the control of virus disease. We know today how practical was his approach for plant breeding and disease control. It has paid out a thousandfold. The leader of that pioneer project now heads the department of genetics at Iowa State College. Under contract with the Atomic Energy Commission, his department is engaged in extensive investigations of the effects of radiant energy on plant and animal life. The studies include research on the well-being and life expectancy of mammals exposed to irradiation and their progeny. A subject that was extremely abstract in 1937 has some very practical applications to humanity in 1951.

The agricultural research scientist of today must therefore be equipped by training and experience to cope with any and all scientific emergencies as they arise in his part of the big field of agriculture. He must be schooled in the elements of cooperative research, because the broad problems of today's agriculture rarely can be solved by a single research department. The situation is becoming more evident daily. Broad and thorough training in the basic sciences of mathematics, physics, chemistry, and thermodynamics seems to be as important in one segment of agriculture as in another. I was impressed by the remark of a former president of the American Society of Agricultural Engineers, a leader in research and teaching in agricultural engineering for a generation: "We have just one science." How true this statement becomes when one delves into the character of the problems facing agriculture today and tomorrow!

I can say with certainty that there is no recognized limit to the knowledge of science that we must have to cope fully with the problems of the agriculture of the future. Atoms remain to be cracked. We have a long way to go in applying mathematics and analytical mechanics of nuclear fission to these phenomena before we have the last word on the use

of atomic energy in agricultural research. Control of the mysterious phenomena of cosmic rays and solar energy must yield sooner or later to the fine analytical mind of some clever young engineer-physicist, who perhaps will help to produce a food crop which is rich in nutrients but will leave the soil enriched in the essential elements of energy and productiveness.

The field of agricultural research is so broad and ever expanding into the dim unknown that there is no safe way of predicting exactly what will be its essential constituents in even the near future. But I believe, from what I have seen even in the relatively recent past, that what we know now is merely a good start. We need to have faith in the future of scientific agriculture.

R. W. TRULLINGER *is Chief of the Office of Experiment Stations and Assistant Administrator of Agricultural Research of the Department of Agriculture. This article is based on a speech he gave before the American Society of Agricultural Engineers.*

LUCK STRIKES in strange places, but it favors the trained observer. Scientific facts, seemingly of only academic interest at the time of their discovery, later prove of immense practical importance—radium, saccharin, dry ice, penicillin, and 2,4–D, for example. Chemicals made for one purpose have a way of popping up in new fields to serve mankind even better than their inventors ever dreamed of.

An insecticide—phenothiazine—later came into wide use for removal of intestinal parasites from farm animals. Today it is manufactured in hundreds of tons. Another chemical—2-acetaminofluorene—was being tested as an insecticide, when pharmacological researchers in the Department of Agriculture learned that it induced cancer in experimental animals. Scientists are now making use of the discovery in their investigations of cancer.

Pentachlorophenol was originally proposed for termite control. More recently, an enterprising company tried it as a spray for rice fields before harvesting, and found that it had an effect on the maturing rice like that of frost. It greatly simplified harvesting. Such a compound may revolutionize our methods of handling rice if the preliminary findings are confirmed, and no objectionable flavor or toxicity in the milled grain results from its use.—*Ernest B. Kester, Western Regional Research Laboratory.*

New and Better Uses for Our Crops

H. T. Herrick

Nearly all our agricultural products must be processed before they are ready for the consumer. It has always been so. The early hunter and tiller of the soil had to preserve by smoking or drying some of his food and the skins he needed for clothing. Down through the ages and well into the past century, the preparation of agricultural products for food, clothing, and shelter was mostly the problem of the individual rather than the community.

Following the industrial revolution of the early nineteenth century, weaving and spinning moved out of homes into the textile mill. The preparation of leather from hides and skins was transferred to the tannery. The preservation of foods was taken over largely by factories. The development of highly mechanized industries for utilizing farm products relieved the individual of much work that once was done in the home, and it greatly expanded the markets for agricultural commodities.

More recently, the development of a highly mechanized agriculture and the substitution of the automobile for the horse released many acres from the production of forage crops and transferred them to other crops. Many farm commodities were in surplus, and low prices caused distress.

THEN CAME THE farm chemurgic movement. In 1935 a group of industrialists, agriculturists, and scientists proposed to relieve the farmers' distress by channeling the crop surpluses into chemical industries for nonfood products. The word "chemurgy" was coined by an industrial chemist from Egyptian and Greek roots, which together mean chemistry at work. It has been accepted as a simple expression to cover a large field of chemical industry in preference to the more cumbersome "industrial utilization of the agricultural raw materials."

The group proposed to meet the situation by discovering new uses for established farm crops, developing new crops for acreages producing surpluses, and making use of agricultural residues and wastes from industries consuming agricultural materials.

Each point had significance.

New uses for established farm crops implied new products that could be made from agricultural surpluses without interfering with existing markets.

It was proposed to reduce the acreage in wheat, cotton, and other crops in surplus and use the land so released for growing new crops for industrial consumption—soybeans for oil, Jerusalem artichokes and potatoes for alcohol, sweetpotatoes for starch, and so on. Such crops, if properly developed, would find their places in a balanced industrial economy.

Finally, profitable uses were to be found for crop residues and wastes, the cereal straws or corn stalks, husks, and cobs, for all of which there is a use, even if it is only to increase humus in the soil. Straw, for example, has a value to the farmer for mulching plants and bedding livestock. It can be used as a packing material or processed into pulp for strawboard. The wastes from industries processing agricultural products (such as fruit pulp, vegetable leaves, the vines and pods, and milk wastes) sometimes are a threat to

6

community health and actually cost money for disposal. If agricultural residues and such industrial wastes can be used for finished products of higher value, the farmer's income should be increased thereby.

For many years, the Department of Agriculture had been giving attention to the utilization of agricultural materials for the manufacture of sugars and sirups, turpentine and rosin, tanning extracts, leather, paper pulp, and other products. It had also given much attention to the introduction of new and specialized crops.

The idea of laboratories specially designed for studying the utilization of certain kinds or classes of agricultural commodities stemmed from several precedents. The Citrus Byproducts Laboratory was started in Los Angeles in 1914. The Cooperative Agricultural Byproducts Laboratory was set up in Ames, Iowa, in 1934. The Cooperative United States Regional Soybean Industrial Products Laboratory was established in Urbana, Ill., in 1936.

The success attained in the various lines of that research, coupled with the interest in the farm chemurgic movement, led the Congress to include in the Agricultural Adjustment Act of 1938 a provision for the establishment of research laboratories in the four main agricultural areas of the country.

Their purpose was: "To conduct researches into and to develop new scientific, chemical, and technical uses and new and extended markets and outlets for farm commodities and products and byproducts thereof. Such research and development shall be devoted primarily to those farm commodities in which there are regular or seasonal surpluses, and their products and byproducts."

Under that authorization, four regional research laboratories were established by the Department of Agriculture in or near Peoria, New Orleans, Philadelphia, and Albany, Calif. Each laboratory cost about 2 million dollars to build and equip, and has received an annual appropriation of about a million dollars for operation. They were named for their regions—Northern, Southern, Eastern, and Western. They went to work on a limited number of farm commodities, primarily those in surplus during the 1930's. The commodity assignments were: Northern Regional Research Laboratory, cereal crops, oilseeds of the area, and agricultural residues; Southern Regional Research Laboratory, cotton, peanuts, and sweetpotatoes; Eastern Regional Research Laboratory, dairy products, tobacco, apples, white potatoes, vegetables, animal fats and oils, hides and skins, and tanning materials; Western Regional Research Laboratory, fruits, vegetables, alfalfa, wheat, and poultry products. Work on other commodities, including rice, wool, honey, and maple sirup, has since been undertaken.

WHEN THE PROGRAM of the regional laboratories was under consideration, we recognized that research in utilization could be approached from several directions. Those are: Utilization of the whole commodity; utilization of individual components; application of a particular method of research; and utilization of anything that will yield the desired end product.

I give a few examples.

The wet milling of corn is based on the whole commodity, because all the components are utilized to get these products and byproducts: Cornstarch, dextrose, corn oil, corn gluten, zein, corn steep liquor, and cattle feed. Cornstarch is used as a sizing and finishing material for textiles, as a food, and as a starting point for chemical derivatives. Corn oil is a good food oil. Corn gluten is the raw material from which zein is extracted and is also used in cattle feed. Corn steep liquor contains most of the water-soluble material of the whole grain and was formerly concentrated and added to the cattle feed. Much of it is now used as a nutrient in the production of penicillin and other antibiotics. Zein, the alcohol-soluble portion of corn gluten, can be used in varnish and in a new protein textile fiber.

Cattle feed is made up of everything in the corn that is not used for special products—the bran and hulls, the residue from corn germs pressed for corn oil, a part of the corn gluten, and the corn steep liquor that is not sold for other purposes.

Utilization of an entire commodity is the aim of a project at the Northern Laboratory. In that undertaking, corncobs are the raw material for the production of the following substances: Dextrose, from the cellulose in the cob; xylose and furfural, from the pentosans; and fuel, from the residue of lignin, which may also be used as a source of vanillin, plastics, and other products. Nothing should go to waste.

Different agricultural commodities contain oil, protein, starch, or sugar, and often are used as alternate sources of such materials. For example, proteins in agricultural goods include albumin in eggs, gluten in cereals, casein in milk, the keratin in hair and feathers, collagen in hides, and other proteins in the various oilseeds. Aside from the great importance of some proteins as foods and the industrial use of certain proteins as adhesives and as the basis of leather, the chief potential development for proteins lies in their industrial use.

Some of the work is still in the experimental stage, and the full expansion of the use of proteins must await further development of fundamental knowledge of those materials. Relatively little is known of the chemistry and properties of the proteins as compared with those of the fats and carbohydrates, but even in the face of our still inadequate knowledge, industries based on the production of synthetic fibers from such important proteins as casein, soybean protein, zein, and peanut protein are in operation or are in an advanced experimental stage.

Fermentation is one of the best examples of a particular method of research that is often applied in attempts to utilize an agricultural commodity or residue. The use of micro-organisms for the production of chemical changes in the agricultural materials has been known for a great many years—as a matter of fact, since prehistoric times. There are several types of fermentation. In one type, yeasts convert fermentable sugars to alcohol, as in the production of wine, cider, and beer. In another type, bacteria in the presence of air convert fermentable sugars or dilute alcohol to acids, as in the souring of milk or the conversion of cider to vinegar. In a third type, molds produce acids and other chemical products from sugars and other nutrient substances. The industrial use of molds to bring about chemical changes is relatively recent. One extensive use is in the production of millions of pounds of citric acid, accomplished by growing the molds on a carbohydrate substrate. Various other substances have been produced in a similar manner, including gluconic acid, kojic acid, dextrolactic acid, and penicillin. While by far the greatest numbers of fermentations are based on a carbohydrate substrate, other types of substrate are sometimes selected. For instance, a mold growing on a substrate composed largely of tannin will yield gallic acid, which is now produced commercially in this manner. Some fermentations require the actual presence of the micro-organism. In other instances the enzyme produced by the micro-organism may be separated and used as desired.

An example of research directed toward the production of a particular end product is the development of fibrous pulp for paper or fiberboard. The materials considered for such utilization naturally have a fibrous structure and do not offer greater returns from such plant components as oil, protein, or starch. They comprise coarse grasses and the lignocellulose residues from field crops, which resemble wood in their chemical composition. Bagasse, the residue after sugarcane has been crushed to recover juices for the manufacture of sugar, is used for the production of fiberboards for structural use and for insulation. Wheat straw is used to produce strawboard and paper.

When we consider all the aspects of chemical utilization, we find that agricultural commodities have some disadvantages as raw materials from the standpoint of chemical and physical properties and costs. Obviously, because of their properties, finished organic materials derived from agricultural commodities could not compete with metal products in which high tensile strength or the ability to withstand high temperature is required. They have a relatively high electrical resistance and cannot be used in contact with acids. On the other hand, such materials can be used for many purposes in which resistance to heat or the ability to stand high stresses is neither necessary nor desirable, as in the manufacture of paints, plastics, and adhesives. Materials from agricultural commodities have their place and, as a matter of fact, may be superior to other materials for the purposes to which they are adapted.

ANOTHER IMPORTANT factor must be considered, however. There is no point in producing a material for industrial use unless it can be sold in competition with other materials in its field. As an example: Ethyl alcohol from grain or other starch materials, if considered purely on the basis of the yield of alcohol from the raw material, does not compete in the open market with synthetic ethyl alcohol. On the other hand, it is conceivable that profitable use may be made of the carbon dioxide, distillers' grains, vitamins, and other byproducts of the fermentation process and that the time may come when the alcohol will be considered as secondary to some other product that sells at a competitive price in the open market.

Also, we should not overlook the fact that, in producing industrial products from agricultural products, we are working at an initial disadvantage in that the farm products must first be produced, while products of the mine and oil well already exist and need only to be taken from the ground. In other words, mineral products that need only to be "harvested" are competing with agricultural products that must pay the farmer a return for management, labor, cost of fertilizer, and investment in land and equipment for bringing them to the condition for harvesting.

AGRICULTURAL raw materials, however, have one basic advantage over nonagricultural raw materials. They are reproducible; field crops can be grown and harvested each year. They are produced naturally in practically unlimited quantities from air, water, and minerals by photochemical reactions. The minerals that are removed from the soil can be replaced by returning manure and plant wastes to the soil and by the use of chemical fertilizers. The mineral contents of agricultural commodities removed from the land are low in comparison with the organic matter in such commodities.

But the petroleum, coal, and other minerals that now constitute the principal raw materials for industry are not reproducible. Nature apparently does not go on manufacturing them, or if she does it is at a very slow rate. As they are consumed, the supply diminishes, and eventually our mineral supplies will be exhausted.

Under present conditions, therefore, our Nation is living on its capital as well as its income. No individual can do that and remain solvent indefinitely. The same is true of a country. Chemical utilization of agricultural raw materials will help to postpone or prevent bankruptcy of important mineral resources.

THE LATE H. T. HERRICK *was director of the Northern Regional Research Laboratory from 1942 to 1946, and later was a special assistant to the Chief of the Bureau of Agricultural and Industrial Chemistry.*

The attention of the reader is directed to the glossary of uncommon terms that is printed at the end of this volume.

How Far Can We Go in Chemurgy?

Wheeler McMillen

The achievements reported in these pages show that unsuspected uses for agricultural raw materials have been created by scientific inquiry. Profitable commercial utilization has been established for farm residues formerly of little or no market value. Entirely new crops have gained a foothold, and some have become important factors in total production. How far can progress go in the fields of chemurgy? Can research profitably be pursued further?

The answer seems completely clear. The place to catch fish is where fish are being caught. Where so much already has been accomplished there must be much more to be done.

At the risk of restating well-known fundamentals, it may be well here to recall the new conditions that have made these advances in chemurgy possible. Agriculture from its primitive beginnings has been an individualistic, unorganized, empirical business. Gains in knowledge came mostly from scattered observations. Little, or indeed almost nothing, of true science existed in agriculture until the latter part of the past century.

During the 1890's organic chemistry began to be important, and Mendel's law, the basic principle of plant genetics, became known. The early part of this century saw the rising application of power to agriculture. These three relatively recent developments in chemistry, genetics, and engineering have made chemurgy possible. They have provided a wholly new set of tools for moving agriculture forward in new directions. Organic chemistry and related sciences enable industry to extract values from plant substances that always before had been inaccessible or were useful only in crude forms. The science of genetics permits plant breeders to improve and intensify the characteristics of a plant species which may prove to be commercially desirable. The developments in power and machinery meanwhile have multiplied human and animal muscle so that materials can be moved, lifted, ground, and processed to degrees that never before were possible.

All those advances have come about within a generation or so. They are so recent that up to now, even with the resources of industry, individuals, and Government, there has been little time to apply them extensively. Only a few of the more obvious opportunities have been undertaken; an abundance of obvious ones remains. Every gain in definite knowledge has been accompanied by practical new questions yet to be answered by further research.

The most natural and most economic primary use of the new tools has been to apply them to existing crops. These efforts seem to have been almost fabulously productive when one contemplates the list of more than 200 consumer items that derive from the corn plant alone, and an equally long list from the relatively new soybean crop. That possibilities for further chemurgic exploitation of present crops are great cannot be doubted. Thus far some have been studied but little. Fundamental scientific facts, such as the precise molecular structure of starch, remain to be determined. Once found, a fact such as this might multiply the usefulness of starchy crops as raw materials.

The number of plants presently cultivated in the United States continues to be surprisingly small in comparison with the abundant diversity of the plant kingdom. Fewer than a dozen species will account for most of this country's agricultural production. Apparently not more than 200 species, if that many, are cultivated to the extent of producing carlot quantities, and probably 150 comes closer to the fact.

In contrast, some 15,000 species of plants are native to the United States and Canada. Estimates vary somewhat according to how far down the list of plant orders one goes, but the world total of plant species may be stated to be more than 250,000 and perhaps as many as 300,000. These are the species that botanists have discovered, classified, and described. Regarding most of them, present knowledge goes little further than description.

Every plant has something in it. Chemical content ranges widely. Since man has ready uses for cellulose, sugar, starch, proteins, oils, and other compounds, he has begun to look for those ingredients. Many other compounds also enter into plant composition, and as scientific knowledge expands there is always the possibility that some once valueless plant may provide a new compound of value and importance. A recent conspicuous example is *Strophanthus sarmentosus,* which has been found to contain a source material for cortisone, the new drug for arthritis. So little was known about *Strophanthus,* other than that it was a vinelike species of African origin, that no one could say whether it might be cultivated successfully in the United States, what its habits were, or how it should be cultivated if supplies were required.

Knowledge regarding most of the quarter of a million species of wild plants on the earth stands at about the same stage.

Chemical records list many thousands of compounds that have been created during the course of experimentation. Whatever is known about any one of these appears in the chemical literature. No practical uses or applications have been found for most of them. However, a chemist, confronted by a new problem, can select from the records a list of these substances which, for one reason or another, seem worth investigation. One after another he tests them against his problem. If he is fortunate, he may find one among hundreds that meets his needs. In some such manner new insecticides, fungicides, and the weed killers have been made available to agriculture.

Little such comparable information yet exists about the diverse members of the vegetable kingdom. The names and shapes and habitats of thousands of plants are set down in the botanical records. Only in chance instances can the chemurgic investigator point to a species and expect that its specifications may meet some urgent need, because the specifications have not yet been determined or recorded.

THIS OPPORTUNITY alone opens up an almost unlimited area for future chemurgic advances. The future will no doubt see the entire flora of the earth, species by species, examined by the instruments and tests of the latest scientific technology. Chemical analyses will be made of leaves, roots, stalks, and fruits. Other scientific determinations will be made and recorded. Future investigators, seeking raw materials for processes to supply new and old human needs, will turn to such records, and will be able to select such plant species as may promise to meet their requirements.

The economic value of such information cannot be estimated. If it were available at this particular period in agricultural history, one would not be rash to expect that new crops would be in the process of becoming incorporated into American farm practices. If one of them were adapted to the Great Plains, and should promise enough profit to be preferred to wheat on a fourth or fifth of the present wheat acreage, the fear of wheat surpluses might quickly disappear. The same result might be expected if a new crop were found to occupy the cotton lands, potato lands, or any other lands where farmers yet have few alternatives to their present habits and methods of operation.

Human needs are by no means abundantly supplied. If a new plant, for instance, were discovered to yield a cure for the common cold, its product would immediately enjoy a tremendous market. Considering that cinchona, a plant once new to Europeans, did provide a cure for malaria, perhaps my example of the common cold is not entirely fanciful. Only a century ago, humankind had little use for rubber, a plant product now indispensable to civilization and, incidentally, a "new" crop in the eastern regions where most rubber is produced. The Hevea tree was introduced into Ceylon and Malaysia from Brazil in 1876–77. For that matter, it is well known that all except a few of the principal American crop plants were transplanted to the western world after Columbus.

A review of the appearance within recent decades of new inventions and new products permits the expectation that future generations will enjoy as common necessities materials which are as difficult for us in 1951 to picture as it would have been for the people of 1851 to foresee the future of rubber.

That an increasing proportion of future industrial raw materials will come from the plant kingdom seems entirely likely. One of the basic facts in chemurgic philosophy is that, as long as the fertility of the soil is maintained, plant substance can be indefinitely reproduced. When ore or oil has been extracted from the earth's crust and consumed, man has no means for replacing it. The remarkable fact that vegetable raw materials are created by sunshine, largely (95 to 98 percent) from air and moisture, and that they are annually renewable, gives reason to hope that, given enough knowledge, increasing future generations can enjoy increasing abundance. •

The defense needs of present times emphasize the urgency of research into plant materials. No warship is now built, or plane flown, or munition made without drawing upon agricultural materials. Chemurgic research made penicillin available during the recent war, made shipment of dehydrated foods practicable, and provided packaging methods which proved invaluable. And, of course, the conservation of mineral resources, upon which war draws heavily, demands maximum utilization of renewable materials.

WHEN THE CHEMURGIC concept was first being elaborated, the development of the nonfood products for industrial rather than edible purposes received major emphasis. At that period through the 1920's and early 1930's, when grain and meat surpluses were notably disturbing, it was remarked that although the capacity of the stomach was limited to about three meals daily the human inclination to consume nonfood products had no apparent limits. However, as chemurgic research has progressed, the chronic world-wide food shortage has become better understood. Because of this, fears have been expressed that chemurgic advances might lessen the inducements to produce food. The contrary is true.

In the first place, almost no food plant is wholly edible. When profitable commercial uses are found for the inedible portions, such as stalks, rinds, cobs, straw, or pits, the total return to the grower can be enough larger that the incentive to produce the plant may be all the greater, and the producer may be able to sell the edible portions for less because he has markets for the inedible portions which formerly he could not sell.

In the second place, chemurgic research in several instances has extended the range of food products. New dehydration processes may be cited, and the brilliant success of frozen concentrated fruit juices. These make foodstuffs available to more people at less cost. Chemurgic research has also shown that in some instances products not usually suitable for market, such as off-size fruits or fruits too ripe for shipment, may be processed into new forms, which find new markets. Food materials thus are rescued from waste.

Chemurgy, rather than creating a diversion from food supplies, tends to add to the total of variety and abundance. Further studies of wild plants not now in cultivation may reveal additional sources of food.

How FAR CAN CHEMURGY ADVANCE? Clearly the answer must be that the possible distance is far greater than the human eye, or even the human imagination, can yet penetrate. Not only is the distance great, but even the directions of advance cannot yet all be foreseen.

The vegetable kingdom remains virtually unexplored. Tens of thousands of species of plants await study. Out of their number some will prove useful for present purposes, and some for purposes yet unimagined. New crops will be added to the agricultural repertoire. The new crops will occupy acres that now are problem acres, either because they still have to be used to produce crops for which demand is inadequate, or because no plant has yet been found that will flourish in the soil of that acre. Within American borders may be found almost every condition and combination of conditions, except the very tropical, required for plant growth. Lands vary from humid to arid, sea-level to mountaintop, peat to granite, semitropical to cold. Nearly all the plant riches of the earth are potentially American riches.

Within the brief span of a few decades extraordinary increases of knowledge about plants have been attained, and important additions to human wealth and well-being have followed. The foundation upon which to build future knowledge is broader than ever before. The dividends for the future will be in proportion to the effort expended.

WHEELER MCMILLEN *is editor-in-chief of the Farm Journal and president of the National Farm Chemurgic Council, Inc.*

THOMAS A. EDISON, responsible for some of this country's greatest inventive research, had to test thousands of different materials by trial and error in order to obtain a satisfactory filament for the first incandescent lamp.

His impatient young assistant once asked him, "Don't you get awfully discouraged after these thousands of failures, knowing that all our research has been utterly in vain?"

"Our research has not been in vain," Edison replied, "for there is also a value in finding out what will not work."

It was upon this foundation of failure, frustration, and chaff that he eventually achieved his goal, the one kernel of truth he was seeking.

Notable also is the example of the early research of Planck and Einstein. Surely nothing important could come from anything so abstract and seemingly innocent as a quantum theory. Pure scientific chaff, we thought then—before we entered this crucial age of electronics, nuclear fission, and hydrogen bombs.

How, then, are we to judge the products of research? Who can properly separate the wheat from the chaff?—*Elmer W. Shaw, "Green Pastures," Lacey, Wash.*

Diversification of Another Kind

W. B. Van Arsdel

Thoughtful men realized long ago that the business risk of growing or processing a crop could be diminished by diversifying the market. Meat-packing concerns were among the first to put the principle into practice. I well remember that just a generation ago "everything but the squeal" was a common byword.

The great crop surpluses of the 1920's and 1930's brought the idea into new prominence. The demand for some food crops is rather inelastic, so that even an oversupply of 10 or 15 percent is enough to depress prices to ruinous levels unless the oversupply can be diverted into some other channel of consumption. Even a relatively small new use for the product may, therefore, have a powerful leverage on the price level for the entire crop. In view of the often-repeated proposition that the human stomach has only a fixed capacity, the emphasis in the search for new uses has usually been placed on the discovery of nonfood uses, even for crops that have been traditionally grown only for food.

In the crude form as I have just stated it, the proposition certainly does not contain the whole truth. Many Americans, even in prosperous times, do not eat enough food to reach an adequate calorie intake. Many, many more do not have a nutritionally balanced diet. New or cheaper food products need not simply displace older food products on the market—if they can reach these malnourished persons, the total consumption of food and total farm income will be increased.

In addition, as our national standard of living rises we consume a wider variety of foods primarily for their flavor, texture, or color appeal, or because we think they are good for us. A dollar spent for orange juice or milk or lettuce does not buy so many calories as to make much difference in our need for energy foods. We cannot forget, either, that a vast hunger exists in other parts of the world and that some day, barring catastrophe, we shall be able to sell our goods freely overseas once more.

But even when we make all these proper qualifications, the fact remains that our need for food products is limited, while our appetite for other material goods seems to be insatiable.

How much of a stake do American farmers have in the market for products other than food or feed, and what are their chances for the future in this limitless field?

MOST FARM PRODUCTS find uses both as food or feed and as one or many of the multitude of other things our industrial civilization wants. Meat animals are the outstanding example. Cattle and sheep are raised primarily for meat, but hides and wool are among the most essential of the raw materials produced by agriculture. I do not know how to estimate the total value to farmers of the nonfood part of these multiple uses. Available statistics do not go far enough. The few figures we have only scratch the surface. The farm value of shorn wool in 1949 was 107 million dollars. In the same year the corn wet-milling industry converted 117 million bushels of corn into starch, sirups, dextrose sugar, dextrins, oil, and feed, but the value of the nonfood, nonfeed part of this to the farmers has not been estimated. Neither do we know the money return to farmers from the use of soybean oil cake in adhesives and soybean oil in paints; or the use of skim milk for making casein; or the sale of hides, fertilizer, and glue by packing plants. We can only say with confidence that several hundred million dollars of farm income must be ascribed to industrial uses of crops grown primarily for another purpose.

Cotton and wood are conspicuous examples of agricultural commodities that are grown for nonfood purposes. The list is not long. It includes tobacco, horses and mules, flaxseed, tung nuts, and broomcorn. Along with wood and the multitude of products derived from it go a number of secondary forest products, such as naval stores and some tanning materials.

The cash return to farmers for the nonfood commodities is impressive. The values for the 1949 production year (omitting a few crops of relatively small total value) were, in millions of dollars:

Cotton lint	2, 380
Primary forest products	2, 100
Tobacco	904
Flaxseed	154
Gum naval stores	37
Horses, colts, and mules	26
Broomcorn	10
Mohair	7
Tung nuts	4
Total	5, 622

The second item, estimated by the Forest Service, includes sawlogs, veneer logs, pulpwood, fuel wood, poles, piling, and posts, estimated in unmanufactured condition at local points of delivery.

The total is approximately one-fifth of the total estimated cash receipts from farming in 1949.

AGRICULTURAL PRODUCTS constitute essential raw materials for a broad segment of American industry. The interaction is two-way; not only are many industries geared to the processing of the farmer's crops, but also in increasing degree the farmer finds that his direct customer is a processing plant.

Self-sufficient farming, nearly independent of cash sales, is today a rarity. But one consequence of that change in our farm economy is that today's farmer has a heavy stake in one or more manufacturing enterprises, and has a right to expect intelligent and efficient handling of his partner's end of the business. By fumbling, the processor may ruin both himself and his farmer-supplier.

The 1947 Census of Manufactures divided American manufacturing industries into 20 broad groups. One of these contains the food industries. Seven of the groups cover mainly nonfood products from the agricultural sources.

The 20 groups are subdivided in the Census into nearly 500 distinct industries. A third of them, about 160, produce nonfood products from agricultural commodities. The 160 industries comprise more than 65,000 separate establishments, employ 4 million wage earners, and in 1947 shipped goods valued at more than 44 billion dollars. The industries range in size from such giants as the cotton-textile and pulp and paper industries down to such modest enterprises as the manufacture of straw hats, neckties, mucilage and paste, saddlery and harness, and brooms.

The seven industry groups concerned mainly with the manufacture of nonfood products from agricultural raw materials are listed here in the order of the value of their products (in millions of dollars):

Textile-mill products	12, 293
Apparel and related products	8, 874
Paper and allied products	7, 052
Furniture and fixtures	6, 565
Lumber and products, except furniture	4, 415
Leather and leather products	3, 381
Tobacco manufactures	2, 541

BYPRODUCTS have a way of becoming the primary products of great industries—cottonseed, for example, was once a waste.

In writings on this subject the words residue and waste are usually given special meanings. A residue is a relatively stable waste portion of a crop generally left on or near the farm when the crop is harvested. The term has been applied particularly to cereal straw and hulls and corn stalks and cobs. Waste is a broader term, embracing not only the residues but also such diverse kinds of things as peach skins and pits separated from the peach flesh in a cannery, broccoli or cauliflower leaves trimmed from the heads at a packing shed, day-old cockerels from a hatchery, whey from a cheese factory, and bark separated from wood in a pulp mill. It is a peculiarity of language, rather than of the things themselves, that the instant a commercial use is made of a waste it ceases being a waste and becomes instead the raw material for a byproduct.

Most of the wastes of agricultural processing plants are major problems in their own right, because of the difficulty and expense of disposing of them without creating a nuisance. The nuisance aspect has, in fact, provided a strong incentive toward the discovery and development of uses which would turn the wastes into raw materials for new byproduct industries. In general, the solid portions of processing wastes, classifiable as garbage, have shown much more promise of useful byproduct development than the liquid sewage.

Many of the industrially successful uses for residues and other agricultural wastes lead to nonfood products, others to highly acceptable livestock feeds.

I MENTIONED THE PROPOSITION that the total market for food products is practically fixed. Even if that were true, it would imply at least that the farmer's food market is safe. People must eat. The case is different for many nonfood farm products. During the past century we have seen natural dyes replaced by synthetic ones, animal and vegetable lubricating oils by petroleum products, tallow candles by electric light. Completely new kinds of plastics, films, and fibers, made from mineral raw materials, have been increasingly successful. Alcohol, glycerin, lacquer solvents, new resins, and many other "organic" materials, which used to be made from farm products exclusively, are now produced from natural gas, calcium carbide, or petroleum-refinery byproducts.

This is a challenge, not a foretaste of disaster for farmers. It means only that no producer has been endowed with such an impregnable monopoly that he can afford complacency. True, he has a long head start over the synthetic chemist. No laboratory is going to come out soon with a synthetic that will replace tobacco in the affections of smokers, or with a real competitor for shoe leather, or with a paper-making fiber synthesized from coal or natural gas. In the long run, indeed, the world must learn to supply its major needs from things that can be grown, quarried, or recovered from the sea, not mined. But in the meantime, let no farmer assume that his product is so secure that it needs no improvement.

The facts of nature are, of course, neutral with respect to the interests of any group of people. When scientists discover new facts, no conspiracy against the farmer's livelihood is implied. On the contrary, there is excellent reason for believing that markets have been lost in the past largely because science was not being applied as vigorously to the problems of utilizing farm products as it was, say, to petroleum utilization. This concept has been recognized by agricultural scientists for several decades.

Three broad objectives characterize nearly all this research work.

It may seek to improve the technology of a processing industry, eliminate wastes, and reduce costs to the point where the product can compete advantageously for a limited market.

Or it may aim to improve the quality of a product until it will appeal to more and more consumers.

Or, finally, it may seek to discover and develop completely new products, thus diversifying and broadening the market for the agricultural raw material.

The record shows that substantial success has been achieved in each of these directions. Hundreds of examples are cited in this book. Dozens more are announced each month. The flow of new ideas accelerates year by year. Diversification of the market for our farm products is really happening—a buckler for peacetime and wartime.

W. B. Van Arsdel *was trained as a* *chemical engineer. He has been connected with scientific and engineering research ever since he was graduated from Purdue University in 1913. For 23 years he carried on research and development for a manufacturer of wood pulp, paper, and heavy chemicals. Since 1937 he has been with the Bureau of Agricultural and Industrial Chemistry in Urbana, Ill., the District of Columbia, and Albany, Calif. He is assistant director of the Western Regional Research Laboratory.*

George Washington Carver was born of slave parents on a plantation in Missouri in 1864. When he was 6 weeks old, he and his mother were captured by a band of raiders and taken to Arkansas. His master, Moses Carver, bought him back from his captors for a race horse valued at $300, but his mother was never heard of again.

The boy attended a one-room school about 8 miles from the plantation. Later he worked and attended other schools when and where he could and finally completed high school in Kansas. He worked, saved his money, and set out for an agricultural college that had accepted his application. But when he arrived and they saw his color, they refused to admit him. He worked for a while in Kansas and then went to Simpson College in Iowa. After a year there, he entered Iowa State College, where he received his bachelor of science degree at the end of 3 years. He worked as assistant station botanist at the college and continued his studies leading to a master of science degree in 1896.

That year, Booker T. Washington invited him to join the faculty of Tuskegee Institute as director of agriculture. He organized the agriculture department there and planned the first building devoted entirely to agriculture.

At Tuskegee he was able to carry on his research—research aimed at making life more abundant for people everywhere, but especially for those of his own South. Farmers appealed to Dr. Carver for help when the boll weevil threatened total destruction of the cotton crop in Alabama. He told them to raise peanuts. Then he set about to find new uses for the peanuts so the farmers would be able to sell them. From them he developed about 300 products, including peanut milk, plastics, stains and dyes, lard, flour, soap, and cooking oils. From the sweetpotato he got more than 118 products—mucilage, starch, molasses, dyes, ink, and vinegar, among them. He developed new products from cotton, soybeans, wastes, and clay.

George Washington Carver died on January 5, 1943. His entire estate, amounting to more than $60,000, he bequeathed to the George Washington Carver Foundation, where it has been used as the beginning of an endowment fund.—*Catherine F. George, Office of Information.*

DEPARTMENT OF AGRICULTURE scientists and economists continually study changes in agriculture. The Second World War brought demands for food and fiber that greatly accelerated changes under way in agriculture and added economic control programs to the responsibilities of Department administrators.

Changes in governmental programs and administration during the war period were made the subject of special study in the Department of Agriculture as part of a Government-wide war records project initiated at the request of the President and the Director of the Bureau of the Budget. The Department's project was organized in the Bureau of Agricultural Economics. The project staff collected and organized documents relating to the wartime administration of the Department. It also prepared and assisted in the preparation of historical accounts of some of the major war programs and of wartime changes in various sectors of agriculture.

One study of general interest was prepared by Walter W. Wilcox, then of the University of Wisconsin, as part of a cooperative project of the university, the Bureau of Agricultural Economics, and the Social Science Research Council. It was entitled *The Farmer In the Second World War* and was published by the Iowa State College Press in 1947.

Studies with a more limited scope were published by the Government and can be obtained from the Bureau of Agricultural Economics. They were prepared by specialists in the Bureau and in other agencies. The first seven were published as War Records Monographs:

Farm Machinery and Equipment, by Erling Hole; *Soil Conservation During the War,* by George W. Collier; *Sugar During World War II,* by Roy A. Ballinger; *War Food Order 135, Veterans' Preference for New Farm Machinery and Equipment,* by F. M. Johnson; *Acquisition and Use of Land for Military and War Production Purposes, World War II,* by Alvin T. M. Lee; *Fats and Oils in World War II: Production and Price-supporting Programs,* by Robert M. Walsh; *Wool During World War II,* by John W. Klein.

Two other publications, *Agricultural Wage Stabilization During World War II,* by Arthur J. Holmaas, and *Citrus Fruit During World War II,* by Ben H. Pubols, have been published as *Agriculture Monographs,* Nos. 1 and 3.

Additional studies dealing with the Department's farm labor program, with meat and meat animals, and with the concentration of food authority, in addition to a chronology of the War Food Administration, were planned.

In addition to war records project studies, which focused attention on governmental programs and their effects on agriculture, the Bureau of Agricultural Economics published a number of studies dealing with changes in agricultural production during the war: *Changes in Farming in War and Peace,* by Sherman E. Johnson; *Changes in Cotton Production in War and Peace,* by E. L. Langsford; *Changes in Hay Production in War and Peace,* by Neil W. Johnson; *Cropland Use and Soil Fertility Practice in War and Peace,* by Donald B. Ibach; *Dairying in War and Peace,* by Olav F. Anderson; *Farm Production in War and Peace,* by Glen T. Barton and Martin R. Cooper; *Feed Grains and Meat Animals in War and Peace,* by C. W. Crickman; *Soybean Production in War and Peace,* by Edwin G. Strand; *Wheat Production in War and Peace,* by Carl P. Heisig, Ernest R. Ahrendes, and Della E. Merrick.—*Gladys L. Baker and Wayne D. Rasmussen, Bureau of Agricultural Economics.*

THESE ARE THE TOOLS

The Chemist Seeks One of Three Goals

Harry W. von Loesecke

If you ask the chemist to find a profitable use for any product that is wasted or overabundant, he will first study the substances of which it is made up and then try to reach one of three goals.

He may process the whole product to see if he can find in it an entirely new item that can be sold at a profit.

He may separate from the raw material a particular constituent that is valuable enough to yield a profit over the cost of material and operations.

Or he may make the material more acceptable to the chemical industry for present uses by learning how to prevent deterioration before utilization, how to purify the material, how to improve the product, or how to utilize the raw material more effectively.

ONE DAY, before the turn of the century, a chemist took some kernels of corn and started an industry that today uses more than 140 million bushels of corn annually. He employed many techniques, operations, and processes in order to separate particular substances, modify the things he had separated, and convert the materials into other chemical entities that have different chemical and physical properties. His methods and accomplishments with corn exemplify the methods and accomplishments of the chemists with other farm products.

One of the first products the chemist obtained from corn was starch. That was comparatively simple. He then set about finding means of making other products from starch and methods of changing the properties of starch so that it could be used for entirely different purposes. For instance, starch does not dissolve in water, but when it is heated under proper conditions, a chemical change takes place that reduces the number of atoms in the molecule, so that the new products thus obtained combine readily with water to form a variety of pastes, gums, and adhesives. The new products are called dextrins. More than 100 different kinds and blends of dextrins are made industrially from cornstarch.

Another product from cornstarch is sugar. The chemist knew that a starch could be changed to sugar if it were broken down by hydrolysis. When the breaking down is carried to completion, the final product is dextrose, the sugar that is in the blood stream of humans. Its common commercial name is corn sugar. It is about half as sweet as cane or beet sugar. If hydrolysis is not carried to completion, a sugar sirup (corn sirup) is the end product.

Even the corncobs themselves can be made into sugars by treating them with sulfuric acid under certain conditions. The sugars can be recovered as a sirup by neutralizing the excess acid with chalk, separating the calcium sulfate formed by the action of the chalk on the sulfuric acid, decolorizing the neutralized sugar solution with charcoal, and, after removing the charcoal, evaporating the sugar solution to a sirup.

The sugar or sirup made from cornstarch is at first dark, as is the sirup from corncobs. The color is removed by adsorption. Quite different from absorption, adsorption is based on the tendency of all solids to hold on their surfaces a layer of any gas or liquid with which they are in contact. A solution of corn sugar is allowed to come in contact with very porous charcoal, which adsorbs the dark substances in the sugar solution.

Corn sugar itself has many uses, but it also is the basic material for making substances of quite different properties. For instance, vitamin C, so essential in the human diet, and found in citrus and other fruits and in green and yellow leafy vegetables, has been prepared commercially in pure form from corn sugar by synthesis. Synthesis is a process in which a chemical compound is obtained by building up or adding elements or simple compounds by a series of reactions. The reactions in the synthesis of vitamin C from corn sugar involve, among others, fermentation, hydrogenation, oxidation, reduction.

WHEN MOLECULES of the same kind unite to form a new substance, which consists of large molecular units and from which the original compound may or may not be regenerated, the change thus effected is said to be caused by polymerization. The new compound is called a polymer. A polymer of corn sugar is dextran, which sometimes is used as a substitute for blood plasma. Condensation is applied to polymerization reactions in which a molecule of water or other substance is split off. Several condensation products of corn sugar have been prepared in the laboratory and may eventually be of use in our agricultural economy.

HYDROGENATION raises the melting point of the oil obtained from the corn germ by pressing. Thus corn oil, which is fluid at room temperature, becomes a plastic fat. Such a product is used as a shortening in cooking. Hydrogenation means the addition of hydrogen, and is probably the most valuable tool of the oil technologist. What happens is that the hydrogen molecule attaches itself to the double bonds that link the molecular chains of the fatty acids that constitute the oil. When that happens, the chemist says the fatty acids have become saturated, because the double bonds have taken on hydrogen and can no longer take on any other element. The final hardness of the oil being hydrogenated can be controlled by the amount of hydrogen permitted to be attached to the double bonds of the fatty acids in the oil.

Hydrogenation of the oil cannot be carried out without a catalyst—a substance that markedly affects the rate of a chemical reaction. Usually the catalyst is present in tiny amounts. Some chemical reactions will not proceed at all without the presence of a catalyst, or the yields are so small that production would be uneconomical. Thus, nitrogen and hydrogen unite to form ammonia when they are mixed and brought in contact with specially prepared porous iron (the catalyst) at high temperature and high pressure. Without the porous iron, the two original gases form ammonia in minute amounts. In the hydrogenation of oil the catalyst generally is nickel, finely divided and specially prepared.

Corn-germ oil, wheat-germ oil, and several vegetables contain substances that probably are related to vitamin E. The chemist has found that the substances can be separated without decomposition if they are distilled at low temperature under a high vacuum. That is called molecular distillation. It is the process of distilling the oil from a thin, heated layer to the nearby condenser across space maintained under such a high vacuum that the molecules being distilled will go by the shortest route to the condenser without bumping into other molecules on the way. Molecular distillation requires rather bulky and expensive equipment and is used chiefly to prepare high-priced substances.

The chemist has found how to make such diversified things as condiments and cloth from the proteins of corn.

When the proteins are treated with acids, alkalies, or certain protein-digesting enzymes (organic catalysts that are produced by a living organism), they are hydrolyzed to peptones, polypeptides, or finally amino acids, which are really the building blocks of proteins. The end product will depend upon the degree of hydrolysis. Thus, when corn gluten, wheat gluten, soybean meal, or Steffens waste (from beet-sugar factories) are hydrolyzed with acid, the end product is monosodium glutamate, which enhances the flavor of cooked meats and some other foods and of which we produce about 9 million pounds a year.

Another product from corn protein is zein, which is obtained from gluten. The zein is made soluble by a proper solvent and then spun into fibers, which are woven into fabrics.

The corn kernel itself can be hydrolyzed to obtain sugar. That usually is done by making a mash of the corn and treating it with an infusion of malt (sprouted barley). The hydrolysis of the starch in the corn is brought about by the enzymes in the sprouted barley.

Now we have a sugar solution. From it we can get alcohol and several other volatile materials or even some non-volatile acids by adding a yeast or a bacterium and permitting it to ferment for a definite period at a specific temperature.

If the material obtained by fermentation is volatile, it can be recovered by distillation, in which the mixture is heated and the vapors are recovered by cooling. The greater the difference in boiling points of the individual constituents, the easier is the separation. As the number of constituents in the mixture increases, the more difficult it becomes to effect separation.

Suppose our fermented sugar solution contains a mixture of acetone, butyl alcohol, and ethyl alcohol, which have been formed by a specific micro-organism we mixed with the mash. In normal fermentation, the mash should contain 6 parts of butyl alcohol, 3 parts of acetone, and 1 part of ethyl alcohol. Under atmospheric pressures, acetone will boil at 133° F., ethyl alcohol at 142° F., and butyl alcohol at 243° F. Thus, the differences in boiling points make it feasible to separate the constituents by distillation.

But what if the mash contains a material that is not volatile and cannot be distilled? Let us suppose it contains lactic acid, because we have used a micro-organism that will produce lactic acid. Lactic acid is the acid of sour milk and cream. The chemist has several ways to recover such a material.

He may rely on precipitation, which generally involves bringing about a chemical reaction in a solution of a substance to be separated so that it forms an insoluble compound. Thus, he could add chalk (calcium carbonate), which would react with the lactic acid to form calcium lactate, a comparatively insoluble substance. The calcium lactate could be separated by filtration and then treated with sulfuric acid, which would change the calcium lactate into lactic acid and calcium sulfate. The sulfate is insoluble and can be filtered off, leaving the lactic acid behind. Indeed, that is one method of making lactic acid commercially.

The chemist may rely on esterification, and make an ester of lactic acid. Esters are organic compounds corresponding to salts in inorganic chemistry. They may be considered as derived from acids by the exchange of the hydrogen of the acid for an alcohol radical. In the case of lactic acid, the hydrogen of the acid can be exchanged for butyl alcohol. The result is butyl lactate, an ester, which can be recovered by distillation.

Lactic acid can be recovered from the butyl lactate by saponification, which here means the conversion of an ester (butyl lactate) into an acid and an alcohol by a mineral acid or an alkali. Thus, the butyl lactate upon saponification will give butyl alcohol and lactic acid; the alcohol can be recovered by distillation and used again to make additional butyl lactate.

Thus we have seen something of the chemist's ways and results with one product. There are many more, and there will be more still. Chemistry, an ever-expanding science, is the farmer's helpmeet, no less than the industrialist's.

HARRY W. VON LOESECKE *is technical adviser in the Bureau of Agricultural and Industrial Chemistry. He is a graduate of Harvard University. Be-* *fore coming with the Government he was research chemist for General Electric Co., American Protein Corp., and United Fruit Co. For 10 years he was in charge of the United States Citrus Products Station at Winter Haven, Fla. During the Second World War he was connected with the Bureau's work on the dehydration of foods at the Western Regional Research Laboratory, and later was industrial specialist with the War Food Administration and Production and Marketing Administration.*

IN RESEARCH it is often necessary to detect and identify minute amounts of materials. Microchemistry is the branch of chemistry that deals with these micro quantities. The chemical reactions involved are no different from those involved in large—or macro—amounts. Microchemistry, therefore, differs from other fields of chemistry in the amount of material handled and in the special techniques and apparatus necessary to work with small items.

The microchemist generally works with only a few milligrams of substance, roughly equivalent to the weight of one-tenth of a drop of water, or approximately one ten-thousandth of an ounce. What place has this branch of chemistry in research on agricultural commodities, which often are measured in billions of bushels, millions of tons, or thousands of carlots?

One of nature's most challenging features is that many extremely important constituents of plants and animals are present in such small amounts that pounds and even tons of material must be processed to obtain minute quantities of them. It is at the end of such isolation or separation processes that microchemistry must be depended upon to make the final separations and purifications, as well as the analyses to determine the nature and purity of the constituents. The microchemist, of course, is not limited to working with naturally occurring trace materials. He has an important part in preparing and evaluating other materials, which occur naturally or are derived from agricultural products. Even when larger quantities of material are available, it is often expedient to work with micro quantities because of a saving in time and money. The savings result from the use of only small amounts of costly materials and chemical reagents and the shortening of the time required.

The ability to carry out chemical reactions on a small scale and to identify and determine the purity of traces of material has helped greatly in advancing our studies on vitamins, hormones, antibiotics, and antiarthritics.—*C. L. Ogg, Eastern Regional Research Laboratory.*

The Tools the Physicist Uses

C. H. Kunsman

Physics, a basic and a far-reaching branch of science, gets right at the heart of many things that affect our life, comfort, and happiness. Agriculture, national defense, transportation, communication, and the control of climate are concerned with the applications of physics in particular fields.

Physics deals with matter and energy. It comprises the use and study of mechanics, heat, light, sound, electricity, magnetism, and atomic physics.

The physicist's tools are simple ones like the measuring rules, weighing balances, clocks or watches, thermometers, speedometers, and the electrical instruments. He also uses more complicated tools like the vacuum tubes, electronic amplifiers, recording meters, spectrophotometers, electrostatic generators, cyclotrons, and the atomic pile.

Physics solves many of the problems that pertain to the processing and utilization of farm goods. A market exists for many an agricultural product simply because of its special physical property. Fibers have values based almost entirely on their physical characteristics—appearance, durability, and wrinkleproofness. Plastics are wanted for their strength, durability, color, and ease of shaping. Processed food, fresh fruit, vegetables, poultry products, and frozen or canned products are bought by housewives according to color, crispness, texture, or moisture content.

Physicists and what they do are less commonly known than chemists or engineers, because so many of them become engineers and technologists when they apply the basic principles of physics to a particular field.

A GREAT DEAL of science (particularly physics, chemistry, engineering, and biology) deals with seeing, sorting, comparing, and measuring the optical properties and dimensions. The microscope makes visible to the eye details not otherwise resolvable. Such devices range from a single lens or reading glass that magnifies type only two times to the electron microscope, developed in the past decade, which has a useful magnification up to 100,000 times. The magnification of this instrument is equivalent to making a period on this page appear to be 300 feet in diameter. In between these developments are the ordinary optical microscope, with a useful magnification of 100 to 500 times, and the ultraviolet microscope, with a useful magnification of 2,000 times.

Because the nature of the light used in microscopy is basic in obtaining definition or useful magnification, many devices have been used to control or modify the illumination. The one most recently made available for general use is known as the phase-contrast microscope, which employs minor changes in the phase relation of the wave fronts, where the crests of some of the light waves coincide with the troughs of others, so that highly transparent objects whose structural details vary only slightly can be seen and photographed. Phase microscopes have been employed in the study of bacteria, molds, yeasts, suspensions in body fluids, muscular tissue, feldspar, dusts, and natural and synthetic fibers. The magnification varies from 300 to 1,000 times.

Because electrons in motion have

25

properties similar to those of light, they are now used as an aid to sight in the electron microscope. The electron has a unit negative charge of electricity. Its weight is one eighteen-hundredth of the weight of our smallest atom, hydrogen. It is a part of all atoms. It is also at the heart of a radio or television set. In the electron microscope, those negative-charged particles are deflected and controlled by electric fields, in much the same way as glass lenses bend and control the light beam in the ordinary microscope. The present limit of vision or resolution of the electron microscope is a solid particle that consists of 100 or more atoms. This powerful pair of eyeglasses therefore helps us to see many of the larger molecules and to get a photographic record of them.

Scientists use the electron microscope for determining the size and shape of very small particles, or for observing very thin sections of substances, such as soils, starches, proteins, dyes, pigments, cellulose, natural and synthetic textile fibers, viruses, and other biological materials. The results are of maximum value when they are used with other information on molecular structure obtained by X-ray, spectroscopic, or light-scattering methods. To the extent that the information is available on these small units of agricultural materials largely depend their uses as foods, feeds, or industrial materials. The information is as important in agricultural research as information on the structural properties of brick and mortar is in the construction of buildings.

The physicist uses the spectroscope for study of the structure of atoms and molecules through the light they emit when in a high state of excitation, as in a flame, electric arc, or spark. Emission spectroscopy gives him a sensitive, accurate, and rapid method of determining, in amounts as small as a few parts per million, essential and desirable . constituents, or harmful and objectionable ones. Lead, tin, iron, and copper from spray residues, processing equipment, and containers used to store foods are examples of substances that may be harmful; calcium and magnesium are considered essential minor, or trace, elements for the growth of plants.

The spectroscopic method also has the advantage that spectra of a number of elements may be recorded on a photographic plate simultaneously and held as an impersonal record for study and analysis later. The spectrograph has been used in agricultural research to determine such trace elements as magnesium, calcium, manganese, copper, iron, boron, cobalt, lead, zinc, tin, and aluminum in soils, fertilizer materials, agricultural products (such as fruits, vegetables, and poultry), and industrial products and byproducts (such as pectin, fats and oils, microbiological culture media, and the fermentation residues).

In spectrophotometry the physicist has a means for studying some of the fundamental physical characteristics of materials. The devices he employs measure the ability of the material to reflect or transmit the electromagnetic waves. As the experimental techniques necessarily vary with the spectral regions, it is natural to divide the subject into visible, ultraviolet, X-ray, infrared, electrical, radio, and microwave spectrophotometry. Those physical methods are important because they give the necessary characterization and identification, without chemical or physical change in the materials under study. They are often the only methods available for obtaining those results.

LIGHT is the part of the spectrum that is ordinarily visible to the eye. A material appears colored because it selectively reflects or transmits light. Color is a significant factor in the acceptability of foods and most items of the home. The more nearly the original color of fruits, vegetables, and poultry products can be kept in processing and storage, the more acceptable they will be to the consumer.

In researches on agricultural products, color is treated only from a physical standpoint. The physicist can state with certainty that two beams of light are identical, or he can determine how two beams of light differ with no reference whatsoever to the eye. A recording spectrophotometer is used in the investigations because it permits a record of the percentage of light reflected from the sample (or transmitted through a clear extract) to be automatically recorded on a chart. The physicist thus can measure quickly and accurately differences in color in the fresh produce or the changes in color due to processing and storage.

Typical curves are given in the accompanying chart for light reflected from an orange, a winesap apple, yellow sweet corn, and fresh green peas, all products of average market maturity. Differences in color are related to differences in percentage of reflectance in the visible range of 400 to 700 millimicrons (4,000 to 7,000 angstroms, the units which are used to measure the wave length of light and which correspond to the colors indicated in the figures). In the chart on page 29, reflectance curves are given for lemons in different states of maturity. You will notice that the most marked differences occur at about 680 millimicrons, corresponding to one of the chlorophyll absorption bands. As the amount of chlorophyll, the predominant green pigment in vegetation, decreases, the lemon becomes progressively yellower. Two important plant pigments, carotene (provitamin A) and chlorophyll, are identified and characterized by their absorption spectra. The deterioration or loss of carotene and the transformation of chlorophyll to pheophytin, a brown pigment, in agricultural products are also followed with the spectrophotometer.

Crystalline quartz is the material used for the optical system in the ultraviolet spectrograph and transmits to about 1,850 A. (angstroms). The useful range covered by such an instrument extends from 2,000 to about 8,000 A.; or from the ultraviolet through the entire visible region of the spectrum. When diffracted, or bent, light rays from the spectrograph are allowed to pass through a quartz cell containing the clear liquid to be characterized, one or more absorption bands usually result.

Because most of the measurements are made on substances in solution, solids as well as liquids can be investigated. Constants and calculations for the spectrophotometric determination of fatty acids, important constituents of fats and oils and having direct bearing on spoilage and rancidity, have been established.

A new spectrophotometric method has been developed at the Western Regional Research Laboratory for analyzing hop extracts for humulon and lupulon, two essential constituents that have antibiotic properties—that is, they prevent the growth of certain bacteria. Although the two substances are colorless, their ultraviolet absorption spectra are different enough to permit the determination of the amounts of humulon and lupulon in a hop extract in about 15 minutes. We do that by measuring the optical density of the extract at two different wave lengths in the ultraviolet region of the spectrum. No satisfactory chemical method existed previously for determining lupulon in the presence of humulon.

THE PRINCIPLES used for measurements in the visible and ultraviolet regions of the spectrum are applied also in infrared spectrophotometry. The only differences are imposed by materials and energy sources and receivers best adapted to infrared radiation. The prisms are usually rock salt, lithium fluoride, or potassium bromide, which are more transparent than either glass or quartz to the longer infrared radiations and also have characteristic dispersions higher for certain bands that may be under study.

Substances of agricultural origin that have been characterized by application of infrared spectrophotometry are cellulose, cotton and wool, vitamin C and related compounds, amino acids

SPECTROPHOTOMETRIC REFLECTANCE CURVES
OF SOME FRUITS AND
VEGETABLES

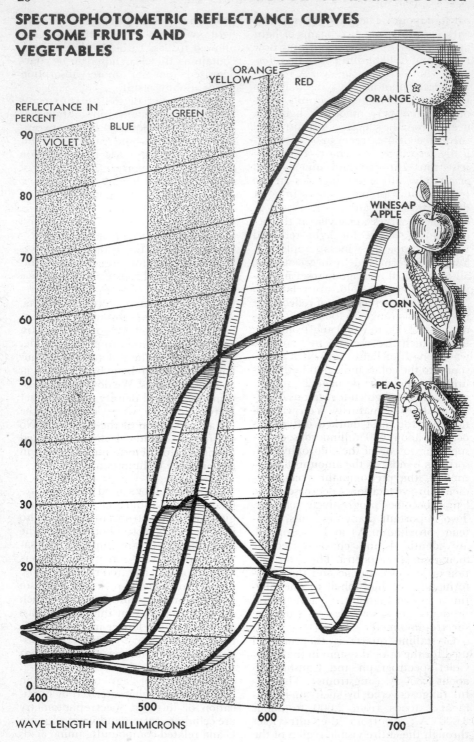

SPECTROPHOTOMETRIC REFLECTANCE CURVES OF LEMONS IN VARIOUS STAGES OF RIPENING

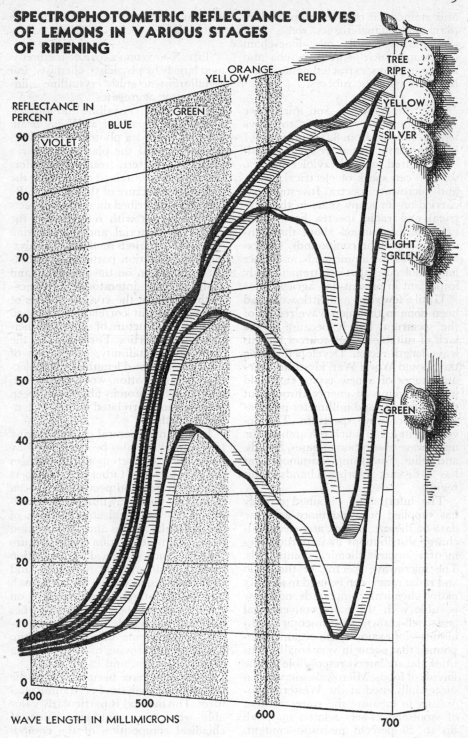

REFLECTANCE IN PERCENT

WAVE LENGTH IN MILLIMICRONS

and amino acid complexes, penicillin, plant and animal tissues, some plant pigments, vegetable oils, long-chain compounds such as gutta-percha and rubber in plants, extracted natural rubbers, and synthetic rubbers.

ELECTRICAL, RADIO, and microwave spectrophotometry applies to wave lengths ranging from 8,000 miles to 0.1 inch in length. Just as we speak of visible, infrared, and ultraviolet spectra, we also can speak of electrical, radio, and microwave spectra. Investigations carried on for many years in the electrical and radio spectra have given valuable information about the high-molecular-weight compounds, for example, proteins, amino acids, and other large molecules that are tremendously important in present-day agriculture.

Until a few years ago, little work had been done in the microwave region of the spectrum, largely because of the lack of suitable energy sources for this wave-length region. Developed during the Second World War, klystrons (vacuum tubes of a new type) can yield useful amounts of energy throughout the centimeter and millimeter portions of the microwave spectrum. The development led to much research on the microwave absorption of gases, liquids, and solids. For example, ammonia gas has 30 distinct absorption bands in this region.

The information obtained already has supplied new and more accurate data on the size, shapes, and electrical-charge distributions in important elementary organic chemical compounds. The microwave spectra, or the radio and radar range, can be used to identify many chemical compounds not now possible with the more conventional and well-known spectroscopic techniques—for example, the organic compounds that occur in very small quantities and are largely responsible for the flavors of foods. Microwaves have been successfully used at the Western Laboratory to measure the water content of wool and closely related material, up to 20 percent moisture content,

without modifying or destroying the materials.

THE X-RAY DIFFRACTION method is used largely by physicists, chemists, and metallurgists to study crystalline solids and organic aggregates.

When some crystalline substance is placed in the path of an X-ray beam directed toward a photographic plate, development of the plate will show a diffraction pattern from which information can be obtained concerning the molecular structure of the material. By following prescribed methods of directing the X-rays with reference to the crystalline material and by applying somewhat laborious methods of analyzing the diffraction patterns, physicists get information on the symmetry and position and interatomic distances of the atoms in the crystal. Studies of this type permit correlations between the internal structure of solids and their physical properties. For example, the degree of crystallinity, orientation of the molecules, and length of the molecular chains in cotton, wool, ramie, flax, and synthetic protein fibers have been obtained and correlated with their tensile strengths.

Important structural changes during processing have also been followed by observation of corresponding changes in X-ray patterns. Other high polymers (such as starch and pectin) have been studied by the X-ray diffraction method. The geometrical configuration of the molecular chains and the variation in interchain separation with moisture content and chemical composition have been determined for pectin and its derivatives, as well as for cornstarch and potato starch. Information on those structural and physical properties has made it possible to develop methods for producing films from pectin. The films are proving of use in coating sticky figs, dates, and candy bars.

X-rays also have been useful for the quantitative analysis of crystalline mixtures. The method is particularly valuable when we want knowledge of chemical composition of the components of the mixture or when chemical properties of the components are sufficiently similar to make chemical analysis difficult or impossible. Electrons, rather than X-rays, are sometimes used in such experiments; they are especially effective for the investigation of the structure of surfaces, thin films, gases, and liquids. Within the past 5 years, neutrons (noncharged particles with a weight close to that of the hydrogen atom) from atomic piles have been used in the same way as X-rays and electrons; no doubt they will supply another tool for obtaining information on molecular structure, particularly in instances in which the other methods cannot be used satisfactorily.

Cooperative investigations by physicists, the electrical engineers, and the food technologists have been carried out at the Massachusetts Institute of Technology on the biological and photochemical effects of high-voltage X-rays and cathode rays. Many microorganisms and organic materials, including food products, have been irradiated with varying dosages of X-rays at potentials up to 4 million volts, and the lethal (or killing) and chemical effects were evaluated. A few tests were made with high-voltage cathode rays or penetrating electrons, which proved to be several hundred times more efficient than the X-rays used. The observed effects were attributed to the excitation and ionization of the atoms of the absorbing material.

The general conclusions drawn from the studies in July 1948, were: Very large doses of approximately 3-million-volt X-rays destroyed bacteria, yeasts, and molds in massive concentrations in pure culture and when they were associated with liquid or solid substances, such as milk, water, apple juice, or ground spices, soil, and catgut sutures. Sporeforming bacteria were less affected than the nonsporeforming bacteria. As usually noted when lethal agents are applied, the destruction was not uniform; that is, most of the bacteria were killed in a short time, but a few survived. It was not very difficult to kill

902722°—51——4

99.9+ percent of the bacteria; to achieve complete destruction, however, often required 10 to 20 times that dosage. Fatty foods, when they were irradiated, showed a tendency to become rancid or to have a rank smell or taste. X-ray treatment gave some reduction of vitamin C in the pure state but somewhat less reduction of the vitamin in orange and grapefruit juices.

HEAT is of primary importance in processing agricultural products, particularly foods. But the benefits gained by heating (for example, blanching or scalding of fruit and vegetables before freezing) are almost always offset by a loss of one or more desirable or essential characteristics of the original material. The physical problem is apparent—in this case, to supply just enough heat to the fruit or vegetable to kill the bacteria that contribute to spoilage and to deactivate or destroy the enzymes that normally would reduce the food value of the product.

Radio-frequency (rf) or dielectric heating would seem to meet that requirement, because the heat required can be rapidly generated within the material in a fairly uniform way.

In contrast, in the more conventional heating methods the temperature gradient is such that the surface must be heated much hotter than the inner parts of the material in order to make sure that every particle of the mass will be heated to the required temperature.

In dielectric heating, the nonconducting material forms the dielectric of a condenser in the circuit of the apparatus designed for the heating process. Rf radiation varies from 100 thousand cycles per second to 300 million cps and forms the radio-wave part of the electromagnetic spectrum where the developments were primarily made for radio. Those frequencies correspond to wave lengths in air of 300 meters and 1 meter, respectively. This method of heating is successfully used in plywood gluing, in setting plastics, and sealing sheet thermoplastics.

Laboratory experiments on rf heating for the drying of vegetables have been carried out by the Western Laboratory. Similar work was done elsewhere at atmospheric pressure and in a vacuum. Uniform internal heating depends on having a homogeneous material; as most agricultural and biological materials are not homogeneous, they are not uniformly heated. Sparking or arcing tends to produce charred spots (which ruin the product for food) on products like peas and potato pieces. Experiments on the thawing of frozen foods by rf heating showed that as the outer portion of the sample is thawed, or the ice melts, that part continues to be heated more readily than the inner or frozen portion; to prevent scorching, the thawed part must be mechanically removed, so that the remainder is still a frozen solid.

During the Second World War, the development of the magnetron and klystron resulted in extending the frequency range for heating from 300 million cps (1 meter wave length) to 30 billion cps (1 centimeter). Sufficient laboratory work has been carried out to demonstrate that in this range of frequencies bacteria are killed and enzymes inactivated. In the studies with both rf and microwaves, however, no specific effect was observed other than that caused by the heat produced in the material by the high-frequency currents.

INDUCTION HEATING is the process of heating conducting materials by setting up electric currents in them at frequencies varying from 500 to 12,000 cps. Induction heating is used primarily in the metal industry, where exact analyses of metal for alloys are required, and in melting, forging, and hardening processes. Induction heating can be used to heat nonmetals in special instances. For example, some meat products have been successfully heated by induction at frequencies of about 1 million cps.

SONIC AND ULTRASONIC FREQUENCIES vary from a few cycles per second in the audible range to as high as 100 million cps in the ultrasonic range. Those sound waves have been known for a long time; but the World Wars intensified developments in connection with their use in submarine and airplane detection.

An early application in the Department of Agriculture showed that colloidal suspensions of very fine particles of soil and other substances in water would be quickly dispersed when subjected to ultrasonic energy. The breaking up and mixing of the milk particles, or homogenization, has also been accomplished by this means. Immiscible liquids, such as water and oil, can be transformed into stable emulsions by ultrasonic waves. Colloidal suspensions of paraffin and water have been produced.

Bacteria are destroyed probably by a mechanical process resulting from the waves and not by the accompanying heat. It is difficult, however, to separate the effect of temperature as such from the mechanical process of breaking up or shattering the bacteria. The biological studies generally are therefore not so conclusive as desired. The process may be compared to a dog vigorously shaking a snake until it is dead and in pieces. Large molecules like those of starch have been split at around 700 thousand cps. The use of high-frequency sound waves in characterizing natural and synthetic rubber has been reported as sufficiently promising that the range of useful sound waves is being extended.

The relative sensitivities of bacteria and viruses to intense sonic vibration have been investigated in conjunction with the use of the electron microscope. Experiments have included such diverse applications as a change in genes with mutation, modification of organic molecules, sterilization of foods by killing the bacteria, enzyme deactivation, and the killing of mosquito larva, weevils in grain, and insects in tobacco.

The value and importance of treating foods by sound waves are difficult to determine at this stage, because the long exposures required to kill most of the bacteria may also substantially decrease the essential organic constituents, such as vitamin C.

PHYSICISTS during the past quarter century have been leaders in studies of radioactivity and gaseous ionization and in developing such devices as Geiger-Mueller tube counters, vacuum-tube electrometers and amplifiers, cyclotrons, and atomic piles, essential in the important radioactive tracer technique. A brief explanation of some of the terms in use follows.

The atoms of an element are not of the same weight, although they are identical in chemical properties. The different kinds of atoms of an element are called isotopes of the element. Most elements have several isotopes; hydrogen has three atomic weights: 1, 2, 3. Oxygen also has three: 16, 17, 18. Elements like radium, uranium, and thorium, which spontaneously give off radiations of either fast electrons (beta particles), gamma rays (similar to X-rays), or positive-charged particles (alpha particles), are called radioactive.

A cyclotron is a device used to speed up electrons and atomic- or molecular-weight particles bearing a positive charge until they can disrupt or break up or modify atoms, some of which have radioactive properties and are known as radioactive isotopes.

The atomic pile, developed in connection with the atomic bomb, is now supplying adequate sources of radioactive carbon and other materials for agricultural research. The fact that the radioactive isotopes emit beta and gamma radiations, which can be followed through various systems by sensitive instruments such as the Geiger-Mueller counter, is the basis of the method. The quantitative determination of radioactivity is based on the ionization effects produced in gases by the radiations emitted from the radioactive materials. The radioactive tracer atoms are substituted for normal atoms in dilutions comparable to one in a million, in all kinds of physical, chemical, and biological systems.

The use of radioactive phosphorus as a tracer in fertilizers and soils and in the growth processes of various crops under wide agronomic conditions is giving promising results.

Similarly, radioactive sulfur, potassium, and calcium now are used to follow the movement of those elements through plant growth. Radioactive iodine and phosphorus are also used in the study of the function of plant hormones. Radioactive carbon in the form of carbon dioxide is used in the synthesis of sugars, amino acids, and other carbon compounds and also is giving promising results in determining the chemical processes involved.

Some experiments are in progress on the use of radioactive carbon in solving problems bearing on food spoilage and radioactive sulfur in the study of wool and mohair fibers.

Other physical methods that are in use in agricultural research will be briefly mentioned.

PHOTOELECTRIC LIGHT-SCATTERING photometer and differential refractometer are instruments that were developed at the Eastern Regional Research Laboratory for determining the molecular weight and particle size of polymerized products in solutions.

The high-molecular-weight compounds studied were casein, starch fractions, synthetic rubber, polymers of fatty acid derivatives, pectins, and proteins derived from agricultural products.

MASS SPECTROMETRY is applied to determine molecular weights and the relative abundance of isotopes, and to the quantitative analysis of complex organic mixtures. In the mass spectrograph, a beam of electrons bombards a column of gas molecules and produces positive ions. The positive ions are deflected by a magnetic field to a degree depending on their mass and are recorded on a collecting and amplifying system.

FLUOROMETRY is based on the property of materials and organic substances of emitting characteristic fluorescent-light spectrums when illuminated with ultraviolet light. The determination of the vitamins thiamine and riboflavin are examples of interest to agriculture.

POLARIMETRY, which deals with the quantitative measurement of the ability of various organic compounds to turn the plane of polarized light passed through them, has been particularly useful in the analysis of sugars for many years. The extent of rotation of the polarized light depends upon the kind of sugar and the amount present.

MECHANICS, including the measurements of the strength of materials, viscosity, elasticity, diffusion, capilarity, and compressibility, finds direct application in food processing and industrial utilization.

The dehydration of agricultural materials, the development of gelling substances, and the packaging, storage, and transportation of fruit, vegetables, and poultry products are processes in which the field of mechanics is a basic part of agricultural research.

JUST AS SWORDS and armor were turned into plowshares, the German nitrogen-fixation process (which was a factor in the First World War) can now supply an unlimited amount of fixed atmospheric nitrogen for use as fertilizer. Products from the atomic bomb, supersonics, and radar (developed for national defense) are being applied to agricultural research and should continue to provide the basis of new ideas for use in the processing and utilization of farm products.

Thus physicists are aiding in the solution of the difficult and important problems facing agriculture today, in close cooperation and teamwork with chemists, engineers, biologists, agronomists, and geneticists.

C. H. KUNSMAN holds degrees from Pennsylvania State College and the University of California. He has been engaged in research in agricultural physics since 1923 in the Bureau of Agricultural and Industrial Chemistry and its predecessors, starting with the Fixed Nitrogen Research Laboratory. He was associated with agricultural research at Pennsylvania State College, New Mexico State College, and the University of California. He served as associate editor of the Journal of Applied Physics and the Journal of Chemical Physics. He was a member of the Advisory Council of Applied Physics, and chairman of the American delegation to the International Congress on Chemical Fertilizers in Rome, 1938.

DURING an armyworm outbreak in central Arkansas, a meeting was held with farmers to explain methods of control of the insect. After our explanation of the procedure to be followed in mixing poison-bran bait and broadcasting it over the fields, the group began discussing certain practical angles of the operation. Prevailing opinion seemed to be that it required too much work. One old gentleman listened to this complaining for some time and then spoke up:

"You boys are right; it is a lot of work. I've baited armyworms before and I know. But the hardest part isn't mixing and broadcasting the bait. The hardest part is trying to make up your mind to do it."—*F. D. Miner, Department of Entomology, College of Agriculture, University of Arkansas.*

Making Use of the Biological Approach

Richard W. Jackson

Biology is the science of life, of the process by which living things begin, grow, change, and die. Agriculture as a whole is primarily biology, to which the sciences of chemistry, physics, and meteorology give support. Indeed, agricultural production is the biological conversion of one kind of material into another. Green plants, for example, convert carbon dioxide, water, and simple forms of nitrogen into carbohydrates, fats, and proteins. Cattle convert plant materials into beef, milk, and hides. Each of these products in turn may undergo a biological change. Hides are tanned and become leather, for which no full-fledged substitute has been found yet. Rennet, the enzyme from the calf's stomach, acts upon milk to form cheese. Beef is digested, absorbed, and converted into new tissue and energy.

The biological approach also is put to use in the manufacture of pickles and soya sauce, in the preservation of eggs, in the investigation of allergens, in the preparation of nicotine and derivatives as insecticides, in the biosynthesis of riboflavin, in the production of feed yeast from waste materials, and in the control and use of enzymes. In many more ways, besides, does biology add to the quality, quantity, and diversity of products that are derived from agricultural commodities.

One way of converting agricultural materials to other kinds of useful products is to submit them to the metabolism of an organism so that the bulk of the material is not destroyed—only changed. For that purpose, plants, animals, and micro-organisms can be used. The higher plants are the most important chemical factories in agriculture for production, but they have limited use as modifying agents. An exception is sprouted barley, or malt, which is used to bring about the hydrolysis of starch to sugar on a commercial scale.

The use of animals as converting agents is expensive—the fact is that the solids contained in milk or meat cost 25 to 100 times as much as the solids of corn or alfalfa.

• BUT THE MICRO-ORGANISMS—the third group of living organisms that carry out innumerable modifications—often do so at relatively little cost. They include the molds, yeasts, and bacteria. Given favorable temperature and moisture, and the necessary food materials, they are exceedingly active. A few do harm to man, animals, or plants. Most of the micro-organisms do not cause disease. They are useful in reducing the substance of dead animal and plant tissues to simple forms in the soil and air for later use. Imagine what a mass of dead trees and other plants and animals would accumulate if the microscopic scavengers were not always at work!

Micro-organisms may be used to produce the simple organic compounds, like acetic acid and acetone, as well as substances of great complexity. Plants and animals produce materials just as complex, but are more prone to deposit them in mixtures that are hard to separate. It is not uncommon, after a fermentation, to filter or centrifuge off the organism and to obtain a good yield of the desired product directly by evaporation or distillation. That is a consequence of the fact that the metabolism of micro-organisms can often be directed, under carefully controlled conditions, to travel one path predominantly, if not exclusively. A high yield has the usual double advantage, because unwanted products generally interfere with isolation of the main product. Although a given chemical is often produced by a number of organisms, the specificity in general is such as to make it possible to pick and choose the organism and conditions which give the most efficient conversion.

Among organic substances known thus far to be produced by micro-organisms are many ordinary chemicals, unique carbohydrates, a variety of enzymes, special proteins, vitamins, fats, strange pigments and dyes, an array of antibiotics (the microbes' instruments of chemical warfare), and a host of odd substances whose use is yet to be suggested.

It is well to emphasize the ability of the micro-organisms to synthesize compounds. In many respects it is greater than that of the higher plants and animals. Plants and animals, for example, always produce the same l-configuration of an amino acid, of which two forms, mirror images of each other, are possible. Likewise, the lactic acid in muscles of animals is inevitably d-lactic acid. Micro-organisms do not confine themselves to the one standardized type of amino acid. They may produce a protein that is a polymer of one amino acid, instead of many, and opposite in form to that in higher plants and animals. Again, they may produce both optical forms of lactic acid. These instances illustrate the amazing chemical versatility of the myriads that inhabit the microscopic realm.

BECAUSE MOLDS, YEASTS, actinomycetes, and bacteria provide working tools for developing new fermentation processes, the research worker must keep on hand a large collection of correctly identified cultures. The culture collection of the Northern Regional Research Laboratory, established in 1940, contains more than 5,000 separate strains, of which about 2,500 are molds, 1,700 are yeasts, and 900 are bacteria. An almost equal number of strains of unknown potentialities also have been collected and are maintained only in lyophilized form, a sort of dormant state. These constitute a potentially valuable reserve series. The collection is particularly rich in groups of micro-organisms known to be especially active biochemically; it is believed to be the largest collection of industrially important strains in the world. A vigorous program has been pursued also to identify and classify new forms or old ones unsatisfactorily described.

The collection is a reservoir of cultures upon which our own investigations are based. It also provides a source of biochemically active cultures for other investigators in this country and abroad. It was particularly important to the realization of large-scale production of penicillin during the war, because it was the principal source of authenticated, high-yielding penicillin-producing molds.

Micro-organisms vary greatly in their dietary requirements. A medium comprising glucose, ammonium sulfate, potassium phosphate, and traces of magnesium, manganese, iron, and zinc suffices for some. Others need supplements of certain amino acids, purines, pyrimidines, and vitamins. Corn steep liquor and soybean protein, among similar materials, are used industrially to supplement the carbohydrate.

Fermentation is sometimes the preferred method in utilizing the second-grade or waste materials. The advantage is most likely to exist in a process involving the stripping, or distillation, of the desired products from the "beer," or fermentation liquor. Impurities, which might cause trouble in isolating a product by direct precipitation or crystallization, would not interfere in removal of volatile chemicals. Thus, the starch of off-grade corn and the sugar of molasses can be used efficiently in the production of ethyl alcohol or of butyl alcohol and acetone. (The fermentation of corn to butyl alcohol is noteworthy in that the organism used possesses its own mechanism for converting starch to sugar; hence the separate and expensive malting procedure is dispensed with.)

But micro-organisms, like other living things, have limits of tolerance toward unfavorable factors, and the utilization by fermentation of some waste materials hinges on the discovery of an especially resistant organism or an economical treatment to eliminate toxic components. An example is the residual sugar concentrate obtained from various industries. When such a concentrate does not ferment like a sugar solution of the same concentration, it might contain too much salt or a toxic organic material that was concentrated or produced in the previous processing steps.

The production of ethyl alcohol by yeast has always been the main commercial fermentation, as well as the chief method for conversion of carbohydrate materials to chemicals and liquid fuel. The manufacture of butanol and acetone by means of bacteria is another. Before the Second World War, upwards of 100 million gallons of industrial ethyl alcohol were made each year in the United States; during the war, production reached a peak of 580 million gallons a year. (These figures do not include the fermentative production of distilled beverage alcohol, which after the war has been equivalent to 96 million gallons of 95-percent alcohol annually.)

Nearly all of this was made by fermentation. Lately, fermentation alcohol has been meeting sharp competition from synthetic alcohol derived from petroleum products. Nevertheless, fermentation is the best method known today for converting carbohydrate substance to liquid fuel of high utility. Aside from this background of commercial importance, the alcohol fermentation has interesting biochemical aspects. For those reasons, the opera-tions will be described to illustrate the general features of industrial fermentation.

YEAST, generally some species of *Saccharomyces,* is the organism universally employed to convert the carbohydrate to ethyl alcohol. Like many others of the micro-organisms, but by no means all, yeast requires its carbohydrate in the form of simple sugar, such as glucose, fructose, sucrose, or maltose. Hence, the starch of corn, grain sorghum, potato, or other commodity is converted to sugar by means of malt or fungal amylase (see page 148). That step can also be accomplished by heating the starch with dilute acid, but the biological procedure is more economical, all things considered. After malting is finished, the mash is inoculated with the yeast culture, which ordinarily exhausts the sugar in 48 to 72 hours. The resulting liquor, or beer, is stripped of its alcohol in a steam-heated column. The distillate then is concentrated progressively to give 95-percent alcohol. (The residual material, or distillery slop, is a valuable stock feed. Generally, it is dried down and sold as "distillers' solubles," "light grains," or "dark grains," depending on how the soluble components and screenings are handled.) In the process, the cooked grain mash is no longer sterile after the addition of malt to saccharify the starch. It is common practice, therefore, before the yeast is introduced, to add traces of fluoride to restrict bacterial growth. Most other commercial fermentations require rigorous sterilization of the medium before the pure culture is introduced.

The starch in 1 bushel of corn, dry basis, may yield as high as 3 gallons of 95-percent alcohol with a conversion efficiency of 90 percent or better.

The basic equation for the alcohol fermentation, as described by Joseph Gay-Lussac more than a century ago, is:

$$(1) \quad C_6H_{12}O_6 \xrightarrow{\text{yeast}} 2CH_3CH_2OH + 2CO_2$$
$$\text{glucose} \qquad \text{ethyl alcohol}$$

The reaction is complicated. It proceeds through a number of compounds, including highly labile phosphoric acid derivatives of sugar and other intermediates, and is catalyzed by a series of enzymes and coenzymes. By the time of the First World War, the Germans were able to exploit their knowledge of the fermentation to produce large quantities of glycerol. In the normal process, the hexose sugar is cleaved into two 3-carbon sugars (triose). Acetaldehyde is produced (equation 2) and is reduced to ethyl alcohol (equation 3). Those reactions proceed simultaneously. The net result is shown in equation 4, which is closely related to the first equation. By fixing the acetaldehyde with sodium bisulfite, the reduction (that is, taking up of hydrogen) was diverted to a 3-carbon sugar fragment to give glycerol (equation 5).

We can thus picture the reactions, in greatly condensed form:

$$(2) \quad CH_2OH \cdot CHOH \cdot CHO \longrightarrow CH_3 \cdot CHO + CO_2 + 2H$$
$$\text{triose} \qquad\qquad\qquad \text{acetaldehyde}$$

$$(3) \quad CH_3CHO + 2H \longrightarrow CH_3 \cdot CH_2OH$$
$$\text{alcohol}$$

$$(4) \quad CH_2OH \cdot CHOH \cdot CHO \longrightarrow CH_3CH_2OH + CO_2$$

$$(5) \quad CH_2OH \cdot CHOH \cdot CHO + 2H \rightarrow$$
$$CH_2OH \cdot CHOH \cdot CH_2OH$$
$$\text{glycerol}$$

There are other instances of abnormal products obtained by chemical intervention of fermentative mechanisms. This approach, like the search for organisms with new fermentative capacities resulting from induced mutation, may be regarded as having good potentialities. We are making both.

Another interesting feature of the alcohol fermentation is the side production of the amyl alcohols that compose fusel oil. Their formation has no direct relationship to that of ethyl alcohol. Rather, they are produced by the yeast from the two amino acids, leucine and isoleucine.

$$CH_3$$
$$\searrow$$
$$CH \cdot CH_2 \cdot CH \cdot COOH + H_2O$$
$$CH_3 \nearrow \qquad | $$
$$\qquad\quad NH_2$$
$$\text{leucine}$$

$$CH_3$$
$$\searrow$$
$$CH \cdot CH_2 \cdot CH_2OH + CO_2 + NH_3$$
$$CH_3 \nearrow$$
$$\text{isoamyl alcohol}$$

Fusel oil is a minor product. Fractionated out by the distiller, it contributes some revenue to the industry. There are other cases of production of two useful substances by one organism—for example, the production of the alcohol, butylene glycol, and the antibiotic, polymyxin, by *Bacillus polymyxa*. Polymyxin is potent and its effective formation, unlike that of butylene glycol, requires only a very small amount of the sugar and other substances present in the medium. Unfortunately, in such cases the optimal conditions are seldom the same for the two products. In general, it has proved most practical to make one product at a time and to raise the yield as high as possible.

OUR DISCUSSION thus far has dealt with biological means of production of utilizable materials from farm crops. In another field also biology serves outstandingly—the field of analysis. Analysis provides information on which to draw conclusions and take action. Analysis of your soil, for example, shows whether it needs lime. Likewise, many different kinds of analysis provide the scientist with the information he needs to solve his problem.

Several branches of chemistry are called analytical. Certainly more than half the average chemist's time is spent in analytical operations. The analytical contributions of biology, at least for industrial use, have been developed more slowly, but the applications have been multiplying rapidly, so that it is common to find bacteriologists, nutritionists, or others trained in biological sciences on company research staffs or in charge of control groups. Most often their work is concerned with utilization of agricultural products, but it is by no means limited to the food business.

The living forms available for assay work range all the way from humans to bacteria and other one-celled forms. One of the most difficult tasks is to appraise the taste and odor of foods and beverages, such as frozen vegetables, condiments, processed fruit juices, coffee, whiskies, and wines. Chemical analysis is often useful, but chemical knowledge of the subtle elements of flavors is yet too limited to offer a complete system for their determination. In some fields, the practice continues of depending upon the expert ability of the professional taster. However, a current trend is toward employment of taste panels with the object of making judgments as uniform and reproducible as possible. Such panels are conducted at the regional laboratories in connection with improvement of the quality of soybean oil and of fruit, vegetable, and confectionery products.

The development of drugs like penicillin and rutin called for large numbers of tests with assorted animals. The potency of penicillin was determined with bacteria on agar plates by measurement of the clear zone where the antibiotic prevented growth. Both penicillin and rutin were shown to be free of toxicity and their modes of action explained as clearly as possible. Finally, experiments were made on healthy and unhealthy humans. Thus, pharmacology, physiology, and clinical medicine appeared on the scene. The basic biological sciences are sometimes called on to resolve questions of health hazard from industrial materials not destined for food or medicine. Flying dust causing allergylike symptoms is an example.

Analysis for vitamins is often required. Let us consider the case of vitamin A. Chemical methods are helpful, but final figures should be obtained with animals, generally albino rats. First, vitamin A is withheld from them until they are clearly deficient; then they are fed graded doses of the "unknown" material and also graded doses of a known standard.

Invertebrate animals are also employed. The development of artificial woollike fiber from casein, zein, and other proteins raised the question of how vulnerable the fibers would be to moths or carpet beetles. The answer was obtained by placing the fiber as the only source of food before the test organism. Likewise, the development of insecticides from nicotine and its derivatives requires their scientific testing on the harmful insect, either in the laboratory or in the field.

Micro-organisms naturally serve as the testing agents in making cotton and leather articles that resist mildew, sand bags that resist the rotting organisms of the soil, or similar products. But they serve a broader function in analysis. They can be employed as the analytical tool in the systematic determination of essential biological compounds. In other words, they play the same role in assays as does the albino rat.

Advantages with the micro-organism are that it can be confined to a test tube or small flask and that its cultivation and maintenance are cheaper than the corresponding operations for animals. Again, the time required to complete experiments is considerably less. Consequently, for a given amount of space and a given budget, many more analyses can be run.

Let us suppose assay is to be made for niacin in corn samples—the individual grains in this particular investigation. Each grain is ground and extracted to afford more than enough material for an analysis. The test bacterium is inoculated into a series of sterile tubes containing a medium that meets all its necessary growth and metabolic requirements except niacin. Niacin is added in graded amounts to one set of tubes. The corn samples, or aliquots, are added to another set of tubes. After a standard growth period, the tubes are compared as to density of growth, or titrated to measure the total acid produced from carbohydrate in the substrate. Either index gives an accurate measure of the amount of niacin present in the corn sample.

The method may be used to assay a number of the water-soluble vitamins and nearly all of the amino acids. Microbiological methods of this type are extremely useful and are finding a wide application. One of their most interesting uses is to show how much of each essential amino acid is present in common foods and food mixtures. We thus come one step closer to knowing the real value of the foods we eat.

Forty years ago, the term "fermentation" was used mostly in reference to production of alcohol, particularly in beverages, and to the manufacture of such products as vinegar and pickles. Nevertheless, the manufacture of lactic acid had begun and, at the time of the First World War, there was initiated the large-scale production of acetone and butyl alcohol by a fermentation method. Next came the microbiological manufacture of citric acid. Similar developments later furnished gluconic acid. In the past decade, fermentation has expanded greatly to include the production of the antibiotics and some of the vitamins. In the light of these developments in so short a time, one can look forward to further discoveries and their use in his daily life. Micro-organisms are like humans and other animals in that, whereas some are harmful,

many are useful. It is our job to find out more about the useful ones and how they can be made to cooperate in producing better or cheaper materials for everyday use.

RICHARD W. JACKSON *heads the fermentation division in the Northern Regional Research Laboratory. He has degrees from Eureka College and the University of Illinois. Dr. Jackson held professorships in the University of Louisville, Yale University, and Cornell University Medical College. He joined the Department of Agriculture in 1939 as chief of the protein division at the Eastern Regional Research Laboratory and served in that capacity until 1947. His research contributions have dealt chiefly with the synthesis, chemistry, and intermediary metabolism of amino acids and other organic acids and with the utilization of agricultural commodities. He discovered the essentiality of methionine in diets.*

As EARLY as the turn of the century, acetone and butanol had been identified as fermentation products. Not until the First World War, however, when acetone was required for the manufacture of cordite, a high explosive developed by the British, and for dope for airplane wings, were plants installed to ferment grains to acetone. Butanol was then considered a byproduct with little value. With the end of the war, acetone was no longer required in large quantities, and, because there had never been a market for butanol, the plants were closed. But a demand soon developed for butanol in the manufacture of automobile lacquers, and the industry was revived. Acetone was then regarded as a byproduct. With the subsequent discovery that the bacteria synthesize riboflavin (an important B vitamin) during the fermentation of grain, the butanol fermentation liquor is now first stripped for the solvents and then dried for use as a valuable vitamin concentrate. Today, few other fermentation processes depending on bacteria play so important a part in the manufacture of chemicals as the butanol-acetone fermentation.—*H. M. Tsuchiya, Northern Regional Research Laboratory.*

The Engineer and His Pilot Plant

Roderick K. Eskew

The physicist, chemist, and biologist study a farm product and discover that something good and useful can be made from it. Using beakers, flasks, filters, stills, and such laboratory equipment, they develop on a small scale a method for making the new product, but before it can be an article of commerce some questions have to be answered: Is there a potential market for it? Is it feasible to make it on a large scale? What sort of factory equipment will be needed? What will it cost?

The chemical engineer undertakes to answer the last three questions. His workshop is the pilot plant. His tools range from buckets and shovels to intricate reproductions of large-scale chemical-processing machinery. With pumps, pipes, meters, and control instruments, he integrates the small-scale units into the equivalent of a small factory, the pilot plant. With them, the chemical engineer usually can find the answers to the three questions.

You might suppose that transferring a laboratory method to a commercial process would be solely one of increasing the scale of operations. It is far more than that, for in the pilot plant there must be answered questions that cannot logically be studied on a laboratory scale and that would be too costly to answer on a factory scale.

For instance, the problem of corrosion. Glass is all right in the laboratory, but it would not be used in factory operation unless less expensive and less fragile materials (such as wood, steel, copper, stainless steel, or Monel metal) could not be used. The chemical engineer must determine the cheapest and most durable material to use, consistent with maintaining quality in the product.

A larger scale of operations may pose another problem—putting heat in or taking it out of the reacting chemicals. In the laboratory one can use a bunsen burner to heat the flask. One can put the flask in a bucket of ice if it gets too hot. In the factory, however, heating may have to be done by electricity, direct firing, or steam. Cooling may have to be done with tap water or a refrigerant. The transfer of large quantities of heat to reaction vessels may entail a problem of design, especially if the materials are viscous or sensitive to heat. The chemical engineer must therefore take economy into consideration and must apply the principles of heat transfer and fluid flow to the design of his equipment. At times he may have to modify the process to make it feasible on a large scale.

A specific example illustrates the pilot-plant stages. Each year thousands of tons of red oil are used to make agents for processing textiles, lubricants, soaps, protective coatings, and other items. Red oil can be considered a crude oleic acid, of which it contains about 70 percent. In the course of research on animal fats and oils at the Eastern Regional Research Laboratory, chemists found a means of producing an oleic acid of 85 to 95 percent purity. They used the same starting materials as in making red oil—inedible animal fats obtained from the slaughterhouses. The cost of the purer product might be higher than that of red oil. In order to find whether there was a potential market for the im-

41

proved product even at a somewhat higher cost, a market survey was made by the Laboratory's industrial liaison representative. He learned that there was a market for the new product. Chemical engineers then undertook to find out whether its manufacture would be feasible on a large scale, what sort of factory equipment would be required, and what it would cost.

The chemists found that by combining hydrogen with the fats, splitting them into their respective acids, and then chilling them in acetone, they could separate the fats into two fractions—a solid one and a liquid one. The liquid fraction comprised the new, purer oleic acid, dissolved in the acetone. The acetone was removed to give the new product.

In the laboratory the chemists used acetone in a 5-gallon bottle to dissolve the mixture of fatty acids, with which some hydrogen had been combined, and chilled the resulting mixture in a refrigerator. They filtered off on a cold suction filter the crystals that formed, again operating in an improvised refrigerator. Then they distilled the liquid drawn off from the crystals to remove the acetone. The new, purer oleic acid remained.

Obviously, merely to scale up these operations would not be feasible commercially. To carry them out batchwise, as the chemists have to do, would cost too much for labor and would waste refrigeration, because the solutions would be warmed by exposure to air while being handled. Pilot-plant studies were therefore planned to make the process a continuously flowing one. If the dissolving, chilling, and filtering could be done in closed apparatus with the liquids flowing steadily through them, the labor would be reduced to merely watching and adjusting the machinery, and the solutions could easily be kept cold. Continuous operation also makes a more uniform product.

Before designing an integrated unit for continuous operation, the engineers experimented to determine the effect of rate of cooling the acetone solution on the character of the crystals and on the completeness of crystallization. Because the crystals had to be filtered on a continuous filter, it was desirable to have them of such a character that the solvent could be sucked away from them rapidly. The results of that work permitted the engineers to design the pilot-plant unit. When this unit is completed, the partially hydrogenated fatty acids and the acetone will be automatically fed to the crystallizer in the proper proportions.

The crystallizer is a long, stainless-steel tube, surrounded by brine at about 40 degrees below the freezing point of water. As the mixture flows through the tube, crystallization takes place, and scrapers remove the crystals from the walls of the tube. When the materials leave the crystallizing tube, the mixture of crystals and liquid passes over a rotating drum covered with filter cloth. The crystals are continuously scraped off the surface of the drum while the liquid fraction flows from inside the drum. The liquid can then be distilled by a continuous process to remove the acetone, which is returned to the system for reuse. When the operation of the unit has been studied experimentally, we shall be able to answer the questions necessary to translate the process into commercial operation.

BUT BASIC RESEARCH on the development of new processes does not always originate in the laboratory. Some new process or product may wait only on the solution of an engineering problem. Take the case of a process that chemical engineers developed for recovering in concentrated, unaltered form the volatile flavoring constituents of apple juice. It had long been known that by vaporizing 10 percent of the freshly pressed juice all the volatile flavors could be obtained in the distillate. The 10-fold concentration, however, was too low to be of practical use, and the aim was to obtain a highly concentrated essence without losing any of the flavors. The problem was an engineering one. It had two aspects. It entailed the design of an evaporator that would make possible the vaporization of 10 percent of the juice under conditions of time and temperature that would not change the flavor of the stripped juice or the essence. Moreover, some means for concentrating the aromas and collecting them without loss had to be devised. If the vaporization were done under vacuum, the aromas were difficult to capture. It thus became necessary to design an evaporator that at atmospheric pressure would achieve the desired vaporization quickly.

When that was done and the evolved vapors were concentrated in a packed column and the vent gases were scrubbed with chilled essence, the aroma fraction was obtained. Cost estimates were prepared, the basic engineering data and operating procedures were compiled, and recommendations for large-scale operation were published by H. P. Milleville and me. Apple essence is discussed at greater length in the next chapter.

The essences of apples and other fruit are now becoming important articles of commerce. They can be used to give the true flavor of fresh fruit to carbonated beverages, candy, ices, and a host of other fruit products.

But the sequel to that account remains to be told. Chemical engineers have started studies of design and pilot-plant research to find out if they can recapture the appetizing aromas that come out of the kettles in which jam, jellies, and preserves are being made. Such concentrates could be used to improve the flavor of the products made in the kettles or as concentrated essences to improve the flavor of beverages, bakery products, and the like.

The technical feasibility of a new process has to be determined. Cost analyses also are required. Industrial utilization of an agricultural commodity will not eventuate unless there is an actual or potential market for the new product and unless the producer can make a profit on the enterprise. The cost analyses are frequently made at more than one stage. Even in the original laboratory studies it is desirable often to make at least a preliminary estimate to clarify the relationship between value of product and probable cost of production. As pilot-plant investigation progresses, several lines of approach may present themselves. A cost estimate at this stage is frequently used as one criterion in making a choice. Finally, when the process has been proved both technically and economically sound, detailed estimates of costs are prepared for publication, along with the basic engineering data, in order that a potential manufacturer may have all details before he decides whether or not to adopt the process.

THUS the chemical engineer, through pilot-plant research, can predict with reasonable accuracy what a new product will cost. He can recommend the type of equipment to be used in the factory and provide basic engineering data for the design and operation of commercial units. Only in this way can the fullest practical use be made of the laboratory researcher's findings.

RODERICK K. ESKEW, *a native of West Virginia, was graduated in chemical engineering from the Massachusetts Institute of Technology. After 18 years in the wood pulp, plastics, and rayon industries, he became head of the chemical engineering and development division in the Eastern Regional Research Laboratory. During the war he traveled in Mexico and Haiti in connection with natural-rubber recovery investigations and in 1947 made a survey in Europe of industrial processing of potatoes.*

Scientists report that there are now more than 10,000 different uses for cotton.

The Step From Laboratory to Industry

R. Henry Morris, 3d

Of the 120 million bushels of apples we produce annually, about one-fifth are culls or surplus. The problem arises as to what should be done to keep them from going to waste.

First, a chemist is assigned the job of developing new products. He familiarizes himself with the chemical characteristics of the apple and then with the actual operations in the various apple-processing plants. From that study, he gets an idea that he develops into a process for making sirup from the juice. The method consists of treating apple juice with lime and heating to 180° F., clarifying, adding acid, and evaporating it to 75 percent solids. The sirup looks good to him, because it is mild in taste, sweet, of good color, and easy to make.

Now that he has a new product, many questions occur to him. What use can be made of the sirup? If it is to be used for food, would it require better apples than if it is to have an industrial use? What would be the difference in price? How much will it cost to make the sirup commercially? What price can he get for the sirup? How much can be sold? Who would make it? Who would use it? Is it worth while to investigate it in the pilot plant?

At that point, the liaison man enters the investigation. In industry, he may be known as a technical salesman, market researcher, industrial liaison specialist, fact finder, or sales serviceman.

In the Department of Agriculture, he is all of those; he bridges the gap between the laboratory and industry. His responsibility is to make sure the maximum value is obtained from the research accomplishment by developing to the greatest possible degree its utilization by industry. One way to describe the bridging process is to continue with the actual example of apple sirup. The description of its commercial development, which begins now, and that of essence recovery, which follows, illustrate the liaison man's procedure.

To reach an intelligent decision on the desirability of pilot-plant operation, more information was needed. As a starting point, the liaison man got from the chemist samples of the sirup and a pamphlet entitled *Production of Bland Apple Sirup from Apples,* which describes the method of preparation, the physical and chemical characteristics of the sirup, and suggestions as to uses.

Then, the liaison man discussed the development with trade associations, publishers of trade magazines, farmers, cooperatives, and representatives of industry. The preliminary inquiries showed enough commercial interest in the manufacture and use of the sirup to justify experimental studies in the pilot plant.

While the liaison man awaited results from the studies, he assembled crop statistics which would be helpful in selecting the best places for plants. The statistics included the quantities of apples available in different areas, percentages of culls and wastes, seasonal availability, prices, and the amount processed for various uses.

In preparation for the commercial tests on the sirup to determine its possible application, he found out the kind and amount of sweeteners and hygroscopic (moisture-holding) substances used by the different industries, because those were the main characteristics of apple sirup. Cane sugar was taken as an example of a sweetener and glycerin of a hygroscopic material.

When substantial quantities of sirup became available from the pilot plant, the liaison man arranged with representative industrial concerns for actual performance tests. He closely followed the tests to discover any problems that might require solution by the laboratory.

As a sweetener, apple sirup was evaluated in beverages, ice cream, candy, drugs, bakery products, and fountain and table sirups, as a modifier of curd tension in milk, and as a source of carbohydrates for infant feeding. It was also tested as a hygroscopic agent and plasticizer—or softener—in cosmetics, tooth paste, cork closures for bottle caps, coated paper, bakery goods, and tobacco. The tobacco industry normally uses 40 million pounds of glycerin a year.

Although all the tests gave promising results, some difficulties made further investigation in the laboratory necessary. A few examples show their nature. When apple sirup was used as a sweetener, especially in table sirups and beverages, a bitter aftertaste developed. The sirup did not mix satisfactorily when used in drugs, cosmetics, and tooth pastes that contain oils and fats. Spray residues from apples used for sirups made for human consumption could be a hazard. The liaison man brought the problems of commercial application to the laboratory for solution. The chemists traced the bitter aftertaste and poor mixing to the relatively high calcium content of the sirup. They remedied the trouble and reduced the spray residue within safe limits by special treatment—ion exchange.

In the instances in which he learned the sirup could be used successfully, the liaison man obtained more complete information, such as a comparison of its performance and price with those of other materials, the potential demand in different industries, advantages and disadvantages, possible modifications in the sirup or method of use, and the industries in the best position to manufacture or use it successfully.

Upon completion of the commercial information and engineering data on plant design, process details, operating constants, yields, and costs from the semiplant-scale studies, a revision of the apple sirup publication was in order. Equipped with the new publication, *Bland Apple Sirup,* which covered all phases of the development, and a supply of the sirup, the liaison man directed efforts to the creation of the largest possible industrial utilization of the process. That he did by disseminating information on the development and by helping commercial concerns in the solution of other problems in connection with large-scale production or use. If it seemed likely that the problems would hamper the utilization of the apple sirup, he referred them to the Government laboratory.

In that stage of the introduction of the development to industry, he found that prospective manufacturers generally were unwilling to undertake the expense of new equipment unless they were assured of a substantial demand for the sirup. The prospective users did not want to assume the cost of thorough application tests unless they were certain of a reliable source of supply. Consequently, commercial interest had to be stimulated in the production as well as utilization of the sirup.

As a result, production got into full swing in 15 plants. Some manufacturers built plants exclusively to make sirup. Others, like plants for evaporating milk and maple sirup, had idle equipment during the fall apple season, since spring was their normal busy period.

The market demand for sirup developed until it exceeded 4 million pounds annually. Most of it was used by the cigarette industry to retain moisture in tobacco. Two manufacturers installed special equipment—ion exchangers—to produce sirup of reduced calcium content for use primarily in cosmetics, drugs, tooth paste, beverages, and table sirup. A large dairy-products company recently developed a modified apple sirup to compete in the 12-million-dollar market of sirups for infant feeding.

After the Second World War, the demand for apple sirup dropped sharply, because more sugar and glycerin were available for civilian uses. The sirup could not compete with glycerin, because it was less efficient as a hygroscopic agent and had a color and taste that were undesirable for certain applications. It could not compete with sugar because of its color, taste, and much higher cost. As a table sirup, it was too expensive, and its flavor was too weak to mix with the cheaper sugar sirups. Urgent requests were received from industry to find a way to remove color and taste. But because any additional processing would result in an even higher price in comparison with competitive sweeteners, evidently the best solution was to remove it from such competition by enhancing its natural flavor characteristics. A laboratory development, apple essence, proved to be the solution. It greatly improved the flavor of apple sirup.

APPLE ESSENCE was the result of several years of investigation by laboratory chemists and engineers to find a method for preparing a full-flavor, concentrated apple juice, which would make a beverage on dilution with water, with all the characteristics of fresh apple juice. H. P. Milleville, a chemical engineer, made the goal possible when he invented a method for recovering and concentrating, unaltered, the volatile flavors, or essence, normally lost during the evaporation of the juice of fresh apples.

To obtain commercial opinion, the liaison man called on representative manufacturers of table and fountain sirups with samples of essence-flavored apple sirup. He was told that the sirup was too expensive to compete success-

fully with the cheaper sugar sirups and too weak for use as a flavor in the sirups. Blending the essence with the concentrated juice from tarter apples finally produced a satisfactory flavor material. The blend made a delicious apple drink when it was diluted with water. Mixed with sugar sirup, it made a good table sirup.

The discussion with industrial concerns disclosed that, although interest was great in essence-flavored table sirup and the full-flavor concentrate used in beverages, far more important was the value of the essence itself as a flavor material for many products. The engineers prepared a publication that emphasized the method for the recovery of the essence rather than the preparation of apple-flavor table sirup or concentrate.

To stimulate the production of essence, the liaison man called on manufacturers of apple sirup, concentrated apple juice, vinegar, and brandy, because they were in a good position to use the essence-stripped juice.

With increased production, the price of essence dropped from 15 dollars to 5 dollars a gallon. The market expanded.

The beverage industry became interested in the essence for use with either the concentrated apple juice or sugar-base sirup, to which they planned to add acid and coloring matter. The inclusion of the concentrate, although preferable from the standpoint of naturalness of flavor and nutritional value and as an outlet for the residual juice from the recovery process, was unsatisfactory because of increased costs and poor stability. Stability problems, the most difficult, were the formation of a cloudy precipitate, loss of flavor, and development of a mold growth. Improvement in methods of clarification or the use of sterilizers corrected the cloud formation. The acid apple-juice concentrate apparently caused the loss of flavor, as the essence was stable when it was stored separately. Beverages that contained fruit-juice concentrates spoiled more quickly than those with refined sugar sirups because sugar sirups do not support so well the growth of micro-organisms as do fruit juices that are high in minerals and nitrogenous substances.

Because the conventional heat sterilization would result in loss of volatile essence, the makers of beverages that contained concentrated juice had to resort to germproof (Seitz) filtration, the addition of preservatives, or the removal of mineral and other nutrients with ion-exchange treatment to check spoilage. Eventually, most of the essence went into beverages.

Many candy manufacturers thought the essence would be too expensive and volatile for large-scale use. The technicians, by a study of the application of essence to many types of candy, found a method for making a pectin-gel type that soon went into commercial production.

Several manufacturers of dairy products reported successful results in the development of essence-flavored milk beverages, ices, sherbets, and ice cream. Later they noted a loss of essence flavor in milk and ice-cream products. They attributed the loss to the absorption of the flavor by the milk fats. Makers of ice cream overcame the difficulty by adding the essence to the ribbon of ice or fruit that is included in some types of ice cream. The industry, impressed by the possibilities of the different fruit essences as flavoring, requested that they be included in standards of identity for ice cream.

Tobacco manufacturers also reported that the essence greatly improved the flavor of a number of products. But, because of its rapid disappearance, essence would be of no commercial value to them unless a method could be found to prevent its loss.

The liaison man referred the problem of retaining the essence flavor in commercial products to the laboratory and flavor specialists in industry. The criticisms and suggestions he received from manufacturers of flavor extracts were especially helpful in making suggestions for improving the essence.

Several industrial concerns pointed out the marked variations they had noted in the strength and quality of different apple essences, concentrates, and mixtures. Some of the concentrates quickly developed a disagreeable odor and taste. Methods were needed to insure absolute standardization and uniformity.

The laboratory studied the influence of apple varieties by separately recovering the essence and concentrating the essence-stripped juice from nine varieties. Marked differences were noted in the quality of the essences and the stability of the concentrates when they were evaluated individually and in beverages, jelly, and candy. The blending of selected varieties seemed to be the solution. The chemists, however, did not discover any satisfactory tests to measure the strength of the essence, because volatile flavors are complicated and intangible. Consequently, the strength continues to be expressed in terms of the relative quantity of juice from which it was recovered. For example, 150-fold essence means 1 gallon of essence recovered from 150 gallons of juice.

A problem arose because of the apparent loss or change of flavor in different commercial products to which the essence had been added. A flavor specialist pointed out the necessity of making an exact determination of the constituents of apple essence before it was possible to develop satisfactory procedures for stabilizing the flavor in different commercial products. A chemist, Jonathan W. White, Jr., was assigned the task. After many months of work, he was able to identify 26 compounds— no small accomplishment, for the compounds represent only about 0.5 percent of the 150-fold essence (50 parts per million of the original apple juice). This information gave industry a basis for studies to find suitable methods for stabilizing essence in different commercial products.

The makers of flavoring extracts directed attention to the fact that the commercial demand for apple flavor was much less than the demand for grape, strawberry, raspberry, peach, cherry, orange, and pineapple flavors. They asked us to develop suitable procedures for recovering the essence from the other fruits. We started studies on grapes, strawberries, and oranges. Commercial manufacturers began to produce grape, peach, raspberry, orange, pineapple, and strawberry essences, some of which have been produced so far on only an experimental scale. Approximately 50 essence units, with capacities up to 5 million gallons of juice a year, were installed.

THE SERIOUS PROBLEM as to the economical utilization of the residual juice after the essence had been recovered was referred to the laboratory. The flashed juice of apples could be used for apple sirup, concentrated apple juice, and such, if there was a market for such products. However, the demand for the sirup was seriously curtailed; the demand for the concentrated juice was limited mainly to the preserve industry. A study was needed of ways to expand present markets for the products. It was not feasible to express the juice of the other fruits for essence recovery. As a result, the laboratory and industry initiated investigations to develop satisfactory procedures for recovering the essence from crushed fruits and the condensate from preserve manufacture.

A request for help was received from a manufacturer who had been informed that the apple, grape, peach, and cherry essences, which he had imported from Canada, were subject to an Internal Revenue tax of 9 dollars a gallon. Analyses of the samples showed that their alcohol content ranged from 1 to 8 percent. Essences containing 0.5 percent or more were subject to the tax. Laboratory engineers who worked on the problem devised a new method for making an essence with only one-third the normal alcohol content—they vaporized only 3 percent, instead of the usual 10 percent, for subsequent concentration.

Several companies complained that the imported essences gave a bitter taste and contributed practically no flavor. They traced the trouble to the citric acid denaturant in the essences they used. Exempt from tax were imported essences that contained a denaturant of 6 ounces of citric or tartaric acid to a gallon or 25 percent of sugar.

A COMMERCIAL DEMAND developed for essences of higher concentration, because they would contribute greater flavor value for the same tax cost and would be useful for flavoring certain dried products. To meet the problem, the engineers worked out modifications in the equipment and process which made possible the production of 800-fold essence.

A later law exempted essence from the Internal Revenue alcohol tax if several requirements were met.

Manufacturers of flavoring extracts directed our attention to the desirability of developing equipment and processes that would combine the best features of the conventional alcohol flavor-extract method and the essence process.

Processors questioned the use of the term "essence" for the product, as it implied an alcoholic extract. They suggested that the phrase "volatile fruit concentrate" would be better, even though it is longer.

SO THE ACCOUNT is brought up to date, as of spring, 1951. It brings out two points: How the gap is bridged between laboratory and industry, and how the laboratory men are alert to help solve the problems of production and utilization that may arise when industry takes the product of the test tube into the factory.

R. HENRY MORRIS, 3d, *is special assistant to the director of the Eastern Regional Research Laboratory. He is a graduate of Lehigh University. After 20 years with manufacturing firms, he joined the staff of the Eastern Laboratory in 1943.*

Between the Farmer and Consumer

Roy W. Lennartson

Marketing is the link between production and consumption.

For half a century the Department of Agriculture has worked on problems of marketing. Grading and standardization of farm products, market news services, marketing agreements, and regulatory acts to prevent fraud were among the services developed to meet the essential needs of the marketing system.

Those services, however, were not enough to keep pace with production and population. The Congress in 1946 recognized the need and enacted the Research and Marketing Act.

A major objective stated in the Act is ". . . . to promote through research, study, experimentation . . . a scientific approach to the problems of marketing, transportation, and distribution of agricultural products, similar to the scientific methods which have been utilized so successfully during the past 84 years in connection with the production of agricultural products, so that such products capable of being produced in abundance may be marketed in an orderly manner and efficiently distributed."

The long-range program is based first on the knowledge of marketing accumulated in the Department over the years. Second is the selection, in consultation among Department officials and committees representing agricultural industries, of the problems for which solutions are most needed. The problems and the plans for their solution are specified formally in project descriptions, which determine the lines along which the work is to proceed. The marketing service programs involve constant and direct contact with farmers and businessmen who deal in farm products, and is an important source of information on marketing and its problems.

The market news service, for example, is Nation-wide. It furnishes information concerning prices, supplies, and marketing trends in nearby and distant markets to producers and traders. The development of standards for grades requires of the workers a knowledge of the elements that make up good quality and attractiveness to the consumer in nearly all farm products. Actual grading and inspection work gives an opportunity to learn the problems of the trade directly from those taking part in the commercial transactions.

From those roots and from periodic conferences of Department workers and representatives of agricultural industries has grown a list of projects to develop new services and to improve the older functions. Cotton, wool, grain, livestock, fruits, vegetables—the whole range of farm products—are touched by the new endeavors.

The projects to improve the movement of products from farm to consumer are of five groups:

First, improved collection and dissemination of basic information on supplies, prices, and the movement of farm products.

Second, expansion of outlets for farm products at home and abroad.

Third, analyses of marketing operations and of the costs and margins associated with them.

Fourth, improvement in the preparation and handling of farm products.

Fifth, evaluation and improvement of the facilities and practices employed in marketing.

THE MEANING of marketing in this program is comprehensive. It includes the preparation of commodities for sale from the farm, their assembly, transportation, packing, packaging, processing, preservation, storing, wholesaling, and retailing—all the steps between producer and consumer. It includes marketing services, facilities, trade practices, and trade barriers.

There has not yet been time for the broader studies to go fully into all aspects of our marketing system, but some of the early results exemplify the scope of the work.

Among the first developments was an electronic scale for weighing livestock at markets. The device, almost completely automatic, eliminates most of the possibility of human and mechanical errors that sometimes affect the ordinary type of weighbeam scale.

A study of the economics of prepackaging sweet corn in Florida for sale in many States revealed possibilities for a large trade in sweet corn grown in the South in winter. It kept its high quality when it was properly refrigerated. Housewives reported that they liked it and found it reasonable in cost. The study demonstrated some interesting possibilities: An additional delicacy might be placed on the Nation's tables in seasons when it had not previously been generally available; it is not necessary to ship the corn husks and trimmings, as has usually been done, but the husks can be used in feeding livestock at the point of production; and spoilage can be reduced materially below the usual rate.

Intensive training courses for retailers of fresh fruits and vegetables have reduced the rates of spoilage of perishables and increased the sales of more than 95 percent of the retailers who reported on results. The training includes instruction on handling of such produce, its preservation overnight, effective display methods, and other practices conducive to less waste and greater sales. Within 2 years after the courses were begun, some 15,000 grocers had taken the training. A survey among them showed that many had adopted in their stores the practices recommended in the courses. Some of the men remodeled their entire produce departments in order to apply the methods more effectively.

A study of self-service merchandising of prepackaged meats provided a guide for retailers who were considering the conversion of their meat departments to the self-service basis, threw light on the costs involved in such a change, and listed the problems that required particular attention.

The value of white potatoes as feed for livestock, particularly the small and low-grade potatoes that sometimes get into commercial channels and discourage purchasers, was pointed out as a result of another study. One series of feeding tests and experiments in which potatoes were used as a part of the rations for cattle, hogs, sheep, and other animals disclosed that such feeding can be profitable to both potato and livestock growers when the size or quality of the product fed is low, and, sometimes, when markets are oversupplied. The report on the experiments set forth that milk production often increased sharply and beef cattle and hogs gained weight fast when potatoes formed a part of the usual rations. The death rate for lambs was reported to be lower when potatoes were included in the rations of ewes.

The quality and staple lengths of cotton most widely used in making each of several major textile products were surveyed in another study. The findings provided a guide to the kinds of fiber regarded as best for the different products and indicated the probable demand for cotton of the various kinds. The results thus may be useful to mills and cotton producers.

A series of investigations of marketing costs and margins pointed out marketing operations in which there is a wide spread between what the farmer receives and what the consumer pays. This type of study indicates the areas in which work might be done to develop more economical marketing practices so that the price spread can be reduced to the advantage of producer, tradesman, and consumer.

SURVEYS of wholesale produce markets in several cities provide bases for needed improvements in facilities and practices. New markets have been built in Jackson, Miss.; Trenton, N. J.; and Greenville, S. C., in line with Department recommendations. Improvements have been made in existing markets at Benton Harbor, Mich.; Miami, Fla.; and Atlanta, Ga., and construction of new markets is under way in St. Louis, Mo.; Columbia, S. C.; and San Antonio, Tex. The market at Dallas, Tex., is being improved and will eventually become a modern efficient market. The Department has submitted plans for new markets in Columbia, S. C.; Boston, Mass.; Indianapolis, Ind.; Tyler, Tex.; Norfolk, Va.; Milwaukee, Wis.; and Tulsa, Okla.

EXAMPLES OF WORK in progress include studies of many operations. Among them are: Ways to improve and extend the use of consumer preferences for products of various kinds and qualities; transportation costs, their effects on marketing, and ways to reduce them; development of new and improved standards for grading products; prepackaging perishable foods; equipment and methods for packing and loading farm products for transportation; improvement of cotton-ginning equipment and methods; the preparation of wool for market; the effects on the citrus industry of the rapid growth in marketing frozen orange-juice concentrate; more efficient refrigeration of fresh fruits and vegetables; ways to retard flavor deterioration and staling of bread; and ways to reduce egg breakage and deterioration during marketing.

Some of that work is being done out-side the Department, for the Congress granted authority to draw upon the abilities of private research agencies as well as those of the Government itself. That is accomplished through a provision in the Act that permits contracts with private agencies or individuals to carry on studies that can be handled better or at less cost in that manner. The State agricultural colleges, experiment stations, extension services, and departments of agriculture and bureaus of markets cooperate in the program.

State departments of agriculture and bureaus of markets undertook work on various problems. They include improvement of the processing of cotton, diversion of low-grade sweetpotatoes for use as livestock feed, better grading and packing of berries and fruits and vegetables, stimulation of the demand for prunes, prospective supplies and qualities of grains on a county basis, and better practices in marketing livestock. The program generally aims at improving marketing practices and facilities on a local, State, and regional basis.

One of their studies showed that one-third of the eggs from the principal producing region were below Grade A at the time the producers sold them. Suggestions were made for faster handling, better cooling, and other improved practices. Another project investigated the quality of potatoes in marketing channels and pointed out to traders the causes of deterioration. Another study disclosed that people would eat more sweetpotatoes if the supply was steady and good.

THE OLDER SERVICES are being improved at the same time.

The market news services now operate through a Nation-wide system of field offices, most of which are connected through a 10,000-mile network of leased wires.

The Production and Marketing Administration gathers and disseminates market news on the supply, demand, movement, quality, and prices of livestock, meats, wool, fruits, vegetables, dairy and poultry products, grain, hay, feed, cotton, cottonseed, tobacco, rice, honey, and other agricultural products. In 1950 some 1,200 newspapers and 1,172 radio stations carried this news daily. It was also disseminated by telephone, telegraph, personal contacts, and bulletin boards.

To help make possible the movement of large quantities of foods from producer to consumer at reasonable cost, designations of grades of products have been developed. They provide precise and acceptable definitions of quality so that producers and dealers miles apart may deal confidently. The several hundred grades now in effect for numerous commodities always are under scrutiny to keep them abreast of changes in production and marketing. Billions of bushels of grain, millions of bales of cotton, and many billions of pounds of other products are graded annually.

To facilitate the orderly marketing of milk and certain fruits and vegetables and tree nuts, the Department of Agriculture and industry cooperate in a system of marketing agreements and orders. The marketing program for milk, for instance, involves the regulation of the prices paid to producers. For some other commodities, it involves regulation of the quality or volume of the commodities moving to market. Action leading toward the establishment of such regulation normally starts with the industry that is in trouble. Details are worked out, and the producers, the trade, and the Department take part in developing the lines of action to be followed. The result usually is an orderly flow of goods to markets where they can be absorbed, the maintenance of quality in the goods the consumer receives, and the prevention of violent swings in price levels. Two-thirds of the eligible producers, either by number or volume, who participate in the referendum must vote favorably before a marketing order can be issued. For certain products, a favorable vote of 75 percent is needed.

Regulatory activities in the interest of fair dealing constitute another Nation-wide function. They are based on the principle that the advantages that accrue to agriculture from production and service programs would be canceled by a marketing system that allowed some persons to benefit at the expense of others. The fruit grower who turns his apples over to a commission merchant is entitled to a correct accounting for the sale of his property. The purchaser of seeds has to rely upon the quality indicated by the label. The user of insecticides should be able to rely on the claims made for the product. To make sure that there could be such reliance, the Congress adopted several regulatory measures dealing with the marketing and distribution of agricultural products. These regulate the business practices of dealers who handle the farmer's products at the market place and the truthfulness of labels on goods sold. For some products, they require the promulgation of standards and their use in interstate commerce under inspection laws.

THESE FEW EXAMPLES of the many aspects of the marketing work in the Department of Agriculture suffice to indicate the new trend and shift in emphasis toward greater activity in solving growing problems of marketing. Greater activity—but at the same time the welding of what looks like individual projects and compartmentalized units into a single (although intricate) pattern of marketing.

ROY W. LENNARTSON, *director, office of materials and facilities, Production and Marketing Administration, joined the Department of Agriculture in 1936 as a member of the Farm Credit Administration to engage in work in connection with the marketing of poultry and eggs. From 1942 to 1945 he was a procurement officer for dairy and poultry products for the Armed Forces. Later, as deputy director of the poultry branch, he was in charge of price-support and research programs on poultry products.*

A Problem in the Grocery Store

Callie Mae Coons

What the housewife buys in a grocery store concerns many persons, each of whom can learn something from the others.

It concerns the earner who supplies the cash, and the ones who will eat the food. It concerns the retailer and wholesaler, who risk losses from damaged goods and fluctuating prices. It concerns the processor, who decides how much of the seasonal crops to pack, freeze, can, or mill and put in storage. It concerns the farmer, who plans far in advance what and how much to grow. It concerns warehouse men and transportation men, who must maintain the correct conditions of temperature and humidity and sanitation, and observe precise delivery schedules.

Finding out what she and her family need and want is a major problem for producers and processors. The research results that guide them can also help the consumers decide what to buy and how to use it to best advantage.

BEFORE DECIDING TO PRODUCE a new food, the processor may need to consider several questions. Will it fill a need? How much will it cost the consumer? How will it compare with the same food in other forms, as to cost, usefulness, and other qualities the buyer looks for? Will it displace other foods? Will it reach a new group of consumers? Will it give a fair margin of profit? Will it be as good as his

reputation—or is it just a tasty and expensive mixture, low in important nutritive values, that may not survive the first advertising campaign?

The housewife wants foods that her family will like and will satisfy their appetite and needs. She assumes that the food will be wholesome, sanitary, unadulterated, and not hazardous to health. She expects it to be priced fairly; sometimes she chooses a higher-priced item because she believes it is of higher quality.

Consumers expect that the chain of research to find new uses for foods and how to handle and distribute them will continued until it yields the correct answers as to the consumer values of the new products. The responsibility for a wholesome food rests with the industry that processes, converts, or manufactures it. The processor is expected to conform to existing sanitary regulations and to food and drug laws governing standards of identity, purity, and labeling. He should be aware of the nutritional and other values of the basic food materials used, and seek to retain or improve them.

The financial security of the processor, however, demands that he be fairly sure of consumer acceptance before he expands too far in the manufacture of a new product. Determination of the usefulness of foods to consumers is a serious problem, sometimes costly for both processors and consumers. In developing a product, a processor may spend a lot of money on research to find out what chances it will have in finding an open and permanent market. If the inquiry is poorly planned and conducted and gives the wrong prediction, still more time and money are spent in pursuing a wrong lead. If the product finds only a temporary market, it fails to move from grocers' shelves, or moves from kitchen

53

pantries into discard. Finally, processors, distributors, and consumers all have to pay for poor research and the business ventures based on it.

Costs and the losses involved in food processing reach consumers in other ways, too. Sometimes, without regard to consumers' needs, vast sums are spent in advertising some new product. This advertising convinces many consumers that they need the new product. In the price of the food the consumer pays the cost of being educated in this fashion. Other buyers may have doubts about a food and may start inquiries through the press, schools, Government agencies, and even the Congress. They want to know whether a publicized product is all that is claimed for it, or whether it possesses some hidden youth-giving quality, or whether it contains some harmful ingredient likely to aggravate human ills. Every inquiry costs time and money.

Occasionally large amounts of public and private moneys are used in hearings and legal proceedings to establish the harmlessness of some processing ingredient or food. Food legislation may prove essential to protect the health of people, and then more money is required to enforce the law.

Research so far has not shown how to measure all desirable consumer qualities of all foods, but some progress has been made. A number of measurements may be necessary to tell whether a food deserves a place in production programs, on grocers' shelves, and in family meals. The housewife judges foods by various practical standards in her kitchen or at her table and decides whether or not to buy again. The market analyst surveys population groups for attitudes and opinions so that he can predict consumer preference. Others test consumer acceptance of a new product by take-it-or-leave-it reactions in stores, homes, schools, and institutions. The food technologist has laboratory tools for measuring some qualities, but not all—measurement of palatability is most baffling. The biochemist and nutritionist analyze the nutrient content and test the food to see how far it will go in supporting life in laboratory animals. Each group analyzing food qualities needs an understanding of what qualities other groups are measuring and how measurements by other yardsticks may affect its conclusions.

SOMEWHERE ALONG THE LINE in the development, processing, marketing, and household use of a new food someone is going to apply tests of usefulness that may spell the success or failure of the product in the market. Judging a new food by the homemaker's yardstick long before it goes to market will minimize losses. Some of the tests are:

Palatability. The crucial test is the response of the people who eat the food. Family members may have limited or widely cultivated tastes. They may prefer mild or strong seasonings. Specific directions for preparing and serving a new food can help it through its first practical tests.

Form. Many processed foods come ready-to-serve, as preserves and baked goods. Others, like soup mixes, frozen foods, and pancake mixes, are ready to cook. Flour, sugar, shortening, and many others require preparation and cooking before serving. Dry forms— dry milk, dried eggs, and potato flour, for example—may require reconstitution, but have the advantage of longer pantry life than do the fresh forms. Ground forms, as in meats, dry beans, or meals, may be cooked quickly, but may not be acceptable indefinitely because of monotonous texture.

Packaging. The amount desired in a package depends on family size and on the rate of use and of deterioration of the product. Visibility of contents may help promote initial acceptance of a superior product, or its continued acceptance if several qualities are available. Ease of opening and removing contents must be considered, too, but reclosing or transferring contents for protection during storage may be even more important. It may be more satisfactory to transfer crackers or ready-to-eat cereals to airtight containers immediately upon opening than to pay the cost of a heavily coated moisture-proof package, which gives protection only while the carton is sealed. The cost of expensive packaging, added to the price of the product, may hinder its continued acceptance. Dual-use packages, such as plastic containers, can be expected to have sales appeal only until consumers have a supply sufficient for the desired secondary uses. The quality of the food in the package is more important than the packaging.

Storage qualities. The storage life required for a product depends on how often the family wants to eat it. Foods should store well at room temperatures or in the refrigerator. Other levels of controlled temperatures are not available in homes in all climates. In some climates or seasons, dried fruits, salad dressings, fats, and such must be kept in the refrigerator, or only small amounts purchased at a time. Space for storage, the size and shape of the package, and the likelihood of exchange of odors with other foods in the same compartment all enter into storage considerations. Designers of food packages need to collaborate with designers of refrigerators and kitchen cabinets for better handling of foods and management of the available space.

Multiple-use foods. A food that combines well in a variety of dishes soon becomes a familiar pantry item. A biscuit mix that can be used also for dumplings, shortcakes, and (with a little change) piecrust, cake, and cottage pudding has wider demand than a prepared pudding mix that makes one kind of dish of one flavor and texture.

Food processors can take cues from the menu patterns of most American families. Soups, salads, juices, and desserts may be served once or twice daily; main dishes, one to three times; vegetables and fruits, two to six times; cereals and breads, two to eight times or more, counting seconds at meals and between-meal snacks. A versatile product, such as dry milk or potato flour, can enter into several of these items each day. On the other hand, a pop-ular ready-to-serve product may find many roles in one item. For example, ice cream may be served for dessert, alone or in combination with cake, pie, pudding, or fruit, and also between meals, at home or at soda fountains, in a beverage or as a frozen confection or other concoction.

Convenience. Homemakers look for time- and labor-saving features in food products and simplicity in handling. Some products, such as the improved shortenings, eliminate motions in conventional methods of preparation or lend themselves to simple, easy new methods. They have a better chance for consumer acceptance than products that require several stages in preparation, much space, and many utensils. So eager are housewives for convenience in the kitchen, especially in times of high incomes, that they may pay ten times the price of constituent ingredients for ready-to-cook mixtures. In recent years, high prices have scarcely hindered acceptance of many costly items. In cities, where eggs, milk, fat, meat, and other ingredients are comparatively expensive, ready-to-cook mixes, like quick bread, baked goods, and packaged soups, puddings, and desserts, may cost no more than the same dishes made from home recipes and may fill a real need in small families and in the small kitchens of employed women. Some of the ready-to-use products in big packages may be used in institutions where the wages of kitchen helpers are high or cooking skills are so low that the quality of cooked food is poor and much food is otherwise wasted. In times of close budgeting and less employment of women, the market for mixes may not be so good.

Cost. Homemakers have several ways of looking at costs. One may compare prices per pound or per can. She may figure the cost of a meal for her family or of a serving. Another may keep account of all food costs and compute the amount to a person for a week. If the total food bill runs high, she begins to figure and sooner or later omits the foods expensive per serving. However, consumers do well to remember that servings differ in size and that in different foods (such as soups and desserts) the portions do not carry the same satisfactions and nutritive values.

No one can predict with surety which foods consumers will accept or continue to use. Market analysts search for ways to find out what consumers want and how they will react to foods, qualities, and prices. The consumer herself often does not know or may not be able to say in advance what she will do in the market. Her attitudes and experience, the pressures at the moment and many other conditions peculiar to her own problem influence her decisions in the grocery store.

Consumer-preference surveys take many forms to find out what consumers want and why. The information is given during interviews with individuals or groups or in mailed questionnaires. The consumer reports, among other things, the kind and color, size, quantities, and qualities of a product she prefers to buy. She is asked whether or not the food is available in her local market, what substitutes she would accept, and how often she uses each product. The report shows what the consumer thinks she wants and would buy.

Surveys of preferences and attitudes are hard to make. The findings have to be interpreted with care. The interviewer's approach, skill in framing questions, and patience may influence the replies. The replies of the person interviewed may be limited by her understanding and attitude and by the extent and nature of her experience with the commodity. Also, she may have too little time and too much on her mind.

The unknown bias in replies may be even greater when the analyst seeks information by mailed questionnaires. For example, a high-school girl served on a Nation-wide teen-age panel for several years. The company liked her careful, complete monthly reports on one commodity after another. She confided to others that when she received a questionnaire she bought the commodity at once, if she was not already a user, so she could always report in the affirmative. With her own report she included all the favorable comments she gathered from her relatives and friends. A manufacturer can be misled by data from such surveys.

Studies of consumer preference have been used widely in industrial surveys—sometimes to discover how much a housewife knows about a little-known item, and sometimes for information on the extent of use of widely known foods that meet strong competition in a changing market. The studies can be used to ascertain attitudes of consumers and opinions that never find expression, unfilled wants and needs for qualities or commodities not available in the market, or types of consumer resistance to be overcome in revised sales-promotion techniques. The results may help processors and distributors understand why a food is or is not selling, what improvements the consumers want, what services they will not pay for, or what characteristics of a new product may interfere with its acceptance.

But on the other hand, consumer-preference studies do not tell how the consumer will act in a real (rather than imaginary) situation. In making a choice among two or three possibilities, consumers often display difficulty at one time or place, and not at another time or in another situation. The shopper may be expected to show more interest, imagination, and even acceptance of foods while buying just before meals, when her own appetite is keen, than soon after a hearty lunch.

The value of a report on preferences depends also on the kind of sample studied. A report from an urban consumers' club or a parent-teacher group may give more useful guidance than one from a group of farm women who seldom buy that food. The findings of neither can be taken as typical of the whole population.

The usefulness of reports depends

also on the location of the population sample whose opinion is sought, the kinds of markets to which it has access, and the kind of market sought for the food. Preferences for whole-wheat flour or whole-wheat bread in a section of the country where an excellent whole-wheat flour is milled and marketed widely and regularly will differ sharply from those in an area where the product seldom appears, or is of poor quality, poorly stored, and slow in sales. In these instances, the time of investigators might better be spent in analysis of the market situation in the two areas or of the qualities of the products and other conditions which seem to contribute to a favorable market.

CONSUMER ACCEPTANCE also implies more than mental response or stated preference. It denotes action, with an opportunity for rejection, which may take place in the market, at the tasting time, or after a series of experiences in using the product. The consumer-acceptance method of testing consumer reaction with samples of foods is being used widely by survey specialists. It is more expensive, and the number of families or the persons tested is usually smaller than in consumer-preference studies. It is used in communities or with groups that are under direct observation. Sometimes it is done by mail, with a panel of families scattered throughout the country. The test may be for acceptance of specific qualities in a product (such as the flavor of baker's bread made with more milk) or for predicting the average acceptance of a new product that has not yet gone into large-scale production.

In one controlled test, for example, a group of third-grade children was ushered into an attractive bus just before lunch and driven to a milk-processing plant to taste a new type of fortified milk. Every detail was made as attractive as possible to induce each child to take at least a taste. Reactions, comments, rejections of first servings, and requests for seconds were the measures of acceptance. The children returned home after school and asked their mothers to buy some of that "good-tasting milk."

A new school-lunch item to be used in a city system may be tested in one or two schools before it is offered on a larger scale. The pre-testing prevents loss through plate waste or refusals when the product could be further improved in the kitchen. For reliable results, the food is served without comment or any coaching, as a part of the usual plate lunch. The percentage of children leaving portions uneaten and the proportion of the serving left as plate waste at the end of the meal are the chief criteria of acceptance, but comments may count.

Another example: Some samples of canned juices or other canned foods may be shipped to cooperating families in different parts of the country. They try out the product according to directions and fill in a questionnaire, which they mail to the distributing concern. The kind of panel, its acquaintance with the product, its standards for quality, the situation under which the food is tasted, and several other factors may affect unduly the results in this kind of testing. If the test panel is an institution, a group of workers at a plant, or some other assembly of persons from different families, the testing may be supervised by a representative of the investigator, but seldom can it be treated as a typical population sample.

Consumer-acceptance studies can predict buying behavior better than preference studies. Consideration must be given to the naturalness of the test situation, the character of the test sample of food, the kind of families, and the kind of market sought. It cannot be concluded that women want medium-size potatoes unless the test situation offers small, medium, and large potatoes, all well labeled, or that eggs in cartons are preferred to eggs by the pound unless they are comparably priced. Packaged vegetables and fruits may be unacceptable if previous experiences in that market have convinced buyers that retail packaging is one way of concealing retail waste. Consumers may have to accept fancy cartons and expensive containers when the commodity comes in no other.

CONSUMER-BUYING PRACTICES are still the most reliable index to what consumers will want and buy next week or next year. The tests of buying behavior come in actual choice-making situations in the retail market. The intelligent buyer presumably has in mind her pantry stocks and stored supplies, her family's likes, her customary needs for the week, and the little extras that she can afford. The test commodity receives its due share of attention, no more.

Food purchases reviewed after the buying is completed, and inventories of stocks on hand made without warning, can also give information on food acceptance and reveal patterns of food preferences. In addition, they provide quantitative data which have many other uses. Quantitative food-consumption studies, together with family menus, afford a basis for estimating consumer demand for one or more products and for analyzing competition among foods. The data help in determining the effect of high and low levels of consumption of a food on the displacement of other foods and on the character and nutritive quality of the diet. With some follow-up questions, the studies can also compare consumer practices with preferences and reasons for the choices, in actual situations of known price, supply, and purchasing power.

WHY AND HOW MUCH families spend for food has long interested agricultural, industrial, and home economists. In 1864, the Congress appropriated money for an investigation of "the nutritive value of the various articles and commodities used for human food; with special suggestion of full, wholesome and edible rations less wasteful and more economical than those in common use." Since then, many studies

have yielded data which now are classics in economics.

People with higher incomes buy more meat, milk, and fruits; those foods may crowd out some in other groups which satisfy hunger at lower costs. However, families with high incomes purchase more of some forms and less of others that may be in the same food group. Or they spend more money for fancy forms without increasing the quantity or even the quality consumed. Even though less of the grain products are consumed at high incomes, more of processed cereals and baked goods, especially the fancy ones, are used by people above the middle-income range. With rise in income, the upward shift in forms of milk used is in more cream, ice cream, cheese, and butter. Among the processed meats, more bacon at higher prices and smoked ham are used, and less salt pork and lunch meats. More fruits in all forms—fresh, canned, frozen, and dried—tend to be used at higher incomes. Among the vegetables, only the frozen and a few fresh ones are used more by the high-income families.

One purpose of food processing is to spread seasonal food supplies around the year and to regions where seasons are less favorable. Today, facilities for transporting fresh foods have done much to remove seasonal differences in market supplies, but the price of fresh food still limits its use. In 1948, the seasonal differences in the use of canned fruits, for example, were more marked among low-income families who could not always afford the fresh.

Families in Birmingham, Buffalo, and Minneapolis-St. Paul used almost twice as much canned fruits and juices and canned vegetables in winter as in fall, when certain fresh vegetables and fruits were plentiful. Frozen fruits and vegetables and dried fruits were also less used in the fall. Seasonal differences in foods used were less marked among San Francisco families, who spent more for foods at all income levels and used more fresh foods year around.

Regional food habits, as well as incomes and seasons, still influence the food choices of many families. In the 1948 study of four cities, Birmingham families led in the use of buttermilk and evaporated and dry milk; the Twin City families in the use of butter, cream, and ice cream; and San Francisco families in the use of cheeses. All bought about the same amounts of whole milk, except the southern families, who bought only about half as much. Families in San Francisco used twice as much canned juices as those in Birmingham, who bought more bottled soft drinks and less milk than did families in any other one of the four cities studied. The Birmingham families used more oleomargarine, shortenings, flours and meals, sugars, and sweets. Buffalo families used more ready-baked goods of all kinds. San Francisco families bought less grain products and more salad oils, fresh vegetables, and fruits.

For a number of years, canned baby foods and junior foods, special mixed cereals, and canned milks have been processed for families with children. In 1948, the urban families with children used more of several processed foods than did families without children. Among them were canned applesauce, ready-to-eat cereals, peanuts and peanut butter, sirups and molasses, soups, prepared desserts, white bread, and canned and fresh milk. Convenience was an important feature of many of the choices. Families with children did not buy more citrus products, lunch meats, and soft drinks for home use, as might have been expected. They used less cream, butter, meats, frozen foods, and baked goods other than bread.

THE FOOD TECHNOLOGIST uses many tests for the purity and sanitary quality of a processed product or its ingredients. The tests usually follow a pattern prescribed by Federal and State regulations. Objective tests for qualities important in grading foods, such as color, sugar content, fat content, and specific gravity, are carried out routinely on some foods. The results may not be of major importance to the consumer because they have little relation to the nutritive quality or to the flavor and other qualities.

The food technologist's concern with problems of palatability has grown with food processing. Much research went into developing processed rations during the Second World War. Processed food mixtures present unusual problems of flavor, texture, odor, and color. Little is known of how the chemicals in or added to foods affect palatability or of how they are altered by processing and storage. Still less is known of the psychological and physiological conditions affecting the taster's rating of foods. Much remains to be done to discover why people find some processed foods acceptable at first and wholly unacceptable after a time. How to measure some of those real or imagined characteristics that interfere with acceptance is a subject of continuing research. A look at a few of the problems involved in palatability judging may help consumers to appreciate its importance and the cost to processors.

THE BEST-KNOWN DEVICE for measuring food flavors is the taste panel or palatability panel. Properly carried out, it is relatively expensive because of the number of judges required, the skill they must possess, and the time the test takes. Several persons are needed to do one job—in contrast to mechanical recording devices for other quality tests, where several devices can be controlled by one person. However, the judging panel is indispensable for appraising some food qualities for which no objective chemical or physical tests have been devised. With stricter laboratory controls and selection of judges, standardized testing procedures, better statistical designs, and better treatments of the scores, palatability judging is becoming a fairly precise and reliable technique. Assays of palatability and related qualities likely to affect continued consumer acceptance of the food are made routinely in some processing plants. Research men use the panels to measure changes in palatability caused by different conditions.

TWO TYPES of palatability panels are in general use: The tasting panel for grading and routine control of quality in food processing; and the expert analytical judging panel for laboratory research.

The expert panel is needed when familiar foods are to be changed or improved and when new ones are to be developed. It is an analytical tool for detecting degrees of differences in such qualities as sweetness, rancidity, and bitterness. The judges must have keen senses for taste and smell. They have to have a fine discrimination for texture and different kinds and degrees of flavors and aromas. Their abilities must be fully calibrated to determine the range over which their judgments are accurate. Like inaccurate thermometers or recording barometers, poor tasters cannot accomplish their purpose or justify their cost. The ratings of an expert tasting panel do not represent average consumer tastes. The expert judges may detect objectionable qualities that not 5 in 100 average consumers would detect. But they must detect qualities likely to become increasingly objectionable during the processing or storage of a product.

Selecting and training an expert panel may take weeks. Usually a volunteer group is screened to find five or more persons gifted in a sense of perception for the particular flavor, aroma, texture, and other qualities of palatability likely to be found in the product to be judged. The screening tests should be made with a food combination similar to that product. A characteristic or objectionable flavor may rate differently in food combinations because of the interplay of flavors, aroma, and texture, as well as because of the associated food experiences of the taster. Tests show that the effect of monosodium glutamate, for example,

rates all the way from pleasing in certain meat combinations to objectionable in some fruit combinations.

The judges are trained to an accepted standard of consistent performance. For comparison throughout the testing, some control or standard reference samples (such as a good product with quality maintained by storage at the proper low temperatures) are tasted along with the experimental samples. All are unlabeled. The judges' record of performance on a known sample is the key to the reliability of their ratings of unknown samples.

Charts of individual performance may reveal erratic judging as compared to a previous record or that of the whole group. Illness, emotional upsets, interest level, and other physiological and psychological conditions may disqualify a judge for a time. Further research on the biological basis for taste, smell, touch, and other phases of palatability may yield figures allowing for the effect of age, fatigue, repeated tasting, smoking, dietary habits, and other factors on the sensitivity of individual judges.

Careful control at the time of tasting is essential over such conditions as lighting, color, and temperature of the room and food, noise or distracting influences, time of day, the interval after a meal, sequence of tasting, and the number of samples that can be judged in succession. The food is served in glass dishes with porcelain or taste-free implements. The judges are isolated by a seating arrangement which precludes observation of the facial expression of others. Water is provided for rinsing flavors from the mouth between tastings.

The palatability panel for routine tasting in food plants is not usually governed by the same rigid controls as the research panel. Neither panel should be used to predict consumer preference or acceptance. Even a panel of 20 to 30 members recruited from all types of workers in a factory is seldom typical of average consumers with respect to origin, age, and food habits.

Another difference in laboratory or plant tasting is that the foods are not eaten along with other foods.

The other items of the diet, its monotony or extreme variety, and its general consistency and texture may limit the acceptability of a product that has passed the most expert panel of judges. It may be significant that a few foods, such as bread, milk, meat, and potatoes, can be basic to most meals because they are accepted repeatedly by a large number of people. They contribute several nutrients in good proportions and help to bring unbalanced diets into nutritive equilibrium.

The causes and consequences of individual appetites are little understood. A rising appetite is associated with tides of growth and with a change in environment or in types of meals and food preparation. It is a favorable time for establishing food acceptance, but not for critical judging of foods. Almost any food may taste good when appetite is keen. A declining or low appetite usually goes with an unhappy or tense emotional state, when a person becomes highly critical of flavors of food. A poor appetite may also accompany the onset of an illness. It is one symptom of diet deficiency in several nutrients, including most B vitamins, the essential amino acids, and some minerals. A person with poor appetite may have a dull sense of delicate flavors and odors or may be an overcritical judge.

THE CONCERN OF NUTRITIONISTS over the changes in nutritive value brought about in food processing may be shared eventually by processors and consumers. People send in many questions about choosing foods on the basis of nutritional quality. The questions often come in waves from consumers, students, educators, and writers and reflect interest in new diet fads, or hearings on food legislation.

Many questions concern processed foods—alfalfa and dried grass for food, citrus juice standing in cans, chocolate milk for children, breads old and new, ersatz foods, trace elements, sodium-low foods for hypertension, and purified diets for neuroses—to name a few.

Processing may improve or harm or have no effect on the nutritive value of foods. Processing for preservation, including drying, canning, and freezing, has been applied to most foods for years and years. In modern preservation, great effort is made to retain the original qualities and nutritive values of the fresh food. Processing by milling or refinement for technological reasons—to improve the shipping, storage, or retailing qualities of foods—is the basis of some of our oldest and largest food industries. Unfortunately, this type of processing often lowers nutritive values, as in the purified sugars, starches, and fats.

Processing by concentration or conversion, aimed at separating and condensing the desirable nutrients, with higher nutritive value in the product than in the original form, is definitely in the consumer's interest. Such developments are comparatively new. They include oilseed flours for protein concentrates, dry skim milk, whey solids, wheat germ, rice polishings, food yeasts, and citrus concentrates.

Processing by compounding or formula making, largely for consumer convenience, is a growing industry. It offers many opportunities for harm and for benefit to human diets, as well as risk for producers. The importance of ready-to-cook mixes may be determined by their content of such ingredients as dry milk and dried eggs, or other nutritious concentrates that contribute important nutrients at a cost below that of the fresh ingredients. If the 50 or more brands of pancake mixes on the market today were equally good in time and effort of preparation, in cost, and in palatability, preference should be given to the ones that are formulated from materials of high nutritive values.

Analysis of the foods themselves before and after processing is the surest way to know what is happening to nutritive values. In many food industries, routine analyses of foods accepted for processing (such as vegetables to be used for canned infant foods) and regulatory analyses of the processed products for conformity with label claims to nutrient content yield data to guide the processor.

Many analyses to determine the effect of various conditions in altering nutritive quality are becoming increasingly important to consumers. Unfortunately, the findings are not always published. Among the analyses are those that reveal changes in nutritive value resulting from commercial and home processing, soil, climate, variety, fertilizer, mode of shipping, storage, temperatures, and humidity. The need for such analyses increases with the complexity of commercial processing, storage, and distribution of food. The data are valuable when processors must choose among several procedures likely to affect the cost and consumer uses of a food.

A GOOD WAY to get an over-all view of the nutritional importance of foods is to look at the nutrients contributed by different groups of food in the food supply of the United States. Some food groups are cornerstones in diet planning—they contribute a fourth or more of several essential nutrients. They are milk for protein, calcium, and riboflavin; meats for protein, iron, thiamine, and niacin; citrus fruit and tomatoes for ascorbic acid; leafy green and yellow vegetables for vitamin A value and ascorbic acid; and grain products for food energy, protein, iron, thiamine, and niacin. Grain holds its position in iron, thiamine, and niacin because of the extent enrichment has been continued since the Second World War.

Processing practices that affect the bread supply of a country are of far greater importance than those that affect some item served infrequently or eaten only by a few people. One can offset the small losses of one or two nutrients by eating more of foods that contain them or by getting them from some more potent source. For example, the pasteurization of milk means a loss of a small amount of vitamin C, but it makes possible a safer supply of milk of acceptable fresh flavor, more economical distribution to neighboring towns and cities, improvements in the diets of more people, and (in this country) a level of consumption unequaled in the world. The loss in vitamin C in pasteurized milk can be made up by greater consumption of citrus fruit or processed citrus juices, which undergo little change in nutritive value.

A COMMON WAY to appraise the nutritional quality of foods is on the basis of nutrient content per pound as purchased. Pound for pound, dry cereals and dry beans or fats cannot be compared directly with foods that contain much water, like leafy vegetables or milk. They can be compared, however, on the basis of the cost of 100 grams of protein or 100 milligrams of ascorbic acid or some other nutrient. Foods were traded among nations in the Second World War on the basis of price per thousand calories—a sensible plan when calories are at a premium. In times of food abundance, comparisons should be for nutrients most expensive and lacking in diets or with due consideration to all nutrients supplied. That method of appraising nutritive value through comparisons of cost of nutrients is easier with individual foods than with groups of foods. Many foods within a group are far better choices than the averages; others are poorer, and the price is neither uniform nor related to nutritive values. For such comparisons, tables of food composition should be consulted.

The chemist likes to define nutritive values on a moisture-free basis to get around the problem of differences in water content. He prefers figures giving the moisture and nutrient content per 100 grams (percentages), so that all nutritive values can be converted to an absolute dry-weight basis for comparisons.

The dietitian and the consumer who is aware of the importance of good nutrition like to compare the values in servings of foods. Such a comparison should supplement comparisons with pounds or 100-gram portions of the food. A 100-gram portion is a common-size serving for many simple foods like fruits, cooked vegetables, juices, and meats. But the average portions of beverages—milk, and cocoa, and tall glasses of juice—contain 200 to 300 grams or more; of breads, only 20 to 40 grams; and of concentrated sweets and fats, about 10 to 20 grams. In practice, the serving portions of a food may be two to five times the average. The actual weight of the portions or of the total eaten in a meal or a day is more useful than a count of servings with no definition of size.

Those facts are recognized by scientists, but consumers are often confused by claims that a food product is the richest known source of a particular nutrient. That may be true weight for weight, but the product may not be the richest source from the standpoint of the amount likely to be consumed. Also misleading are statements that dried fruits or legumes contain three to four times as much nutrients as the fresh foods. Such statements disregard the fact that the water removed in the processing must be replaced in the diet before digestion and assimilation are complete.

The food economist likes to have the nutritionist look at foods from still another angle. After families have made their customary choices of foods, what did they get for their money and how could the choices have been improved? Did emphasis on some food group result in unbalanced diets? Were choices made within groups poorer than average or were the prices paid so high that needed foods were crowded out?

URBAN FAMILIES, in the spring of 1948, chose to spend their grocery money on a few inexpensive foods, as potatoes and grains, which furnished generous portions of several nutrients at low cost, and on other inexpensive foods, some of them highly processed,

as sugars and oils, which actually may be costly because they supply chiefly a single nutrient and have to be counter-balanced by foods of better than average quality to safeguard nutrition.

With prices as they were in the spring of 1948, grain products took about 11 percent of the food money of urban families in the United States and supplied 11 percent or more of five of the nine nutrients calculated. That same spring, milk, cheese, and cream took around 15 percent of the food money and supplied 15 percent or more of five of the nine nutrients. Eggs, dry beans and peas, tomatoes and citrus fruit, and leafy green and yellow vegetables accounted for a share of at least five nutrients in proportions equal to their cost. Other vegetables and fruits carried their proportionate share of only one nutrient. Meats, poultry, and fish at 1948 prices took the largest share of food money, 27 percent; they furnished 27 percent or more of four nutrients and in addition half this percentage of three others of the nine nutrients calculated.

An economical investment of money is in the groups that contribute two or more nutrients in twice the proportions the group takes from the total food budget. First in this rating (on the basis of 1948 prices) were grain products and potatoes, each of which supplied five nutrients at twice the level of the proportionate cost. Dry beans and peas carried a double share of four nutrients; dairy products and leafy green and yellow vegetables, two important nutrients each. Meats, citrus fruit and tomatoes, sugars and sirups, and fats and oils furnished a double share of only one nutrient each when compared to the cost. Lower prices for the food, better choices within the group, or higher nutritive value per pound would bring other groups into the class bearing a double share of several important nutrients. It would mean better diets with the same or less money.

Some nutrients become part of our diets through many foods. Calories and phosphorus are so widely distributed that no one group of foods is a prominent main source. Except in a very restricted diet or food economy, gains or losses in these nutrients through processing—for example, in amounts of sugar added to canned fruits and vegetables, and fat added to bread during baking—may be relatively unimportant. Carotene is widely distributed and seems to be little affected by processing, but its true value in vitamin A nutrition is limited by its low availability from some foods.

The few foods that supply calcium, riboflavin, or ascorbic acid usually have high priority in food production, management, and processing, either for wider distribution or to guard against losses. This principle explains the esteem in which nutritionists hold all kinds of milk as a source of calcium and riboflavin and citrus fruits as a source of ascorbic acid. The amount of ascorbic acid available from green leafy vegetables as a group is significant. However, analyses of foods *as served* show that commercial, home, and institutional processing or cooking of the vegetables often destroys most of the ascorbic acid in the vegetables. To retain as much of the ascorbic acid as possible, vegetables should be cooked covered and quickly, in as little water as possible, and served promptly.

Thiamine comes chiefly from cereals, some meats, and legumes. Like some other nutrients, it is largely lost in the milling or polishing of grain because it is concentrated in the germ and bran layers. Low-income families, who depend heavily on grain products and less on meats in their diets, are affected most by the losses through milling. Replacement of some nutrients by enrichment (as of flours and bread) is commendable, but it does not cover the loss of all nutrients.

Niacin comes from a few natural food sources, mostly expensive ones, but is little affected by common processing treatments. Less is needed in diets containing much tryptophane, one of the amino acids in protein. The production of synthetic niacin and other derivatives of nicotinic acid at low cost for enriching foods has eased some of the concern about possible shortages of niacin in our diets.

Little is known of what heat processing does to the amino acid content of proteins. Lysine, for example, is damaged by treatments at temperatures used in extraction of cottonseed oil from the meal containing the protein. Meats and other protein-rich foods are exposed to high temperatures during canning under pressure. It is a problem, too, in the protein of ready-to-eat or toasted cereals. The effect on different amino acids needs to be investigated. If such damage cannot be avoided, recognition of it should enter into planning the use of such processed foods in diets.

Eventually, the food processor or producer of new products may be affected by the problems relating to the importance of the nutritive value changes brought about by processing. At first he may reason that if a processed product tastes good, is convenient to use and is moderately priced, and holds a strong competitive position in comparison with possible alternates, it is a good product, meeting a public need. Later, however, the processed product of low nutritive quality may find its market position insecure. At times in the national economy the criterion of nutritive values comes to be the deciding factor between products of similar price, quality, and palatability. Each decade, through research and education, finds people increasingly better informed on the importance of nutritive values in foods.

CALLIE MAE COONS *has been assistant chief of the Bureau of Human Nutrition and Home Economics since 1945. She is a native of Texas and a graduate of the University of Chicago and has lived 1 to 10 years in each of 11 States. Dr. Coons has been a homemaker for 30 years, shopping for groceries for a household of two to eight persons. Her university training has been in nutrition and biochemistry.*

Nutritive value per pound and percentage of nutrients furnished by groups of food [1]

Food group	Food energy	Protein	Fat	Carbohydrate	Calcium	Iron	Vitamin A value	Thiamine	Riboflavin	Niacin	Ascorbic acid
	Calories	Grams	Grams	Grams	Mg.[2]	Mg.[2]	I. U.[3]	Mg.[2]	Mg.[2]	Mg.[2]	Mg.[2]
Dairy products, except butter (milk equivalent)	300	16	17.1	20.9	530	0.4	700	0.14	0.75	0.5	5
Eggs	655	52	46.5	2.8	220	10.9	4,600	.39	1.17	.3	0
Meat, poultry, fish	935	65	73.1	.5	60	9.7	1,400	1.00	.86	18.7	4
Fats and oils, including fat cuts and butter	3,565	11	392.5	1.4	30	1.0	3,700	.42	.13	2.2	0
Dry beans and peas; nuts, soya flour	2,005	102	99.4	202.9	560	23.0	100	2.40	.89	28.4	5
Potatoes, sweetpotatoes	335	8	.6	76.8	50	2.7	3,500	.40	.16	4.2	66
Citrus fruits, tomatoes	150	4	1.1	35.9	70	1.8	2,100	.23	.12	1.7	136
Leafy green and yellow vegetables	115	7	.9	24.1	170	3.6	9,900	.28	.31	2.1	108
Other vegetables, fruit	205	4	1.3	49.9	70	2.0	1,300	.15	.16	1.6	34
Grain products	1,655	47	5.7	346.5	80	9.3	100	1.31	.72	10.9	0
Sugars, sirups, preserves	1,695	0	0	437.9	30	2.3	0	0	.01	.1	(4)

Food group	Percent	Percent	Percent	Percent	Percent	Percent	Percent	Percent	Percent	Percent	Percent
Dairy products, except butter	13.5	25.5	17.7	7.6	75.0	3.7	12.4	11.4	47.2	3.7	5.6
Eggs	2.6	7.4	4.3	1.0	2.7	8.6	6.8	2.7	6.4	(5)	0
Meat, poultry, fish	12.5	29.9	22.7	0	2.5	25.8	7.2	23.2	15.9	42.7	1.6
Fats and oils, including fat cuts and butter	19.4	2.1	49.0	0	.6	1.2	7.7	3.8	.9	2.1	0
Dry beans and peas; nuts, soya flour	2.7	4.3	2.8	2.2	2.4	6.1	.1	5.4	1.7	6.3	(5)
Potatoes, sweetpotatoes	3.3	2.1	0	5.9	1.5	5.5	12.7	6.5	2.1	6.8	16.9
Citrus fruit, tomatoes	1.3	1.1	0	2.4	2.0	3.1	7.2	3.8	1.7	2.6	31.6
Leafy green and yellow vegetables	1.1	2.1	0	2.0	5.0	6.7	36.2	4.9	4.3	3.2	27.4
Other vegetables, fruits	3.9	2.1	.7	7.6	4.0	7.4	9.3	4.9	4.3	5.3	16.9
Grain products	24.1	23.4	2.1	40.0	3.5	27.0	.4	33.4	14.6	26.8	0
Sugars, sirups	15.1	(5)	0	31.1	.8	4.3	0	0	(5)	(5)	0
Miscellaneous	.5	(5)	.7	.2	0	.6	0	0	.9	.5	0

[1] Based on estimates of food quantity by Bureau of Agricultural Economics, as of April 1949.

[2] Milligrams. [3] International Units. [4] Less than 0.5. [5] Less than 0.05 percent.

Percentage and cost of nutrients in diet of urban families[1] in the United States[2]

Food group	Food cost	Food energy	Protein	Calcium	Iron	Vitamin A value	Thiamine	Riboflavin	Niacin	Ascorbic acid
	Percent	Percent	Percent	Percent	Percent	Percent	Percent	Percent	Percent	Percent
Dairy products, except butter	15.8	15.0	23.5	65.9	2.9	13.6	10.2	42.0	3.3	4.2
Eggs	4.4	2.6	6.9	2.4	8.0	6.1	3.0	7.1	(3)	0
Meat, poultry, fish	27.4	13.9	29.4	2.1	24.6	8.4	25.1	16.9	43.8	1.2
Fats and oils	9.2	17.3	2.0	.6	1.7	9.7	3.4	.8	1.7	0
Dry beans and peas; nuts	1.4	2.6	3.9	1.6	6.9	.1	3.8	1.5	5.4	(3)
Potatoes, sweetpotatoes	2.2	3.4	2.9	1.2	5.1	4.4	6.4	1.9	6.6	12.6
Citrus fruit, tomatoes	4.9	2.6	2.0	3.7	5.1	9.1	6.0	2.3	4.1	44.2
Leafy green and yellow vegetables	4.6	1.6	2.9	4.6	8.0	41.2	6.0	4.9	3.3	22.2
Other vegetables, fruits	8.3	4.2	2.0	3.6	7.4	6.9	4.7	3.8	4.1	15.0
Grain products	10.7	25.0	23.5	13.6	28.0	.5	31.4	18.4	27.3	(3)
Sugars, sirups	4.9	11.8	1.0	.7	2.3	(3)	(3)	.4	.4	.6
All food	[4]93.8	100	100	100	100	100	100	100	100	100

[1] Of two or more persons.
[2] Based on nutritive value of diets of urban families, United States, spring 1948. Preliminary Report No. 12, Bureau of Human Nutrition and Home Economics.
[3] Less than 0.05 percent.
[4] Does not include 6.2 percent for miscellaneous food accessories.

NATURE HAS A PART

The Nature and Preparation of Enzymes

A. Laurence Curl,
Sigmund Schwimmer

All the living things contain small amounts of a number of curious chemical substances that assist the cell in performing all its life processes. Their mere presence or contact with the changing contents of the living cell speeds up the chemical reactions that go on there—growth, respiration, the metabolism of food. The acceleration seemingly goes on without using up or altering the substances themselves. These accelerators are the enzymes.

Enzymes are made only by living cells. All living cells contain them, for they are essential to life as we know it. Every agricultural product in the natural state therefore contains the enzymes that it made for its own use. Enzymes can often be separated from plant or animal products and used to accelerate chemical reactions in laboratory or factory.

Extracted enzymes greatly speed up certain chemical reactions. They therefore are catalysts, which are substances that hasten chemical reactions without themselves being changed or destroyed in the process. The reactions that are catalyzed, or quickened, are always reactions of value to the cell that made the enzyme.

Enzymes have yet another function. They select one from a number of possible reactions to be speeded up. Often the chemicals in a cell could react together in several different ways. The enzyme determines in which of the ways the reaction will actually proceed. The result of this selective influence is that each reacting chemical in a living organism is transformed by a particular enzyme in a particular way. This directive effect is known as specificity.

In a sense the action of an enzyme is analogous to that of a mechanical corn harvester. Picking corn by hand is slow; the machine hastens the work. But merely to hasten the process would do no good if the corn were spilled on the ground and the stalks put away in the crib. The corn harvester separates the ear from the stalk, then the husk from the ear and sometimes also the grain from the cob, and puts each one in its proper place. The harvester speeds up the process and separates the final products, but it does not, or at least it should not, enter into the final products. At the end of its job it is still, we hope, in as good condition as when it started.

Much labor has been spent to find out how enzymes are produced by living organisms and what the stuff is of which they are made. We have some general ideas, though no facts, on the first point. We know that the characteristics of a living thing are determined by bodies called genes. The genes are transmitted by inheritance and can multiply. Genes are now considered to be the agents responsible for the formation of enzymes. Thus the red color of a rose is due to the presence in the flower petals of a red substance, which is produced from a colorless precursor by the work of one particular enzyme. The enzyme is in turn elaborated by the gene responsible for the production of red color in that variety of rose. When that gene is absent in the flower, the enzyme will be missing and the rose will be white. The gene seems to act like a mold in which the enzyme is produced.

We have much more information on what enzymes are. Chemists have succeeded in extracting, purifying, and sometimes isolating enzymes. Several chemists have received Nobel prizes for work along those lines. All the enzymes whose constitution is definitely known are proteins.

Sometimes the enzyme appears to be a simple protein. Sometimes it is combined with metals, such as iron or copper. Again, the protein is known to be united with other organic substances, the coenzymes, which usually are of simple structure. Curiously enough, vitamins (particularly those of the B complex) often have turned out to be a part of the coenzyme. These facts may explain why a deficiency of vitamins and minerals in the diet causes some form of disease.

Once in a while a vitamin (like niacin) will combine with several proteins to form different enzymes. The enzymes then have an over-all similarity, but an indiscriminate combination of vitamins and proteins as a rule would not lead to substances of any enzymatic activity whatever.

The effects of enzyme action on foods and feeds are discussed in the next chapter. When enzymes stay active after harvesting, the crop is likely to keep poorly; it might even spoil. As a rule, the food processor is interested mainly in getting rid of enzyme action. Usually he does so by heating the material to denature the proteins, as in canning fruits or vegetables. Many enzymes have been found useful in speeding up chemical reactions in industry, however; consequently, methods for their extraction and concentration have been worked out.

Enzymes are utilized in many ways in the production of various commodities.

One way is to treat a substance, such as sucrose (common sugar), with a micro-organism—a yeast, mold, or bacterium—that contains an enzyme or enzymes which can convert the sucrose into something more valuable. An example is the fermentation of sucrose by yeast to ethyl alcohol and carbon dioxide. The process is involved in the preparation of all varieties of alcoholic beverages and in the manufacture of industrial ethyl alcohol. The carbon dioxide is often utilized in the form of dry ice. Sugars may be converted also into glycerol (glycerin), citric acid, gluconic acid, acetone, butanol, and other valuable products. Alcohol solutions are converted into acetic acid, usually as a dilute solution known as vinegar, when they are treated with bacteria of the genus *Acetobacter*.

Penicillin is formed by the action of certain molds on a sugar solution. One of the steps in the manufacture of synthetic vitamin C involves the use of bacterial oxidation.

Enzyme preparations, usually much more concentrated than the original material, are often made from bacteria, molds, and yeasts. They are still impure and often contain several enzymes. The preparations are mainly amylases and proteinases, which attack starch and proteins, respectively.

One of the most widely used enzyme preparations is pancreatin, which contains enzymes that react with fats, proteins, and starch. Pancreatin is prepared from the pancreas of hogs or cattle, and is thus a byproduct in the meat-packing industry. The dried and powdered whole pancreas may be used for some purposes. A more concentrated preparation can be made by mincing the glands, mixing with water, and allowing to stand in a moderately acid solution (pH 4 to 5) for 24 hours. The enzymes dissolve and are removed from the solid material by filtering. The filtrate is evaporated to dryness at a low temperature in a vacuum or in a current of air. A still more concentrated preparation is obtained by adding ethyl alcohol or acetone to the filtrate and filtering and drying the resulting precipitate. Pancreatin is used medicinally as an aid to duodenal digestion and in lienteric diarrhea. It is used commercially in making leather, gelatin, glue, and peptones, and in laundering and dry cleaning to remove proteins and fats. Peptones are water-soluble products formed by the partial digestion of proteins, such as meat, by enzymes. They are used in preparing bacteriological nutrient media.

Pepsin, another commonly used enzyme preparation, is obtained from the mucous membrane of the stomachs of hogs and cattle. It is prepared in much the same way that pancreatin is, except that a much more acid medium is used for the extraction. Unlike pancreatin, pepsin contains only proteolytic enzymes. Pepsin is used medicinally for some stomach deficiencies, for the manufacture of peptones, and in the motion-picture industry to remove gelatin, a protein, from waste photographic films to facilitate recovery of the silver.

Papain is another commonly used proteolytic enzyme. It is prepared from the green fruit of the papaya (*Carica papaya*), a tropical fruit. Several scratches are made on the skin of the fruit while it is still on the tree, and the latex that seeps out is collected and dried. The crudest commercial products are merely sun-dried, and so lose a good deal of activity. Stronger preparations are obtained by drying the latex to a powder in a vacuum. Papain has also been prepared in a satisfactory and stable form by adding common salt to the moist latex and removing part of the water. The result is a paste that can be stored for long periods without loss of activity.

Papain is used medicinally in treating some digestive ailments, for tenderizing meats, in the manufacture of leather, and in clarifying beer. Papaya leaves have long been used for tenderizing meat in tropical America. Most of the papain imported into the United States probably goes into "chillproof" beer. Ordinarily beer contains proteoses—partially split proteins—which

are soluble in beer at room temperature but precipitate as a cloud if the beer is chilled in the ice box. The addition of a little papain breaks down these precipitatable protein fragments still further—in fact, to the point where they will no longer fall out of solution in the ice box. The beer then may be chilled without turning cloudy.

The latex of certain fig trees contains a proteolytic enzyme, ficin. The sap has been used as an anthelmintic, or intestinal-worm medicine, in Central and South America, and has also been used to curdle milk and prepare cheese. Pineapple juice, which contains bromelin, an enzyme similar to papain, has also been used as a meat tenderizer and as an anthelmintic.

Another important proteolytic enzyme is rennin, or rennet. This enzyme occurs in the gastric juice of the fourth (true) stomach of the calf, but has not been found in the young of other mammals. To prepare rennet, calf stomachs are dried, finely ground, and stirred slowly for several days with a solution of sodium chloride and a preservative, such as boric acid.

The extract is poured off, and a little hydrochloric acid is added to precipitate one of the impurities, mucin. The precipitate is filtered off. Solid sodium chloride is added until the solution is saturated. The precipitated rennet is filtered off and dried at room temperature. Rennet converts the soluble casein of milk to the less soluble paracasein, which forms a curd. The curd is processed in various ways to form the different types of cheese.

Commercial preparations of proteinases have also been manufactured from bacteria and molds.

One of the more important commercial applications of proteinase preparations is in the manufacture of leather, in the process known as bating. The bating of hides, originally a secret process, has been practiced for a long time. The purpose is to prepare dehaired skins for tanning by removing various undesirable residual protein materials, such as hair and glands. Bating was

Interrelations of some of the substrates for which vitamin-enzymes are known [1]

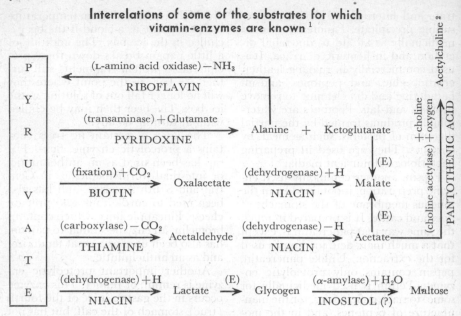

[1] This table shows some of the chemical reactions of pyruvate, a key substance in the metabolism of carbohydrates, proteins, and fats in most living organisms. The reactions, catalyzed by enzymes (in parentheses above the arrows) containing vitamins (in capitals beneath the arrows), give rise to end products (metabolites) which can be further transformed by other enzyme reactions (E). Other substances, such as ammonia, carbon dioxide, hydrogen, and water (NH_3, CO_2, H, and H_2O), which participate in or are transferred during these reactions, are shown above the arrow.

[2] This is a simplified version of a complicated series of reactions which has not yet been elucidated.

first carried out by soaking the dehaired skins in a warm suspension of dog or bird dung. After it became known that the action of the dung was due to the proteolytic enzymes present, bates containing such enzymes as pancreatin or papain were substituted.

Enzymes that attack starch are known as amylases or diastases. The first enzyme to be discovered was probably the amylase of wheat, which in 1811 was observed to digest starch. The amylases are generally found in animals, plants, and micro-organisms. Good sources are sprouted starchy seeds, the pancreas of higher animals, and the saliva of man, pigs, and rats.

There are two types of amylases. One type, known as α-amylase, breaks down the very large molecule of starch into large fragments, called dextrins, which are soluble in water. The second, known as β-amylase, breaks starch

down into much smaller fragments, particularly maltose, a soluble sugar.

BARLEY MALT is the most extensively used source of starch-digesting enzymes for commercial purposes. The production of barley for malting amounted to about 93 million bushels in 1946, with a value of 160 million dollars.

The first problem in barley-malt production is the purely agronomical one of obtaining barley varieties that contain large amounts of amylase after malting. The Department of Agriculture has a malt laboratory, which cooperates with many State experiment stations to get such information. Thus malt for the brewing industry need not be especially high in amylase, but the distiller sets a premium on high enzyme concentrations. The enzyme content of each kernel does not vary much; to obtain a high-amylase malt, therefore, the smaller kernels can be selected, because that will mean a higher potency per unit weight.

After cleaning, barley is put into large steel tanks and soaked for about 48 hours to eliminate minute amounts of a naturally occurring substance which acts as an inhibitor of germination. After draining, the grains are kept in a moist, fresh atmosphere for a week, or sometimes longer. During this period, the amount of available (soluble) amylase is increased, and a new starch-digesting enzyme (α-amylase) is formed. The combination of those two enzymes is effective in degrading starch to sugars. After drying and removal of sprouts, the malted grain is ready for use.

In the brewing and distilling industries, malt is ground and added to the cooked starch upon which it is to act. Rice, corn, wheat, milo, or potatoes can be used as adjuncts.

The enzymes of malt are used in many industrial processes. As a desizing agent in textile industries, the malt enzyme is prepared as a thick sirup. The ground malt is soaked in water and then filtered. The clear liquid is evaporated in a vacuum so that a moderate temperature can be maintained, because high temperatures would destroy the enzyme. Many processors add a calcium salt, such as gypsum, to the sugary sirup, because it has a stabilizing effect on at least one of the components of the starch-digesting enzyme system present in malt. The treatment concentrates the malt enzymes (an advantage in shipping) and eliminates some of the less soluble impurities in the extract. Furthermore, the sugar present acts as a stabilizing agent. Further purification can be achieved by precipitating the enzyme with alcohol and drying the product.

In the baking industry, malted wheat is prepared as a flour to be added to a regular wheat flour to improve baking characteristics.

Amylases are also prepared from micro-organisms, especially in the Orient, where the mold *Aspergillus oryzae* is grown on moist rice. The enzyme is obtained by extracting the moldy product with water and precipitating with alcohol. The product is known as Taka-diastase. Wheat bran has also been used as a medium for the growth of *Aspergillus oryzae*. Bacterial amylases have been prepared from *Bacillus mesentericus*. Vera-diastase is an enzyme preparation which is made from the pancreas of the pig.

THE PREPARATION OF A PURE enzyme is much more complicated and difficult than commercial preparation. Pure enzymes are mainly used at present for scientific purposes—that is, to study the properties and behavior of enzymes—but some pure preparations may have found an application in medicine. In order to purify an enzyme beyond the degree usually practiced in industry, it is necessary to obtain a clear idea of its stability.

All enzymes, being protein in nature, are inactivated by heat, some much more readily than others. Furthermore, acids destroy some and alkalies destroy others. Various metals, oxygen, or certain chemical compounds, known as inhibitors, may affect the activity or stability of an enzyme. Special methods of preparation must therefore be worked out for each enzyme. Most of the methods fall into one of three groups.

Salt or alcohol precipitation: To the solution of the enzyme in water, a water-soluble organic solvent (such as ethyl alcohol or acetone) may be added. By adding the solvent gradually, one often can obtain several precipitates, which may differ in their content of the enzyme. In that way, a small precipitate in which the enzyme activity is concentrated can be had. Instead of using an organic solvent, fractional precipitation of enzymes may be carried out by adding varying quantities of a salt, such as sodium chloride, ammonium sulfate, or magnesium sulfate. The method is very common because usually it does not destroy any of the enzymic activities.

Adsorption: When certain water-insoluble solids, such as aluminum hydroxide, iron hydroxide, or starch, are added to enzyme solutions, the enzyme is sometimes adsorbed on the solid. Impurities may remain in solution or may be removed by washing the solid with water or with salt solutions. Finally the enzyme is dissolved by treatment with a faintly alkaline or acid solution. Enzyme preparations of a high degree of purity can sometimes be made by this method.

Dialysis: Enzymes often can be purified by dialysis. The solution, in a cellophane bag, is immersed in water or dilute buffer solution. Impurities such as sugars and inorganic salts pass slowly through the walls of the bag, while the enzyme remains behind. After dialysis, the enzyme can be obtained as a dry powder by lyophilization. The solution of the enzyme is frozen and the ice is evaporated in a vacuum. When the operation is carried out properly, the solution remains frozen until all of the ice is gone, and the enzyme is left as a fluffy powder of low moisture content.

Final purification: It is quite usual to employ all of these procedures in turn before complete purification is attained. When complete purity is approached, the enzyme protein frequently crystallizes. The crystals may then be centrifuged, or filtered off, and further purified by recrystallizations. This is a good way to purify enzymes when the exact method of purification leading to crystals is known, because crystallization removes many impurities that are difficult to take away otherwise, particularly other enzymes.

When an enzyme preparation is contaminated by inert material, the result is often not very serious, but only a little contamination by another enzyme is needed to complicate the results of experimental work. Sometimes an enzyme preparation is referred to as enzymically pure. That means that it fails to give a test for any other known enzyme. But because a great many enzymes remain unknown and their effects are unrecognized, this designation is of limited value. A "chemically pure" enzyme preparation would consist of one protein only.

Several physical methods are available for testing the chemical purity of enzymes.

In one method, an electrical current is passed through the solution, and analyses are made to find out whether all the protein migrates at the same rate under the influence of the current. A mixture of proteins usually separates under these conditions, each protein migrating at its own rate. The operator can thus detect the presence of an impurity in the enzyme protein.

Another test is based upon the solubility of the enzyme protein. If the enzyme protein is added a bit at a time to a given solvent, usually a salt solution, it will continue to dissolve until the solution is saturated. Thereafter no more protein will dissolve if the protein is pure. If the protein is not pure, the impurity will continue to dissolve. This difference in behavior can be detected by appropriate analytical methods, and thus can be used to demonstrate the purity of a given preparation. The method is not limited in its application to enzymes or proteins; it is based on a general principle of chemistry discovered about 70 years ago by Josiah Willard Gibbs, an American scholar.

We outline the preparation of two crystalline enzymes as illustrations.

Chymotrypsin from beef pancreas: Freshly-removed pancreas is freed from fat and connective tissue and minced. The enzymes are removed by extracting twice with cold dilute sulfuric acid. Solid ammonium sulfate is added to precipitate some of the impurities; a second fraction is precipitated by adding more ammonium sulfate. The second precipitate is redissolved in water, and more impurities are precipitated by adding ammonium sulfate. Following this, more ammonium sulfate is added to precipitate the desired fraction, which contains chymotrypsinogen (the precursor or zymogen of chymotrypsin), trypsinogen, and an inhibitor.

The fraction is again dissolved in water, ammonium sulfate is added, and the solution is made more alkaline (pH 5.0). On standing, chymotrypsinogen separates out as crystals, which are filtered off after 2 days. The filtrate may be worked up for trypsinogen or trypsin.

The chymotrypsinogen is then recrystallized eight times by dissolving in very dilute sulfuric acid and adding ammonium sulfate and then sodium hydroxide (to pH 5.0). Chymotrypsinogen crystallizes out within an hour.

Chymotrypsinogen is converted to chymotrypsin by treating with trypsin. The eight-times recrystallized chymotrypsinogen is dissolved in dilute sulfuric acid and made slightly alkaline (pH 7.6) with phosphate buffer and sodium hydroxide. A small amount of trypsin is added and the mixture is permitted to stand at 5° C. for 2 days. It is then made to pH 4.0 with sulfuric acid and precipitated with ammonium sulfate. The precipitate is again dissolved in a small amount of dilute sulfuric acid and allowed to stand at 20° C. Crystalline chymotrypsin will separate within 24 hours. The crystallization is helped by the use of a few seed crystals. Chymotrypsin may be recrystallized by dissolving in a little dilute sulfuric acid and cautiously adding ammonium sulfate until crystallization begins.

α-Amylase from malt: The starting material is a concentrated malt extract like the one used in the textile industry for desizing cloth. It contains many enzymes besides the α-amylase, which is being sought. Most of these, including a β-amylase, which is present in considerable amount, are destroyed by heating the extract to 70° C. and filtering off the coagulated protein.

The α-amylase is next precipitated along with other proteins by adding ammonium sulfate. The precipitate is filtered off and may be washed with ammonium sulfate solution to remove adhering sugars. It is dissolved in dilute alcohol and poured through a column packed with raw starch granules. The enzyme is adsorbed on the starch, while the impurities pass on. The remaining impurities are washed off with dilute alcohol, and the enzyme is removed from the starch by pouring a solution of calcium sulfate through the column. The enzyme in this solution now is practically pure. It is concentrated by precipitating once more with ammonium sulfate. The precipitate is then redissolved in a small amount of calcium sulfate solution, from which the protein crystallizes in a few hours. Solubility tests have shown that the crystalline enzyme is at least 95 percent pure. In the original malt the enzyme is present to an extent of about 1 part in 5,000.

A. Laurence Curl *is a chemist in the enzyme research division at the Western Regional Research Laboratory. He received his training at Miami University and Ohio State University, and has been engaged in research with the Department of Agriculture since 1935.*

Sigmund Schwimmer *is a chemist in the same division. He studied at Ohio State University, George Washington University, and Georgetown University. He has been engaged in research with the Department of Agriculture since 1936.*

Some 3.5 million families—about 75 percent of them on farms—rented more than 4 million frozen-food lockers at locker plants in 1950. The highest concentration of locker plants was in Iowa, which had more than 350,000 individual lockers for a population of 2.5 million.

Enzymes in Foods and in Feeds

Eugene F. Jansen,
Arnold Kent Balls

Enzymes are constantly changing the products in which they exist. The changes, during the growth and ripening and even after the harvesting of a plant, may be good or bad, depending on circumstances.

Once in a while it is easy to remove unwanted and destructive enzymes. For example, the sugar in sugarcane deteriorates rapidly because of the action of the enzyme invertase, which changes the cane sugar to invert sugar. The invert sugar eventually goes into the molasses. When a cane is first cut, most of the invertase is at the top. Therefore topping the cane immediately removes a great part of the harmful enzyme, and the rest of the cane can be kept many hours longer until it can be ground conveniently.

But such simple methods cannot be applied to processed foods. They are usually heated to destroy the enzymes. The process is termed blanching, scalding, pasteurization, and the like, according to the industry and the particular methods used to raise the temperature. It is ordinarily thought of as a method for reducing the population of micro-organisms, which it does; but the destruction of enzyme material by that means is also a matter of moment, particularly when other methods are to be used for minimizing the growth of bacteria—as, for instance, when the product is to be kept frozen or is to be dried.

In canning foods, there is little or no enzyme problem, because the temperatures employed are usually adequate for the destruction of enzymes. The refinements required in heating technique to reduce the little to practically nothing are today the study of many food technologists.

The destruction of enzymes during the heat treatment depends on three things—the time of heating, the temperature, and the nature of the enzyme. Obviously all three variables need to be considered, and the work of considering them and developing definite heating times and temperatures is now going on, but it is by no means completed. Indiscriminate heating cannot be used—it would surely inactivate all enzymes, but it entails other disadvantages. The canning of orange juice is one example among many. The flavor of orange juice is imparted mainly by the suspended particles. There exists in oranges an enzyme (pectinesterase) that causes the particles to coalesce and settle, resulting in a bland juice. Pectinesterase is unusually resistant to heat. To inactivate it, temperatures higher than those needed for ordinary pasteurization are necessary. To prevent heat damage (that is, the formation of a burnt flavor) many ingenious methods have been devised to inactivate pectinesterase by a short exposure to a high temperature, followed by rapid cooling.

The importance of enzymes in the preservation of frozen fruits and vegetables was not recognized at first. In 1929 the pioneer company among frozen-food firms selected and froze thousands of pounds of fresh peas. It was a bitter experience to find that, after a few months of storage at $0°$ F., the peas had developed a foul odor and flavor. At that time, H. C. Diehl and C. A. Magoon, of the Department of

Agriculture, suggested that scalding—blanching—might improve the keeping qualities of the peas by inactivating the enzymes. Accordingly, the 1930 pack was scalded with steam before freezing. This time the peas kept well at the temperature at which the former lot had spoiled. Hence it is not enough merely to slow down enzyme reactions by holding vegetables at very low temperature—the reactions must be completely stopped by a scalding process, which destroys most or all enzymic activity before freezing.

The experience gained from the peas opened up the whole question of enzyme inactivation in the freezing of vegetables. A measure of the scalding necessary had to be determined by trial and error for each vegetable.

Aside from the taste of the product, other advantages are gained from scalding. The color of green vegetables becomes brighter. The bacterial count is lowered. The bacterial count becomes a factor only during the defrosting (thawing out), however, whereas the enzymes keep on decomposing the material throughout the whole storage time, even though the storage temperature is so low that the decomposition goes on very slowly.

We do not know which of the enzymes are responsible for off-flavor in frozen vegetables. There is no good proof that well-blanched products deteriorate in storage because of enzyme action, except that if they are not scalded the deterioration is thousands of times faster. The destruction of various enzymes by scalding has been measured many times and in many agricultural products. It not only takes place, but the rates are known in many cases, so there is no doubt of the efficacy of scalding.

At present (and we report on a rapidly developing subject), the situation seems to be that with unscalded fruits and vegetables the deterioration is almost all due to action of enzymes. When the same products are scalded, it may be caused by the last remnants of enzymes, or by the natural reactions no longer catalyzed by enzymes, or a slower catalysis caused by pieces of the enzyme that have been decomposed by heat. To illustrate the last point: Some enzymes are iron compounds; others are compounds of copper. Traces of iron and copper are known to cause foodstuffs to deteriorate, though very slowly when compared with what the enzyme would do. Nevertheless, in a storage warehouse a lot of time is available to enzymes or copper or anything else.

In raw fruits and vegetables, when kept in cool storage, it may well be that the formation of off-flavor is not due to direct enzyme action but rather to the lack of it.

R. Plank advanced such a theory for the cold-storage (not frozen) injury to fruit. Grapefruit cannot be stored below approximately 50° F. without harmful results. Green bananas chilled below 46° F. will not ripen properly. Plank's explanation is that some enzymes of the extremely complicated biochemical system are retarded more than others at the low temperature, thus permitting the accumulation of the products from the enzymes of first attack. Such midproducts can cause off-flavors or other effects. It is doubtful if this is the case with processed foods, in which most enzymes have already been destroyed, but it is very likely that this sort of action is responsible for many of the troubles that develop in the cool-storage shipment and marketing of unheated agricultural products like fresh fruits and vegetables. The best-known example of a comparatively harmless change from cold is the sweetening of potatoes at temperatures slightly above 32° F. At lower temperatures the velocity of sugar formation from starch is retarded less than the rate of decomposition of sugar due to respiration. The result is a higher concentration of sugar in the potato.

Two other troublesome details cause complications.

The first is that some enzymes, notably peroxidase, are known to regenerate themselves after being heated. It must be said that this has never been demonstrated for any practical food product. But because it occurs every day in the laboratory (under rather special conditions), we suspect that other enzymes, today unknown, might do the same thing even better and thus be giving us trouble.

The second is that harmless bacteria (of which there are always a few in "commercially sterile" food products) may not grow in the product but may still be able to excrete their enzymes into the product, and thus make trouble again.

The fact remains that scalding has got rid of most of the trouble in keeping canned or frozen foods. The rest of the difficulty may be due to remaining enzymes, maybe to something else, or maybe to both. In any case, it is a slow process. Most persons associated with the frozen-pack industry believe that these slow deteriorative changes in stored processed foods are due to enzyme action; only a few believe that off-flavor formation may occur because of slower (nonenzymic) reactions.

The argument of the majority who believe in the enzyme hypothesis is that when certain enzymes, for which tests can easily be made, have been inactivated by heat, the product keeps well in the frozen state.

It is therefore of great industrial importance to have tests for the efficiency of a scalding process when it comes to inactivating enzymes.

Two enzymes have been used as an index. One is catalase, which decomposes hydrogen peroxide to water and oxygen. The other is peroxidase, which decomposes hydrogen peroxide when any one of a number of other oxidizable substances is present—for example, catechol. Both enzymes are easily measured, and their disappearance on heating is taken to signify the destruction, or near destruction, of all the other enzymes as well. Packers disagree as to whether catalase or peroxidase makes the better index. Catalase is destroyed by less heat treatment than

peroxidase. Testing for peroxidase therefore is a more rigorous measurement—perhaps too rigorous. A need exists for research to determine the enzymes actually responsible for off-flavor formation in order that tests for them can be used, rather than an index enzyme, which apparently has little to do with the process of deterioration.

THE PROBLEM OF ENZYME CONTROL in frozen fruits is different from that in frozen vegetables. Let us first take up tree fruits, such as peaches and apples. Tree fruits contain an enzyme called polyphenoloxidase. Most of them contain a natural, tanninlike substrate, which in the presence of oxygen causes darkening at the cut surfaces. In untreated frozen-pack peaches most of the darkening occurs during the defrosting. Such peaches also develop an off-flavor.

THE CONTROL of polyphenoloxidase has taken three approaches.

The first is to scald the fruit. But if the enzyme is destroyed by scalding there is no advantage in freezing precooked peaches over canning them. Hence other methods were sought.

The second method was through plant breeding. The Sunbeam peach, although it contains polyphenoloxidase, does not darken, because it lacks tannin. Some of the new crosses with the Sunbeam peach darken only slowly. Although these new peaches have good quality, many persons think they are not equal to an Elberta.

The third method, the one most widely used on peaches and apricots, is to exclude oxygen during packing. Packaging peaches in sugar sirup also helps keep oxygen from coming in contact with the cut surfaces, but that alone is not enough.

C. W. DuBois and D. K. Tressler found that the addition of vitamin C completed the job. That vitamin functions in this manner: The first oxidation products of the tannin formed by polyphenoloxidase and oxygen are reduced by the vitamin C (which is thereby oxidized), and no darkening takes place as long as any of the vitamin remains. This method is now widely used.

The technique used for the control of polyphenoloxidase in the preservation of frozen apples is somewhat different from that used for peaches, because apples are a good deal more porous than peaches. The porous nature (vacuoles) of the apple makes necessary the control of the enzyme throughout the slices, but with peaches one has to control only the enzyme on the cut surfaces. Scalding techniques have the disadvantage of precooking the fruit and also cause excessive leaching, because a temperature of 190° F. must be reached throughout the whole slice before enzyme inactivation takes place.

Apples therefore are treated with sulfur dioxide to control the enzyme. A good method to get penetration of the sulfur dioxide is to place the slices in a sirup containing the SO_2 and subject them to a partial vacuum. Air is admitted again; when the atmospheric pressure is restored, the sirup and SO_2 have filled the vacuoles. As much as 5 to 8 percent of sirup is thus introduced into the slices. An equally good job of control can be done by substituting vitamin C for the sulfur dioxide, but for such a use the cost of the vitamin is rather high.

The problem of enzyme control in bush fruits is not an important factor in preservation by freezing. Strawberries tend to become dull gray, presumably because of an enzymatic reaction. That, however, is controlled simply by adding solid sugar to the berries. The sugar draws juice from the berries and gives them a protective coating, thus excluding oxygen. With raspberries and blackberries no enzyme problem seems to exist.

Like all chemical reactions, enzyme actions go faster at higher temperatures. But in going on, many of them (like the oxidation of sugar in fruit) develop more heat. So the warmer the product is to start with, the faster it gets hotter—a vicious circle.

Much has been done, particularly by F. Kidd in England, to reduce the damage that occurs in shipping fruit by cooling the fruit beforehand. That simply increases the time interval before the fruit gets warm enough to heat up rapidly and thus to deteriorate rapidly. In the meantime it ripens somewhat. The precooling method has been used in transporting South African fruit to England; it is really the method used in refrigerated railroad transport, which usually starts cooler than it ends.

The preparation of cucumbers for pickling consists of curing the cucumbers by a fermentation in salt brine. The resulting product, called salt stock, may be kept for some time before being desalted and made into pickles. The softening of the salt stock, particularly in warmer climates, has constituted a very serious economic loss to pickle manufacturers. Cooperative work by T. A. Bell and J. L. Etchells, of the Department of Agriculture, and I. D. Jones, of the North Carolina Agricultural Experiment Station, has shown that pickle stock softens when an enzyme—pectinase—is present in the brine. The presence of pectinase in the brine is a valuable indicator of impending softening. It shows that softening is definitely connected with an enzyme action—a big step toward the ultimate goal of preventing that form of spoilage.

From the foregoing you gather that enzyme action can cause serious losses of quality and even of the product itself. To eliminate enzyme actions, some form of scalding or heating is generally employed; to delay enzyme actions, some form of cold is helpful. It is too bad that some other methods of destroying or delaying enzyme actions are not practicable. The future may well see inventions to do so.

One other method of lowering the enzymatic spoilage, however, has proved its worth and is occasionally used. It consists of withdrawing as much water as possible from the material. All the known enzymes require water for their action. When the material is perfectly dry, enzyme action (as far as we know) ceases entirely. The withdrawal of water is neither simple nor inexpensive—it must be almost complete, and it is hard to withdraw the last few percentages of water from an agricultural commodity. Nevertheless, the preservation of dried eggs has been markedly improved by practically dehydrating them.

The withdrawal of water has been of practical use to the processor and to the farmer. Probably the biggest single agricultural loss in this country occurs when freshly cut grass or alfalfa is allowed to dry slowly in the field. The food value of the hay depends largely on its sugar content, which is reduced rapidly by enzymic oxidation after cutting. The grass becomes warm, and the oxidation goes all the faster before the hay dries out enough to stop it. Artificial drying stops the loss at once—but artificial drying is expensive. Nevertheless, it might pay the farmer to compare the two potential losses for the particular conditions under which he works: The loss of food value by enzyme action and the cost of artificial drying. Obviously, in a dry climate the weather dries hay for the farmer without cost. In a wet climate he usually gets much more hay per invested dollar but loses some of its value before he dries it. The right answer is an individual matter, but the situation illustrates the necessity of figuring on enzyme action in agricultural products.

ENZYME TESTS have been devised for determining the efficiency of pasteurization. Normal milk contains phosphatase. That enzyme disappears on heating, and the higher the temperature the faster the disappearance. By measuring what is left, one can set up an accurate test to determine whether a given sample of milk has been heated at the legal pasteurization temperature for the required time. *Mycobacterium tuberculosis*, the most heat-resistant of the pathogenic organisms likely to occur in milk, is more rapidly destroyed by heat than is the phosphatase. The test was first used in Great Britain and has been widely adopted in this country. B. Axelrod, of the Department of Agriculture, has developed a similar phosphatase test as an index of pasteurization in citrus products.

The annual production of cheese in the United States since the Second World War has averaged more than a billion pounds. The manufacture of most of it requires the use of the enzyme rennin.

Rennin coagulates the casein of milk and thus forms the insoluble curd (calcium paracaseinate), which, after undergoing various other processes, constitutes the cheese. The formation and finishing of the curd, based on physical and chemical details in processing, determine the final nature of the cheese. For soft cheeses the coagulation is carried out at a low temperature. The amount of rennin used is such that 2 hours or more are needed for the coagulation. For hard cheeses, the coagulation is carried out at a higher temperature and in a shorter time. After the curd has been separated from the whey and pressed, the ripening begins. The ripening process depends on the enzyme system of certain bacteria or molds, according to the kind of cheese to be made. However, the rennin in some cheese continues to hydrolyze the curd during the ripening.

The tenderizing of beef during the hanging period is due to the autolytic enzymes present in the beef. Usually the beef is kept for several weeks at a temperature slightly above 32° F. That temperature is a compromise between the temperature needed for the optimum action of the enzymes and that needed for keeping down the bacterial and mold growth. By preventing the growth of mold and bacteria by ultraviolet radiation, meat can be tenderized in 3 days at 60° F. Thereafter the meat is held at the customary refrigeration temperatures, pending sale.

Raw pineapple juice contains a proteolytic (protein-hydrolyzing) enzyme called bromelin. As many a bride has found out, there is no point in putting fresh pineapple into gelatin, because it liquefies. This enzyme is being used to tenderize sausage casings. The sausages are sprayed with pineapple juice.

Fruit juice can be clarified by enzymes. Practically all the clear apple juices marketed today have been clarified by the use of pectin-hydrolyzing enzymes (pectinase) derived from molds. The opaque juice obtained by pressing the apples is treated with a relatively small amount of the enzyme preparation. After an incubation period, which allows enzymes to act in the juice, it can be filtered clear; untreated juice cannot be filtered so because of technical difficulties.

Enzymes are important in bread making. The enzymes known to be involved are amylases (enzymes that convert starch to sugar), proteinase, and the fermentation enzymes of yeast.

A. K. Balls and W. S. Hale, of the Department of Agriculture, and H. Jørgensen, of Denmark, independently discovered in 1935 the importance of the protein-digesting enzyme in wheat. This proteinase is a typical plant proteinase in that it must be in the reduced form to be active. Oxidizing agents inhibit its action. The proteinase must be adequately controlled in order to obtain a good loaf. Too much proteinase makes a flat, small loaf; too little gives a tough bread. The proteinase in a flour that contains too much of the enzyme can be reduced by several methods—by the miller, who can either bleach (oxidize) the flour or store it 6 to 8 weeks for natural oxidation to occur, or by the baker, who can incorporate such oxidizing agents as bromates in the dough. The proteinase in a flour that contains too little of this enzyme can be increased by the addition of flour from malted wheat. The malted wheat flour also contains α-amylase and therefore is added to practically all flours. Usually not enough sugar is added to dough to enable the yeast to produce enough carbon dioxide for the desired degree of rising. The amylase added as malt flour converts some of the starch to sugar, which the yeast ferments to carbon dioxide.

Another enzyme sometimes used in bread making is lipoxidase. It oxidizes carotenoids, which are yellow, to colorless substances. The enzyme is added to dough in the form of soybean flour by the baker when he uses unbleached flour. The result is a whiter bread.

Proteinases are used in the manufacture of leathers. Amylases are used for the conversion of starch to sugar before the production of alcohol by fermentation. Amylases are also extensively used to remove starch from textiles, particularly from cotton cloth after the operation of printing. All fermentation processes, such as the production of penicillin, butanol, and acetone, depend on the enzymes of the microorganism used in the process.

ENZYMOLOGY has a variety of industrial aspects. Certainly it is a wide field for future development. But a word of caution: Two pitfalls await those who would base new industrial processes on enzyme action—the difficulty of avoiding contamination by unwanted molds and bacteria during the enzymatic part of a process, and the difficulty of competing with processes of straight chemical synthesis which are often also catalyzed at very high temperatures by inorganic catalysts.

It seems now that adventurers in enzyme technology would do well to consider more the specificity of enzyme actions, rather than the speed-up in reaction rate that enzymes cause.

EUGENE F. JANSEN *is a biochemist in the enzyme research division at the Western Regional Research Laboratory. He received his training at George Washington University and has done research in the Department of Agriculture since 1929.*

ARNOLD KENT BALLS *is head chemist of the enzyme research division at the Western Laboratory. He received his training at the University of Pennsylvania and Columbia University and in Europe.*

Allergens of Agricultural Products

Henry Stevens

Allergy is a comparatively new term of medical origin. Its modern, everyday meaning, however, is told in an old saying, "What is one man's food is another man's poison." Freely applied, as proverbs usually are, this one can be fitted to all the familiar and widely varied symptoms called allergy.

Continual sneezing and smarting eyes torment the victims of hay fever. Their distress is seasonal; it lasts from the beginning to the end of the blooming period of one or more species of trees, grasses, or weeds. Air-borne pollens from those plants act as poisons in the air passages and eyes of people who are allergic to them. Pollen hay fever or, worse, pollen asthma, is the result. But for most persons the same pollens are entirely harmless and can be neither seen nor sensed in the air they breathe.

Food allergy may be recognized by a brief but annoying outbreak of hives— a familiar penalty of overindulgence when wild strawberries are bearing in abundance. Far more serious and persistent disorders of the skin, the air passages, the digestive system, and other organs, however, may signify allergy caused by food. One or several usually wholesome ingredients of a varied diet may be, in fact, another man's poison.

Allergy, regarded as disease to be identified and treated, is a medical problem requiring the special knowledge and skills of a physician. However, most allergens—the substances that provoke allergy—are found among products and byproducts of farming. Thus, agriculture has a stake in problems involving the identity of allergens as minor, but important, components of farm products. I give one example.

Among the hundreds of farm products examined and cataloged by allergists in their search for and evaluation of allergens, cottonseed proved to be especially impressive. Clinical evidence derived from testing allergic subjects with extracts of the cottonseed kernel or cottonseed press cake demonstrated the presence of an allergen of exceptional potency. The allergen was presumed to be a protein, but extracts diluted beyond the limit of chemical detection of the compounds still exhibited the capacity to induce allergic reactions. Lacking knowledge of the chemical and physical properties of allergenic components, or any means other than clinical tests to detect them, the allergists concluded that complete avoidance of all cottonseed products should be advised when the allergic persons showed positive reactions to test with cottonseed extract. Because derivatives of cottonseed were presumed to carry the seed allergen, particular emphasis was given to strict avoidance of foods containing refined, edible cottonseed oil and hydrogenated shortenings. Also recommended was avoidance of mattresses and other furnishings containing cotton linters. Two products, edible cottonseed oil and cotton linters, which account for the major industrial value of cottonseed, thus were recognized by clinicians as probable or actual sources of the cottonseed allergen.

The clinical evidence against cottonseed oil and the cotton linters appeared incontestable. No identifying chemical or physical properties of the

82

allergen were known. No one had isolated an allergen. No one knew whether an allergen would retain its activity if purified. Therefore, the presence or absence of the allergen could not be proved by chemical analysis of the edible oil and linters. Moreover, medical consensus supported the conviction that a clinically significant quantity of cottonseed allergen would be determinable by clinical evidence alone.

To test the conclusions of the clinicians required first the isolation and chemical characterization of cottonseed allergen. The objective involved chemical fractionation of the cottonseed kernel to find a component of unknown chemical and physical properties and recognizable, therefore, only by its biologic activity as an allergen.

All the previously known proteins of cottonseed were separated, purified, and evaluated for allergenic activity. Together, the proteins comprised the major nitrogenous substance of the cottonseed. But none exhibited sufficient allergenic activity to account for the potency attributed to the crude extracts employed by clinicians in assembling their evidence or in reaching their conclusions.

Fractionation was then directed to the components of cottonseed that can be extracted with water alone. That approach was successful. The principal allergen of the cottonseed was identified with a minor protein component combined with a complex carbohydrate. This protein component of cottonseed had not been previously recognized. Moreover, it differed significantly from all proteins previously classified and named. This unusual component had both allergenic specificity and potency of a degree to account for the allergenic properties of the crude seed-extract.

Isolation of the principal allergenic component of the cottonseed made possible the first comprehensive examination of an industrial oilseed and its commercial derivatives. The results proved conclusively that the principal allergen of cottonseed is a natural proteose of the seed embryo. In relation to other components of the seed, the proportion of this protein would be insignificant except for its exceptional allergenic properties. This allergenic component of the seed embryo is not a component of the linters or hulls of cottonseed. The allergen of the seed embryo is stable under conditions employed in the milling of cottonseed for recovery of the oil, meal, and edible flour. Both cottonseed meal and edible cottonseed flour contain significant amounts of the allergen. However, the conventional industrial refining excludes the allergen from edible cottonseed oil, which is also the source of hydrogenated shortenings and other edible fats.

The findings have led to revision of firmly established clinical opinion on the management of cottonseed allergy. No justification remains for avoidance of foods containing edible cottonseed oil or hydrogenated cottonseed oil, regardless of clinical sensitiveness to cottonseed allergen. Among the edible products of cottonseed, only the flour need be excluded from the diet to avoid the cottonseed allergen. Cotton linters of all grades are free from the cottonseed allergen. Accordingly, substitution of other filling for mattresses and upholstered furnishings is not essential when one tries to avoid exposure to cottonseed allergen.

Investigations prompted by the significance of allergens to the utilization of agricultural products have continually produced evidence of immediate value to processors and consumers of farm products, and of collateral importance, also, to clinicians whose first concern is relief of allergic symptoms.

HENRY STEVENS *heads the research on allergens of agricultural products for the Bureau of Agricultural and Industrial Chemistry. Dr. Stevens found his chief interest in chemical reasons for disease while a student of agricultural chemistry at the University of Wisconsin.*

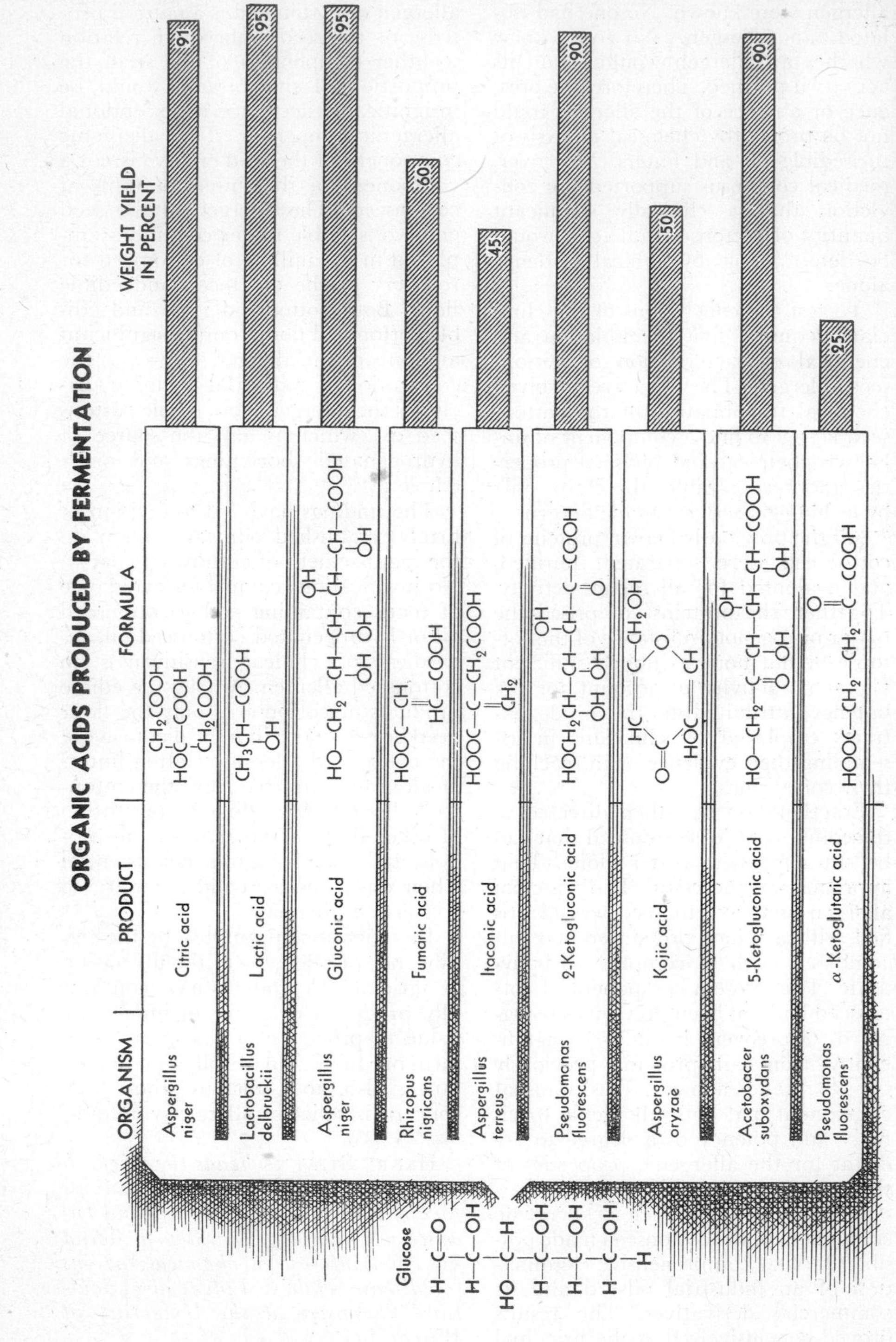

ORGANIC ACIDS PRODUCED BY FERMENTATION

ORGANISM	PRODUCT	FORMULA	WEIGHT YIELD IN PERCENT
Aspergillus niger	Citric acid	CH_2COOH $HOC—COOH$ CH_2COOH	91
Lactobacillus delbruckii	Lactic acid	$CH_3CH—COOH$ OH	95
Aspergillus niger	Gluconic acid	$HO—CH_2—CH—CH—CH—CH—COOH$ OH OH OH OH	95
Rhizopus nigricans	Fumaric acid	$HOOC—CH$ $HC—COOH$	60
Aspergillus terreus	Itaconic acid	$HOOC—C—CH_2COOH$ CH_2	45
Pseudomonas fluorescens	2-Ketogluconic acid	$HOCH_2CH—CH—CH—C—COOH$ OH OH OH O	90
Aspergillus oryzae	Kojic acid	$HC = C—CH_2OH$ $O = C$ O $HOC = CH$	50
Acetobacter suboxydans	5-Ketogluconic acid	$HO—CH_2—C—CH—CH—CH—COOH$ O OH OH	90
Pseudomonas fluorescens	α-Ketoglutaric acid	$HOOC—CH_2—CH_2—C—COOH$ O	25

Glucose

$H—C = O$
$H—C—OH$
$HO—C—H$
$H—C—OH$
$H—C—OH$
$H—C—H$

Fermentation Acids in Industry

Frank H. Stodola,
Richard W. Jackson

To most persons, an acid means a strongly corrosive substance that eats holes in pipes, clothes, fingers, and other things it touches. Yet there are acids that are mild in action and even edible. They are the organic acids, as distinguished from the mineral acids. They are important to us because of their diverse uses in the preparation of foods, beverages, and many other materials from medicinals to inks and plastics.

We meet the organic acids almost daily. Citric acid occurs in grapefruit, lemonade, and orange juice. Lactic acid makes milk taste sour and gives buttermilk its tang. Gluconic acid, as a vehicle for calcium, is often of great help to dairymen in treating cows for milk fever. A less known organic acid, itaconic acid, is valuable in making plastics. These are merely a few of the organic acids used in industry.

A great deal of effort has been directed toward making the organic acids by new and ingenious chemical methods. Fruitful as the chemical methods have been, however, they have limitations that at times bar their use in the preparation of the more unstable or complex organic acids. Fortunately, in micro-organisms we have the means of making some organic acids by the use of those delicate and specific substances known as enzymes.

Fermentative action has long been known and utilized in the manufacture of alcohol and vinegar, but only in recent years has it been widely adopted by industry. Such developments as those leading to the production of citric acid, sorbose, gluconic acid, butyl alcohol, acetone, penicillin, and streptomycin illustrate the diversity and importance of fermentation processes today.

LET US SEE how fermentation is employed in the commercial production of citric, lactic, gluconic, and fumaric acids, and glance at some acids of coming importance, such as 2-ketogluconic, kojic, 5-ketogluconic, α-ketoglutaric, pentonic, and bionic acids.

Many complicated syntheses are so readily carried out by the molds, yeasts, and bacteria as to make one wonder at the remarkable synthetic powers of those simple forms of life. Each species, in its own way, by changes subtle or profound, can so manipulate the atoms of glucose (corn sugar) as to produce one of many different acids. That these products are not merely incidental to the existence of the organisms but, rather, represent their life work is shown by the yields of the fermentation products obtainable. Possibilities for new commercial processes are enhanced by the increasing diversity of available organisms and by the expanding assortment of sugars, alcohols, and other substances that serve as starting materials.

CITRIC ACID is the most important acid produced industrially by microbiological means. From a rather discouraging start in the closing years of the nineteenth century, the fermentation method for the preparation of this useful compound has been developed by research to a point where it is the principal commercial source.

Citric acid was first isolated from lemon juice by Carl Wilhelm Scheele

85

in 1784. Its chemistry was elucidated by Justus von Liebig in 1838. In 1893 began the history of the industrial utilization of molds. In that year C. Wehmer in Germany reported the production of citric acid by a mold of the genus *Penicillium*. Realizing the commercial possibilities of his discovery, Wehmer at once started large-scale production in a factory in Alsace. The effort failed, however, because of technical difficulties. Another attempt in Germany in 1914 also failed because of the war.

Meanwhile, B. Zahorski disclosed in an American patent the important discovery that good yields of citric acid could be obtained with the mold *Aspergillus niger*. As Wehmer had maintained that this species of *Aspergillus* produced only oxalic acid (which occurs, for example, in rhubarb), a detailed study of the group was made by Charles Thom and J. N. Currie of the Department of Agriculture. They showed that Zahorski was indeed correct in his claim that citric acid production is a characteristic of many *A. niger* strains. This new turn prompted Dr. Currie to undertake research on the conditions that govern citric acid production by the organism. His study laid the foundation for the large-scale manufacture of citric acid in the United States.

The first commercial unit for citric acid production was in operation in New York City by 1919. Production was increased gradually to the point where this country no longer depended on Italy for citric acid. Italy in 1922 used waste citrus fruits to produce approximately 90 percent of the world's supply of the calcium citrate from which the acid was obtained. Most of it was imported by the United States. By 1927, however, we became practically independent of foreign sources, so successful was the fermentation method.

Because of its commercial importance, the citric acid fermentation has received much attention in university, Government, and industrial laboratories. The Department of Agriculture

has investigated the organism, the interrelation of carbon source and inorganic salts, the hydrogen-ion concentration, the temperature, the ratio of surface area to volume of solution fermented, and the oxygen supply. All are important factors.

Several investigators have found that a large number of molds can produce citric acid. Among them are *Aspergillus niger*, *A. clavatus*, *Penicillium luteum*, *P. citrinum*, *Paecilomyces varioti*, *Mucor piriformis*, *Ustulina vulgaris*, and *Botrytis cinera*. Commercially, however, only *Aspergillus niger* can give high yields of citric acid, with small amounts of oxalic acid—an unwanted byproduct. This organism also has fairly uniform biochemical characteristics and is easily cultivated.

Citric acid can be produced from many organic substances, particularly sugars, including 2-, 3-, 4-, 5-, 6-, 7-, and 12-carbon compounds. Of these, sucrose and glucose give the highest yields. For industrial fermentations, sucrose, technical glucose, and molasses are used. In general, a concentration of sugar between 15 and 25 percent is required for high yields of citric acid. Nitrogen is usually supplied in the form of ammonium salts. The only other essential elements are potassium, phosphorus, magnesium, sulfur, and traces of iron and zinc.

It is important to acidify the fermentation liquor with hydrochloric acid to an acidity of pH 3.5 before inoculation in order to limit the formation of oxalic acid, prevent undesirable spore formation, and minimize the danger of infection by other organisms. It is known that contamination difficulties were at least partly responsible for the failure of early commercial attempts in Europe—the neutralization of the citric acid by calcium carbonate allowed the invasion of undesirable organisms. The process is usually carried out between 77° and 95° F., although temperatures as low as 68° and as high as 104° have been used. The optimum temperature depends somewhat on the organism used.

Acids produced by fermentation

Acid	Price per pound (October 1950)[1]	Recent production
	Cents	Pounds
Citric, crystalline........	27 [2]	26,000,000
Lactic, plastic grade......	[3] 35	[4] 4,538,000
Fumaric, crystalline......	32	[5] 2,691,000
Gluconic...............	[6] 28	[2] 871,000

[1] Price given is lowest quoted for high-quality product in large quantity (carload, barrels, or drums).

[2] 1945.

[3] Price is for 80-percent lactic acid; 50-percent lactic acid is quoted at 19 cents a pound.

[4] 1949.

[5] 1948.

[6] Calculated on anhydrous basis. Actual quotation was for 50 percent gluconic acid at 14 cents a pound. A large percentage of the acid is sold as the calcium salt, which was quoted at 65 cents a pound.

The relation between the area of the fungus mat on the surface and the volume of the underlying solution is important for satisfactory yields. Because the conversion of sugar to citric acid occurs entirely in the mold cells, diffusion processes must play a significant part in the transfer of sugar into and of the product away from the organisms. Shallow pans of solution therefore are used industrially to effect the most efficient conversion of sugar to acid. Extensive studies have determined the surface-volume ratio that will give the maximum yield in the shortest time. Air supply is an important factor. Although little information concerning it is available, it appears likely that only relatively small amounts of air are needed to supply the necessary oxygen for the mold. It is known also that large amounts of air adversely affect yields of acid.

Citric acid has been produced industrially by fermentation in this country for 30 years, but the methods are kept secret, and details about them have not been published. We can give at least a general picture of the surface process, however.

The fermentation is conducted in shallow pans made of high-purity aluminum to avoid the harmful effect of other metals. The process is started with spores of a tested organism and the fermentation is conducted in a room with constant temperature and humidity and regulated air flow. A continuous mat of mycelium forms over the entire surface of the solution within 2 days. Formation of citric acid proceeds rapidly after the fourth day. The fermentation is usually complete in 7 to 10 days after inoculation. The solution is then drained off and the mat pressed. The acid is crystallized directly, or it is removed as the insoluble calcium salt, from which it can be regenerated by sulfuric acid. The weight yield is probably 60 to 70 percent, although A. J. Moyer, P. A. Wells, and O. E. May, of the Department of Agriculture, obtained as high as 91 percent. Because of the pan requirements and handling difficulties involved in the process, several organizations are working to develop a submerged-growth process that would permit the use of large tanks instead of shallow pans for the fermentation. It is not unlikely that the submerged-growth method has already been tried commercially.

Citric acid is soluble in water and crystallizes from it in large prisms, which contain one molecule of water of crystallization. Chemically, it is a tribasic acid forming three series of well-defined salts. On heating, citric acid decomposes first into aconitic acid and then into itaconic acid, which, in the form of its esters, can be used in making plastics.

Some of the salts of citric acid, particularly the calcium salt, are used in medicine. The free acid is used for the preparation of soft drinks, flavoring extracts, and confectionery. In industry, citric acid is used as a silvering agent, as an ingredient of engraving inks, and in dyeing and calico printing. Considerable interest centers in the esters of citric acid, which can serve as plasticizers of synthetic resins. Thus, tributyl citrate may be used in lacquers and triethyl citrate in vinyl resins; both of these esters plasticize phenolic resins as well as cellulose ethers and esters. As plasticizers, they serve to increase the flexibility and extensibility of the plastic.

LACTIC ACID has been of concern to man since earliest times because of its appearance in sour milk, but only recently has its production become an important enterprise. From humble beginnings in 1881, the industry has grown until in 1949 about 5 million pounds of lactic acid was produced in this country, all of it by fermentation.

Despite its simple chemical nature, lactic acid has a variety of properties, such as strong acidity and edibility, which make it of value technically. Such a diversity of uses has developed that four distinct grades of acid, based on purity, are now distributed. The so-called crude grade finds its greatest application in deliming hides and plumping leather, in vegetable tanning, and in dyeing textiles. The edible grade is used in confectionery, extracts, fruit juices, essences, soft drinks, olives, pickles, yeast, and sirups. The plastic grade can be converted to plastics by way of methyl acetoxypropionate and methyl acrylate, and lactic acid esters can be used as plasticizers. The United States Pharmacopoeia grade of lactic acid is widely used in the drug industry, particularly in the form of its calcium and iron salts.

Lactic acid is produced by the growth of micro-organisms on a cheap carbohydrate source to which have been added inorganic salts, a crude organic nitrogenous material, and calcium carbonate. Many carbon sources can be fermented by lactic-acid-producing organisms, but the choice for commercial production is determined by factors like cost, availability, and the amount of preliminary treatment required. The most widely used carbon sources now are molasses, whey, and starch hydrolyzates prepared by acid or enzyme treatment.

The bacteria used in the fermenta-

tion belong to a group called the homofermentative lactic acid bacteria, which produce lactic acid as the principal end product of their activity, as contrasted with the heterofermentative lactic acid bacteria, which produce (besides lactic acid) considerable amounts of volatile acids and carbon dioxide. Just what member of this group is used depends primarily on the kind of carbohydrate to be fermented and the rate and temperature of fermentation desired. For the fermentation of the lactose in whey, *Lactobacillus bulgaricus, L. casei,* or *Streptococcus lactis* can be used. The molasses and starch hydrolyzates are readily converted to lactic acid by *L. delbrueckii, L. leichmannii,* or *L. bulgaricus.* It is not uncommon to use several kinds of organisms together to produce a desired effect.

In industrial practice the details of the fermentation may vary widely, but all processes have several features in common. It is desirable to use thermophilic bactria, which exhibit their optimum activity at 122° to 131° F. Such a fermentation eliminates most contamination problems and permits the use of simple pasteurization, rather than sterilization. The carefully selected organism is first grown in seed tanks that have about 5 to 10 percent of the capacity of the large fermentors to be inoculated. The concentration of sugar in the large fermentors is usually 15 percent, and this produces just about the amount of calcium lactate that will saturate the fermentation liquor. The precipitation of the product during fermentation is undesirable. The fermentation requires from 20 to 96 hours, depending on the carbohydrate used.

When the fermentation is complete, any one of a number of methods for the isolation of the lactic acid can be employed. Crude lactic acid of commerce can be prepared by removing the calcium ion from the fermentation liquor by means of sulfuric acid. If lactic acid is desired for edible use, the crystalline calcium lactate is removed from the fermentation liquor by filtration or centrifugation and is treated with the calculated amount of sulfuric acid. If the United States Pharmacopoeia or plastic grades are wanted, three basic procedures are available for obtaining the acid of high purity from the acidified fermentation liquors: Extraction with solvents, steam distillation under relatively high vacuum, and distillation of the methyl ester followed by hydrolysis. C. H. Fisher and his group developed new methods at the Eastern Regional Research Laboratory for recovering lactic acid from the fermentation liquor. They also prepared many derivatives of potential industrial use from lactic acid.

GLUCONIC ACID is used mainly in the form of its calcium salt as an ingredient of pharmaceutical preparations. Administration of the salt, orally or by injection, is a safe and effective way to supply calcium to tissues during pregnancy and lactation and in cases of fractures, dental caries, allergic conditions, and rickets. Humans find calcium gluconate easier to take than other calcium compounds, because it has no unpleasant taste and does not upset the digestive tract. The injection of calcium gluconate, which is quite soluble, into cows with milk fever caused by a calcium deficiency has produced startling cures. Calcium gluconate is also used in some dentifrices.

Gluconic acid itself is used in tanning compounds and metal polishes and has industrial possibilities for use in acid baths for pickling iron and steel, and for baking powders, pectin jellies, processed cheese, and laundry preparations.

Gluconic acid differs from glucose only in that the aldehyde group of the glucose has been oxidized to a carboxyl group. The transformation can be brought about by chemical means, but the preparation by mold fermentation has proved so superior that all gluconic acid here and abroad is made by fermentation. As early as 1880, L. Boutroux showed that gluconic acid could

be produced by bacteria. In 1922, M. Molliard found that molds could also carry out the direct oxidation of glucose, and later work, largely by H. T. Herrick, O. E. May, A. J. Moyer, and P. A. Wells of the Department of Agriculture, made it a successful commercial process.

The ability to produce gluconic acid occurs particularly in certain species and strains of the genera *Aspergillus* and *Penicillium*. From them, strains of *A. niger* have been selected for ability to give high yields of gluconic acid in a short time and to sporulate abundantly, as required for the inoculation of new fermentations. It will be remembered that citric acid is also produced by *A. niger;* the difference in behavior of the mold is due to the difference in hydrogen-ion concentrations used for the two fermentations.

Industrially, the raw material for the fermentation is corn sugar (glucose monohydrate). Other materials in the medium include ammonium phosphate, magnesium sulfate, potassium phosphate, and corn steep liquor. Calcium carbonate is added to prevent the development of an acid reaction, which interferes with the smooth conversion of glucose to gluconic acid. The concentration of glucose can be as high as 25 percent if a small amount of boric acid or a borate is added so as to prevent the precipitation of calcium gluconate. Otherwise, the concentration of glucose must be limited to 11 percent.

The fermentation is carried out in vertical-tank fermentors equipped with aerators and stirrers or in rotary-drum fermentors. Yields of 95 percent can be had in less than 24 hours. When the fermentation is complete, the solution is separated from the mycelium, which is added to fresh nutrient solution. In that way, the same mycelium can be used to carry out at least 12 fermentations. The solution from the fermentor, on concentration, yields crystals of calcium gluconate, which can be separated by filtration or centrifugation. If the free acid or its lactone is desired, the calcium can be removed by sulfuric acid.

The formation of fumaric acid by molds was first reported by F. Ehrlich in 1911. Since then we have learned that this unsaturated acid is produced by various species of the genera *Rhizopus, Circinella, Cunninghamella, Mucor, Aspergillus,* and *Penicillium.* Ordinarily, molds produce only small amounts of the acid, but J. W. Foster and S. A. Waksman, of the New Jersey Agricultural Experiment Station, found that one strain of *Rhizopus nigricans* can convert up to 50 percent of the sugar consumed to fumaric acid. As with other fermentations, the effect of strain differences is profound. It is likely that all fungi, and probably all living cells, produce fumaric acid during the oxidation of carbohydrates. In most cells, the acid is metabolized as soon as formed so that only traces exist at any one time. In a few exceptional organisms it appears that some derangement of the usual cycle has occurred, and fumaric acid accumulates.

It is probable that in industrial practice a selected strain of *Rhizopus nigricans* is grown in submerged culture on either starch or refined corn sugar. Salts are added to provide sources of nitrogen, potassium, magnesium, phosphorus, and sulfur. Calcium carbonate is used to prevent the culture medium from becoming too acid. It has been found that zinc must be kept at low levels if high yields of fumaric acid are to be obtained. The principal industrial use of fumaric acid is as a mordant in textile dyeing. It appears that it could find application as a replacement for tartaric acid in leavening agents, as well as in the manufacture of resins and plastics for special purposes. (Cream of tartar is a salt of tartaric acid.)

Besides the acids produced commercially, a number of others await exploitation. Scientists in the Department of Agriculture have demonstrated that 2-ketogluconic, kojic, 5-ketogluconic, α-ketoglutaric, and various sugar acids can be got in good yield. If we can find some use for them, we believe we can produce them in quantity.

Itaconic acid is formed by *Aspergillus itaconicus.* The process was first reported by K. Kinoshita in Japan in 1931. English workers discovered in 1939 that certain strains of *A. terreus* also produce the acid. Studies in the Department of Agriculture by Lewis B. Lockwood, A. J. Moyer, Kenneth B. Raper, and others on the selection of strains of *A. terreus* and the modification of cultural conditions have resulted in a marked increase in the yield. In surface culture, it is now possible to get 37-percent weight yields in 12 days at about pH 2.2. With submerged fermentations, yields as high as 45 percent have been obtained in 5 days at a pH of 1.8. Itaconic acid, now available commercially, has possibilities in the preparation of resins and plastics because it is a substituted acrylic acid.

2-Ketogluconic acid is produced by the action of various species of bacteria of the genus *Pseudomonas* on glucose in aerated cultures in the presence of calcium carbonate. Weight yields of 90 percent can be obtained in a 30-hour submerged fermentation and 100-pound lots have been prepared in Department laboratories. This keto acid is of interest in that it can be converted to *d*-araboascorbic acid, which is a good antioxidant for food use. In this capacity, it could serve in the preservation of flavors in the canning industry and in preventing the development of oxidation flavors.

Kojic acid can be produced readily in yields of more than 50 percent by molds growing on a variety of carbon sources. Best results have been obtained from glucose and xylose, with the use of members of the *Aspergillus flavusoryzae* group. It is a very reactive compound chemically, and many derivatives have been prepared from it.

5-Ketogluconic acid is produced by various species of *Acetobacter* in weight yields exceeding 90 percent. Aerated cultures are used with calcium carbonate added for neutralization. When oxidized by air in the presence of vanadium pentoxide, it is converted to *d*-tartaric acid in good yield.

α-Ketoglutaric acid can be produced in a 25-percent yield when the fermentation of glucose by *Pseudomonas fluorescens* is allowed to proceed beyond the 2-ketogluconic acid stage to the point where no more reducing value is observed. This reactive acid is a vital step in the oxidative breakdown of carbohydrates, but its production in any quantity by fermentation had always been despaired of because investigators supposed that it was metabolized as soon as it was formed. This fermentation illustrates how accumulated knowledge has permitted the manipulation of a series of enzymic reactions for a specific purpose. It is possible that still better ways will be found to produce known products by fermentation. It is certain that many new fermentation products will be disclosed.

The bionic acids: Until recently no organism was known that would carry out the simple oxidation of the reducing disaccharides to corresponding acids. Heretofore such microbiological oxidations failed because enzymatic splitting of the disaccharides into monosaccharides always accompanied oxidation. This search for the proper agent was successful when Frank H. Stodola and Lewis B. Lockwood in the Department of Agriculture reported in 1947 that good yields of maltobionic and lactobionic acids could be obtained by the action of *Pseudomonas graveolens* on maltose and lactose.

The pentonic acids: It has been demonstrated also by investigators in the Department that various members of the genus *Pseudomonas* will oxidize *d*-arabinose, *d*-xylose, and *d*-ribose to the corresponding *d*-arabonic, *d*-xylonic, and *d*-ribonic acids in good yield.

PRESENT PRODUCTION figures and prices, insofar as they are available, are presented in the table. A more complete accounting of production according to process employed would be useful. Official statistics involving a small number of companies, as in this instance, however, are sometimes withheld to protect trade secrets. It can be assumed that all the quantities listed are produced by fermentation, except perhaps a small percentage of the citric and a part of the fumaric acid. Market prices, ranging from 27 to 35 cents a pound, are relatively low. It is worthy of note that in 1919, before the fermentation method was put in operation, the price of citric acid was well over a dollar a pound. For comparison, the prices early in 1950 on some other organic acids were: Formic, 13 cents; acetic, 13.5 cents; butyric, 34 cents; oxalic, 14.5 cents; glycolic, 9 cents; and tartaric, 32 cents.

One important item in the cost of production is the carbohydrate substrate. If high-quality sugar from crops grown in the United States is to be used, corn is the most economical source. Potatoes cost on the average about the same per pound as corn, but they contain only 25 percent starch compared to 70 percent in corn. Cane and beet molasses, to the extent they are available and of suitable quality, are used as cheap sources of sugar. Since the First World War, blackstrap molasses has varied from less than 3 cents to more than 30 cents a gallon. When it was 8 cents a gallon, as in early 1950, the sugar cost slightly more than 1 cent a pound. This may be compared with pure corn sugar, then selling at 6 cents a pound. Milk whey has been used in one lactic acid plant since 1939.

One has to consider the market position of the organic acids now being manufactured by fermentation and to appraise, as best one can, what changes may be forthcoming. A chemical reaction may be a classroom oddity in one decade and a chief industrial process in the next. Looming on the horizon at the moment, for example, is the Fischer-Tropsch process and the accompanying large amount of useful by-product chemicals. Nevertheless, certain points regarding the fermentation acids appear worthy of mention.

The structure of citric acid is hardly suggestive of any cheap synthesis from simpler chemicals. Much the same is true of gluconic acid, although its chemical conversion from glucose is known and this process might conceivably be made so efficient as to become the method of choice. Lactic acid is a simple molecule, but the relatively high price of hydrogen cyanide militates against its use in the production of lactic acid from acetaldehyde.

The commercially produced fermentation acids have their appropriate outlets in chemical industry. Itaconic and fumaric acids, if sufficiently cheap, could also flow into plastics. The same is true of citraconic acid, which may be derived chemically from citric acid. In addition, this group is outstanding as acidulating agents in foods. Citric, lactic, and gluconic acids are known to be safe ingredients of the diet and are extensively employed in foods, soft drinks, confectionery, and pharmaceuticals. The uses have been increasing constantly. Applications for 2-ketogluconic, 5-ketogluconic, α-ketoglutaric, and kojic acids, among others, are mainly yet to be worked out. The organic acids obviously have unique applications, and the method of fermentation has been responsible for an increasing number and amount of these substances. The future is bright for further developments.

FRANK H. STODOLA *is in charge of the chemistry section of the fermentation division in the Northern Regional Research Laboratory. After receiving his doctor's degree in organic chemistry from the University of Minnesota in 1933, he spent 3 years at Yale University as a National Tuberculosis Association fellow. After a year at the Kaiser Wilhelm-Institut für Biochemie, he did research for 2 years at the Mayo Clinic on the adrenal gland hormones. Before joining the Department in 1942, he taught in Columbia University.*

RICHARD W. JACKSON *is head of the fermentation division in the Northern Laboratory. He is a native of Illinois and was trained in chemistry and biochemistry in Eureka College and the University of Illinois. His research contributions have dealt chiefly with the synthesis, chemistry, and intermediary metabolism of amino acids and other organic acids and with the utilization of agricultural commodities.*

CONTAMINATION of cultures is a frequent and bothersome accident in microbiological laboratories. It is a major problem in the fermentation industries. But it brought rare good fortune to a group of research workers in the Department of Agriculture a few years ago. They were trying to make the vinegar bacteria, which produce 5-ketogluconic acid from glucose, produce instead the more valuable 2-ketogluconic acid. They found accidentally that a common soil organism, *Pseudomonas fluorescens,* which contaminated their culture of vinegar bacteria, produced 2-ketogluconic acid in good yield. The accident opened up a new series of biological oxidations, which has given us new and improved methods of making several organic acids, some of which may have industrial and pharmaceutical applications.—*Lewis B. Lockwood, Northern Regional Research Laboratory.*

FOOD OR FEED OR FABRIC

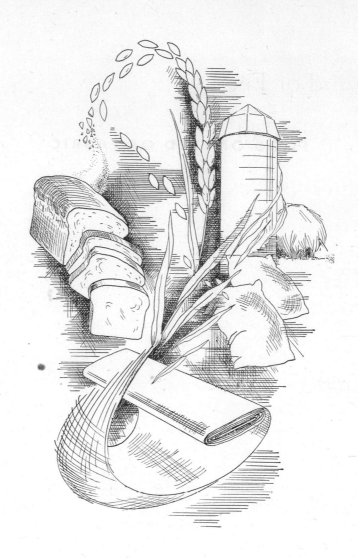

Food or Feed in a Period of Change

W. D. Ramage

Before undertaking an analysis of the current use of farm goods as food and feed, it may be useful to review the changes in the Nation's food habits, because they are the basis for our present agricultural pattern.

During the latter part of the eighteenth century and the early part of the nineteenth, Americans generally ate plenty of food but, even on the farms, they did not have a diet that in the light of modern knowledge could be considered good. Corn was the main cereal. Pork was the principal meat. Small use was made of milk, vegetables, or fresh fruit.

A few persons agitated for the increased use of natural foods, but made little progress because of the difficulties in keeping fruits, vegetables, and milk in satisfactory condition during distribution. The dearth of those foods was especially marked in the cities because of inadequate transportation facilities. The introduction of refrigerators helped to relieve the shortage.

The development of railroad transportation in the middle of the nineteenth century made fresh foods much more available. One of the most important forward steps was the invention of the refrigerator car. Commercial cold storage of perishable foods was first tried just before the Civil War began.

Canned foods gradually assumed a more important place in the diet. Canned fruits, vegetables, and milk were supplied to the armies in the Civil War. After the war, canned goods became generally available in the retail stores.

Except in a few backward areas, the use of protective foods greatly increased in the period following the Civil War, with a corresponding improvement in the general health. The national diet shifted toward more varied foods. An important contributing factor was the lowering of food costs in relation to wages. During the latter part of the nineteenth century and the early part of the twentieth, many further improvements were made in the methods of food production and handling. Dairy herds were tested for tuberculosis. The meat supply was more carefully inspected. The use of preservatives was regulated. Laws were passed against adulteration of foods. The concept of scientific analysis of the diet began to develop. Several investigators studied the protein and carbohydrate needs of humans under various living conditions. The distinction between complete and incomplete proteins was established. It was shown that only animal proteins contain all the essential building blocks for a complete protein diet and that some animal protein is ordinarily needed in the diet to maintain good health. The importance of calcium, iron, and phosphorus in the diet was shown. Scientific evidence on vitamins began to develop.

But the dietary improvement during this period was partly offset by the increased use of refined foods that resulted from the advances in processing technology. White flour, for example, came to be preferred over whole-wheat. Despite greater knowledge on the subject, some economists and even nutritionists still objected to fruits and vegetables because of their relative high cost. With such difference of opinion, wide variations in both quantity and quality of food in different areas were inevitable.

During the First World War, rationing, public education, and war gardens effected conservation of the food supply. They further raised the average person's level of diet. More people became aware that certain foods supply large amounts of such health-protecting elements as vitamins and minerals. The proportion of the family food budget for protective foods increased to about 40 percent, from approximately 10 percent in the latter part of the nineteenth century. Increases in stature and health resulted from this better diet, especially in the upper economic level of wage earners. As late as 1929, however, the production of protective foods was inadequate for the whole population. The increased use of refined cereals contributed to the deficiency. The protective elements removed in the refining processes were not always supplied in sufficient quantities by other protective foods in the diet. The addition of vitamins and minerals to those products had not yet begun. Public education on the use of protective foods was advanced by spectacular cures of deficiency diseases in certain areas by the use of milk, fresh meat, fruit, and leafy vegetables.

Adequacy of diet suffered in some respects during the depression years. Milk consumption fell below the level of the 1920's. Distribution of surplus agricultural commodities through relief channels was successful on the whole in preventing widespread malnutrition. Farm diets were generally good, as a result of home canning.

The minimum annual cost of an adequate diet in 1932 was approximately 100 dollars a person; even that was too high for many large nonfarm families whose incomes were low. The purchase and distribution of surplus commodities by relief agencies continued even in the late 1930's; surplus farm products were distributed under the food-stamp program. The school-lunch program also contributed materially to improvement in the general adequacy of the diet.

Notwithstanding the ups and downs, food habits have improved during the twentieth century. Production of agricultural commodities is being directed more and more toward satisfaction of the health needs of the Nation. Processing technology has advanced, with resulting improvements in product quality. The nutritive and flavor values in manufactured foods are better preserved during processing and the shelf life of the food products is greater than ever before. The rapid improvement in quality and variety of frozen foods is especially noteworthy. Freezing preservation for retail distribution is becoming an important factor in the availability of protective foods.

THE PRODUCTION and general distribution of food and feed crops in a representative recent period are indicated in the first table. Another (page 100) shows the approximate cash received by farmers for these food and feed crops in a prewar year, a war year, and a postwar year. Ignoring for the moment the question of production volume (which is roughly proportional to population), we find this production picture quite different from the one that existed in the early days of American agriculture. The modern production pattern is higher in the proportion of protective foods.

The noteworthy increases in consumption of milk, eggs, vegetables, and citrus fruits during the Second World War are significant from the standpoint of diet adequacy. Equally significant is the enrichment of white flour and wheat cereals, which began before the war and became general during the war period. The gains were

Production of food and feed crops in the United States

Commodity	Average production			Major areas of production
	1935–39	*1942–45*	*1946–49*	
Fruits, including melons (commercial production)...................thousand tons..	14,700	17,200	18,800	Calif., Fla., Wash., N. Y.
Vegetables (commercial production).....do....	21,900	27,200	28,400	Calif., Fla., N. J.
Cattle and calves...........million pounds..	14,200	19,200	18,400	Iowa, Tex.
Hogs...............................do....	13,500	21,600	18,800	Iowa, Ill., Ind.
Sheep and lambs.....................do....	1,940	2,070	1,480	Tex., Wyo., Mont., Colo.
Poultry...........................do....	2,900	4,800	4,500	Del., Va., Iowa.
Eggs...........................millions..	28,000	46,000	48,000	Iowa, Minn., Pa., Tex.
Milk produced on farms......million gallons..	12,000	14,200	13,800	Wis., Minn., N. Y.
Edible fats other than lard or butter million pounds..	1,700	2,500	3,100	Ill., Iowa, Ind., Ohio, Ga., N. C.
Rice....................thousand cwt. bags..	22,000	30,000	37,000	La., Ark., Tex., Calif.
Wheat (as food).............thousand tons..	14,300	14,500	14,500	Kans., N. Dak.
Field corn for food products...........do....	5,200	6,200	6,100	Iowa, Ill., Minn., Ohio, Ind., Mo.
Oat food products....................do....	450	740	670	Minn., Iowa., Ill., Wis.
Sugar beets.........................do....	9,600	8,400	10,700	Colo., Calif.
Sugarcane..........................do....	5,700	5,900	5,900	La.
Grains as feedstuffs..................do....	89,000	106,000	121,000	Iowa, Ill., Minn.
Hay harvested......................do....	84,000	106,000	101,000	N. Y., Wis., Minn.
Oilseed cake and meal................do....	3,300	6,100	6,700	Ill., Nebr., Mo., Tenn., Tex.
Animal protein feeds.................do....	2,800	2,900	2,400	Ill., Iowa, Nebr.
Other byproduct feeds...............do....	8,300	9,800	10,300	Ill., Minn., Mo.

Computed by W. L. Shaw from data issued by the Bureau of Agricultural Economics and the Bureau of the Census.

largely held during the period of high employment in the postwar period.

Despite their enrichment, grain products have become less important as sources of protective elements in the diet. Vegetables and fruits, especially citrus, have become more important. Nevertheless, the average annual consumption of food has been remarkably constant for the past 30 years, in terms of total weight and energy requirements. The over-all nutritional adequacy has increased markedly, however, since the beginning of the First World War.

A lower consumption of potatoes has accompanied the downward trend in use of cereal products. In 1949, the Americans consumed less than two-thirds of the average quantity of potatoes consumed annually between 1910 and 1915. The decline in the use of corn meal has been especially large. The consumption of corn meal in 1949 was less than a third of the average quantity consumed in the 1910 through 1915 period. Partly offsetting the decrease in energy value resulting from less use of potatoes and cereal products, there has been a larger use of sugar, except during the war.

The use of meat and eggs has been fairly stable. Vegetable proteins, such as beans, peas, and nuts, have gone up somewhat in volume. Manufactured dairy products have increased steadily in volume since the First World War. There has also been some increase in the use of fluid milk. We eat only slightly less butter—notwithstanding the large increase in the use of margarine.

The use of fresh fruit has been fairly constant, but the shift from apples to citrus fruit has been marked. The consumption of apples is about two-thirds of the level before the First World War. We eat and drink more than three times more citrus fruit and fruit juices. The general increase in the consumption of vegetables during the past 25 years has been marked by a shift toward the leafy green and yellow vegetables and by an increased use of tomatoes.

Calculating from the nutritive value of the daily per capita food supply, the Bureau of Agricultural Economics finds that, although the caloric intake has gone down 6 percent over the past 40 years, intake of other values more important in the diet has increased as follows: Calcium, 22 percent; iron, 13 percent; vitamin A, 14 percent; thiamine, 15 percent; riboflavin, 25 percent; niacin, 10 percent; and ascorbic acid, 17 percent. (Food values taken in capsule form are not included.)

THE DISTINCTION between food and feed uses of agricultural commodities was more clearly drawn when horses were the principal motive power for agricultural machinery. With a largely mechanized agriculture, the distinction has become less definite, as the feeding is done mainly for ultimate food uses. An arbitrary distinction is still made, however, largely on the basis of primary use.

One respect in which this distinction between food and feed is important lies in the value of agricultural end products for food use. If the end-product balance is on the side of the high-unit-cost products, such as meat, produced by diverting low-value cereals to feed use, the danger of overproduction is greatly lessened. A somewhat smaller population can be supported, but at a higher nutritional level. The inelasticity of food consumption is such that overproduction always results in years of bumper crops unless a large part of the cereal grains is diverted to feed use, with a view to ultimate consumption as higher-value food products. The interdependency of food and feed uses thus becomes apparent.

Another way in which the distinction between food and feed uses has become important is in the development of a commercial feed industry. This amounted to only about 1 million tons a year before the First World War. By 1929, it had grown to 13 million tons and during the Second World War it grew to more than 30 million tons. The potential market for commercial feeds is probably much greater—perhaps 100 million tons.

From the table introduced to show the production of most feed grains and other feed concentrates during the prewar, war, and postwar periods, it is apparent that corn is the outstanding feed concentrate. No food commodity stands out in the same way among the feed materials. Eighty to 90 percent of the corn grown is used for feed, mostly on farms where it is raised. Although only about 5 percent is used for food directly, the corn fed is the basis for much of our meat supply and our dairy products. Indirectly, corn is thus still the most important single food crop, as it was in Colonial days.

Although most of it is fed on farms, corn is one of the three most important ingredients of the commercial mixed feeds. The other two are soybean meal and alfalfa meal.

As most agricultural crops are seasonal, it is necessary to store quantities for use throughout the year. Some grains tend to heat in storage, but the grains and oilseeds generally hold their quality fairly well if harvested in prime condition and stored dry in tight bins. Fruits and vegetables, however, require carefully regulated conditions of temperature and humidity if their storage life in the fresh state is to be extended beyond a very short period. Freezing of

Production of feed grains and concentrates in the United States

	Average production		
	1935–39	*1942–45*	*1946–49*
	1,000 tons	*1,000 tons*	*1,000 tons*
Corn..	64,900	84,000	88,900
Oats...	16,700	20,700	22,100
Barley...	5,700	7,800	6,600
Sorghum grains...	1,600	3,500	3,400
Wheat, rye, and imported grains........................	5,100	12,400	5,300
Oilseed cake and meal..................................	3,300	6,100	6,700
Animal protein feeds...................................	2,800	2,700	2,400
Other byproduct feeds..................................	8,300	9,800	10,300
Total...................................	108,400	147,000	145,700

Computed by W. L. Shaw from data issued by the Bureau of Agricultural Economics.

the fresh products is not permissible because of the damage to texture which often results and the rapid spoilage which follows thawing. Freezing is usually permissible after moderate processing, but it yields a product not directly competitive in price with the fresh material. Potatoes and apples are more readily stored than most other vegetables and fruits. Careful control of the humidity and temperature to which these products are exposed in cool storage keeps them in satisfactory condition for many months. Citrus fruits may also be stored. Their effective storage life is extended by delaying their harvest.

Even under the best conditions of storage, the life of many fruits and vegetables is so short that the stored materials have no significant effect on the total consumption. Canning, freezing, pickling, and other preserving operations are the direct outgrowth of the perishability of these commodities and the desire to make them available over a longer season.

Retail prepackaging of fresh fruits and vegetables has developed rapidly in recent years. Although it brings about no great extension of storage life, the practice has resulted in bringing the fresh products, especially leafy vegetables, to the consumer in better condition than when marketed in bulk.

Keeping the prepackaged vegetables at refrigerator temperatures during marketing operations increases their salable life two or three times.

The processing which most cereal crops undergo to render them more suitable for food use makes their subsequent handling more critical. Thus, flour is more exacting in its storage and container requirements than the wheat from which it was made. Processed cereal grains are, in general, more subject to spoilage than the whole grain.

Some feed materials lose part of their nutritive value in storage. This is especially true of alfalfa meal. The carotene content of alfalfa meal decreases rapidly under commercial storage conditions. It has been estimated that the actual cost of storing alfalfa meal is often much less than the value of the carotene lost during storage. That is due to the fact than many buyers of alfalfa pay a graduated price, based on the carotene content. If most of the carotent is lost, the marketability of the alfala may be seriously impaired. Extensive research is in progress toward the solution of the problem.

The growing of agricultural commodities for nonfood and nonfeed uses has paralleled the general agricultural development. Some nonfood crops, for example cotton, tobacco, and flax, became important in agriculture even be-

Returns to farmers in the United States from sale of food and feed commodities

Commodity	Average returns 1935–39	1942–45	1946–49
	Million dollars	Million dollars	Million dollars
Fruits and tree nuts..	470	1,260	1,330
Vegetables..........	640	1,480	1,900
Cattle and calves.....	1,150	2,690	4,670
Sheep and lambs.....	161	318	380
Hogs...............	870	2,560	3,480
Poultry.............	313	980	1,120
Eggs...............	490	1,320	1,730
Dairy products......	1,480	3,040	4,000
Grains.............	840	2,140	4,220
Wheat...........	440	1,060	2,200
Corn............	260	600	1,160
Oats............	50	160	295
Barley..........	30	110	160
Rice............	40	130	220
Other...........	20	80	165
Sugar beets........	51	76	116
Sugarcane for sugar...	18	28	37
Hay harvested.......	72	183	276
Oilseeds for food and feed.............	193	760	1,150

Computed from data issued by the Bureau of Agricultural Economics.

fore the production of food crops was adequate. The development of non-food and nonfeed outlets for food and feed crops resulted, at least in part, from the growing excess of food production over food needs.

Many food- and feed-processing operations result in byproducts which have value mainly as feed materials. After the oil has been removed from cottonseed for use chiefly in food products, the meal remains as a valuable high-protein cattle feed. The byproducts from flour production also constitute an important source of feed material. In general, it can be said that there is no real waste material in the processing of cereal grains.

On the other hand, with the exception of citrus wastes, only a small portion of the enormous waste from fruit and vegetable processing is converted into byproducts. Citrus wastes are largely dried for cattle feed. A small part of the citrus peel from juice operations is used for the production of pectin. The high moisture content of most fruit- and vegetable-processing wastes works against their economical utilization.

Research in the fields of feed and food processing will open up broader possibilities for improvement. Marked advances are being made in our knowledge of dietary requirements. New methods of handling food and feed commodities will make it possible to satisfy these requirements.

Recent surveys show the Nation's progress toward the goal of a good diet for everyone. Among the low-income families the trend is toward the use of more meat, poultry, milk, eggs, fruits, and vegetables. In the spring of 1948 about 70 percent of our families were consuming enough calcium to meet their needs. In 1936, only 33 percent were getting enough calcium. In 1948, more than 80 percent of the families surveyed were getting adequate amounts of the essential vitamins.

The improvement in diet is directly related to our ability to consume the agricultural commodities we produce. We can consume more of our production when we use a high proportion of secondary agricultural products, such as meat, eggs, and milk, along with fruits and vegetables.

Further improvement in the quality of preserved and prepared foods will certainly result from research now in progress.

It appears reasonably certain, also, that more and more prepared foods will be used in the future. The average housewife now has less help and more outside interests than the housewife of 50 years ago. The quality and variety of prepared foods have increased greatly. It is a safe prediction that food habits, especially in the urban areas, will be increasingly influenced by standardized products of large food manufacturers. The importance of food research in this development is sure to be great.

W. D. RAMAGE *was graduated in chemical engineering and received his doctorate in physical chemistry from the University of California. From 1930 to 1935 he was assistant director of research for the Great Western* *Electro-Chemical Co.; from 1935 to 1941 he was a consulting chemical engineer. He joined the Department of Agriculture in 1941. He is head of the engineering and development division of the Western Laboratory.*

Estimated food consumption in the United States

Commodity	Average per capita consumption		
	1935–39	*1942–45*	*1946–49*
	Pounds	*Pounds*	*Pounds*
Dairy products...............................	386	449	444
Fluid milk and cream.............................	300	356	346
Ice cream...	5	7	11
Evaporated and condensed milk...................	19	23	26
Cheese...	6	6	7
Buttermilk (dry, cultured, natural)...................	53	49	46
Other dairy products (cottage cheese, dry skim and dry whole milk, whey, malted milk, sherbet).....................	4	8	8
Vegetables..	372	414	393
Fresh (sum of retail weights)...........................	324	349	326
Tomatoes.......................................	23	28	25
Potatoes..	124	122	110
Sweetpotatoes..................................	19	18	14
Other...	158	181	177
Frozen..		2	2
Canned (including tomato sauces and catsups, baby foods, soups)...	34	46	51
Dry beans and peas; soya grits and flour..................	10	11	10
Peanuts (shelled).....................................	4	6	5
Fruit...	194	198	215
Fresh (sum of retail weights)...........................	167	166	169
Apples...	38	31	30
Citrus..	44	59	52
Melons...	31	34	34
Other...	54	42	53
Frozen (including juice and juice concentrates).............	1	2	3
Canned (including juice and juice nectars).................	19	23	36
Dried...	6	6	4
Nuts (including desiccated coconut and tree and bush nuts, shelled)...	1	1	1

Estimated food consumption in the United States—Continued

Commodity	Average per capita consumption		
	1935–39	1942–45	1946–49
	Pounds	Pounds	Pounds
Grain products...	203	200	178
Wheat products (flour and cereal).......................	163	160	145
Corn products (meal, flour, starch, breakfast cereal, hominy, grits)..	27	26	21
Rice (milled heads)....................................	6	5	5
Oat products (primarily oatmeal).......................	4	4	3
Rye products (primarily flour).........................	2	3	2
Barley products (malt equivalent)......................	1	2	2
Meats, fish, poultry, eggs.............................	173	205	209
Beef and veal (retail cuts)............................	52	55	60
Pork (retail cuts, except large bacon and other fat pork).....	37	47	47
Lamb and other meat (retail cuts of lamb and mutton, plus edible offal of slaughtered animals, plus game)...........	16	20	17
Chickens (dressed, not eviscerated).....................	18	28	24
Turkeys (dressed, not eviscerated)......................	3	4	4
Fish (edible portion).................................	11	9	11
Eggs..	36	42	46
Sugars and sirups.....................................	110	102	103
Refined sugars (excluding those used in production of frozen and canned products, salad dressing, unskimmed sweetened condensed milk, tobacco products).....................	96	83	88
Sirups (maple sugar, maple sirup, cane sirup, sorgo sirup, refiners' sirups, edible cane molasses)..................	13	17	14
Honey...	1	2	1
Fish and oils...	64	65	65
Butter..	16	12	10
Margarine..	3	4	5
Lard (estimated at 28 percent of pork carcass weight).......	11	12	13
Shortening...	12	9	10
Bacon and salt pork...................................	16	21	20
Other edible oils (cooking and salad oils in salad dressing, mayonnaise, baking products).........................	6	7	7
Beverages..	16	15	19
Coffee...	12	11	15
Tea...	1	1	1
Cocoa...	3	3	3
Total retail weight equivalent	1,518	1,650	1,626

Computed from data issued by the Bureau of Agricultural Economics and the Bureau of Human Nutrition and Home Economics.

Animals and animal products handled in commercial channels in the United States, by region, selected years

	Meat				Milk products manufactured			Poultry sold				
	Live weight produced 1949	Dressed weight produced 1947	Consumption[1] 1944	Milk sold 1949	Cheeses 1948	Evaporated milk (unskimmed) 1948	Dry whole milk 1948	Chickens 1949	Broilers[2] 1949	Turkeys 1949	Eggs 1949	Fish frozen 1949
	Percent	Percent	Percent	Percent	Percent	Percent	Percent	Percent	Percent	Percent	Percent	Percent
North Atlantic............	3.3	10.0	28.0	23.3	8.3	3.6	10.0	19.5	14.4	7.7	18.2	56.3
East North Central........	22.5	24.3	22.1	39.7	62.1	50.6	59.4	21.5	6.8	12.1	21.2	1.4
West North Central........	39.8	35.0	9.5	12.3	11.9	10.3	20.6	29.5	4.3	25.9	30.1	0.7
South Atlantic............	5.8	6.8	12.3	5.5	0.1	4.9	....	6.2	51.3	8.7	7.1	3.9
East South Central........	6.2	4.4	6.6	4.1	7.0 }	[3]12.7 }	0.6 }	6.4	4.4	1.2	4.9 }	[3]10.1 }
West South Central........	10.9	8.0	8.9	2.8	2.8 }	}	0.6	8.4	12.6	10.7	7.8 }	}
Mountain................	7.3	3.4	2.8	2.7	3.8	5.1	0.6	2.8	0.4	8.2	2.8	[4]12.2 }
Pacific..................	4.2	8.1	9.8	9.6	4.0	12.8	8.8	5.7	5.8	25.5	7.9	}
	Million pounds	Million pounds	Million pounds	Million pounds	Million pounds	Million pounds	Million pounds	Million pounds	Million pounds	Million pounds	Millions	Million pounds
Total produced, sold, or manufactured...............	41,099	[5]21,710	[5]21,381	73,114	1,094	3,383	170	1,966	1,482	756	48,319	286

[1] Office of Temporary Controls, January 1947.

[2] Production.

[3] Published for "South Central"; breakdown for East and West not available.

[4] Published for "Pacific"; State breakdown not available. (Percentage for Alaska was 15.4.)

[5] Excluding lard.

Compiled from U. S. D. A. Production Records, Bureau of Agricultural Economics, Statistical and Historical Research.

Animal products processed in the United States, 1949

Dairy products: [1]	Million pounds	Meat products—Continued	Million pounds
Market milk	57,480	Sausage—Continued	
Butter (creamery)	1,409	Dried or semidried	116
Cheese:		Loaf and head cheese	175
Whole milk (and part skim)	1,193	Cooked meat:	
Skim milk [1]	2	Beef	29
Cottage (curd and creamed) [1]	504	Pork	598
Evaporated and condensed milk (unsweetened):		Canned meat:	
Whole	3,009	Beef	80
Skim	508	Pork	492
Condensed milk (sweetened):		Sausage	77
Whole	144	Soup	408
Skim	212	All other	392
Condensed buttermilk	179	Bacon, sliced	713
Dried milk:		Lard:	
Whole	130	Rendered	1,821
Skim:		Refined	1,423
Food	918	Oleo stock	95
Feed	20	Compound	215
Buttermilk	45	Oleo	25
Whey [1]	125	Miscellaneous	99
Ice cream	554	Egg products:	
Chocolate and fermented milk	2,000	Liquid eggs:	
Milk sugar, crude	22	Whole	375
Casein	20	Mixed emulsions	64
Meat products:		Whites (albumen)	89
Placed in cure:		Yolk:	
Beef	111	Plain	20
Pork	3,371	Sugared	20
Smoked and dried:		Salted	18
Beef	51	Emulsion	2
Pork	2,025	Dried eggs:	
Sausage:		Whole	69
Fresh	238	Albumen	2
Smoked and cooked	965	Yolk	4

[1] 1948.

Compiled from U. S. D. A. Production Reports, Bureau of Agricultural Economics, Statistical and Historical Research.

Approximate production of animal products in various parts of the world, 1949

Region	Beef and veal [1]	Pork, excluding lard [1]	Mutton and lamb [1]	Carcass meat [1][2]	Milk [1][3]	Chickens [4]	Eggs [4]
North America	12,970	11,584	671	25,253	138,750	540	60,326
Western Europe	[5] 16,743	[5] 7,040	[5] 820	[5] 15,042	[5] 122,571	[3] 568	33,074
U. S. S. R. [3]	2,855	3,459	978	7,292	....	....	....
South America	7,457	881	646	9,061	....	[3] 110	4,057
Union of South Africa	682	104	175	971	....	16	1,200
Oceania	1,685	280	1,465	3,430	22,877	[3] 19	1,893

[1] Million pounds.
[2] Includes goat and horse meat.
[3] Figures are for 1934–38.

[4] Millions.
[5] Not including Bulgaria, Hungary, Poland, Rumania, and Yugoslavia.

About the Use of Animals for Food

Paul E. Howe

The production of animals for human food needs to be considered from three viewpoints: Their relation to the total world food supply; the unique contributions of animal products to the health and satisfaction of man; and the direction that research should take to make the best use of the total food supply. Questions to be answered are: To what extent do animals compete with man for food? How can one make the best use of animal foods?

As the population of the world increases, man will reserve more and more of the foods, especially the cereals and grains, for his own use. He will give preference to animals that can produce and grow on foods least acceptable to him and to methods of feeding them that will contribute to the same results. The feeds allotted to animals will be those that are not acceptable to man, such as the coarser grains, roughage, and pasturage. The leafy green plants are an important part of man's dietary. There will be some competition between man and animals for the grasses. This is evident even now in the United States, where wheat and alfalfa and other plants in the early stage of growth are commercially cut and dried, so far principally for poultry feeding, but also packaged for human use. As a matter of fact, the product is a good vitamin supplement. Another example is the use of young green alfalfa and green grass for human food in regions of the Near East.

Byproducts from the processing of food for man are available for animal feeding. As competition increases, however, man will undoubtedly take for his own use the more important portions of what are now byproducts. This may create new problems.

Justification for the production of animals for human food lies in the unique nutritive values of their products. In addition, the inedible parts of animals are valuable because they may be converted into products useful to man.

Animal products owe their importance as food to their proteins and other essential nutrients, such as the vitamins, hormones, and calcium. Man's interest in them, however, is strongly associated with the fats—the fat of meat and the cream or butter of milk. So far as we now know, everything of nutritional importance, except vitamin A, in the fats of animals can be obtained from plant fats. As a matter of fact, man obtains most of his vitamin A from the carotenoids of plants. Search should continue for evidence of the special nutritive value of fats. In general, however, animal fats serve to make animal products more palatable and to add flavor to bland vegetable foods.

The importance the average man places upon the fat of animal products has unfortunately led to failure to utilize fully the more nutritionally important parts of the animal. Thus butter commands a premium in the market, and skim milk, with its protein, calcium, riboflavin, and other important nutrients, is fed to farm animals. Often when cheese is made the whey is thrown away or fed to animals. Industry has taken steps to conserve nutrients; the whey of milk with its riboflavin is being converted into cheese and other palatable products. In the case of the meat animals and eggs, the bones and shells, sources of calcium, are discarded or made into fertilizer. Industry is making some moves to utilize the calcium of those products to increase the value of other foods. Thus, in one country, bones are finely ground and cooked with meat in canning; in another, very finely pulverized bone has been used advantageously in the manufacture of confections. In some countries the bones of small fish are an important source of calcium in the diet.

Standards of quality of the meat that is needed to supplement effectively a diet based on grains and leafy vegetables must include vitamins, in addition to other components. Fat should not be the primary criterion of quality that it tends to be today.

Strains of animals that grow rapidly, with maximum muscle development and quality and the minimum of fat, would be a reasonable goal. Quality of meat may then be an inherent characteristic of particular strains of animals and perhaps of methods of feeding, rather than degree of fatness, at present often the only measure.

All these problems are a challenge to the animal breeder and feeder. Animals and animal products will continue to contribute pleasure and profit to man and to serve as a source of nutrients. If my assumptions are correct, the experimental animal breeder and feeder must set his goal far in the future, looking toward the types of animals I have indicated and at the same time meeting immediate demands.

Meat and animal products are perishable. To assure their use as human food, the processor must study and develop ways that will preserve them and make them attractive to the consumer. The changes that occur in processing and preservation of food may affect its nutritive value and even our health. The objective of the processor, therefore, must be to retain the maximum nutritive value compatible with an acceptable product.

In most diets, animal foods are a major source of all nutrients except carbohydrates and vitamin C. The nutrients that are particularly modified in preparation of animal foods in the home and in commercial processing are the proteins, thiamine (vitamin B_1), and pantothenic acid. Of these, thiamine is especially susceptible to change upon storage for long periods of time and at high temperatures. What the changes mean to an individual depends on the quantity and quality of the protein and of the vitamins in the remainder of the diet.

When the diet depends largely on the animal products for thiamine, the losses in processing and home preparation may be serious. Riboflavin is readily destroyed upon exposure to light, but it is not destroyed by heat. Milk is susceptible to loss of riboflavin on exposure to light. In the United States, milk supplies the largest proportion of riboflavin to the total daily intake; hence milk must be protected against such a loss. Vitamin A and carotene are destroyed upon exposure to oxygen. In animal foods, those vitamins are in the fat, which helps to protect them from oxidation.

The general high quality of the proteins of animal foods is an accepted fact. Heat when too high and too continuous lowers the nutritive value of protein by reducing the availability of the amino acids, especially lysine, through combinations and diminished digestibility. The best commercial processes and home cooking methods do not cause sufficient change to affect seriously the nutritive value of the usual mixed diet. Malnutrition, however, results from such practices as the steady use of a processed food of reduced nutritive value in diets on the border line of nutritional adequacy in proteins, vitamins, or minerals. In such instances, the same amount of the original food would assure at least the minimum of the nutritional value of the nutrients lost in processing.

FOOD HABITS—likes and dislikes of food and prejudices for or against certain methods of preservation—often interfere with our acceptance of food. Acceptance or rejection of food may act as a two-edged sword. When it is good, it helps assure an adequate dietary; when it is harmful, it excludes necessary foods or makes us eat too much of the wrong kinds and too little of their supplements.

In the course of processing or preserving foods, there is often a loss of one or more of such important nutrients as vitamins or minerals (or even a change in the nutritive value of the proteins) that are characteristic of the unmodified food. On the other hand, some nutrients may be concentrated.

When people use processed foods in which the appearance, flavor, and attractiveness are retained but the nutrients lost, the danger is that they may not appreciate the significance of the change that has taken place. They may continue to satisfy their appetites by following their old habits, but in so doing they may fail to satisfy their requirements for specific nutrients. Unknowingly, they suffer from hidden hunger. That happened in the last war, not because the nutrients were not provided in the rations but because the soldiers neglected to eat the supplementary foods, such as lemon powder and sometimes vitamin pills, that were furnished to compensate for the losses in vitamins that had taken place in processing and storage. Too, they often failed to use all the milk products provided them because they were accustomed to drinking fresh milk and were indifferent to the canned and dried products that were available.

The Food and Nutrition Board of the National Research Council made good use of one of our food habits when it proposed the addition of vitamins and iron, valuable dietary supplements, to bread, flour, and corn meal, because everyone eats bread. The British added calcium to their 85-percent extraction flour, partly to compensate for the phytic acid (which interferes with absorption of calcium) and partly to assure a better calcium intake.

The preference of rice-eating people for white rice, which has lost most of its thiamine, even when they know that beriberi is likely to occur, has resulted in procedures of fortifying rice that will still be white and fit the methods of preparation.

THE DANGER that malnutrition will result from the introduction of new and useful processed foods, because they may be improperly fitted into established food patterns, may be lessened in two ways.

First, the investigator and processor who develop and produce the food should make every effort to retain as much as possible of the natural nutritive value.

Second, the processor should include in his advertising program information on the composition of his product and its value in the dietary. He should also state on the label of his package the quantity of the important nutrients affected by processing that are present, or the proportion retained, as compared with that in the average natural product.

With such information, the person responsible for feeding people, whether in homes, armed forces, institutions, or public eating places, can make the correction necessary to insure the health of those for whom he is responsible. It will also make it easier for people generally to know the essentials of a good diet and to modify their food habits accordingly.

THE NEED TO RETAIN the maximum nutrients in processing is as important in animal products or byproducts intended for animal feeds as in those for human food. State and Federal laws require statements of the composition of animal feeds on all labels. In the past, the laws have covered protein, fat, carbohydrate, fiber, and ash. With the development of the science of nutrition, they are beginning to require data on vitamins and specific minerals in feeds sold as supplements to the common feeds.

The percentages of animals or animal products sold or manufactured through commercial channels in the United States are given in a table on page 103. The data with regard to meat from the larger animals—beef, pork, lamb, and mutton—illustrate the general movements of animals from West to East and far West as they are produced, slaughtered, processed, and finally consumed in the more densely populated areas. They reflect primarily the finishing of cattle and sheep, not the origin of animals in the West and Southwest that move into the Middle West and East to be finished before slaughter. A larger proportion of the milk, eggs, and pork, originates near the centers of population. These foods can move to the consumer without processing other than refrigeration, while poultry and hogs fed garbage can also be produced on small areas of land near the cities.

Another table, printed on page 104, shows the production of animals, meat, milk, chickens, and eggs in various parts of the world. The numbers are more representative of North America, parts of South America, Western Europe, and Oceania than for the rest of the world. In the world, as in the United States of America, animals produced in the less populous pasture or range and surplus-grain-producing areas are processed near the place of origin and then moved to the centers of population. Likewise, a higher proportion of the world's supply of eggs, poultry, or milk is produced near the manufacturing centers of high population or in countries near them.

The extent to which edible animal products are processed is set forth in a third table. The production of animal products has a seasonal variation, related to the availability of grains and pasture and range grasses and to the effect of temperature and sunlight on the animals' reproductive processes. Farming practices have been modified to minimize these natural cycles, especially in milk cows and poultry to provide fresh milk and eggs throughout the year. Processing of animal products, other than those of refrigeration, is necessary to care for seasonal surpluses or for high production in areas at a distance from those of high consumption.

The quantity of animal products consumed by man is determined in part by the laws of supply and demand and in part by the financial return to the producer. Man should conserve the maximum of animal products that can contribute to his health and satisfaction. There are times of surpluses or low costs when the producer is justified in utilizing his animal products as supplements to his farm-produced feeds in the rearing of animals. That is especially true of skim milk and buttermilk used in the rearing of calves, pigs, and poultry. These products, however, contain protein, vitamins, and calcium that are valuable human foods.

The general tendency in the science and technique of processing and preserving animal foods today is to preserve in stable form more and more of the eggs, milk, meats, and animal byproducts for human consumption. As dried and canned foods, they can be stored and transported without the special precautions of refrigeration. The practice of removing inedible portions and packaging animal products before quick freezing has reduced the space required for storing, simplified handling, and has contributed to their market acceptability.

The possibilities of recovering more of the minor parts of animals, such as the organs and trimmings, blood, and bones, under conditions suitable for their manufacture into human food or into byproducts that can be fed to animals have increased with the practice of collecting animals and animal products at central points to facilitate their processing.

Man and animals compete continuously for the food of the world. Animals, particularly ruminants, can obtain more nutriment from the coarser foods than can man. In animals, also, the need for vitamin and protein supplements is reduced through the activities of micro-organisms in the intestinal tract. The micro-organisms also help to digest the feed and compensate for some of its nutritional deficiencies—particularly among ruminants.

In general, man should have priority for food unless the animal can make better utilization of it or can produce a product of greater value for man's health and comfort.

I find it difficult to justify the diversion of edible animal foods (such as casein or egg albumen) to nonfood uses. It involves consideration of the innate nutritive value of the product and of the quantity available. The importance of the nutritive value is determined by whether or not it is possible to supply similar nutritive value with supplements from plant or manufactured products. The quantity available depends on such factors as acceptability, custom, availability to the consumer, and the farmer's welfare.

The technical competition between edible food products and synthetic or vegetable products is one of superiority and cost. The cost is determined in part by the presence or absence of a surplus and the ability to move animals or their products to market.

The nonfood use of edible animal products has been based upon the properties and relative abundance of animal proteins and fats. Insurance of their greater use for food requires protection of the original products from contamination and deterioration until they can be consumed or processed and protected through canning, drying, and packaging.

Protection of the original product calls for the proper care of milk and eggs on the farm, for proper transportation to milk stations, better egg-storage or egg-breaking plants, and proper slaughter centers where the products can be processed and where miscellaneous animal parts too small to be used in small units can be collected, combined, and sent to larger centers for processing. In such centers it is possible that some of the nonedible parts of animals—wool, hides, and feathers, for instance, or at least their byproducts—may be converted into supplements to animal rations, which in turn make for more economical production of animal foods and for other commercial uses.

Greater use of edible animal products for food would divert considerable quantities of some of them, particularly egg white and casein, from their present technical uses. The nonfood use of animal proteins in the past originated in the ease with which they could be separated from the fat and minerals and in the unique properties of the proteins. For example, the ease with which casein can be separated from milk and egg white from the yolk simplified the discovery of its nonfood uses. Technological developments in the modern synthetics are due largely to the use of animal proteins and fats in the past and to attempts to synthesize as substitutes products having similar values and properties, or to improve upon the product or the effect obtained with animal products. This progress applies to the use of fats as well as of proteins.

Edible animal products possess properties that have made them valuable for uses other than food, such as the use of casein for adhesives, artificial fiber, and plastics, and the use of eggs as adhesives and stabilizers. Research and developments of technology should be directed to the discovery of new or better substitutes for edible animal products now used for other purposes, to the preservation and modification of edible animal products for human consumption and to retain their maximum nutritive value, and to greater utilization of animal products for food.

PAUL E. HOWE *is nutrition consultant, Bureau of Animal Industry. Since 1924 he has been in charge of nutrition investigations and the biochemistry of animal products and has made extensive studies of the nutritive value and quality of meat, eggs, and goat's milk. During the war he served as nutrition consultant in the Public Health*

Branch, Supreme Headquarters, Allied Expeditionary Force, in Europe and afterward in General Headquarters, Supreme Commander Allied Forces, in Japan. He is a graduate of the University of Illinois.

In discussing the animal foods, Dr. Howe reflects his observations on the diets of segments of the world's population which, for one reason or another, have existed on short rations often with different food habits from those of the United States. Under these conditions it was necessary to make the

best use of the animal foods available. This was also at a time when the appreciation and enjoyment of animal foods were heightened by their scarcity. As a colonel in the United States Army and Director of the Division of Food and Nutrition, Office of the Surgeon General, Dr. Howe was also concerned with the nutrition of our soldiers in the United States, where they had the foods to which we are accustomed, and overseas, where of necessity they lived largely on processed foods and missed the fresh foods of home.

THE BIOLOGIST signalled to the man at the winch to lower away, and the fine-mesh net splashed into the warm tropical sea alongside the slowly moving vessel. A few minutes later the biologist was hunched over the curious catch that had been swung up on deck—hundreds of pounds of a pinkish jelly that quivered here and there with minute squirmings. He thought momentarily of the thousands of square miles of ocean that surrounded him, and of the little scoopful that had yielded this swarming life, and he marveled once more at Nature's ways. Plankton, he called the jelly. Sorting it out, he could distinguish scores of completely different families of tiny animals and beings on the border line between plant and animal. Fish food, that's what it was. But at least 99 percent of it was plain sea water, and that's what it would taste like—sea water with a slight fishy flavor. A fish would have to strain gallons of it to make a square meal.

The ocean is no desert. People living in the Scandinavian and Baltic countries, in the Canadian Maritime Provinces, in Alaska, in Japan, in Polynesia know that and live by the knowledge.

For a hundred years some men have been worrying about the ultimate capacity of this earth to support a growing population. Land areas suitable for cultivation are limited. Sometime there just will not be enough. What then? What about the ocean?

Nobody really knows the limits of the ocean's productivity, but we can be sure there are limits. Already the good fishing grounds are parcelled out by solemn treaty agreements. The ocean deeps are not heavily populated; fishing is good mainly in the shallower waters near continental coasts—in waters where sunlight can penetrate to grow the tiny water plants that feed the plankton that feed the fish. The amount of human food obtainable from the ocean is limited by the amount of sunlight that can be captured by green plants in the ocean—exactly the same limitation that confronts us on dry land.—*W. B. Van Arsdel, Western Regional Research Laboratory.*

IN THE LABORATORY

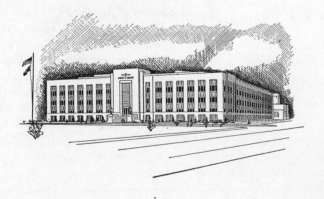

ON THE PRECEDING PAGE *is a drawing of the Southern Regional Research Laboratory at New Orleans. Inside and out-side it is much like the other three regional laboratories of the De-partment of Agriculture.*

On the next pages are shown a few of the everyday activities in laboratories.

Seeing and measuring are a large part of science. For that, a scientist may use an ordinary microscope that magnifies an object up to 500 times. Or he may use this electron microscope, which has a useful magnification up to 100,000 times and can make the dot at the end of this line appear to be 300 feet in diameter.

RADIOACTIVE CHEMICALS *furnish valuable new tools in agricultural research. Two examples of their use: They can be used as tracers to follow the movement of ordinary chemicals through plants or animals to learn what happens to them. Added to dried egg, radioactive glucose shows how glucose operates to hasten spoilage. George W. Irving, Jr., of the Bureau of Agricultural and Industrial Chemistry, protected by rubber gloves, long-handled instruments, and a lead shield, against harmful radiations, here transfers to a synthesizing apparatus a small amount of a radioactive iodine solution from a lead-shielded shipping bottle.*

WITH THIS *tensile testing machine, engineers measure the plasticizer efficiency, or strength, of a bar of a plastic composition and thereby evaluate its usefulness to industry. The bar contains a standard plastic mixed with the plasticizer under test to see if it can toughen the plastic. Plasticizers can be developed from intermediate compounds, which in turn come from lactic acid, obtained by the fermentation of starch, sugar, whey, wood, or other products.*

INTO TWO *of the tiny glass cylinders is put penicillin solution of known strength, for comparison. The other three are filled with newly made penicillin solution of unknown strength. The plates in which they stand contain a medium that has been inoculated with disease bacteria. The penicillin, spreading from the bottom of each cylinder, prevents the growth of the bacteria within a certain radius. The diameter of the zone of clear medium in the area made milky by the bacterial growth, as measured by a special ruler after a suitable interval, shows the strength of the penicillin solution under test.*

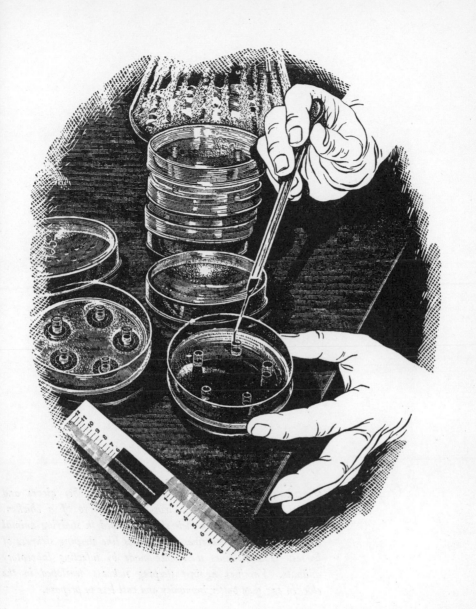

SO DANGEROUS *it must be handled with rubber gloves and special instruments is this virus-loaded embryo of a chicken. Live chicken embryos in their shells are used in studying animal disease viruses and vaccines for diseases like sleeping sickness of horses. The vaccines were once made by infecting laboratory animals. Vaccines against sleeping sickness developed in the chicken egg give better immunity and cost less to prepare.*

WITH THIS *self-contained, portable assembly, designed and built at the Eastern Regional Research Laboratory, one can obtain the concentrated essence of fruit and vegetable juices. It vaporizes part of the juice so fast that there is no heat damage and distills the odorous constituents out of the vapor. The essences are used to restore the original fresh flavor to processed juices and jellies. Sometimes they are added to candies and ices.*

RAW MILK *contains a phosphatase enzyme, which can be destroyed by heat. The absence of the enzyme in milk, cream, or manufactured dairy products indicates adequate pasteurization. Its presence indicates underpasteurization or none at all. That fact is the basis of a test developed by George P. Sanders and Oscar S. Sager of the Bureau of Dairy Industry. Here, Dr. Sanders performs one of the eight steps in the test, which is so sensitive that it will reveal the presence of 1 pound of raw milk in 2,000 pounds of properly pasteurized milk. On the following page is shown one of the many new procedures that improve the ginning of cotton. To test whether cotton contains no more than the normal number of immature fibers, a factor that determines quality, a slide is prepared for the microscopic examination of a composite sample.*

Basic Methods of Processing Food

John R. Matchett

Enormous quantities of food are lost each year through attack by living organisms that are too small to be seen by the naked eye. The organisms, bacteria, yeasts, and molds, seem to be everywhere. They can use a great variety of materials for food if moisture is present. They can live and grow in a fairly wide range of temperatures.

In present-day technology we rely on low temperatures to preserve frozen foods and on low moisture content to protect dried foods. But we generally sterilize foods to be preserved some other way and pack them so that living organisms cannot get inside the package. The process is the modern adaptation of the discovery of the Frenchman Nicholas (or Nicolas) Appert less than 150 years ago. Appert learned that food placed in a bottle and then heated would keep if it were tightly stoppered while hot. That he should have achieved success with the crude containers of that day is astonishing, surrounded as he was by the world of microscopic enemies, which even today we have not learned to control completely.

Several interesting problems have been solved in the course of the development of preserving foods by heat treatment. Of these, the most basic ones have to do with the relative merits of various foods as media of growth for bacteria, yeasts, and mold, and the resistance of the organisms to destruction by heating. An important distinction may first be drawn on the basis of the acidity of the products being preserved by heat. Few of the bacteria dangerous to health grow in acid surroundings; all are easier to destroy by heat in an acid environment. Thus, canning of most fruits is relatively simple and can be accomplished by merely boiling in water.

The canning of vegetable and meat products is not so simple, because generally they lack the acidity that sensitizes bacteria, yeasts, and molds to destruction by heat. Then, too, meat and vegetables constitute a good material for the organisms to grow in.

Meat and vegetables then must be heated at temperatures higher than the boiling point of water. That is done by placing the food, sealed in the final container, in a steel tank strong enough to withstand steam pressures that will give temperatures of 240° to 250° F.

The most difficult problem in processing vegetables and other nonacid foods is the assured destruction of the bacterium known as *Clostridium botulinum*. Under favorable conditions it produces a virulent toxin. The toxin is quite easily destroyed by heat. The bacterium itself is harmless enough. It is the toxin that does the damage. Unfortunately, the bacterium has the faculty of retreating when it encounters adverse conditions into a dormant form—a spore. These spores are resistant to heat. When conditions become favorable, they change back into the active (vegetative) form, ready to pour out toxin. The bacterium will not grow in the presence of air, nor will it grow in acid surroundings; hence it constitutes a health hazard only when it survives its competitors that cause souring. For this reason, food-processing schedules that destroy the spores with ample factors of safety have long since been adopted and well enforced.

In some ways the most interesting of the organisms that vex food processors are the thermophiles (Greek, *thermē,* heat; *philos,* loving), because they may survive the processing temperatures and grow rapidly while the canned goods are cooling, producing a condition in the can known as flat souring, that is, the can does not show swelling, but the contents have a sour taste. None of these bacteria produces disease.

These heat-loving bacteria, along with others like the brightly colored micro-organisms of hot springs, must live through some sort of biochemical system involving enzymes and other proteins much different from those that function at ordinary temperatures. Micro-organisms whose chemical activity sustains life at ordinary temperatures would be killed in an environment most favorable to growth of the thermophiles.

But microbial activity in foods and beverages is not always undesirable. Organisms that produce undesirable changes in some foods are responsible for desirable changes in others. The fermentation industries (pickle, cheese, and sauerkraut making and olive processing) and the farmer who ensiles his crops depend on the chemical changes brought about by yeasts and bacteria. Thus, fermented milks have been prepared for ages and were used by nomadic tribes that could not keep milk in its fresh condition. Through observation over the centuries and through research in more recent times, strains of micro-organisms best adapted to the intended use have been selected. These are used in pure culture in many instances; careful control is exercised to avoid contamination by ever-lurking enemies, which would ruin the food through the unwanted chemical reactions they may bring about or through interference with growth of the desired organism.

A demand for variety and savor in foodstuffs developed early in the course of Western civilization, and trade records indicate that herbs and spices constituted important items of trade. The long caravan route from India and the East witnessed an enormous traffic in spices, along with silk and dyes. Closing of the route in 1453 motivated the search for sea routes that led to the discovery of the New World. Thus, long ago man developed preferences for pleasant flavors and set for himself increasingly rigorous standards of quality that could be met only through sanitary processing of raw material well suited to a particular use.

Man learned to judge food products on the bases of color, flavor, and texture. He found that varieties of plant materials differed substantially with respect to each of these and that similar differences occurred among breeds of livestock. As knowledge of human and animal nutritional requirements accumulated, vitamin and mineral content of foods became of increasing concern. Selective breeding programs on animals and plants undertaken long since have resulted in the highly specialized products of agriculture today, each of which is designed for a specific purpose.

Such considerations provide the ground work for the second basic principle of food processing—the selection of the raw material. It goes without saying that the material must be harvested at its optimum maturity and so handled after harvest that its color, flavor, texture, and nutritive value will be unimpaired when processing begins. Material that has deteriorated will not be made better by any manner of treatment. Protection against micro-organisms must be maintained with care.

It is equally necessary to avoid damage that can result from disturbing the enzyme systems in the raw products. That would cause several undesirable changes, such as darkening of cut or bruised fruits, development of off-flavors in certain vegetables, and destruction of vitamin C. Rapid handling and lowering of temperature are practical means of control.

In some instances, however, enzyme

activity is necessary, if it can be controlled. Many fruits, for example, cannot be picked and transported when fully ripe. Therefore they are harvested "green" and permitted to ripen (a process brought about by enzymes in the fruit) under favorable conditions at the processing plant. Once the fruit is ripened, immediate processing is necessary to avoid damage by the very mechanism used for ripening. Even some meats frequently are made more tender by their own enzymes, controlled through the action of suitable temperatures.

THE FINAL BASIC PRINCIPLE in food processing involves the processing proper, which must be carried out in such a way as to develop or to retain the qualities of color, flavor, texture, and nutritive value to the greatest extent.

This means, in general, that enzyme action must be controlled, that contact with air must be kept as brief as possible, and that high temperatures of processing must be the shortest consistent with accomplishment of the purpose.

Enzymes are generally made inactive at the processing plant by treating for a short period with hot water or steam (blanching). For reasons I have mentioned, this step must be carried out at the earliest stage possible after the plant tissues have been damaged by peeling or cutting. Sometimes blanching is not applicable, and chemical treatment must be used. Sulfur dioxide treatment is used on most fruits to be dried. Vitamin C is commonly employed in certain fruits to be frozen. Those methods are treated in more detail elsewhere in this volume.

The adverse effects of contact with air mostly develop rather slowly. Consequently, they appear more often after storage of the product, rather than during actual processing. Control of such effects is attempted by pumping as much air as possible out of the container, then putting in a gas that would have less effect than air, and sealing the container. Vitamin C and carotene (the latter changes to vitamin A in the body) are important constituents affected by air. Foods containing fat may become rancid in the presence of air, and certain constituents that impart flavor to foods may also undergo unfavorable changes, the chemistry of which is now but little known.

High processing temperatures affect color, flavor, and the way the food feels when you chew it. The green and yellow colors of vegetables are altered, becoming brown under some conditions. Sometimes this browning is desirable. The color and flavor of maple sirup, for example, are brought about by high temperatures. So is the golden brown of bread crust. But high-temperature treatments required to assure sterility in canned foods are generally more severe than desirable, and research is devoted to finding means of reducing processing times consistent with safety. Agitation of cans during processing allows heat to penetrate faster. Quick cooling after processing helps to keep down deteriorative effects. It has been possible to process some products by very rapid heating outside of the container and then quickly cooling and packing into sterile containers without contamination by micro-organisms floating about in the air.

Unfavorable changes brought about by processing at high temperatures are not confined to the processing period. All processed foods should be stored at the lowest practicable temperature to avoid such changes.

CANNING, FREEZING, AND DEHYDRATING are the three basic methods wherein the principles outlined find application in commercial practice. Let us consider briefly the factors governing the relative popularity of these methods. These factors will determine the trends in food technology in years to come.

First is the long-time trend toward improved conservation of color, flavor, and nutritive value of the fresh product. Equally important are economy and convenience in preparation for the table. Fruits, vegetables, fish, and meat approach the quality of the fresh product more closely when frozen than when preserved by any other means. Frozen foods must be stored at low temperatures (usually 0° F.); otherwise they will spoil. They are thus protected against deteriorative changes caused by high temperatures.

Though not always interchangeable or directly comparable, frozen and canned foods are about equally convenient to prepare for the table. Canned foods thus far have been less expensive in general, and many products retain quality as well when canned as when frozen. Some do not freeze well at all, and some are not readily adaptable for canning.

Properly prepared dehydrated foods are of excellent quality, but their greatest advantage lies in economy. This economy is not in price alone, but in ease of handling because of reduction in weight and bulk. It is for this reason that they are indispensable in wartime, when huge quantities of food must be transported over vast distances. Advantage in handling and storage is important in the home, too; with convenience in preparation, it is responsible for the increasing popularity of prepared mixes for soups, cakes, pies, and many other foods.

Recently methods have been found for removing part of the water from certain fruit juices without noticeable changes in flavor or color. These partially concentrated juices are then frozen and kept in that condition until consumed. As the frozen material is in the form of a slush, it can be readily diluted with water back to the strength of the original commodity. Examples of this type of product are frozen concentrated orange juice, grapefruit juice, grape juice, and (to a lesser extent) apple juice.

FOODS of the future will probably be those that combine the characteristics of quality, economy, and ease of preparation for the table. It is hardly conceivable that we will be satisfied to swallow a pill that by itself constitutes a balanced diet, or that we will permit ourselves to be talked into consuming a powder that might taste like a steak, but isn't. Man likes something he can sink his teeth into, that he can chew, taste, and enjoy.

JOHN R. MATCHETT *is an assistant chief in the Bureau of Agricultural and Industrial Chemistry. He is charged with coordinating the Bureau's research on fruits and vegetables. A native Hoosier, he was trained in chemistry at Earlham College, Purdue University, and the University of Chicago. He joined the Department of Agriculture in 1941 after 14 years as a chemist in the Treasury Department.*

BY PHOTOSYNTHESIS, 16 billion tons of carbon is assimilated each year by the land plants for eventual conversion to starch and sugars, proteins, fats, or other complex materials manufactured by plants and used by man for food, feed, and industrial purposes. This ability of green plants to manufacture, in the presence of light and chlorophyll, complex organic chemicals on such a gigantic scale from carbon dioxide, water, and other simple materials is responsible for life on earth as we know it. You can see then why photosynthesis is called the greatest chemical reaction in the world.—*I. A. Wolff, Northern Regional Research Laboratory.*

Changes in the Bread You Buy

Esther F. Phipard

Our consumption of grain products—notably wheat flour—has declined greatly during the past 40 years. We can infer from that fact that we eat less bread, although we cannot say precisely how much less, for no year-by-year figures are available that take into account the unknown amount of bread baking in the home as well as in bakeries.

The main reason offered for the downward trend in consumption of bread seems to be that we are eating more of other foods—dairy products, except butter; citrus fruits; vegetables; and sugar.

Nearly everybody eats bread. Ninety-eight percent of the families included in a Nation-wide sample of urban areas bought bakery bread. The study, made in the spring of 1948 by the Bureau of Human Nutrition and Home Economics, gave information on the kinds and quantities of foods used in the household during a week and on the money spent for them. Purchases of bread of different types and the percentage of households using each kind in a week were:

	Pounds	Percent
Bread, all kinds_____	6. 14	97. 6
White, enriched____	4. 69	86. 5
White, unenriched__	. 21	3. 4
Whole-wheat_____	. 56	22. 1
Cracked-wheat, rai-sin, rye_____	. 68	28. 6
Rolls, biscuits, muffins__	. 27	23. 6
Crackers (not sweet)___	. 40	49. 2

White enriched bread, by far the leading item in the group, accounted for more than two-thirds of the total breadstuffs purchased. Most families enjoy variety now and then, as shown by the percentages that ate other types as well. More than a fifth used whole-wheat bread; more than one-fourth used cracked-wheat, rye, raisin, and other specialty breads. Ready-made rolls, biscuits, or muffins were bought by about one-fourth of the families and unsweetened crackers by nearly one-half. The figures do not include homemade bread, rolls, muffins, or corn bread, which were reported in terms of flour or meal.

Among four large cities studied by the Bureau of Human Nutrition and Home Economics in the winter of 1948, families in Buffalo, N. Y., bought the largest amounts of bread, averaging more than 2 pounds a week a person. Next in order were Minneapolis-St. Paul, San Francisco, and Birmingham, Ala. Farming in Birmingham used only about 1.5 pounds of bakery bread a week a person; hot biscuits and corn bread made at home more than made up for the difference.

Family income made little difference in the amount of bread purchased, except in Birmingham. There, as incomes rose, a marked shift to more ready-made bread and other bakery products occurred, but less flour and corn meal was used. The percentage of Birmingham families using whole-wheat bread also rose with income.

Grain products are among the cheapest sources of calories—a fact that accounts largely for their prominence in diets of many population groups. Fortunately for people who depend heavily upon them for food, grains furnish many of the nutrients needed for good nutrition.

City families in the United States in

the spring of 1948 spent about one-tenth of their total food money for grain products, from which they obtained about one-third of the thiamine, one-fourth of the calories, protein, iron, and niacin, one-fifth of the riboflavin, and one-seventh of the calcium in their diets. Grain products would thus be considered economical sources of those nutrients. Ready-baked bread took about 4 percent of the food dollar, but returned more than that proportion of several nutrients.

Processing changes affect the quality of bread. Basically, bread is made from flour and water or other liquid, to which is added a leavening agent, usually yeast. Other substances may be added to enhance flavor and texture or to promote the growth of yeast. The mixture then undergoes processes of mixing or kneading and rising before baking. That was as true years ago as it is today, but today's bread, dead-white in color, is quite different from the bread of, say, a century ago. To begin with, the flour is different. In the early days when wheat was ground between millstones, all parts of the kernel were ground down together. When the resulting product was sifted through bolting cloth, some of the brownish particles of bran and the more yellowish parts from the germ and aleurone layer also passed through. The stone-ground flour was therefore creamy in color with flecks of brown.

Beginning in 1880, stone grinding of wheat came to be almost completely replaced by the use of steel roller mills, a great technological advance. The chief difference was in the cleaner separation of the starchy endosperm from the outer branny layers of the kernel, and the nearly complete removal of the germ or embryo. The result is a finer, whiter flour, which makes a finer and whiter loaf.

Today's bread is different for other reasons, too. Consider how it is made and what goes into it. In the past few decades, laboratory testing of flours has revealed much about the relation of their chemical composition to the

properties of the dough and the resulting bread. Methods have been devised for determining the elasticity and potential strength of the dough. As a result, there is better control of the flour going into various products, to the satisfaction of consumers and bakers.

Yeasts have been improved and standardized. The discovery that the kinds and amounts of natural salts in water supplies affected the activity of the yeast and the behavior of the dough led to the development of so-called yeast foods, commonly used in commercial bakeries.

Each of these developments has contributed to production of uniform quality in bread. Perhaps even more important is the physical control of the bakery processes. Large-scale bakeries are largely mechanized from the blending of ingredients to the slicing and wrapping of the finished loaf. Control of time, temperature, and humidity helps to bring laboratory precision into the production of the modern staff of life. Even small bakeries, while they do not have the elaborate equipment used in large plants, make use of mechanical mixers and controlled oven heat.

Consumers have come to expect freshly baked bread and to associate freshness with softness. It is now known that certain chemical substances when added in small amounts to bread dough impart a softness to the loaf which lasts somewhat longer than would otherwise be the case. Whether or not this practice is desirable from the standpoint of the consumer has been under review. The kinds and quantities of these and other ingredients which may be added to commercial bread have been studied with a view to publication in a proposed booklet, *Definitions and Standards of Identity for Breads, Rolls, and Buns,* to be promulgated by the Federal Food and Drug Administration, Federal Security Agency.

A grain of wheat, like all seeds, contains the nutriment needed for germination and growth of the seedling. Protein, minerals, B vitamins, fat, and carbohydrates are present in the right proportions for the new plant. Actual concentrations of the several nutrients may vary widely with the type and variety of wheat and other factors. The nutrients are distributed unequally in the three major parts of the kernel. The outer coating, or bran, contains most of the fiber and a large share of the minerals and vitamins. The germ, or embryo, although a very small part of the kernel by weight, contains most of the fat, a large proportion of the vitamins, and protein of superior quality. The endosperm, or starchy portion, provides most of the carbohydrate and some of the protein, but much lower concentration of the minerals and vitamins.

White flour, as it is milled today, is largely the endosperm of the wheat. The removal of the bran portion and the germ has removed also the greater part of the minerals and vitamins and much of the protein.

According to B. K. Watt and A. L. Merrill, in *Composition of Foods— Raw, Processed, Prepared,* the differences in the average composition of whole-wheat flour and white flours made from hard wheat and suitable for bread are:

	Values per 100 grams	
	Whole- wheat flour	Patent flour
Food energy_____calories	333	365
Protein_____grams	13. 3	11. 8
Fat_____do__	2. 0	1. 1
Carbohydrate _____do__	71. 0	74. 7
Fiber_____do__	2. 3	0. 3
Calcium_____milligrams	41	16
Phosphorus_____do__	372	95
Iron_____do__	3. 3	0. 9
Thiamine _____do__	0. 55	0. 08
Riboflavin _____do__	0. 12	0. 06
Niacin_____do__	4. 3	1. 0

Whole-wheat flour is higher also in other known nutrients not listed here and possibly in some still to be identified.

The slightly lower caloric value of the whole-wheat flour indicates the effect of the fibrous bran on the completeness of digestion of the protein and carbohydrate. In ordinary mixed diets of normal persons, a moderate amount of indigestible roughage is desirable. It gives bulk to intestinal residues and helps maintain normal functioning. An excessive amount of bran in the diet, however, may prove too irritating.

From the standpoint of calories, the slightly lower digestibility of the longer-extraction grain products is of little practical importance in American dietaries. It is more than compensated for by the larger amount and better quality of the protein and by the greater contribution of minerals and vitamins from the whole wheat. The figures show about twice as much calcium and riboflavin in the whole-wheat as in the white flour; from three to four times as much phosphorus, iron, and niacin; and seven times as much thiamine.

THAT WHOLE-GRAIN, or nearly whole-grain, products are nutritionally superior is not a new idea.

To quote from Frederick Accum's book, *A Treatise on the Art of Making Good and Wholesome Bread,* published in London in 1821: "The finest bread, says an eminent physician, is not always the best adapted for answering the purposes of nutrition. Household bread which is made by grinding the whole grain and only separating the coarse bran, is without doubt, the most wholesome. . . . But bread is often spoiled to please the eye. . . . The baker is obliged to suit the caprice of his customers, to have his bread light and porous and of a pure white color."

Most consumers prefer white bread for day-in and day-out use. It is significant, however, that more than one-fifth of the city families surveyed in 1948 used some whole-wheat bread. That might suggest that more and more persons appreciate the facts on the relative values of dark and light breads. On the other hand, as total quantities consumed were small, it may reflect only a fondness for variety.

The movement to restore some of the nutrients lost in the milling of wheat gained momentum early in the Second World War. Surveys in the middle 1930's had shown an alarming prevalence of poor diets. Under threat of war, the dietary situation was considered precarious. Flour was deemed a suitable carrier for an increased distribution of thiamine, niacin, riboflavin, and iron, as flour and bread are used by nearly everyone, and are especially important in the diets of low-income families.

The enrichment program was officially launched at the National Nutrition Conference in May of 1941. Standards for enriched flour were promulgated by the Food and Drug Administration (*Federal Register,* May 27, 1941; amended July 3, 1943). The levels adopted for iron, thiamine, and niacin are such that they approach the content of whole wheat. Levels of riboflavin were set higher than in whole wheat, on the grounds that it was more frequently deficient in American diets.

Comparable standards were proposed for bread. Enrichment of all white bakery bread and rolls was made mandatory under War Food Order No. 1. Upon its expiration, many groups were interested in continuing the practice, which they felt was in the interest of public health and welfare. By early 1951, 26 States and Hawaii and Puerto Rico had enacted legislation requiring that all bread and flour sold within their borders should be enriched. For the whole country, it is estimated that about two-thirds of all white flour used reaches the consumer in enriched products.

Nutritional benefits to people from the enrichment of grain products are hard to measure because other influencing factors cannot be controlled as might be possible with laboratory animals. Calculations of the nutrient content of diets, however, show the contribution made by such foods. In diets of urban families in 1948, the addition due to enrichment of grain products ranged from 3 percent for riboflavin to 16 percent for thiamine. The contribution was greater at a low-income

Effect of flour and bread enrichment on nutritive value of urban diets, spring 1948 [1]

	Addition to diet due to enrichment			
Annual income class	Iron	Thiamine	Riboflavin	Niacin
	Percent	Percent	Percent	Percent
All classes.........	12	16	3	13
$1,000-$2,000.....	14	20	5	15
$5,000-$7,500.....	10	13	2	9

[1] From 1948 Food Consumption Surveys, Bureau of Human Nutrition and Home Economics.

level than at a high-income level.

Enrichment with iron and three vitamins has made a substantial improvement in the nutritional quality of white bread. Additional values are obtained when certain foods are incorporated in the bread formula. Milk solids, for example, contribute good-quality protein, which has high supplemental value for wheat protein; calcium; riboflavin; and other nutrients in small amounts. Nonfat dry milk is frequently used in commercial bread in varying quantities, averaging perhaps 3 to 4 percent on the flour basis. Even higher levels are consistent with a good product and contribute added food values. Other food materials sometimes used in special breads include soy flour, wheat or corn germ, and special yeasts.

Under the program for better bread in New York State, C. M. McCay, at Cornell University, reported that some 90,000 patients in 27 mental hospitals were receiving bread made with 6-percent high-fat soy flour and 8 percent nonfat dry milk solids. Similar nutritious breads are being used also in New York City schools, hospitals, and corrective institutions.

Improved bread formulas have been developed by the Bureau of Human Nutrition and Home Economics for use in school lunches and in hospitals and other institutions. High nutritive value is obtained through using enriched white flour along with 6 to 10 parts by weight of nonfat dry milk, and in some formulas by using wheat germ, whole-wheat flour, or soy flour. These bread

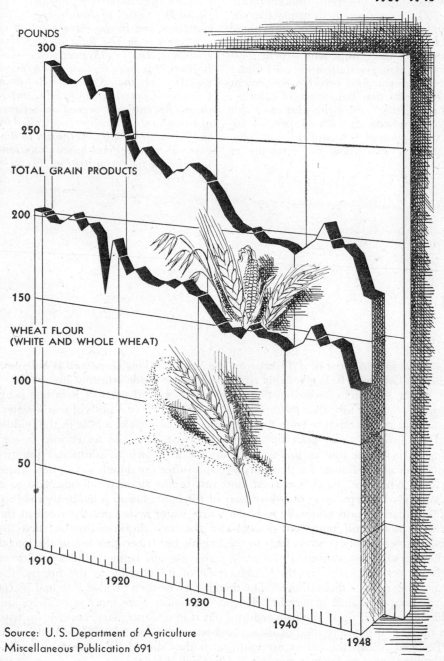

PER CAPITA CONSUMPTION OF TOTAL GRAIN PRODUCTS AND WHEAT FLOUR IN THE UNITED STATES
1909–1948

Source: U. S. Department of Agriculture
Miscellaneous Publication 691

recipes have been tested by a large baking company using standard equipment. The products have met with favor in tests of consumer acceptance in school-lunch programs and hospitals.

The more prominent its place in the diet, the more important it is that bread be as nutritious a food as possible. Some of the groups who benefit most from a stronger staff of life are: Older people, who find bread a convenient and easily digested source of calories; hungry boys and girls, who make for the bread box after school; people who carry sandwiches to work; low-income families, who know the economy of bread.

ESTHER F. PHIPARD *is assistant head of the family economics division, Bureau of Human Nutrition and Home Economics. During her 15 years of service with that Bureau she has been engaged in studies of family food consumption and in the interpretation of the findings in the light of nutrition problems. Among other activities, Mrs. Phipard has been for several years a member of the National Research Council's Committee on Food Composition. Recently she served on a panel of consultants at a conference called by the Tennessee Valley Authority to discuss soil-plant-animal-human relationships in the field of nutrition.*

FREDERICK ACCUM in *A Treatise on the Art of Making Good and Wholesome Bread,* London, 1821, gives this recipe for "home-made wheaten bread":

"Take a bushel of wheaten flour, and put two-third parts of it in one heap into a trough or tub; then dilute 2 pints of yeast with 3 or 4 pints of warm water, and add to this mixture from 8 to 10 ounces of salt. Make a hole in the middle of the heap of flour, pour the mixture of yeast, salt, and water into it, and knead the whole into an uniform stiff dough, with such an additional quantity of water as is requisite for that purpose, and suffer the dough to rise in a warm place. When the dough has risen, and just begins again to subside, add to it gradually the remaining one-third part of the flour; knead it again thoroughly, taking care to add gradually so much warm water as is sufficient to form the whole into a stiff tenaceous dough, and continue the kneading. At first the mass is very adhesive and clings to the fingers, but it becomes less so the longer the kneading is continued; and when the fist, on being withdrawn, leaves its perfect impression in the dough, none of it adhering to the fingers, the kneading may be discontinued. The dough may be then divided into loaf pieces (of about 5 pounds in weight). Knead each piece once more separately, and having made it up in the proper form, put it in a warm place, cover it up with a blanket to promote the last rising; and when this has taken place, put it into the oven. When the loaves are withdrawn they should be covered up with a blanket to cool as slowly as possible."—*Esther F. Phipard.*

STARCH HAS MANY USES

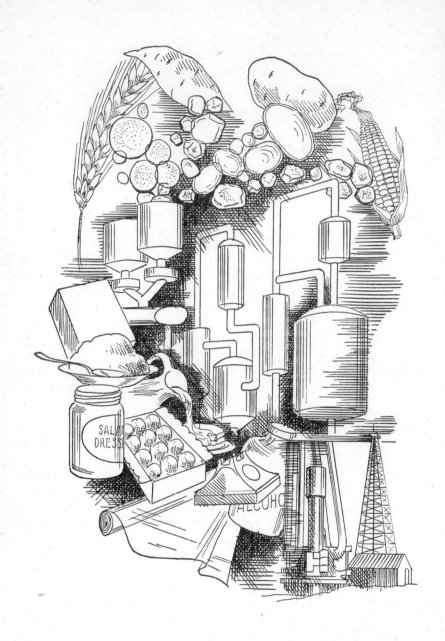

A Source of Our Daily Energy

I. A. Wolff, M. M. MacMasters

Starch is the main source of the energy we must have for the many activities of our daily lives. We get most of our starch from cereal crops, like wheat and rice, and from roots and tubers, like potatoes and sweetpotatoes. We eat much of our starch in the form of natural foodstuffs, but some of it we eat only after it has been removed from the natural source.

To gain an idea of the importance of starch in our everyday foods, let us imagine ourselves seated at the dinner table in a typical American home. Perhaps our meal starts with a fruit cup prepared from canned or frozen fruits. The fruits may contain glucose sirup or dextrose sugar as a sweetening agent. About 5 percent of the country's corn-sirup production is so used. The sirup sweetens the fruit; it also helps preserve its firmness. The natural color of the fruits has been preserved by the addition of ascorbic acid, or a related product, made chemically from starch.

Soup comes next. If it is a canned cream soup, possibly some starch has been added for thickening. If it is home-made, small pieces of prepared tapioca starch may serve the purpose.

The crackers eaten with the soup contain cornstarch and corn sugar. Ten percent of starch, based on the weight of the flour, may have been used in making the crackers to improve their texture.

Cornstarch may be the thickening agent in the cream sauce on the peas and in the gravy for the potatoes. The salt in the gravy and on the food contains starch to keep it from caking in damp weather. The sugar-cured ham owes part of its flavor to the dextrose-containing curing ingredients.

If one of our vegetables is cream-style corn, starch may have been added to it just before canning. As sweet corn matures, the ratio of sugar to starch goes down. For the best flavor, an optimum starch-sugar ratio must be maintained by adding starch to young corn and sugar to the older corn as it is canned.

The baking-powder biscuits with our main course also contain starch. Baking powder consists of an acid and a carbonate which, when wet and warm, form carbon dioxide, the leavening agent. The addition of starch as an inert ingredient keeps the two chemicals from reacting during storage, but permits them to react when moisture and heat are applied. It also helps to keep the baking powder from caking.

The jelly, jam, or preserves for the biscuits may have been sweetened with corn sirup. In them, the sirup has another function. It keeps sugar crystals from forming in the finished product. The action is like the one that occurs when vinegar is added to the other ingredients in making candy. The vinegar converts part of the cane sugar (sucrose) to two other sugars, glucose and fructose.

We may have mayonnaise on our lettuce, but if the cook wanted a dressing that is less rich, we have a mayonnaise-type salad dressing in which starch is one of the main ingredients. The use of starch as an emulsifying agent permits the use of less oil and less egg and makes the dressing cheaper. The starch usually consists of one-third to two-thirds cornstarch; the rest is tapioca.

To end our meal we have a dessert that also contains starch and its products. Be it chocolate pudding or cream or berry pie, starch is the thickening ingredient and dextrose sugar is the sweetener. Possibly ice cream is served in a sugar-wafer shell, in which starch is an ingredient; the ice cream or sherbet is sweetened with glucose sirup or dextrose sugar, which is used to retard crystallization. The ice cream also contains emulsifying agents, hexitol derivatives, derived from starch.

The cookies or cake bought at the bakery to eat with the ice cream contain both cornstarch and glucose sirup. Dextrose sugar is in the flavoring extract used in the cake. (If the cake had been made at home from a prepared mix, it would have contained cornstarch and probably refined dextrose.) The caramel icing is sweetened with corn sirup; the caramel color comes from corn sugar.

Dextrins, obtained by roasting the starches, are an ingredient of the instant coffee which may be served with the dessert.

The after-dinner sweets contain dextrose sugar and glucose sirup in the fondant centers, chocolate coatings, fudge, nougats, and hard candies. Gumdrops contain large amounts of starch and glucose sirup and, like marshmallows, are shaped in molds composed completely of cornstarch of a special type.

THE FOOD USES of starch and derived products are even more extensive than we have indicated. Many fermentation products, such as wine, brandy and cordials, vinegar, and lactic acid, originate from the action of microorganisms on the sugars derived from starch. In the manufacture of beer, specially prepared cornstarch is often used in the form of small particles called grits. Dextrose sugar sweetens canned fruit juices. Glucose sirup is used in cheese spreads and condensed milk.

Or, put it this way: How many common items of food can you name that do not contain starch?

NEW FOOD PRODUCTS from starch are being developed all the time.

One, known as starch sponge, was developed by G. E. Hilbert and M. M. MacMasters at the Northern Regional Research Laboratory. A crunchy chocolate candy can be made by impregnating a block of the sponge with sweet chocolate. The chocolate can also be incorporated into the sponge itself and the piece, dipped to coat it with chocolate, makes a light, crisp confection. Ground or shredded starch sponge can be used in chocolate to make bars, coatings, or icings.

The finely ground sponge shows promise as a holder for excess moisture to prevent the slipping and melting of icings. Compressed sponge is a concentrated carbohydrate and can be used in emergency rations and sportsmen's packs—alone, or flavored, or with vitamin concentrates, proteins, and other foods.

I. A. WOLFF *received his graduate training at the University of Wisconsin. In 1941 he joined the staff of the Northern Regional Research Laboratory, where he is now in charge of research on starch derivatives and starch conversion products in the starch and dextrose division.*

M. M. MACMASTERS *is in charge of research on the properties of starch granules and the structure and chemistry of cereal grains, in the starch and dextrose division of the Northern Laboratory. In a poll conducted by the Chemical Bulletin, a publication of the Chicago section of the American Chemical Society, she was named one of the most able starch chemists in the United States.*

Starch Is a Number of Materials

M. M. MacMasters

Starch (in the form of tiny granules) is deposited in large quantities in the storage organs of various plants.

Many processing methods have been developed for separating the starch in pure form from the other plant materials, thus making starch available for industrial use. Cornstarch, for example, is obtained by a wet-milling process, which is described on page 142.

The application of this process to other cereal grains has been studied at the Northern Laboratory. With minor modifications, starch can be separated from grain sorghum and wheat by the method. Similar separation from barley, oats, and rye is possible although not economically practical at ordinary market prices of those grains.

Three methods are now in use in this country for the production of wheat starch from flour.

In one, the Martin process, which has been used for many years, the flour is mixed with water to make a dough about the stiffness of bread dough. It is allowed to stand for an hour or longer to permit the gluten to become cohesive. The dough is then kneaded under a water spray to wash out the starch, which is purified by sieving and gravity separation.

The second method is similar to the Martin process, but minor changes have been introduced to make it a continuous, rather than a batch, operation.

A third method, known as the batter process, was developed by C. E. Rist at the Northern Laboratory in 1943. It was adopted by industry during and after the Second World War, to produce wheat starch for conversion into glucose sirup, dextrose sugar, and industrial alcohol. Flour is mixed with water to form a uniform, elastic batter. When the batter is broken up mechanically in excess water, the starch and gluten separate quickly while the gluten forms small curds, or lumps. The starch is then removed on a mechanical screen and is further purified by gravity separation.

STARCH GRANULES vary in size and shape, depending on the kind of plant in which they have been formed. They are usually spherical or more or less egg-shaped, although often they appear flat in photographs.

In some plants, such as rice and wrinkled-seeded varieties of peas, compound granules are common. The groups of many simple granules are closely pressed together into globular masses, which only partly break up into the simple granules as the starch is removed from the plant.

The diameter of starch granules varies from 2 microns to more than 100 microns. (A micron equals 0.001 millimeter, or 39.37 millionths of an inch.) If 100 starch granules each 10 microns in diameter were laid in a row, the length of the row would about equal the thickness of a dime.

In bulk, starch is white, like new-fallen snow, but under the microscope the granules are transparent. Seen microscopically between crossed Nicol prisms, each granule is gleaming white with a dark cross dividing it into four segments. The cross may be regular or very eccentric, depending upon the shape of the granule. This appearance between crossed Nicol prisms, known as birefringence, indicates that there is an orderly arrangement of starch molecules within each granule.

STARCH GRANULES are heavier than water, a property used in purifying starch by gravity separation during processing of plant material for starch production. Dry starch seems light in weight, however, because a large amount of air surrounds the granules.

When they are heated in water, as in making paste, starch granules undergo peculiar changes. Birefringence is lost within a certain temperature range, which is characteristic for each kind of starch. The range usually is 9° to 18° F., and for most starches lies somewhere between the approximate limits 130° and 175° F. Birefringence disappears first around the intersection of the arms of the cross, then outward to the periphery of the granule. The temperature at which a granule has just lost all birefringence (and is therefore invisible when viewed between crossed Nicol prisms) is known as the gelatinization temperature. The individual granules of a starch sample have different gelatinization temperatures, but all lie within the gelatinization temperature range for that kind of starch.

As starch granules are heated in water above their gelatinization temperature, they swell and usually lose some of their starch molecules into the surrounding water. The molecules seem to seep out, as the granules are not necessarily broken at this time. The greater the swelling, however, the more fragile the granules become. Sometimes the jostling of adjacent granules is enough to cause each of them to break into several large pieces. If the suspension of swollen granules is stirred hard enough, the granules break into fragments less than 1 micron in diameter. Such behavior partly explains the decrease in viscosity of starch paste during prolonged stirring—a point of importance in industry.

Gelatinization and swelling of starch granules can be brought about at room temperature by treating the granules with solutions of certain chemicals, especially those that are alkaline.

Swollen starch granules form a viscous paste if the concentration of starch is high enough. The viscosity depends on the kind and concentration of starch and on how much the granules have swollen and the amount of breakage they have undergone. Under ordinary conditions, though, a paste containing 2 percent potato starch is viscous and long, while a 5 percent cornstarch paste is less viscous and short. A long paste forms "strings" if a rod is dipped into it and pulled out; a short paste breaks away as the rod leaves it.

Starch paste sets to a gel when it cools. The type of gel depends on the kind of starch used. Cornstarch, for example, forms a rigid, nearly opaque gel. Tapioca forms a clear gel, which does not hold its shape. Stiff gels, such as those of cornstarch, tend to lose water as they age.

WHEN WE SPEAK of starch, then, we speak of a number of materials, alike in a broad sense, but actually differing considerably from one another in both physical and chemical properties. We might compare the term "starch" with the term "dog"—while all dogs are alike in a general way, a St. Bernard is quite different from a Pekingese.

All starches do have one thing in common: They can be broken down into glucose sirup containing dextrose sugar. If the breakdown is carried only a little way, dextrins are obtained. Their molecules are similar to those of starch but contain less glucose residues. Dextrins, glucose sirup, and dextrose sugar, both crude and purified, have important uses in industry.

Although starch can be separated from literally hundreds of kinds of plants, only a few are economical sources of starch for industry. Corn, wheat, grain sorghum, potato, and sometimes the rice and sweetpotato starches are made in the United States. The tapioca and sago starches we use are imported.

About 98 percent of the starch produced in the United States is obtained from corn, because that grain is the cheapest and most plentiful source of starch that we have. If starch is to be used for the production of glucose sirup or dextrose sugar, any kind will serve, and about a third of the cornstarch produced in 1948, for example, was so used. In that year our corn wet-milling industry produced more than 3½ billion pounds of starch, of which about 1,389 million pounds was sold as such, while the remainder was converted and sold as approximately 158 million pounds of dextrins, more than 1,333 million pounds of glucose sirup, and about 712 million pounds of dextrose sugar. A considerably smaller amount of glucose sirup was made from wheat starch. Relatively minor quantities of potato, wheat, and possibly rice starch were also produced, mainly for special uses.

About two-thirds of the starch sold as such is for industrial nonfood uses. The largest consumers are paper mills and paper-box manufacturers, who use nearly 22 percent of the total; textile manufacturers, who take over 19 percent; and home and commercial laundries, which use 13 percent. More than 5 percent is utilized by the laminating and corrugating industry, and a like amount is used by makers of pastes, adhesives, and dextrins. Lesser amounts go into asbestos products, gypsum and mineral board, explosives, and other products. Cornstarch also has some relatively minor uses—as a binder in cores for castings, as a component of drilling mud used in sinking oil wells, as a dust on the surface of rubber articles to limit tackiness, as a constituent of dry batteries, as a raw material for making such chemicals as levulinic acid, and as a filler in soaps, cleaners, and insecticides.

The starches other than cornstarch that are produced in small quantities in this country go into special uses. Potato starch is employed chiefly in the textile industry, where the nature of its pastes

makes it especially valuable for some types of sizing. Potato dextrins are used as adhesives. Rice starch is used for textile sizing, in face powders, and as a laundry starch. Because of the small size of its granules, rice starch penetrates textile fibers well and also makes cosmetics spread smoothly.

Most of the wheat starch produced in the United States is used by laundries. For this purpose it is sometimes mixed with cornstarch. Wheat starch is especially suited for laundering because it contains both large and small granules. The small granules penetrate the threads; the large ones give the surface coating.

Sweetpotato starch, of which little is available, has characteristics that make it particularly suitable for use in the textile industry.

Tapioca and sago starches compete with cornstarch in the textile and paper industries on a cost basis. Their dextrins have been preferred to those of other starches for some uses, however, and in this field these starches found an outlet before the Second World War, even when they cost more than cornstarch. For example, tapioca dextrins were desired for use on envelope flaps and stamps because of their lack of flavor and quick adhesive properties. Tapioca dextrins were also used for making plywood adhesives. During the war, cornstarch products were developed for many uses for which tapioca- and sago-starch products had previously been employed. The results were so satisfactory that cornstarch probably will continue to be used in those fields. Waxy-corn starch was used in place of tapioca in some specialty fields when tapioca could not be imported from Java, its usual source. Workers in the Northern Laboratory, the Bureau of Plant Industry, Soils, and Agricultural Engineering, the State agricultural experiment stations of Iowa, Wisconsin, and Nebraska, and industry helped in the development of waxy-corn starch during that period. It is still being produced. For some industrial uses it has advantages over tapioca, a fact that favors its continued production in competition with tapioca, even if tapioca should again be imported in large quantities and sold at low cost.

DEXTRINS, the products obtained by partly breaking down the starch molecules, are made by heating the starch alone or with a small amount of acid. They can also be produced by the action of enzymes on starch. They have industrial uses chiefly as adhesives and in sizings. They are used in sealing cigarettes, in binding abrasives, for billboard posting, for bookbinding, in library and wallpaper pastes, in gums, glues, and mucilage, for pasting such different products as shoe counters and straws, in match heads, for holding the abrasive on the match box, and in making chalk crayons and linoleum cement. Dextrins are also used in the sizing and finishing of paper and of textiles, including window shades and shade cloth, in the backing of rugs and carpets, in bluing, dyes, ink, and silvering compounds, in the manufacture of shotgun shells, soap, and molded toys, as an ingredient of dynamite and fireworks, in the manufacture of linoleum, and in the tanning of leather.

Glucose sirup and dextrose sugar are used in making synthetic rubber, in adhesives, dyes, and explosives. Both are employed in paper and textile manufacture and in boiler compounds. The sirup enters into the composition of hydraulic-brake fluid, inks, and boot polish, and is used in making hot patches for tire repair. It is sometimes employed in tobacco products.

DEXTROSE SUGAR, both crude and refined, is used in tanning leather and also as a plasticizing agent and in hairwaving preparations. The refined sugar is used in the preparation of lactic acid, calcium lactate, sodium lactate, acetic acid, mannitol, and other chemicals—also in electroplating and galvanizing, in explosives, and in boiler compounds.

Even though starch and its immedi-ate products—dextrins, glucose sirup, and dextrose sugar—are used in such a multitude of ways, their industrial possibilities are far from exhausted. Chemists in the Northern Laboratory have developed a spongelike physical modification of gelatinized starch which is useful as a surgical dressing. It is absorbed if left in the body. In clinical studies, an obstetrician and gynecologist found the material to be excellent for stopping hemorrhage following childbirth and surgical operations. Other surgeons have used it to control bleeding following many different types of operations. Its surgical use is now well-established, and commercial production is expected.

The development grew out of a study of the physical characteristics of starch pastes, which was begun in 1941 with a view to finding starches fitted for special uses.

In 1950, chemists in the Northern Laboratory conducted investigations into the possibility of making films and coatings from starch. They also started some experiments on the production of transparent films and textile fibers from the amylose fraction of starch. Chemical compounds derived from starch are showing promise for use in making plastics, surface-wetting agents, and detergents. Other chemicals being prepared from dextrose will be tested for medicinal uses.

M. M. MACMASTERS *obtained her graduate degrees at the University of Massachusetts, and spent 5 years, chiefly in research on starch pastes and gels, at the Illinois Agricultural Experiment Station. She joined the staff of the starch and dextrose division of the Northern Regional Research Laboratory in 1940, where she is now in charge of research on the structure and chemistry of cereal grains and the properties of starch granules. Her work at the Northern Laboratory has included studies on processing cereal grains for starch production and on industrially useful properties of starch pastes.*

The Chemist Looks at Starch

R. J. Dimler

When a chemist looks at starch, he tries to find out what it really is, why it behaves the way it does, why some starches are different from others. He draws a mental picture of the chemical structure of starch to see how it is put together. With this picture and his studies of the behavior of starches, he can show the way to new products, new uses, and more satisfactory adaptations of the present uses of starch.

Starch is a type of compound the chemist calls a polymer; that is, one in which the molecules are built up by the chemical union of hundreds or thousands of molecules of a simpler substance. In starch, this simpler substance, or building block, is D-glucose, or dextrose, which combines with itself chemically through a dehydration reaction to make the starch molecule.

Starch can be broken down again to dextrose by acid hydrolysis or by enzyme action. The first is a step in the commercial production of dextrose. The latter is involved in the digestion of starch in the body. All starches are alike in that they are built up from dextrose and can be broken down, therefore, into dextrose.

The chemist has a diagrammatic picture of the dextrose molecule (shown in the first figure), which he uses to indicate how starch molecules are built up. The carbon atoms (C) are numbered for ease in indicating the position of linkages. The relative positions of the hydroxyl (OH) groups and the number of carbon atoms distinguish one simple sugar from another, such as dextrose from galactose, each of which is a 6-carbon sugar (or hexose), or from xylose, which is a 5-carbon sugar (or pentose). When two molecules of a simple sugar, or monosaccharide, are linked chemically, the result is a disaccharide (such as maltose) or, with two different monosaccharides, sucrose (cane or beet sugar) or lactose. Maltose is obtained from starch by enzyme action; its structure typifies the kind of chemical linkages between the dextrose units in starch.

A fragment of a starch molecule as the chemist diagrams it is charted also on page 130. Here the dextrose units have been combined by a type of linkage known as an α-1,4-glucosidic linkage. It links carbon atom No. 1 of one dextrose unit to carbon atom No. 4 of the next. For many years, the chemist thought starch consisted of only one type of molecule. Now he knows that in starch there are at least two different types, amylose and amylopectin. Since the discovery of methods by which the two types can be separated from the starch granule, the chemist can look at the amylose and amylopectin individually.

The most satisfactory processes for separating, or fractionating, starch depend on the ability of certain organic chemicals to combine physically with the amylose fraction, giving an insoluble complex that can be removed mechanically from the mixture. The amylopectin fraction remains in the solution, from which it can be removed if desired. Among the chemicals that have proved particularly useful for separating amylose from amylopectin are butanol, Pentasol, 1-nitropropane, 2-nitropropane, nitrobenzene, and stearic, oleic, and other fatty acids.

PRINCIPAL SUGARS OBTAINED FROM STARCH BY HYDROLYSIS

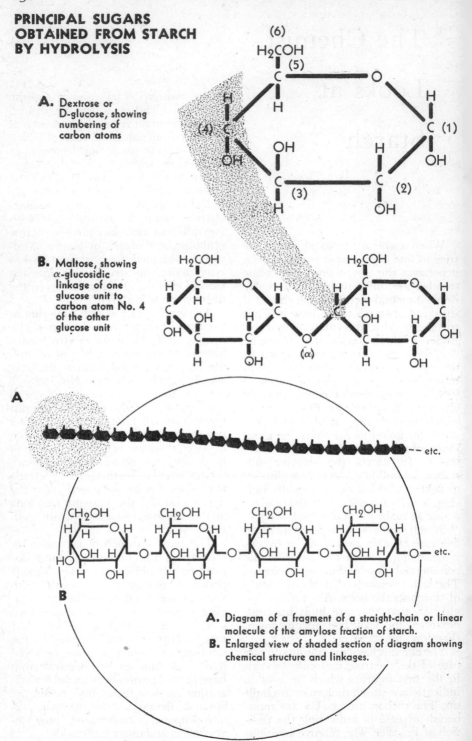

A. Dextrose or D-glucose, showing numbering of carbon atoms

B. Maltose, showing α-glucosidic linkage of one glucose unit to carbon atom No. 4 of the other glucose unit

A. Diagram of a fragment of a straight-chain or linear molecule of the amylose fraction of starch.

B. Enlarged view of shaded section of diagram showing chemical structure and linkages.

With butanol, for example, the fractionation procedure consists of first saturating a 3-percent solution of starch in hot water with the butanol (about 10 percent). The mixture is allowed to cool slowly for about 24 hours, when the amylose-butanol complex forms, usually as miscroscopic needles or rosettes, which are removed by centrifuging. The crude amylose fraction thus obtained can be purified by redissolving it in hot water saturated with butanol. On slow cooling, the insoluble complex again forms and is removed as before. The wet cake, or thick paste, of either crude or purified amylose-butanol complex is carefully dried, frequently by dehydration with ethyl alcohol. Special methods have been developed for this step to keep the product from being horny or gritty and therefore hard to dissolve or react with chemicals, as for the production of acetates or other derivatives.

After the amylose-butanol complex has been removed, the amylopectin fraction remains in solution in the water saturated with butanol. To recover the amylopectin fraction in dry form, the solution is added to a large excess (5 to 10 parts) of ethyl alcohol with vigorous stirring. The amylopectin separates, or precipitates, in finely divided form. It is removed and dried, again using special methods to insure a light, fluffy powder.

Now THAT the chemist has the amylose and amylopectin fractions before him, he can look at their molecular structures. At this point he reminds us that these are fractions of starch, not definite compounds. Each fraction probably contains a mixture of rather similar molecules, which vary in size and other fine points of structure. The chemist's molecular pictures therefore represent composites, which show the distinctive characteristics of the two fractions. The most important difference he sees between amylose and amylopectin molecules is in the way they are put together. Amylose has linear or straight-chain molecules, while amylopectin molecules are branched, perhaps bushlike in shape. As we shall see, this difference has a marked effect on the behavior of the two fractions.

All the dextrose units in amylose are linked one to the next by the α-1,4-glucosidic linkages that are predominant in starch. Roughly, 500 or more dextrose units are thus combined like the links of a long chain.

Amylopectin molecules seem to be combinations of short lengths of the same type of chain, containing 20 to 25 dextrose units per length. The short lengths have been linked together, the No. 1 carbon atom of the end dextrose unit on one chain being attached by an α-glucosidic linkage to the No. 6 carbon atom of a dextrose unit somewhere along the next length of chain, as shown on the next page. That gives a branched, more or less spherical structure, in which the exact arrangement of the branches is still unknown. The entire amylopectin molecule apparently contains more than 50 of these short lengths of chain linked together, giving a total of more than 1,000 dextrose units.

These are large molecules—macromolecules—from the chemist's viewpoint. Yet they are still very small in terms of actual measurements.

If starch molecules are so exceedingly small, how can we picture the details of their structures? The chemist has drawn his picture from the way the starch fractions behave. Much of the behavior of the amylose and amylopectin fractions of starch is what would be expected of linear and branched molecules, respectively. In addition, some properties point to the type of linkage involved in the branching.

THE BREAKDOWN OF STARCH and its fractions by enzymes is an important reaction from both the standpoint of seeing the molecular structure of starch and of using it in industry, as in fermentation.

Barley malt contains two enzymes, α-amylase and β-amylase, which act

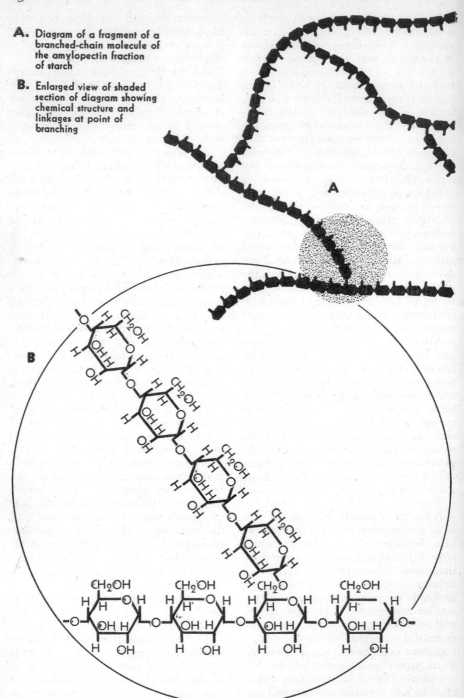

A. Diagram of a fragment of a branched-chain molecule of the amylopectin fraction of starch

B. Enlarged view of shaded section of diagram showing chemical structure and linkages at point of branching

differently in breaking down starch. α-Amylase first breaks the starch down rapidly to fragments called dextrins. Each dextrin molecule contains 7 to 15 dextrose units. The dextrins are then more slowly broken down, or hydrolyzed, to dextrose and maltose, both of which are fermentable. Some nonfermentable carbohydrate is always left and presumably comes from the points of branching, which are not broken appreciably in the hydrolysis of the amylopectin molecules.

The other enzyme, β-amylase, produces maltose immediately. A marked difference exists in the action of β-amylase on the linear amylose and on the branched amylopectin. Amylose is almost completely broken down to maltose. Amylopectin, however, is only about half hydrolyzed to maltose. The molecule of amylopectin is reduced to about one-half its original size by this hydrolysis. To explain the incomplete hydrolysis of amylopectin, the chemist pictures the enzyme as "chewing" maltose molecules (two dextrose units) one after another off the free ends of the branches. When the point of branching, or linkage of one length of chain to another, is reached the enzyme stops. It lacks the ability to hydrolyze the linkage at that point and cannot get beyond to continue the hydrolysis.

Even the combined action of α- and β-amylase, as in treatment with malt, will not convert starch completely to fermentable sugars. The point of branching of the amylopectin is left intact. The isolation of this unfermentable residue and its characterization have helped the chemist see what type of linkage is present at the branch point in the amylopectin molecule.

The physical behavior of the amylose and amylopectin fractions also indicates the linear and branched structures of the molecules of the fractions. Thus, amylose acetate readily forms strong films and fibers similar to those of cellulose acetate. This property is typical of linear molecules of high molecular weight. Amylopectin acetate, in contrast, forms a weak, brittle film, indicating a nearly spherical molecule. The formation of films and fibers with good strength is pictured as depending on the ability of the linear molecules to line up alongside each other, at least in part. In such an alined position, attractive forces develop and hold the structure together, giving the film or fiber its strength. The bushlike shape of the amylopectin molecules gives little chance for lining up long sections, and therefore little development of strong binding forces.

Gel formation also indicates the linearity of the amylose and the ability to bind the molecules together. Amylose forms a firm gel. Amylopectin gives a soft, fluid gel, even at high concentrations. Here again the more or less spherical shape of the amylopectin molecules prevents the formation of the rigid network that makes up a firm gel.

When the concentration of the starch fraction is too low for good gel formation (1 percent or less) or if stirring interferes with formation of the network, the amylose molecules will still get together, or associate, finally forming visible particles, which are insoluble. This formation of an insoluble precipitate is known as retrogradation. The amylose fraction retrogrades from solution very rapidly, while the amylopectin fraction retrogrades extremely slowly, if at all. The development of a milky appearance in starch pastes and gels on standing is also referred to as retrogradation. It probably is caused by somewhat the same sort of clumping together of molecules, particularly the linear amylose molecules.

ANOTHER WELL-KNOWN PHYSICAL PROPERTY of starch is the blue color that it gives with iodine. The amylose and amylopectin fractions of starch show a marked difference in this characteristic. Amylose gives a deep-blue color, amylopectin a reddish-purple color. The blue color seems to result from the formation of a complex between the amylose and iodine, much after the fashion of the formation of the colorless amylose-butanol complex. The amylopectin forms no such complex with iodine.

Having seen the marked difference in structure and properties between the linear amylose and branched amylopectin, you probably have been wondering how much amylose there is in the starch granules. In most cases, roughly one-fourth of the starch is amylose. Thus the common cereal starches (corn, wheat, sorghum, rice) contain 20 to 30 percent amylose.

A few starches are well outside that range of amylose content. The starches of waxy corn, waxy sorghum, and waxy rice have become of particular interest because they contain no amylose or linear fraction. In contrast, the starch of wrinkled-seeded varieties of garden peas contains 60 to 70 percent amylose. Because of the potential industrial value of starches of unusual amylose content, the Department of Agriculture is including the determination of amylose content of starches in some of the surveys of the characteristics of different varieties of starch-bearing plants.

The properties of the amylose and amylopectin molecules naturally contribute to the properties of the starch in which they are found. The effect of the amylose component is well shown by a comparison of cornstarch, which contains about 25 percent of linear amylose molecules, with starch of waxy corn, which contains none. Cornstarch gives a milky paste, which sets to a firm, rigid gel and is colored blue by iodine. Those are properties we have seen in amylose, whose molecules are able to associate or bind together easily and form complexes. Waxy-corn starch gives a clear paste, the gel is soft and fluid, and the color with iodine is reddish purple, as would be expected of amylopectin.

Wrinkled-seeded pea starch, with 60 or 70 percent amylose, is difficult to gelatinize, indicating a high degree of association of the molecules within the granules. Acetylation of the starch of wrinkled-seeded peas gives an acetate that forms strong films and fibers, quite different from the brittle films of cornstarch acetate. As might be predicted, in wrinkled-seeded pea starch the amylose properties predominate.

NOT ALL THE PROPERTIES of different starches are explained, however, on the basis of the properties on the constituent molecules. A good example is the similarity of waxy-corn and waxy-sorghum starches to tapioca starch. The amylose content of tapioca starch is about 20 percent, which is very near that of cornstarch, while the waxy-grain starches contain no amylose. Yet the properties of the starches are so similar that the waxy starches have been substituted for tapioca starch in food and industrial uses.

Our knowledge of the structure of starch is important in its utilization. We know that starch is used for a wide variety of things. In many of them the starch is changed chemically before or during its use. The relatively new discovery of methods of fractionating starch opens the way for a study of these treatments in terms of their effect on the starch molecules.

For the fermentation industry, the study of starch has shown probable reasons for incomplete conversion of the starch in the grains to fermentable sugars. The branch point of the amylopectin molecules is resistant to breakdown by most enzymes, such as those in barley malt. Workers with enzymes are now seeking practical sources of enzymes that will break the linkage at the branch point. The success of their efforts will lead to more efficient fermentation of starch.

Retrogradation and gel formation of starch pastes are undesirable in some uses, in the textile field for example. Since the linear amylose fraction is apparently largely responsible for this property, attention can be centered directly on amylose in seeking ways of overcoming such difficulties.

The fractionation of starch also opens up the possibility of making a new type of material, the linear amylose, available for industrial use. Its film- and fiber-forming properties hold particular interest. The observation of a starch of high amylose content, such as that of wrinkled-seeded peas, stimulates interest in unusual types.

Although the chemist has shown the world many things about starch, much is still unknown. If the linear amylose fraction, for example, is to be used industrially, we must either perfect practicable methods for fractionating starch or find more practical sources of made-to-order starches with a high content of amylose. The latter has already been done for amylopectin, which is the sole constituent of the waxy-sorghum and waxy-corn starches. There is still much to be learned about the relationship of starch structure to the behavior of starch and ways to control that behavior, and in the field of chemical reactions and new products from starch.

R. J. DIMLER *joined the staff of the Northern Regional Research Laboratory in 1941 after graduating from Bradley University and receiving his doctorate at the University of Wisconsin. He has conducted research on carbohydrate structure and on starch production and has developed an alkali process for the production of starch from cereal-grain flour. Dr. Dimler is now in charge of research on the structure of starch in the starch and dextrose division of the Northern Laboratory.*

LEONARDO DA VINCI, who was a pioneer in aviation, proposed to stiffen the wing fabric of flying machines with starch.

The use of starch as a hair powder is said to have originated in France in the sixteenth century. Near the end of the eighteenth century large quantities of starch were used for the purpose.

Starch is a common ingredient of face powder, as are kaolin, magnesium carbonate, light precipitated chalk, and zinc and titanium oxides. Rice starch, because of the small size of its granules, is often used for the purpose. Recently some manufacturers have added magnesium and zinc stearates to face powders. They help to keep the powder from being wet from perspiration. Wet face powder loses part of its power to reflect light and becomes less visible. In order to give the desired "bloom" to the skin, the powder must be visible.

Holland was noted for the high quality of wheat starch produced there in the Middle Ages. Then and later starch was used mostly in the laundry for stiffening fabrics and was an expensive luxury afforded only by church dignitaries, aristocrats, and other wealthy persons. Apparently starch was first used in England during the reign of Elizabeth, who is reported to have appointed a laundry starcher as a special court official. Later the manufacture of starch from wheat more than once was prohibited in England because wheat was considered to be more useful as a food.

In the seventeenth century, laundry starches were colored. Yellow starch was ultrafashionable for men. The Cavaliers often used green starch; the Roundheads, blue.—*M. M. MacMasters, Northern Regional Research Laboratory.*

Chemicals From Starch and Sugar

E. A. Talley, I. A. Wolff

Starches and sugars belong to the important group of substances known as carbohydrates. Because they are an essential part of all plants, carbohydrates occur everywhere and in a supply that is replaced each year.

The name of the group comes from the simplest formula, CH_2O, for the central compound, D-glucose—or dextrose, as it is known commercially. D-Glucose contains only carbon, hydrogen, and oxygen. In most of the principal members of the group, hydrogen and oxygen occur in the same ratio as in water. In fact, the French, who did the early research in this field, named the group *hydrate de carbone* (hydrate of carbon). The Germans translated it as *Kohlenhydrate,* and in English it became *carbohydrate.*

Dextrose, or D-glucose, is outstanding among the carbohydrates, both chemically and biologically. It is the product of photosynthesis in the green leaves of plants in the presence of sunlight. In the process, the raw materials are carbon dioxide and water; oxygen is formed as a byproduct. The energy of the sun is stored in green leaves in this way.

Sucrose, the sugar that is obtained from sugarcane and sugar beets, is made up of one unit of glucose and one unit of fructose. These two simpler sugars differ only in the structural arrangement of their atoms. Sucrose is found in the sap of nearly all plants and is stored in fairly high concentration in the sugar beet.

Glucose is the fundamental unit of two other important plant materials, cellulose and starch, which differ only in the structural arrangement of the glucose units. Cellulose is a structural building material of plants. Starch is the form in which carbohydrates are stored in many plants. It occurs as small granules, which are rather easily separated in pure form from the rest of the plant.

MANY OF THE INDUSTRIAL USES of starch as such are based on its physical characteristics: It can form a thick paste in water, and it is a white, finely divided, and free-flowing powder that can be incorporated in foodstuffs. Its most important chemical characteristics are that it may be broken down into simpler units and that it is a polyhydroxy alcohol. Starch may be broken down into its simplest unit, D-glucose, by acid or enzyme hydrolysis. By reaction with suitable chemical reagents, such as acid anhydrides or alkyl halides, it is possible to prepare, from starch, ester and ether derivatives, the properties of which differ greatly from those of the raw material itself although the size of the starch molecule is essentially retained. If the substitution is limited, the product, like starch itself, is insoluble in organic solvents but dispersible in water. More completely substituted starch derivatives, on the other hand, are usually more soluble in organic solvents and less soluble in water.

In 1948 more than 8 million pounds of cornstarch was used by the explosives industry, part as a nonexplosive ingredient in fireworks and dynamite, but much of it, after nitration, as an explosive agent. These starch nitrates, or nitrostarches as they are sometimes less correctly called, are esters formed by the reaction of nitric acid with starch in the presence of either sulfuric acid or phosphoric acid as a catalyst. The use of phosphoric acid leads to starch nitrates, which are more stable than those obtained with sulfuric acid.

Starch phosphate, another ester of starch with an inorganic acid, also has interesting and valuable properties. When phosphorus oxychloride is allowed to react with starch granules in the presence of pyridine, which is an organic base, approximately one hydroxyl group in each of the repeating units of the starch molecule can be converted to a phosphate ester. This starch monophosphate, insoluble in hot or cold water and in organic solvents, and containing strongly acidic groups, has valuable ion-exchange properties. That is, the compounds can be used to soften water or to remove the metallic ion of many inorganic salts from solutions containing them—a desirable procedure in such industrial processes as the demineralization of sugar sirups. The nature of the starch phosphate obtained under similar conditions of reaction is greatly influenced by the variety of starch used. The starches with smaller granules show the greatest reactivity with the phosphorylating reagent.

Starch normally swells in hot water to form a paste. Water-resistant starches that are completely unaffected by boiling water, or even by heating above the boiling point in an autoclave, can be prepared by treating starch with appropriate chemical reagents. Organic diisocyanates, such as hexamethylene diisocyanate, react with starch in the presence of pyridine to form cross links, or bridges, between the carbohydrate chains. These cross-linked products are notably inert, and may find uses as dusting powders, insecticide carriers, or fillers for plastics. Treatment of starch under suitable conditions with such other reagents as formaldehyde, glyoxal, dibasic acid chlorides, or phosphorus oxychloride can also convert it to products that swell little if at all under conditions that completely gelatinize untreated starch.

Acetates of whole starch or of each of its fractions may be prepared by treatment with acetic acid-acetic anhydride mixtures in the presence of catalysts. The acetates of whole starch or of amylopectin are too brittle and weak to form fibers or plastics. But the amylose triacetate (and other saturated aliphatic triesters) can be formed into cellophanelike films, which are lustrous and pliable. Amylose triacetate can also be converted into fibers resembling acetate rayon by a process known as dry spinning, in which a viscous chloroform solution of the amylose triacetate is forced through tiny holes of a spinneret into a hot-air chamber for evaporation of the solvent. The resulting threads are wound on a reel. Mixed acetyl with higher acyl radicals (such as the mixed acetate-propionate of amylose) are thermoplastic and can be molded into plastic articles. More extensive use of the valuable properties of the amylose derivatives depends on economic factors.

Other esters of starch (such as the propionate, benzoate, xanthate, palmitate, thiocyanate, sulfate, and chloride esters) and ethers (such as the methyl, ethyl, and benzyl derivatives) have been prepared. Many of these are being investigated with a view to possible industrial use.

Of particular importance are esters of the starch-containing unsaturated groups. Starch methacrylate can readily be polymerized to form insoluble materials, and may thus be of value as a plastic or as a coating compound.

An interesting compound is obtained by the reaction of chloroacetic acid with starch in the presence of sodium hydroxide. The product, called carboxymethyl starch, is said to be a potential replacement material for various natural gums in foods, cosmetic preparations, pharmaceuticals, and some other products where a stable thickening agent, constant in properties from batch to batch, is required.

The allyl ether of starch, another important unsaturated derivative, is prepared by heating starch, a strong alkali solution, and allyl chloride in a closed vessel. The ether formed is a doughy material, which dissolves readily in organic solvents. Sprayed or painted on surfaces, the solutions form a film that dries tack-free in a short time. On exposure to air, the material behaves like a drying oil in that it takes up oxygen to form an insoluble hard resin. It is useful as a coating material, an adhesive, and an ingredient in printing inks. Sulfur may be substituted for oxygen in the polymerization process. Mixtures with sulfur may be used to form rigid plastics and laminates.

Allyl starch has been successfully tested for the following applications:

As surface coatings for furniture finishes, interior wood finishes, and metal finishes.

As bronzing liquid, thermosetting adhesive, overprint and finishing varnish, and printing-ink vehicle.

Other miscellaneous uses such as solventproofing paper and greaseproofing paper, fast-drying undercoats, plastic for wood and other laminates, leather dressing, synthetic enamels, and dope for aircraft finishes.

For each of those uses, proper formulation (addition of plasticizers, resins, driers) must be used.

Samples and limited commercial quantities of allyl starch are available.

Allyl sucrose (made from ordinary cane or beet sugar) has properties similar to those of allyl starch. Unlike allyl starch, allyl sucrose is compatible with drying oils.

Alkoxides of starch have been prepared in which a metallic atom or ion takes the place of a hydrogen atom on a hydroxyl group of the starch. Sodium starchate has been prepared by heating the starch in an organic solvent containing dissolved sodium hydroxide. Other metal derivatives have been prepared from the sodium derivative. The evidence indicates that only the hydroxyl on the second carbon atom of the anyhydroglucose unit is attacked. The sodium atom may be replaced by treatment with metal salts, alkyl halides, and other reagents. The copper derivative is a mildew-proofing agent. Other derivatives are being studied, and new uses are being sought for compounds prepared by use of the starch alkoxides as intermediates.

Thus far we have discussed the chemical products from starch in which little or no breakdown of the molecule has occurred. One possible product from the more drastic degradation of starch is l-glucosan, an anhydride of the beta form of glucose. When starch is heated to 350° C. in an evacuated system, 60 percent of the original weight distills over as a brown viscous sirup. Treating this distillate with boiling acetone gives crystalline l-glucosan, which, after recrystallization, is a white, alkali-stable, anhydro sugar that contains three hydroxyl groups. The crystalline material is neutral in reaction, free from unstable reducing substances, and stable to light and air. On acid hydrolysis, it is converted quantitatively to dextrose. The process for the preparation of l-glucosan from starch has received considerable study in the research laboratory. Because no expensive chemicals need be used in the degradation, but only heat and simultaneous distillation under reduced pressure, economical production will probably be possible if suitable uses are found for it or its derivatives.

The cleavage of starch, dextrose, or sorbitol by hydrogen at high temperatures and pressures in the presence of a suitable catalyst, such as finely divided nickel, results in their conversion in good yield to a mixture of propylene glycol, ethylene glycol, and glycerol. In times of national emergency when our supply of glycerol from natural fats is inadequate, the process may have particular significance. In Germany during the Second World War, a mixture of glycols and glycerol, obtained by the hydrogenolysis of carbohydrates and called "glycerogen," was marketed as an antifreeze and for other purposes.

Levulinic acid, a 5-carbon γ-keto

cid, has been prepared industrially by heating dextrose-containing materials or starch in aqueous solutions of mineral acids. It is used pharmaceutically in the form of its calcium salt and has promise as a chemical intermediate for use in plastics and in the synthesis of other organic chemicals.

We have discussed a number of chemical products from starch, but the subject is by no means exhausted. A host of other products—such as acetone, butyl alcohol, 2,3-butylene glycol, lactic acid, citric acid, and ethyl alcohol—result from the fermentation of carbohydrate substrates. Many further uses are being explored, and other new starch compounds are being made for examination of their properties and industrial utilization whenever possible. Now let us consider the sugars.

A NUMBER OF SUGARS are actually and potentially available for use as chemical raw materials.

Dextrose is manufactured from cornstarch in pure form in the United States to the extent of more than 600 million pounds annually. The same product can be obtained from other starches. In northern Europe, where little corn is grown, it is usually prepared from potato starch.

Dextrose also has been prepared from wheat starch in this country in recent years to supplement that available from cornstarch.

Sucrose is produced in quantity from sugarcane and sugar beets.

Maltose is potentially available in large quantities from starch by hydrolysis with enzymes.

Lactose is the sugar from milk.

Raffinose may be obtained as a by-product in the manufacture of sucrose from sugar beets.

Xylose, or wood sugar, can be obtained in large quantities from crop residues. It is the sugar from which comes most of the furfural, an important industrial chemical, when agricultural residues are treated with hot dilute acid.

Arabinose, from which furfural can also be obtained, occurs in combined form in various plant polysaccharides.

Galactose can be obtained from lactose by hydrolysis.

Fructose, or fruit sugar, can be derived from sucrose by hydrolysis. It can also be obtained from inulin from the Jerusalem artichoke and other inulin-bearing plants, or it can be prepared chemically by the action of a mild alkaline catalyst on dextrose.

THOSE SUGARS the chemist divides into two classes—reducing and nonreducing. Sucrose and raffinose are nonreducing sugars; they do not reduce copper and silver salts under certain conditions. Their chemical reactions are those of alcohols only, unless the molecules are broken down in some way. Both give reducing sugars on hydrolysis. The other sugars all have the property of reducing copper and silver salts under specified conditions.

The reducing sugars have another active group, besides the hydroxyl or alcohol groups of the nonreducing sugars. Because of the presence of this other active group, the reducing sugars are capable of forming a class of compounds known as glycosides. The corresponding derivatives of glucose or dextrose are termed glucosides.

THE GLYCOSIDES as a class are important biologically. Living organisms often render toxic materials harmless by converting them to glycosides. The essential principles in a number of pharmaceutical preparations are glycosides. Digitalis is one of the cardiac glycosides that stimulate the heart. Rutin, obtained on a commercial scale from buckwheat, is a flavanol glycoside. Another flavanol glycoside, hesperidin, was formerly thought to be identical with "vitamin P." Natural dye materials often are glycosides; indican, from which indigo was formerly obtained, is an example. Streptomycin, an important antibiotic, is a glycoside of a previously unknown disaccharide.

The glycosides we have mentioned are obtained from natural sources, although they can be prepared by synthesis. Glycosides of higher alcohols can be prepared; they are nonionic surface-active substances and may be used as emulsifiers. The solubility of these materials in water is improved by treatment with materials like ethylene oxide. The formation of a glycoside may be used to increase the water solubility of a pharmaceutical preparation—for example, the glycosides of 2-alkyl-1,4-naphtho-hydroquinone, an antihemorrhagic agent. Sometimes the action is changed by such treatment. The glucoside of sulfapyridine is reported to have appreciable activity against cholera, in contrast to sulfapyridine itself.

THE REDUCING SUGARS can be converted to the sugar alcohols by catalytic or electrolytic reduction processes. Then the reducing group is no longer present. For example, the hydrogenation of dextrose under neutral or acidic conditions yields principally the hexahydric alcohol sorbitol, which is a white, odorless, crystalline, water-soluble compound. Sorbitol is an established article of commerce used for its humectant or conditioning properties. It is a chemical intermediate in the manufacture of vitamin C; when it is esterified with fatty acids, it forms edible, nonionic emulsifying agents used in ice cream and other food products and in pharmaceutical preparations. Drying oils prepared from sorbitol esterified with long-chain unsaturated fatty acids are said to be rapid-drying and to give hard, alkali-resistant coatings. Fatty acid esters have been suggested as plasticizers for polyvinyl chlorides, polyvinyl chloride acetates, and polyvinyl butyrals. They have been recommended also as textile lubricants, and the monoesters as textile sizes. In many of its derivatives, sorbitol actually exists as an anhydride, sorbitan, resulting from the loss of water during derivative formation. Reduction of dextrose under alkaline conditions gives a mixture of sorbitol and mannitol, both hexahydroxy alcohols which differ only

in the spatial arrangement of their constituent atoms. Similar products are obtained from both. Nitrated mannitol is used as an explosive and in medicine as a vasodilator.

Xylitol is potentially available in large quantities, because it can be obtained by the hydrogenation of xylose. This pentitol (5-carbon sugar alcohol) would be expected to have properties similar to those of the hexitols (6-carbon sugar alcohols) mannitol and sorbitol. A rare pentitol, ribitol is one of the units in the structure of riboflavin, vitamin B_2. This naturally occurring vitamin may be synthesized in several ways.

The polyols, or sugar alcohols, can be converted readily to their anhydrides by heating with catalytic amounts of strong mineral acids or other dehydrating agents. They are formed often during the preparation of their derivatives. The anhydrides as a class are reported to be humectants, particularly for tobacco, and softeners for papers and textiles. Isomannide from mannitol, has been patented as a diuretic. Styracitol, from mannitol forms an explosive tetranitrate. The anhydride dinitrates show depressor action, similar to that of glycerol trinitrate and mannitol hexanitrate.

The oxidation of glucose, either electrolytically or by the action of hypohalites, gives gluconic acid; its nitric acid oxidation gives the dibasic saccharic acids. Other sugars give similar acids. Shorter-chain acids can be prepared by oxidation of dextrose under different conditions. Tartaric and oxalic acids can be obtained from glucose by oxidation with nitric acid in the presence of vanadium salts. Good yields are reported. Glucuronic acid, another valuable oxidation product of glucose, has received attention recently as a remedy for certain types of arthritis.

A NUMBER of ether and ester derivatives, like those prepared from starch, can be prepared from the sugars. Their properties differ in some respects because of the great difference in molec-lar size. The methacrylyl esters and llyl ethers of the sugars form inoluble resins on exposure to air in the ame way as the corresponding compounds from starch. The allyl ethers of he sugars dissolve in a wider range of olvents than those of starch, but their oatings do not dry tack-free in a short ime, as do those of starch, because the ugar ethers are liquids at ordinary emperatures. If the allyl ethers of the ugars are first blown with air, they dry much faster. Sucrose octa-acetate has been used in a special formula for denaturing alcohol, as a gum contituent of lacquers, as a plasticizer in anhydrous adhesives, and in the treatment of paper.

CERTAIN BODY STRUCTURES composed of lightweight atoms do not show up in X-ray pictures. If some heavy atom could be introduced into the structure in question, X-ray shadow pictures would be formed. Iodo derivatives of galactose and of methyl glucoside have been found useful as contrasting agents. These derivatives are rapidly excreted through the kidneys after intravenous injection and are present in sufficient concentration to render the kidney structure opaque to X-rays.

Vitamin C (L-xyloascorbic acid) is synthesized from sorbitol, which, as we mentioned before, is a sugar alcohol obtained from dextrose. Bacterial oxidation converts the sorbitol to the sugar sorbose, which is then oxidized to ascorbic acid by chemical means. Other ascorbic acids can be prepared, for example, D-araboascorbic acid, which has but one-twentieth the antiscorbutic activity of vitamin C. The compounds differ only in the relative arrangement in space of the groupings in the molecule. Fatty acid esters of ascorbic acids have been used to inhibit rancidity in fats. Ascorbic acids are used to prevent the darkening of fruits during canning or freezing.

Many chemicals have been prepared from sugars by fermentation. These are discussed elsewhere in this volume.

Mention will be made of one process on the border line between fermentation and the usual chemical modifications of carbohydrates. That is the process for making methanol, or wood alcohol, from the gases obtained as a byproduct in the fermentation to produce butyl alcohol and acetone. The mixture of gases consists almost entirely of 60 percent carbon dioxide and 40 percent hydrogen. They are combined under high pressure in the presence of a suitable catalyst to give methanol and water. Methanol is readily converted to formaldehyde, an important chemical in the plastics field.

FROM THE EXAMPLES given, it is apparent that the field of potential chemical uses for the starches and sugars is exceedingly great. Many other chemical reactions of carbohydrates are known. Lactic acid may be obtained in fair yields by treating carbohydrate materials with strong alkali. Ordinarily it is obtained by fermentation methods. Under conditions of high temperature, carbohydrates have been converted in the laboratory to products resembling oil and bituminous coal, which some chemists believe were formed naturally from the carbohydrate materials of plants in past geologic ages. Starches and sugars will become more important sources of chemicals as we learn more about their reactions and the products thereof.

E. A. TALLEY grew up on a farm in Virginia. He was granted the doctor's degree in the field of carbohydrates by the Ohio State University. He has been with the carbohydrate division of the Eastern Regional Research Laboratory since 1942 and has done research on carbohydrate ethers and esters.

I. A. WOLFF holds a bachelor's degree from the University of Louisville and a doctor's degree in organic chemistry from the University of Wisconsin. He has been a member of the starch and dextrose division at the Northern Regional Research Laboratory since 1941.

Wet Milling of Cereal Grains

Robert L. Zipf

Orlando Jones, an Englishman, was a pioneer whose work in 1840 founded a multimillion-dollar industry that touches all our daily lives. Every early starch producer used his process, in which an alkali was used to recover the starch. The process worked so well that the industry grew by leaps and bounds until, by 1880, this country's yearly consumption was estimated at 200 million pounds. Thus the cornstalk industry was born.

Wet milling, which has been considerably modified from Jones' original method, now consists of grinding the soaked grain and then separating the starch with water. Eleven companies were operating 14 wet-milling plants in 1950. They used about 6 percent of our corn crop, or 140 million bushels. Three of the plants have occasionally wet milled grain sorghums since about 1945. Another firm has announced plans for wet milling about 2 million bushels (56,000 tons) of grain sorghum annually. Wheat starch and rice starch have been made by various wet-milling procedures. Starch also has been obtained from barley and oats in the laboratory.

This use of the cereal grains has given the starch industries the advantage of a raw material high in starch, easy to store, and available in quantity. Every cereal grain can be wet milled by modification in equipment or processing. Because of the differences in the physical properties of starch from various sources, the starches may not be interchangeable for some purposes. Therefore, the production of starch from cereal or tuber crops depend upon the demands of industries for products most satisfactory for their purposes.

Cereal grains can be roughly classed as waxy and nonwaxy, or common. The terms do not imply the presence or absence of wax, but are merely descriptive of the physical appearance of the inside of the whole kernel. Waxy varieties are found in corn, grain sorghum, barley, rice, millet, and Job's tears. Commercially, only small amounts of the waxy corn and sorghum have been processed for starch.

Because sound grain yields the most starch with the least processing difficulty, wet mills as a rule process grain of grade No. 2 or 3. Only corn and sorghum are wet milled today.

THE OLDEST WET-MILLING METHOD for extracting wheat starch is the Halle or fermentation process, in which the grain, softened by steeping in water, is ground and made into a mash with water and allowed to ferment a week or two. The modified gluten can then be washed out of the starch. A second method, known as the Alsatian process, consists of steeping, grinding, and washing out the starch, without previous fermentation. The methods have been replaced by the Martin process and the batter process, both of which are wet-separation, not wet-milling, methods. Wheat starch was also made during the Second World War by a modification of the corn wet-milling process developed at the Northern Regional Research Laboratory.

Rice starch is obtained by steeping the grain for 24 hours in 0.3 percent caustic soda solution, then grinding it with additional caustic soda. The starch is obtained after screening, sedimentation, and centrifuging. Sulfur dioxide has also been used instead of the caustic soda.

The process as described for extracting starch from corn applies generally for grain sorghum.

MOST STARCH FACTORIES start with shelled corn delivered in railroad boxcars, each holding 1,200 to 1,800 bushels. A sample is collected from each car and analyzed. The grain is unloaded by means of power shovels, air conveyors, or tilters. It is weighed and then may go to either storage bins or a cleaner to remove dust, chaff, cobs, stones, rodent excreta, insects, broken grain, and other foreign material. In some plants the cleanings, except the larger particles, are conveyed to the feed system and mixed to form part of the gluten feed.

The cleaned grain is stored in bins in an amount sufficient to fill a steep tank. Some of the larger wet-milling plants are equipped with grain driers to dry high-moisture grain. Corn with a moisture content under 16 percent can usually be stored safely during the winter, but corn that contains more than 16 percent moisture is turned in the bins periodically.

Steeping, or soaking, is the most important step in wet milling. It loosens the bond that holds the starch granules together in the kernel; it removes solubles, mainly mineral matter, from the germ so that it is lightened and can be floated off in the germ separators; and it softens the kernel for grinding. Steeping does not harm or modify the starch very much.

Sulfurous acid water is used for the purpose. Steeping is done in a series of tanks in which lactic acid fermentation is controlled by a countercurrent flow of steep water and the addition of sulfur dioxide. Each tank holds 2,000 to 3,500 bushels of grain.

The sulfurous acid is made by burning sulfur and absorbing the sulfur dioxide in gluten settler water. This acidic steep water, amounting to 7 to 14 gallons per bushel and containing 0.07 to 0.25 percent sulfur dioxide, is heated to 116° to 133° F. and put on the oldest corn in the steeping system. The acid water is transferred countercurrently through the steeps and at times is circulated over each steep. The oldest corn, therefore, is soaked or steeped with water containing the smallest amount of solubles and the newest corn with water containing the largest amount of solubles.

The corn is completely covered during the steeping. The steeping time varies from 28 to 48 hours. The temperature of the contents of each steep is maintained at 116° to 133° F. by means of tube and shell heat exchangers or by sparging (injecting) the steam directly into the water. The water drained off the newest corn is called light steep water. It amounts to 4 to 10 gallons to the bushel and varies greatly in its composition. Soluble or colloidal matter amounting to 1.5 to 9.5 percent of the dry substance of the original grain is removed in steeping. The steeped corn, when withdrawn, has a moisture content of 40 to 55 percent, depending upon the condition of the grain used. More sulfur dioxide is required for steeping moldy and heat-damaged corn.

The starch is separated from the steeped corn in four steps. In the first, the grain is ground by degerminating mills to free the germ, which is then floated off in large tanks known as germ separators. Then, the underflow from the separators is screened and the resultant hull and grits are ground by means of buhrstone mills or vertical hammer mills. The third step is screening to separate coarse and fine fiber from a starch and gluten slurry. The germ, coarse fiber, and fine fiber are washed free of starch and gluten by a countercurrent flow of water over three or four sets of screens. The starch is separated from the gluten in the fourth step by tabling or centrifuging.

The trend today is to replace the tables with centrifuges because there is less chance of any contamination, processing time is shorter, less floor space is required, and results are better.

The starch from the tables or centrifuges is filtered and washed on the filters to remove soluble matter.

Starch from the filters is dried to 5 to 18 percent moisture by kiln, belt, rotary, vacuum, spray, or shelf driers.

The starch that leaves the driers with 10 to 14 percent moisture is known as pearl starch. It can be packed in 140-pound jute, burlap, or cotton bags, or in 100-pound paper bags. This starch will have a protein content of 0.26 to 0.38 percent on a dry basis and contain 0.5 to 1.2 percent total impurities, which include protein, ash, solubles, and oil.

Pearl starch is pulverized to produce food and powdered starch. The main difference between them is that food starch must not contain more than 0.005 percent of sulfur dioxide. Pearl starch may be dried further either before or after it is pulverized. To avoid explosions the moisture content has to be kept above 7.5 percent while the starch is being pulverized. Therefore, to reduce the moisture below 7.5 percent the starch is dried after pulverizing. The powdered starch is sifted through 200-mesh screens and bagged. Pulverized starch contains 5 to 14 percent moisture, depending upon its intended use.

BYPRODUCTS are recovered by drying the wet material from the milling system in flash driers, rotary fire driers, or rotary steam-tube driers. Two passes are generally used to maintain a more uniform moisture content in the product. Flash driers are used to dry gluten feed, gluten meal, and zein. In other installations, rotary fire driers are generally used for the first pass and steam-tube driers for the second pass. The rotary driers are used to dry gluten feed, gluten meal, and germ.

The washed germ from the screens is pressed with a screw- or disk-type water extractor and then dried with two passes through rotary driers. The dry germ will contain 42 to 50 percent oil and 14 to 18 percent protein. The oil is recovered by screw-type oil presses or by a combination of screw presses and solvent extractors. The resulting cake or meal, which contains 0.5 to 15 percent oil, 19 to 22 percent protein, and 3 to 6 percent moisture, is called oil cake or corn-germ meal. It may be sold as such, but most of it is added to the gluten feed. The oil is shipped out as crude corn oil or is refined in the plant.

The gluten liquor or overflow from the tables or first-pass centrifugals is concentrated by centrifuges or settlers. Most of the gluten settler water or overflow from the settlers is used to make the steep acid. The rest is mixed with the other process waters and used to wash the germ and fiber.

The settled heavy gluten is mixed with some fine fiber and filtered with recessed-plate presses or a string-discharge drum filter. The filtrate is mixed with the other process waters to wash the germ and fiber. The filter cake is dried by two passes through rotary driers. The tailings from screening the dried material pass into a hammer mill and can be added to the gluten meal or gluten feed. The material through the screen is called gluten meal and will contain 40 to 45 percent protein and 8 to 14 percent moisture. About 75 percent of the gluten can go into gluten meal and the remaining 25 percent into gluten feed.

The light steep water is evaporated from 2° to 5.5° Baumé (average about 4° Baumé) to 19° to 26° Baumé. Small plants commonly use single-effect and larger plants triple-effect evaporators. The heavy steep water, which contains 35 to 48 percent dry substance protein and 2 to 16 percent dry reducing substances, is loaded into barrels or tank cars or is mixed in the gluten-feed system.

The coarse fiber from the screens is dewatered with screw- or disk-type water expressers. The excess, about one-third of the fine fiber not used to make gluten meal, is used in making gluten feed. In some plants all the gluten and fine fiber go into a gluten feed of 27 to 29 percent protein. The chaff and screenings from the grain elevator may be added to the dewatered coarse fiber; then heavy steep water is added, and the mixture is passed through driers. If all the gluten is used, it is best to dry it separately through one pass of driers. The dried mixture from both sets of driers can be soaked with more heavy steep water and dried to a final moisture content of 9 to 14 percent. The oversize from the gluten-meal system and refinery mud (cake from the dextrose and sirup filters containing about 30 percent oil and 15 percent protein) is added before the final drying. The dried gluten feed will contain 23 to 28 percent protein, depending upon the amounts of constituents added. Tailings from the pulverized-starch and dextrin screens and off-grade batches of starches or dextrins are also added to gluten feed.

Sweet gluten feed is made by adding hydrol, a byproduct molasses from dextrose manufacturing, to the gluten feed before the final drying.

Starch can be converted into a number of simpler substances. Almost any acid can be used to catalyze the reaction of starch with water to form them. Time of conversion, temperature, and acid concentration are factors that can be varied to produce different conversions. Enzymes also can be used to convert starch into sirups.

The greatest acid conversion yields dextrose; lesser conversion yields maltose and the dextrins, along with smaller amounts of dextrose. The degree of conversion is expressed as dextrose equivalent (D. E.), which is a determination of the total reducing substances as dextrose. Products with a lower dextrose equivalent, that is, D. E. 30 to 70, are glucose sirups; those of a higher dextrose equivalent, D. E. 70 to 90, are dextrose sirups from which dextrose sugars are isolated by crystallization.

In the past, this conversion to sirups or dextrose took 4 to 14 hours under atmospheric pressure in large wooden tanks. Today the conversion takes 5 to 30 minutes under pressure in bronze batch converters or in pipe continuous converters.

Starch that contains the smallest amount of impurities is preferred for conversion. The starch cake from the filters is suspended in water to attain a gravity of 10° to 26° Baumé. This slurry is mixed with acid to obtain a pH of 0.9 to 2.4, approximately 0.02 to 0.50 percent acid. The higher acid concentrations are used for dextrose sugar conversions; the lower ones for glucose sirup conversions. The mixture is pumped continuously through a steam-jet heater into a chamber attached to the hydrolysis coil. A valve at the end of the coil controls the flow of the material and thereby the pressure and temperature. A vacuum flash chamber at the discharge is used for a partial concentration of the liquor. The retention time in the continuous converter will vary from 15 to 30 minutes. The liquor is mixed with a diatomaceous filter aid and pumped through a precoated filter to remove insoluble protein and fats (refinery mud). A partial or complete (4.0 to 5.5 pH) neutralization may be employed before the filtration. Some of the proteins and fats may be recovered by using skim tanks ahead of the filters and after the neutralizer.

The clarified juice is run through a triple-pass ion exchanger to remove the impurities. The ion-exchange resins are regenerated with acids and alkalies. The liquor from the ion exchanger at a pH of 4.5 to 6.0 has residual color removed by activated carbon. This treatment consists of contacting the juice at a temperature of 178° to 190° F. with activated carbon for ½ to 2 hours. Boneblack (char), activated carbon, or resinous absorbents may be used. Sodium bisulfite is added to the juice to preserve it, to aid bleaching, and to maintain 0.002 to 0.005 percent sulfur dioxide in the finished sirup. The liquor is evaporated to 42° to 45° Baumé for glucose (corn) sirup. The sirup is sold in tank cars, drums, cans, and bottles. It also may be spray dried.

The process of converting the starch to dextrose sugar starts the same way, except that more acid and a higher temperature or 'longer time are used. The deionized, bleached, and clarified liquor is evaporated to 38° to 40° Baumé and pumped into crystallizers. Because dextrose can crystallize in different forms, the liquor in the crystallizer is seeded with dextrose crystals from previous batches. From 20 to 30 percent of the dextrose goes back as "seed." After 80 to 140 hours of gradual cooling, the mass from the crystallizer is transferred to centrifuges to separate the dextrose crystals from the mother liquor (hydrol). The crystals are dried in two passes through rotary driers using clean hot air. The dextrose sugar may be packed "as is," or it may be ground to pass a 200-mesh screen. Generally, only 100-pound paper bags are used because of the hygroscopic nature of product.

Crude corn sugars are made by cooling the heavy dextrose liquor in forms. In this case the hydrol is included along with the dextrose. The lumps are broken up and then packed.

THE MODIFIED STARCHES include those that have been modified to form products of varied chemical and physical characteristics. These can well be grouped as the acid-modified, alkali-modified or pH-adjusted, and special starches and starch blends. The acid-modified starches yield thin-boiling (thin-bodied) or low-viscosity starches; the alkali-modified or the pH-adjusted starches yield thick-boiling (thick-bodied) or high-viscosity starches. Various chemicals are used to form special starches, such as nitrated starch, allyl starch, solvent-extracted starch, cold-water-soluble starch, chlorinated starch, chlorine-treated starch, and aldehyde-treated starch. Starch or any of the modified starches may be blended together or with other substances, such as tapioca flour, sago flour, wheat flour, oils, sulfonated oils, soaps, borax, and various chemicals, to form starch blends. The blends are used mainly for adhesives.

The acid-modified starches form the bulk of modified-starch production. They are prepared by treating starch slurries in large wooden tanks with sulfuric acid or hydrochloric acid maintained at a temperature below the gelatinization point of the starch for 10 to 24 hours. Acid of 0.002 to 0.8 percent concentration in the slurry is used. When the desired fluidity (viscosity) is reached, the conversion is stopped by adding an alkali such as caustic soda or soda ash. The resultant modified starch is filtered and dried like regular pearl starch. Some of the acid-modified starches may be pulverized. They are packed in 140-pound jute, burlap, or cotton bags, or 100-pound paper bags.

The alkali-modified starches are prepared by treatment with alkaline chemicals, followed by filtering and drying in the ordinary manner, or by pumping the slurry directly on to a rotary drum drier.

Brewers' grits is a special starch which is partly gelatinized by heating a starch slurry just under a gelatinization point. Unless great care is taken, the starch in the tank will gel or filtering and drying the product will be difficult.

Another special starch, which is used as a core binder and an additive to drilling mud, is made by gelatinizing and drying table liquor on a rotary drum drier. It contains 4 to 7 percent protein.

DEXTRINS ARE starch degradation products yielded by the dry conversion of starch of 5 to 10 percent moisture content with various catalysts. As in all the other conversions, time of conversion, type and amount of catalyst, and temperature are governing factors, which are varied to obtain different dextrins. Heat-degraded starch products can be classified as white dextrins, yellow (canary) dextrins, British gums, and blends. The commercial dextrins are not true dextrins but a mixture of dextrins. Most British gums are made without a catalyst.

Pulverized starch for dextrin conversion is stored in a bin. From there it is conveyed to an acidifier—a blender that is a horizontal oblong enclosed wooden tank with openings and a horizontal mixing agitator. Dilute hydrochloric acid or other chemical catalyst is sprayed in over the starch and mixed in. After thorough blending, the starch goes into dextrinizers, where it is held at a fixed temperature between 150° to 400° F. for 1 to 18 hours. Indirect heating with steam or Dowtherm is preferred owing to the fire and explosion hazard of this operation. A totally enclosed jacketed steel kettle is used. It is also very important to avoid undue local overheating. The batch is dropped from the dextrinizer when it approaches the color and fluidity of a standard. It is then cooled, screened, blended with other like batches, and packed in 140-pound jute, burlap, or cotton bags, or 100-pound paper bags.

A certain dextrin may be blended with any of the starch products, that is, starch, modified starch, another dextrin, or British gum, or with chemicals to obtain blends with special properties. These blends are generally used for adhesives.

Adhesives have such varied uses that it is difficult to describe manufacturing procedures without mentioning each particular adhesive. They can be classified, according to their physical state, as liquid, paste, and dry. Dry adhesives may be modified-starch blends, dextrin blends with other materials, or drum-dried products. Dry adhesives can be further classified as to their solubility in hot or cold water.

Various chemicals are used to impart certain properties to an adhesive. Borax is used in almost every one to increase the viscosity and tack. To obtain a still greater viscosity and tack, alkalies, such as caustic soda or soda ash, are added. Urea, iodides, thiocyanates, chloral, and other chemicals are added to increase the cold-water solubility of an adhesive. Wetting agents like sulfonated castor oil are used in adhesives as defoamers and to wet difficult surfaces and thereby increase the bond. Hydroscopic materials, such as glycerol, ethylene glycol, sorbitol, glucose, calcium chloride, ammonium nitrate, urea, and sodium acetate, are used to keep the adhesive film from drying out and becoming brittle. Preservatives are required for almost every liquid or paste adhesive. Among the compounds used for this are sodium salt of o-phenylphenol (Dowicide A), sodium salt of pentachlorophenol (Dowicide G), formaldehyde, formalin, copper sulfate, zinc sulfate, fluorides, benzoates, sodium bisulfite, and mercury compounds. To impart more body and lessen the tendency for the liquid adhesive to set back, flours from wheat, rye, or sago may be added.

In general, the liquid and paste adhesives are made in small batch tanks. The various ingredients are added to hot water and held at a certain temperature until the desired product is obtained. A number of small batches are blended to yield a more uniform liquid adhesive, which is then barreled.

ROBERT L. ZIPF *is a graduate in chemical engineering of Case Institute of Technology. From 1947 to 1950 he was in charge of the cereal grains section, engineering and development division, of the Northern Regional Research Laboratory. Previously he was employed in private industry as development engineer, chief chemist, and chemical engineer.*

The preparation of starch from cereal grains was described by Marcus Porcius Cato in 184 B. C. Pliny the Elder attributed the first extraction of starch from grain to the inhabitants of the Isle of Chios. Until the latter part of the eighteenth century, starch was practically always obtained from wheat.

Mold Agents in Conversion of Starch

H. M. Tsuchiya, R. H. Blom

The bases for industrial processes of saccharifying starch—that is, converting it to sugar—were laid early in the nineteenth century.

The first announcement that it was possible to saccharify, or hydrolyze, starch came in 1811, when G. S. C. Kirchoff, a Russian chemist, reported that starch would yield sugarlike substances on treatment with acid. Five years later, M. Kirchhoff stated that starch could also be degraded by a treatment with diastase, an enzyme from plant sources.

Both procedures have been adapted to industrial operations. In the method that involves acid hydrolysis, a starch slurry is treated, at high temperatures, with hydrochloric acid or nitric acid as a catalyst. The conditions of saccharification, the neutralization of acid, and the removal of residual solids by filtration vary according to the product desired.

In the enzymatic hydrolysis, water is added to starch or starch-containing material, the slurry is heated to gelatinize the starch, and an enzyme (an organic catalyst) is added. Depending on the product desired, the conversion conditions in the enzymatic saccharification of starch may be varied.

Diastases, or amylases, are the enzymes that hydrolyze starch to dextrins and two sugars, maltose and dextrose.

These amylolytic enzymes are of two types: The dextrinogenic enzymes, which primarily convert starch to dextrins (carbohydrates intermediate in molecular size between starch and sugar); and the saccharogenic enzymes, which saccharify the higher polymers of dextrose to sugars.

The dextrinogenic enzyme can hydrolyze the two types of molecules in starch—amylose (a straight-chain or linear molecule) and amylopectin (a branched-chain or ramified molecule). The saccharogenic enzyme can split off sugars from the terminals of amylose and amylopectin molecules. Neither enzyme can hydrolyze the chemical linkages at the branch points in amylopectin. The dextrinogenic enzyme, however, can cut the molecular chain of glucose units in amylopectin at other points. The products formed, like those resulting from the activity of the dextrinogenic enzyme on amylose, are dextrins. The saccharogenic enzymes in malt then attack the free terminal ends of dextrin molecules and split off more sugar molecules.

AMYLASES are found in the seeds of such plants as barley, wheat, and soybeans and also in animal glands, such as the pancreas, and in body fluids, such as saliva, blood, and urine. Diastases occur in micro-organisms, such as bacteria and fungi.

Of the higher plant sources, barley seed is used most commonly on an industrial scale to saccharify starch. Because activity is enhanced by malting the grain, the seed is steeped in water, allowed to sprout, and then dried. When the grain germinates, the dextrinogenic activity of the material is increased substantially. Apparently the dextrinogenic, or α-amylase, enzyme is synthesized during germination. Moreover, the saccharogenic enzyme, or β-amylase, is released from its bound, or inactive, form. The germinated and dried barley seed is known as malt. In the fermentation of grain to ethyl alcohol, the conversion of starch to maltose has depended almost entirely on the use of barley malt, at least in this country. Other amylolytic materials have been considered from time to time, however.

Both α- and β-amylases are found in wheat and rye malts in amounts and proportions approximately comparable to those in barley malt. They are also present in ungerminated cereals like barley, wheat, and rye.

In an attempt to exploit the amylases in ungerminated cereals, the Balls-Tucker process was developed to extract and utilize the enzymes in wheat. The process involves the extraction of ground wheat with a weak solution of sodium sulfite, and the addition of the sulfite-diastase mixture thus obtained to cooked grain to saccharify the starch. The amylolytic activity in the soybean and sweetpotato is of the β-amylase type.

Pancreatic diastase is the only amylolytic enzyme of animal origin now used to any extent in industry. This enzyme displays α-amylase activity but not the saccharogenic characteristics of β-amylase.

CERTAIN MICRO-ORGANISMS produce enough starch-hydrolyzing enzymes under favorable conditions to merit industrial consideration. Some of the bacteria, especially certain members of the genus *Bacillus* (gram-positive, aerobic, sporeforming rods), elaborate α-amylase when they are propagated in either submerged or surface cultures. The dextrinogenic enzymes of bacteria display extraordinary stability in heat; some can withstand boiling temperature for short periods and still rapidly liquefy starch.

Some mold species also produce amylolytic enzyme systems that degrade starch to dextrins and fermentable sugars. The organisms in the crude amylase preparations used in the Orient are primarily of the *Aspergillus flavus-oryzae* group. The mold-bran

process, a refinement of the Oriental practice of propagating molds on moistened rice and other grains, has been developed in the United States. L. A. Underkofler and his associates at Iowa State College have tested the organisms used in the process for their ability to convert starch to fermentable sugars, as measured by the production of alcohol from grain mashes saccharified with mold bran.

The 27 mold cultures tested included strains from 4 genera—*Aspergillus, Mucor, Penicillium,* and *Rhizopus.* All strains of *Aspergillus oryzae* were effective in the conversion of starch. Although *Mucor rouxii* and *M. circinelloides* were as effective as the *Aspergilli,* the strains of *M. javanicus* and of *Penicillium chrysogenum* and *P. purpurogenum* were inferior. Of the 14 strains of *Rhizopus* tested, all but 1 produced active mold-bran preparations.

In the amylo process for the production of alcohol, *Rhizopus japonicus, Mucor rouxianus,* and other related molds have been used to convert starch to sugar. When investigations were originally undertaken at the Northern Regional Research Laboratory to develop a submerged-culture process for the production of fungal amylase, more than 350 strains of 5 genera—*Aspergillus, Rhizopus, Mucor, Penicillium,* and *Monilia*—were tested for their ability to elaborate α-amylase.

Of 278 *Aspergillus* strains, representing 41 species, only 34 produced dextrinogenic amylase under mold-culture conditions. As was to be expected, the enzyme production varied among the strains within a species. Certain strains of *A. niger, A. oryzae,* and *A. wentii* were particularly active. Of 80 *Penicillum* cultures, 8 displayed dextrinogenic activity of low order. Of eight cultures of *Rhizopus, Mucor,* and *Monilia,* none demonstrated any marked α-amylase activity, but one strain of *Rhizopus* was capable of saccharifing grain mashes.

Other strains of *Rhizopus* and *Mucor* behaved the same way, suggesting

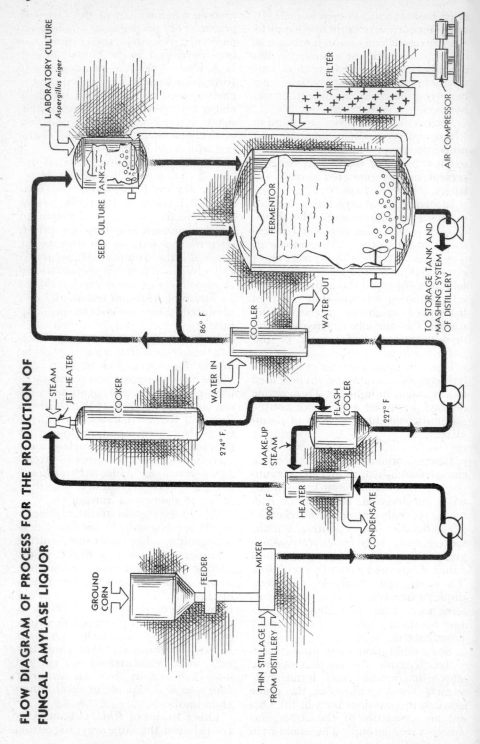

FLOW DIAGRAM OF PROCESS FOR THE PRODUCTION OF
FUNGAL AMYLASE LIQUOR

that those organisms possess amylolytic systems other than the dextrinogenic or liquefying enzyme. Some of the properties of the diastatic systems elaborated by molds in submerged culture were then studied. The properties were compared to those of other starch-hydrolyzing enzymes, particularly barley malt.

Early in the investigation on fungal amylase, chemists observed that the yield of alcohol from grain mashes saccharified with mold-enzyme preparations did not correlate with the α-amylase activity of the preparations. Although a low, but definite, concentration of the dextrinogenic amylase was required and, indeed, essential for satisfactory alcohol production, the alcohol yield depended also on the presence of other amylolytic enzymes. β-Amylase was absent in fungal-amylase preparations, but at least two other enzymes, which displayed maltase activity, were present. Evidence has accumulated that "maltase" can hydrolyze the higher polymers of glucose directly to the simple sugar. As it hydrolyzes maltose as well as the higher carbohydrates, this enzyme is most conveniently measured by its action on the disaccharide. The importance of maltase lies in the fact that alcohol yields from grain mashes saccharified with fungal amylase correlate well with the maltase activity of mold preparations, provided a low but significant activity of α-amylase is also present.

There are certain fungal-amylase preparations of high maltase activity that can hydrolyze isomaltose, a disaccharide that differs from maltose in that the chemical linkage between the glucose residues is of the α-1,6 type in isomaltose, whereas it is of the α-1,4 type in maltose.

The ability to hydrolyze isomaltose is significant because the linkages at the branch points in the amylopectin fraction (branched-chain molecule) of starch are of the 1,6 type and are completely refractory to the hydrolytic action of other common amylolytic enzymes. Fungal amylase thus might cleave the linkages at the branch points of the amylopectin molecule as well as the common 1,4 linkages in the linear portion of the molecule. Maybe that explains why the yields of alcohol from grain mashes saccharified with mold-enzyme preparations are slightly higher than those from mashes converted with malt. Although it can be said that fungal amylase hydrolyzes the isomaltose, not enough evidence is at hand to state that maltase is responsible for the cleavage.

Eric Kneen, of Milwaukee, has presented evidence that a saccharifying enzyme other than the α- or β-amylase may be present in certain malt, bacterial, and fungal-amylase preparations. He believes that this enzyme hydrolyzes limit dextrins to fermentable sugars. His hypothesis is that malt-limit dextrinase hydrolyzes the α-1,6-glucosidic linkages to fermentable sugar, presumably maltose.

We should note that the α-amylase of mold preparations does not liquefy starch to the same extent as does the α-amylase of malt or bacteria. Furthermore, it is more heat-sensitive than the α-amylase of malt. In that respect it is comparable to pancreatic α-amylase. Certain compensating advantages, economic in nature, however, follow the use of fungal amylase to replace malt as the converting agent in the production of alcohol from grain.

FUNGAL ENZYMES have been used in China and Japan to prepare alcoholic beverages, sauces, and other food products from soybeans, wheat, rice, and sorghum. In general, the products are made by the action of amylolytic and proteolytic enzymes on the starch and protein of the grain or beans. The appetizing aroma and pleasant taste of the sauces and foods are results of the slow chemical changes by which amino acids, esters, and the organic acids are formed.

The enzymes are produced by the culturing of molds, usually *Aspergillus oryzae*, on various starchy materials. A mixture of enzymes is made, but amylolytic, or starch-degrading, types predominate. These are most important in the production of saké, Japanese rice wine, for which the rice starch is converted to sugars, which yeast can ferment to ethyl alcohol. The fungal preparation used for starch conversion is known as koji. The use of koji by the Japanese in the production of beverage alcohol is comparable to the utilization of barley malt to make whisky and beer in this country.

Credit generally is given Jokichi Takamine for the first industrial production and application of fungal-enzyme preparations in the United States. The processes for the industrial preparation of the materials are basically the same as those used by the Chinese and Japanese to produce koji. Indeed, Takamine gave the name Taka-Koji to his product, which was prepared from wheat bran, to distinguish it from the Japanese material, which is a culture on steamed rice. The product is now called moldy bran or mold bran.

Several manufacturers produce mold bran in this country. So far as known, the processes they employ are modifications of the method described by Takamine in 1914.

In Takamine's procedure, wheat bran is moistened and steamed to sterilize the material and gelatinize the starch. The mass is cooled to about 100° F. and inoculated with a small quantity of spores of *A. oryzae,* which are intimately mixed with the bran. The mixture is transferred to a room where the temperature and humidity of the air can be controlled. It is put on trays, which are mounted one above the other in a specially constructed rack. The trays are fitted with bottoms of screen so that the bran is aerated from both above and below. During the first several hours of incubation, the temperature is held at about 86° F. by the introduction of steam directly into the room. Within 16 hours, the mold spores germinate and the growth of mycelium begins. During the period when the fungus is multiplying rapidly, it generates a great deal of heat, and

the temperature of the room must be reduced by circulating cool air through it. The circulating air is saturated with water to keep the bran from becoming too dry for proper propagation of the mold. Growth is complete in about 48 hours. Because the material is susceptible to bacterial infection when it is moist, it must be dried promptly.

In the United States, one concern at least produces mold bran by the tray method. During the Second World War, a large tonnage of mold bran was made by this method, mostly in a midwestern plant, which had a capacity of about 10 tons a day. One or more distillers utilized the output of the plant in place of, or to supplement, barley malt in the production of industrial alcohol from grain.

Another procedure used industrially to prepare mold bran differs from the tray method in that a drum is used for culturing the *A. oryzae* on wheat bran. Large drums that can be rotated are charged with bran and water, and the material, sterilized by steam, is introduced directly into the vessel. After it has been cooked, cooling of the medium is hastened by the passage of cool, clean air through the drum. The bran is then inoculated with spores, which are mixed into the medium by the rotation of the drum. Growth takes place at 85° to 104° F. under conditions of controlled temperature and aeration.

Mold bran can be used directly as a source of enzymes. It also may be extracted with water, and from the solution a purified and concentrated enzyme preparation can be made. The main use for the saccharifying enzymes in crude mold bran is as the converting agent in the production of ethyl alcohol from grain by fermentation. That use has been advocated for many years, but only in 1945–47 was the material prepared on a large scale for use in alcohol plants. A large amount of mold bran was utilized by a producer of industrial alcohol in the propagation of yeast and for the saccharification of grain mashes.

A midwestern alcohol plant conducted large-scale tests in 1945 to determine the value of mold bran and mixtures of mold bran and barley malt as saccharifying agents. The average alcohol yield from six fermentors of mash converted with mold bran was 5.24 proof gallons (2.76 gallons of 190-proof alcohol) per standard bushel of grain (12 percent moisture). From 3.9 to 4.8 percent mold bran was used for conversion. An average yield of 5.13 proof gallons (2.70 gallons of 190-proof alcohol) per bushel was obtained from malt-converted mash.

After the tests, a factory was built to produce mold bran. It operated for several years. Most of its output, some 8 or 10 tons a day, was used by a producer of industrial alcohol from grain. When the demand for industrial alcohol diminished and its production from grain became uneconomical, the mold-bran plant closed down.

Mold bran could be used to make beverage alcohol. Distillers of whisky and spirits have been reluctant to use fungal preparations, however, for fear that the flavor and odor of the products might be affected detrimentally or altered markedly. In 1950, no plants were using mold bran as a saccharifying agent in the production of industrial or beverage alcohol.

Several factories produce a mold bran and extract it with water for the preparation of refined enzyme products. Many of the operations are trade secrets, but the general process is known. After incubation, the moist mold bran is charged into vessels called percolators, and the enzymes are recovered from the substrate by countercurrent extraction with water. Four percolators can be used. The liquor drawn from the last percolator is a concentrated solution of the enzymes. It is clarified by filtration, and the clear extract is treated with ethyl alcohol to precipitate the enzymes, which are separated by filtration (or centrifugation) and dried. After the product is analyzed for enzyme activity, it is blended with a diluent to a standard potency. Several commercial preparations of this type have enzyme activities 10 to 20 times greater than that of mold bran.

PURIFIED OR REFINED enzymes are used to prepare sizes and adhesives and to desize textiles. They are used for the clarification of beverages and fruit juices, and in the preparation of table sirup from starch. In each application, the initial action of the dextrinogenic and saccharogenic amylases is upon starch to achieve a certain result. When the desired action has been obtained, the enzymes may be destroyed by the application of heat.

In the production of fabrics from raw fibers, the fibers are spun into threads; these threads are woven into fabrics, which are finished by bleaching, dyeing, and printing. Before weaving, the threads usually require strengthening or sizing. Sizing often is done by coating or impregnating the warp threads with modified starch or dextrin that has been prepared by the action of amylases on starch. Before a raw fabric is dyed or bleached, it must be freed of the sizing material. Modified-starch sizes may be removed by immersing the fabric in a bath containing amylase. Fungal enzymes can be used for the purpose, but bacterial amylases are preferred because they can be employed at relatively high temperatures, at which they act fast.

In the preparation of a beverage like beer, there is a possibility that small amounts of starch, insufficiently modified by malt, may be dissolved in the wort. The starch may precipitate later as a haze in the finished product. Fungal enzymes can be used to complete the solubilization of the starch and thus prevent the undesirable haze.

In the production of pectin from apple pomace, difficulties are caused by the starch that is present in the raw material. Diastatic enzymes, especially fungal amylases, overcome the trouble by converting the starch to a soluble form.

Many bottled or canned fruit juices tend to develop a haze in standing. It can be prevented by treating the juices with a mixture of enzymes that are capable of attacking pectins and starches, which are most likely to cause the cloudiness. Refined products prepared from cultures of the mold *A. oryzae* contain both types of enzymes.

A comparatively large-scale application for refined fungal amylase is in the production of a sweet table sirup from starch. In one process, a slurry of cornstarch is modified by acid conversion to a solution containing dextrins and a small proportion of the sugars dextrose and maltose. The mineral acid used for hydrolysis is neutralized, and fungal enzymes are added to the solution. The diastatic enzymes act on the dextrins to form more sugar and, simultaneously, to transform a large part of the maltose to dextrose. When enzyme conversion is terminated, the solids in solution are composed principally of dextrose and maltose, with a preponderance of the former. About 20 percent of the original starch is present as dextrins. The finished sirup is very sweet and has no unpleasant flavors. It is difficult indeed to prepare a sirup of comparable sweetness by acid conversion alone, because undesirable byproducts are formed when that high degree of conversion is attained.

Amylases produced by molds in submerged culture may be used in the fermentation of grain to alcohol when the enzyme preparation can be employed without concentration or purification.

IN THE AMYLO PROCESS, developed by A. Calmette in 1895 and modified somewhat since then, the mold (generally a species of *Mucor* or *Rhizopus*) is grown submerged in the grain mash itself; the starch, saccharified by the action of mold enzymes, is fermented to alcohol by yeasts. The process, in which the cultures must be absolutely pure, involves several steps. The grain mash is cooked in the conventional manner. It is subsequently pretreated with 1 to 2 percent malt so as to liquefy the starch to render the mash suffi-

ciently fluid. Instead of malt, acid can be used in this liquefaction step.

The contents of the cooker are blown into closed containers, where the mash is first sterilized and then cooled. The mash is inoculated with the desired mold strain, and sterile air is blown into the contents of the fermentor. The mash is agitated to help maintain aerobic conditions. The mold multiplies for some 24 hours and elaborates the amylolytic enzymes, which hydrolyze starch to fermentable sugars. A yeast inoculum is added, and the aeration is ended shortly thereafter. The alcoholic fermentation is generally completed 72 hours after the mash has been pitched with yeast. Modifications (such as the simultaneous inoculation of the mash with mold and yeast) have been attempted.

Two disadvantages have limited the acceptance of the process by industry: Rigid pure-culture conditions must be maintained in large volumes of mash; an enormous amount of air is required to maintain aerobic conditions in the grain mash during the propagation of the mold and production of amylolytic enzymes.

In 1909, A. Woolner, Jr., and A. Lassloffy described the use of a "diastatic slop" or "fungi-diastase" as a converting agent in the production of alcohol from grain mashes. Distillers' thin stillage, handled with aseptic precautions from the time it left the "beer" still, was inoculated with *Aspergillus oryzae*.

The mold was grown in submerged culture under aerobic conditions for 36 hours. The grain mash was first treated with a small amount (3 to 5 percent) of malt. The mold culture was then added, at the rate of 8 gallons per 56-pound bushel of grain, to the completely liquefied (but only partly converted) mash and the yeast was added. The alcoholic fermentation was completed in 60 hours.

During the Second World War, an unprecedented demand developed for industrial alcohol that required a five-fold increase in production. Although fermentation of molasses and synthesis from ethylene provided a small part of our industrial-alcohol requirements, the bulk was produced by the fermentation of grain, especially corn and wheat. The increase in production required correspondingly greater quantities of converting agent. So great was the demand for barley malt that the supply was inadequate; in fact, for a time curtailment of grain-alcohol production appeared imminent. Thus, the war situation gave impetus to the study and use of fungal amylase as a replacement for malt.

N. M. Erb and F. M. Hildebrandt, at Baltimore, in 1946 described a process in which both fungal amylase produced in submerged culture and malt were used for saccharification. They employed a strain of *Rhizopus delemar* and incorporated granular wheat flour, stillage, and malt in the mold-propagation medium. In addition to 2 percent malt, they used 2.3 to 4.6 gallons of mold culture per bushel of granular wheat for saccharification.

An interesting process was developed at the Northern Laboratory to produce fungal amylase in submerged culture. It resembles somewhat the Woolner-Lassloffy and the Erb and Hildebrandt processes, but it differs in that no malt is used for conversion—the organism employed, which was discovered in the survey of molds for α-amylase, is especially active as a starch-converting agent.

At the Northern Laboratory, we do it this way: A sterilized mash of grain and distillers' thin stillage is inoculated with a liquid culture of *Aspergillus niger* NRRL 337. Aerobic conditions are maintained by blowing air into the fermentor. In large installations, agitation of the mash may help disperse the air. The mold is grown at 86° F. for 50 to 60 hours, when the production of fungal amylase is at a maximum. The entire culture is added to the grain mash, previously cooked and cooled, at the rate of 3 gallons, or less, for each 56-pound bushel of corn. The grain mash is then inoculated with yeast, and

the alcoholic fermentation is complete in 72 hours. In pilot-plant tests, the yield of alcohol from grain mashes saccharified with fungal amylase was 5.2 proof gallons per bushel of corn. The yield from mashes converted with malt was 5.15.

Fungal amylase produced by the submerged-culture process promises to be as effective as malt in the conversion of moldy and heat-damaged corn, and wheat, milo, sorghum, and potato mashes for the production of alcohol.

The concentrations of the constituents in the medium employed for the production of fungal amylase influence markedly the yield of amylolytic enzymes. As the quantity of corn is raised from 1 to 5 percent, an increase is noted in the production of maltase. As the amount of distillers' thin stillage solids is raised from 1 to 7 percent, an increase is noted in the production of α-amylase. Other materials are not required in the medium used to propagate the mold and develop the amylases.

Alcohol yields from grain mashes saccharified with fungal amylase at 140° to 149° F. for 5 to 10 minutes are no higher than those obtained from mashes saccharified at 122° to 131° F. for 20 to 30 minutes. The former conditions of conversion are preferable, however, because the liquefaction of the mash proceeds further than under the latter conditions. The more fluid the mash, the more readily it can be pumped through the plant lines. In plant-scale tests of the process, a conversion temperature of 155° F. was found desirable. The retention time used was 15 minutes. The mash was liquefied satisfactorily, the alcohol yield was not adversely affected, and no difficulties in plant operations were encountered.

Investigations have also been conducted at the Northern Laboratory on the preparation of maltose sirup from granular flour. Fungal amylase was used as the converting agent. Experimental work proved that malt and mold amylase, produced in submerged culture, were comparable in their ability to hydrolyze starch. The finished sirups produced with both of the converting agents were equally good with respect to protein content, color, and clarity.

THE METHODS of starch conversion or saccharification that are important industrially utilize acid or enzymes to catalyze the reaction. Each agent has characteristics that influence its application. When acid is employed, the principal end products are practically the same as the ones obtained when enzymes are used, but the relative proportion of each varies. The rate and extent of the reaction differ with the conversion agent, and, because of the conditions of hydrolysis, some decomposition of starch to deterimental byproducts is obtained by acid conversion.

Acid is commonly used for the conversion of starch to corn sirup and dextrose. The reaction is conducted under pressure and at a temperature above 250° F. in closed vessels constructed of an acid-resistant alloy. The conversion is rapid—a matter of a few minutes. The acidity of the starch slurry, temperature, and retention time are varied according to the type of product desired. If the product is to be sirup, the conditions are relatively mild, so that the hydrolysis is incomplete—that is, 30 to 35 percent of the starch is degraded no further than dextrins, while 65 to 70 percent is converted to maltose and dextrose. If dextrose sugar is to be made, starch is hydrolyzed under more vigorous conditions. Almost all of the starch is converted to dextrose and small amounts of byproducts, which interfere in the recovery of crystalline dextrose and appear to be somewhat toxic to microorganisms.

In contrast to the speed with which acid hydrolysis proceeds, enzyme conversion of starch under industrial conditions is slow. Up to 25 or 30 hours may be required for maximum hydrolysis. As with the acid catalyst, the end products are dextrose, maltose, and dextrins; but, while practically complete conversion to dextrose is possible by the acid reaction, such is not the case when the degradation is catalyzed by enzymes.

If a slurry of starch is gelatinized, cooled, and treated with diastatic enzymes, hydrolysis will proceed, and ultimately the product will have a certain composition in terms of dextrose, maltose, and dextrin. Usually this equilibrium composition does not change; if it does, it changes very slowly with additional time of conversion. But if dextrose is withdrawn from the system (for example, by yeast, which converts the dextrose to alcohol), the equilibrium is disturbed, and more dextrose will be formed by the enzymes at the expense of the maltose and dextrins. Eventually, practically all of the original starch will have been converted to dextrose to be utilized by the yeast. It is believed that, besides amylases, other enzymes have a part in the total degradation of starch to dextrose.

Of the two methods for splitting starch into sugar, the process in which acid is employed as the catalyst is undoubtedly more economical. Each method has certain characteristics which make it unique, however, and therefore they should not be compared in all instances on the basis of economics alone. As we have pointed out, enzymes are unsuitable for the production of dextrose from starch. Either catalyst—enzymes or mineral acid—can be used in the preparation of sirups of low sweetness. Certainly, for this application, the acid process is the cheaper; the cost of the catalyst is lower, a more concentrated slurry of starch can be converted with acid than with enzymes, and less time is required for the acid reaction than for enzymic hydrolysis.

For the saccharification of starchy materials, such as grains, in the production of alcohol, enzyme conversion is the more suitable method. The formation of sugar is relatively slow, but it is fast enough during the fermentation to satisfy the requirements of the yeast. The ultimate conversion of the starch to fermentable sugar is good. Because dextrose and maltose are fermentable sugars, it seems that the acid hydrolysis of starch grains to dextrose could be applied to the process for the production of alcohol. To attain essentially complete conversion, however, the conditions are such that some toxic substances are formed, and a small portion of the sugar is destroyed or made unfermentable. The result is a lower yield of alcohol than can be obtained from grain mashes saccharified with enzymes.

One of the largest consumers of enzymatic materials is the industry based on the production of ethyl alcohol from such starchy substances as grains. In that process, barley malt is the source of the diastatic enzymes that are employed to convert the starch of the grain to sugars fermentable by yeast. Malt is comparatively expensive, and investigations have been conducted to develop a cheaper source of enzymes. The preparation of fungal amylase by submerged-culture methods and its utilization as a converting agent are developments of the Northern Laboratory. Large-scale tests of the process have shown it to be practicable.

LET US COMPARE the costs of raw materials required in the production of 1 gallon of 190-proof alcohol from corn when the grain is saccharified by malt in one case and fungal amylase in the other. Let us assume that the yield in each case is 2.74 wine gallons of 190-proof alcohol per bushel (56 pounds) of grain containing 12 percent moisture; that other costs and credits are not affected by the choice of converting agent; and that the quantities of agents required for the conversion of 1 bushel of grain are 10 percent malt (5.6 pounds) and 3.0 gallons of fungal-amylase liquor. We assume also that corn costs 2.4 cents a pound ($1.34 a bushel), that barley malt costs 6 cents a pound, and that fungal-amylase liquor can be produced for 1.7 cents a gallon. The table gives the amounts

Comparison of fungal-amylase conversion with malt conversion in the production of 2.74 gallons of 190-proof alcohol

	Malt conversion	Fungal-amylase conversion
Materials:		
Corn............pounds..	50.40	[1] 56.00
Converting agent....do....	5.60	[2] 3.00
Cost:		
Corn..............cents..	120.96	134.40
Converting agent....do....	33.60	5.10
Total cost.........do....	154.56	139.50
Cost per gallon....do....	56.41	50.91
Relative cost....percent..	100.00	90.25

[1] Includes corn used in preparation of fungal amylase.

[2] Gallons.

and costs of the materials needed in the production of identical quantities of alcohol with the two enzymic substances.

THE CALCULATIONS show that it is possible to lower the production cost of alcohol by 5.5 cents a gallon through the use of fungal amylase in place of malt. By using the fungal-amylase preparation, a distillery mashing 5,000 bushels of grain a day may reduce its cost of operation by as much as $750 a day.

The practicability and economic feasibility of the fungal-amylase process were tested in a series of plant-scale experiments. The runs were made in 1949 under a contract between the Department of Agriculture and the operators of a Government-owned alcohol plant in Muscatine, Iowa. Fungal amylase was prepared in quantities of about 20,000 gallons, and each batch of liquor was used in place of malt for the conversion of 5,000 to 7,000 bushels of corn. The operators of the plant concluded that it was entirely practical to produce fungal amylase in conjunction with the operation of a distillery, that the yield of alcohol obtained from mashes converted with the mold agent was no less than the yield with malt, and that significant savings in the production cost of the alcohol could be achieved through the application of the fungal-amylase process.

H. M. Tsuchiya *is a bacteriologist in the fermentation division, Northern Regional Research Laboratory. Dr. Tsuchiya received the master's degree at the University of Washington and the doctor's degree at the University of Minnesota. He was on the research staff of the University of Minnesota until 1947, when he joined the laboratory in Peoria. He has been investigating factors affecting the industrial production of ethyl alcohol and butyl*

alcohol by fermentation procedures, as well as the production and utilization of the enzymes of potential use in industry.

R. H. Blom *is assistant head of the engineering and development division at the Northern Laboratory. He has been engaged in chemical engineering work since 1933. Since 1943 he has specialized in fermentation technology, especially the production and utilization of enzymes of microbial origin. Mr. Blom completed his formal training in chemical engineering at the Armour Institute of Technology and received his master's degree in 1933.*

The origin of freeze-drying of potatoes apparently goes back to the Incas of ancient Peru, who spread potatoes on the ground of the high plateaus to freeze by night and thaw by day. Freezing renders the cell walls of the potato more permeable and shears groups of cells from other groups. As a result of the shearing action, avenues are created that permit escape of the juice through breaks in the skin. After 12 to 15 days of alternate freezing and thawing, the Incas trampled on the potatoes to expel the juice. Then they left the potatoes for 15 or 20 days longer to undergo further dehydration by action of sunlight and frosts.

Chuno, the name given the product by the Incas, was a mainstay in their diet, and its preparation has continued up to the present time in Peru. It is ground into flour for bread making. Pieces of chuno are reconstituted in water to be later cooked and eaten instead of fresh potatoes.

The practice of the Peruvians seems to have been largely forgotten in this country until a group of potato growers in North Dakota, led by William M. Case, executive secretary of the Red River Valley Potato Growers Association, tried it in 1947. Cull and surplus potatoes were spread out on pastures and allowed to freeze and thaw alternately during the winter. In the spring, livestock was let out to eat the "mummified" potatoes, so-called because they shrink and become wrinkled during the natural drying.

Both dairy and beef cattle did well on rations in which the dried potatoes were an important part. The stand of grass on the pastures improved noticeably as a result of the protein and mineral nutrients of the potato juice, which had drained into the soil.

The natural freeze-dehydration of potatoes also has been carried out successfully in upper New York State and experimentally in Aroostook County, Maine, and on Long Island. This method of converting potatoes to a stable feedstuff may help solve the problem of using up subgrade potatoes.—*R. H. Treadway, Eastern Regional Research Laboratory.*

New Uses for Waxy-Cereal Starches

John H. Martin,
Merle T. Jenkins

Waxy starch exists in the endosperm of the grains of some varieties of corn, sorghum, rice, millet, barley, and Job's tears. The term "waxy" refers to the waxlike appearance of the endosperm of the grain when it is cut or broken; it does not indicate the presence of true wax.

In the Orient, waxy grains are called glutinous; it is because of the gluelike character of the cooked or the wetted grain, flour, or starch. Glutinous varieties of rice and also millet have been known in China for many centuries, and glutinous sorghum has been grown there for at least 300 years. Many varieties of waxy rice, millet, and sorghum are grown in China and other Eastern countries. A few waxy rices have been grown in the United States at times to supply special holiday delicacies to Oriental people living here. The chromosomes in the reproductive cells of corn occasionally undergo sudden changes and give rise to waxy grain.

It remained, however, for the Chinese to discover this new type in a crop that originated in the Americas. The existence of waxy corn (or maize) became known in 1908 when a missionary in China, the Reverend J. M. W. Farnham, sent a sample to the United States Department of Agriculture.

Amber waxy sorghum from China reached the United States about 1854, and that variety or selections from it have been grown here since that time.

Its waxy character was unknown, however, until about 1933, when J. C. Stephens discovered that several other American varieties also were waxy.

From 1944 to 1947, 20,000 to 40,000 acres of waxy corn and sorghum were grown and the grain processed in the United States each year. About 32,000 acres of waxy corn and 5,000 acres of waxy sorghum were grown in 1949.

Waxy-cereal starch produces pastes with higher viscosity and less rigidity than does ordinary cornstarch. Those characteristics make it adaptable to many special industrial uses. The properties of waxy starch resemble those of tapioca starch. We are all familiar with the difference between soft tapioca pudding and stiff cornstarch pudding. Waxy and ordinary starch also differ in their molecular structure.

WAXY STARCH is entirely amylopectin, a type in which the molecules are arranged with many branches. Ordinary starch is a mixture of the amylopectin (71 to 72 percent) and amylose (28 to 29 percent) types. The amylose molecules are arranged in straight unbranched chains. Tapioca starch is about 80 percent amylopectin and 20 percent amylose.

One of the distinctive characters of waxy starch and grains is that they stain red when they are treated with iodine. Ordinary starch stains blue. The difference was discovered in France by A. Gris, in 1860. In 1921, F. R. Parnell, an Englishman working in India, discovered that the pollen of waxy cereals also stains red rather than blue when treated with iodine. Starch in the stems, leaves, and seed coats of waxy cereals gives a blue reaction to iodine, which indicates that the waxy type of starch is formed only in the endosperm and in the pollen. Apparently the factors of heredity in waxy

902722°—51——12

barley, and at least one waxy gene in corn, do not effect complete conversion to waxy starch, because the starch of the mature grain contains 2 to 3 percent of amylose.

THE FIRST ATTEMPT to promote industrial use of waxy grain in the United States was made by R. E. Karper, of the Texas Agricultural Experiment Station. In the early 1930's he crossed the Batad variety of waxy sorghum, introduced from Java, with a domestic kafir variety. From that cross he developed a new waxy variety otherwise like the kafir parent. When the grain supply had been increased to about a ton, he offered it to several processors with the suggestion that it might have special uses. Karper then had visions of new types of baby foods, health foods, or desserts. But no processor could be interested in undertaking the development of products from this strange grain, and so the waxy kafir was used in a hog-feeding experiment. The hogs thrived as well as but no better than did those consuming ordinary kafir.

Interest was revived after 1936 with the discovery of the similarity between waxy starch and tapioca starch. The discovery was made at the Iowa Agricultural Experiment Station by R. M. Hixon, after separating the starch from waxy corn and sorghum supplied by the writers. In 1938, F. H. Thurber, of the Department of Agriculture, made some limited tests of starch which he had separated from waxy and nonwaxy sorghums. Chemists at the Kansas and Nebraska Agricultural Experiment Stations started experiments shortly thereafter.

The war cut off our supplies of tapioca flour from the Netherlands Indies, which had furnished about 97 percent of the 300 million to 400 million pounds we imported annually. The emergency focused attention on waxy grains. Representatives of the starch industries began experimenting with the waxy starches for various uses and also with commercial methods for separating the starch from waxy grains.

For several years, work had advanced toward the development of a waxy hybrid corn similar to the non-waxy hybrid, Iowa 939. Each of the inbred lines used in producing that hybrid had been crossed with a waxy corn. Waxy progenies from the crosses were backcrossed repeatedly upon the original inbred lines until the waxy counterparts were recovered. The first test of the new waxy hybrid (Iowax 1), in 1939, indicated that it yielded only slightly less than did the ordinary hybrid, Iowa 939. Waxy kernels frequently weigh 3 to 5 percent less than nonwaxy kernels, with a corresponding reduction in yield. Unfortunately, in the fall of 1941 less than 2 bushels of Iowax 1 seed was available. Only 335 and 3,800 kernels, respectively, of the two single crosses and limited quantities of seed of the four inbred parental lines needed to produce the hybrid were on hand at that time. The seed supply was increased in large greenhouses at Beltsville, Md., in the winter of 1941–42, and in the field at Ames, Iowa, during the following summer. In 1942, 326 acres of the second-generation hybrid of Iowax 1 was grown, harvested, and processed. That was the beginning of the waxy-corn industry. The growing of such lower-yielding second-generation hybrid corn was merely a temporary expedient. By 1944, some 10,000 acres of the first-generation hybrid was grown; since 1946, about 20,000 acres of waxy corn has been grown annually. An open-pollinated variety of waxy corn developed at the Nebraska Agricultural Experiment Station was grown to some extent for a time.

Breeding operations to convert additional inbred lines of corn to the waxy condition were expanded immediately with the development of interest in the commercial production of waxy corn. Hybrids involving the additional lines were released as rapidly as they became available. As a result, there have been rapid shifts in acreage to the improved hybrids. Iowax 2 was released in 1945, and by 1947 it comprised the bulk of the crop. That hybrid now has been largely replaced by Iowax 4 and Iowax 5. Small acreages of the waxy counterparts of U. S. 13 and Kansas 2275, a white hybrid, were grown in 1948. The acreage of waxy U. S. 13 was expanded in 1949. Waxy hybrids developed by a commercial hybrid-corn company also have been grown on a limited acreage.

At the beginning of the war we had more waxy sorghum than waxy corn, but no methods for processing the grain. The two leading waxy-sorghum varieties then being grown commercially, Leoti and Schrock, had colored seeds that were difficult to process. Unless bleached, the starch from Leoti was about the color of a strawberry sundae; the Schrock starch resembled malted milk. It was found that by grinding the grain in a wheat-flour mill the bran could be separated from the flour, which would yield a white starch. The waxy-sorghum industry started on that basis, but satisfactory wet-milling procedures have since been developed. By this time, the waxy white kafir that had been unacceptable a few years earlier was in demand, but only 100 pounds of seed was available in 1941. This was increased in 1942, and several thousand acres were harvested and processed in 1943. For several years, A. F. Swanson, of the Bureau of Plant Industry, Soils, and Agricultural Engineering, cooperating with the Kansas Agricultural Experiment Station, had been experimenting with several strains of waxy sorghum selected from crosses with the Leoti variety. The best of these, a Leoti-Club kafir derivative later named Cody, was increased in 1942 from a seed supply of only 24 pounds. In 1943 this was planted in early spring in southern Arizona and California, and the crop threshed in June was shipped to Kansas and Texas for growing the same year.

From 1944 to 1946, all the waxy sorghum processed was the Cody variety, grown on 10,000 to 20,000 acres annually. Cody grain was entirely free from objectionable pigments. Now several varieties of suitable grain type are available. A waxy white-seeded sorghum called Ellis was distributed to Kansas farmers in 1947. Although this is a sweet-stalked variety grown for forage, the seed can be threshed and processed whenever there is sufficient demand for it. About 5,000 acres of a new variety called Miloca was grown in western Texas and Kansas in 1949 for processing. This variety was developed and distributed by the Texas Agricultural Experiment Station. This station also developed some combine-type waxy white-seeded kafirs.

Waxy sorghum, like waxy corn, requires special handling in growing and marketing. It is desirable to avoid contamination with the pollen of nonwaxy varieties. When pollen from a nonwaxy variety fertilizes the flowers of a waxy variety, the grain produced is nonwaxy because of the dominance of the gene that controls the inheritance of the nonwaxy character of the endosperm starch. It is possible to utilize waxy grain that contains not more than 5 percent of nonwaxy kernels. Nevertheless, the seed stocks must be kept pure, and pollen contamination and mechanical mixtures with ordinary corn should be avoided. Like waxy corn, most strains of waxy sorghum tend to yield less than corresponding nonwaxy strains. Thus far, waxy corn and sorghum for processing have been grown under contract and have sold at a premium over the price of nonwaxy grains, because of higher production costs.

Breeders of sorghum have tried to develop waxy varieties and hybrids that are sufficiently productive and otherwise desirable for growing as a feed crop. Manufacturers could then select the lots reaching the market that are pure enough for processing, probably by paying a small premium to encourage the shipment of reasonably pure waxy grain. Such a procedure, which is now followed by processors of barley and oats, would result in lower costs of the raw material.

The starch of waxy corn and waxy white-seeded sorghums can be separated from the germ, bran, protein, and cellulose of the grain by the procedure that is used in the wet milling of the nonwaxy grains. The waxy starch, however, requires special handling, and the mill must be thoroughly cleaned before changing from one type of starch to the other. Mixtures of waxy and nonwaxy grain or starch cannot be processed satisfactorily. In a large wet-process mill, there are several miles of pipes, besides numerous containers, that must be cleaned before shifting to another type of starchy material. Therefore, the processing can be justified only when large quantities of waxy grain are available. Because larger mills may have capacities of 10,-000 to 30,000 bushels a day, it is necessary to assemble 100,000 to 300,000 bushels for a 7- to 10-day run on waxy grain.

Waxy-corn starch has been used chiefly for making adhesives for articles in which tapioca starch formerly was used, and for textile and paper sizings. The adhesives are used on stamps, envelopes, gummed tapes and labels, corrugated cardboard cartons, and ordinary plywoods for indoor use.

Waxy sorghum was first used industrially for preparing Minute Dessert to replace Minute Tapioca during the Second World War. Its manufacture was stopped when tapioca starch from Brazil became available in 1947. Pure waxy-sorghum starch produces a softer gel than does tapioca. For this reason it may require less cooking to reach the right consistency. Some of the first Minute Dessert was not of the most uniform quality, but methods of manufacture have since been perfected. At present prices, waxy-sorghum starch competes satisfactorily with tapioca starch for food purposes. However, it cannot be marketed as tapioca, which is a recognized product with an established trade.

Waxy starch is excellent for many adhesive uses because it makes a free-flowing paste with much less water than is possible with ordinary starch. Thus the waxy-starch gums can be applied to paper without leaving the paper appreciably wet. The resultant thin-gummed layer is remoistened easily when sticking stamps or paper.

The soft puddings made from waxy starch are pleasant to eat. They are especially good for people unable to swallow solid food following a tonsillectomy. There are possibilities for a great variety of food products from waxy starch besides the two that already have been marketed in the United States. Waxy corn makes a tasty corn bread. People of the Orient make many different cakes, confections, puddings, and other foods from waxy (or glutinous) grains. The future industrial uses of waxy starch in the United States may include adhesives, paper and textile sizings, and drilling muds, as well as several new food and industrial products.

Glutinous rice is suitable for the manufacture of waxy starch, but it usually costs considerably more than either corn or grain sorghum. Also, broken rice and rice flour, which are byproducts of milling, already have special uses. Waxy barley shows no superiority over nonwaxy barley for malting, but other possible uses have received little attention. An adapted variety of waxy barley was developed by repeated backcrossing, the waxy character having been derived from a variety from Japan. Waxy varieties of millets and Job's tears are not grown in the United States, and are unlikely to be established here. The Job's tears plant is a coarse grass that produces beadlike, hard-shelled seeds. The grain is sometimes eaten in the Orient.

JOHN H. MARTIN *has been engaged in cereal research since 1914 and has had charge of sorghum investigations in the division of cereal crops and diseases, Bureau of Plant Industry, Soils, and Agricultural Engineering, since 1925.*

MERLE T. JENKINS *has conducted research with corn since 1919 and has been in charge of corn investigations for the same Bureau since 1934.*

Production of Sweetpotato Starch

F. H. Thurber, E. A. Gastrock, W. F. Guilbeau

Sweetpotatoes are a big crop, and a highly variable one.

Of all the vegetable crops, they are second only to white potatoes. The fluctuations in production from year to year often have been enormous. In 1930 the yield was 54,517,000 bushels. In 1932 it was 86,594,000. In 1936 it was down to 59,765,000 bushels. Many factors influence the marketing of farm crops, but when such variations occur in supply it is difficult or impossible to establish a stable food market for a perishable crop. For that reason, the Department of Agriculture has had many requests for help in finding profitable industrial uses for sweetpotatoes to supplement the food outlets.

One approach was to develop procedures and equipment (which are now in commercial use) for drying sweetpotatoes for feed. Another was to investigate the possibilities in the fermentation industries, which use enormous amounts of carbohydrates in making industrial alcohol, lactic acid, and yeast. Sweetpotatoes have been successfully used for making all those products experimentally.

A third way is to isolate and purify the principal components and find profitable markets for them. It is with this third approach that we are here concerned. More than 72 percent of the solid content of sweetpotatoes grown for industrial utilization is starch. (Other materials are present in such small amounts that their recovery would be profitable only as byproducts.) To find an industrial outlet for sweetpotatoes, therefore, we concentrated on the determination of the properties, uses, and production of the starch—although we were well aware that a tremendous amount of starch is used each year and that the production of cornstarch, the leader, could be expanded. Our point was that no two starches are exactly alike.

In cotton mills, pastes made by heating starch with water under controlled conditions are used for sizing warp and for finishing. The warp is passed through the hot paste and dried. The hardened film of starch on the fibers is tough enough to prevent breaking of the warp during weaving. Sweetpotato-starch paste was used for sizing cotton threads in the laboratory. After drying, the threads were found to be coated with a tough, rubbery film of gelatinized starch. Technologists, who tried out large samples of the starch, believed that it would be satisfactory for warp sizing. Later, when the starch was made in larger quantities, this rubbery gel and tough, film-forming characteristic proved to be outstanding. Besides warp sizing, the starch was found useful for finishing some types of cloth, for laundry work, and for many other purposes where a smooth, tough film is required, such as paper finishing, insulating fabrics, and coatings in dry batteries. The same qualities appear to carry over to dextrin made by heating the dry starch with acid under controlled conditions. The dextrins, with hot water, form clear solutions, which remain fluid when cold and thus handle well in spreaders used to apply them to postage stamps and other surfaces. They have excellent remoistening properties.

For food use, one starch should be

about as good as another in actual food value, but the clear, stable gel with a high water-holding capacity formed with sweetpotato starch created a ready market for the starch as an ingredient in prepared food products.

Pioneer experimental work on sweetpotato starch in the United States was begun at the South Carolina Agricultural Experiment Station in 1895 and was continued for about 15 years.

Sweetpotato starch has also been produced under the name of Brazilian arrowroot. For many years it has been manufactured in Japan, where it is used in laundries, for sizing textiles and paper, for foods, and in cosmetics.

But the starch produced there—like the starch first produced in the United States—was gray and of poor quality; it did not meet the standards of United States buyers. If a market was to be developed for sweetpotato starch manufactured in the United States, we had to find procedures and equipment to produce a white, pure starch.

SWEETPOTATO STARCH granules are 1.633 times heavier than water. A few granules are large, but generally they range in diameter from about 27 microns (about one-thousandth of an inch) to 2 microns. Many samples average 12 microns in diameter. Some of the granules are spherical, some are ellipsoidal, and others are irregular. If we assume that all are spherical, the surface area, volume, and number of granules per unit weight can be calculated. Such calculations are not strictly accurate because the granules are not all spherical, but they give an idea of the volume and surface area of the particles to be washed in developing a starch-purification system. They show that a pound of the 27-micron-diameter granules would contain about 27 billion particles having a surface area of about 95,000 square inches, while the same amount of 2-micron-diameter granules would contain 66,000 billion particles with a surface area of more than 1 million square inches.

Those properties are used in devising means of extracting and purifying starches. Grinders (such as saw-blade rasps, hammer mills, and attrition mills) are used to break the cell membranes which enclose the starch granules. The resulting mass is stirred with water, and the starch is separated from the pulp with silk, nylon, or metal screens. The starch granules are so much smaller than most of the pulp particles that they are washed through the screen along with the solubles, protein, gums, and other solids, such as fine pieces of fiber. The heavy starch granules soon settle; then the water, containing solubles and some of the lighter solids, can be siphoned off to leave a fairly pure starch. More solubles and more of the light solids can be removed by repeating the settling process. In cool climates, where the fermentation of the sugars does not interfere, the process has given excellent results.

Tabling, a refinement of the settling process, is one of the most efficient means of separating starch from solid impurities. Starch tables are long, smooth, flat-bottomed troughs that have a slope of about one-thirty-second inch per foot. For large-granule starches, the tables may be as short as 30 or 40 feet and for small-granule starches as long as 120 feet. Starch from the screening system or from settling tanks is pumped to the head of the table at a predetermined constant rate. The heavy starch granules form a constantly increasing semisolid layer on the bottom of the table that behaves almost like a heavy liquid and forces the lighter solid particles to the top. Water from which the starch has separated flows along the surface and carries the lighter particles to the lower end of the table, where they either flow off the end or are deposited on the lower sections. In refining small-granule starches, the starch content of the overflow from the table is too great to be discarded, and settling tanks are used to recover that starch.

In the Department's experimental work with sweetpotatoes, starch was separated by settling, by tabling, and by means of centrifugal separators. The tests showed that settling alone would not produce a satisfactory yield of high-grade starch. When tabled, starch from the centrifuge or from the settling tanks was relatively clean, but it still had a yellowish cast.

Exposure to the air causes darkening on the cut surface of a sweetpotato. The use of a reducing agent, such as sulfur dioxide, prevents the darkening. R. T. Balch and H. S. Paine, Department chemists, found that a white starch resulted when the grinding and screening process was carried out in a solution that contained a small amount of sulfur dioxide, after which sodium hydroxide was added to dissolve color-forming compounds. When iron equipment was used, however, the tannin-like substances in the sweetpotatoes produced dark compounds with the iron that was not removed by the alkaline treatment. Sodium hydroxide, together with a trace of sulfur dioxide, was finally used throughout the process to keep the iron from dissolving. With that procedure, high-viscosity white starch was produced in pilot-plant equipment in which iron tanks and iron pipe lines were used.

IN 1933, WHILE LABORATORY WORK was still in progress, many requests for aid in utilizing surplus sweetpotatoes were received. Surveys were made to determine the probable cost of producing sweetpotatoes and the probable selling price of sweetpotato starch. Cotton-mill technicians believed that the starch could be used in their work but that the price might be somewhat higher than that of cornstarch. The selling price, it seemed, might be about 4 cents a pound. In a small plant with a capacity of 2,000 bushels (60 tons) of sweetpotatoes a day, the processing and sales costs were estimated to be 20 cents for each bushel of potatoes; that would leave only 20 cents a bushel that could be paid to farmers for sweetpotatoes that would yield one-sixth of their weight in finished starch.

Some growers believed they could make a profit on sweetpotatoes at 20 cents a bushel if they were assured a steady market for field-run potatoes. The crop was being produced almost entirely by hand labor, but at that time farm labor costs were computed at the rate of 10 cents an hour.

In 1934 the Federal Emergency Relief Administration established a small starch plant at Laurel, Miss., to ensure a market for sweetpotatoes in that area and so provide an income for farm families that would otherwise be on relief. Department engineers and chemists assisted in designing, building, equipping, and operating the plant at first. It was then turned over to a local cooperative for operation.

After experience was gained in the plant, some changes in equipment and procedures were made. The capacity of the screening system was increased; limewater was substituted for the sulfur dioxide-sodium hydroxide solution; sodium hypochlorite was used to remove the last trace of color in the starch; and settling tanks were added to increase capacity and starch recovery.

After the changes, the capacity was about 16 tons of starch and 7 tons of byproduct pulp a day. The pulp proved to be an excellent feed for dairy cows and was all sold nearby. Some of the starch was sold to the local cotton mill for warp sizing and some to other cotton mills and laundries; some went into prepared food specialties; some was used in dry batteries and some in the manufacture of dextrin.

In 1937, farm labor costs rose, and farmers could no longer produce sweetpotatoes for 20 cents a bushel. Growers therefore were granted a small subsidy, and the Laurel plant continued to manufacture starch and byproduct pulp until 1944, when operations were suspended. During the war years, farm labor costs increased so rapidly that they far outstripped the savings that could be introduced by agricultural engineers. Consequently, the costs of growing the sweetpotatoes became so great that the starch made from them could not be sold at a profit.

In 1936 the United States Sugar Corporation began experimental work on growing sweetpotatoes for starch production. In 1941 its agricultural program had progressed to the point where plans were outlined for a well-equipped factory with a daily capacity of 600 tons of sweetpotatoes or other root and tuber crops.

In that year also, the Department's investigations were consolidated and broadened and intensified as the sweetpotato-utilization project of the Southern Regional Research Laboratory in New Orleans. Engineers and research workers of the United States Sugar Corporation, the Southern Laboratory, and the Laurel plant cooperated with representatives of machinery manufacturers to conduct pilot-plant tests to determine the efficiency of equipment suitable for a 120-ton-a-day plant. The results formed the basis for designing the new starch plant at Clewiston, Fla.

The over-all flow sheet of operations used in the new plant was approximately the same as that used in the Laurel plant. Within the limits allowed by this flow sheet, however, efforts were made to devise a rapid and continuous process with low labor requirements for the production of a clean, high-quality starch. One of the greatest changes was in the use of continuous centrifugals, which took up a part of only one floor in the processing plant in place of the acres of settling tanks and tables used in older plants. We believe this to be the first commercial plant in the United States in which the starch purification was made entirely with centrifuges and without the use of tables or settling tanks.

The factory was completed in 1945. It was operated that season and the next, but the yields per acre were disappointingly low. Consequently, the costs of the potatoes delivered to the plant were too high to enable the company to sell starch at a profit.

The development of the Laurel enterprise stimulated efforts to develop improved varieties of sweetpotatoes of high yield, high starch content, and good processing qualities. From a regional program started in 1939 by the Bureau of Plant Industry, Soils, and Agricultural Engineering and several agricultural experiment stations in the South, came two new varieties suitable for industrial utilization. One, Pelican Processor, was released by the Louisiana Agricultural Experiment Station and was grown extensively for the Laurel starch plant in 1944. It averaged 25.5 percent starch, compared to 22 percent in an older variety. White Star was released by the Department of Agriculture in 1948. It has not been used commercially, but the laboratory tests indicate that it has excellent processing qualities.

New strains of sweetpotatoes that will simplify mechanical problems may perhaps be developed. Selections of the bunch-type Porto Rico sweetpotato have been under observation at the Georgia Coastal Plain Experiment Station for many years and have entered commercial production in that section. A similar strain has more recently attracted attention in Texas. The top of the plant is in the form of a small bush rather than a vine. The plants can be cultivated throughout the growing season to keep down the weeds. One grower reported that the root crowns of this variety were strong enough to hold the potatoes together so that harvesting could be done with an ordinary potato digger. One man with a potato digger, he said, did the work of seven men with plow-type digging equipment.

We believe that the growers, machinery manufacturers, agricultural engineers, pathologists, entomologists, and horticulturists together can solve the problems of sweetpotato-starch production. Agricultural engineers have made progress in the design and construction of machinery for setting sweetpotato plants in the field. We believe that all the operations connected with the growing of the crop can be mechanized on a scale comparable to the mechanization of cotton production.

Scientists at the Southern Laboratory have started research on improvements for small factories like the Laurel plant.

Because the transportation of root crops is expensive, some growers believe a factory should be small enough to get all its raw material within a radius of about 15 miles.

Another item in the studies has to do with the efficient use of labor. The Laurel factory required a considerable amount of manpower. Also, the recovery there was only about 72 percent of the starch. The starch in the pulp amounted to about 18 percent—meaning that about 10 percent of the starch was lost. Some of the loss was due to fermentation in the settling tanks, some to the loss of fine-granule starch.

In the Southern Laboratory's latest pilot-plant arrangement of equipment for the process, the starch is purified by four passes through centrifuges, combined with a countercurrent screening system. The first centrifuge is a high-speed, horizontal, continuous-type machine, perfected since the Laurel plant was put into operation.

Afterwards, the starch is made up with clean water and screened through a 180-mesh nylon screen. It is again centrifuged, taken up in water, and re-screened and further purified with a continuous nozzle-type centrifuge. The overflow from the centrifuge is collected as second-grade starch. The underflow is treated with sodium hypochlorite solution to remove the last trace of color, and is then dewatered with a perforated basket-type centrifuge and dried. A high-grade starch is produced in the pilot plant, and the labor requirements are reduced to a minimum. All but approximately 1 to 2 percent of the starch is recovered as first- or second-grade starch or in the pulp, which is sold for cattle feed.

The improved process of starch production is available to industry. It could be used by large or small producers. That the potential market for sweetpotato starch is large was demonstrated by the ready sale of the output of the Laurel factory.

F. H. Thurber is a senior chemist in charge of the properties section in the protein and carbohydrate division in the Southern Regional Research Laboratory. He is engaged in research on sweetpotato starch and the processing of sweetpotatoes. He designed and directed the construction of the Laurel starch plant and helped design the Clewiston plant. Dr. Thurber is a graduate of Lawrence College and the University of Chicago.

E. A. Gastrock is head of the engineering and development division of the Southern Laboratory. A graduate of Tulane University, he has had industrial experience in the commercial hydrogenation of vegetable oil, in the manufacture of paint, varnish, and enamel, and in quality control and mill research of fibrous structural insulating board. He has been with the Bureau of Agricultural and Industrial Chemistry since 1937.

W. F. Guilbeau is a senior chemical engineer and coordinator of operations in the engineering and development division in the Southern Laboratory. Before joining the Department of Agriculture in 1942, he worked for the Hershey Corp. in Havana, where he was superintendent and did chemical engineering work in the sugarcane refinery and in the sunflower- and peanut-oil expeller plant and refinery. He is a graduate of Louisiana State University.

DURING THE FIRST WORLD WAR the famous tulips of Holland were used for making starch. Tulip bulbs have considerable quantities of starch. Starch also was produced from horsechestnuts.

Production of White-Potato Starch

R. H. Treadway,
W. W. Howerton

Starch from white potatoes was first produced in the United States in 1831 in a plant at Antrim, N. H. The industry grew rapidly. By 1880, more than 150 factories were operating in Maine, New Hampshire, Vermont, Michigan, Wisconsin, Ohio, and Minnesota.

In some States, particularly Maine, varieties of potatoes were grown specifically for starch. They were not of high quality for cooking, but contained much more starch than the common varieties now grown. The practice of growing different types of potatoes for eating and for nonfood uses still is followed in the Netherlands and Germany.

Late in the nineteenth century the industry began to lose its strong position to cornstarch, which could be manufactured to sell at a lower price. Potato starch then became one of the specialty starches, which it still is.

Several points account for the lower cost of cornstarch. Although the acre yields of starch from potatoes and corn are comparable, corn is better adapted to mechanized methods of farming, which lower production costs. Corn dries out on the cob to a moisture content of 12 to 15 percent; in that condition it can be shelled, easily transported, and stored indefinitely before processing. Potatoes contain about 80 percent moisture, which means added bulk and weight in transportation, and they are so perishable that they require special methods of storage. The ease of storage of corn has made it possible to build large factories, which can process the raw material throughout the year, but potato-starch factories operate ordinarily only about 8 months of the year, from October through May. Valuable byproducts in corn wet milling (oil and gluten feed, for example) aid materially in making the industry profitable. The potato-starch industry has no byproduct except the extracted pulp, which a few manufacturers recover and sell as feed.

The higher cost of making potato starch affected the industry greatly. By 1900 the number of potato-starch plants had fallen from more than 150 to 63. Moreover, the industry tended to be concentrated in Aroostook County, Maine; 45 of the 63 factories were there. Aroostook County became a center for production of table-stock and seed potatoes, and the starch industry provided an outlet for the culls. In 1920, the twenty-odd factories in Maine had a daily capacity of less than 75 tons of starch. In 1940, Aroostook County had 27 starch factories, whose total daily capacity was more than 150 tons of starch. This greatly increased capacity was due mainly to construction of three modern continuous-process plants in 1938 and 1939. Now, 20 potato-starch factories in Maine have a capacity of about 135 tons a day.

In 1941, two plants were built in Idaho—one at Blackfoot and one at Twin Falls. The Twin Falls plant was rebuilt on a larger scale in 1948. A third plant was built in 1942 at St. Anthony. Another was established at Menan in 1944, but was later moved to Idaho Falls. With the construction of another plant at Idaho Falls and conversion of a glucose-sirup plant at Jerome to starch manufacture in 1948, Idaho now has six potato-starch factories with a total capacity of about 140 tons a day. The country's total capacity for potato-starch production, therefore, is now approximately 275 tons a day, or 110 million pounds for a 200-day operating year. Because the industry uses cull and surplus potatoes, the supply of raw material is not constant, and the industry rarely if ever operates at capacity for as much as 200 days a year.

ABOUT 98 percent of the starch we produce is made from corn. Nearly two-thirds of the total cornstarch produced, however, is used for manufacture of glucose sirup, dextrose, and modified starches. About 90 percent of the starch used as such in the United States, or 1,389 million pounds a year, is cornstarch. The maximum production of the potato-starch industry is believed to be approximately 89 million pounds, attained in the 1946–47 season, when Maine produced an estimated 44 million pounds and Idaho 45 million pounds. The average production in recent years has been somewhat below that record.

Potato starch is used in industry in about the following percentages: Textiles, 30; foods, 20; paper, 20; dextrins, 15; confectionery, 5; and miscellaneous, 10.

The textile industry uses potato starch mainly in sizing cotton warps, but some also for sizing spun rayon and worsted warps. Potato-starch pastes revert slowly to the gel state upon cooling and thus penetrate better into the interstices of the warp than do pastes of some other starches. Better penetration results in a better anchored film, which protects the warp from abrasion in the loom. Potato starch is outstanding in the strength it imparts to paper in beater sizing. Potato dextrins give relatively flexible films, which resist checking and remoisten readily.

The Eastern Regional Research Laboratory has undertaken studies to compare the physical and chemical properties of potato starch with those of other commercial starches. The aim is to find new uses for potato starch. Since 1944, various techniques and specialized equipment have been employed there in the search for ways in which potato starch is unique among starches.

THE SIZE, STRUCTURE, AND SHAPE of the starch granules have undergone scrutiny by technicians using the optical microscope. The molecular arrangement has been studied in detail by X-ray specialists. The structure of the granules has been further explored with the electron microscope. The molecular weight of potato-starch fractions have been determined with specially designed light-scattering equipment.

Factors influencing the paste consistency and gel firmness of potato starch have been investigated at length. Although it has long been known that the presence of calcium lowers the consistency of pastes, workers in the Eastern Laboratory found that even traces of calcium have a pronounced effect. So sensitive is the paste consistency to minute amounts of calcium that changes in the hardness of processing water from season to season result in changes in the final product, previously unexplained.

Little by little the fundamental causes for the unique properties of potato starch—its large granule size, its relatively high molecular weight, and the peculiar packing of matter in its molecule—are being unfolded. Research on technical applications will follow the fundamental studies. The largest potential fields of expansion appear to be in the paper and food industries.

Apparently it is not economical now for American farmers to grow potatoes just for industrial use. Starch manufacture, however, is to be regarded as an integral part of a well-organized potato industry, which markets its best potatoes for eating and processes the substandard grades. Marketing agreements in the potato industry are leading to these practices now more than ever before. Starch factories provide an outlet for potatoes that should be kept off the food market in order to make effective the slogan, "Sell the best— and process the rest." The higher price that the public will pay for uniformly high-quality potatoes should make it possible to place a lower value on sub-standard potatoes diverted to industrial processing.

IN OUR MORE MODERN potato-starch factories, the operations are essentially continuous. A typical Maine factory can produce about 10 tons of starch in a 24-hour day, for which it will use 80 to 90 tons of potatoes. An analysis of the potatoes processed shows these components, in percentages: Starch 13; protein, 2; cellulosic material, 1.5; sugars, 0.5; mineral (ash), 1; miscellaneous minor constituents, 1; water, 81. (Potatoes received by the Idaho starch plants average 15 or 16 percent starch.)

Storage facilities in the factory can handle as much as 4,000 barrels, each weighing 165 pounds, of potatoes.

A description of the process used by one of the modern plants is given here, but we must stress that the equipment and methods used in other modern factories may differ in some respects from the one we describe.

The potatoes to be processed are removed from storage by a flume to a conveyor, which dumps them into a washing trough where they are tumbled in water to free them of dirt. The potatoes are then elevated to a hopper and metered through a screw conveyor to a rasp, which reduces them to a slurry. The slurry is diluted with water containing sulfur dioxide and is pumped to a screening battery, in which most of the cellulosic material, or pulp, is separated from the starch granules. The screening battery has a series of screens and sieves, one mounted above the other in this order: Shaker screen, bottom rotary brush sieve, top shaker screen, and top rotary brush sieve.

The potato slurry from the rasp is pumped onto the bottom sieve, which has perforated holes 0.03 inch in diameter. Here the starch milk (principally starch granules suspended in water) passes through, and the pulp discharges over the end of the sieve. The pulp is diluted with water and passes into an attrition—or disc—mill for further grinding-rubbing to release more starch. The mill has two carborundum-type plates mounted closely together, one of which rotates. The starch milk, along with finely divided pulp from the bottom sieve, falls onto the bottom 80-mesh shaker screen. The starch milk runs through, and most of the fine pulp drops off the end of the screen and is combined with the reground pulp from the attrition mill. The combined pulp is pumped to the top sieve (which has perforated holes 0.02 inch in diameter) and is washed with a spray of water. The fine pulp and starch milk pass through the sieve and drop onto the top 100-mesh shaker screen. The starch milk continues through to the bottom shaker screen, and the fine pulp from the top shaker screen and the coarse pulp from the top sieve combine and are discharged to the sewer.

The starch milk from the screening battery—that is, the starch milk through the bottom shaker screen— goes to a continuous centrifuge, where the protein water is removed from the starch and discarded to the sewer. The protein water contains about 1 percent total solids, which comprise mainly soluble protein, with some fine starch and fine pulp. The starch from the separator is diluted with water and pumped to a 120-mesh shaker screen, where more fine pulp is removed. The starch milk then passes to starch tables for final purification. At that stage, the starch settles on the tables, and any residual fine pulp passes off the end. The tables are about 40 feet long, with a slope of about one-thirty-second inch to the foot. They fill up in about 4 hours. The starch cake from the tables is shoveled into a conveyor, where it is diluted with water; then it flows into a storage tank or pit. The density of the starch milk is adjusted in a make-up tank. Then the milk is fed to a continuous rotary vacuum filter, which dewaters the starch to about 40 percent moisture and delivers it as a broken cake to a continuous-belt, hot-air drier. The pieces of starch cake, dried to a moisture content of about 16 percent, are transferred to a pulverizer, where they are reduced to a powder. The starch is loaded into 200-pound, kraft-lined burlap bags.

The finished starch typically has the following composition in percentages on a moisture-free basis: Starch, 98; ash, 0.3; and cold-water solubles, 0.1. It has traces of nitrogen and sugars.

THE DISPOSAL OF WASTE MATERIALS from starch factories remains a problem. It is becoming more acute, particularly since Federal and State regulations on stream pollution have become more stringent. A factory that produces 10 tons of starch a day discharges about 4,500 pounds of waste pulp solids and 6,500 pounds of protein water solids during that period. The pulp contains about 4 percent solids.

Analysis of a sample of dried waste pulp showed the following percentage composition: Moisture, 4.5; starch, 54.6; uronic acid anhydride, 16; pectin, 12; pentosans, 9.5; crude fiber, 15.6; ash, 1.0; fat, 0.4; protein, 5.9; sugars, a trace. (The total is more than 100 percent, probably because of overlapping in the uronic acid anhydride, pectin, and pentosan determinations.)

The following procedure is suggested for recovery of the waste pulp; it is based on experience in recovering pulp from 2 million pounds of potatoes and on German technical processes:

The pulp would first be discharged into a tank and mixed with lime. The limed pulp would be partly dewatered on a vibrating screen, further dewatered by passage through continuous rotary presses, and then dried in a steam-tube rotary drier.

Wet waste potato pulp is frequently used as hog feed in Europe, and has been so used in the United States. The dried pulp has also been fed to livestock, usually mixed with a high-protein feed.

The protein water from a potato-starch factory contains about 1 percent total solids—about 0.6 percent protein, 0.1 percent starch, and the remainder principally fiber and sugars. No economical method is known for recovery of the solids from protein water because of the great dilution.

R. K. Eskew, of the Eastern Laboratory, made a survey of potato-starch processing in Europe in the summer of 1947. He reported that protein is recovered in starch factories, particularly in Germany, by diluting the potato slurry, immediately after the initial grinding, and passing it through a Jahn or Uhland continuous centrifugal separator to recover the protein solution in more concentrated form than ordinary "protein water." The protein is then coagulated by heat or chemicals, dewatered, and dried. Protein water is also reported to have been concentrated under vacuum at 113° F. to 48 percent solids and then dried in admixture with dewatered pulp. During periods of protein shortage, potato protein has been recovered in Germany for enrichment of soups.

Apparently an economical method, used in some European countries, for preventing stream contamination with waste protein water is to spray the effluent on fields after the potatoes have been harvested. Some benefit is gained through action of the effluent water as a fertilizer.

A PILOT PLANT has been set up in the Eastern Laboratory for studying the technology of manufacturing white-potato starch in order to develop practical methods of improving quality, increasing starch yields, simplifying operations, and recovering waste materials. To provide a background for planning the plant, we studied processing operations in the factories in Maine and Idaho.

We have not had time to study completely the operations and make recommendations for best processing methods. Grinding the potatoes is one operation that we began to study in 1950. We are experimenting with several types of grinding machines to determine which will release the most starch without excessive power consumption and excessive production of fine pulp. The fine pulp is objectionable, because it goes through the screens with the starch milk during subsequent screening operations, making purification of the milk more difficult.

Preliminary experiments have shown that a vertical-type hammer mill is about equivalent to a rasp in releasing starch. If this is confirmed in further experiments, it will be advantageous—the hammer mill is commercially available, whereas the rasp is not. (Some of the starch factories now use vertical-type hammer mills.)

In current operations, about 10 percent of the starch present in the potato remains in the waste pulp, because it has not been freed in the grinding. On the dry basis, the starch ordinarily constitutes about 45 percent of the weight of the waste pulp. We will try to reduce the amount of starch that goes to waste by further study of the grinding operations.

Screening is another important operation in the starch process under investigation. Experiments have shown that the purity of the starch milk at that stage is appreciably improved by using finer mesh screens for separating the pulp than are now generally used.

These are only two of the phases of starch manufacturing under investigation. Other studies are planned. One has to do with the recovery of waste materials. Even though the potato-starch industry is old, we believe that opportunities exist for improving the engineering aspects of the processing. Because it is an industry of many small manufacturers, the companies themselves have not had adequate technical staffs to undertake such research and development. By thorough modernization along lines that will give high-quality starch in maximum yield, the starch manufacturer should continue to serve as an important adjunct to the table-stock potato industry and to supply consumers who demand the special properties of potato starch.

R. H. TREADWAY *was born in Indiana and did undergraduate and graduate work at Indiana University. From 1936 to 1941 he was engaged in chemical research with the E. I. du Pont de Nemours & Co. and the A. E. Staley Manufacturing Co. Since 1941, Dr. Treadway has been employed as a chemist in the carbohydrate division of the Eastern Laboratory.*

W. W. HOWERTON *is a native of North Carolina and is a graduate in chemical engineering of the Georgia Institute of Technology. From 1936 to 1941 he was employed by Swann & Co. and Joseph E. Seagram & Sons in research and production work. During the early part of the war he engaged in chemical warfare development with the Chemical Corps. Since 1942 he has been employed as a chemical engineer at the Eastern Laboratory, where he has worked on process development of natural and synthetic rubbers and potato starch.*

AFTER A FIRE in a Dublin, Ireland, textile mill many years ago, it was noticed that the starch stored there for sizing purposes had turned brown, but that its usefulness as an adhesive had greatly increased. The roasted starch, unlike the original material, was soluble in cold water and could be made into a paste of high solids concentration. Today, more than 150 million pounds of dextrins, or roasted starches, are produced annually in the United States for use on postage stamps, envelope flaps, and gummed paper.—*I. A. Wolff, Northern Regional Research Laboratory.*

Louis Lumiére in 1904 made the first successful color screen for the unit process of color photography. Mixing dyed starch grains in the ratio of four green to three red to one blue, he dusted them on a glass plate at the rate of approximately 147,000 to the square inch. The space between the grains he filled with a fine powder, such as carbon black. Over all he then spread a thin layer of photographic emulsion, thus producing a color-sensitive photographic plate. Lumiére's method with its starch screen was widely used until it was replaced by the subtractive process—a modern method of recording color.—*L. J. Gundrum, Northern Regional Research Laboratory.*

DISEASE-PRODUCING BACTERIA that are resistant to antibiotic drugs have not developed to the extent once predicted. Resistant forms do occasionally arise, however, as with penicillin and more frequently with streptomycin. Some bacterial forms have literally acquired a taste for streptomycin and will not grow in the absence of that drug. Professors Miller and Bohnhoff, of the University of Chicago, first experienced this change in a meningococcus variant, type B. Other workers have since isolated several bacterial types which require streptomycin for growth. Theoretically, these streptomycin-requiring organisms are interesting from the standpoint of their metabolism; practically, they can be used to determine quickly whether an unknown *Streptomyces* is producing streptomycin or some other antibiotic.—*Robert G. Benedict, Northern Region Research Laboratory.*

THE LATE Dr. A. J. Pieters of the Department of Agriculture told me in 1923 how the first packet of Korean lespedeza seed was almost discarded. The seed came with a letter from the Rev. Ralph G. Mills of Seoul, Korea. The letter stated the plants resembled *Medicago sativa,* the botanical name for alfalfa. Probably because of this statement the packet of seed went to R. A. Oakley, who was handling the Department's alfalfa work. He routed it to Dr. Pieters, who had taken over the lespedeza investigations. The statement that lespedeza plants resembled alfalfa raised a doubt in Dr. Pieters' mind about the judgment of the seed collector. He held the seed about a year before he decided to plant them. A superior new species of annual lespedeza of multimillion-dollar value to the farmers of this country started with this planting. The time element of this story checks with the recorded introduction in 1919 and the first planting in 1921.—*Paul Tabor, Soil Conservation Service, Spartanburg, S. C.*

SORGHUM to many people means a crop used for making molasses. But that use accounts for only about 1 percent of the domestic acreage, and less than 0.05 percent of the world acreage in this crop. The importance of sorghum for food, feed grain, and forage, as well as for various industrial uses, is not generally known. And the same holds true for flax. Every schoolboy learns that linen is made from flax. Relatively few people know that less than 0.05 percent of the American flax crop, and less than 20 percent of the world flax crop, is for making linen. Most of the acreage is seed flax grown for the manufacture of linseed oil and linseed cake.—*John H. Martin, Bureau of Plant Industry, Soils and Agricultural Engineering.*

THE GROWING DEVELOPMENT of organic raw materials for the use of industry in war and peace intensifies the need for conserving the soil and water that produce them. Efficient land use will support this development; continued waste of soil and water would retard and weaken it.

This country's remaining productive land is called on to meet twin pressures: Steadily growing population to be fed and rapidly increasing use of farm-produced raw materials in manufacturing. The land-produced materials of industry include crops grown specifically for that purpose and for other purposes. Most of them cannot be returned to the land to renew the productivity.

Regardless of its end use, any crop requires so much land and so much soil fertility to produce it. Our acreage of good productive land is limited. Approximately 460 million acres of this good land can be considered available for continued safe cultivation. It includes about 70 million acres not yet in use but which can be developed for cultivation. It excludes some 70 to 100 million acres, which now is in use but is not suitable for cultivation. All but about 100 million acres of this 460 million acres must be protected from erosion and waterlogging.

Clearly, then, the more we draw on this fixed acreage of good, productive land for food, industrial raw materials, and so on for our growing population, the more necessary becomes the permanent maintenance of that land's producing ability.

Of particular concern from the standpoint of national defense, in which productive land is so vital, is the fact that we cannot stockpile soil as we can metals and other essentials. Neither can we replenish wasted soil by digging a new supply up out of the earth or shipping it in from other countries.

Productive land, unlike other natural resources, is characterized by the element of life—fruitfulness—placed by nature in the thin mantle of productive soil occurring over a limited portion of the earth's surface. We must maintain the productiveness of the land while we use it.

By the same token, water conservation becomes of increasing importance on farm lands and pasture lands and in forests. That calls for planning ahead for watershed protection for all new installations, including processing and manufacturing plants located within reach of land-produced raw materials. The conservation measures that control soil erosion and other damage to the land also help prevent wasteful run-off of rain and snow water. They lessen flood damage, silting up of power and other reservoirs, and water shortages affecting key manufacturing plants and urban interests.

The first requirement is to look at the land and the way it is being used, from the standpoint of both soil and water wastage—or better, soil and water conservation. Such an inventory shows the productive capabilities of the land, as based on such interrelated factors as soil, slope, past erosion, and susceptibility to future erosion and run-off. Thus we establish the only sound base for treatment and use of each kind of land for its continued safe and economical utilization, whether that be for food or industrial crops, pasture, timber, or wildlife.

Future use of industrial raw materials produced from the soil unquestionably will increase, not decrease. Soil and water conservation is the natural teammate for this development in progressive American agriculture. It increases yields, protects the land, conserves water, and reduces siltation of streams, ditches, harbors, and reservoirs.—*H. H. Bennett, Soil Conservation Service.*

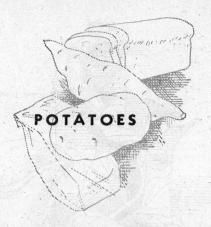

POTATOES

Food and Feed From White Potatoes

Roderick K. Eskew,
Paul W. Edwards

In times of surpluses of potatoes it is hard to realize that the acreage in potatoes is probably less now than it was in 1882. The surpluses arise because efficiency of production has gone up and the average person's consumption of potatoes has gone down.

From 1943 through 1950, the surplus was never less than 3.5 million bushels in any year. In 1946 it was more than 108 million bushels. Those surpluses were extensively utilized to produce industrial alcohol, starch, and livestock feed; millions of bushels were exported. But in normal times all those uses would not be profitable. Molasses is usually too cheap for potatoes to compete with it as a source of alcohol. Extensive research is going on therefore to increase food consumption and to develop efficient and profitable ways to use surplus and cull potatoes.

Why are we eating fewer potatoes than formerly? Perhaps it is because the population is becoming more urban. A farmer rising before sunup to do heavy work requires a hearty breakfast that may include fried potatoes. The city dweller may do with fruit juice, toast, and coffee. Then, too, our diets are more varied today because quick-frozen and canned perishable foods are more common than a decade ago. Partly to blame, perhaps, is the mistaken belief that potatoes are unduly fattening.

Research in the Department includes studies of ways to raise consumption by improving the quality and widening the variety of foods made from potatoes.

Prepeeled potatoes, needing only to be cooked, are becoming increasingly available to restaurants and housewives. Potatoes may soon be marketed according to their adaptability to different uses. A high-starch potato will bake well but will be too soft for salad; the best type for frying may not be best for mashing.

The problem of nonfood uses is not simple. Potatoes are bulky and perishable. They may rot in storage or lose some of their starch. They contain about 80 percent water, and are costly to ship or to dry.

Raw potatoes contain about 12 percent starch, which is the most valuable constituent as a source of industrial chemicals. Research is being done at the Eastern Regional Research Laboratory to determine how they may be used for lactic acid. Potatoes also contain proteins, minerals, and vitamin C, which are valuable in food or feed. The first thing to be done was to find a cheap way of drying potatoes to preserve them and to reduce their bulk so that they could be shipped economically and used industrially throughout the year.

The dehydration of potatoes for food was studied widely during the war and successful techniques were developed, but until recently little had been done in this country to find cheap drying methods for feed or industrial

FEED FROM DRIED WHITE POTATOES

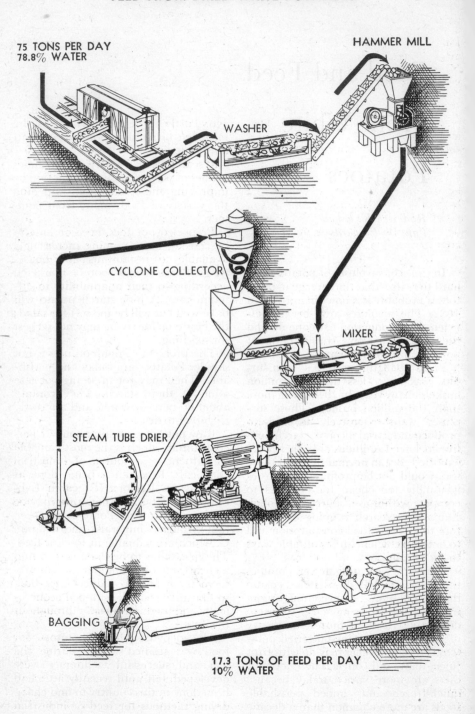

75 TONS PER DAY
78.8% WATER

HAMMER MILL

WASHER

CYCLONE COLLECTOR

MIXER

STEAM TUBE DRIER

BAGGING

17.3 TONS OF FEED PER DAY
10% WATER

use. In certain European countries, notably Germany where the agricultural economy was based on potatoes, a great deal had been done on this aspect. A survey was made of European techniques for processing potatoes. New methods of cheap drying were developed at the Eastern Laboratory.

ONE OF THE CHEAPEST WAYS to dry potatoes is to wash them, grind them in a hammer mill, and dry them in a steam-tube drier. But ground raw potatoes are soupy; if fed directly into the drier they would bake on the hot steam tubes. That can be avoided by mixing with the raw ground material about an equal weight of dry product to reduce the average moisture to about 43 percent. Such a mixture can be efficiently dried in a steam-tube drier. The product is granular and light brown in color, and contains the carbohydrates, proteins, and minerals originally in the potato. From its analysis it should have a feed value nearly equal to that of corn.

A plant using the process shown on the opposite page would cost about $80,000, would have a capacity of 75 tons of raw potatoes each 24 hours, and would yield slightly more than 17 tons a day of finished product that contains 10 percent of water. The cost of the product would be about $24 a ton, including everything except the cost of the potatoes and the cost of selling the product.

It is possible to add a small amount of lime to the ground potatoes and press out nearly half of the water, thereby saving on the drying costs, but because up to 20 percent of the potato solids may be lost in the press waters, it is questionable that any real over-all economy is achieved. Furthermore, disposing of the expressed juices may prove a serious problem in some places.

Ground raw potatoes may also be dried in high-temperature rotary driers that use gas, oil, or coal as a source of heat. Here again some of the dried product must be mixed with the raw ground material to prevent sticking. In this type of drier, care must be taken to prevent a spark from coming in contact with the finely divided material suspended in air near the outlet of the drier and in the dust collectors, because explosive mixtures of starch and air can form. A means of reducing the explosion hazard is to recycle only that portion of the dried material that will not pass through a 100-mesh screen.

BECAUSE OF THE FOOD SHORTAGE in Europe in 1948 and the need for transporting food in compact form, there arose a demand for approximately 450 million pounds of potato flour—some 10 times the normal United States output. To meet the demand, to utilize surplus potatoes, and to put idle equipment to work, two processes for producing potato flour were developed at the Eastern Laboratory.

One was a simple modification of the steam-tube-drier process developed for producing feed. It was only necessary to add less than 0.1 percent of sulfur dioxide, based on the weight of raw potatoes, to the ground potatoes to maintain their color, and then, after drying as already described, to grind and screen the product to a proper fineness for flour. Much of the equipment necessary for making flour by this method was available in the dry houses of idle distilleries. Even if idle equipment were not available, the entire process could be set up for about $87,000 and operated to produce a potato flour at about $39 a ton. This includes all costs except that of the potatoes and selling costs on the product. It assumes a capacity of 75 tons of potatoes a day. The process is shown in the drawing on page 180.

The second process also utilizes idle distillery dry-house equipment. It is a modification of the conventional process of using specially designed drum driers to dry mashed potatoes, which have been cooked whole. But since the drum driers in distilleries are of a different design, it was found necessary to "cream" the cooked potatoes by hammer milling them while hot and then

FLOUR AND MEAL FROM DRIED WHITE POTATOES

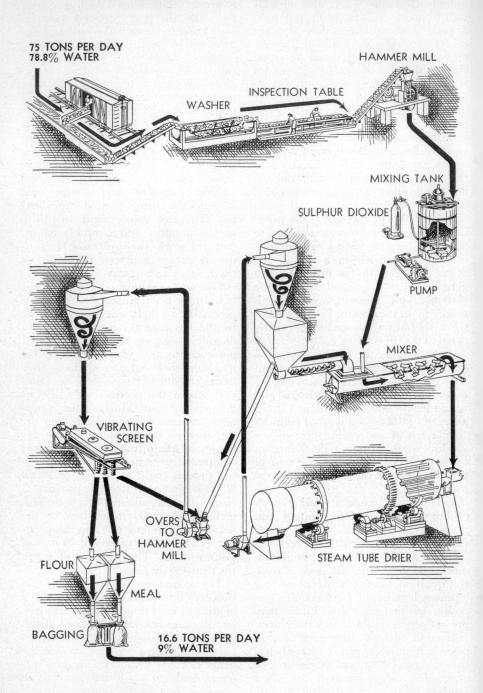

75 TONS PER DAY
78.8% WATER

HAMMER MILL

WASHER

INSPECTION TABLE

MIXING TANK

SULPHUR DIOXIDE

PUMP

MIXER

VIBRATING SCREEN

OVERS TO HAMMER MILL

STEAM TUBE DRIER

FLOUR

MEAL

BAGGING

16.6 TONS PER DAY
9% WATER

FLOW SHEET FOR POTATO FLOUR MANUFACTURE

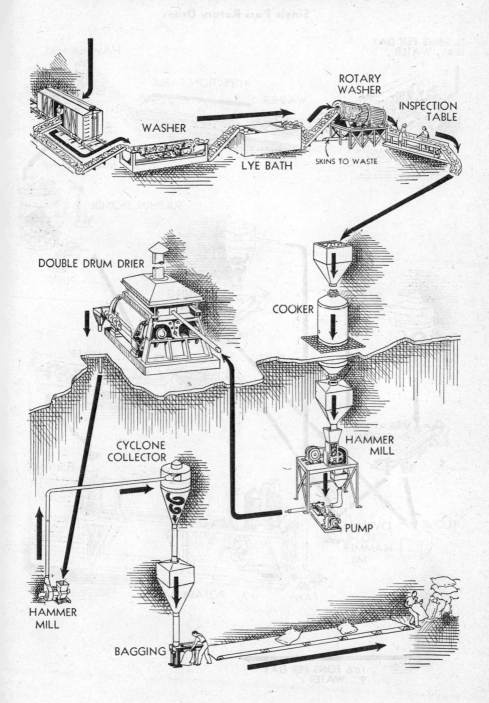

FLOUR FROM GROUND WHITE POTATOES
Single Pass Rotary Driers

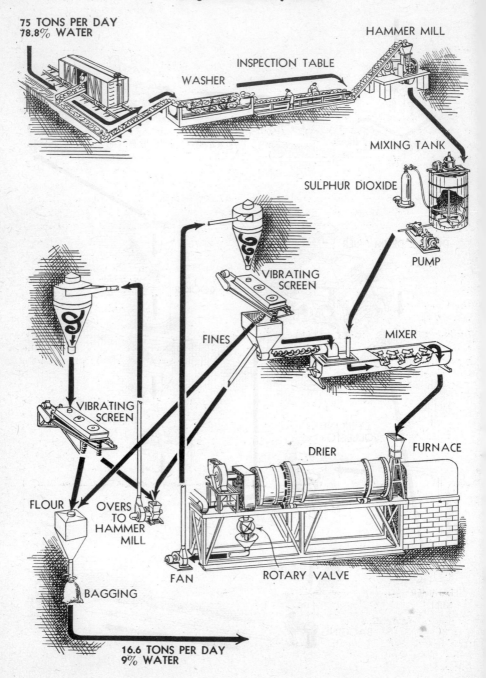

75 TONS PER DAY
78.8% WATER

HAMMER MILL

INSPECTION TABLE

WASHER

MIXING TANK

SULPHUR DIOXIDE

PUMP

VIBRATING SCREEN

FINES

MIXER

VIBRATING SCREEN

DRIER   FURNACE

FLOUR   OVERS TO HAMMER MILL

FAN   ROTARY VALVE

BAGGING

16.6 TONS PER DAY
9% WATER

feed them to the driers at a temperature above 150° F. This process is shown on page 181.

A third method of producing potato flour cheaply comprises grinding the washed potatoes in a hammer mill, treating them with sulfur dioxide, and drying them in a direct-heat, high-temperature rotary drier. The dried product is passed over a 100-mesh screen. The part that passes through the screen is used as flour. A portion of that remaining on the screen is re-cycled and mixed with the freshly ground potatoes to reduce their moisture content to about 43 percent so that they will not stick in the drier. The excess overs from the screen are ground for flour. The elimination of fines by screening before recycling greatly reduces the explosion hazard. The fourth figure shows this process diagrammatically—page 182.

Between July 1948 and the middle of 1949, 348 million pounds of potato flour was exported to Germany. It is impossible to say how much of this was made by the processes developed at the Eastern Laboratory. However, it is known that two of the methods mentioned were in commercial operation

during the period and that the flour was exported. It is understood that much of the flour produced during the period in question was flown into Berlin in the air lift.

RODERICK K. ESKEW, *a native of West Virginia, is a graduate in chemical engineering of the Massachusetts Institute of Technology. After 18 years in the wood-pulp, plastics, and rayon industries, he became head of the chemical engineering and development division at the Eastern Regional Research Laboratory in 1940. During the Second World War he traveled in Mexico and Haiti in connection with natural-rubber recovery investigations and in 1947 made a survey in Europe of industrial processes for processing potatoes.*

PAUL W. EDWARDS *is a chemical engineer in the division of chemical engineering and development in the Eastern Laboratory. He joined the Department of Agriculture in 1921, and until 1940 did research on the prevention of dust explosions. Since 1940 he has been engaged in the development of processes for the utilization of surplus farm commodities.*

CORN IS the No. 1 food crop of the people of El Salvador. It is ground between stones or by machines and is then made into tortillas. The native corn is white. The people were accustomed to it and ordinarily objected strenuously when yellow corn was offered them for making tortillas. One of the prominent farmers of the country received some yellow corn from the Cooperative Experiment Station and found it to be 30 to 40 percent more productive than the native type. He had observed that his workers were feeding only yellow corn to their fighting cocks. When he asked them why they used yellow corn, they replied that it made the cocks stronger and better fighters. He pointed out to them that if yellow corn was better for the fighting cocks it also would be better for them. They saw the point and before long began using yellow corn to make tortillas.— *James M. Watkins, Director, Centro Nacional de Agronomia, Santa Tecla, El Salvador.*

The Processing of Potatoes for Food

Francis P. Griffiths

Potatoes are grown in all parts of the country and are harvested in one place or another in each of the four seasons. Even in winter, from Florida and the lower Rio Grande Valley in Texas, we can get new potatoes. So, because potatoes are widely grown and easily available, until relatively recently there was little purpose in processing them.

Today, however, we process about 22 million bushels of the 300 million bushels of potatoes we produce for food each year. Potato chips use up 18 to 20 million bushels more, and other products account for 2 to 4 million bushels. We use normally an additional 2 million bushels for potato flour. About 20 million bushels of potatoes were dehydrated the last 2 years of the Second World War.

Why do we not process all the potatoes we do not eat fresh so that none will be wasted? Part of the answer is that processing serves one of two purposes: It makes for more convenient use, or it makes specialty products available. In times of war, dehydrated potatoes are important because— dried, compressed, and packaged— they take up much less space and weight in transportation and storage. In times of peace, the problems of preparing acceptable processed products are different, but even more numerous than under the necessities of war. Each product must meet with the approval of the American public. Is it

better than the one it is meant to replace—or at least as good? Will it save time, money, or effort? Is it attractive in appearance? Is it appetizing?

Such practical demands must be met if a new product is to succeed. If it competes with or replaces another made from a different vegetable or fruit, it must be as good as the old one—preferably better.

Frozen prepared foods are an example of a new type of processed foods that combine availability and palatability with great savings of time.

Dried potatoes and canned potatoes meet the housewife's demands for less waste, more time saved, greater convenience. Both are successful products. Such specialties as shoestring and hash-brown potatoes, french-fries, and potato chips meet the requirements and are appetizing as well. Hence their success with the public, especially chips, which are the leading potato product.

DEHYDRATION OF POTATOES had grown considerably by the end of the First World War. In 1919, when the technique was still in its infancy, about 7 million pounds of dehydrated potatoes were produced. But because of limited technological information and failure to produce a top-quality product, the industry declined.

The Second World War gave it fresh impetus. But neither our technique of handling food nor our scientific and engineering knowledge of dehydration was sufficiently advanced to meet fully the large wartime demands. Dehydrated potatoes and other vegetables deteriorated rapidly in storage. We did not know what caused the deterioration or how to prevent it. The Government set to work on those problems. Much valuable information was accumulated, but some of it came too late for use in the war. Although consumption of dehydrated food declined after the war, several companies have remained in the business, and research on the subject has continued. This continuation of production and research now provides a nucleus for effective orientation and expansion of the industry to meet the 1951 national defense needs.

Which potatoes are best suited for dehydration? First, the variety selected must be grown in a district and under conditions to which it is adapted and where it will give the best yields. The type that becomes white and mealy when cooked is preferred. Katahdin in the East and Russet Burbank in the West are two of the best varieties for dehydration.

At the beginning of the Second World War, improper blanching (heating with steam) was a common fault in commercial operations. Overblanching of the high-density potatoes causes what is known as popcorn effect. The potato puffs up; each ball has a hard shell and a hollow center, so that it is excessively mushy when prepared for the table.

But underblanching, or incomplete destruction of enzymes, causes potatoes to darken excessively during processing. Such improperly blanched potatoes are difficult to reconstitute, and they deteriorate rapidly in storage.

Why blanch potatoes before dehydration? Obviously, the potatoes are blanched to inactivate enzymes. But that answer disregards the even more important questions: Which enzymes are involved in the blanching process? What treatment can be used to eliminate the enzymes that are deleterious?

The role of each enzyme in producing the changes is not yet completely understood. Research, however, has developed a test for enzyme inactivation which defines proper blanching time—a large forward step in the field of dehydration.

Factors that hasten deterioration are being isolated and methods of combating them developed. Storage tests have disclosed the harmful effects of high temperatures on the dried potatoes and other dehydrated vegetables. Treatment with sulfur dioxide, packing in containers with a gas such as carbon dioxide or nitrogen, or putting in the container a sort of auxiliary container holding a substance that will take up moisture (called in-package desiccation) are being studied in relation to this problem. Already, by a combination of these techniques, deterioration has been reduced.

Treatment of fruits and vegetables with sulfur dioxide to prevent darkening has been known in this country for some time, but the public has viewed it with disfavor. Because technical data on its application were lacking, it was sometimes used without discrimination. The result was a food so unpalatable that the public rejected not only the food but the process as well. Used in proper amounts, sulfur dioxide is a valuable aid to dehydration. Potatoes require less sulfur dioxide than either carrots or cabbage. Application of 400 to 500 parts per million of sulfite markedly improves the color in dehydrated potatoes, as it keeps them from graying during dehydration. Moreover, it increases their ability to retain vitamin C and improves their storage quality. In proper application, sulfur dioxide leaves no unpleasant taste.

In-package desiccation of dehydrated food is a recent development, and a significant one. The method was adopted shortly before the end of the Second World War in new procurement specifications by the Army Quartermaster Corps. It is simple. By means of calcium oxide (lime) stored in the container in such a way that it does not come in contact with the food, the moisture content of the package is lowered from the 6 to 8 percent that is obtained by the usual dehydration methods to between 2.5 and 4 percent. The use of in-package desiccation extends by about sixfold the storage life of dehydrated potatoes at room temperature. The process may become important in any future Army procurement program for dehydrated food.

Deterioration of dehydrated foods during processing and storage causes important changes in the palatability.

Even before war lent urgency to the problem, scientists were puzzling over the changes and their cause. Little was then known of the mechanism of these causes.

A series of investigations has shown what happens to vegetables during dehydration. Vegetables, particularly potatoes, pass through a zone of moisture content where heat damage is at a maximum. For potatoes, the maximum rate of damage by high temperature appears when the moisture level is 10 to 15 percent.

Browning, which is characteristic of heat damage, is related to sugar content. Under ordinary drying conditions, there is a marked moisture difference within each piece. Such a difference brings about a migration of dissolved substances, including sugars, toward the centers of the pieces. Even when the average sugar content is low, the centers may behave like high-sugar potatoes. Such conditions lead to brown centers in the dehydrated pieces. Once a scientist establishes at what rate these undesirable changes occur, he can set about devising methods for combating them.

One method that has been developed for studying the deterioration of potatoes is that of photometric measurement. The pigment responsible for darkening is leached from the potatoes and its amount determined by measurement of light passing through a definite thickness of the leached liquid.

Potatoes at the extremes of the density range, either high or low, are usually unsuited for commercial use. Low-density potatoes are watery and waxy. They make a translucent product of poor reconstitution qualities. Potatoes of high density often do not stick together well after dehydrating. They slough and go to pieces on cooking. The cause of the peculiarities is obscure, although it may be a property inherent in the starch particles.

The Department of Agriculture has devoted time and effort to designing and engineering dehydrators. In the light of that research, it is possible for the first time to separate the effects on drying time of such variables as air temperature, humidity, velocity, size and shape of the cut potato piece, and the quantity that can be loaded on the drying tray or conveyor.

Research is continuing on some phases of the problem. We have given special attention to the determination of drying rates where internal diffusion of moisture is the controlling factor.

PREPEELED POTATOES are an item of potential importance, once production difficulties are overcome. Peeled or sliced for french-fries, they offer particular advantage to hotels and restaurants. Preliminary preparation, which involves labor, time, and space, has been completed. The supply is quickly available. The user can depend upon a good product.

For prepeeling, potatoes of good quality and medium or large size, with smooth surfaces free from irregularities, are selected. After being thoroughly washed, they are mechanically peeled, usually by an abrasive peeler, sometimes by steam or lye peelers. The peeled potatoes are sorted. Eyes and other defects are removed by hand trimming. Then they are washed again. In some processes, sulfur dioxide is used to prevent darkening and to aid in preservation.

Packaging and delivery of the potatoes should follow immediately. If the potatoes are kept for any length of time, refrigeration at 40° to 50° F. under humid conditions is desirable.

CANNING OF POTATOES was discouraged during the Second World War as not essential to the war effort, but canned potatoes returned to the market shortly after the war.

Potatoes for canning are usually selected on the basis of preliminary processing trials. Those that slough or cook to pieces are rejected. Those selected are graded for size and freedom from any defect. They are then usually lye-peeled and thoroughly washed in cold water. Whole tubers are usually packed in cans with boiling 1.5- to 2.5-percent brine. The sealed cans are then processed; the time and temperature of processing vary with the size of the can.

Large quantities of potatoes are marketed as quick-frozen french-fries. Potatoes with a low sugar content are selected. After washing, they are heated by steam at 50 pounds pressure for 45 to 55 seconds. The peel is then removed by high-pressure blasts of cold water. After inspection and trimming, the potatoes are sliced in strips. The slices are fried in vegetable oil or shortening and cooled by blasts of cold air. After cooling, they are packed in cartons, weighed, sealed, and quick-frozen. For consumer use, the fries can be quickly reheated in hot fat, or they can be thawed and placed for a few minutes in a hot oven.

Many other items can be made from potatoes. One of them is a prepared mashed-potato mix. It requires only the addition of hot water and stirring before it is ready for use. Methods for preparing ready-to-use potato products were studied during the war under the sponsorship of the Army Quartermaster Corps. The problem was found to be essentially one of avoiding breaking of the cell walls in the potatoes and preventing the gelatinization of starch granules liberated from broken cells. If more than 15 percent of the cells are ruptured, the product will be pasty or rubbery. It was found that cell structure of cooked potatoes could be toughened by freezing and thawing.

For the mix, potatoes are washed, peeled, and trimmed in the usual way. They are then sliced and cooked 30 minutes in steam at 212° F., cooled, and frozen. Upon thawing, about one-half of the original water in the cooked potatoes can be removed by light pressure. The remaining pulp can be disintegrated without serious damage to the cells. It is then carefully dried in a blast of warm air to produce a granulated potato product which can be reconstituted to light and fluffy mashed potatoes.

FRANCIS P. GRIFFITHS *is special assistant to the director of the Western Regional Research Laboratory. He is a graduate in chemistry of the University of Washington and received advanced training in food technology at Massachusetts State College. During the Second World War he was acting head of the Department of Food Technology at Massachusetts State College.*

THE ORIGIN of bread making antedates recorded history. Bread is mentioned several times in Genesis, and leavened bread in the time of Moses. The first bakers are believed to have been Egyptians. Baking was regarded as a fine art in ancient Rome, where bakers enjoyed high prestige and special privileges.

Bread grains—wheat, rye—are least used in southeastern Asia, where rice is the staple cereal. In these countries, prewar consumption of bread grains ranged from almost none to about 80 pounds a year per person. At the other extreme is central and southeastern Europe, where consumption of bread grains is particularly high. In rural households, bread or other cereal foods are the mainstay of the diet, often furnishing 70 percent or more of the total calories. In most of those countries the bread has been traditionally made from the whole grain, whether of wheat, rye, corn, or barley—a nutritional advantage in such restricted dietaries. As the standard of living has risen, there has been a tendency for some of the rye and corn to be replaced by wheat, especially the more highly refined wheat.—*Esther F. Phipard, Bureau of Human Nutrition and Home Economics.*

The Making

of Potato

Chips

R. C. Wright, Martha E. Davis,
Carl E. Hendel

Production of potato chips jumped from 45 million pounds in 1936 to nearly 260 million in 1946. In terms of potatoes utilized as chips, production rose from 3 million to 15 million bushels a year during that period. Consumption in 1949 was about 20 million bushels and the capital investment in the industry was about 25 million dollars.

The industry is of importance to American farmers also as an outlet for domestic vegetable oils. Potato chips owe their relatively high food value chiefly to their carbohydrate and fat content. They contain from 30 to 50 percent fat. Using 40 percent as the average fat content, we figure that the fat used for making chips increased from 13 million pounds in 1936 to about 100 million in 1949.

The steady increase in the production of chips results partly from improvements in machinery, which make it possible to turn out more high-grade chips, and in merchandising (packaging and sales) methods that aid in keeping a fresher and more-attractive product before the consumer, and from the increased consumption of manufactured rather than the home-cooked foods.

The processing of potato chips is a fairly routine and easy procedure, but knowledge and experience are necessary to obtain and handle raw stock from which good chips can be made.

For quality the finished product depends largely on the source and variety of the potatoes used. Some varieties, notably Russet Rural, Russet Burbank, Irish Cobbler, and the new Kennebec and Canus, are more suitable than Green Mountain, Bliss Triumph, Pontiac, and some others, which usually cannot be used because the chips from them are often too dark brown.

Storage temperatures are important. When potatoes are kept at a relatively low temperature, too much sugar builds up at the expense of the starch content. A small increase in amount of sugar over that present in tubers at digging turns the chips too dark. Usually during January chip manufacturers begin to have extra trouble in obtaining suitable potatoes because of low temperatures in storages. The potatoes can be desugared, or conditioned, by exposure to a temperature of about 70° F. for 1 to 4 weeks if they are of the right variety and have not been too cold too long.

Potatoes that have been stored at 40° F. for more than 10 days are not likely to be suitable for chipping without first being conditioned. Stock held at 50° can be processed directly without being conditioned, because at that temperature the sugar content remains about the same as when the potatoes were harvested. Furthermore, excessive sprouting will not occur at 50° until 2 to 5 months after digging, depending on the variety. A little sprouting is not harmful—in fact, most chippers prefer stock with some sprouting. Chippers who can control their stock may follow this "magic 50°" program, which will keep them in potatoes for chipping through February and possibly March. If they want stock for late spring or before southern new-crop potatoes are available in good quantities, they can store an additional supply of potatoes at 40° and condition this stock as needed.

Steps in processing include peeling, slicing, washing the slices, frying, salting, and packaging. Cooking operations may be on a small scale, as in the batch-frying process, in which hand-operated kettles are used. Or, they may be on a large scale, by the mechanized continuous-frying process. It is fascinating to watch the finished chips delivered from the huge cookers, which have a capacity up to 500 pounds an hour. Almost before they are cool the chips are bagged, put in cartons, loaded on motor trucks, and hurried on their way.

In the continuous process, the potatoes first are peeled in abrasive peelers, which grind off the outer surfaces by a whirling motion. Inspection and trimming by hand follow. The use of abrasive peelers often results in definite loss of potato flesh as well as skin, because of uneven action and irregular-shaped potatoes. Other types of peelers, such as those that use steam or direct flame, have possible application as means of reducing the loss.

The peeled potatoes are sliced in rotary slicers. The thickness of the slice varies with each lot and has an important effect on the degree of curl and the ultimate appearance of the chips. The number of slices usually varies from 15 to 20 to the inch. The slices are washed in a mesh cylinder, which rotates in a trough of water. Fins within the cylinder move the slices along as they are tumbled over and over. Washing removes granules of free starch and small bits of potato, which would otherwise char during frying. The slices then move over a mesh conveyor belt to the cooker.

A long, shallow, covered trough, heated from below, contains the frying oil. The slices enter at the hot end of the fryer and are kept submerged in the hot oil as they are moved at a regulated speed to the front end. The large volume of steam and other fumes is exhausted through a flue to the outside. Near each end is a thermometer. The temperature is held at about 375° F. or a little higher at the hot end and 325° F. at the outlet end. The frying temperature is varied to compensate for the browning tendency inherent in some raw material. Higher temperatures increase browning; lower ones decrease it. The fried chips fall on a mesh conveyor, where they drain before passing under a salt sprinkler and then to the packing room.

Vegetable oils or fats, most commonly cottonseed oil, corn oil, and peanut oil, in either liquid or solid hydrogenated form, serve as the usual frying medium. The kind of oil used is determined by price and also by local preference for certain tastes resulting from the oil in which chips are fried. Recent studies at the Plant Industry Station at Beltsville have shown some differences between varieties of potatoes, but practically none between oils, in the amount taken up in the chips. It was also found that chips from potatoes of high starch content are less oily than chips from potatoes with less starch.

Several methods of treating potatoes at the factory are being tested to determine what characteristics of certain varieties or what handling or storage practices cause the excessive browning that has been so troublesome. Some of them are based on extraction of the browning reactants from the raw slices before frying. Another method of approach being studied at the Western Regional Research Laboratory is based on the dehydration of raw sliced potatoes shortly after harvest and their storage for later use in order to avoid the results of prolonged cool storage of fresh stock.

R. C. WRIGHT *is a physiologist in the fruit and vegetable division of the Bureau of Plant Industry, Soils, and Agricultural Engineering.*

MARTHA E. DAVIS *is a chemist in the food research division of the Western Regional Research Laboratory.*

CARL E. HENDEL *is a chemist in the vegetable processing division of the Western Laboratory.*

The Chemicals We Get From Potatoes

R. H. Treadway, T. C. Cordon

The carbohydrates, proteins, and minerals that make potatoes an excellent food for our bodies also furnish excellent nourishment for molds, bacteria, and other microbial forms of life. In the language of the microbiologist, the potato is a good substrate for the growth of micro-organisms. The liquor from boiled potatoes, "potato broth," has long been established as a nutrient medium in experimental microbiological work. That is to say, in culturing, or growing, bacteria and molds in order to identify species, determine numbers, or increase their concentration preparatory to putting the micro-organisms to practical use, potato liquor provides the necessary stimulation for growth.

Potatoes contain about 20 percent solid matter and 80 percent water. Starch, by far the most important solid constituent, accounts for 65 to 75 percent of the potato on the dry basis. Potatoes ordinarily contain little sugar, but the starch can be converted into the fermentable sugars maltose and dextrose.

About 10 percent of the dry matter is protein, much of which is present in soluble form. Free amino acids, the simple building blocks of protein, are also present. A good part of the protein content of the potato, therefore, is in a readily available condition for utilization by micro-organisms. Essential inorganic elements, such as potassium, phosphorus, and magnesium, occur in adequate amounts among the mineral constituents of the potato. Other necessary growth factors are also present.

Large tonnages of potatoes have been fermented to produce ethyl alcohol, the common beverage and industrial alcohol. During periods when grain is scarce or costly, potatoes have been used to great advantage when they were available in sufficient quantity. In 1946, 29 million bushels of potatoes were used by alcohol distilleries. Most of the potato spirits has gone into industrial alcohol; some has appeared in blended whiskies and liqueurs. In 1947, 13.3 percent of the alcohol produced in the United States came from potatoes (compared to 16.5 percent from grain), with ethyl sulfate—a synthetic method starting with petroleum—and molasses serving as raw materials for most of the production.

An attempt was made during the Second World War and immediately afterward to popularize the blended whisky containing potato alcohol. Through the period of hostilities, the production of grain alcohol for beverage purposes was banned because industrial alcohol was sorely needed in the war effort. It is likely that people associated the potato alcohol with the idea of an inferior, temporary war substitute. At any rate, when potable grain alcohol again became available, little or no market remained for potato alcohol in beverages. Europeans have long used potato alcohol in vodka and other liquors. Actually the difference in taste between grain and potato alcohol is negligible.

Butyl alcohol, which is valuable in the formulation of lacquers and in the synthesis of organic chemicals, also is obtained by fermentation of potatoes. We do not know how many potatoes have been used in the fermentation of butyl alcohol, but the quantity has been large since 1946. Late in 1948 the price of fermentation butyl alcohol dropped from 32 cents to 17.5 cents a pound on tank-car lots, largely because millions of bushels of surplus potatoes were available at low cost through the Government's diversion program. The price drop placed fermentation butyl alcohol in direct competition with the synthetic grade, an unusual situation. Eighteen percent of the 35 million bushels of surplus potatoes from the 1947 crop went into the production of ethyl and butyl alcohols. From the 1948 crop, 34 percent of the 133 million bushels acquired by the Government were used in the fermentation of those two alcohols.

IN THEORY IT IS POSSIBLE to produce almost any fermentation product from potatoes. For various reasons, however, it would not be feasible to use potatoes in all fermentations. In some, the non-carbohydrate constituents may interfere with fermentation of the sugar, uncontrollable side fermentations may occur, or insurmountable difficulties may arise in isolation and purification of the desired product.

The Eastern Regional Research Laboratory undertook a study to determine the suitability of cull and surplus potatoes for various fermentations. Early in 1947, P. A. Wells, the director, suggested using potatoes in a novel way in fermentations. He pointed out several advantages of potatoes for this use. Potatoes might be of value in culturing and propagating organisms that produce the amylases (starch-splitting enzymes), which are necessary agents in forming the sugars so that fermentations can proceed. The potato nutrients also would be expected to promote the fermentation of the sugars. Hence, he suggested that the conversion of potato starch to sugars and the fermentation of the sugars to other products might be carried out simultaneously. Chemists and microbiologists joined forces in developing this line of work.

We estimate that if potatoes were carefully graded and only the best grades sold for table use, a supply of subgrade stocks of 50 million bushels or more a year would exist. A fermentation industry based on such a large quantity of raw material would seem entirely feasible. Assurance of a constant supply of raw material is a requisite for the development of any large-scale industrial processing.

The problems associated with utilization of potatoes in industrial fermentations arise from their perishability and the high water content that gives them their great bulk and weight.

Freshly dug potatoes go through a rest period for about 2 months after harvesting. During that time they will not sprout, even at relatively high temperatures. Afterwards, they must be stored in a cool place or treated with a sprout inhibitor to keep them dormant and prevent sprouting. In the Northern States, where there are facilities for storage over the winter, processing of fresh potatoes can be spread over about 8 months of the year. The intermediate crop of potatoes—which is harvested in midsummer and late summer—is stored for only a few months. Practically no early-crop potatoes are stored in the Southern States.

Because potatoes are four-fifths water, they are bulky and heavy to transport and comparatively costly to handle, unload, store, and process at industrial plants. The ideal situation is to have processing plants in the potato area where transportation costs are kept down. It also appears advisable, though, to have facilities for dehydrating potatoes to convert them into stable form. A stockpile of dehydrated potatoes would enable processors to operate the year around through both low- and surplus-production years.

Potatoes have only a low value as raw material for fermentation of ethyl and butyl alcohols, in which they must compete with cheap blackstrap molasses and the synthetic processes. Cuban blackstrap molasses was available in Philadelphia at a cost of only about 4 cents a gallon (in February 1950). At that low cost, the fermentable sugars are worth about 0.6 cent a pound. Potatoes containing 14 percent fermentable carbohydrate would thus be worth only 8.4 cents a hundred pounds, delivered, in competition with blackstrap molasses at 4 cents a gallon. Nevertheless, surplus potatoes costing approximately three times that figure, delivered, were used in Philadelphia in February 1950. Apparently the supply of cheap molasses is inadequate at times.

Ventures in alcohol production from cull and surplus potatoes have failed in Idaho and Maine in the past few years. Because there was little demand for industrial alcohol in the vicinity of each distillery, the output had to be shipped great distances to heavy industries that constituted markets. We believe it is possible, however, that alcohol can be produced successfully in regions of large potato acreages if alcohol comes into common use for supplying automotive power. Maine, Minnesota, North Dakota, and Idaho—potato States far from cheap industrial alcohol—might then find it economical to use alcohol manufactured from locally produced potatoes for blending with gasoline to provide fuel for cars, busses, trucks, and tractors.

Potatoes admittedly are worth only a trifle now in competition with blackstrap molasses in the fermentation of ethyl and butyl alcohols, but research workers are constantly on the alert for new fermentations in which potatoes may have sufficient superiority to command a higher price than their carbohydrate content alone would warrant.

Minor differences in nutrients and traces of essential constituents present sometimes mean a lot in fermentations. For example, lactose (milk sugar) is used instead of the much cheaper sucrose (cane or beet sugar) in the *Penicillium notatum* fermentation to produce penicillin. Lactose has the same chemical elements and molecular weight as sucrose, but it gives a better yield of penicillin.

Although blackstrap molasses costs little as a fermentation material, it has so far been unacceptable in its impure state for some fermentations, such as the production of lactic and citric acids. We hope to uncover practical fermentations in which cull and surplus potatoes are an economical raw material.

The production of lactic acid, which was first studied, illustrates what might possibly be done with other fermentations.

IN THE LACTIC ACID fermentation, clean potatoes are first ground and cooked. The next step is to convert the starch to sugars by hydrolysis, a process in which the starch takes up water and breaks down into the sugars maltose and dextrose with dextrins as the intermediate products.

Hydrolysis of the starch is necessary in order to convert the relatively large starch molecules of complicated structure into simple, readily soluble sugar molecules that will undergo fermentation. The hydrolysis of starch is catalyzed by the addition of mineral acids, such as hydrochloric or sulfuric acid, or by the presence of enzymes (biological catalysts). Amylases (starch-splitting enzymes) produced by strains of the mold *Aspergillus niger* were employed in the starch conversion. Investigations at the Northern Regional Research Laboratory, at Joseph E. Seagrams & Sons, Inc., and at U. S. Industrial Chemicals, Inc., have shown that these strains of *A. niger* can produce amylases when grown in submerged culture on distillery wastes. It was found at the Eastern Laboratory that potato mash could also serve as an excellent nutrient medium for culturing the mold strains in the production of the enzymes. After growth for 5 or 6 days on a potato mash that contained 5 percent potato solids and 1.5 percent calcium carbonate, the mold culture was ready for use in saccharifying potatoes (converting their starch to sugar). After the saccharification of the potatoes had been allowed to proceed for a while, a culture of a bacterium capable of producing lactic acid from dextrose (*Lactobacillus delbrueckii* or *Lactobacillus pentosus*) was added. An excess of calcium carbonate was maintained in the mash to neutralize the acid as it was formed during the fermentation. Otherwise, the acidity would stop the growth of the bacteria. Three to four days were required to complete the fermentation. By the process, 80 to 90 percent of the starch originally present in the potato was converted to lactic acid.

A manufacturer of lactic acid— Clinton Foods, Incorporated, of Clinton, Iowa—has produced several commercial scale batches of the acid from potatoes by the process tested at the Eastern Laboratory. The company had no unusual difficulties in carrying out the fermentation.

A RESEARCH WORKER IN INDUSTRY— Dr. O. K. Sebek, then in the employ of a firm of distillers—has found that *l*-2,3-butanediol can be produced by the fermentation of white potatoes with *Bacillus polymyxa*.

l-2,3-Butanediol is an alcohol that is potentially valuable as a solvent, reactant, and antifreeze. To produce it, the potatoes were diced, macerated in a food blender, and diluted with twice their weight of water. The mash was heated to 158° F., and 1 percent of malt (based on the potato weight) was added to thin it down to a consistency that could be easily stirred. After the mash had been heated to boiling to cook the starch, it was cooled, 1 to 1.5 percent of calcium carbonate was added, and fermentation was started by inoculation with *B. polymyxa*. This bacterium produces its own amylase and no additional saccharifying enzyme is needed.

Investigations by E. A. Weaver at the Eastern Laboratory in 1949 indicate that amylases can be produced in high yields by certain strains of the mold *Aspergillus niger* when grown submerged on whole-potato media.

Growth is very rapid, but the amylases are held within the young cells. They can be released, however, by breaking down the cell walls. By including this process of comminution, high yields are obtained in 15 to 18 hours fermentation time, whereas 4 to 5 days are required to reach high potencies if the amylases have to diffuse through the cell walls. If the excellent laboratory results can be reproduced on a commercial scale, potatoes may become a cheap source of amylases.

OTHER PRODUCTS that might be produced by fermentation of potatoes include glycerin and five acids—citric, gluconic, fumaric, itaconic, and kojic.

Potatoes might also be used as a culture medium in other microbiological processes, as, for example, the production of antibiotics by molds, actinomycetes (organisms having characteristics intermediate between bacteria and molds), and bacteria.

Dr. Harry Humfeld, of the Western Laboratory, has shown that the mushroom fungus *Agaricus campestris* produces the mushroom flavor when grown submerged. Potatoes might possibly be used as a food for this organism.

Preliminary results indicate that potato mash saccharified with mold amylase can be used for the production of feed yeast. As yeasts multiply, they convert the carbohydrate and other constituents of the potato into protein. In order to produce a high-protein yeast and increase the amount of protein synthesized, it is necessary to provide additional nitrogen. The nitrogen comes from both the soluble form present in the potato and from inexpensive sources, such as ammonia, ammonium salts, or urea. The protein that is produced is obtained by harvesting the yeast cells.

It should be borne in mind that, with the exception of the ethyl and butyl alcohol fermentations, much that has been said about fermentations of potatoes is conjecture. Several of these potential fermentations have given promising results in preliminary laboratory work, but it will take many months to determine their commercial practicability.

So it appears that a well-developed pattern for utilization of substandard and surplus potatoes must include their use in the fermentation industry and various microbiological processes. Starch production, flour production, and livestock feeding all have their proper places in the economy of the potato industry, but those old-established methods of utilization must be supplemented by industrial fermentations if all off-grade potatoes are to be used. The potato has long been known as an excellent substrate for microorganisms. The challenge to research is to find practical fermentations based on potatoes in which their use is economical. A solution to this problem would not only be a boon to agriculture but a bulwark in national defense. Particularly during periods when grain and molasses are scarce and potatoes are abundant, it is important to have information available on methods of converting potatoes into needed chemicals and other products of microbiological reactions.

R. H. TREADWAY *did undergraduate and graduate work at Indiana University. From 1936 to 1941 he was engaged in chemical research with E. I. du Pont de Nemours & Co., Inc., and with the A. E. Staley Manufacturing Co. Since 1941, Dr. Treadway has been employed as a chemist in the carbohydrate division of the Eastern Regional Research Laboratory.*

T. C. CORDON *holds degrees from Utah State Agricultural College and Rutgers University. Before he joined the Eastern Laboratory in 1942 as a bacteriologist in the division of hides, tanning materials, and leather, he was engaged in research at the New Jersey Agricultural Experiment Station, at the University of Idaho, and in industry.*

SEVERAL YEARS ago somebody suggested wet milling of grain sorghums as a means of obtaining starch. The method had long been used for corn, but the concensus was that it would not work with grain sorghum. Corn grains are 10 to 15 times larger than sorghum grains, but the two grains have the same composition and the starch manufactured from them is identical. In fact, one laboratory spent $10,000 trying to find some difference between the two starches that would be useful for identifying the source of starch used in commercial products. It found no difference. Laboratory trials showed that only a few modifications of the wet process were necessary in order to separate sorghum starch from the other constituents of the grain. The procedures worked also on a large factory scale. But the experts had been right; you just could not put grain sorghum through a corn wet mill without changes. This is why: The small sorghum grains fell through the coarse screens at the bottom of the corn steep vats. But when finer-mesh screens were placed over the corn screens, everything clicked, and grain sorghum wet milling became a reality. Thus the size of a hole may be as important to an industrialist as it is to a mouse pursued by a cat.—*John H. Martin, Bureau of Plant Industry, Soils, and Agricultural Engineering.*

Sweetpotatoes:

More Than

Starch

P. R. Dawson, I. H. Greathouse,
W. O. Gordon

Starch, the chief component, aside from water, of sweetpotatoes is the only one that has been separated, purified, sold, and utilized commercially. However, the more important nonstarch portions have been isolated and identified in the laboratory. They affect the nutritional value of sweetpotatoes, as well as the conditions of processing the crop for starch, fermentation products, feed, and food products. They add up to so much less than the starch and water, however, that processing sweetpotatoes to recover them, except possibly as byproducts, is generally considered impractical.

Sweetpotatoes vary in composition with the variety, the soil and climate where they grow, and the duration and conditions of handling and storage after harvesting. At the time of digging, water and starch make up about 90 percent of most sweetpotatoes. The moisture ranges from 75 to 60 percent; the starch, from 15 to 30 percent. The rest consists of 2 to 3 percent of sugars, 1 to 2 percent of protein, 1 to 3 percent of pectic substances, about 1 percent of mineral matter, and smaller percentages of fat, cellulose, hemicelluloses, resins, coloring matter, organic acids, enzymes, and vitamins.

As soon as sweetpotatoes are separated from the vines, the sugar content begins to rise—as much as twofold to threefold, with a corresponding decrease in starch, in 10 to 30 days. The rate and extent of change in the sugar and starch content during that time and in later storage vary with the variety, temperature, and humidity.

INVESTIGATORS AT the Southern Regional Research Laboratory have explored the possibilities of recovery and utilization of some of the nonstarch components as byproducts, or coproducts, of sweetpotato-starch manufacture. The investigations had the dual aim of increasing the byproduct credit (extra income from byproducts) and of simplifying the waste-disposal problem.

We found that sweetpotatoes of the improved high-starch L–5 variety, later named Pelican Processor, had approximately the following average composition when ground for starch in the factory at Laurel, Miss. (in percentages):

Moisture	64. 5
Starch	25. 5
Total sugars	2. 8
Crude protein (total nitrogen × 6.25)	1. 5
Pectic substances	2. 2
Crude fat	. 6
Mineral matter	. 9
Other	2. 0

When 100 tons of sweetpotatoes of such composition are processed daily, the following quantities of components are fed into the plant in the raw material (in tons):

Water	64. 5
Starch	25. 5
Sugars	2. 8
Crude protein	1. 5

In the starch-extraction process, sweetpotatoes are ground with about 3 parts of limewater, and the liberated starch is separated from the pulp by washing over a series of fine screens. The suspension of crude starch thus obtained is allowed to settle or is centrifuged to separate the starch from the process liquor.

The liquor, often called fruit water, is actually a limewater extract of ground sweetpotatoes. It contains most of the sugar in the original potatoes at a concentration of 0.75 to 1.0 percent and 80 to 85 percent of the nitrogenous matter at a concentration of about 0.4 percent, or as high as 0.7 percent if the potatoes have a higher protein content. The fruit water also contains small amounts of other organic substances and mineral matter, which are in solution or so finely suspended that they are not separated in settling or centrifuging. Often it also carries a little fine starch, the amount of which depends on the efficiency of the sedimentation or centrifuging system.

In the commercial sweetpotato-starch plants that have operated so far, the fruit water has gone to the sewer, along with the effluent (waste) waters from other stages of starch refining or plant clean-up. The waters carry variable amounts of very-fine-grain or contaminated starch, the recovery of which is impracticable. The effluents have constituted the major waste-disposal problem in the manufacture of sweetpotato starch. The pulp remaining on the screens after washing out the free starch has not gone to waste.

When commercial-scale sweetpotato-starch manufacture was undertaken at Laurel, the workers recognized that the rapid spoilage of the wet pulp would create an intolerable nuisance if it were dumped in the waste and would prevent its disposal as feed unless immediately dried. They also recognized that the potential byproduct value of the pulp would offset the cost of converting it to stable form. Hence, the spent pulp has been pressed and dried and sold for feed. The dried pulp contains 40 to 50 percent of starch and 20 to 30 percent of other digestible carbohydrates, about 2 percent of crude protein (representing about 10 percent of the protein in the original potatoes), and about 11 percent of crude fiber. It makes a good carbohydrate feed and has readily sold at a price that has afforded a fair byproduct credit in the manufacture of starch.

The fruit water is the most troublesome waste. The water from typical sweetpotatoes contains 1.5 to 2 percent of organic matter, mostly in dissolved or highly dispersed form. In a factory that grinds 100 tons of sweetpotatoes every 24 hours, the daily fruit water, about 70,000 gallons, carries 5 tons or more of such organic matter. In it is more than a ton of nitrogenous matter and 2 tons or more of sugars on a dry-substance basis.

Such an effluent cannot be tolerated in the smaller watercourses. It can easily overload small municipal sewage systems. Recovery of the protein and sugars that comprise most of the organic matter in the fruit water and their conversion to some usable product would help eliminate the waste-disposal problem and might reduce the costs of starch manufacture by the revenue from byproducts. Such possibilities have been under investigation at the Southern Laboratory since 1942.

THE PROTEIN remains in solution, or is very highly dispersed, in the fresh fruit-water effluent, which is alkaline from the limewater. With other organic material, it separates out as a flocculent precipitate if the liquor becomes acid through fermentation on standing.

Previous investigators had found that sweetpotato protein is largely precipitated from water solution if the acidity drops to about pH 4.0. Our recovery process is based on this behavior. We found that most complete precipitation takes place at pH 3.8. If hydrochloric acid is added to the alkaline fruit water until the pH is 3.8 and the liquor is heated to 176° F., about three-fourths of the nitrogenous matter in the fruit water is coagulated into a light flocculent precipitate. Heating to this point does not increase the proportion of the total nitrogen actually coagulated, but it causes a denser precipitate, which is more easily separated by sedimentation and filtration.

Half to two-thirds of the dry substance in this precipitate is protein, as computed from the total nitrogen by use of the conventional factor 6.25. The remaining dry substance is a mixture of other organic material, dissolved or finely dispersed in the fruit water and thrown down with the protein coagulate. Hence the precipitate is really a crude protein concentrate.

Because of the high dilution, it is impracticable to filter or centrifuge the coagulated concentrate directly from its mother liquor. If it is precipitated under the best conditions, however, the coagulate will settle in 6 hours to about one-tenth the volume of the total fruit water, and 90 percent of the water can be removed by drawing off the overlying clear liquor. The settled suspension still contains up to 95 percent water. Further water can be effectively removed by filtration under carefully controlled conditions. The coagulate gives a highly compressible filter cake. As long as the mass is fluid, therefore, only a very light force must be applied through the filter. An effective procedure is to allow the settled concentrate to spread over a rather open filter in a layer not exceeding 2 inches in depth and let it drain until the mass begins to show definite plasticity.

For successful settling and filtration, the starch content of the original fruit water must be reduced to 0.2 percent or less before coagulation. Otherwise, gelatinization of the starch during heating causes the liquor in the settled concentrate to have enough viscosity to retard settling and to make filtration very slow. Also, agitation during coagulation must be kept to a minimum—just enough to effect even distribution of acid and heat. Otherwise, the curd structure of the coagulate is broken up and gravity filtration is impeded. A new kind of filter cloth, made of synthetic plastic fabric, facilitates this type of filtration.

After the filter cake begins to show plasticity, a suction of not more than 5 centimeters of mercury may be applied until a puttylike consistency is reached. The vacuum may then be increased to 70 centimeters of mercury. At that stage the cake must be covered or pressed down to prevent cracking and consequent loss of vacuum. The concentrate is removed from the filter as a stiff paste, which has 80 to 85 percent moisture.

The material may then be dried directly to low moisture content for preservation. For use as a feed supplement, however, the most practicable procedure is to mix the wet protein cake from the filter with the wet pressed residual pulp from the starch-extraction process and dry the mixture in one operation. If the two components are combined in the proportion in which they are recovered from a given quantity of sweetpotatoes, the byproduct feed contains 10 to 12 percent of crude protein, rather than only about 2 percent where the protein is not recovered.

A large-scale pilot plant has been designed and installed to carry out the protein-recovery process in conjunction with the operation of the starch pilot plant at the Southern Laboratory. The overflow of fruit water from the centrifugal used in the first stage of starch refining is passed through another solid-basket centrifugal to remove small amounts of starch that may be carried over. Improved centrifugal equipment, which recently became available commercially, makes it possible to keep the starch in the fruit water so low that this step may eventually be dispensed with. The water is then fed, at a rate of 200 to 250 gallons an hour, through a tank, in which the protein concentrate is precipitated by continuous addition of acid and heating, with gentle agitation and sufficient holding time to effect good flocculation. The process is fully automatic, with electronic controls, and is easily handled by a single operator.

The dilute suspension flows into a 1,000-gallon insulated conical settling tank of special design. After the precipitate has settled to about one-tenth the volume of the dilute suspension, the clear overlying liquor is drawn off from the top of the tank and conveyed to the yeast-propagation system or the sewer.

In commercial operation, this effluent would be cooled in a heat exchanger to conserve heat. When thus cooled to 95° F., the liquor would be ready for feeding directly to a yeast-propagation system. It is already pasteurized by the heating, and the degree of acidity is about correct for yeast propagation. Only the addition of supplementary nitrogenous nutrient is needed.

The concentrated precipitate is drawn off from the bottom of the tank and fed continuously to a specially designed gravity filter of rather open-texture plastic fiber. The filter has power-driven scraper blades, which slowly convey the concentrate across the surface and discharge it when it has drained to plastic consistency. The concentrate is transferred to large suction filters, which are fitted with special plastic cloths, and further dewatered, at first with very slight suction and finally with a higher vacuum. The fabric used in both stages of filtration is woven from a heat-resistant, continuous-filament yarn, which is not affected by the hot slurry and releases the cake readily. The final stiff paste, still containing 80 to 85 percent of moisture, is mixed in a power mixer with the wet pressed pulp from the starch-extraction process and dried in a rotary drier.

Repeated runs in this pilot plant have shown that, although the absolute quantity of protein concentrate recovered varies with the protein content of the sweetpotatoes, the process can be depended on to recover 70 to 75 percent of the nitrogenous matter in the fruit water, or 55 to 60 percent, sometimes more, of the nitrogenous matter entering the starch-extraction process in the sweetpotatoes. More than 3,000 pounds of the protein-enriched pulp have been recovered for evaluation in feeding trials.

With sweetpotatoes that contain 25.5 percent of starch and 1.5 percent of crude protein, commercial plants recovered 18 to 20 tons of commercial starch and about 8 tons of byproduct pulp for every 100 tons of potatoes ground. Nearly a ton of protein, which could have been recovered by our new process, went down the sewer. Recovery of the protein as a concentrate that is returned to the pulp would yield at least 9.5 tons of byproduct feed with a protein content of 10 percent or more, instead of 8 tons of straight pulp with a protein content of only about 2 percent.

Will recovery of feed protein as a byproduct of sweetpotato-starch manufacture prove profitable in itself? The answer depends on its nutrient value for livestock, the quantity of recoverable protein in the potatoes, the efficiency and cost of the recovery procedure, and the credit in saving on waste disposal.

A thorough chemical examination of the crude sweetpotato protein recovered by the process has been made by H. M. Robinson and L. C. Mallory at the Southern Laboratory. In amino acid content, it seems to compare well with other vegetable proteins. It contains an unusually high proportion of the amino acids essential to balanced nutrition and important proportions of some that are inadequately supplied by certain protein feedstuffs readily available in the South.

The only direct study of the nutritional value of sweetpotato protein heretofore reported was by an American missionary school in China during the Sino-Japanese fighting before the Second World War. It was found equal to other plant proteins.

The protein-enriched byproduct pulp prepared in our pilot plant has been tested at the Florida Agricultural Experiment Station. Calves fed rations in which about a third of the total protein was supplied by the enriched pulp gained in weight at a rate as high as when this protein was supplied by cottonseed meal. We need more data, however, before we can make definite recommendations.

The value of the recovered protein concentrate, or of the byproduct pulp in which it is incorporated, will be determined by the current value of other sources of feed protein to which it proves equivalent.

Several conclusions are possible from the pilot-plant operation of our process for recovering proteins as a byproduct in the manufacture of sweetpotato starch. The process is technically feasible. The cost of equipment and operation on a commercial scale will be moderate. Allowing nothing for the saving in waste disposal, the byproduct will at least pay for the process and probably will yield a profit if it is recovered in the quantity described and compares reasonably well in nutritional value with vegetable protein from other sources.

The 1.5 percent protein content of the starch sweetpotatoes used in our work is about the mean of the extremes we have found in sweetpotatoes grown on upland soils in Mississippi and Louisiana. It will more often be higher than lower. Under some conditions, as in the Florida Everglades, protein contents may be as high as 4 percent.

THE LIQUOR that remains after precipitation and separation of the protein concentrate contains almost all the sugar extracted from the sweetpotatoes, at a concentration of 0.75 to 1 percent, about 0.1 percent of soluble nitrogenous compounds not precipitated with the protein, and other soluble matter from the potatoes. Recovery of the sugar as such or its conversion to alcohol by fermentation is hardly practicable because of the high dilution.

However, we discovered that the liquor made a nearly perfect medium for the growth of feed yeast (*Torulopsis utilis*). Laboratory experiments by N. Porges, G. S. King, T. J. Klatt, and others showed that the liquor contained enough of all the food elements necessary for maximum growth of the organism except nitrogen. The soluble nitrogen carried over from the protein precipitation is readily assimilated, but

it supplies only one-third to one-half of the total requirement for the amount of sugar present. The deficit must be made up by adding ammonia or ammonium salts. We found that if ammonium hydroxide were used to neutralize the acid liquor after protein precipitation, by adjusting the pH from 3.8 to 6.5, the quantity required was generally sufficient for the yeast growth. If the effluent liquor from protein recovery is neutralized in this manner, inoculated with an active culture of Torula yeast, and vigorously aerated at a suitable temperature, the sugar and nitrogen are rapidly consumed and the yeast multiplies at a corresponding rate. After 8 hours, the yield of yeast on a dry basis amounts to 40 to 50 percent of the sugar initially present, and the sugar content of the liquor is reduced to about 0.05 percent.

The process was then made continuous. A vigorous starting culture is allowed to build up in the propagator until the sugar is largely consumed and the rate of yeast increase is at a maximum. Fresh liquor is then run into the propagator, with withdrawal of yeast growth. If the effluent liquor from process proceeds with continuous flow. For maximum yields it has been found necessary to use two or three propagators in series. The culture from the first-stage propagator flows into the second propagator, in which the yeast increases further with complete depletion of sugar. From the second generator, the culture flows to a third generator for aging or goes directly to the recovery system, where the yeast is separated by centrifuging and then dried. With this system, yields of yeast equivalent to 45 percent of the sugars supplied can be maintained with a rate of continuous flow per hour equivalent to about 40 percent of the volume of culture in each propagator.

This continuous process was developed from the laboratory scale first to a small pilot plant and then to a large pilot plant for three-stage continuous operation at a rate of feed up to 200 to 250 gallons an hour. The plant was planned for experimental operation under commercial factory conditions where enough waste water for protracted continuous runs would be available. Unfortunately, suspension of commercial sweetpotato-starch manufacture has so far prevented such tests.

Under another project, however, the plant and process were operated successfully on citrus-waste press juice in a commercial cannery in Florida. Continuous propagation was maintained for as long as 30 days without objectionable contamination or depletion of the culture.

The propagation system in this pilot plant consists of three cylindrical closed steel tanks about 40 inches in diameter and 12 feet high, each with a total capacity of about 750 gallons and a working capacity of about 500 gallons of the culture. Each tank is equipped with aeration tubes in the bottom and with cooling coils. Air for aeration is supplied by a high-capacity rotary compressor.

In operating with sweetpotato-starch waste water, 500 gallons of vigorous starting culture would be built up in the first propagator. The clarified liquor from the protein-recovery system, already pasteurized by the heating in that process, is cooled to 95° F. by running through a heat exchanger and is then fed into the first propagator at a rate of 200 to 250 gallons an hour.

Simultaneously, ammonium hydroxide or ammonium salt solution, in the proportion necessary to supply the nutrient supplement and to maintain the pH at optimum, is fed in. This nutrient feed is regulated by an automatically controlled proportioning system. The culture flows by gravity from the first propagator to the second until the latter is filled to working capacity, when, in turn, the third propagator is filled and eventually culture with maximum yield of yeast overflows to the centrifuge feed tank. With the system in equilibrium, the levels in all three propagators are automatically maintained, and the overflow from the third

is at the same rate as that at which the liquor is fed into the first tank. Aeration at the required rate is maintained in all propagators. The temperature of the culture is held at about 95° F. by regulation of the flow of the cooling water. Excessive foaming is prevented by a simple device.

The mature culture is concentrated to about 12.5 percent dry-weight solids in a small-capacity yeast centrifugal of standard design. The yeast cream is dried in an atmospheric double-drum drier.

The feed yeast produced in sweetpotato-starch fruit water has about the same composition as that produced in other waste media, with a protein content of about 50 percent.

With typical sweetpotatoes containing 2.8 percent sugars, about 2.5 tons of the sugars appear in the fruit-water effluent for every 100 tons of the potatoes processed for starch. The results of our experiments seem to indicate the sugars could be converted to about a ton of feed yeast containing a half ton of protein. A valuable protein feed supplement would be recovered and the sugar would be practically eliminated from the final waste waters.

Recovery of that byproduct is still in the experimental stage. Further data from large-scale trials, as well as further information on the value of the product and the outlet for it as a protein and vitamin feed supplement, are needed before we can pass on its practicability for commercial application. The vigorous aeration required takes much power and large volumes of very dilute liquor must be handled. But the cost of nutrient addition is less than for other wastes that are used to produce feed yeast. The only amendment needed is ammonia and the amount required is moderate because of the assimilable nitrogen already in the waste water. We must still determine whether the return from the yeast produced will pay for the processing costs, even with credit for the saving in waste-disposal treatment.

The pectin content of 2.2 percent

shown for the typical high-starch sweetpotato is approximately the average of the values of 1 to 3 percent reported by various investigators. When sweetpotatoes are processed for starch, nearly all the pectin remains in the pulp after extraction of the starch, with a concentration as high as 30 percent of the dry pulp. The recovery of pectin from this pulp has been investigated at the Southern Laboratory. With the use of limewater in the starch-extraction process as carried out commercially, the pectin is so fixed in the pulp that it cannot be extracted in any quantity by any procedure so far devised. If the pulp is prepared without limewater, about two-thirds of the pectin can be extracted. To obtain a high-quality product, however, the residual starch, which makes up 40 to 50 percent of the pulp, must be completely removed before extraction of pectin.

Such removal of starch must not cause appreciable loss or degradation of pectin. It cannot be done mechanically. By treatment with a suitable enzyme preparation, the starch can be made completely soluble, so that it may be washed out of the pulp without appreciably affecting the pectin. The pectin can then be extracted without contamination by starch. Sweetpotato pectin thus extracted appears to be comparable to apple pectin and has good gel-forming characteristics.

Practical and economical recovery of sweetpotato pectin as a byproduct of starch manufacture would depend on the elimination of limewater in the starch-extraction process. Such modification of the process might be possible with some of the improved varieties of starch sweetpotatoes. Recovery of pectin would still be impracticable unless effective use could be made of the solution of sugars resulting from dissolving out the starch retained in the pulp. Fermentation and production of yeast are possibilities.

Consideration has been given to the recovery of pectin from the peel and trim waste of sweetpotato canneries. Here, also, to make the process feasible, use would have to be made of the starch, which must be separated before extraction of pectin.

SWEETPOTATOES owe their color—yellow, orange, or salmon—principally to carotene. Sweetpotato carotene has been found to be nearly all, if not entirely, β-carotene, which is readily converted to vitamin A in the body and is therefore sometimes called provitamin A. Widely grown improved selections of the Porto Rico variety commonly contain 30 to 50 parts of carotene per million parts of fresh sweetpotatoes. Breeding and selection in recent years have developed some new varieties that contain more than twice as much carotene as the best Porto Ricos grown under comparable conditions. The sweetpotato has a high rating as a source of provitamin A in the human diet and in the livestock ration.

Consideration has been given to the possibilities of using the high-carotene sweetpotatoes as a source of pure carotene or carotene concentrates, for which there is some demand for food and feed supplement, food coloring, and scientific purposes.

Carotene preparations now on the market are derived principally from leafy green material, such as alfalfa leaf meal, carrots, and vegetable oils that contain carotene. As far as we know, however, the processing of sweetpotatoes for carotene preparations has been investigated to only a limited extent.

In experiments at the Southern Laboratory, both fresh and dehydrated Porto Rico sweetpotatoes were used. In further experiments at the Alabama Agricultural Experiment Station, the dehydrated potatoes were extracted with solvents and the dissolved carotene was concentrated and purified by several procedures. Most of the extracted carotene could be accounted for in concentrated fractions and in more or less pure β-carotene; but the yield of purified material was rather low.

The results indicate that high-carotene sweetpotatoes can be used advantageously for laboratory preparation of small quantities of carotene where the biologically active β-carotene is required in pure form, free of α-carotene. The practical absence of α-carotene in sweetpotatoes eliminates the problem of its removal in the purification process. α-Carotene accompanies the beta form in other plant materials used as sources of carotene.

However, the investigations were not carried far enough to determine the best conditions and procedures for extraction and purification and to appraise the practicability of commercial production of carotene from sweetpotatoes as compared with other sources.

Sweetpotatoes of the highest carotene content now grown in quantity are still lower in the pigment than are well-colored carrots on a fresh-weight basis and much lower on a dry-matter basis. The carotene content compares favorably with that of alfalfa and other leafy material, but with such material added returns are received from the chlorophyll and xanthophyll recovered.

So far, the combined high raw-material costs and probable high processing costs in proportion to the value of the carotene likely to be recovered have not encouraged exploration of the possibilities of commercial production of carotene from sweetpotatoes.

If, or when, sweetpotatoes of as high carotene content as a number of new varieties or selections now under test become established in production, the picture may alter. It has been suggested that, with such sweetpotatoes, it might be possible to solvent-extract them for carotene in conjunction with production of dehydrated feed.

Direct extraction of fresh sweetpotatoes requires the use of large volumes of water-miscible solvents, such as acetone or alcohol, to remove most of the water before carotene can be extracted effectively. An efficient but quite expensive solvent-recovery system would be involved. Dehydration of the sweetpotatoes before extraction greatly reduces the volume of solvents needed and simplifies the solvent-recovery problem. The cost of drying must be added to the other processing costs and an appreciable loss of carotene is incurred, however. In both instances the extraction residue could be used as a carbohydrate feed, or for fermentation purposes, if objectionable solvent residues were effectively removed. Of course, it would lack most of the original carotene, and in the case of the residue from fresh potato extraction, much of the sugar content and possibly small amounts of other nutrients would have been extracted. The fresh potato-extraction residue probably could also be used for starch production. If either of the extraction processes should ever prove practicable, it is likely to be the one that uses dehydrated material. The savings in solvents and solvent recovery would probably more than offset the cost of direct drying and the attendant loss of carotene.

A new method for the recovery of carotene or a carotene concentrate from sweetpotatoes has been devised at the Southern Laboratory. It was found that when sweetpotatoes of the Porto Rico type were processed for starch, most of the carotene was dispersed in the process water. When the fruit water from the first stage of refining the crude starch was treated for recovery of a protein concentrate, an amount of carotene equivalent to more than half of that in the original potatoes was carried down with the coagulate. Thus, with carotene-containing sweetpotatoes, this coagulate constitutes a concentrate of both protein and carotene. After drying, the protein cake contained as much as 2100 parts per million of carotene, a concentration equivalent to 44 times that of the original sweetpotatoes. This concentrate affords a material for economical extraction of carotene or for use as such as a feed supplement.

Production of carotene or carotene concentrate from sweetpotatoes by such a process, without the recovery and utilization of the starch and residual pulp, would hardly be practicable. In a starch plant incorporating the protein-recovery process, the carotene concentrate would be obtained with no modification of the process and with no extra cost. Of course, in the commercial sweetpotato-starch enterprises that have operated so far, the sweetpotatoes processed have been for the most part of the high-starch, white-fleshed type that have little or no carotene in them. Such sweetpotatoes are preferable for starch manufacture because of the higher yields of starch and the less exacting refining procedures needed to produce a high-quality white starch. When the subgrade or surplus sweetpotatoes containing carotene are available for processing, however, the increased byproduct credit from the carotene concentrate might well offset the lower starch recovery and higher starch-refining costs, and perhaps leave a margin. If the added return from the carotene concentrate were high enough, as it might be with new sweetpotatoes of very high carotene content, it might be more profitable to operate entirely on such potatoes. Development of varieties that combine high starch and high carotene contents is not out of the range of possibility.

Some other components of sweetpotatoes, though small in amount, affect the nutritional value of the potatoes and their behavior in processing for food or industrial products. Among them are vitamins of the B series and vitamin C. The amounts are significant to the food value of the crop, but they are not so high as in some other vegetables and fruits.

Sweetpotatoes also contain enzymes, which are active in the transformation of starch and sugar. The Porto Rico and similar varieties are particularly rich in β-amylase, which is responsible for the high conversion of starch to maltose and dextrins when these potatoes are cooked.

A. K. Balls and his coworkers of the Enzyme Research Laboratory of the Bureau of Agricultural and Industrial Chemistry have isolated a pure crystalline protein, high in β-amylase activity, from the expressed juice of sweetpotatoes. The oxidases, or oxidizing enzymes, in sweetpotatoes accelerate the formation of dark substances from tanninlike compounds, also present in sweetpotatoes, when cut surfaces are exposed to the air.

The familiar milky sap, or latex, which exudes from freshly cut sweetpotato roots or vines, becomes very sticky on exposure to the air, and eventually sets to a hard resinous material, consists of an emulsion of a resinous substance. A Japanese investigator identified the substance as jalapin and concluded that its presence was the reason sweetpotatoes had found some use in Japan as a boiler compound for steam boilers. The latex is responsible for much of the gumming up and clogging of screens in manufacturing starch from sweetpotatoes. Some varieties have such a high content as to make them undesirable for starch production. Superficially, sweetpotato latex resembles the latex of rubber-bearing plants, but it contains only the merest trace, if any, of substances that resemble rubber.

P. R. DAWSON *is an industrial analyst and special assistant to the director of the Southern Regional Research Laboratory. He joined the Department of Agriculture in 1921.*

L. H. GREATHOUSE *is a chemical engineer in the engineering and development division of the Southern Laboratory. He first joined the Department of Agriculture in 1915. From 1920 until 1935 he was engaged in a private engineering enterprise.*

W. O. GORDON *has been a member of the Bureau of Agricultural and Industrial Chemistry since 1938. He was on the staff of the former Bureau of Chemistry from 1911 to 1916, and during the ensuing 14 years was engaged in industrial processing of food products. From 1930 until he rejoined the Department of Agriculture, he was with the National Bureau of Standards.*

Sweetpotatoes for Food and Feed

P. R. Dawson

In the United States, sweetpotatoes are used primarily for human food. Some culls and other unmarketable subgrade potatoes are fed to livestock, but such use is essentially a salvage measure.

Well over 90 percent of the sweetpotatoes used for food are prepared as needed from the fresh raw product and are stored, shipped, distributed, and purchased by the ultimate consumer in this form. Because of the bulk and perishability of sweetpotatoes, many efforts have been made to process them into food products that could be stored and distributed without loss and prepared for the table without waste and with little time and effort. However, canning is the only process in general use today for the preservation of sweetpotatoes.

SWEETPOTATOES have been canned commercially for more than 50 years. Around 100,000 cases were packed in 1899 for the United States as a whole. Production rose to a peak of some 769,-000 cases in 1925, and then dropped, reaching a low of 159,000 cases in 1933. The financial depression contributed to this recession, but another factor was the stiffened competition with fresh sweetpotatoes, which were becoming available in better quality and distribution over a longer season. The solid or mash packs, the only styles in use up to that time, were not satisfactory substitutes for the fresh vegetable.

After 1933 the production of canned sweetpotatoes again took an upward trend, until in 1940 a pack of some 800,000 cases for the first time exceeded the previous high of 1925. Vacuum packing of whole small sweetpotatoes of the Jersey type, which could be so processed without objectionable softening, had been introduced in the Middle Atlantic States. The vacuum-packed product was more attractive to consumers who favored the drier, or more mealy-fleshed, sweetpotatoes. In the late 1930's the sirup pack was introduced. Varieties which have a greater tendency to soften in processing than do the Jersey types retain their shape and firmness when canned in sirup. The development made possible a very attractive pack of the Porto Rico variety of sweetpotato widely grown in the Deep South. It found ready consumer favor and gave impetus to expansion of sweetpotato canning in the South Central and the Southeastern States.

With the added impetus of defense and lend-lease demands, the output of canned sweetpotatoes more than doubled in 1941. Production dropped back abruptly in 1942, and, while progressively increasing in 1943 and 1944, was kept below its 1941 level by wartime restrictions on sugar and tin plate. In 1945, however, 2,260,000 cases set a new high, which was topped by the 1946 production of more than 3 million cases.

Greater activity of canners in the Deep South, particularly in Louisiana, was responsible for the recent increases in the production of canned sweetpotatoes. At one time Maryland and Virginia were the leading sweetpotato canners. Mississippi put up about 21 percent of the national pack in 1919, but in the succeeding 12 years dropped to 7 to 10 percent and in 1935 and 1937 to 2 to 3 percent. In the record season of 1946, Louisiana alone accounted for nearly 40 percent of the total production reported by the National Canners' Association.

The solid or mash packs have been largely displaced by the whole pack in sirup and the vacuum pack.

The 1946 pack was greater than the demand and resulted in a surplus that was difficult to move. The inferior quality of some of it gave the industry a setback the following season. However, with disposition of the surplus and more widespread adoption of improved practices in selection of raw material and in preparation and processing, canned sweetpotatoes are finding a steadily expanding outlet. Some of the newer varieties and selections of sweetpotatoes offer promise for further improvement of the canned product. Solution of some processing problems which still hamper output of a uniformly high-quality product should expand the market still further.

DEHYDRATED sweetpotatoes made an important contribution to the supply of dehydrated foods for our Armed Forces in the Second World War. From 1942 through 1945 more than 4 million bushels were processed to produce close to 40 million pounds of dry product.

For many years there had been recurrent efforts to prepare a stable dehydrated sweetpotato product. Preservation of sweetpotatoes for home use by simple drying procedures is common in rural sections in China, Japan, and other countries where the crop is commonly grown. Small-scale drying was rather common in our Southern States before modern storage methods made it possible to keep the fresh roots in good condition for longer periods after harvest. However, the products from simple drying of sweetpotatoes without cooking or blanching leave much to be desired with respect to retention of color and flavor and reabsorption of moisture when prepared for the table.

A number of patents were granted on processes for dehydrating sweetpotatoes before 1900. In 1899 the South Carolina Agricultural Experiment Station undertook investigations to improve the dehydration process. Attempts to commercialize dehydrated sweetpotato products, however, met with little success until the Second World War. Then modern dehydration of sweetpotatoes for food use became a substantial enterprise.

Early in 1942 a Louisiana enterprise which had pioneered in the dehydration of sweetpotatoes for stock feed submitted to the Army Quartermaster Corps sample lots of sweetpotatoes dehydrated for food use by the latest procedures. A substantial order followed. The plant was converted to food dehydration and was in full production in the 1942–43 season. By 1944, 20 or more plants were dehydrating sweetpotatoes under Army contracts. Close to 40 million pounds were turned out from 1942 to 1945 and more than 4 million bushels of sweetpotatoes were processed.

There was some hope that dehydrated sweetpotatoes might find an outlet in civilian consumption after the war ended. Some producers placed limited quantities on the market; but not much consumer demand developed. Production dropped off abruptly in 1946 and since then it has become negligible. Most of the wartime plants have been dismantled or have been converted to canning. Apparently, they have found it difficult to compete with good canned sweetpotatoes where a stable packaged product, easily prepared for the table, is desired.

There is opportunity for further improvement in the quality of dehydrated sweetpotatoes by use of new varieties of superior quality for drying and by further improvement in processing methods. However, in 1951 there was relatively little activity in this field.

FLOURS OR MEALS prepared by grinding and screening the dehydrated sweetpotatoes have recurrent interest as supplements to wheat flour in bakery products. From time to time attempts have been made to manufacture and exploit them commercially, but, as a rule, the production was only experimental and lasted but a short time when carried to the commercial scale.

From 1900 to 1906 Henry S. Morris, of Philadelphia, manufactured a flour by grinding and bolting sliced and dried sweetpotatoes. During the First World War sweetpotato flour was used to some extent, but the products were not such as to encourage production after the emergency had passed.

In 1919 the Bureau of Chemistry prepared flour from sweetpotatoes by the flake process which had been used for white potatoes. The steamed potatoes were dried in a steam-heated double-drum drier and the resulting flakes were ground into flour. The results were unsatisfactory. Some years later, light-colored flours of high starch content were prepared experimentally from sliced air-dried sweetpotatoes, and in further experiments stable flours were obtained by grinding sweetpotatoes that had been dehydrated after a treatment with a cell-plasmolyzing agent and pressing out the excess water and solubles. It was thought that such products might be useful in brewing or in baking and in the manufacture of adhesives, but no commercial development followed.

For several years just before and during the Second World War a flour or meal prepared from dried sweetpotatoes was marketed in small quantities by a Texas concern. Its manufacture was discontinued when no demand developed.

Most of the sweetpotato flours produced up to this time have been prepared from potatoes that were dried without precooking or blanching. Such products deteriorate rather rapidly in flavor on keeping.

Toward the end of the Second World War some interest developed in the production of a flour by grinding and screening dehydrated sweetpotatoes prepared by the improved blanching and drying procedures used in supplying the Armed Services. One processor in Louisiana made and distributed such a flour for a short time. It was superior in flavor and keeping quality and found some use as an ice-cream stabilizer when stabilizers previously used were in short supply. It appeared to offer promise as an ingredient of pie fillings, puddings, and cakes. However, the producer suspended operations in 1947 and the flour disappeared from the market.

A NOVEL LINE of processed food products from sweetpotatoes has been developed experimentally by L. M. Ware and associates at the Alabama Agricultural Experiment Station. The sweetpotatoes are baked slowly until fully cooked, with maximum conversion of starch to maltose and dextrins, then peeled and pulped to a puree. The puree, with admixture of other ingredients where desired, is extruded onto trays and dried, with a final toasting in a bake oven. The product has a moisture content of only 2 to 3 percent. The size of the extruded strips, the character of added ingredients, such as coconut, sugar, and orange, and the degree of toasting are varied to produce confections of the taffy type, snacks, breakfast foods, and the like. The products are very attractive in appearance and flavor. Limited quantities, produced on a pilot-plant scale, have received favorable response when marketed on a trial basis.

Another product, a precooked flour, is prepared by grinding the dried extruded puree in a buhrstone mill. It makes a highly satisfactory ingredient of cakes, cookies, puddings, and icings. Milk shakes containing it were well received at a soda fountain in Auburn.

The Alabama Experiment Station products have not yet been exploited commercially. However, they seem promising if the process can be adapted to economical operation on a commercial scale.

Encouraging consumer reactions to several of the products were obtained in Nation-wide acceptance tests conducted in 1949–50 with the cooperation of the Bureau of Agricultural Economics.

Sweetpotato confections prepared by processes similar to those used in the preparation of candied or crystallized fruits are said to be popular in some South American countries, but have not been exploited to any extent in the United States.

FREEZING as a means of preserving sweetpotatoes for table use has been investigated at the Georgia Agricultural Experiment Station, with promising results. Precooked potatoes are frozen in the form of slices or a puree. No extensive commercial development has been reported. Freezing has been found an effective means of storing the puree used for the Alabama Experiment Station products.

SIRUP is another sweetpotato product that has been investigated. Utilization of sweetpotatoes for production of an edible or fermentable sirup has been the subject of recurrent interest and some experimentation for a great many years.

Fresh-dug sweetpotatoes contain from 1.5 to 3.0 percent of sugars, mostly sucrose, depending on the variety and environment. The sugar content increases, rising to 5 or 6 percent or higher, after curing and storage. More than 100 years ago, Robert Hare, of the University of Pennsylvania, reported the preparation of a sirup by concentration of a water extract of sweetpotatoes and noted its similarity to molasses or malt sirup. However, with either fresh or stored sweetpotatoes, the sugar content is too low to justify processing the roots directly for recovery of the sugar as such, or as a sirup, without conversion of the starch.

When sweetpotatoes are cooked the total sugar content is increased by the action of β-amylase, an enzyme which, when activated by the temperatures of cooking, converts the starch to maltose and dextrins before it is inactivated by

the higher temperatures in the final cooking. Sweetpotatoes of the Porto Rico variety are particularly high in β-amylase, and after curing and storage nearly all of the starch can be converted by slow baking.

Back in 1870 a patent was granted to Charles DeLamarre of New Orleans for a process in which cooked and pulped sweetpotatoes were treated with barley malt to convert the starch. The resulting mash was diluted with water and the juice was separated by decantation and pressing the sludge. The juice was purified and evaporated to a sirup.

Some 50 years later, H. C. Gore and associates in the Bureau of Chemistry conducted experiments on production of a high-maltose sirup by a similar process. They found that if the cooking conditions were properly adjusted most of the starch was converted by the native enzyme of the sweetpotatoes and that only enough malt to complete the conversion needed to be added. The juice was separated by pressing and refined by successive evaporation, dilution, and filtration. The filtered sirup was evaporated to about 70 percent solids content. The process was carried experimentally to a small commercial scale in a pilot plant in Georgia. The sirup produced was described as bland and sweet, with a distinct flavor. It was considered to have possibilities for a variety of uses. However, its color and taste restricted its usefulness and the manufacturing costs were rather high. The product, it was believed, could not compete commercially with corn sirup under normal conditions.

Glucose sirup has been prepared experimentally from sweetpotato starch by procedures essentially the same as those used in manufacture of glucose from cornstarch. The product does not differ appreciably from corn glucose.

The combined costs of raw material and processing have kept the commercial production of sirup from sweetpotatoes from becoming an attractive proposition. During the Second World

War the shortage of sugar stimulated some revival of interest in the possibilities. However, with the heavy demands on the crop for food purposes and the high prices prevailing, the supply, even of culls, available for other purposes was not enough to warrant exploitation.

G. A. SHUEY, of the Tennessee Agricultural Experiment Station, has described a procedure for home preparation of a jelly from the juice expressed from cooked sweetpotatoes.

In the Argentine, gelled sweetpotato products are manufactured on a comparatively large scale. A gelling agent, such as agar or Irish moss extractive (carragar), is incorporated with the sweetpotato pulp and sugar to form a very firm gel.

G. L. Baker and C. W. Woodmansee, of the Delaware Agricultural Experiment Station, have conducted experiments on the production of similar gels. The cooked and pulped sweetpotatoes were mixed with suitable proportions of the gelling agent, cane and corn sugar, and spice seasoning and boiled down to the point where the mixture would set to a strong gel when cooled. Powdered mixes which would produce gels upon adding water, heating, and cooking were also prepared from powdered dehydrated sweetpotatoes and the other ingredients in dry form.

SWEETPOTATO CHIPS can be prepared by methods similar to those used for white-potato chips. So far, production has been on an experimental or home-kitchen basis, and little or no commercial exploitation is reported. Sweetpotatoes are drier and tougher in structure than white potatoes and have a higher sugar content. Production of a uniformly satisfactory chip is a little more difficult. However, with proper conditions and precautions it is possible to prepare a very attractive and palatable product with a distinctive color and flavor quite different from those of the white-potato chip.

Some very acceptable chips were prepared experimentally from several varieties of orange-flesh and white-flesh sweetpotatoes at the Southern Regional Research Laboratory. The products from the orange-flesh potatoes are more attractive in appearance and somewhat sweeter. The products from the white-flesh sweetpotatoes, with a higher starch content, have a less pronounced sweetpotato flavor and more nearly resemble white-potato chips, although still distinctive.

J. G. Woodroof and S. R. Cecil, of the Georgia Experiment Station, who conducted more extensive investigations on the preparation of sweetpotato chips, have published recommendations as to the conditions and precautions in preparation of the slices, frying, draining, and packaging to yield a high-quality product.

PRODUCTION OF stock feed by dehydration of cull and other subgrade sweetpotatoes has attained considerable proportions in some parts of the South, especially Louisiana, since the end of the Second World War. Such feed affords a potential outlet for a greatly increased production of sweetpotatoes in the South, where livestock enterprise is expanding rapidly and locally produced carbohydrate feed is generally in deficient supply. However, with the present and prospective high costs of growing sweetpotatoes, processing for feed is restricted to the portion of the crop which cannot be moved in the food market.

Raw sweetpotatoes have for many years been fed to livestock, and farm surpluses or culls are commonly disposed of in this way. Raw sweetpotatoes are equivalent to about a third their weight of shelled corn in feeding value. The relatively high carotene content of Porto Rico and similar varieties gives them an added value, especially for dairy stock. However, the high water content and perishability of fresh sweetpotatoes place limitations on their use for feed. Dehydration puts the crop in a stable condition, in which it can be stored, handled, and distributed like corn and in which it is nearly equivalent to corn in feeding value.

Sweetpotato dehydration for feed as now carried out really had its beginning in experiments conducted by the former carbohydrate research division of the Bureau of Chemistry and Soils at the starch plant in Laurel, Miss., in 1938 to 1941. The pressed and dried byproduct pulp from sweetpotato-starch manufacture had been shown to make a good carbohydrate stock feed and had found a ready market for this purpose. Why not grind and dry the whole sweetpotatoes to make an even better feed containing all the nutrient material of the original potatoes? Experiments had been undertaken to explore the possibilities of dehydration as an economical means of preserving sweetpotatoes for starch extraction, so that the factory could operate beyond the end of the harvest season on stored material. For this purpose it was considered advantageous to remove much of the water and soluble matter of the original sweetpotatoes by mechanical pressing before dehydration. The drying costs would be reduced and it was hoped that the product would be more suitable for extraction of starch than if dried down with all the soluble matter present. A process was developed by which 50 percent or more of the water and solubles could be removed by disintegration in a cutter grinder, treating the ground pulp with a little hydrated lime, and pressing in a continuous squeezer press.

In the fall and winter of 1939 to 1940 more than 150 tons of sweetpotatoes were processed in this manner and dehydrated to produce about 50 tons of dried product. Drying was carried out in a specially constructed truck-and-tray drier and in the pulp drier at the starch factory. Enough material was obtained for a factory-scale trial of starch extraction and for cattle-feeding tests at three southern State experiment stations.

Processing of the dehydrated sweetpotatoes for starch was not very successful. The yield and quality of the starch recovered were very poor. On the contrary, the results of the feeding trials were very encouraging.

Further investigations of the dewatering and drying processes placed major emphasis on the production of feed, including direct drying of the disintegrated sweetpotatoes without pressing. The most effective method of disintegration was shredding the potatoes with beet knives in a simplified form of cossette cutter. Several models of such shredders were designed and constructed. The shredders now rather widely used in dehydration of sweetpotatoes are for the most part based on the designs developed at Laurel.

The results of this early work on production of dehydrated sweetpotato feed and the results of the feeding trials aroused interest in the possibilities of commercial feed manufacture, as well as farm-scale production. Experimental work was undertaken by other agencies, both State and private. In 1940 the processes developed at Laurel were carried over to the pioneer commercial-scale sweetpotato-feed dehydration plant at St. Francisville, La. A year later a commercial-scale experimental plant was set up at the State Prison farm at Atmore, Ala. Other commercial-scale enterprises were projected and further experimental work was undertaken in several quarters to develop driers and processes suitable for operation on a farm or small community scale.

After the outbreak of war in 1941 further development was retarded by the stringency of materials and diversion of activity to food dehydration. However, during the war a large sweetpotato packing and shipping enterprise installed a commercial-scale feed plant at Opelousas, La.

Toward the end of the war, manufacturers and individuals in Louisiana and other States undertook further development of commercial- and farm-scale dehydrators. By the end of 1946 as many as 150 or more driers had been installed in the South Central and

Southeastern States. Most of them were moderately small units, with capacities of 600 to 800 pounds of dry product an hour. As many as 75 plants were reported in Louisiana alone by early 1947. Of these, 54 processed sweetpotatoes in the 1946–47 season, with a total production of 8,500 tons of feed from about 974,000 bushels of sweetpotatoes, about 9 percent of the total State crop. In the 1947–48 and 1948–49 seasons the volume of operations dropped to 6,500 to 6,750 tons of feed, respectively, representing about 10 percent of the total crops. The numbers of plants operating were 47 and 37, respectively. Several of the plants installed never operated or suspended operations because of insufficient supplies of sweetpotatoes for processing. In all seasons many operated at too low a volume for profit. Where sufficient volumes of sweetpotatoes were available for sustained operations at full capacity, good returns were reported at the prices obtainable for the product. It should be noted, of course, that many of the plants in Louisiana have the advantage of very low fuel costs, with abundant natural gas available.

Dehydration for feed appears to have become established as an outlet for low-value unmarketable sweetpotatoes, and for trim waste from cannery plants, as long as the prices obtainable for the product in competition with other feeds allow a profit over and above raw-material and manufacturing costs, and as long as the volume of sweetpotatoes for processing is sufficient to sustain operation of the plant at an economical level.

When produced from sound raw material, reasonably free of rots and trash, dehydrated sweetpotato feed is an excellent product. It has found favor, even in competition with shelled corn, for beef and dairy stock. If, or when, the costs of growing sweetpotatoes can be sufficiently reduced to allow profitable diversion to feed of a larger proportion of the crop which should be kept out of the fresh-food market (No. 2's) or to make profitable the production of sweetpotatoes primarily for feed, the feed-dehydration enterprise can expand.

P. R. DAWSON, *an industrial analyst and special assistant to the director of the Southern Regional Research Laboratory, was head of the former sweetpotato products division of the Southern Laboratory from 1940 to 1949. He is a graduate of Clark College and the University of North Carolina.*

AMERICANS EAT more chop suey than the Chinese do, but the Chinese and Japanese eat 10 pounds of sweetpotatoes to our one. The Japanese alone raise at least twice the crop that we do and in some years five times as many pounds per capita. Sweetpotatoes are one of the basic foods in Japan. The crop there would provide enough carbohydrate and a large part of the protein needed to feed the entire population of the islands for 2 months. One reason for selecting this crop is not far to seek. In a country where food-producing land must be used to the utmost and cheap hand labor is available, sweetpotatoes can yield as much food to the acre as any crop raised in temperate climates.—*L. H. Greathouse, Southern Regional Research Laboratory.*

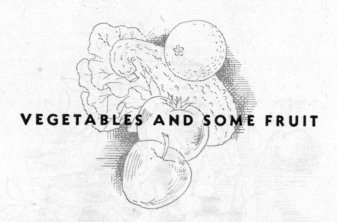

VEGETABLES AND SOME FRUIT

Our Second Largest Food Group

Francis P. Griffiths,
Harold S. Olcott,
W. Lawrence Shaw

The increased American demand for green and leafy vegetables has contributed to an enormously expanded production of truck crops in the past half century. This advance has been aided not only by improved farming practices, but also by effective methods of processing and distribution. In the years 1940 to 1949, the commercial growers marketed a yearly average of about 400 pounds of vegetables per person in our country. Many relatively local truck farms have provided a further quantity, which, although not recorded, is another sizable amount to include. Innumerable farm and city home gardens still provide additional vegetables. Into the American kitchen is going an increasingly larger amount of vegetables, both fresh and processed. A noteworthy portion of the vegetable crops is purchased already canned, frozen, and, in some cases, dried or pickled.

Next to milk and milk products, vegetables lead all other food groups in production and consumption in the United States.

Coupled with a growing consumption of fresh vegetables has been a growing population. Commercial farming has expanded to meet this market. Between 1940 and 1949, production averaged more than 25 million tons a year. Farm value was more than a billion dollars. In 1946, when our farm machine was going full tilt, we raised more than 30 million tons of vegetables; farm value soared to 1,600 million dollars.

We eat the roots or tubers of some plants—potatoes, carrots, beets, turnips, and sweetpotatoes, for example. We eat the stalks of others—celery, rhubarb, asparagus, and broccoli. We eat the leaves of still others—spinach, lettuce, chard, cabbage, beet greens, brussels sprouts, and kale. And we eat the ripened portion of some plants that are, or contain, or produce the seed for propagation—peas, beans, cauliflower, artichokes, and cucumbers. We call all these parts vegetables.

Nearly all vegetables are available in fresh form for use in the home kitchen during certain parts of the year. Most of them can be processed for use in winter. Generally speaking, the vegetables most commonly canned are those that are the end product, or near-end product, of the plant (peas, beans, corn, and tomatoes) or the root portions (beets, carrots, and, to a limited extent, potatoes). Asparagus and rhubarb of the stalk group are excellent when canned. Spinach is about the only leafy vegetable canned in quantity.

Freezing preservation widens the field of vegetable types that are processed. To the group that has already been mentioned for canning, we should add broccoli, brussels sprouts, artichokes, and cauliflower as vegetables that make fine frozen products. Other vegetables, notably cucumbers and cabbage, are processed by pickling and fermenting, or both.

213

Commercial production of vegetables in the United States, 1940–49 average

	Production [1]		Approximate farm value		
Vegetables	1,000 tons	Percent of total	1,000 dollars	Percent of total	Major producing areas [2]
White potatoes [3]......	12,280	45	506,500	36	Maine, Idaho, N. Y., and Calif.
Tomatoes............	3,680	14	141,000	10	Calif., Ind., N. J., Md.
Sweetpotatoes........	1,680	6	102,300	7	Southern States.
Cabbage............	1,400	5	36,900	3	N. Y., Wis., Tex., N. J.
Sweet corn..........	1,150	4	22,100	2	Minn., Ill., Wis., Iowa.
Dry beans and peas.	1,100	4	140,000	10	Calif., Mich., Idaho, Wash., Colo.
Lettuce.............	1,000	4	79,000	6	Calif., Ariz.
Onions.............	940	3	49,000	4	N. Y., Tex., Colo., Calif.
Celery.............	640	2	43,800	3	Calif., Fla., Mich.
Carrots.............	590	2	32,300	2	Calif., Tex., N. Y., Ariz.
Snap beans.........	460	2	52,500	4	Fla., N. Y., Calif., Oreg., N. J., N. C., Md.
Green peas..........	440	2	41,600	3	Wis., Wash., Oreg., N. Y., Minn., Calif.
Cucumbers.........	340	1	21,300	2	Mich., Calif., Wis., Fla., N. C.
Cauliflower.........	200	1	13,900	1	Calif., N. Y.
Spinach.............	200	1	13,800	1	Tex., Calif., Ark., Okla., Va.
Beets..............	180	1	4,100	1	N. Y., Wis., Tex., N. J.
Asparagus..........	160	1	27,700	2	Delta area of Calif., N. J., Wash., Ill.
Others [4]............	450	2	37,700	3	
Total of 34 vegetables.	26,900	100	1,365,500	100	

[1] Includes quantities used for seed, feed, and other nonfood uses.

[2] Indicates only largest producing areas of vegetables. Some vegetables, particularly white potatoes and sweetpotatoes, are produced commercially in many areas too numerous to list here.

[3] About 81 percent of the potato crop is normally used for food, 5 percent for seed, and 14 percent for nonfood purposes.

[4] Artichokes, broccoli, brussels sprouts, eggplant, escarole, garlic, greens (other than spinach), green peppers, kale, lima beans, okra, pimientos, popcorn, pumpkin, rutabagas, shallots, and squash.

The production and consumption of vegetables have followed varying trends. We eat, on the average, 50 pounds a year more fresh vegetables, other than potatoes, than we did 25 years ago, and 20 pounds more processed vegetables. On the other hand, we are eating 40 pounds less potatoes.

RESEARCH and education have contributed to the trend. During the past 20 years we have become more aware of leafy green vegetables as protective foods, which provide vitamins and other food constituents.

Some vegetables formerly of little commercial importance have taken an increasingly prominent place on the menu. Examples are broccoli, chard, and squash.

Vegetables supply us with minerals and vitamins, and also with proteins and carbohydrates. Experiments have demonstrated that the vegetable proteins, particularly those of leafy plants, are high in nutritive value. Carbohydrates, when digested, provide energy. Legumes, roots, and tubers contain more total nutrients than do the leafy green vegetables.

Although Americans now use many more vegetables than formerly, the

Composition of vegetables, edible portion

Vegetable	Water	Protein	Fat	Carbohydrate	Ash	Calories per pound
	Percent	Percent	Percent	Percent	Percent	Number
Asparagus....................	93.0	2.2	0.2	3.9	0.67	120
Beans, lima..................	66.5	7.5	.8	23.5	1.71	595
Beans, snap..................	88.9	2.4	.2	7.7	.77	190
Beans, snap (canned)...........	94.3	1.0	.1	3.3	1.3	80
Beet greens..................	90.4	2.0	.3	5.6	1.7	150
Beets, red...................	87.6	1.6	.1	9.6	1.11	205
Broccoli.....................	89.9	3.3	.2	5.5	1.1	170
Brussels sprouts..............	84.9	4.4	.5	8.9	1.3	260
Cabbage.....................	92.4	1.4	.2	5.3	.75	130
Carrots......................	88.2	1.2	.3	9.3	1.02	205
Carrots (canned)..............	89.6	1.0	.3	7.6	1.5	170
Cauliflower..................	91.7	2.4	.2	4.9	.85	140
Celery......................	93.7	1.3	.2	3.7	1.08	100
Chard.......................	91.8	1.4	.2	4.4	2.2	115
Corn, young, fresh.............	80.3	2.9	.8	15.4	.56	365
Corn (canned)................	76.0	2.5	.9	19.6	1.0	440
Dandelion greens.............	85.8	2.7	.7	8.8	2.0	235
Kale........................	86.6	3.9	.6	7.2	1.7	225
Lettuce.....................	94.8	1.2	.2	2.9	.9	85
Okra, fresh..................	89.8	1.8	.2	7.4	.84	175
Onions, fresh................	87.5	1.4	.2	10.3	.58	220
Parsnips....................	78.6	1.5	.5	18.2	1.15	380
Peas, young.................	81.4	5.4	.3	12.1	.77	330
Peas (canned)...............	85.7	4.0	.4	9.3	.60	260
Peppers, green..............	92.4	1.2	.2	5.7	.50	135
Potatoes....................	77.8	2.0	.1	19.1	.99	385
Spinach.....................	92.7	2.3	.3	3.2	1.53	110
Squash, summer.............	95.0	.6	.1	3.9	.44	85
Sweetpotatoes...............	68.5	1.8	.7	27.1	1.07	565
Tomatoes...................	94.1	1.0	.3	4.0	.57	105
Tomatoes (canned)...........	93.5	1.0	.2	4.3	1.00	105
Turnips....................	90.9	1.1	.2	7.1	.73	155

amount is still less than required for an adequate diet. Dr. Hazel K. Stiebeling, of the Bureau of Human Nutrition and Home Economics, estimated that we should double our consumption of leafy green and yellow vegetables and increase by at least 70 percent our use of tomatoes and citrus fruits.

Technical development has had an important part in providing us with a much greater variety of vegetables, in making them available either canned or frozen during the entire year, and in keeping fresh vegetables grown in California, the Rio Grande Valley, or Florida on eastern markets during winter. The use of ice as a refrigerant became widespread in the first half of the nineteenth century. Thomas Moore patented a refrigerator in 1803. By 1840 the household use of refrigerators was common. Iced shipments of perishable fruits and vegetables by rail began about 1850; in 1865, 30 freight cars were converted to "ice boxes on wheels" for the shipment of fresh meat and other perishables from Chicago to the East. The modern era of mechanical refrigeration began about 1870, when successful refrigeration machines were introduced into the United States. Most recently, field

Production of important vegetables for processing in the United States

	Average production	
	1918-22	1945-49
Vegetable	1,000 tons	1,000 tons
Potatoes [1]	10,518	12,892
Tomatoes	1,087	2,975
Sweet corn	511	1,225
Dry edible beans [1]	360	820
Green peas (shelled basis)	140	432
Cabbage	91	190
Cucumbers	78	241
Snap beans	29	204
Spinach	[2] 28	72
Asparagus	25	105

[1] Data not segregated as between fresh and processed use.

[2] No data for year 1918; average for 1919-22.

Calculated from U. S. Bureau of Agricultural Economics data.

packaging and rapid long-distance trucking have become important in delivering fresh vegetables to market.

Methods of can manufacture and food-sterilization techniques improved rapidly. By 1880, canning was a well-established industry, and canned foods were available to all city dwellers.

The last technical development to make fresh foods more available has been the frozen-food industry. Commercial freezing started about 1865, when fish were frozen by being placed in covered cans surrounded by ice and salt. The use of frozen small fruits for jams, jellies, pies, and ice cream began in the East in 1905 and was followed by the rise of the berry-freezing industry in the Pacific Northwest about 1910. The commercial freezing of vegetables attained industrial importance in 1929 and has expanded rapidly since then. More than 100 million pounds of fresh frozen peas were marketed in 1949.

About 25 percent of the vegetables produced between 1940 and 1949 were used in processing (canning, freezing,

pickling, and sauerkraut manufacture). The dehydrators used more than a million tons of potatoes from 1941 to 1945—more than half of all vegetables dehydrated in that period. Of increasing importance is the manufacture of potato chips, which in 1949 took more than 600,000 tons of potatoes. To utilize surplus stocks, hundreds of thousands of tons of potatoes have gone into potato flour for export since 1945, and in the 1948–49 season the total was more than a half million tons.

PROCESSING offers a major outlet for many vegetable crops, notably tomatoes, green peas, asparagus, sweet corn, cucumbers, spinach, snap beans, and lima beans.

The consumption per person of commercially processed vegetables has more than doubled through the past 25 years. The average annual consumption of the canned vegetables increased from 19.5 pounds a person during 1918 to 1922 to 39.3 pounds during 1942 to 1946. The consumption of frozen vegetables in 1946 was perhaps 3 pounds a person, compared with practically none 25 years earlier.

FRANCIS P. GRIFFITHS *was graduated in chemistry from the University of Washington and received his advanced training in food technology at Massachusetts State College. He joined the staff of the Western Regional Research Laboratory in 1947 as special assistant to the director.*

HAROLD S. OLCOTT *is a chemist at the Western Laboratory. He has been with the Department of Agriculture since 1941 and head of the vegetable processing division since 1948. In 1936 he received the Eli Lilly award in biochemistry from the American Chemical Society.*

W. LAWRENCE SHAW, *after majoring in economics at Pomona College, did graduate study at Claremont College and the University of California. He is a member of the industrial analysis section of the Western Laboratory.*

Nine Principles

for Freezing

Vegetables

James A. Berry, F. E. Lindquist

Food spoilage—putrefaction or fermentation—is due to the activities of micro-organisms, which break down organic matter in their search for food and energy.

Decay is most marked at high temperatures. It proceeds slowly at low temperatures. It stops at hard-freezing temperatures. Plant and animal tissues deteriorate after harvest or slaughter because of the activities of enzymes. Though responsive to temperature, enzymes are more tolerant of cold than are bacteria, yeasts, and molds. Hence, in the freezing preservation of vegetables, the inactivation of enzymes by heat is a routine preparatory step.

When the natural deteriorative processes have been checked, a frozen foodstuff will keep indefinitely if steadily exposed to sufficiently low temperatures. Because freezing alters the fresh character of foodstuffs least of all the preservation methods, the freezing industry has grown rapidly in recent years.

SUCCESSFUL FREEZING preservation rests on nine well-defined principles.

The foodstuff must be naturally adapted to the method. For example, peas freeze satisfactorily, but cucumbers do not.

The variety or strain must be of proved suitability. Garden-type peas, for instance, are superior to canning varieties for freezing.

The maturity or general character of the raw product must be of the best. Freezing preserves defects as well as good qualities.

Handling between field and plant and in the plant itself must be prompt. During unavoidable short delays, produce must be kept cool to check deterioration by respiration and microbial growth.

Natural enzymes, capable of lowering quality while the product is in freezing storage, must be inactivated. Scalding is thus obligatory for vegetables intended for freezing.

Freezing must be rapid enough to assure retention of quality in the product, give capacity to the plant, and yet be economical.

The plant must be kept sanitary, and the line clean. Molds, yeasts, and bacteria, if present in a frozen product in excess of reasonable limits, are regarded as proof of a poor sanitary history.

Packing must be such that practically no loss of moisture from the product occurs during a year's storage.

Storage temperature must be uniform and must not exceed 0° F.

The vegetable-freezing industries, which may be said to date from 1929, have grown rapidly. At first people were doubtful about the method. The behavior of vegetables at freezing temperatures was but little understood, and experience in fruit freezing, an older industry, offered only limited help. However, when it was proved that bad odors and tastes in frozen vegetables were due to action of enzymes that could be inhibited by a short scalding treatment before packing, the first hurdle was cleared.

Scientific work in the Department of Agriculture, State experiment stations, and private agencies has kept pace with commercial development—not infrequently has it made such development possible. Mention may be made of the establishment of times and temperatures for the scalding of various vegetables, the engineering of suitable freezing systems, determination of the relationships between storage temperature and product quality, the adaptability of varieties or strains of vegetables to freezing preservation, and the development of knowledge in such important matters as packaging, distribution, and public health protection.

The pioneer packs of frozen vegetables—about a million pounds in 1930 —were of peas, which are still the most popular commodity. The garden, or fresh-shipment, types were recognized as superior to canning varieties, and, as their vine growth is heavy and makes good ensilage, farmers in many sections came to find pea raising for frozen pack a profitable venture. The feasibility of freezing other vegetables (such as snap beans, spinach, corn, and asparagus) had been demonstrated by 1934. New concerns quickly entered the business. Some were offshoots of already established food-processing firms. Others were newcomers to the industry. Also, with expansion and diversification of output, the industry became more widespread geographically. Operators in quest for more raw material naturally came to depend on areas more remote from their processing plants. The resulting long hauls created problems of bacterial growth and deterioration in quality through respiration, which were met by icing lug boxes or establishing precooling stations. The perishability of harvested vegetables, especially shelled peas, and the close relationship between quality of raw material and that of frozen product early impressed itself on the industry and shaped its practices.

SCALDING, or blanching, vegetables to inhibit the enzymes is a key operation in preparation for freezing. If it is not done, the enzymes will function slowly at low temperatures and cause the development of undesirable odors and flavors in the frozen vegetables. Heat, either hot water or steam, is used to destroy the enzymes. The scalding operation obviously must be adapted to the product so that the necessary enzyme destruction causes minimum sacrifice of fresh quality. Peas, for example, are scalded for about 1.25 minutes and asparagus for 3 minutes at 212° F. Incidental advantages of scalding are intensification of color in green vegetables; slight wilting, which facilitates packing; and reduction in numbers of bacteria.

THE TERM "QUICK FREEZING," often heard in connection with food freezing, has no definite meaning. Probably most commercial vegetable freezing may be called quick; that is, the product is frozen to a temperature of about 0° F. in an hour or less. The packer is guided more by practical considerations of plant output, often paramount during harvest peaks, than by a conviction that such a freezing rate is absolutely necessary to insure good quality in the product. In vegetables like snap beans and asparagus, the rate of freezing may be reflected in the ice patterns, but such differences are of minor significance when the products are cooked and served. On the other hand, temperature of storage is recognized as being highly important. Deterioration in color and probably in eating quality takes place in frozen vegetables stored, for example, at 15° F., apparently irrespective of rate of initial freezing.

Various freezing systems have been advocated for vegetables. The basic consideration is the rapid transfer of heat to effect a hard-frozen state— about 0° F.—quickly and economically.

Most vegetables now are frozen in one of three ways. (1) With the refrigerated-plate method, the packaged food is placed between adjustable refrigerated plates, and pressure is applied to insure close contact and rapid freezing. (2) The air-tunnel system consists of a woven-steel belt moving slowly in a tunnel in which refrigerated air is circulated. Products like peas, lima beans, and cut corn can be frozen loose on the belt and packaged afterwards in a low-temperature room. (3) With the tray method, the vegetables, packaged or not as necessary, are spread on shallow trays in portable racks and frozen in rapidly moving refrigerated air in an insulated chamber.

Good frozen vegetables are produced by all three systems.

A flow sheet for frozen peas shows the following steps: Mowing; vining; icing (unless vining is done at the plant); cleaning; washing; sizing; scalding (steam or hot water, 200° to 212° F., for about 1.25 minutes); cooling; quality grading; inspecting; packaging and freezing, or freezing on refrigerated belts or trays and packaging; casing; and storing at −10° to 0° F.

Because frozen vegetables are used directly as such in the kitchen rather than in the manufactory as are most frozen fruits, they are put up in small packages, 12 or 16 ounces for retail trade and 2.5 or 5 pounds for institutions. Vegetable freezing in packages larger than 5 pounds might prove inadvisable because of bacterial growth due to slow freezing. If, however, peas or lima beans are loose-frozen on trays or belts, as is often done, the size of the final container does not matter. Some packers store part of their frozen peas in barrels or bins during the peak of the harvest season, pending development of market needs to determine container sizes. Vegetables like asparagus and snap beans do not lend themselves to loose freezing, because efficient and compact packaging in the frozen state cannot well be done. The usual container for frozen vegetables is a carton with a heat-sealable bag of transparent moisture-vapor-proof material.

THE PACK of frozen vegetables in the United States in 1949 was about 400 million pounds. Most of it was produced in about 60 plants. Peas, the leader, account for some 30 percent of the total pack. The Pacific Northwest is the outstanding region in pea freezing. Lima beans, frozen mainly in the Eastern States and California, are in second place—about 15 percent of the total pack. Frozen snap beans, asparagus, cut corn, corn-on-the-cob, spinach, broccoli, and brussels sprouts have become commercially important. Packs of carrots, cauliflower, squash, and pumpkin increased during the war. The States prominent in commercial vegetable freezing, not listed in strict order of their output, are Washington, Oregon, California, Minnesota, Wisconsin, Michigan, New York, New Jersey, Maine, Maryland, and Pennsylvania. Federal grades have been issued for all important frozen vegetables.

The most advantageously situated plants are those that can draw on a wide variety of produce, both fruit and vegetable, and may start with asparagus in spring and follow through steadily with berries or fruits, peas, beans, and corn, to late crops like spinach, broccoli, and brussels sprouts.

THE TRANSPORTATION SYSTEM developed for frozen vegetables is essentially the same as that for frozen fruits. Refrigerator cars holding from 45,000 to 50,000 pounds are first precooled and quickly loaded with material direct from storage at 0° F. or below. The bunkers are replenished with ice and about 25 percent salt as required en route. While a cross-country consignment may be in transit 9 days or more, and some increases in temperature in the outer parts of the load usually are noted, especially in hot weather, spoilage losses are low. Local distribution is preferably by refrigerated truck, although short hauls in cool weather may be made without refrigeration.

About 90,000 retail stores in 1950 had refrigerated cabinets for their frozen vegetables. In practice, the desired zero temperature is not always held.

Though actual spoilage under prevailing conditions is rare, many feel that retailing methods could be improved. Domestic refrigerators with a

0° F. compartment are now being made. They enable the housewife to buy and safely store a small supply of frozen foods for use as needed.

During the Second World War, frozen vegetables made some contribution to the feeding of the Armed Forces. Army authorities bought 71 million pounds in 1943 alone. The vegetables, used, of course, within the United States, freed an equivalent amount of canned or dried food for shipment overseas. The decision was made on the strength of laboratory tests by the Department of Agriculture simulating camp conditions, supplemented by use tests in camps. The tests proved that frozen vegetables remain usable in cool storage for several days, especially when packages are in the unbroken case. The rise in temperature and deterioration of the vegetables then are gradual at 40° F., so that refrigerators need be stocked only twice a week.

RESEARCH PROBLEMS of the industry include improvement of varieties from the cultural and utilization standpoints. Such improvement involves greater resistance to diseases, increased yields, earlier maturing, and better appearance and table qualities.

Important also is the identification of changes in texture and flavor, sometimes noticed in frozen vegetables, with a view to their elimination. For example, frozen snap beans tend to be limp, and frozen peas sometimes have an unnatural haylike flavor. There is also need of rapid, easily applied tests to determine optimum harvest maturity of vegetables, and of improvement in transportation so that all parts of the load are steadily held at the low temperature required by the frozen product.

Considering the similarity of frozen vegetables to fresh in appearance, taste, and nutritional qualities, and the fact that the per capita consumption in the United States is only about 2.5 pounds a year, most observers believe that a steady expansion of the frozen-vegetable industry is certain—even after making full allowance for factors tending to limit the rate of progress. The public appetite is only so big, and the use of a pound of frozen vegetables in a household means that a pound of the selfsame commodity in the more familiar canned, dried, or fresh form will not be needed. Supplanting the more familiar foods to any marked degree with frozen foods calls for a change in the buying habits of the public. Also, to the average consumer, frozen vegetables do not seem cheap. In fact, the heaviest buyers are in the upper-income brackets. Then, too, the perishability of the frozen pack at ordinary temperatures imposes conditions of storage and distribution that cannot always be met.

THE BASIC NEED for packers to produce only one grade of frozen vegetables—the best—bears restatement. Poor frozen vegetables are very poor indeed. However, there can be no gainsaying the unique quality of good frozen vegetables. Their cost is not prohibitive, and as distribution and retail facilities improve more people will become familiar with them and use them regularly. The question of the 1930's, "Are frozen vegetables here to stay?" is no longer heard. The question of today is "How far will they go?"

JAMES A. BERRY *was until recently a senior bacteriologist in the Western Regional Research Laboratory. He holds degrees from Michigan State College and the University of Washington. He joined the Department of Agriculture in 1931 and did research in the Frozen Pack Laboratory in Seattle. From 1941 to June 1950 he was stationed at the Western Laboratory.*

F. E. LINDQUIST *is a chemist in the same laboratory. He received his training at Fresno State College, the University of California, Stanford University, and the University of Pennsylvania. He taught biochemistry at Baylor University College of Medicine before joining the Department in 1942.*

The Art of Drying Vegetables

James A. Berry, F. E. Lindquist

Preserving food by reducing its water content is an old art. Dried raisins and figs were used in ancient times. The American Colonists cut corn from the cob in the sugar stage and dried it in the oven. Dried meat was a food many centuries ago. Thus the art of dehydration preceded the science.

We know today that dried foods keep simply because the molds, yeasts, and bacteria in or on the foods are deprived of the water necessary for their growth. The foods are not free from live microorganisms, but as long as the water content is kept low and the concentration of sugars and other solutes is high, the micro-organisms cannot multiply and thus give rise to fermentation or putrefaction. Conversely, the addition of water makes a dehydrated food perishable and, depending on temperature and rate of microbial growth, the rehydrated food will sooner or later harbor active micro-organisms and undergo spoilage. Because enzymes, the compounds necessary for life processes, may not be inactivated by removal of water and may bring about undesirable changes in appearance, composition, and flavor of the dried product, special methods to inhibit their activities generally must be employed. (Onions and garlic are exceptions.)

In Napoleon's day the necessities of war launched the canning industry; the Civil War saw the beginning of vegetable dehydration in the United States. In the South African War (1899–1902), some dehydrated foods were used by the British, who, as noted by Kipling, had already experimented with pea sausage (Erbswurst). The First World War greatly stimulated the production of dehydrated food; about 9 million pounds of potatoes (the largest single item), carrots, onions, turnips, and soup mixtures were shipped to the army overseas. As the foods were often of indifferent quality and appealed but little to civilians, production fell off after the war. A few specialties like dried onions and soup mixtures continued to find a market, but the total value of dehydrated vegetables produced in the United States in 1937 had shrunk to less than $150,000. The Second World War gave a tremendous impetus to vegetable dehydration. The pack in 1944 was nearly 209 million pounds, of which about 40 percent was white potatoes.

THIS GROWTH was not, however, haphazard. It was guided by research in the Department of Agriculture and other agencies. The aim was to develop a sound technology to replace rule-of-thumb methods, so that the dehydrated products for the Armed Forces and lend-lease would be of better quality than before. To this end, extensive studies were made of the suitability of raw material, the effect of handling practices and method of preparation on the quality of the dried product, dehydration systems and their operation, sanitation, reconstitution of the foods, their appraisal, determination of nutritional values, packaging methods, and deterioration of commodities during storage.

Two training schools, each lasting 2 weeks, were held by the Department in 1942. They offered plant operators courses in the application of scientific findings to practical dehydration. Also, in 1944 the Department issued a 218-page manual for the guidance of the industry. As was foreseen, however, packs of dried foods decreased with the coming of peace. The national output of dehydrated vegetables for 1947 was the comparatively small total of 51 million pounds, made up almost entirely of potatoes, peppers, onions, garlic, and carrots.

Some people have the mistaken idea that inferior vegetables will do well enough for dehydration. It is true that potatoes and onions, because of their good keeping qualities, need not be freshly harvested to yield a good dehydrated product, but the green vegetables should literally be harvest-fresh. The reason is that vegetables continue to respire and deteriorate in quality after they are harvested. Peas, for example, quickly lose their sugar, and spinach its vitamin C, on standing. Furthermore, if vegetables are held for more than a few days, even at low temperatures, there is a possibility of incipient spoilage by growth of bacteria. Cull vegetables as a rule are unsatisfactory because of excessive wastes in preparation. It is well recognized that operators of dehydration plants should either grow the vegetables themselves or contract with local growers to supply material of known history and sound quality. Reliance cannot be placed on open-market purchases.

Not all vegetables are suitable for dehydration. For example, asparagus when dried does not rehydrate well and it is tough and unappetizing. Other vegetables that are not very well suited to dehydration, or at least have not been commercially dried in quantity, are brussels sprouts, cauliflower, and squash.

The better adapted vegetables are white potatoes, sweetpotatoes, cabbage, carrots, beets, peppers, onions, garlic, parsley, snap beans, green lima beans, sweet corn, and green peas.

MATURITY OF VEGETABLES for dehydration is fully as important as for canning or freezing. White potatoes stored until their sugar content is high become dark when dehydrated. Woodiness in carrots and beets, or stringiness in snap beans, are serious raw-material defects that will appear in the finished product. Practical experience has amply shown that dehydration is in no sense a leveling or remedial process. It preserves defects as well as good qualities.

One of the outstanding differences in vegetable dehydration during the two world wars lies in the blanching, or preparatory heating operation. Most of the vegetables dehydrated in 1917 to 1919 were not blanched—scalded, that is. Most of those prepared from 1942 on were. Authorities agree on the value of blanching, except for onions and garlic. The advantages are easier drying, reduction of bacteria, better retention of vitamins and color, and quicker reconstitution. These outweigh the disadvantages of additional time and expense and some loss of extractives that blanching may entail.

Blanching is preferably done in steam. The times and temperatures must be carefully regulated according to the product. Underblanching does not inactivate enzymes. Overblanching destroys the texture of the vegetable and causes excessive leaching of nutrients.

Many types of food driers are in use. Some are suitable for specific purposes only. The operator selects a type combining the requirements of proved efficiency for his products and economy in operation. There are six main types of driers.

Spray driers consist essentially of a chamber into which the liquid or very finely divided material is fogged into currents of heated air. The product dries as it falls and is recovered in a collecting chamber. The system is adapted to juices and pulps.

In a drum drier the product is dried on the outside surface of internally heated cylinders and scraped off in powder or flake form.

The type in which the drying takes

place inside a revolving cylinder is generally called a rotary drier. In it, a current of heated air flows through the drier along with the wet material. Drying takes place as the material tumbles through the hot air.

Compartment driers have a drying chamber divided into several compartments in which stacks of loaded trays are run. A main duct carries heated air, which is diverted to each compartment. The air usually moves across the trays and may be discharged or reheated for further use. Compartment driers are especially suitable for small-scale operations.

Tunnel driers are the most widely used type for dehydrating vegetables. A typical tunnel is 40 feet long, 6 feet high, and 6 feet wide. It can be built of metal or of concrete and hollow tile. The product to be dried is spread on slatted trays of wood or metal, which are stacked on trucks. The tunnel accommodates 6 to 14 or more trucks. The whole string of trucks is periodically moved along one step, and a truckload of dry product is taken out at one end of the tunnel. A truck loaded with the freshly prepared vegetable is then run in at the other end. A high-capacity blower forces a strong current of heated air lengthwise in the tunnel through the spaces between the loaded trays.

The conveyor, or draper, type of tunnel drier is becoming increasingly important. In such driers, the product is spread an inch or more deep on a perforated metal conveyor belt, which moves slowly through the drying chamber. Heated air is forced through the perforations in the conveyor and through the layer of moist food. At the point where the conveyor leaves the drying chamber, the dry product falls into a collecting hopper.

Oil, gas, or coal can be used as fuel. The simplest system, direct heating, is widely used where gas or clean-burning oil distillate is relatively cheap. Hot air from the combustion chamber is mixed with fresh or recirculated air to moderate its temperature and then passed directly into the drying area. Indirect heating, requiring more complicated equipment, must be used if coal or heavy oil is the fuel. The most satisfactory indirect-heating system is a combination of steam boiler and steam radiator. In some of the older dehydrators, the air is heated by circulation over an extensive system of sheet-metal flues, which carry the hot gases of combustion from an oil-burning furnace.

The countercurrent system of air flow is the one most widely used. As the hottest and driest air is in contact with the nearly dry product, the low moisture content that is necessary for good keeping quality in dehydrated vegetables may be more certainly reached or approached. The allowable temperature of the hot air entering the tunnel is set by balancing several considerations. The hotter the air, the shorter will be the drying time and the greater will be the drying capacity of the dehydrator. The risk of scorching the product also will be greater. In practice, the best compromise has been found to lie in the range between 120° and 170° F., depending on the sensitivity of the particular vegetable to scorching.

Attainment of a sufficiently low moisture content is sometimes so difficult that a secondary final-drying step is necessary. A moderate degree of further drying—and, often more important, an equalization of moisture content and elimination of wet spots in the primary product—can be attained in a bin drier. The product from the dehydrator is charged several feet deep into a bin having a perforated bottom, and slightly warm, very dry air is blown up through the mass for several hours.

During the Second World War an entirely different method of final drying—desiccation in packages—developed by the Department of Agriculture reached the point of large-scale tests. Along with the normally dehydrated product, such as diced white potatoes, a small package of a strong water absorber, such as quicklime, is packed in the hermetically sealed metal shipping cans. In the course of several months of storage at ordinary temperature, water vapor diffuses from the vegetable pieces to the lime, and the moisture content of the food is reduced by 3 or 4 percent.

The operator of a dehydration plant must give constant thought to sanitation. His aim should be to produce a food as free from micro-organisms and foreign matter as possible. The plant must be kept rodentproof and insectproof. Because particles of vegetables left on the preparation line soon harbor enormous numbers of bacteria, making them a source of contamination to products being handled, all machinery and carrying belts should be frequently cleaned. Plenty of hot water, a good cleanser, scrubbing brushes, and willingness to use them are indispensable. All water used should be safe to drink. Frequent removal of waste, such as trimmings and peelings, should be routine. Finally, only healthy persons should be allowed to work, and they should be encouraged in cleanly personal habits by the provision of washrooms that are convenient, adequate in size, and well appointed.

The disposal of wastes from a dehydration plant may tax the ingenuity of the sanitary engineer. Solid wastes, such as peelings, may be used for stock feed, but the voluminous liquid wastes, which contain soluble or finely divided organic matter from the washing of cut vegetables, often present a problem. It is inadvisable to run them into a stream or ditch, for the organic matter combines with dissolved oxygen in the water, so that anaerobic fermentation, which stinks and creates a public nuisance, takes place. Public sewage systems as a rule are unavailable.

Sometimes the waste water can be run into lagoons, from which it will seep away if the soil is deep and open. If that cannot be done, the engineer must fall back on a system of screening, chemical treatment, and settling in a tank. The liquid from the tank may be used for irrigation, though sometimes it must be passed over trickling filters, which permit aeration. Because a dehydration plant, using, say, 100 tons of potatoes a day, may give rise to as much waste organic matter as is contained in the sewage from a town of 40,000 population, the problem of waste disposal clearly does not admit of haphazard solution.

IN DRYING white potatoes, the most important dehydrated vegetable, operators pay much attention to the quality of the raw material. New potatoes are not suitable. If the potatoes have been stored for a time at about 40° F., their sugar content may be too high and give rise to a dark color on drying. The condition may be rectified by holding them at about 65° F. for a few weeks.

The preliminary step is washing, usually in a "squirrel cage" machine equipped with sprays. Peeling processes were improved materially during the Second World War. Abrasive methods were generally abandoned because of excessive waste. Peeling by immersion for a few minutes in a boiling dilute caustic soda solution was widely used, and is still considered a satisfactory method. It has been partly superseded, however, by a method that loosens the potato skins by subjecting the potatoes to steam under pressure for several minutes and then quickly releasing the pressure. Subsequent spraying to remove the split and loosened skins should be prompt and thorough. Hand trimming to remove eyes and discolored spots follows. Peeling and trimming losses may run from 10 to 25 percent.

The peeled and trimmed potatoes are mechanically cut into slices not more than a fourth of an inch thick, strips not less than three-fourths of an inch in length and not more than three-eighths of an inch wide or thick, or cubes from three-sixteenths to three-eighths of an inch on a side. Surface starch is washed off in strong sprays. Cut potatoes are susceptible to discoloration; hence delays between operations must be avoided. The potato pieces are blanched, usually on a wire belt moving in a tunnel fitted with steam outlets above and below it. The operation is complete when a test for the enzyme peroxidase is negative. At that point, the product is sometimes exposed to a spray of dilute sodium sulfite solution. The slight amount absorbed helps prevent darkening of the final product and deterioration of its flavor during subsequent storage, especially if the storage temperature is relatively high. The potato pieces are loaded onto trays, care being taken to insure uniformity and suitable weight, usually about 2 pounds to the square foot.

Experience shows that during drying the temperature of potato pieces should never exceed 150° F. The rate of drying is far from constant. Loss of moisture is rapid for the first hour, but soon slows up. In the process, marked changes take place in the product. At first plump and tender, the pieces shrink in size, are distorted in shape, become firm, and end up hard, somewhat glassy, and brittle. One hundred pounds of prepared pieces entering the drier will yield about 22 pounds of dried product.

The drying of other vegetables is not essentially different from that of potatoes, although the preparation varies with the product.

For example, cabbage is trimmed, cored, and cut by machine into 1/4-inch strips. Blanching time is about 2 minutes in flowing steam. Cabbage, like potatoes, is sometimes treated with sodium sulfite to give better stability during storage.

Onions and garlic do not require blanching but may be injured by a temperature above 140° F. Also, as their moisture content should not exceed 4 percent, drying is usually finished in a bin.

Yields of dried products vary with the commodity. Based on the weight of the raw unprepared product, they range from 4 to 10 percent for cabbage, to 20 to 30 percent for sweetpotatoes.

Dried vegetables are bulky. The idea of compressing them to save storage and shipping space was tried by all the warring nations during the Second World War. With pressures of about 650 pounds to the square inch, it is possible to produce blocks weighing 55 pounds or more per cubic foot. Except with potatoes, there is no perceptible loss in quality from the process.

PACKAGING dehydrated vegetables is more important and more difficult than you might think. The ideal container is strong enough to withstand rough handling, a quality especially important in supplying soldiers on combat duty. It should permit hermetic sealing. It should resist penetration of moisture and be capable of retaining carbon dioxide or nitrogen, when gas packing is practiced. It should remain unaffected by normal extremes of heat and cold. Obviously, too, it should be insectproof and verminproof, and impart no foreign odor or flavor to the product.

Only a metal container satisfies all these requirements. Steel is scarce in wartime, and a perfect substitute has not been found. Single-sheet materials, even when heavily waxed, break down under rough treatment. Laminations of two or more sheets are better, but a lacquered fabric built of different materials, including metal foil and asphalt, is the most satisfactory. A bag of that sort will hold a partial vacuum when properly heat-sealed. When it is encased in a stout shipping container, it will withstand a good deal of abuse. Requirements for small-package retail distribution are naturally less exacting than those for overseas shipment.

DIRECT HOUSEHOLD USE of dehydrated vegetables is confined almost entirely to dehydrated soup mixes and certain condiments, such as onion salt, garlic salt, and chili powder. Substantial quantities of dehydrated potatoes and onions are, however, being used in such manufactured foods as corned-beef hash and catsup. Dehydrated potatoes and potato flour were among the foods flown into blockaded Berlin.

Packages of dehydrated vegetables usually have directions for use printed on the labels. Theoretically, as much water should be added as was removed in dehydration, plus enough to permit cooking without scorching. Fleshy vegetables, such as beets, carrots, and potatoes, can be reconstituted by soaking in cold water for about 30 minutes and boiling until tender. Leafy vegetables, like spinach and cabbage, are usually dropped directly into the cooking water. One pound of reconstituted vegetable is derived from about 2.4 ounces of dried beets, 2.7 ounces of potatoes, 3.3 ounces of carrots, and 1.5 ounces of cabbage.

Dehydration causes a concentration of proteins, fats, carbohydrates, and minerals. A loss of vitamins—hardly significant in some cases, but rather serious in others—has been reported. Further reduction in vitamin content occurs during storage. These facts should not be urged too strongly against dehydrated vegetables, because vitamin impairment follows other methods of preservation, as well as the standard methods of transporting and handling fresh produce. Also, it is possible that with wider choice of raw material, better handling and preparation, and improved packaging and storage, both the nutritional value and palatability of dehydrated vegetables will increase.

Granted good uniform quality and long shelf life, dehydrated vegetables should prove a great deal more than a wartime expedient, and could become the basis of a stable industry of considerable importance in the economic life of the Nation.

A NEW PROCESS of vegetable preservation, dehydrofreezing, has been under study by the Department of Agriculture for some time. The method partakes of both dehydration and freezing, the object being to effect economies in packaging, storage, and transportation, without altering the essential fresh quality of the vegetable. The water content of vegetables runs from 75 to 90 percent. Advantage is taken of the fact that in dehydration the evaporation of water is at first rapid and economical. Weight reductions in vegetables up to 40 or 50 percent are easily effected. At about 30 percent weight reduction, the product is little distorted. In particular, peas dehydrofrozen under pilot-plant conditions reconstitute well and are excellent in appearance, texture, and flavor. Also, potato slices and strips dehydrofrozen when the sugar content is optimum are superior for the production of chips and french-fries.

The water content in the partly dehydrated product is still high enough to permit growth of bacteria, yeasts, and molds; therefore the vegetables must be promptly frozen and stored at −10° to 0° F., like other frozen foods.

JAMES A. BERRY *was formerly a senior bacteriologist in the Bureau of Agricultural and Industrial Chemistry.*

F. E. LINQUIST *is a chemist in the same Bureau.*

THE ARMY put lemon powder in the K-ration as a source of vitamin C. The soldier considered it a drink and did not always use it—practically never unless the water was cold. But he found other uses for it: To bleach summer uniforms, clean stoves and floors, and reduce a supposed moldy taste in bread. He used the powder as a hair rinse and, in Italy, he combined it with GI carbonate tooth powder to make biscuits.—*Paul E. Howe, Bureau of Animal Industry.*

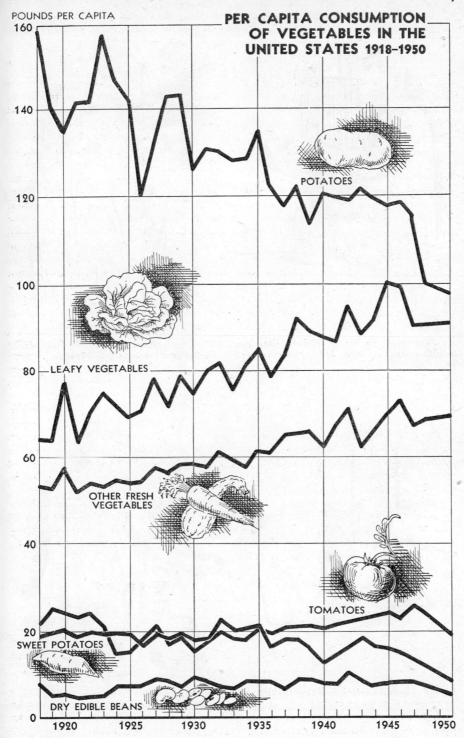

POUNDS PER CAPITA

PER CAPITA CONSUMPTION
OF VEGETABLES IN THE
UNITED STATES 1918–1950

POTATOES

LEAFY VEGETABLES

OTHER FRESH
VEGETABLES

TOMATOES

SWEET POTATOES

DRY EDIBLE BEANS

160

140

120

100

80

60

40

20

0

1920   1925   1930   1935   1940   1945   1950

An experiment to see if calcined lime can lengthen the storage life of dehydrated potatoes.

A patron removes some of the food placed earlier in a freezer storage locker.

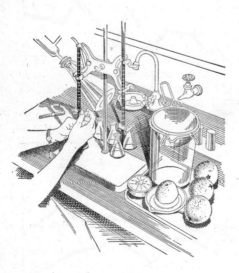

A food chemist determines by titration the vitamin C value of orange.

An inspector tests the quality of canned apricots and peas.

Advances in Cucumber Pickling

John L. Etchells, Ivan D. Jones, Thomas A. Bell

In this country the manufacture of cucumber pickles requires annually about 240,000 tons of pickling cucumbers. The crop is the fourth largest in acreage of the national truck crops (122,000 acres). A typical annual crop is about 10 million bushels and is valued at about 16 million dollars by 50,000 growers. About one-half the acreage is centered in Michigan and Wisconsin and one-fifth in the South Atlantic States.

The industry has three major operating fields. The first is manufacture of salt stock and genuine dills from green cucumbers by natural fermentation in brine. The second is the manufacture of such staple items as sweet, sour, and mixed pickles from the brine-cured cucumbers. The third is the pasteurization of various pickle products from green cucumbers, which is essentially a canning operation.

In each field, the industry has made notable advances in the past decade. Basic studies on the fermentation of salt stock have pointed out the complex nature of the microbial, chemical, and physical changes that take place. More information on how to spice pickles has made it possible to improve the finished products. Pasteurization has resulted in increased consumption of pickle products, by reaching new consumers and by giving packers a standardized procedure for preserving and maintaining the quality of their products. Storage problems have received renewed attention, and much that is advantageous has been learned. Many of these developments are the result of cooperative research by the Department of Agriculture and the North Carolina Agricultural Experiment Station.

The use of salt for the preservation of food began early in man's efforts to store edible material for his future consumption. During the years, salt preservation, or brining, has been gradually replaced by other methods, such as canning and freezing, for the bulk of commodities required for table use between seasons of production. Brining, however, is still used to produce cucumber pickles.

In times of national emergency, as during the Second World War, salt is used to preserve other vegetables, particularly when they cannot be frozen or canned because of wartime restrictions. During the period from 1942 to 1945, our research efforts turned to brine preservation of green beans, green peas, lima beans, wax beans, corn, lettuce, carrots, tomatoes, celery, okra, and certain leafy vegetables. Recommendations were given in a bulletin for the salting and brining of such vegetables for nonpickle use on both home and commercial scale. Information gathered during the 1943 season showed that several million pounds of vegetables such as corn, green peas, green beans, celery, and okra were successfully salt-preserved by commercial concerns for use in food products. Substantial amounts were also preserved in the home by this method.

In the cucumber-pickling industry, brine salinity is usually recorded in terms of degrees salometer, as measured by a hydrometer calibrated in percentages of saturation with respect to sodium chloride (0° to 100° sal.). For the convenience of the reader, degrees salometer have been converted to the approximate equivalent in percentage of salt by weight (for example, 20°, 30°, and 40° sal. brines would approximate brines with 5, 8, and 10 percent of salt).

Cucumbers are brined in wooden vats ranging in capacity from 200 to 1,200 bushels. In the South, where fermentation is relatively rapid, the vats are filled with green cucumbers, either graded to size or mixed, and fitted with loosely constructed wooden board covers keyed down firmly with wooden 2 by 4's or 4 by 4's. Salt brine of suitable concentration is added to a level of a few inches above the cover in each vat. Next, dry salt is added on the cover of the vat to maintain the initial brine concentration, which otherwise would be diluted by the water in the cucumbers. The initial concentration ranges from 8 to 10 percent salt, depending on the individual pickling plant. Usually the brine strength is gradually raised by adding enough dry salt on the cover to give a holding strength of 16 to 18 percent at the end of 4 to 6 weeks. Under these conditions and with brine temperatures of 75° to 80° F., salt-tolerant micro-organisms grow for at least 4 months. The micro-organisms that cause the fermentation come from the cucumbers and adhering particles of soil. They use as food the soluble nutritive material, principally sugar, that diffuses into the brine from the cucumber as the result of the action of salt solution on the tissue.

The growth of the micro-organisms, or fermentation, produces lactic and acetic acids, alcohols, and gases. The type of fermentation, with respect to the microbial groups involved and the end products formed, is greatly influenced by the starting brine strength and by the rate at which it is increased. At the end of the curing process, about 3 months, the cucumbers have changed from a green, opaque, buoyant fruit to olive-colored, translucent, gas-free salt stock.

In the North, the brining procedure is different. There the intake of cucumbers is slower, and therefore the vats are not filled so rapidly as in the South. The salting method, usually a combination of brining and dry salting, consists of adding a few inches of brine as a cushion in the vat and gradually filling the vat with cucumbers and dry salt. Some of the brine is formed by action of dry salt on the cucumbers. The initial brine strength used is usually in the range of 6 to 7.5 percent and is not generally raised according to any set schedule but is dependent mostly on temperature conditions and progress of the acid fermentation. The aim is to have the stock cure out as much as possible before cold weather—otherwise, vigorous gaseous fermentation takes place in the spring as the brine warms up. Another feature characteristic of northern brining stations is that most of the vats are sheltered. Shelters, which range from high sheds to enclosed buildings, prevent the dilution of the brine by rain or snow, but provide ideal conditions for the film-forming yeasts, which are absent from the brine surfaces of vats in the open and exposed to direct sunlight.

During the natural fermentation of cucumbers for salt stock, the following salt-tolerant microbial groups may be present: Acid-forming bacteria, yeasts, coliform bacteria (*Aerobacter*), and obligate halophilic (salt-loving) bacteria. As a result of the growth of these organisms, lactic and acetic acids, alcohol, and gases are formed.

UNDER SUITABLE CONDITIONS as to temperature and brine strength, an active acid fermentation, resulting from the growth of salt-tolerant, acid-forming bacteria, begins within a day or so after the cucumbers are brined and continues for 4 to 6 weeks. The preserving effect of the brine is due chiefly to the combined action of the salt and the developed acidity. There is a direct relationship between numbers of lactic acid bacteria and the brine strength used. For example, in 5-percent brines upward of 200 million bacteria per milliliter are found. Correspondingly smaller populations are found as salt concentrations increase. At 15 percent concentration or stronger, little or no growth by the acid-producing bacteria is observed. The effect of salt on the growth of these organisms is shown by the degree of developed acidity. Fermentations at salt concentrations of 5, 10, and 15 percent result in decreasing brine acidity—0.7, 0.4, and 0.1 percent total acid calculated as lactic.

Identification studies on cultures of lactic acid bacteria from commercial fermentations at 5, 8, and 10.5 percent salt showed that the bacteria were *Lactobacillus plantarum*. Additional cultures from commercial brines at 11 to 12.5 percent salt were also identified as this species.

Yeasts associated with the cucumber brines are of two general groups: Those that produce a gaseous fermentation in the brine; and those that produce luxuriant films on the brines exposed to air but sheltered from direct sunlight. The two groups are frequently confused in the reports on cucumber pickling.

Yeasts capable of gaseous fermentation have a high tolerance to salt and acid. Fermentations are found in brines ranging from 2.5 to 20 percent salt by weight. As a rule, the salt content governs the time yeast growth starts, as well as the duration of activity. Carbon dioxide is evolved from the brine surface as long as yeasts are present. At brine temperatures of 75° to 80° F. and fermentations at 5 percent salt strength, yeast growth usually starts within 2 to 3 days and populations drop sharply after 7 days of activity. At 10 and 15 percent brine strengths, yeasts start growing in 7 to 12 days, respectively, and the gaseous fermentation continues for a much longer period than at 5 percent. The reason for the more active development in the stronger brines is that the lactic acid bacteria are inhibited as the brine strength is increased and more fermentable material remains for the yeasts, which are not similarly inhibited.

The principal subsurface yeasts, isolated and identified during fermentation of 42 commercial vats of cucumbers at two plants, fell into the following six genera in the order of frequency of isolation: *Torulopsis*, 721 cultures; *Brettanomyces*, 588; *Zygosaccharomyces*, 59; *Hansenula*, 49; *Torulaspora*, 6; and *Kloeckera*, 1. Two new species, *Torulopsis caroliniana* and *Brettanomyces versatilis*, accounted for 88 percent of the total cultures. These results are based on fermentations under southern conditions. First results in studies on cultures obtained from northern brines indicate that yeast activity also forms part of the general fermentation of cucumbers brined in Michigan, Indiana, and Wisconsin. Several of the species—*Torulopsis caroliniana*, *Brettanomyces versatilis*, *Hansenula subpelliculosa*, *Torulaspora rosei*, and *Zygosaccharomyces* spp.—were found in both brining areas.

Film-forming yeasts do not depend on sugar for growth but use organic acids or alcohol in the brine as a source of energy. Their growth causes a decrease in brine acidity. In 1939, E. M. Mrak and Lee Bonar, of the University of California, found that the surface films on seven samples of cucumber salt stock at 18 to 20 percent salt were the result of growth by film-forming yeasts belonging to the genus *Debaryomyces*. However, films on seven samples of dill-pickle brines at 4 to 6 percent of salt were identified as species of the genera *Mycoderma* and *Picha*. Work by the writers shows that species of *Endomycopsis*, *Candida*, and *Zygosaccharomyces*, in addition to *Debaryomyces*, produce films on commercial cucumber brines.

A third type of fermentation frequently takes place during salt-stock production. This fermentation is characterized by the evolution of hydrogen. Bubbles of this gas forming on the brine surface may be exploded by ignition with a flame, thereby giving a ready practical test for this type of fermentation. Hydrogen fermentation in the cucumber brines is caused by two groups of bacteria and the gas formed is a mixture of carbon dioxide and hydrogen. One group has been established as belonging to the genus *Aerobacter*. The other, unidentified, is closely related, but differs in that at least 5 percent salt by weight is required before it will grow. Both groups are very salt-tolerant, but also very sensitive to the acid produced by the acid-forming bacteria and to added organic acids, such as vinegar and lactic acid. This sensitivity to acid stops the hydrogen fermentation in the 5 percent salt range owing to the simultaneous rapid growth of acid-forming bacteria. In certain seasons, however, these organisms seem to predominate on the cucumber, and 10.5- and 15-percent brines develop gaseous fermentations that are very vigorous to violent.

The lack of sufficient oxygen and the salt content of the brine are factors that discourage the growth of molds beneath the brine surface. Molds are usually present at the start of brining, but decrease rapidly and disappear within a few days. Under sheltered conditions, molds may be found growing along with film yeasts. But molds have appeared on the surface of brines even under outside conditions during periods of cloudy and humid weather. In experiments with cucumbers at 10.5-percent brine, and wax beans at 4-percent brine, unrestricted mold growth softened the vegetables to the extent that they were not usable.

Salt-stock spoilage is of two kinds. One is the formation of "bloaters," or hollow cucumbers, as a result of gaseous fermentation; the other is softening of the stock, which is attributed to pectin-splitting enzymes.

Bloater formation may be of either the "balloon" or the "lens" type. In the balloon type, the carpels of the cucumber separate because of internal gas pressure and are pressed flat toward the skin, leaving a large gas- or liquid-filled cavity. In the lens type the gas pockets in the cucumber tissue are smaller and lens-shaped. Lens bloaters are generally restricted to the smaller cucumbers. Leaders of the industry estimate the loss due to bloaters at $750,-000 annually. This loss actually is in the reduced value of the cured stock, because bloaters cannot be used as whole pickles but only as cut pickle or relish. Although gaseous fermentation by yeasts is responsible for most of the bloaters, sporadic hydrogen fermentation also contributes to bloater formation. Hydrogen fermentation may affect cucumbers of any size; yeast fermentation, however, usually turns only the larger ones into bloaters. The influence of the initial brine strength on the percentage of bloaters in the large cucumbers is shown by averaged results from 28 vats over a 4-year period: At brine strengths of 5, 10.5, and 15 percent salt, the percentages of bloaters formed were 6.5, 22.9, and 43.6.

Softening of salt stock by pectin-splitting enzymes does not result in yearly losses like those due to bloaters, but may be more severe in some years than others, and in some brining areas than in others. This condition may develop at plants using different brining treatments and different varieties of stock and with vats either outside or inside. In other words, softening may sometimes be widespread and take place under varied conditions of plant procedure. The softening may be only slightly noticeable or it can progress rather rapidly so that the stock cannot be used because of lack of firmness.

To date there has been no clear-cut demonstration that any one group of micro-organisms is responsible for the softening of salt stock in commercial cucumber fermentations. A large number of organisms, including different genera of bacteria, yeasts, and molds, have been reported as capable of producing the pectin-splitting enzymes that would destroy cucumber tissue.

Whether one or more of these groups could develop in brines would depend on the adaptation of certain strains to salt tolerance.

We have approached this softening problem from the standpoint of detection of the specific softening enzyme in the brine. We have learned that a pectin-destroying enzyme corresponding in chemical behavior to commercial pectinase is responsible for the loss in firmness of salt stock and have made progress in correlating pectinase activity of the suspicious brines with the degree of softness of the salt stock. We are using this approach also in determining pectinase activity of the different groups of the organisms isolated from the fermentations.

So far, a total of 143 yeasts, representing 66 species in 15 genera, have been screened for their ability to produce the salt-stock softening enzyme. This total included representative species of yeasts responsible for the gaseous fermentation of brined cucumbers, as well as those responsible for film formation on brines. Thirty-three of the species tested came from other collections. None of the yeasts from cucumber brines was found to be a potential source of the softening enzyme (pectinase). However, most of the film-forming species were capable of changing pectin to pectic acid. Four yeasts from sources other than cucumber brines were able to produce the softening enzyme.

The cucumber plant and its fruit have also been studied as a possible source of the salt-stock softening enzyme. An enzyme very similar to that responsible for softening of brined cucumbers has been found in dry cucumber seeds, male flowers, fertilized female flowers, and also in the ripe cucumbers. A second enzyme, known as pectase, has been found in various parts of the cucumber plant and the fruit. Working alone, this enzyme probably would not damage the cucumber as far as firmness is concerned.

However, pectase is important because it has the property of speeding up the action of the softening enzyme (pectinase). During the growth of a cucumber, from a very small fruit to maturity, the enzyme pectase remains at a rather constant level. This is in sharp contrast to the tomato where the enzyme content increases rapidly as the fruit ripens. Our enzyme studies demonstrate that the cucumber itself may be an important contributing factor to the spoilage of salt stock resulting from softening.

VARIOUS TYPES OF finished pickle products are made from completely cured salt stock by a series of operations—leaching out most of the salt, souring with vinegar, and sweetening with sugar.

The leaching, or desalting, operation is called processing by the industry. The 15 to 18 percent of salt in the cured stock is reduced to about 4 percent by at least two changes of water. In the last change the water is heated to about 130° F. and turmeric is added for coloring and alum for crisping or firming. After desalting, the stock is covered with distilled vinegar. This is referred to as souring. Sour pickles and processed dills are made directly from the souring operation and are made to contain about 2.0 and 0.8 percent acetic acid, respectively.

The sweetening operation is usually carried out in small tanks of 40- to 100-bushel capacity, although some packers prefer to sweeten in barrels. To make sweet pickles, the processed stock, after souring in distilled vinegar, is covered with liquor, or sirup which contains all the vinegar and some of the sugar to be used. The remaining sugar is added gradually until the desired sweetness is reached; otherwise the pickles will shrivel badly.

No legal requirements have been set for the sugar content of sweet pickles. From the manufacturing standpoint, enough vinegar and sugar must be added to prohibit fermentation.

The sugar content of the commercially made pickles may vary from 36 to 51 percent (20° to 28° Baumé) and the acid content from 1.6 to 2.1 percent acetic acid (16 to 21 grains vinegar). As the sugar content is increased, less acid is required for preservation. For example, a product finished at 51 percent sugar would require at least 1.6 percent acetic acid, as compared to one finished at 36 percent sugar, which would require at least 2.1 percent acetic acid. To prevent fermentation, sweet pickles containing less than 2.0 percent acetic and 36 percent sugar are pasteurized according to the procedure described later.

Proper blending of the spices is important in the preparation of pickles. Commercial formulas vary, depending on the product, the individual manufacturer, and customers' preferences. The common whole spices used are allspice, cloves, coriander seed, yellow mustard seed, celery seed, cardamon seed, dillweed seed, ginger root, bay leaves, cassia, mace, Japan chilies, and black pepper. In the past 10 years rapid development has been made in the use of spice oils and oleoresins as replacements for whole spices in some pickle products. F. W. Fabian, of Michigan State College, who provided this list of spices, has contributed much to the knowledge of spicing pickles with such oils as clove, cassia, allspice, or pimento, in combination with the oils of nutmeg, ginger, thyme, and cardamon.

YEASTS AND LACTIC ACID BACTERIA usually will grow in finished sweet pickles that do not have sufficiently high levels of sugar and vinegar. The growth of yeasts in jars of whole sweets imparts a "fermented" taste and usually causes bloaters. Yeast fermentation may also develop during the sweetening process in tanks if the acetic acid content drops below 2.0 percent, causing bloater formation if it goes far enough. Molds and film yeasts may develop on the liquor surface of pickles, including sours and dills, chiefly as the result of faulty jar closure. Too much head space in low-acid products, such as dills made from salt stock, may result in the growth of film-forming yeasts.

Plant sanitation is important in connection with spoilage problems. Yeasts can develop high tolerance to acid or sugar or both when their growth is unrestricted by lack of cleanliness in a plant. In a recent outbreak of spoilage of finished pickle products, we isolated an acid-tolerant yeast belonging to the genus *Zygosaccharomyces*. Under laboratory conditions, this yeast was capable of fermenting liquors containing various amounts of acid, sugar, and benzoate of soda. Three solutions containing the following ingredients were fermented: (1) 10 percent sugar and 3.0 percent acetic acid; (2) 10 percent sugar, 1.5 percent acetic acid, and 0.1 percent benzoate of soda; (3) 60 percent sugar.

PASTEURIZATION rapidly has become of major importance. It is estimated that at least 20 percent of the domestic crop of pickling cucumbers now goes into fresh pasteurized products. Pasteurization has made it possible to add a new line of products to the standard sweets, sours, mixed pickle, and relish. The characteristic crispness and fresh appearance and flavor of the pasteurized fresh dills and fresh sweet slices make them popular with consumers. The moderate requirements of sugar, vinegar, and spices in their manufacture make them popular with packers, too.

Probably a dozen or more types of pickles made from fresh or partially fermented cucumbers require pasteurization. These products may be classed as fresh or unfermented, partly fermented, or fully fermented. Pasteurization is required for the first group to prevent fermentation, for the second to stop the fermentation under way, and for the third to prevent the further growth of organisms or the action of fermentation byproducts that might reduce the firmness of the pickle during storage.

No doubt the bulk of the pasteurized pack is composed of the sliced fresh cucumber pickle, commonly called bread-and-butter pickle, and the fresh dill pickle. A number of closely related types of dills that require pasteurization should be mentioned. These differ chiefly in the duration of the natural fermentation period allowed before packaging, or in the amount of acid, salt, and spices used during preparation. Quite often, partly fermented dills are referred to as Polish, Hungarian, overnight, or fresh-fermented dill pickles. The addition of garlic and more spicing may be sufficient reason for the packer to label any one of the various types of dills a kosher-style product. Ordinarily such a pickle is relatively low in acid and salt and is rather highly seasoned, particularly with garlic.

Genuine dills, when properly pasteurized, retain most of their firmness over a storage period of many months. Loss of firmness in genuine dills either before or after marketing has been an important reason for the marked reduction in their manufacture. Even though the problem of retaining the firmness after packing has been solved by pasteurization, sales resistance has developed because of the milky brine, which is the result of the activity of the organisms of the natural fermentation. The customer has been sold on substitutes in the form of processed dills from salt stock which have clear brines. A genuine dill with an added clear brine is not the answer, because the original flavor produced by the fermentation is changed and the cost of fermenting the dills in barrels or tanks exceeds that for substitute products.

Pasteurization is also required for the sweet pickle made from salt stock, which differs from the usual sweet pickle in that it lacks enough sugar and vinegar to prevent fermentation.

The pasteurization treatment has been developed for the industry by carefully conducted experiments under commercial conditions to determine the correct amount of heat required to kill the organisms responsible for spoilage, yet retain most of the characteristic appearance and crispness of the fresh cucumber tissue. On the basis of this work, a procedure involving the use of a maximum product-interior temperature of 165° F., followed by prompt cooling, has been recommended for pasteurized pickle products containing required amounts of vinegar. The process is adaptable for both continuous and batch pasteurizing operations.

Spoilage occurs in products of this class when they are improperly pasteurized, and is caused chiefly by yeasts or acid-forming bacteria, or both, that survive faulty heat treatment. Molds and film yeasts are spoilage factors in cases of poor jar closure. Excessive heating of pasteurized products gives them a cooked flavor and soft texture.

CUCUMBER VARIETIES used in pickling may be divided into two general groups—white-spined varieties and black-spined varieties. Most of the pickles manufactured commercially are made from black-spined varieties. We have recently shown that the quality of salt-stock cucumbers and manufactured pickle products is closely related to the variety of cucumber used. Such factors as shape, crispness, skin color, skin toughness, and the presence of bitter flavors account for the differences between varieties.

A number of white-spined varieties have recently been developed for use in pickling. Several have certain advantages over black-spined cucumbers. For example, some are more productive, ship better, and can be held in temporary storage as fresh stock with less spoilage than can black-spined varieties. However, the type or variety of cucumber best suited to an individual pickling company depends on the location of the processing plant, the type of product being manufactured, and customers' preferences.

THE ULTIMATE OBJECTIVE of any changes in cucumber pickling is to place this industry among the controlled-fermentation industries. Clearer understanding of fermentation and identification of increasing numbers of microbial groups and their byproducts contributing to the fermentation bring the controlled-fermentation goal closer. Control procedures cannot be developed until the basic information is collected and understood. Practically the only control the packer has today is the use of salt. Actually, salt has no effect on some micro-organisms that cause difficulty, and may actually foster their growth. Numerous experiments on a commercial and semicommercial scale have definitely proved that no one brining treatment is capable of giving the same degree of firmness of stock consistently from one year to another.

Pasteurization, with its new line of pickle products, has been a notable advance in the industry. The practice will undoubtedly continue to increase.

In the past decade there has been a marked increase in the number of technically trained employees and a decided improvement in laboratory facilities at pickling plants. With a better knowledge of chemistry, bacteriology, engineering, and food processing, packers can develop more standardized procedures that will result in improved quality of products, reduction of spoilage, and better sanitation.

JOHN L. ETCHELLS *is in charge of the food-fermentation investigations of the Bureau of Agricultural and Industrial Chemistry. He is a native of Michigan and received his doctorate at Michigan State College. Since entering the Department in 1935, he has been engaged in research relating to the bacteriological changes during the fermentation of brined and salted vegetables, especially cucumbers.*

IVAN D. JONES *is research professor of horticulture, in charge of fruit and vegetable processing at North Carolina State College of Agriculture and Engineering. For the past 15 years he has been engaged in research covering a wide field of problems dealing with the cucumber-pickling industry. He received his doctorate in agricultural biochemistry at the University of Minnesota.*

THOMAS A. BELL *is a native of South Carolina and a graduate of Wofford College and North Carolina State College of Agriculture and Engineering. He is a chemist in the Bureau of Agricultural and Industrial Chemistry and since 1940 has done research on chemical changes in brined vegetable fermentations.*

ACCEPTANCE of the results of advancement in science is sometimes delayed. Take vitamin A. Investigators in Wisconsin demonstrated that there seemed to be an association of the vitamin A potency of food with yellow color. Investigators in Missouri, however, had shown that color is not necessarily associated with the vitamin A in eggs. It took some years and the discovery of yellow carotene as a precursor of vitamin A to discover the reason for the discrepancy. Vitamin A is practically colorless, but carotene is one of the yellow pigments of plants, milk, and milk fat—but not of egg yolk.

The association of yellow color with the presence of carotene in green leaves has been one of the most practical discoveries made in nutrition for popular education in the feeding of both man and animals. It leads, in part, to the designation "leafy green and yellow vegetables" as an important group of foods.—*Paul E. Howe, Bureau of Animal Industry.*

Floating Peas To Clean Them

A. M. Neubert

Froth flotation, a technique first used by the mining industry for concentrating and enriching ores, has been adapted to the commercial cleaning of vined green peas to be canned or frozen. It reduces labor in inspecting and sorting, improves the quality of the packaged product, and saves for market large tonnages of peas that would otherwise be discarded because of heavy contamination with foreign material.

Present methods of processing green peas exemplify the efficiency that can be achieved in the commercial production and preservation of a highly perishable food through the application of science. Advances made by the industry now permit operations on a tremendous scale. A number of processors in the Blue Mountain area of Washington and Oregon harvest 7,500 to 12,000 acres of peas annually and are equipped to process from 300 to 500 tons of shelled peas a day. Labor requirements in harvesting, preparing, processing, and warehousing canned peas have been reduced in some cases to less than 1⅓ man-days a ton of peas processed, or about 25 seconds of labor for each 20-ounce can.

By the proper selection of land, varieties, and planting schedules, the processor obtains a continuous supply of green peas of prime maturity over a period of 30 to 60 days. Seeding, insect control, and harvesting are highly mechanized and provide shelled peas for processing with little hand labor.

The pea viner, a special type of thresher that removes the peas from the pods on the vine by a controlled beating action, may be considered the key to the industry. It permits the recovery of the tender green peas from the cut vines without picking and shelling the pods by hand. Processing operations consist of washing the vined peas, removing foreign material, sorting the peas by size and maturity, blanching, packaging, preserving by heat or freezing, and warehousing. Here again, mechanization and technical controls have greatly reduced the need for hand labor.

Although the pea viner makes large-scale commercial processing practical, it contributes a difficult problem to later preparation. The beating action of the viner breaks some of the more tender peas, which, with the debris from pods and leaves, contaminate the shelled peas. Other more serious contaminants are the seeds and flowers from weeds that grow in the fields and are harvested with the pea vines.

Many of the preparation steps in the processing plant were developed for the purpose of removing dirt, debris, and foreign materials from the vined peas. Preliminary sizing removes material that does not fall within the size range of the peas. Air separation removes material less dense than peas. A water wash removes dirt and also makes a separation based on density. Stones and other heavy material are trapped in riffles, and material that will float in water is skimmed off the surface of the washer. The washed peas may be graded for size and passed through reels or shaker screens, where some additional debris is removed on the basis of size.

Those steps remove most of the

debris and foreign material from the vined peas, but the burden of assuring completely clean peas rests on hand sorters. In normal operations, where peas are practically free from weed parts, hand-sorting requirements are not excessive in the larger sizes. Sorting costs are considerably higher, however, for the very small peas, which contain most of the broken peas and skins.

The sorting problem is seriously complicated when the vined peas contain weed parts that cannot be removed by the common mechanical cleaning methods, notably nightshade berries, dogfennel flowers, and tarweed seeds.

The problem of removing such material by hand becomes clearer when one realizes that a 20-ounce can will hold more than 1,500 small peas. If the peas are contaminated with only 1 percent of foreign material, for example, it becomes necessary to pick out more than 15 pieces of such material for each can. If even one piece is overlooked, the peas will not meet the rigid requirements for Fancy peas.

Because only a limited amount of foreign material can be removed by hand in commercial processing, it has frequently been necessary to slow up the sorting line or discard the contaminated peas entirely. Nightshade berries are particularly troublesome, because their resemblance to peas in size, shape, and color makes complete removal by hand difficult, even if they are present in only small amounts. Losses due to contamination with nightshade berries alone in peas grown in the Blue Mountain area of Oregon and Washington were estimated by various canners at 3 to 10 percent of the 1941 crop. It was to remove these foreign materials from the vined peas that the froth-flotation process was developed.

DIFFERENCES in size, shape, or density are the basis for the separation of foreign material from sound peas by the conventional mechanical cleaning methods. As broken peas and the trou-

blesome weed parts do not differ suff ciently from sound peas in those prop erties, some other physical characte istic must be selected as the basis fo separating them.

The froth-flotation process employ differences in wettability (the propert that determines how readily a solu tion will spread on a surface) to sepa rate the sound peas from foreign mat ter. Materials of the same density, bu differing sufficiently in wettability, ca be mechanically separated on the basi of the property by being placed in . suitable solution. The material not eas ily wetted will float; that easily wette will sink. This type of separation ca be made, even though the density o the floating material greatly exceed that of the supporting solution.

In practical applications of the prin ciple, the materials to be separated ar usually introduced into a solution con taining air dispersed as fine bubbles By control of the wetting properties o the solution, bubbles are attached t materials that are not easily wetted The attached bubbles buoy such mate rials up so that they float. Easily wette materials, however, sink through th solution and bubbles. Thus separatio is effected.

In early applications of froth flota tion, some success was achieved in th separation of foreign material from peas by careful control of the wetting properties of a water solution through the addition of synthetic detergents o salt.

Slight natural differences in wettabil ity between peas and foreign material particularly nightshade berries, were not great enough, however, to make it complete removal from peas practical solely by control of wetting propertie of the separating solution. Further experiments showed that the differences in wettability could be greatly increased by conditioning the surface of the peas and contaminating materials with a light mineral oil. After such conditioning, sound peas could be made to sink in a foaming solution of controlled wetting properties, so that a sharp separation could be made from night-shade berries and other foreign materials which floated. It was possible also to float cracked and broken peas, pea skins, and other viner debris because of the attachment of bubbles to the broken or torn surfaces. These preliminary observations were adapted to large-scale pea processing by the development of suitable equipment and controls.

On the basis of laboratory and pilot-plant studies, sodium lauryl sulfate, a synthetic detergent employed extensively for washing dishes and clothing, was selected for use in controlling the wetting properties of the separating solution. A deodorized, low-viscosity mineral oil was found most suitable for conditioning the surface of the peas. The most convenient form of the oil was an emulsion, which could be prepared by adding 0.5 to 1.5 percent oil to a water solution of the detergent. In that way, the detergent served to control the wetting properties of the solution, to emulsify the solution and thus disperse the oil, and to stabilize air incorporated into the solution as small bubbles.

As FINALLY DEVELOPED for commercial use, the froth-flotation process consists of two steps. A preliminary treatment conditions the surfaces of the materials by simple immersion in a water solution of detergent containing oil in the form of an emulsion. This step is conveniently accomplished by means of reels, a circulating pump, and a flume or pipe arranged as shown in the treater section of the chart on page 240. The treated and drained peas pass to the separator section, where foreign materials (floaters) are separated from the sound peas (sinkers). The separation takes place in an emulsion of oil in a water solution, the wetting properties of which are controlled by the addition of detergent. A large volume of air is introduced into the emulsion in the form of finely dispersed bubbles by the circulating pump. Both floaters and sinkers are continuously

carried from the separator by the separating emulsion, which is then recovered by reels and recirculated by the pump.

Because the actual separation of peas from foreign material depends on selective wetting, careful control of the wetting properties of the separating emulsion is essential during operation. Sodium lauryl sulfate is added to the separating emulsion to increase its wetting properties, and the amount added must be such that sound peas are selectively wetted out from the foreign material. The detergent requirements can easily be determined by observing the efficiency of the separation during actual operation. If sound peas float with the debris, the wetting properties of the emulsion are not great enough, and detergent must be added until the sound peas sink. If foreign material sinks with the peas, the wetting properties are too great, indicating the presence of too much detergent. Care must be taken to avoid adding too much detergent, because that error is difficult to correct.

During operation, the wetting properties of the separating emulsion continually change, and frequent adjustment is necessary. The net effect of the change results in a lowering of wetting properties below the point required for efficient separation, so that detergent must be added frequently. The efficiency of the cleaning under manual control therefore depends on the skill and attentiveness of the operator in adding detergent.

In the experimental development of the process, we observed that the amount of air introduced into the emulsion by the circulating pump depended on the wetting properties of the emulsion. This relationship was used in the design of a regulator for automatic control of wetting properties of the emulsion and, in turn, of the separating efficiency. The regulator, which is activated by changes in density resulting from variations in the amount of air dispersed in the solution, adds detergent as needed for efficient

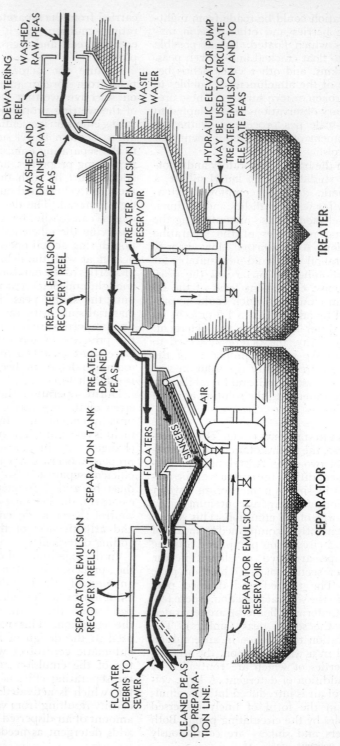

SCHEMATIC FLOW DIAGRAM
OF FROTH FLOTATION PROCESS

DEWATERING REEL

WASHED, RAW PEAS

WASHED AND DRAINED RAW PEAS

WASTE WATER

TREATER EMULSION RESERVOIR

TREATER EMULSION RECOVERY REEL

HYDRAULIC ELEVATOR PUMP MAY BE USED TO CIRCULATE TREATER EMULSION AND TO ELEVATE PEAS

TREATER

TREATED, DRAINED PEAS

SEPARATION TANK

FLOATERS

SINKERS

AIR

SEPARATOR EMULSION RECOVERY REELS

FLOATER DEBRIS TO SEWER

CLEANED PEAS TO PREPARATION LINE.

SEPARATOR EMULSION RESERVOIR

SEPARATOR

separation. This regulator simplifies the preparation of the emulsion and makes cleaning more efficient. It also eliminates the need for constant supervision and reduces the loss of peas that occurs when the separation is controlled by hand.

The best place for the froth-flotation equipment in the preparation line is immediately behind the first washer. Preliminary washing and draining reduce contamination and dilution of the separating emulsion with plant juices and thus simplify control of its wetting properties during continuous operation. Installation at that point means, however, that the equipment must be of sufficient capacity to handle the entire volume of peas flowing through each line.

In plants where peas are segregated by size, it is usually more economical to install the cleaning equipment between the size graders and the blanchers. It is then possible to clean all the small peas, usually less than 25 percent of the total, with a more limited froth-flotation capacity. Auxiliary equipment is desirable for use on the larger peas that require special cleaning because of weed contamination. Since useful differences in wettability are destroyed by steam or water blanching, the process cannot be used after the blanching step. The heat treatment during the blanching reduces oil residue to a trace, which cannot be detected in the finished product.

The froth-flotation process gives growers and processors a means for avoiding their former large losses from weed-contaminated peas. The efficiency of the process is not affected by the degree of contamination—even highly contaminated peas can be salvaged. Labor required for sorting has been greatly reduced for the smaller peas, which contain most of the viner debris. The quality of such peas is improved, because the removal of debris by froth flotation is much more complete than is possible by hand.

A number of other uses have been suggested for the process. It has been found useful in cleaning green lima beans and green soybeans for processing. The equipment, when used with water in place of the separating emulsion, has also been found efficient in removing chaff and other debris from cut sweet corn. In that application, the sap from the cut corn acts as a surface-active agent to stabilize the foam.

A. M. Neubert, *a native of Washington, obtained his undergraduate and graduate training in the State College of Washington in Pullman. He has been employed at the United States Fruit and Vegetable Products Laboratory in Pullman since 1937 and has been in charge of it since 1944.*

The story is told of a South African farmer who found in his field a rough, peculiar-looking stone, which he used for many years as a doorstop. It was too light to be an effective doorstop, however, and his wife threw it into the yard several times. The farmer always retrieved it. After many years they were amazed when somebody told them that their old stone was really a huge rough diamond. The stone was being utilized, of course, but it required the knowledge and skills of the mineralogist and diamond cutter to put it to a more important and valuable use. And so it is with many farm products—effective utilization comes only after we learn the real nature of our raw materials and then apply modern tools of chemistry and engineering.—*Roderick K. Eskew, Eastern Regional Research Laboratory.*

Production of Mushroom Mycelium

Harry Humfeld

Growing mushrooms has become an important industry in the United States. Of the estimated annual production of 62 million pounds, 20 million reach the consumer as fresh mushrooms, 18 million in cans, and 24 million as flavoring in soups.

Consumption might be even greater if production costs could be reduced. With the trend towards packaging prepared, ready-to-serve food products, the use of mushroom flavor in a number of such preparations doubtlessly will increase. The problem is to incorporate mushroom flavor without markedly increasing the cost of the product.

The mushrooms in the retail markets are really the fruits of a plant that grows as a mat of fine strands or threads on the organic material in the soil or in a mushroom bed. When conditions of temperature, moisture, and food supply are right, such a mat, or mycelium, periodically forms mushroom fruits near the surface of the soil. These are the familiar buttons and caps. Soon after they push up through the bed they are ready for harvest.

Although people over the world eat mushrooms of several species, in the United States only one species—*Agaricus campestris*—is grown commercially.

In 1947, I discovered that the vegetative, or underground, part (mycelium) of that species will grow under conditions of submerged propagation.

The technique offers the possibility of greatly cutting the cost of a mushroom-flavored food material, although the physical form and texture usually associated with mushrooms must be sacrificed.

The principles of the method are based on the fact that when a liquid that contains the required chemicals and food supply is continuously stirred vigorously at the right temperature and mixed thoroughly with a constant supply of air, many micro-organisms reproduce in it with great rapidity. The method is used commercially in the production of baker's yeast and feed yeast. More recently it has been applied to the large-scale production of antibiotics, such as penicillin and streptomycin, as well as to the manufacture of citric and gluconic acids.

The mycelium proved to be not too particular about the medium on which it will grow, but it does have certain requirements. It seems now that a good commercial product can be grown on any medium that contains a suitable sugar and other essential nutrients, that does not contain an ingredient inhibitory or toxic to the growth of the mycelium, and that does not impart a characteristic flavor of its own during its use as a medium.

To obtain pure-culture mushroom mycelium, we either germinated mushroom spores or made tissue cultures of various parts of the mushroom. Then we grew the mycelium on an agar medium in order to maintain the pure cultures. The cultures may be inoculated into sterilized compost, grain, or tobacco stems, and allowed to grow to provide the material known in the trade as mushroom spawn. The spawn, when planted in mushroom beds, produces the mushrooms sold commercially.

For the submerged propagation of the mycelium, the procedure now in use consists in transferring some of the mycelium grown on agar in a test tube to 50 milliliters of sterile liquid medium in a 250-milliliter Erlenmeyer (conical) flask. The flasks are shaken on a machine in a room at 77° F. until a heavy growth of mycelium has developed. The time usually required is 5 to 6 days. This inoculum is then transferred to 2 liters of medium in fermentors made from Fernbach (spherical) flasks and incubated to maximum growth. This culture suspension is used as inoculum in the larger fermentors with a culture-medium capacity of 16 to 20 liters.

It has been necessary to consider variations in so-called strains of *Agaricus campestris*. Plant species, like animal species, have familylike variations. Therefore I have isolated and tested more than 40 cultures of strains of *Agaricus campestris*.

Among them I have found three that are well able to adapt themselves to growth in an agitated, aerated liquid medium. Each has characteristic mushroom flavor. Each can be distinguished from the others by a characteristic difference in flavor. Two of the strains were isolated from mushrooms of the white variety and one from the cream or brown variety of *Agaricus campestris*. All have certain characteristics in common. They grow more rapidly than the other isolations. The hyphae, or mycelial threads, are more slender. They produce an abundance of so-called secondary spores in the liquid medium. The secondary spores were first described by Albert Kligman in 1932 at Pennsylvania State College. He found them in old cultures on solidified (agar) medium. From observations up to the present time, it seems likely that the ability to produce the secondary spores may account for the ability of the strains to adapt themselves to submerged growth in a liquid medium.

The process also has been carried successfully through a semipilot-plant stage. That is, we have grown all three strains in 40-gallon batches in our pilot-plant fermentor. Each batch has produced 35 to 38 pounds of mycelial cake with good mushroom flavor.

In both the Fernbach and the larger fermentors, a rate of air flow of 1 liter of air a minute per liter of culture medium gives rapid growth. Lower rates give slower growth. Higher rates do not materially increase the growth rate.

We harvest when good growth and good mushroom flavor have been produced in the large fermentors by taking out half to three-fourths of the culture and adding an equal volume of fresh sterile culture medium. In this manner a number of consecutive harvests are obtained without contamination of the culture medium.

Immediately after harvesting, we separate the mycelium from the culture liquid by centrifuging. Then we resuspend the mycelium cake in water and again centrifuge.

We pack the mycelium into suitable cans and seal and sterilize the filled cans at 15 pounds of steam pressure for 20 minutes. In some cases we have frozen it and stored it in a freezer until used. Drying the mycelium, either by lyophilizing (drying under vacuum from the frozen state) or on a drum drier, has been tried, with some loss of flavor in both cases.

We have obtained good yields on media composed of juices pressed from various fruit and vegetable wastes, such as asparagus butts and pear waste. Our more recent investigations show that a desirable product is obtainable from media made from pear waste, a rice-bran extract, or beet molasses, and also from a synthetic medium containing dextrose and inorganic salts. Media containing asparagus juice or alfalfa juice seemed to impart the flavor of those constituents and were deemed less desirable.

Basic studies in progress in 1949 demonstrated that the essential nutrient requirements for the growth of the mycelium of *A. campestris* are comparatively simple. Sources of nitrogen utilized include ammonia, urea, peptone, monosodium glutamate, a mixture of amino acids, and probably a number of other nitrogen compounds. Most of the sugars tested, which included hexoses, pentoses, and disaccharides, give good growth. The polysaccharides (soluble starch and dextrin) also are suitable sources. However, a form of soluble cellulose (sodium carboxymethyl cellulose) cannot be fermented. Apparently a wide range of carbohydrates can serve as sources of energy for growth of mycelium of *A. campestris*.

We have determined approximate optimum concentrations for the various elements required and have developed a basal medium which contains the required amounts of sugar, nitrogen, phosphorus, potassium, magnesium, sulfur, calcium, and the trace elements, iron, manganese, zinc, and copper.

The development of this synthetic medium of know composition and the determination of the nutrient requirements and utilization of various nitrogen and energy sources aid in investigations on the suitability of various media made from fruit and vegetable wastes. If the composition of the press juice of a particular waste material is known, a preliminary forecast can be made on the suitability of the waste as a source of substrate for mushroom mycelium production.

During the continuous-fermentation tests in the Fernbach and in the larger (20-liter) fermentors, successive harvests were made as soon as enough mycelium had been produced to give a good yield. We discovered that when this procedure was followed, much of the characteristic mushroom flavor was lost. To assure the production of a good-flavored mycelium, it was found necessary to grow each stage of development of the culture until a full mushroom flavor had developed.

We are investigating the effects of rates of aeration, agitation, length of time of fermentation, and the composition of the medium on the development of the intensity of the mushroom flavor.

Our tests on the possibilities of spawning mushroom beds by spraying the liquid culture on the compost gave negative results. The mycelium grows very rapidly, forming a white mat over the surface of the compost bed overnight, and then disappears nearly as quickly. The hyphae apparently are unable to penetrate into the compost or are unable to compete with the other micro-organisms present. This method of seeding beds of compost, if successful, would help reduce the costs of the commercial grower who supplies the commercial trade with mushroom fruit caps.

We have grown these cultures in our laboratory on rye grain by the method used in making commercial grain spawn. When we used grain spawn to start beds in the customary commercial manner, the hyphae formed an excellent fluffy growth on the grain, but again were unable to grow and spread into the compost. It may well be that these strains are spontaneous mutants, which can reproduce themselves only vegetatively in pure culture medium.

Results of analyses of mushroom mycelium produced by submerged fermentation show a protein content (nitrogen x 6.25) of 49.1 percent, fat 3.1 percent, and mineral constituents, as ash, 8.1 percent, calculated on a moisture-free basis. The mycelium of the white variety contained, in micrograms per gram of dry mycelium, the following vitamins: Thiamine, 8.7; riboflavin, 47; niacin, 190. For the cream variety, the figures were 8.7, 90, and 290, respectively. Both showed only a trace of ascorbic acid. The results compare favorably with those for commercially grown mushrooms.

The centrifuged mushroom mycelium looks like a fresh yeast cake and contains about 25 percent solids, as compared with 10 to 12 percent solids in fresh mushrooms. The mycelium should be suitable for use in soups, gravies, and condiments, wherever it is not essential that recognizable pieces of mushroom be present. It is likely, of course, that people will continue to want whole mushrooms, even though the mycelial cake may be made for flavoring.

The advantage of mushroom mycelium over fresh mushrooms would seem to be largely that of more economical production, although the assurance of a constant and reliable supply might also be an important factor.

After the production of the mycelium of *A. campestris* has been carried through the pilot-plant stage, the use of mycelium of other mushroom species known to have desirable flavor characteristics remains to be explored. The mushrooms of many edible species are now available only in limited quantities and only for short periods during the year. A reliable and constant source of supply of mycelium of desirable species would seem to offer

possibilities for the development of palatable food materials. Other species might be suitable as sources of feeds of high nutritive value or for the production of enzymes, antibiotics, toxins, and other organic compounds.

Another direction that research might take is toward basic factors in the medium that might enhance or otherwise modify and improve the concentration and quality of the flavor. Flavor substances are very important commercially. They are complex chemically and constitute an important and interesting field for the agricultural chemist and microbiologist.

HARRY HUMFELD, *a microbiologist at the Western Regional Research Laboratory, has been engaged in research in microbiology in the Department since 1927. He is a native of Holland and has degrees from Oregon State College and Iowa State College.*

CITRUS MOLASSES is no good with hot biscuits, but to Florida cattle it's ice cream and cake. On the big ranches of central Florida, cattle greedily slurp up the black, sticky molasses as it trickles from 1,000-gallon drums into feeding troughs, or they chew their bulky feeds with more gusto if the molasses has been poured over them to make a sort of hay à la mode. This use of citrus molasses is an answer to one waste-disposal problem.

About 60 percent of Florida's huge citrus crop was processed in 1950, and the refuse from the processing plants created a serious disposal problem. Citrus molasses has eased the problem somewhat.

Florida cattlemen, scientists, and processors joined in the effort to turn the waste into livestock feed. Scientists found that it could be converted into citrus pulp and a brownish-black sirup, which they called citrus molasses.

The University of Florida ran trials on the value of the two products as cattle feed. The results were satisfactory. The Florida Agricultural Experiment Station found that citrus feeds can contribute to thickness of flesh, glossiness of coat, and flow of milk, and add to general body tone of cattle. Florida produced about 180,000 tons of citrus pulp and 80,000 tons of citrus molasses in 1950. Most of the pulp went to dairy cattle; most of the molasses to beef cattle. The supply and demand are expanding rapidly.—*Fred P. Lawrence, Agricultural Extension Service, University of Florida.*

Commercial production of fruit in the United States, 1940–49 average

Fruit	Average production 1,000 tons	Proportion of total fruit crop Percent	Major areas of production
Oranges and tangerines.........	3,700	22	Central Fla., southern Calif.
Grapes......................	2,800	17	Calif., Great Lakes region.
Apples......................	2,600	16	Central Wash., Shenandoah Valley, upper N. Y., southwest Mich.
Grapefruit...................	2,000	12	Central Fla., Rio Grande Valley.
Peaches.....................	1,500	9	Central Calif., Ga., southwest Mich.
Melons (including cantaloups)...	1,300	8	Calif., Ga., Fla., Tex., S. C., Ind.
Pears.......................	750	4	Central Calif., Pacific Northwest.
Plums (including prunes)........	670	4	Do.
Lemons.....................	510	3	Southern Calif.
Apricots....................	220	1	Central Calif.
Cherries....................	190	1	Western Mich., western N. Y., central Calif.
Strawberries.................	160	1	Southern States, Mich., Pacific Coast States, Mass.
Others [1]...................	270	2	Calif., Fla., Mass., Wash.
Total.................	16,670	100	

[1] Avocados, bush berries, cranberries, dates, figs, limes, olives, persimmons, pineapples, and pomegranates.

The four main types of fruit processing in the United States, 1940–49 average

Fruit	Proportion of total crop processed Percent	Canned 1,000 tons	Dried 1,000 tons	Frozen 1,000 tons	Crushed [1] 1,000 tons	Major processing areas
Oranges...................	26	......	......	......	950	Fla.
Grapes...................	79	20	1,030	7	1,150	Calif.
Apples...................	26	220	130	27	300	N. Y., Shenandoah Valley, central Wash., Calif.
Grapefruit................	51	89	......	......	920	Rio Grande Valley, Fla.
Peaches..................	40	480	130	17	......	Calif.
Pears....................	38	260	18	......	5	Calif., Pacific Northwest.
Plums (including prunes)....	73	30	450	5	3	Calif.
Lemons..................	32	......	......	......	160	Do.
Apricots.................	71	64	83	9	......	Do.
Cherries.................	52	65	......	30	2	N. Y., Mich., Wis., Pacific Northwest.
Strawberries..............	21	1	......	32	1	Pacific Northwest, Southern States.
Others [2]................	72	62	93	31	10	Calif., Fla., Mass.
Total..............	41	1,291	1,934	158	3,501	

[1] Includes fruit used for making juices and for fermented products, brined (in the case of cherries) and some quantities used for preserves, jams, and jellies.

[2] Avocados, bush berries, cranberries, dates, figs, limes, olives, persimmons, pineapples, and pomegranates. Prepared from U. S. Bureau of Agricultural Economics data.

Production and Food Uses of Fruit

R. R. Legault,
Clyde L. Rasmussen

We eat fruits because they taste good, look good, and satisfy appetite. They are protective foods because they furnish in abundance carbohydrates, minerals, and vitamins. We like to eat raw fruit when we can get it. When we cannot, modern manufacturing methods give us excellent preserved fruits in many forms. The processing of fruit also evens the supplies, come winter and poor growing seasons.

Almost half of the commercially produced fruit in the United States is processed by canning, drying, freezing, or fermenting. Most of the grapes, plums, apricots, cherries, cling peaches, grapefruit, and olives go to consumer markets in a can, bottle, or other package. Apples, oranges, freestone peaches, lemons, pears, and strawberries are still sold mostly as fresh fruit. Recent developments in the production of canned and frozen juices and concentrates, however, may mean that larger amounts of many fruits, including several in the second group, will be consumed as processed juice. In 1950, one-half of the Florida crop of oranges was sold as canned or frozen juice or concentrate.

Many factors favor the commercial processing of fruits for the housewife. Convenience in the kitchen is one of the most important. It is much easier to serve orange juice from a can of frozen concentrate, for example, than it is to squeeze the juice from the fresh fruit.

Most housewives find it impractical to make juices and nectars from such fruits as apples, apricots, prunes, and grapes. Even with the necessary presses or pulpers, the task takes too much time, in view of the demands on her time and the limited amount of domestic help at her command. Thus, it has become increasingly necessary to rely on processed foods, particularly those requiring little or no preparation for table use. As processed juices fit very well into this category, it seems likely that in the future we will drink more and more of our fruit and eat less and less in fresh form.

BECAUSE SEVERAL YEARS are needed to bring new trees and vines into bearing, the acreage devoted to the production of fruit is relatively constant. But the production of fruit varies greatly from year to year, depending on the weather and the grower's ability to overcome adverse conditions by irrigation, spraying, and fertilizing. Production in the irrigated areas in the West generally varies less than in other sections.

Between 1940 and 1949, a typical period, our commercial production of fruit averaged about 17 million tons a year.

Of that, just more than 40 percent (approximately 7 million tons) was processed. Nineteen percent of the total was canned, 28 percent dried, 22 percent crushed (including juice production), and 2 percent frozen.

All parts of the United States produce fruit. Which kind is grown where depends on the cultural needs of the fruit. Apples, perhaps the least exacting as to weather, grow in quantity throughout the North. Citrus fruits require a subtropical climate and can be produced only in the South and Southwest. Oranges, apples, grapes, grapefruit, and peaches are grown in largest quantities.

California produced more than a third of all of the commercial fruit in 1940 to 1949. Florida grew more than a sixth of the total. Texas, Washington, and New York were next. Many other States produce large quantities of fruit for the market, besides that in home gardens and small orchards.

The general inelasticity of supply (the result of the relative permanence of production facilities) and the unpredictable yearly production have complicated the problem of marketing, although processing has provided a means of stabilizing production and making fruits available in one form or another throughout the year. Processing also makes it possible to ship fruits greater distances.

Several kinds of fruit can hardly be sold unless they are processed. Because cling peaches, sour cherries, and olives have limited value in the fresh form, practically their entire volume is directed into processing. Increased acreages of these tree fruits were generally accompanied by increased processing capacity, and the production and processing industries, so to speak, grew up together.

The production of fruit for special processing to get a product different from the original is exemplified in the grapes grown for wine. Grapes for raisins might be considered in this category. In both instances, the demand for the final product influenced greatly the expansion of fruit-producing facilities.

TRENDS IN FRUIT production vary according to variety. Since 1909, the production of nearly all major fruits, except apples, has increased. Most spectacular was the tenfold gain among citrus fruits. The production of grapefruit amounted to about 2 million tons a year from 1945 to 1949, compared to only 60 thousand tons from 1909 to 1915. Late trends indicate a fairly constant or even a declining production of some fruits, among them grapes,

prunes, and apricots. The trend in the production of apples has been downward since 1920.

Our consumption of fresh fruits per person changed little between 1918 and 1948. We ate fewer fresh apples but many more oranges, grapefruit, lemons, and limes. The per capita civilian consumption of fresh fruits in 1918 to 1922 and 1944 to 1948 was (in pounds):

	1918–22	1944–48
Apples	51. 3	24. 4
Citrus	24. 0	57. 6
Melons (including cantaloups)	32. 6	37. 9
Other	54. 8	54 .1
Total	162. 7	174. 0

The use of commercially processed fruits has increased markedly in the past 25 years. The greatest increase was in canned products, particularly canned juices. The per capita civilian consumption of processed fruits during 1918 to 1922 and 1944 to 1948 was (in pounds):

	1918–22	1944–48
Canned juices	0. 3	15. 5
Other canned fruit	8. 4	18. 0
Dried	5. 8	4. 6
Frozen	---	3. 0
Total	14. 5	41. 1

As a result of the increases in per capita consumption and the greater population, the total consumption of fruit in the United States has increased at least 70 percent since 1925.

OTHER COUNTRIES also grow a great deal of fruit, as shown by the reports of the Office of Foreign Agricultural Relations. In 1946 to 1950, France produced almost 25 percent of the total reported production of apples in the world, and used 87 percent of the total for cider. The United States was second, with about 23 percent of the total production. Germany produced 7 percent; the United Kingdom, more than 5 percent; and Switzerland and Italy, about 4.5 percent each. A quarter of the world total of about 12 million tons went into cider. The pattern of world apple production has changed since before the Second World War. Production in the leading countries has decreased, while production has increased materially in many of the smaller countries, such as Belgium, Denmark, Netherlands, Sweden, and Switzerland.

The United States accounted for 40 percent of the reported world's apricot production that averaged 600 thousand tons yearly from 1945 to 1949. Spain and Iran each produced about 10 percent of the total.

It is estimated that total banana production in the world approximates 10 million tons a year. Only about 2 million tons were exported from producing countries annually from 1945 to 1949, of which the United States imported two-thirds. Central America exported almost three-quarters of the total; South America, one-seventh; and the Canary Islands, one-twelfth. Trade in bananas has gone down since before the Second World War; the average during 1935 to 1939 was almost 3 million tons a year.

The reported world's cherry crop averaged about 1 million tons a year from 1945 to 1949. The United States produced about 20 percent of the total; Germany, 14 percent; and Italy, more than 10 percent. France, Czechoslovakia, and Yugoslavia are also important cherry producers.

The orange crop, largest of the citrus fruits, averaged more than 9 million tons a year in 1945 to 1949. The United States accounted for more than 40 percent of the total; Brazil, 13 percent; Spain, 9 percent; Mexico, Italy, and Argentina, about 4 percent each; and Palestine and Japan, about 3 percent each. The world crop of oranges during 1945 to 1949 was one-quarter larger than the crop a decade earlier. The United States production in the same period increased more than two-thirds.

The United States accounted for 93 percent of the total annual production of grapefruit of 2.3 million tons in 1945 to 1949. During the same period, the United States produced about 48 percent of the average lemon crop of almost 1 million tons; Italy, 28 percent; Argentina, 5 percent; and Chile, 3.5 percent.

The production of grapes in the world undoubtedly exceeds that of any other fruit. From 1945 to 1949, the reported annual production averaged 33 million tons. Italy produced 18 percent of the total; France, 17 percent; Algeria, 11 percent; and the United States and Spain, about 9 percent each.

Thirty-three percent of the grape crop (1945 to 1949) in the United States was dried into raisins and currants, but only 7 percent of the world production was processed in that manner. Forty percent of the United States production was crushed commercially for wine. In contrast, 80 percent of the world production was used for wine.

Peaches are an important fruit crop and averaged 2.75 million tons a year from 1945 to 1949. The United States produced almost two-thirds of the total. Italy and Argentina accounted for 9 and 6 percent, respectively.

The reported world production of pears has increased considerably since before the Second World War and in 1945 to 1950 averaged more than 3.5 million tons a year. The United States accounted for more than 20 percent of the total. France produced about 15 percent, of which three-quarters was used for cider. Germany, Italy, and Switzerland each produced about 9 percent of the total. Austria, Belgium, and the Netherlands are also important producers of pears; the latter two have increased pear production threefold since before the war.

From 1945 to 1949 the United States accounted for about one-half of the reported world production of dried fruits.

Data on production of fruits in Russia are not available, hence they are not included in our statistics.

FRUITS CONTAIN water, carbohydrates, acids, proteins, fats, minerals, ethereal substances recognized as flavors, pigments, tannins, and vitamins. Water and carbohydrates are the main components—raw apple tissue, for example, may contain 85 percent of water and 14 percent of carbohydrate substance. But the other components (except fats and proteins perhaps) contribute a great deal to the food value of fruits.

We can classify the carbohydrates of fruits as to constitution and function. Some are simple sugars, such as sucrose, dextrose, and levulose, which make fruits taste better and sweeter, and are sources of readily available energy. The caloric value of fruits lies mainly in the sugars. The starches are present in much smaller amounts in ripe fruits, but they also are sources of body energy. Cellulose and pectins are important food factors, because they provide bulk and roughage, which are considered essential for proper functioning of the alimentary tract.

Tannins account for much of the astringency of fruits. Many fruits owe much of their characteristic flavor to a blend of sugar, acid, and tannin substances. A less desirable characteristic of tannins is their tendency to change to dark-colored substances under certain conditions. This color change is usually associated with the development of bitter flavor.

Enzymes are important protein-bearing substances in fruits. In minute amounts, enzymes influence greatly the rate of chemical processes. They are important in plant life and, perhaps, in the development of natural fruit flavors, but they are generally known for the difficulties they cause in fruit preservation. The darkening of cut surfaces of fresh fruit, such as peach, is an enzymatic process involving at least enyzmes, tannins, and oxygen. Several kinds of enzymes occur in fruits. Some are suspected of being involved in the development of undesirable flavors during processing, while others affect textural qualities.

The flavors of ripe fruits in the raw state are distinguishing characteristics, which markedly increase palatability. The volatile flavors are present in minute amounts as essential oils and certain organic compounds, alone or in combination. Being delicate and transitory, the pleasant fruit components are easily lost or altered during processing. One of the most important of current activities in food processing is the development of means for capturing and concentrating the volatile components, sometimes referred to as the high notes of the scale of fruit flavors.

The brilliant colors of fruits add to their attractiveness. The principal ones, known chemically as anthocyanin pigments, generally account for the red and blue colors. Sometimes, as in the canning of strawberries, a breakdown of the pigments bars the full exploitation of the process.

Fresh fruits contain most of the known vitamins. They are particularly good sources of vitamin C, ascorbic acid. Certain carotenoid pigments, which are converted to vitamin A in the human body, occur widely in fruits. Ascorbic acid is susceptible to change when it is in contact with oxygen. Thus modern fruit-processing methods are designed to minimize contact with air.

R. R. LEGAULT *was reared on a farm in northern Minnesota. He holds degrees from the Universities of South Dakota, Maryland, and Chicago. He carried out chemical research on natural products at the University of Chicago and has taught chemistry at Bucknell University. Since 1942 he has been a member of the staff of the Western Regional Research Laboratory, where he is in charge of the fruit-processing division.*

CLYDE L. RASMUSSEN *received his training at the University of Utah and the University of California. He has worked in the fields of economic and cost analyses with several Government agencies and has had production experience in various food-processing plants. He is in charge of the industrial analysis section of the Western Laboratory.*

What Makes Flavor in Fruit?

Justus G. Kirchner

Without their aromatic flavors, fruits are insipid pulps. If the volatile oils are removed from citrus juices, for example, there remains a juice having only a sweet taste and an acid taste, which come from the sugars and the acids. The characteristic fruity flavor is gone. The juice has no further appeal.

We speak of the taste of a fruit, but actually we are referring to its flavor. Taste is one component of flavor. The other is odor. We sometimes hold our noses when we swallow an unpleasant-tasting medicine; actually we are keeping the olfactory organs from being brought into use.

Taste includes four qualities, singly or in combination: Sweetness, sourness, saltiness, and bitterness. Hotness, as in pepper, and coolness, as in menthol, are sometimes also classified as taste sensations.

A sweet taste is best detected by the tip of the tongue, a salty one by the forward edges, a sour one by the back edges, and a bitter one by the back. This variation explains why we do not taste many bitter substances until after we have swallowed them.

We usually associate a sweet taste with sugars, although there are compounds having no relation to sugars that are also sweet—sometimes even sweeter than sugars. An example is saccharin, which is almost 500 times sweeter than sugar.

Sweetness is generally attributed to the molecule as a whole, but in some instances, notably in certain inorganic compounds, it is associated with ionic stimuli. Beryllium salts are sweet, for example, and this sweetness is associated with the beryllium part of the molecule, which in solution takes on a positive charge and becomes an ion.

Salty and sour tastes are associated with salts and acids, respectively. Sodium chloride (common table salt) has the taste generally associated with salt. Not all chemical salts have this taste, however; many are intensely bitter.

The acid taste may be detected in most fruits. It ranges from the mild banana to the sour lemon. Tartness depends on the amount of acid and on the kinds and amounts of other substances present. For example, two solutions that contain exactly the same amounts of acid, as measured by chemical standards, but with different amounts of sugar, will differ in their sour taste. In other words, the sugar does not destroy the acid but merely tends to mask the sour taste.

ODOR IS MUCH MORE COMPLICATED than taste. It cannot be broken down easily into classifications. Sweet and bitter and salty and sour are distinct classes of taste, but there are no corresponding classes of odors.

Numerous attempts have been made to set up a classification system for odors. The most recent is that of E. C. Crocker and L. F. Henderson, of the Arthur D. Little Laboratories. They recognize four fundamental odors: Fragrant, or sweet; acid, or sour; burnt; and caprylic, or goaty. Each is subdivided into eight divisions, based on intensity. To facilitate classification, a set of eight standard chemicals has been set up for each of the four fundamental odors. Every odor can then be classified by a four-digit number, the size of each digit depending on the intensity of the particular fundamental odor. For example, toluene would be coded by the number 2424 and citral would be 6645.

The aromatic part of fruit flavors arises from the presence of minute quantities of volatile chemical constituents. These are compounds that travel through the air and affect the olfactory organs and give rise to a flow of saliva and related activity. They impart to the fruit its characteristic flavor. The aromatic constituents are extremely sensitive to physical and chemical treatment, and they may be lost or changed as a result of processing.

One of the biggest problems in processing fruits is to preserve the natural fresh flavor and prevent the development of unpleasant off-flavors. Processing techniques have been developed mostly from the standpoint of engineering rather than of the effects on the flavor of the product, primarily because little has been known about the chemistry of the flavoring constituents. This is not surprising, because the isolation and identification of the flavoring constituents are not simple tasks. For one thing, the flavoring components are present in such small quantities that tons of fruit are required to yield a few grams of the aromatic flavoring material. Because the flavor substances of fruits are complex mixtures, separation into their constituent parts results in the collection of only small fractions of a gram for study.

THE CANNING OF CITRUS JUICES presents a particular problem in the preservation of natural flavor, in both the freshly canned and the stored product. During pasteurization, a cooked flavor often develops; during storage, a separate and distinct off-flavor arises, the result of time and temperature of storage.

The development of off-flavors is also different in each fruit. It is most intense in the lemon and a little less intense in orange and grapefruit. The cooked flavor of canned citrus juice is preferred by some to the fresh juice flavor, but the storage off-flavor is unpleasant to everyone.

The solution to the problem of eliminating or preventing off-flavors in canned citrus juices lies in a knowledge of the chemistry of the flavoring constituents in the fresh and processed products.

California Valencia orange juice is the only citrus juice that has been investigated to any great extent. J. A. Hall and C. P. Wilson, of the California Fruit Growers Exchange, crushed whole oranges, removed the peel oil, and recovered 182 grams of juice oil from more than 10,000 gallons of juice. Even that amount was not enough to identify all the flavoring components. As might be expected from the character of the metabolic products of plant tissue, the Valencia orange juice contained small quantities of ethyl alcohol and, in addition, the esters of terpene alcohols, along with the usual aldehyde compounds. But the major part of the alcohol fraction was an unidentified compound, whose physical constants closely resembled those of the terpene alcohol, linaloöl.

BECAUSE COMMERCIALLY processed orange juice contains small amounts of peel oil from the juicing operation, it might be possible that this material has a role in the development of off-flavors. In contrast to the oil from the juice sacs, orange peel oil has been thoroughly investigated. It is 90 to 95 percent d-limonene. The remaining part contains aldehydes and terpene alcohols.

Many investigators have believed that the volatile oils in citrus juices account for the development of off-flavors in the canned product. Their experiments showed that canned juices with an oil content of less than 0.007 percent developed no off-flavors after 18 months in storage, while those with an oil content of 0.01 percent or more readily developed off-flavors.

Other investigators have supported the theory of the deterioration of the essential oil, believing that the unsaturated hydrocarbons or alcohols are responsible and that the *d*-limonene fraction of the oil also has a part in causing off-flavors. On the other hand, workers in the Department's laboratory in Winter Haven, Fla., concluded that the off-flavor might be due partly to an oxidation of the fatty material in the juice. The addition of antioxidants to the canned products, however, did not appear to have any stabilizing effect.

LITTLE IS KNOWN about the chemistry of the flavoring constituents of the other citrus fruits. The navel orange presents an interesting problem, because its juice turns extremely bitter shortly after it is extracted. For that reason, the housewife does not prepare navel orange juice in the evening and hold it overnight in the refrigerator for breakfast the next morning.

The peel, section membranes, and center core of this orange contain a compound that is extracted into the acid juice during the reaming process and turns bitter from contact with the acid in a few hours. The bitter principle is called limonin, and its presence prevents the use of navel orange juice for commercial processing. Somehow the presence of the bitter principle is closely related to the maturity of the fruit. It is more prevalent in immature oranges and decreases as the fruit ripens. It is also more intense in some growing seasons than in others.

Grapefruit is something of an anomaly. Some persons believe that grapefruit juice owes its bitterness to the presence of quinine. Instead, it is the bitter glycoside, naringin, in the peel, section membranes, and center core. Naringin differs from limonin (which also is present in the peel, section membrane, and center core) in that it is bitter in its natural form and imparts a bitter flavor to the juice if too much pressure is used in the reaming process, particularly if the fruit pulp is pressed

to obtain a higher yield of juice. Naringin is also associated with the maturity of the fruit. It is more intense at the beginning of the season and gradually drops toward the end.

Little work has been done on lemon juice. L. Francesconi, however, has tentatively identified an alcohol and an acid, other than citric acid, in the juice.

The Department's research laboratory in Pasadena has started a study of the chemistry of the flavoring constituents of fresh, canned, and stored citrus juices. The aim is to determine the constituents present in fresh juices and what happens to them after being heated in cans and stored.

Attempts have been made to return the volatile flavoring materials removed in the low-temperature concentration of citrus juices to the product to provide a full-flavored concentrate. As the process is now carried out, the juice is concentrated to a 5 to 1 ratio—meaning that 4 parts of water would have to be added to 1 part of concentrate to obtain the consistency of the original juice. To the concentrate is then added 1 part of fresh juice, giving a 4 to 1 concentrate as it is sold in the stores. That means that 1 part of citrus juice is furnishing the volatile flavoring materials for 5 parts of concentrate, a considerable dilution of the original flavor. If that flavor dilution could be prevented by capturing the oils lost during the concentration, the housewife would enjoy a more flavorful product. The processor in turn wants to do so because of the cost factor; by stopping at the 4-to-1 ratio of concentration he would save one-fifth of the cost of the present concentrating method.

The volatile flavoring material as recovered from the concentration of citrus juices is extremely unstable, and, until ways are found to stabilize it, the fortification of the flavor of the concentrate will be impossible. The Pasadena laboratory is investigating this problem in connection with its related study on basic flavoring constituents.

Often the identification of all the flavoring constituents in a fruit is not the work of one man or one group, but rather the cumulative efforts of several laboratories over a period of years. Research on the flavoring components in apples is a good example.

SOME OF THE early work on apples was started in 1911 by C. Thomae, a German chemist, who obtained a few drops of a yellow oil by steam distillation of apple peelings. He reported that the oil had the fragrant odor of apples, but he made no attempt to identify any of the constituents.

Later, F. B. Power and V. K. Chesnut, in this country, steam-distilled a large amount of peelings from Ben Davis apples to obtain a watery distillate that contained the aromatic flavoring materials. The amount of the flavoring oil was too small for complete analysis, but the presence of certain alcohols and acids was shown. The two investigators obtained compounds of the same type in distillates from Springdale apple and crab apple peelings. As might be expected from the differences in flavor of the varieties, there is some difference in the compounds isolated. The amount of volatile oils found in the Ben Davis apple peelings was 0.0035 percent by weight, as compared to 0.0043 percent in the crab apple peelings.

MOST OF THE volatile flavoring materials in apples can be collected in the first 10 percent of the apple-juice distillate. If this fraction is put back into the concentrate, a large part of the original apple flavor can be retained. This investigation was advanced in the Eastern Regional Research Laboratory. Pilot-plant results were so satisfactory that the process was applied commercially by a number of firms. The volatile essences from the experiments provided abundant material for studying the flavor components of apples.

Eight alcohols, comprising approximately 92 percent of the flavoring

agents, and six aldehydes, comprising 6 percent, were found. The remaining 2 percent of the flavor—the ester fraction—contained six compounds, only two of them in any amount. All these compounds together were in the original apple in a concentration of only 50 parts per million. A synthetic flavor made up of the identified compounds approaches, but is not identical with, the natural apple flavor; there are still minute quantities of unidentified materials that have a profound effect on the flavors.

THE DIFFERENCE in the flavoring components of different varieties of fruits has also been shown with grapes. Native *Vitis labrusca* grapes, which are grown in the eastern part of the country, contain methyl anthranilate, but the *Vitis vinifera* grapes, chiefly grown in California, do not.

Zinfandel grapes, although not particularly tasty, are used in making raisins and wine because of their high sugar content. A. J. Haagen-Smit, F. N. Hirosawa, and T. H. Wang found that these grapes owe their flavor to nine compounds, ethyl alcohol, acetaldehyde, acetic acid, *n*-butyric acid, *n*-caproic acid, glyoxylic acid, *n*-butyl phthalate, leaf aldehyde, and acetylmethyl carbinol. Of these, ethyl alcohol is present in the greatest amount. An idea of the small amounts of flavoring materials present, and consequently of the large volume of fruit necessary for this type of work, can be gained from the quantity of one of them—*n*-caproic acid, which is present to the extent of 0.0015 gram per 1,000 kilograms of fruit—that is, 2 tons of fruit yields approximately one-tenth of an ounce of the flavoring constituent. But small as the amounts are, they strongly influence the flavor of the fruit.

JUST AS THERE are differences in the composition of the flavoring constituents of different varieties of a fruit, so there may be differences in composition caused by seasonal variations. For example, the summer crop of pineapples has a much sweeter and fruitier flavor than the winter fruit. This difference in flavor is reflected in the volatile-oil content. The summer fruit contains 86.8 milligrams of oil per pound of fruit. The winter fruit contains only 7 milligrams of oil. Most of the difference is in the amounts of ethyl acetate and ethyl alcohol found in the two fruits. The summer fruit has 54.4 milligrams of ethyl acetate and 27.5 milligrams of alcohol per pound of fruit, whereas the winter fruit has only 1.3 milligrams of ethyl acetate per pound of fruit and contains no alcohol. One other important difference between the oils of the summer and winter fruits is that, except for the ethyl acetate, all the esters in the winter fruit are methyl esters, while those in the summer fruit are mainly ethyl esters.

One type of compound found in pineapple juice has not been found in any other fruits thus far investigated. It is a volatile sulfur compound identified as methyl-methyl thiolpropionate, having the formula $CH_3SCH_2CH_2COOCH_3$. It is present in the juice in very small amounts, 0.45 milligram per pound of fruit, but it is important as a flavoring constituent of the pineapple.

USUALLY FRUITS can be placed in one of two classes, depending on the compounds in their flavoring material—either terpene compounds or aliphatic esters and alcohols. Citrus fruits belong to the terpene class; pineapples and apples to the aliphatic ester class. Strawberries contain a mixture of terpene esters and aliphatic esters. Raspberries belong in the aliphatic ester class; besides, they contain two aromatic ring compounds.

A few other fruits have been investigated somewhat. Montmorency cherry juice, it has been learned, contains benzaldehyde, alcohols, and a trace of a terpene alcohol. Methyl alcohol constitutes 35 percent of the total alcohol fraction; in other fruits that contain it, methyl alcohol occurs only in trace amounts. Montmorency cherries are

also a fruit in which the flavor is due mainly to one component—that is, benzaldehyde.

F. Rothenbach and L. Eberlein, in 1905, were the first to isolate and identify the volatile flavoring constituents of a fruit. They found amyl isovalerate in bananas and mentioned the possible presence of amyl acetate, the so-called banana oil. A few years later, C. Kleber isolated a volatile oil from bananas by steam distillation and confirmed the presence of amyl acetate.

WE KNOW that the flavor of a fruit grown in one locality differs from that of the same fruit grown in another locality. But we cannot express this difference in chemical terms. Nor do we know what causes it. Is it temperature, sunlight, or variations in the soil? Or, perhaps, a combination of all?

The subject is of interest not only to chemists, processors, and consumers but also to horticulturists who seek to develop new varieties of fruit that will taste better than any now grown in this country. Isolation and identification of the elusive compounds that give fruits their flavor are an essential part of food research. They provide the key to more attractive foods for the family table and to new products and markets for growers and processors.

JUSTUS G. KIRCHNER, *a chemist in the Bureau of Agricultural and Industrial Chemistry, in Pasadena, Calif., holds a doctor's degree in chemistry from Iowa State College. From 1939 to 1945 he was employed as a research chemist at the California Institute of Technology, working on the isolation and identification of the chemical constituents in pineapples and onions. Dr. Kirchner was employed by the Desert Grapefruit Industries from 1945 to 1948, determining the flavoring constituents of grapefruit juice.*

Some of the Eastern Laboratory's work on apple essence is discussed in an earlier chapter, page 44.

Many Are the Values of the Apple

Claude H. Hills, J. J. Willaman

Of our 120 million bushels of apples a year, 65 million go into retail channels; 10 into vinegar; 8 into sauce; 5 each into canned slices, evaporated slices, and export; 4 into cider for roadside stands; 4 into apple juice, and 2 each into frozen slices and apple butter. Ten million bushels are used in a few other ways or are left in the orchard. No other American fruit can approach that combination of volume and diversity.

In the United States, apples are grown primarily for sale as fresh fruit. Our leading commercial varieties are Red Delicious, Winesap, McIntosh, and Jonathan, noted for their attractive appearance, aroma, and good eating quality. Two others, Rome Beauty and York Imperial, are used extensively in cooked products.

The demand for fresh apples is fairly constant. In a normal year it amounts to about 55 percent of the crop. Only Fancy grades (large, well colored, and free of defects) can be sold profitably as fresh fruit. The proportion of fruit that will grade Fancy depends on weather, effectiveness of spraying, cultural practices, and care in picking and handling. Even under the best conditions, 10 percent or more of the crop will be culls; sometimes the proportion may be as high as 50 percent.

Dr. A. E. Murneek, of the Missouri Agricultural Experiment Station, gives lack of size and color as the principal reason for grading apples as culls. Although less attractive, cull apples have approximately the same flavor, composition, and nutritive value as Fancy market fruit.

Something must be done with the culls. Here is where the processing plants come into the picture. Today they play an integral part in the orderly marketing of the crop, at the same time providing a great variety of food items and at least two industrial products.

APPLE FLESH contains about 84 percent water and 16 percent solids. Three readily assimilated sugars constitute more than 80 percent of the carbohydrates. They are: Levulose, 60 percent; glucose, 25 percent; and sucrose, 15 percent. The levulose enhances the sweetness. The acid present is almost entirely malic acid. Green apples may contain a small quantity of starch, but mature fruit contains only a trace. Besides small amounts of protein, fat, and fiber, apples contain ascorbic acid and traces of vitamin A, thiamine, and other B vitamins. Apple flesh and, especially, peel are high in pectin. That is why dried apple wastes are an important source of pectin for the jelly and preserve industry.

WHEN APPLES GO TO THE FACTORY they may be converted into any one of 17 primary products. Two potential products, wax and malic acid, are not yet produced on a commercial scale.

Products from apple flesh are prepared from the Utility grade—ripe fruit that is relatively free of defects and 2¼ inches or larger in diameter. Because the first step is peeling and coring, size is important in reducing waste and in raising the output per machine. For example, 100 pounds of 2¼-inch apples will yield only 53 pounds of slices, but the same weight of 3-inch apples will yield 78 pounds of finished product. The difference in output by machine or man-hour is even greater in favor of the larger fruit.

A sizable apple-slicing industry has developed near some large cities to supply bakeries with fresh slices for pies. The amount thus used probably exceeds 2 million bushels a year. Many large orchards, particularly in the East, have installed peeling and slicing equipment in connection with their packing and cold-storage facilities. The usual procedure is to pack the Fancy grades, place the Utility-grade culls in cold storage, and dispose of the smaller culls for juice or vinegar. With a proper choice of varieties and adequate storage, the grower can supply a bakery with fresh slices daily the year around.

Apple tissue contains a catechol-tannin pigment and oxidative enzymes, which cause the slices to turn brown when they are exposed to the air. Dipping the slices in a salt brine of 1 or 2 percent delays browning for several hours. The addition of small amounts of sulfur dioxide or of sulfites to the brine extends the effective holding period to several days. Fresh apple slices so treated have been sold at retail in 1-pound packages in New England.

Many of the summer and early fall varieties, and even the firmer-textured winter varieties, tend to become mushy when baked into pies. The soft slices may be firmed by dipping in dilute solutions of calcium chloride, and it is possible therefore to use many apples that used to be considered too soft for baking.

Canning apples has been a sizable industry for three decades or longer. The principal canning areas are New York, Pennsylvania, Virginia, and Washington. About 5 million bushels a year are so used. Most plants can three or four varieties selected for flavor, color, and texture. Apple slices to be canned usually are blanched to soften them, to destroy oxidative enzymes, and to expel air from the tissues so as to reduce corrosion of the cans. Canned apples are easily sterilized because of their acidity. If the blanched slices go into the containers hot (175° to 180° F.), very little additional heating is required. Most canned apples end up in pies or sauce. Calcium salts also are used now to firm canned slices. Another development is the canning of baked apples, a process suggested by workers at the Massachusetts Agricultural Experiment Station. At least one company has put on the market a retail-size jar of apple pie filler ready for the crust.

Frozen apples are relatively new, but they are going strong. Prevention of discoloration, particularly the internal browning on thawing, is the chief technical difficulty in preparing frozen apple slices. Several procedures have been developed. Steam blanching is rather effective, but it softens the tissues and leaches out part of the soluble sugars. Another method is to dip the slices in a solution containing 0.2 to 0.3 percent of sulfur dioxide or an equivalent concentration of various sulfite salts. Other methods remove air from the slices by applying a vacuum and subsequently filling the air spaces with a salt or sugar solution. More recent is the use of ascorbic acid to prevent discoloration.

Applesauce is a smooth and nearly colorless, slightly sweetened product from apple pulp. To comply with Department of Agriculture grade specifications, sauce must be prepared from peeled and cored fruit. It can be made more cheaply from whole fruit, but the product is darker and contains more defects (peel and calyx particles). Texture is important. A granular, rather than a pasty, texture is desired. Commercial sauce is commonly packed in No. 2 cans for the retail market or No. 10 cans for institutions. Some frozen applesauce is put up in 1-pound cartons.

Dehydrated apples appear on the market as slices, rings, or cubes. The demand for dried slices has fallen off in recent years, partly because of the increased production of frozen slices. The tan-colored, sun-dried slices commonly prepared on the farm are just about out of date commercially. In the factory, apples are always exposed to the fumes of burning sulfur before drying, in order to bleach the surface of the fruit and to prevent further browning. The sulfured pieces are usually dried in kilns or on trays under controlled conditions of temperature, humidity, and air flow. Dried apples are graded on texture and appearance, rather than flavor. Varieties that are firm and yield a white product are preferred. Most of the dehydration plants are in California and Washington. The preferred varieties for drying are Newtown Pippin, Spitzenberg, and Gravenstein.

Apple nuggets are crisp, popcorn-like granules of low moisture content. Dehydrated apples (24 percent moisture) are cut into ¼-inch cubes and dried to less than 2 percent moisture in two stages, the second of which requires a vacuum drier. The product is highly concentrated. It contains nearly 70 percent of sugars and must be packed in moistureproof cartons. One pound of nuggets, with added water and sugar, will make 9 pounds of applesauce. This found a place in Army cookery. The boys probably complained about this applesauce, but then proceeded to enjoy it.

Chops are another common form of commercially dried apples. For them, small culls can be used, because peeling and coring are not required. The whole apple is sliced horizontally into discs about an eighth of an inch thick and dried without sulfuring. Chops are used in apple butter.

Apple powder, prepared by spray drying a slurry of peeled fruit, is another dehydrated product, but its demand is limited to medicinal use. It has been approved by the American Medical Association for the treatment of certain types of diarrhea.

Cider and hallowe'en have belonged together for generations. Because cider is the freshly pressed juice, not pasteurized, it does not keep very long and can be produced only while fresh or storage apples are available. It is such a refreshing drink, however,

that as soon as flash pasteurization of juices was developed, about 1937, cider was put up in cans or bottles for year-around consumption. The product is usually called apple juice, although no official distinction is made between the words. The peak of consumption comes in October, but we now drink apple juice the whole year. Although cider and apple juice together amount to some 25 million gallons a year, that is only about one-sixth of a gallon a person—the Swiss drink 2 gallons. We predict a steady increase in the use of apple juice. It is an excellent way to use up surplus apples. When it is made from a good blend of ripe fruit, it is a delight to the palate.

The ascorbic acid in raw apples is almost completely lost during processing. Addition of the vitamin to juice became widespread in this country during the Second World War. For several years it was compulsory in Canada, because it was a way to provide vitamin C in the absence of an adequate supply of citrus fruits. Ascorbic acid, an antioxidant, also helps maintain flavor during storage.

A new type of product, called liquid apple, is apple juice plus finely pulverized pulp in stable suspension.

Frozen apple juice in retail-size containers has been popular in California. A frozen juice concentrate similar to frozen orange concentrate is now being developed.

Several agricultural experiment stations have undertaken the study of blends of apple and other fruit juices—apple and cranberry blends in Massachusetts; apple and various small fruits at the station in Geneva, N. Y.; and grape-apple blends at the Ohio station. Apple-lime blends were favorably received in commercial trials in Canada. The next few years will determine whether these specialty items have sufficient merit to create a large demand.

APPLE ESSENCE is the volatile fraction of the fruit. These volatiles are a complex mixture of acids, esters, alcohols, and aldehydes.

J. W. White, Jr., of the Eastern Regional Research Laboratory, who studied the composition of the mixture, identified 26 different compounds. The total amount of the substances in fresh apple juice is about 50 parts to the million. They evaporate so easily that they are completely lost in the preparation of sirup, concentrate, and evaporated slices, and are lost to some extent in pasteurized juice, canned apples, and sauce.

The process of recovering the volatiles in concentrated form, which was developed by H. P. Milleville and R. K. Eskew of the Eastern Laboratory, consists of three steps: Rapid vaporization (in 15 seconds or less) of 10 percent of the fresh juice; separation of the vapors from the liquid; and fractionation of the vapors to obtain a one-hundred-fold to one hundred and fifty-fold concentration. One gallon of one hundred and sixty-fold essence would contain all the volatile flavors from a ton of apples. The essence can be prepared economically from juice that is intended for sirup or concentrate, because the volatiles would be lost anyhow during vacuum evaporation. When a small amount of the essence is added to apple concentrate of a good grade and reconstituted with water, the product is indistinguishable from fresh apple juice. As might be expected, the character of the essence varies with the variety of apple from which it is produced. In general, the more aromatic varieties, such as McIntosh and Red Delicious, produce stronger, more aromatic essences.

Products improved by the addition of apple essence include jelly, candy, sauce, and sirup. Apple concentrate fortified with essence could be used as a fountain sirup. Several carbonated soft drinks are flavored with apple essence. It has also been suggested as a flavoring for pharmaceuticals like cough sirups and tooth paste.

Several sirups and concentrates are made from apple juice. If the juice is boiled down in an open vessel, the product is called boiled cider; it is rather dark and has a strong taste. If it is evaporated under vacuum, the product is called concentrated apple juice, or merely apple concentrate; it is lighter in color and milder in flavor, although still sharply acid. If the acidity of the juice is removed or neutralized and the juice evaporated under vacuum, one of several types of apple sirup is produced.

The pectin in apple juice is sufficient to cause gelation if the juice is concentrated beyond 55 or 60 percent of soluble solids. A depectinized juice may be concentrated to 68 or 70 percent of soluble solids without gelation; that is the usual product of commerce. Its sugar content is enough to make it self-preserving. Apple concentrate is used chiefly in jellies and apple butter.

Apple juice may also be concentrated by freezing out the water. Such concentrates contain all the volatile aroma present in the original juice because the juice has not been heated, or subjected to a high vacuum.

APPLE SIRUP, developed at the Eastern Laboratory in 1942, is light amber, bland, and slightly sweeter than honey. Because of its high levulose content, it was used during the war as a substitute for glycerin in conditioning tobacco. The estimated 10 million pounds of sirup produced in this country and Canada between 1943 and 1947 utilized nearly 1.5 million bushels of cull apples.

The original process, using lime to neutralize the acidity and remove pectin, gave a product having a slightly bitter taste of calcium malate. A better flavored sirup, suitable for table use, may be prepared by removing the acid on a bed of ion-exchange resin. Malic acid would be a byproduct of this process, once it is put into commercial operation. Apple sirup cannot compete with corn sirup on a cost basis, but there may be a market for blends of apple and corn sirups or blends of apple and low-grade maple sirups, which have an excess of maple flavor.

Studies by C. C. Flora and C. W.

Holdaway at the Virginia Agricultural Experiment Station have shown the value of apple sirup for reducing curd tension of milk products for infant feeding

OF THE FERMENTED PRODUCTS from apples, the most important is cider vinegar. It is prepared by the fermentation of sugars to alcohol by yeasts, followed by oxidation of the alcohol to acetic acid by acetobacter, commonly called mother of vinegar. An apple juice that contains more than 9 percent of sugars should produce a vinegar containing more than the legal minimum of 4 percent acetic acid. The wild yeasts present in all fruit juices usually produce an inefficient fermentation. It is more efficient to add pure yeast cultures for the first fermentation and to use vinegar generators with controlled temperatures and air-flow rates for the second stage.

Several alcoholic beverages can be prepared from apple juice. The term "hard cider" often signifies a partly fermented apple juice that contains 4 to 6 percent of alcohol and several percent of residual sugar. Apple wine is prepared by adding pure wine yeast to a mixture of apple juice and sugar. Apple brandy is a distilled beverage. These products are prepared in relatively small amounts and utilize only a small quantity of cull fruit.

EVEN THE PEELS AND CORES of apples are used. In the manufacture of nearly all apple products, except apple butter, a large proportion (30 percent or more) of the apple is left as peels and cores or pomace. The peels and cores can be further ground and pressed to yield pomace and juice, which is suitable for sirup, concentrate, or vinegar stock. In an average year, the total volume of processing residues exceeds 200,000 tons.

The most profitable use for dried apple pomace is to make pectin for jams, jellies, and preserves. Many jelly manufacturers buy dried apple pomace and make their own pectin concentrate

as needed. Others buy pectin as a liquid concentrate or as a dry powder.

Another type of pectin, called low-ester pectin, has been developed. Unlike ordinary pectin, it does not require a high sugar concentration to produce gelation, but will form a gel in the presence of a small concentration of calcium. With this modified pectin, jellied fruit desserts and aspics can be made with a small proportion of sugar, or none at all. Jellies made with 35 to 45 percent of sugar have more of the natural fruit flavor than those made with the customary 55 percent. During the war, the Army used nearly 20 million 4-ounce cans of jellied fruit cocktail made with low-ester pectin.

BESIDES their many food uses, pectin or pectin derivatives may serve as thickening agents in pharmaceutical preparations, in pastes and salves, and as an agar substitute in preparing bacteriological culture media. Nicotine pectate has been suggested as an insecticide. Crude pectate solutions have been used in baths for quenching steel. Chemists at the Western Laboratory have developed pectinate films, which provide nonsticky, edible coatings for frankfurters, dried fruits, and candy.

Because of the limited demand for pectin and the serious competition from citrus pectins, probably less than half of the available apple-processing wastes are used in manufacturing pectin. Fresh apple pomace, or marc, contains about 30 percent solids and is rich in digestible carbohydrates.

F. B. Morrison, the well-known authority on animal feeding, wrote that apple pomace is "a good substitute for corn silage in feeding dairy cows, being approximately equal to corn silage in value per ton." In areas near processing plants it is customary to feed fresh or ensiled pomace. Dried pomace is relatively nonperishable and may be stored for years. It is usually fed with molasses or other concentrates.

Several hundred tons of dried apple pomace is used annually as a carrier for insect bait. It attracts grasshoppers and other insects and may be used in place of wheat bran. Dried pomace contains nearly 1 percent of peel wax, and the seeds contain more than 30 percent of oil. The total quantities of these materials would be too small to justify their recovery unless they were found to have special useful properties.

SECONDARY APPLE PRODUCTS are those prepared from one or more of the primary products we have described. They include apple jelly, candy, pie, mincemeat, and dozens of home dishes made with apples.

Apple pie, the great American dessert, is the end product of some 10 million bushels. Most of the commercially prepared canned, frozen, and fresh apple slices reach the consumer between crusts. The restaurant trade requires firm slices, which make its pies attractive in cross section. Only the firmer varieties of apples were formerly used for commercial pies, but many of the summer and early fall varieties, which have excellent flavor, may be treated with calcium salts to provide firmness.

Apple and apple-base jellies contain two apple products, pectin and concentrate. According to Federal regulations, apple jelly must contain 45 percent of apple juice or an equivalent amount of concentrate, plus added sugar to give a final concentration of 65 percent soluble solids. Apple-base jellies usually are blends of apple and some other fruit juice, such as grape, cherry, blackberry, or raspberry.

APPLE BUTTER is prepared from fresh fruit, barreled pulp, or dried chops. As a rule, boiled cider or concentrate is added and the entire mass heated for several hours in an open kettle. Concentration of the pulp under vacuum would yield a lighter product, but the deep-brown color of apple butter has been one of its distinguishing characteristics since pioneer days. After the desired consistency and color have been reached, sugar and spices are added, and the pulp is passed through a finisher that has one or more fine screens, which remove particles of peel, seeds, and stems.

Other commercial items that contain apple products are mincemeat, full-flavored apple concentrate, and various soft drinks fortified with apple essence. An apple ice, containing small bits of ground apple slices and flavored with apple essence, has been prepared on a pilot-plant scale but is not yet a commercial reality. A series of fruit products called Velva Fruit, containing a high proportion of ground fruit plus suitable amounts of sugar and gelatin for stabilizing, has been developed at the Western Laboratory.

IN THE HOME, apples are used in quantities beyond our ability to estimate—for baking, boiling, frying; in pie, dumplings, brown betties; in salads, cakes, pinwheels, and pandowdy. The New York and New England Apple Institute, 43 Crown Street, Kingston, N. Y., compiled a list of more than 200 recipes featuring apples.

CLAUDE H. HILLS *did graduate study in horticulture at Missouri University and biochemistry at the University of Minnesota. His post-doctorate research has been chiefly in the fields of meat proteins, low-ester pectin, and apple products. Dr. Hills joined the staff of the Eastern Regional Research Laboratory in 1941 and is head of the fruit products section.*

J. J. WILLAMAN *is a plant chemist, with degrees from the Universities of Wisconsin and Chicago. For many years at the Minnesota Agricultural Experiment Station and then at the Geneva, N. Y., station, he investigated such subjects as the chemistry of plant diseases, the manufacture of sorghum sirup, and the maturity of canning peas. He then spent some time in the commercial production of enzymes. Dr. Willaman joined the staff of the Eastern Laboratory in 1940 as head of the biochemical division, in which work is under way on the utilization of tobacco, fruits, vegetables, and honey.*

FRUITS, IN GENERAL, are at the same time more sweet and more sour than vegetables. The sweetness is due to the sugar content. The sour, or tart, taste is due to organic acids, which are much weaker than such mineral acids as hydrochloric, nitric, and sulfuric. They are about as strong as acetic acid, which is responsible for the sour taste in vinegar. Like acetic acid, they contain only the elements carbon, hydrogen, and oxygen.

Malic and citric acids are by far the most common of the fruit acids. Most fruits contain both. The term "malic" comes from *Malus*, the generic name of the apple; "citric" comes from *Citrus*, the generic name of such fruits as oranges and lemons. In apples, the acid may be entirely malic acid, or may contain also a little citric acid, depending on the variety. Citric acid is the principal acid of citrus fruits, but small amounts of malic acid are also found. Lemons and limes may contain 6 percent, or even more, of citric acid.

Malic acid is the predominating acid in such fruits as cherries, plums, and quinces; citric acid, in blueberries, currants, pineapples, raspberries, and strawberries. The late E. K. Nelson, of the Department of Agriculture, discovered that the principal acid of eastern bush blackberries is isocitric acid, the first time that this substance was found in nature. It has since been found in other plants.

Grapes contain some malic acid, a little citric acid, and considerable amounts of tartaric acid. Tartaric acid has not been found in more than traces in any other fruit except the tamarind, a tropical plant.

Oxalic acid has been found in small amounts in a number of fruits, but apparently it is the predominating acid only in the tropical carambola. Oxalic acid is rather poisonous. It is absorbed rapidly from the intestine, but is not readily oxidized in the body, as are malic and citric acids. It interferes with carbohydrate metabolism and combines with calcium.

Cranberries are unique in that they contain benzoic acid, in addition to citric and malic acids. Benzoic acid is a mild antiseptic, sometimes used (usually as the sodium salt) in preserving foods like catsup and fresh cider.—*A. Laurence Curl, Western Regional Research Laboratory.*

WHILE I WAS Vice Consul in Manaos, Amazonas, Brazil, it was my duty to take trips on the old-fashioned, wood-burning river boats, which often took a month. On such trips, I often had a great desire for fresh fruit, but rarely was any fruit available at the small river landings where we stopped. Once, on a trip from Manaos to Iquitos (Peru), we stopped at a rather large settlement where I was surprised to find a good supply of bananas, oranges, guavas, papayas, avocados, and many other fruits. I asked the owner of the fruit why he had such an abundance, when there was none at other landings along our route. The fellow, a wrinkled old Indian, dressed in nothing but a pair of almost worn-out shorts, looked at me a long time before answering, and then remarked that any fool should know that without a market there was no need to grow fruit just for the monkeys and birds to eat. I should have observed that his was the only port in many miles where large ocean-going ships could tie up alongside and did not have to anchor in midstream. He said that the crew and passengers could come ashore and easily take on board all the fruit they wanted. Farmers throughout the world produce in quantities when they have a profitable market.—*Hubert Maness, Agricultural Attaché, American Embassy, Montevideo, Uruguay.*

Chemistry and Technology of Citrus

M. K. Veldhuis

In the years between the First and Second World Wars, oranges ceased to be a rarity to be hung on Christmas trees or to be enjoyed only at certain seasons and became one of our most common foods.

Modern transportation has made fresh oranges and other citrus fruits available in regions far from producing centers. Developments in the technology of canning have transformed them into grocery staples. The fresh orange spoils in less than 3 weeks after picking, but its processed juice can be preserved for consumption the year around.

Five States supply all our citrus fruits. Florida grows more than half of our oranges and grapefruit and nearly all our limes. California is next in oranges and produces most of the lemons. Texas and Arizona grow large quantities of grapefruit and some oranges. Louisiana produces a small orange crop.

Only 20 years ago Florida groves were fast becoming nonproductive. Then a spectacular improvement in cultural practices—the inclusion of small amounts of minor elements in fertilizers—helped to rejuvenate the citrus trees there, so that production in Florida alone is as large as the entire national apple crop. The production of oranges in Florida rose from 12 million boxes in 1931 to 57 million boxes in 1950.

Including tangerines, lemons, and limes, as well as oranges and grapefruit, the production in all producing areas in 1950 was more than 150 million boxes, against 85 million boxes in 1936.

This increased production made it necessary to can a larger part of the crop. In Florida, in 1950, 31 million boxes of oranges—nearly half the crop—were processed, compared to about one-eighth before 1936. In 1936, about one-third of the grapefruit was canned; now half the crop is sold as canned products. Total processing operations now consume nearly 3 million tons of citrus fruits. That means that 11 large cans of juice are available annually for each person in the United States.

The number of canneries has also increased in the past 15 years. In Florida about 50 canning plants processed citrus fruits in 1950.

The manufacture in recent years of much larger amounts of a high-carbohydrate cattle feed and a citrus-molasses feed as byproducts of cannery wastes has helped the economy of the industry.

Canning at first was a salvage operation to use fruits rejected from fresh shipments because of blemished skins or unpopular sizes. Now much of the fruit moves directly from the grove to the cannery. In fact, the biggest part of the crop in Florida is grown just for canning.

Fresh and processed citrus fruit compete somewhat, but because fresh citrus fruits also compete with other fresh fruits, the greater convenience to the housewife of the canned citrus may actually give the crop a means of holding its own in the competitive market.

A POPULAR NEW frozen concentrated orange juice is an example of joint research by the Florida Citrus Commission and the Department of Agriculture and illustrates the forward march of processing techniques. The new product is an orange juice of fourfold concentrated strength so like the fresh juice in flavor and taste when it is rediluted and so convenient to use that its consumption has about trebled each year it has been in production. During the 1950 season, 21,647,000 gallons of it was produced in Florida. Within 5 years of its introduction, the juice has become the most popular frozen food. It is simple to use; all one does is to empty a can of the concentrated juice into a container and add to it three times its volume of water. Not even ice is necessary because the readily diluted concentrate cools the drink. Orange juice is a good source of vitamin C, nearly all of which is retained in the concentrate.

Several other citrus products marketed in cans are in demand—fruit sections, sherbet purees, beverage bases, and marmalade. Powdered orange juice has been produced, but it was not available in large quantities in 1950.

CANNED PASTEURIZED single-strength juices are the largest single type of product. Until 1943, grapefruit juice was packed in the largest amounts. Then, with advances in the technology of canning and a better understanding of what was required, canned orange juice surpassed grapefruit in volume. Blended orange and grapefruit juices are also canned in large quantities and tangerine and lime juices in smaller quantities.

Pasteurized juices retain satisfactorily the nutritive value of the original fruit. Even during storage, the rate of loss of vitamin C (ascorbic acid) is low. For instance, more than 80 percent of vitamin C is found in juice that has been stored for 6 months at a little above room temperature, provided the juice has not come in contact with copper or brass. Other components of the juice—acids, sugar, and minerals—are almost unaffected by processing.

Pasteurization, however, does affect the flavor. To be satisfactory, canned juices must retain their pleasing flavor after several months of storage at 70° to 90° F. The flavor of pasteurized juices differs from that of fresh juice and further changes in flavor occur later during storage. Significant off-flavors develop after about a year's storage at room temperature. With cooler storage, the juices can retain flavor longer. Grapefruit juice has the longest storage life. Blended orange and grapefruit juices come next.

Changes in fatty materials, peel oil, and other volatile or nonvolatile compounds cause off-flavors during storage. Research organizations are making progress in determining the cause of the gradual flavor deterioration and in devising means of preventing it.

The pasteurization of single-strength juices is the least expensive of the various ways of processing citrus fruits. It can be done rapidly—the processes are largely automatic and are adaptable to large-scale operations. Some canneries process more than 1,500 tons a day in this manner.

METHODS of processing have been greatly improved in the past few years. Almost all equipment has been remodeled so that it is more efficient and easier to clean and maintain. Stainless-steel equipment is almost universally used.

Although nearly every plant uses a variation of the method, and employs different types of machinery, practically all include six steps in sequence. The fruit is washed and conveyed to extractors, which remove the juice. Seeds and excess pulp are screened out. The juice is passed through deaerators, which rid it of dissolved oxygen. Then it is pumped through continuous, rapid pasteurizers, where micro-organisms are destroyed and enzymes are inactivated. The hot juice flows directly to the can-filling and can-closing equipment. The closed cans are cooled rapidly by rotation under sprays of cold water.

Washing consists of soaking the fruits in large tanks that contain soaps and germicides, then passing them through a machine equipped with scrubbing brushes, and rinsing by spraying with clean water.

A conveyor usually carries the washed fruit to automatic extractors for juicing. Modern extractors are fast and deliver juice of high quality. Most types cut the fruit into halves and press or ream out the juice in much the same way as does an orange juicer in the kitchen. A recently developed extractor squeezes the whole fruit and forces the juice out through a tube inserted through one side of the orange. This juice contains pulp, seed, and peel, or other suspended solids, so it is run through a screw-type finisher or a series of vibrating or revolving screens of successively finer mesh. The screens remove all but the desired amount of solids.

THE JUICE is collected in stainless-steel tanks and mixed, and the content of acid and total solids is determined. These values provide a check on the quality of the fruit being used. If a sweeter product is desired, sugar is added at this point.

To remove dissolved oxygen, the juice is injected into a closed chamber under a high vacuum. The deaeration makes canning more efficient and may also prevent oxidative and flavor changes in the finished juices.

Because consumers may object to peel oil in the juices, some canneries use deoilers, in which a small fraction of the juice is vaporized under vacuum at a comparatively low temperature and a major part of the oil in the juice goes off with the vapor.

The next step, pasteurization by heating, is carried out rapidly in stainless-steel, tubular heat exchangers, in order to minimize changes in flavor due to the heating. Pasteurization destroys organisms that might cause the product to spoil by fermentation and inactivates enzymes that might cause undesirable changes in the juice, such as clotting of the suspended matter. Citrus juices are acid, and heating to about 160° F. is sufficient to destroy the micro-organisms, but heating to 190° or above is needed to inactivate the enzymes. The temperature required varies with the time of heating. In one type of pasteurizing equipment, the juice is heated for 40 seconds to 193° to 200°; in another, to 240° to 265° in about 4 seconds. The juice generally is cooled to 185° to 190° before being run into cans. The filled cans are closed and cooled rapidly by spinning under sprays of cold water.

CONCENTRATED pasteurized juices are popular in the preparation of beverages, sherbets, and candies. The juice is extracted and concentrated under moderately high vacuum at a temperature of 120° F. The process reduces the volume of the juice to about one-seventh. Then the concentrate is heated to pasteurize it, run hot into cans, and rapidly cooled. The product differs from fresh juice in that it lacks aromatic and some other flavor characteristics. Just the same, it is an acceptable product and retains well the vitamins and food value of the original juice. It keeps well under refrigeration at 40° but will deteriorate in a month or two at room temperature.

FROZEN SINGLE-STRENGTH JUICES are produced in limited quantities. The process is the same as for canning, except that the juice is not usually pasteurized before being frozen. Sound, ripe fruits are selected, and great care is taken in processing to insure cleanliness because of the health hazards involved when juices are not pasteurized. The juice is run through a refrigerated heat exchanger, to lower the temperature to 30° to 35° F., and then into cans, which are sealed under a vacuum and rolled or spiraled through a conveyor filled with refrigerated brine. Some juice is frozen in air-blast tunnels. Frozen juices should be stored at 0° to −10°. An objection, which has limited the acceptance of the product, is its slowness to thaw when about to be used.

To develop the basic process for the preparation of a frozen orange concentrate, research workers in the Florida Citrus Commission and the Winter Haven, Fla., laboratory of the Bureau of Agricultural and Industrial Chemistry first centered their attention on producing a high-quality concentrate by high-vacuum evaporation. The scientists learned that if they evaporated the juice rapidly at 80° F. or somewhat below, no cooked flavor or off-flavor developed, but the product tasted flat and lacked the aroma of the fresh juice, because nearly all the volatile flavoring materials had been removed with the water vapor.

To FIND a way to restore the aromatic volatile substances lost in the evaporation, the technicians developed the idea of using "cut-back" juice. The concentration is carried beyond the logical stopping point (to about 60 percent soluble solids) and this concentrate is cut back with freshly prepared single-strength juice until the desired final strength is obtained (42 percent soluble solids). The cut-back juice restores fresh aroma and flavor. The cut-back juice is specially prepared in such a manner that it contains a comparatively large amount of coarse suspended solids and even some whole juice sacs, so that with proper dilution the product even resembles in appearance fresh juice as it is normally prepared in the home. After the cut-back juice has been added, the concentrate is rapidly frozen in continuous slush freezers, run into cans, and stored at zero or below. Because the concentrate is not pasteurized, sanitary precautions are taken to insure the minimum count of micro-organisms. Specially designed evaporators are arranged so that the process can be operated continuously. No off-flavor is noticeable.

The method is widely used by the industry. In the first season of commercial production (1944 to 1945), 225 thousand gallons was produced in

Florida. Production in 1948 to 1949 reached 10 million gallons and 21 million gallons in 1949 to 1950. New plants are being installed, and the capacity of present plants is being increased. Several plants have also been installed in California and more are being planned.

When production facilities have expanded to meet the demand, it is likely that more attention will be given to frozen concentrates of grapefruit, tangerines, and blended orange and grapefruit.

POWDERED ORANGE JUICE has been made possible because of the recent advances in high-vacuum technology and experience gained in the manufacture of penicillin.

The juice or concentrate to be used as the base is kept frozen by the application of high vacuum, and the water is removed by vaporization from the solid state. The resulting product is friable and of good quality and has better storage qualities than the original concentrate but still deteriorates rapidly at room temperature. It contains less than 1 percent moisture, but readily absorbs moisture from the air and must be kept in sealed containers until used. As with other citrus products, the retention of vitamin C is high, 95 percent or better. The cost of manufacture of powdered juice is higher than for juices and concentrates, however; the product will have difficulty on a normal market, but may have special application where it is difficult to obtain the canned citrus juice or concentrate. Although powdered orange juice is not now available in commercial quantities, the processing has been conducted successfully on a commercial scale and the requirements are known.

FROZEN CITRUS PUREES have been prepared experimentally by a simple and effective process. Sound, mature fruit is sorted, washed, trimmed, and passed through a screw press, producing a pulpy juice, or puree. Sugar is mixed in, 1 pound for each 5 pounds of puree, to assist in preserving the product. The sweetened puree is packed in suitable containers, which are sealed or closed, and subjected to subzero temperatures. The canned product is stored at zero or below. The method has been adopted on a commercial scale in both California and Florida.

Orange, lemon, and tangerine purees have been the principal products. They are particularly useful in making sherbets to which they give a superior flavor. The purees also find use in the preparation of pies, cakes, and puddings.

CANNED GRAPEFRUIT SECTIONS, or Hearts, were one of the first successful citrus products. They are flavorful, have a good storage life, and are popular in fruit cocktails, salads, and desserts. Before 1936 they exceeded in volume any other canned citrus product. Some mixed orange and grapefruit sections and some orange sections are also packed, especially for use in salads.

For sections, large, select fruits are first immersed in hot water for about 5 minutes to plump and loosen the peel, which is then removed by hand. The fruit is immersed for about 30 seconds in a 2 percent lye solution to remove the outer membranes. The lye is afterwards removed by spraying with water. The sections are removed with a wide-bladed triangular knife and packed with sirup in cans, which are heated in a steam box to remove air, sealed, pasteurized in hot water, and cooled. The individual sections are fragile, and care has to be taken to keep the pieces whole.

FROZEN citrus sections are prepared in a similar manner, except that they are never heated and are packed in paper containers instead of tin cans. Because the product is not heated, extra precautions are necessary to keep down the microbiological count. The frozen sections are of high dessert quality, but have not enjoyed the popularity they deserve, chiefly because of the length of time required for defrosting before using—the need for the product must be anticipated a few hours in advance of use. Frozen grapefruit sections have been the principal item, but some orange and mixed orange and grapefruit sections have also been packed.

THE CITRUS-BYPRODUCT industry, using the waste peel rag and seeds from citrus canneries, has been speeded up by the developments in canning and processing. Nearly all the waste is utilized in the production of dried citrus pulp, citrus molasses, peel oils, seed oil, pectin, and alcohol.

Although the field of citrus processing has been amazingly active in the past few years, many problems still remain. Citrus processors and research organizations are aware that products of the highest quality can be developed only through the discovery of better processes to inactivate enzymes and to reduce the development of off-flavors. The great appeal of the convenience of citrus products makes improvement especially desirable as a means of stabilizing the industry. Uses of citrus products must also be expanded and new products developed to avoid problems if surpluses of the crop should some time accumulate.

Many regard the processing of citrus as the most important means of increasing the per capita consumption of these desirable fruits.

M. K. VELDHUIS *has been a member of the Bureau of Agricultural and Industrial Chemistry since 1935. He was engaged in investigations on cucumber pickles at Raleigh, N. C., and for 4 years was in charge of the work at the United States Fruit and Vegetable Products Laboratory, Pullman, Wash., where he initiated the work on the cleaning of vined peas. He has been in charge of the United States Citrus Products Station in Winter Haven, Fla., since 1944. He holds degrees from Montana State College and Iowa State College.*

Making Use of Tons of Citrus Waste

Harry S. Owens, M. K. Veldhuis, W. Dayton Maclay

More than 2 million tons of pulp, peel, and rag remain each year after citrus fruits are processed into juice, frozen concentrate, and sections. What to do with those mountains of waste?

When the industry was young, the only wastes were the culls and surplus fruit, which were dumped on wasteland or used as soil conditioners on cultivated land. Solid wastes from early canneries were handled in the same way. The liquid wastes were ponded or flushed into streams, lakes, or sewers. All such makeshifts were unsatisfactory and dangerous. A pile of rotting orange peels soon begins to stink; underground water supplies are contaminated; and the increased biochemical oxygen demand kills aquatic life or exceeds the capacities of sewage-treating plants.

Industrial, State, and Federal research organizations investigated the increasingly serious problem. From their efforts came several economically valuable products. Now 80 to 90 percent of citrus wastes are converted into usable products, such as dried pulp, molasses, pectin, essential oils, brined peel, citric acid, limonene, feed yeast, and biologically active materials.

From the waste peel, marc, and seeds that came from the processing lines, research men developed dried pulp, which is used extensively for feeding dairy and beef cattle and is suitable for feeding other animals. It contains about 8 percent moisture, 6 percent ash, 6 percent crude protein based on total nitrogen, 6 percent crude fat, 14 percent crude fiber, and 66 percent nitrogen-free extract. Although it must be supplemented with some other feed, it contains significant amounts of protein, fats, and minerals.

To make dried pulp, fresh peel is first ground in a hammer mill. One-half to 1 percent of lime is added to the peel immediately after grinding; the amount is carefully measured in order to get the best pressing characteristics. The lime neutralizes the acids and catalyzes the de-esterification of the pectin in the peel to form calcium pectate, which facilitates pressing and drying. Formerly the peel was allowed to stand in bins for about 45 minutes before pressing or drying to allow time for the lime to react. Now the time of reaction is shortened to 15 minutes or so by stirring the peel constantly as it moves slowly through a pug mill. Continuous presses remove as much liquid as possible. In some processing plants the pulp is heated by direct steam injection to about 120° F. during this step to facilitate the pressing. The weight of liquor removed is about equal to the weight of the pressed pulp. Direct-fired or steam-heated rotary kiln driers are used to remove the moisture from the pulp. In some mills the pulp is given a preliminary drying in direct-fired units and finished in steam-heated units. Careful control of the drying rates and temperatures is necessary to produce the fluffy, light-colored feeds that are considered desirable. About 1 ton of feed is obtained from 10 tons of cannery waste. In the past 10 years, production of dried peel has increased to approximately 200,000 tons a year.

Press or drain liquor from citrus peel contains 5 to 7 percent sugar and a total of 10 to 12 percent soluble solids. It cannot be flushed into sewers or ponded unless care is taken to reduce the biochemical oxygen demand or to prevent bad smells. Most of the press liquor is concentrated to produce molasses. Multiple-effect evaporation is commonly used. One plant in Texas uses direct heating with a submerged gas flame, followed by two stages of evaporation.

The first stage of a multiple-effect evaporator is operated under positive pressure (up to 26 pounds) and the last stage under negative pressure (down to 26 inches of mercury). Intermediate stages may be used to increase the number of pounds of water evaporated per pound of fuel consumed. Evaporators may be constructed of mild steel. Corrosion is something of a problem if not all of the acid is neutralized by the lime. A more serious problem is scaling of the heat-exchanger tubes in the evaporators, because the scale builds up rapidly, interferes with heat transfer and circulation, and must be removed about twice a week by boiling with lye. The exact nature of the scale has not been determined, but it probably is composed largely of calcium citrate, calcium pectate, and fibrous material. Trouble is encountered primarily in the first effect of the evaporator. Some operators give the press juice a preliminary heating to 212° F. or higher in an auxiliary heat exchanger, which can be cleaned easily. The heating precipitates some material, which is removed in a continuous clarifier, and lengthens the time the evaporators can be operated between cleanings.

In a recent installation, submerged gas burners are used to give the press juice a preliminary heating and concentration to about 22 percent solids. Carbonation by the products of combustion forms a precipitate, which is removed in continuous thickeners. Either method reduces the amount of suspended matter in the final product and improves the quality. Analyses of 13 samples of Florida citrus molasses showed an average of 71.4 percent total solids, 42 percent sugars, 3.8 percent crude protein, 1.1 percent pectin, and 4.8 percent ash. The pH value was 4.7.

Citrus molasses is dark brown and bitter. It is used mainly in cattle feeds, in which it is usually mixed with other materials, although it can be fed full-strength. Some is mixed with wet citrus pulp and then dried to make a feed. The amount of total digestible nutrients in the molasses is about 57 percent. Some is used as a fermentation substrate in the production of alcohol.

Production of citrus molasses increased from none in 1940–41 to nearly 42,000 tons in the 1949–50 season.

ANOTHER USE for press juice is in the production of yeast, particularly *Torulopsis utilis,* which grows rapidly and is therefore less susceptible to contamination than other yeasts. It is rich in vitamins of the B complex and is a good supplement in feeds. About half the dried yeast is crude protein. It is deficient in methionine, one of the essential amino acids, which, however, is present in cereal proteins. A ration containing this yeast with some cereal would provide all the essential amino acids.

Research workers in the Southern Regional Research Laboratory, the United States Citrus Products Laboratory in Winter Haven, Fla., and a commercial cannery worked together to develop a process for the production of feed yeast. Their experiments included the operation of a 200-gallon-per-hour pilot plant. They developed a continuous method, which gives a good yield. The juice from the feed mill is first passed through an 80-mesh screen to remove particles of pulp. Then it is diluted with water to a sugar concentration of about 2 percent, heated to 200° F. to destroy micro-organisms, cooled, and pumped continuously into the yeast propagator. A concentrated nutrient solution is metered into the propagator in proportion to the feed rate. The propagator is kept thoroughly aerated by air introduced through porous stone candles in the bottom of the tank. The product from the propagator flows continuously into a collecting tank and thence to special centrifuges which separate the yeast as a thick cream. The yeast cream is dried on a drum drier, pulverized, and packaged.

As nutrients, phosphates and nitrogen compounds must be added. Some benefit can be obtained from the phosphorus in the juice, but it must be supplemented. About 0.19 pound of ammonium sulfate, 0.045 pound of anhydrous ammonia, and 0.045 pound of 75 percent phosphoric acid are required per pound of yeast. The acidity in the propagator is easily controlled within the range of pH 4 to 4.5 by varying the ratio of ammonia to ammonium sulfate. With the method of aeration used, from 500 to 700 cubic feet of air was required per pound of yeast produced. Cooling coils were installed in the propagator to dissipate the heat of fermentation and maintain a constant temperature of 95° F.

A pure culture of *Torulopsis utilis* is grown in the propagator. Continuous feeding of the pasteurized press juice and nutrients is started and maintained as soon as the actively growing culture fills the propagator. No new culture is needed so long as the yeast grows rapidly. The problem of foaming is controlled by closing the top of the propagator and providing a large overflow tube to a collecting tank where the foam is broken.

Fermentation proceeds rapidly and the rate of feed an hour can equal one-third the propagator volume. This means an average retention time of only 3 hours, which is considered short for fermentations. Yields of yeast are progressively smaller with increasing sugar content of the feed. At a 2 percent concentration, the yield is 44 percent of the sugars consumed. Utilizations better than 95 percent of the sugars and two-thirds of the total organic matter were obtained. The drum-dried yeast analyzed 47 percent

crude protein and 3.3 percent phosphate (as the pentoxide). The product is light in color, fluffy, and, though not washed, only slightly bitter.

THE ISOLATION OF OIL from the rind of the lemon is one of the earliest chemurgic applications of citrus fruit. Hand pressing of the peel against sponges has been practiced in Sicily since the 18th century; at one time the United States imported nearly a half million pounds of lemon oil annually. Machinery has made possible the production each year of more than 1,500,000 pounds of oils from citrus peels.

The whole fruit, waste cannery peel, or flavedo, the colored part of the peel, can be used. The material is ground and pressed in screw extractors or pressed between fluted rolls to yield an oil emulsion. A recently developed juice extractor, which presses the whole fruit, delivers separately the edible juice and an oil emulsion. The emulsion is screened and the oil separated by centrifuging. The centrifuged oil is placed in cold storage, where waxes separate, the wax-free product being known as cold-pressed oil. These methods are used particularly with lemons, oranges, and grapefruit. Less than half the peel oil in the fruit is recovered from the fruit used. These oils are sometimes concentrated under vacuum to produce concentrated oils in which a major part of the limonene has been removed.

Distilled oils also are prepared from limes, oranges, and lemons. The whole fruit, peel, or liquid effluent from cold-pressed oil preparation is subjected to steam distillation. The oil separates readily from the distillate. Distilled oils are generally inferior to cold-pressed oils. A distilled oil of excellent quality is obtained in some juice canneries by flashing the juice under vacuum. Additional distilled oil is obtained during the manufacture of molasses from the first effect or during flashing of the press juice, but it has little value for flavoring purposes.

Cold-pressed oils are used for flavorng, especially in bottled and fountain beverages, cakes, candies, and pies. Some oils, particularly the distilled, are used to perfume soaps. The amount that can be used for these purposes is limited and much less than the potential supply. Scientists are trying to find other uses in plastics and as solvents; particularly are they seeking further use for the distilled oil that is recovered during other operations. Other outlets are needed; the potential supply from waste cannery peel is about 20 million pounds annually.

The principal constituent in all the citrus-peel oils is d-limonene, which constitutes 90 percent or more of the oil. It contributes little to the flavor of the oil, and its presence results in somewhat less stability. Aldehydes (citral), higher alcohols, higher acids, esters, and hydrocarbon compounds give flavor and aroma to the oil.

Citrus seeds are a source of food oils. Some seed oil was produced in Florida in the late 1930's, but operations were suspended until 1946. During the 1948–49 season the estimated oil recovery was between 300 and 400 tons in Florida. The potential supply from wastes from Florida citrus canneries is estimated at more than 5,000 tons. Some varieties of citrus fruit, such as the navel orange and the Marsh seedless grapefruit, have few seeds, but others, the Seedling orange and Duncan grapefruit, for example, contain many.

In the extraction of juice from fresh fruit, the seeds accompany the juice and are removed by screening, along with some pulp. The adhering pulp is removed by further screening, after which the seeds are dried in rotary driers and sent to oil-extraction plants, where the oil is removed by screw presses or hydraulic presses. The yield of oil is about 600 pounds a ton of dried seeds. The fresh oil is pale amber and extremely bitter, but the bitterness can easily be removed and the oil refined by the methods commonly used with other seed oils. Seeds of grapefruit and oranges are processed to-

gether. The oil is used in cooking oils, including a hydrogenated modification, and in detergents. The principal constituents of the seed oils are glyceryl esters of oleic, palmitic, and linoleic acids, and smaller amounts of the esters of stearic, arachidic, and linolenic acids.

JUICE FROM PROCESSED LEMONS is used primarily to make citric acid. A ton of lemons yields 15 to 50 pounds of citric acid. The whole fruit first is passed through presses and washed to remove the juice. Then it is placed in fermentation tanks to liquefy some constituents, coagulate others, and ferment the sugars. It is then heated and filtered, and the citric acid is precipitated with lime and calcium carbonate. Citric acid is released from the lime salt by adding sulfuric acid. Water is removed by evaporation, and crystallization proceeds in lead tanks. The purification procedure is somewhat complicated. It involves decolorization and treatment with charcoal, sulfide, and ferrocyanide to prepare citric acid of acceptable pharmaceutical quality. Eighty-five percent of the acid in the lemons is recovered. In this country, citric acid is used primarily as a food-flavoring acid and in plasticizers.

Citrus peel, left after the juicing or peel-oil operation, is a good source of pectin, which has been used in making jelly since the eighteenth century. It was isolated and named in 1825. Work on it progressed sporadically until 1912, when patents on its production were obtained. The patents stimulated further activity, particularly after 1930. New uses are being discovered constantly; if some of the promising ideas are developed commercially, production should exceed the present 6 million pounds a year.

MOST COMMERCIAL PECTIN in the United States is obtained from citrus peel, which is one of the richest sources; about 2 million tons of the raw material is available annually. Fresh peel contains 3 percent or more of pectin;

washed, dried peel contains at least 30 percent. Dried apple pomace, the only other source of pectin that has been used on a commercial scale in this country, contains less than half that much pectin.

When peel is used as a source of pectin it must receive more gentle treatment than that used in processing for feed or soil conditioning. The procedure developed at the Western Regional Research Laboratory includes blanching and washing in a continuous jacketed washer that has a screw conveyor. Blanching destroys an enzyme in the peel which changes the properties of pectin; washing removes sugar and colored and bitter constituents. Leached peel can be used directly for pectin extraction or stored dry to provide for year-around operations. It can be dried by artificial heat or in the sun.

Common commercial practice employs a hot-acid extraction of pectin from citrus peel in a batch process. Vigorous stirring during the 1-hour extraction period causes disintegration of the peel. The liquor then requires screening or pressing and a filtration for clarification. The high viscosity of the dispersion must be reduced by maintenance of a fairly high temperature, which causes some degradation of the pectin. Methods for extraction designed to simplify the process and maintain high quality of pectin are being investigated at the Western Laboratory.

The liquor can be concentrated and sold as such, provided food-grade acids are used in the extraction, or it can be treated with alcohol or with calcium or aluminum salts to isolate the pectin. When precipitation is by a salt, the salt must be removed by washing with acidified alcohol. The pectin as finally obtained is dried and ground and sold by its ability to form a jelly with 65 percent soluble solids. In 1950 no standard for that grade had been established, but definite moves were under way to do so.

Pectin is purified by several precipitations in dilute alcohol or by formation of a precipitate with certain metal ions, which are later removed by means of acidified alcohol. Citrus pectin contains about 85 percent anhydrogalacturonic acid, about 5 percent methylene groups present as methyl ester, and smaller amounts of sugars such as arabinose, galactose, and rhamnose.

Citrus pectin has a relatively high molecular weight, ranging from 60,000 to 120,000, which partly accounts for its ability to form jellies, films, and fibers.

The use of pectin in jellies, marmalades, candies, and jams is generally well known, as is its use in pharmaceutical preparations for digestive disturbances. The more recent development of low-methoxyl pectin, which increases the usefulness of pectic substances, is of special interest.

Pectin, when treated with alkali, acid, or an enzyme called pectinesterase, contains free acid groups that will react with small amounts of calcium salts. No sugar or other solids are required in order to make a gel with low-methoxyl pectin.

A procedure for making low-methoxyl pectin, worked out at the Western Laboratory, comprises treatment of the cooled extraction liquor with ammonia to cause removal of part of the methoxyl groups from the pectin, and then precipitation of the altered pectin by addition of acid. The washed low-methoxyl pectin gel may then be partly neutralized, dried, and ground.

The uses of low-methoxyl pectin are many and varied. The usual type of milk pudding can be prepared by adding low-methoxyl pectin and sugar to milk, heating, and stirring until the pectin has dissolved. Flavoring can be added and the whole allowed to cool. This pudding is smooth and not pasty. The gelling agent in this case is the low-methoxyl pectin, which combines with the calcium ion in the milk.

A quick dessert for housewives, campers, and sportsmen can be prepared with low-methoxyl pectin. Milk powder, flavoring, and a combination of sugar and pectin are mixed, then

vigorously stirred into cold water. In
5 minutes a fluffy pudding is ready for
eating or for a pie filling.

Those who like a gelatin dessert, but
do not care to eat gelatin or much
sugar, can make low-solids gels from
low-methoxyl pectin and a calcium salt,
like calcium monohydrogen phosphate.
The flavor may come from fruit juices
or from synthetic flavors. Color and
sugar or saccharin are added as desired.

Low-methoxyl pectin lightens dinner problems in another way. A fruit
mix, like canned fruit cocktail, can be
processed with this pectin and sugar to
form a canned gelled salad or dessert.
The Army used nearly 30 million cans
of this dessert during the Second World
War. Canned tomato aspic also is made
possible by low-methoxyl pectin.

Sparkling, clear, bright films can be
prepared with low-methoxyl pectin.
The ability of the calcium to hold together the pectin molecules, like rivets
fastening steel beams, makes this possible. Spraying sticky stuff, such as candied fruit, with, or dipping it into, a
solution of sodium pectinate and then
a solution of a calcium salt covers it
with a gel of sodium calcium pectinate.
The gel is rapidly dried, after which it
is impervious to sugar and is relatively
nonsticky. Candied fruit, when coated
in this way, can be packaged mechanically instead of manually.

Salted oily nuts have always been a
messy food item. Coating almonds or
other nuts with pectinate containing a
food dye and salt gives a clean, colorful, and tasty product. Other food
flavors, such as smoked salt, cloves, or
chocolate, could be incorporated in the
film. Vitamins for health can be included. The possibilities for use of the
film seem endless.

Fibers and films of certain salts of
low-methoxyl pectin are easily prepared and are water-insoluble and fire-
resistant. The cost of these materials
may restrict their utilization to specialty purposes, but the attractive possibilities of their use in open-weave
fabrics, decorative ribbons, and meat
casings have not been explored.

Low-methoxyl pectin is now available from commercial concerns. Further investigation of its properties
probably will lead to other new uses.

The conclusion might be reached
that extraction of pectin destroys the
feed value of the peel. The possibility
exists, however, that the liquor from
the blanching and washing operation
can be concentrated to produce molasses, the peel from the extractor can
be dried, and the ammonium sulfate
solution from the peeling operation can
be concentrated. By suitable mixing of
the three components, a feed or soil
conditioner could be obtained. Thus
the peel would be utilized completely.

Research has converted citrus waste
into new, valuable products. Practically all of it is used; hardly any goes
down the sewer. Citrus molasses and
dried citrus peel go into feeds; citrus
essential oils and citric acid are used in
foods; citrus pectin makes a jelly failure almost impossible, and has been
altered for use in puddings and films.
Grower, processor, and consumer have
benefited. Further work is needed on
uses of some of the byproducts, such as
pectin and limonene, to develop new
uses for citrus molasses or the press
liquor from which it is made, and to
improve present processing methods.

HARRY S. OWENS *is in charge of the
carbohydrate section of the Western
Regional Research Laboratory. He received degrees from the University of
Idaho and Columbia University. From
1935 to 1942, when he joined the Laboratory staff, he was engaged in research on utilization of farm and forest
products and taught biochemistry and
colloid chemistry in the University of
Idaho.*

M. K. VELDHUIS *has been a member
of the Bureau of Agricultural and Industrial Chemistry since 1935. He has
been in charge of the United States
Citrus Products Station in Winter
Haven, Fla., since 1944.*

W. DAYTON MACLAY *is head of the
biochemical division of the Western
Laboratory. He is a native of Nebraska,*

and holds degrees from the University of Nebraska. He taught chemistry in the Municipal University of Omaha and afterward conducted fundamental carbohydrate research at the National

Institute of Health in Washington. He joined the staff of the Laboratory in 1940 and has been engaged in research related to the utilization of fruit and vegetable byproducts.

PREPACKAGING fruits and vegetables at the farm shipping point offers obvious advantages in the reduction of shipping costs and in the utilization of wastes on the farm, but it cannot be widely recommended until certain problems are solved.

No package will improve the quality of its contents. All highly perishable commodities decline in quality after harvest. The best handling methods only slow down the rate of decline. Studies made since 1948 by the Department of Agriculture in cooperation with the Dickman Farms, Ruskin, Fla., highlight the importance of adequate refrigeration at every step along the way from the time a product is harvested until it is sold to the consumer.

For example, packaged broccoli retained a good green color for 15 to 20 days when held at 40° F. or below, but turned yellow in 2 or 3 days at 70°. Sweet corn lost sugar at the rates of 3.5 percent at 32°, 20.8 percent at 50°, and 59.4 percent at 86° during the first 24 hours after picking. Prepackaged sweet corn delivered in New York at temperatures in the 40's was graded as good to very good in quality but that delivered at temperatures above 50° was inferior.

In tests so far, chemical treatments of various types appear to offer little benefit. Dips in ascorbic, citric, or hydrochloric acid did not prevent discoloration in corn and cauliflower. Instead, these solutions accumulated great numbers of micro-organisms.

Chlorine used in the hydrocooler water—where the vegetables were precooled immediately after harvest—did not completely sterilize the surfaces of the vegetables. It reduced the micro-organism count, however, and held it to a reasonable minimum. Approximately 100 parts per million of chlorine gave as satisfactory results as higher concentrations.

In general, the results show all packages should be perforated to allow for exchange of gas or air. Normal leaks through seams or poor seals do not provide sufficient ventilation to prevent fermentation. In turn, off-flavors and off-odors soon develop when the packaged vegetables are held at high temperatures.

Some products can be packaged more successfully near the terminal than at the distant farm market. For example, tomatoes need to be ripened to a marketable stage before they are packed. Otherwise they ripen unevenly and make an unattractive package. Also they may develop decay in the several days required to put them into retail channels.

For continuous growth of the prepackaging industry, marketing facilities must keep pace. At present, most wholesalers and retail stores lack refrigeration facility to handle adequately a line of prepackaged produce.—*Harold A. Schomer, Bureau of Plant Industry, Soils, and Agricultural Engineering.*

The Oldest Way To Store Fruit

William Rabak

Drying, the oldest form of fruit preservation, is a well-established industry. It dates from ancient times, when man depended on this easy way to store food between crops.

The term is general. It indicates drying by any means, although once it was restricted to sun drying. The words "evaporated" and "dehydrated" generally imply drying in specially constructed dehydrators and under controlled temperature, humidity, and air flow.

The drying of fruits, which reduces the amount of water they contain and concentrates the juices, establishes unfavorable conditions for the yeasts, molds, and other micro-organisms that cause spoilage.

Subjecting light-colored tree fruits—apples, apricots, figs, peaches, pears—to the fumes of burning sulfur (sulfur dioxide) has long been a predrying treatment to prevent enzymatic oxidation, or darkening. All those fruits contain tanninlike compounds, which are readily oxidized by atmospheric oxygen through the catalytic effect of the fruit enzymes when the cut or bruised surface of the fruit is exposed to the air or the fruit cells are killed by the drying process. Such oxidation results in discoloration, commonly called browning, and causes an undesirable change in flavor.

Sulfur dioxide is a reducing agent and an enzyme inactivator or retardant, depending on its concentration in the fruit. It prevents enzymatic oxidation and tends to restore the fruit to its natural color by its reducing action when slight discoloration occurs during the preparation of the fruit for drying. Certain dried fruits are subject to nonenzymatic discoloration upon prolonged storage if insufficient sulfur dioxide is present in the tissues of the fruit. The growers and packers of dried fruit learned from long experience and research just how much sulfur dioxide each of the fruits must contain to prevent both enzymatic and nonenzymatic discoloration over the normal period of storage between harvest and consumption.

Because accurate control of temperature and humidity during the drying process has been found to be generally advantageous, the designs of some driers are elaborate and complicated.

In recent years, many innovations have been made in equipment for dehydration. For example, vacuum dehydrators have come into use. The process removes water from commodities under vacuum at relatively low temperatures. It has certain advantages over conventional drying systems in that the product is not exposed to high temperatures or large volumes of air, which cause oxidation of certain food constituents. The resulting products have better color and reconstitute more readily because there is no surface crust. Products of this type are utilized in dry mixtures, which generally require only the addition of sugar and water. Ready-mixed apple pie is an example. It will keep for some time at ordinary temperatures.

Many other dried-fruit mixes are in the offing; it has been found that certain dried fruits improve the texture and flavor of bread and other baked goods. The possibility of dried-fruit ingredients for jams and jellies has been experimentally proved—simply add water, bring to a boil, and cool. The product is made.

Yet another innovation—freeze-drying—subjects fruit juices to a vacuum at below-freezing temperatures. Under those conditions the water evaporates readily.

Dried fruits undergo chemical and physical changes that affect quality, depending on the moisture content of the commodity and the humidity of the climate. They tend to absorb water vapor from humid air and to lose moisture to dry air. Among the unfavorable changes are crystallization of natural sugars, surface hardening or toughening, loss or alteration of flavors, and impairment of colors. To control such impairments and to guard against bacterial spoilage and insect infestation, more effective packaging is needed.

Tight packages made from sheet materials, like waxed paper, regenerated cellulose, rubber hydrochloride, and polyethylene, provide satisfactory protection in most instances. Certain sensitive products require airtight containers, such as tin cans or glass jars.

DEHYDROFREEZING, a new method of food preservation, combines two well-established processing methods. The name was coined at the Western Regional Research Laboratory to designate a process that has been under investigation since 1945.

The preparation of the fruit for dehydrofreezing is similar to that for freezing preservation or dehydration. To avoid enzymatic discoloration during or after processing, the products are treated with sulfur dioxide before the partial dehydration process, which removes approximately two-thirds of the moisture.

Experiments at the Laboratory indicated that during an ordinary dehydration process the major processing impairments—discoloration, the surface hardening, off-flavor developments, and losses in nutritive values—

occur near the end of the dehydration period. Halting the dehydration before removing the last third of "removable" moisture materially reduced these impairments. Furthermore, freezing the product at that point resulted in less damage to the plant structure and juices than is encountered in ordinary freezing preservation. This was indicated by a marked reduction in the loss of juices after thawing.

After freezing, the product is protectively packaged and kept in freezing storage until used. The dehydrofrozen fruit is quickly and easily restored to a condition closely approximating that of the fresh fruit by covering the pieces with cold water and bringing to the boiling point. Pies made from dehydrofrozen apples and apricots were as acceptable to tasting panels as those made from fresh fruit.

THE EXPERIMENTERS listed the following advantages of the new method of preservation:

The products are readily reconstituted for use.

Savings in transportation and storage costs are considerable.

Substantial economies are effected in the packaging materials.

Partial dehydration reduces the load on the refrigeration system.

The knowledge gained from the age-old preservation by drying and from the infant food-freezing industry combined to bring dehydrofreezing into existence. Like all things new, its value, acceptability, and permanence will be decided by the united efforts of the research worker, the processing industry, bakers, and housewives.

WILLIAM RABAK, *a specialist in food technology in the Western Regional Research Laboratory, has been a chemist in the American Medical Association, the United States Food and Drug Administration, the Biscuit and Cracker Manufacturers Association, and the United States Frozen Pack Laboratory of the Bureau of Agricultural and Industrial Chemistry.*

Preservation of Fruits by Freezing

William Rabak

Preserving fruits by freezing is a practical and desirable way to retain most of their natural food qualities and characteristics. It is a simple and an effective method, and suited for use in the home.

The first research on the process in the Department of Agriculture was with raspberries and strawberries and was conducted in 1904 and 1905 by S. H. Fulton, who recorded the results of his research in Bulletin 108, issued in 1907. He gave this glimpse of the start of a new industry:

"Frozen strawberries for ice cream have been in use in a limited way by confectioners for some time (before 1905), while frozen blackcap raspberries, currants, blackberries, huckleberries, and other small fruits are now being used successfully for pies and other pastries by a few restaurateurs and bakers. A large pie bakery in a central western city is successfully using frozen blackcaps, gooseberries, blackberries, currants, and huckleberries in large quantities. When made into pies the flavor of the frozen fruit is said to be practically equal to that of fresh fruit. Considerable quantities of cherries and damson plums are also frozen by this company for use in pies. . . . Frozen huckleberries and currants can be easily and successfully held for many months. In 1905 the firm referred to froze 14 carloads of huckleberries, using the fruit for pies months after the fresh fruit had disappeared from the markets."

H. S. Baker, once a druggist in Denver, Colo., established the freezing preservation of fruit as a continuing independent industry in 1909 in Salem, Oreg. From that beginning, the industry (particularly the freezing of berries in the Pacific Northwest) grew to importance. In 1928, a total of 60 million pounds was frozen. The pack before then was entirely in large containers for use by manufacturers of preserves and ice cream.

The early processors found by trial and error that to avoid fermentation before freezing the berries had to be handled quickly, kept cool, and stored promptly at refrigerating temperatures. The need for careful washing, inspecting, and grading and the importance of good varieties of fruit became apparent later. Subsequent experiments indicated the best proportions for packing with sugar or sugar sirup, and the need for prompt freezing and constant low-temperature storage. Fluctuating temperatures may cause loss of quality because of the acceleration of chemical changes, excessive moisture losses, and crystallization of sugar. Shipping tests have demonstrated the importance of proper refrigeration during transit to guard against quality impairment and economic losses.

Since 1929 the packing of frozen fruits for retail or household use in small containers has developed steadily. Our total pack of frozen fruit in 1949 was almost 500 million pounds. About one-third of the pack was citrus concentrate (primarily orange), followed by strawberries, other berries, and red sour cherries. Freezing is the newest of the four main ways (drying, canning, freezing, and pickling) of preserving fruits. Dehydrofreezing, a combination of partial dehydration and freezing, has not yet been introduced into commercial practice.

PRECAUTIONS must be taken to retain inherent quality after preparation and during storage. The quality of a product when it is eaten is the standard by which any method of preservation must be judged.

Freezing maintains many natural characteristics of fruits, but changes in quality do occur. Laboratory research and the industry have done much to obviate the changes in quality, but, because of the many and diverse causes, continuing investigations are essential.

Chemical changes, although of many types, fall into two general categories—ordinary and involved.

Ordinary chemical changes result from the combination or splitting of natural compounds, with the production of different compounds. Examples are the reaction between metals and fruit acids (organic salts) ; the splitting of common sugar to form simple sugars, such as glucose and fructose (hydrolysis) ; and the union of compounds that results in a new and different substance, such as production of starch from simpler components—by synthesis, that is.

Unusual color development in fruits, from red through purple to blue, can be prevented by avoiding undue contact with certain metals during processing and storage. Tin and iron are the worst. The color developed is due to the formation of metallic salts with the natural ingredients of fruits, such as tannins or anthocyanin pigments.

The occasional change of the brilliant red of strawberries (anthocyanin pigment) to brown during long storage is probably due to chemical changes that occur in packages that are not airtight.

In 1939 I began examining strawberries that had been packaged and stored for 7 years at 15° F. in both nonairtight (paperboard) and airtight containers (machine-sealed tin cans). I found that the red color of the fruit packed in the nonairtight containers had changed to varying shades of cinnamon brown, while the normal red color was retained in the sealed cans. I also found that the ascorbic acid (vitamin C) was well retained in the enamel-lined tin cans but was practically lost in the paperboard.

Involved chemical changes are induced by the natural enzymes of fruits, an example of which is the browning of cut surfaces of fresh fruits like apples, peaches, and apricots. In this instance, the oxidative enzyme effects a reaction between (catalyzes) the oxygen of the air and complex constituents of the plant cells, so that the tissues are darkened. This oxidative reaction also takes place in improperly processed frozen fruit after thawing and in fruit only partly frozen, that is, above or near 20° F.

A GREAT DEAL of research has been directed toward overcoming this undesirable development. Early experimenters partly solved the problem by quickly immersing the cut fruit in sugar sirup to minimize contact with air or by rinsing in a dilute acid solution, such as 0.5 to 1.0 percent citric acid.

Experiments carried out in 1933 by M. A. Joslyn and G. L. Marsh at the University of California showed that the judicious use of sulfur dioxide would effectively inhibit oxidative discoloration. Immersion of the fruit in a solution of sodium sulfite is the usual method of application. More recently, D. K. Tressler and C. W. DuBois discovered that ascorbic acid is effective in the prevention of oxidative browning. The use of ascorbic acid for the purpose is advantageous because, unlike sulfur dioxide, it does not affect flavor and adds to the nutritive value of the fruit.

SOME OF THE IMPAIRMENTS during the freezing of plant tissues are physical rather than chemical. Because plant juices are essentially water solutions of soluble materials, expansion occurs during freezing as a result of the formation of ice. Earlier investigators believed that the ice crystals ruptured the plant cells. Whether or not the cells are torn by crystal formation, the properties of the cells are so modified by freezing that they no longer can hold the cell juices. Even if the cells are not ruptured, as happens during quick freezing, there will still be leakage of juices. This phenomenon is less striking in some frozen plant tissues than in others; the differences probably are due to variation in cell constituents and plant structures.

The loss of water vapor from inadequately packaged frozen fruits during prolonged storage often leads to quality, impairment because of the drying, or desiccation, of surface tissues. Storage temperatures at or above 15° F. or too great fluctuations in temperature are conducive to this condition. The remedy is to use tight packages and uniform storage temperatures at or below 0° F. Gastight packages have distinct advantages.

ONE AIM IN freezing fruits is to destroy or impede the development of bacteria, molds, and yeasts, which were put in that order of decreasing importance by C. A. Magoon, who did pioneer work in the Department of Agriculture on the freezing preservation of strawberries. In 1932 he proved that about 90 percent of the microorganisms can be killed during the first 24 hours of freezing, but always enough are left to cause spoilage if the temperature rises high enough to thaw the frozen material completely.

James A. Berry, at the United States Frozen Pack Laboratory in Seattle, reported in 1933 that some bacteria persisted for 2 years at below-freezing temperatures but that most yeasts were destroyed after several months of storage.

Because the low temperatures merely halt the growth of some live organisms, frozen foods cannot be considered sterile in the same sense that canned foods are. Unless frozen products are promptly consumed after thawing,

therefore, the surviving organisms will grow and make the foods unfit to eat.

STANDARDS for evaluating and comparing quality are essential to progress in research on processing methods. Such tests involve the evaluation of the factors that affect quality and are divided into two general categories: Objective tests (chemical, physical, and bacteriological); and subjective tests (human acceptability, which is decided by general appearance, color, odor, flavor, texture, and related qualities).

The objective tests are designed to check factors like color retention, losses of juice on thawing, and sugar content and to determine molds, yeasts, bacteria, enzymes, and vitamins.

The subjective tests, which are the final criteria in judging quality, are based on proving the pudding by eating it. They are conducted by groups of trained individuals, who form taste panels. The method is practical and reliable and, with laboratory evaluation methods, has led to higher quality in commercially frozen fruits and fruit products.

FROZEN FRUIT PRODUCTS include Velva Fruit and fresh-fruit spreads.

Experimental work in 1931 and 1932 by D. G. Sorber, at the Department's Laboratory of Fruit and Vegetable Chemistry in Los Angeles, led to the development of a new frozen dessert from fully ripe fruit. It was prepared from fresh pulps and sugar by quick-freezing at very low temperatures. It had the fine flavor of natural ripe fruit.

Later, H. J. Loeffler, at the Western Regional Research Laboratory, developed an entirely new dessert, which was named Velva Fruit to distinguish it from ice cream, sherbets, and ices. Unlike other frozen fruit purees, it contains gelatin and has the smooth texture of ice cream. It is unlike sherbets, because no milk or milk solids are used in the formula. It has the natural full-ripe flavor and nutritive value of the fresh-fruit pulp that is used in its preparation. It can be made with many fruits, but best from those with pronounced flavors.

Out of studies on the freezing preservation of gelled cranberry sauce by Gestur Johnson and Mildred Boggs in 1944 and 1945, came the development of frozen-fruit spreads, which retain natural flavors very well.

The spreads, which are prepared from fruits, juices, or fruit purees, are unique in that the losses or changes of flavor, color, and vitamins are held to a minimum during preparation. The reason is that their preparation requires no heating or cooking, which drives away some natural flavors, destroys vitamins, and breaks down the natural color.

The method of preparation consists in adjusting the acidity to pH 3 with citric acid, mixing the fruit juice or puree at room temperature with sugar and pectin in correct proportions, and transferring it to suitable containers. Under properly controlled conditions, the spread sets at room temperature. When stored at below-freezing temperatures, the spreads will keep for long periods, and they can be used like jams, jellies, or preserves.

PACKAGING is an important factor in the retention of quality of frozen foods because efficient packages, among other things, prevent drying out (desiccation), contact with air (oxidation), and loss of the natural, fresh flavors.

To differentiate between packaged frozen foods and canned foods, various types of nonairtight packages have been used. This has been unfortunate. It has encouraged all sorts of makeshift packaging, resulting in loss of quality, spoilage, and, in some cases, a prejudice against this method of food preservation.

Because of the natural tendency to release moisture constantly to the atmosphere through the smallest openings, merely wrapping frozen foods in moisture-resistant materials leads to a false assumption of protection. Effec-

tive sealing of seams is essential, but sometimes the very act of heat sealing affects the water-vapor resistance of a wrapping material by changing the physical characteristics of the coatings or the sheet itself.

IN 1941 AT THE WESTERN LABORATORY, I began the development of a simple but effective method for protectively packaging frozen foods.

The method, known as dip-coating, consists in dipping the frozen food, or the package containing it, in molten plasticized microcrystalline paraffin. The cold surface causes instant solidification of a continuous film of the coating over all of the commodity, regardless of shape. Such a film excludes air, resists moisture, and obviates seams and sealing. Because of its simplicity and effectiveness in packaging irregularly shaped frozen foods, such as meats and poultry, dip-coating is now in use by a large part of the frozen-food locker-plant industry.

It is possible that the future of the frozen-food industry will be affected greatly by the progress of packaging. Not only distinctive but also protective packaging is essential if the pace of progress is to be maintained.

Although freezing is the youngest of the presently established methods of food preservation, it is enjoying a healthy growth. We can expect new developments and marked improvements.

WILLIAM RABAK *is a specialist in food technology in the Western Regional Research Laboratory. He received his scientific education in the University of Wisconsin. After teaching in Northwestern University and the University of Nebraska, he was consecutively affiliated as chemist with the American Medical Association, the United States Food and Drug Administration, the Biscuit and Cracker Manufacturers Association, and the United States Frozen Pack Laboratory of the Bureau of Agricultural Chemistry and Engineering.*

Vegetables and Fruits for Lockers

J. S. Caldwell, W. M. Hurst, Harold D. White

The locker plant is a recent adaptation of mechanical refrigeration for the use of families and individuals in preserving and storing food. It and the home freezer have brought the general practice of preserving food by freezing to towns, the rural communities, and homes.

Although out-of-season and frozen fruits and vegetables are available in local markets, farm people generally prefer to eat their own produce. Patrons of community processing plants usually give one or more of the following reasons: It tastes better; it costs less; the product would go to waste as we don't have enough to sell; or, we can't afford to buy all we need from the store. Agricultural economists sometimes refer to the practice as marketing through processing for home use.

A cold-storage company in California rented space for holding household quantities of meat, game, and fish in boxes under refrigeration in 1908. A few years later, it provided covered boxes with locks for the customers, and in 1917 it constructed and equipped a room with tiers of wooden drawers.

The commercial freezing of small fruits began in the United States about 1905 and that of vegetables about 1929. The industry has had a phenomenal growth. There were more than 11,000 locker plants in the United States in July 1949.

A commercial plant for freezing fruits and vegetables requires a large volume of produce, usually of only a few kinds. To obtain a product of uniform high quality at a reasonable cost, all operations from planting through processing must be mechanized and controlled. The plants normally contract with farmers for the kind and quantity of crops desired and specify the variety, as well as the kind and quantity of fertilizer, when to plant, and when to harvest.

A locker plant must handle a wide variety of products received in small lots with little control over quality and condition when received. Although they began as places to store food under refrigeration, and continue to rely on locker rental as a major source of income, locker plants have taken on many extra services. Auxiliary sources of income are needed because of high building and operating expenses. Many plants perform all the operations in transforming live animals into frozen cuts and such byproducts as lard and sausage. They dress poultry and process fruits and vegetables for their patrons and for sale.

The floor plans of locker plants vary widely, depending partly on the produce handled and on the local practices. However, the floor plan in the drawing of a hypothetical plant shows refrigerated rooms and processing areas common to locker plants. Opinions differ as to the best location and arrangement of the rooms and processing areas for efficient operations. Moreover, the lay-out will depend somewhat on the specialty lines anticipated, such as country-cured hams, berries for making ice cream, frozen fruits and vegetables, or dressed poultry. Locker plants sometimes provide chilling and aging rooms for local meat markets, and bulk frozen-food storage for hotels and restaurants.

281

FLOOR PLAN OF A HYPOTHETICAL LOCKER PLANT FOR PROCESSING MEATS, POULTRY, FRUIT, VEGETABLES, AND EDIBLE BYPRODUCTS

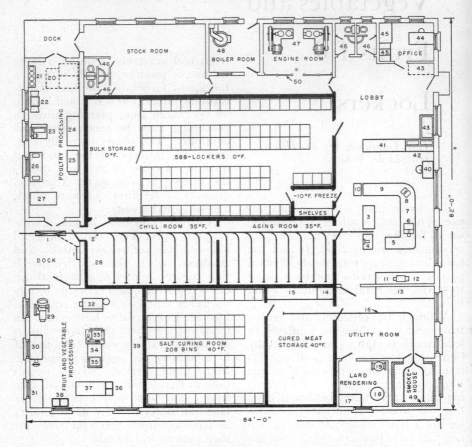

IDENTIFICATION OF EQUIPMENT

MEAT PROCESSING

1. Meat receiving track scale
2. Overhead meat track
3. Meat block
4. Power floor model meat cutting saw
5. Bulk meat table
6. Meat grinder (No. 11) can be mounted under table here if so desired
7. Cutting-up table
8. Computing counter scale
9. Wrapping table
10. Freezing truck
11. Meat grinder
12. Byproducts table
13. Utility table
14. Ham curing pump and scale
15. Salting table
16. Overhead track to smoker
17. Lard utility table
18. Lard rendering kettle
19. Lard press

POULTRY DRESSING

20. Coops of live birds to be dressed
21. Wall type kill-bleed funnels size to suit capacity desired
22. Electric or steam-heated scalder. If electric, it should have at least a 3,000-watt element.
23. Picker with working width of at least 30 inches and equipped with feather collector
24. 30 by 72 by 36-inch pinning table
25. 24 by 60 by 24-inch steel cooling tank on wheels for New York Dress birds
26. 30 by 72 by 36-inch stainless steel eviscerating table with faucets
27. 180 birds steel poultry cooling racks on wheels
28. Space for poultry cooling racks

FRUIT AND VEGETABLE PREPARATION

29. String bean cutter
30. Corn cutter and table

31. Utility table
32. Pea sheller
33. Washer-blancher-cooler, water and steam
34. Table
35. Steam peeler
36. 2-compartment sinks
37. Utility table
38. Lye peeler
39. Wrapping and packing table

MISCELLANEOUS

40. Memorandum desk
41. Sales counter
42. Refrigerated display case
43. Frozen food display case
44. Manager's desk
45. Record files and table
46. Toilets for men and women
47. Refrigerating compressors and accessories, ammonia condensors on roof
48. Oil-fired steam boiler
49. Fire brick lining
50. Pipe guard rail and gate

In the early days of the locker industry, no sharp-freeze room was provided. The patrons then merely placed packages of food in containers in a room held at a temperature of about 0° F. With this procedure, freezing was slow, and the warm product naturally raised the temperature of surrounding packages. New plants have a room for freezing a product quickly before it is placed in the storage lockers.

The size and type of a freezing unit are determined by the number of lockers in a plant and whether larger-scale commercial freezing is to be done. The unit may be plate, coil, or air-blast. A temperature of at least 0° F. is recommended for the air-blast unit and −10° F. or below for the plate or coil types. Employees like to have convenient access to the sharp-freeze room from the meat-processing area. This usually requires a reach-in door installed to minimize the number of times a day the large door is opened. Or the entrance may be through a refrigerated room or vestibule.

Some States have regulations governing features of plant design and operations affecting sanitation. One requires a separate room or enclosed area for processing meats. A city ordinance may prohibit the slaughtering of animals within the incorporated area. The locker plant then must be located in the country if the abattoir is a part of it.

In a plant like the one in the drawing, meat carcasses received from the farm or abattoir pass through the chilling and aging rooms to the meat-processing area, where regular meat-market equipment is used. Cuts to be frozen are wrapped, labeled, and loaded on freezer trucks or placed directly in the freezer. Other parts of the carcass are routed to appropriate departments. Cuts of meat and other small items that do not require processing are wrapped or put in a container, labeled, and placed directly in the freezer.

Poultry is drawn and dressed in the usual manner and chilled before wrapping and freezing. Some plants chill birds in trays or wire baskets in the chill room; others use cooling racks on casters. Processing equipment in small poultry-dressing plants is commonly used also in locker plants.

For processing fruits and vegetables in a locker plant, operators have been handicapped by the lack of equipment suitable in capacity and price for their use. Machinery used in commercial freezers is generally too large and expensive for intermittent operations on small batches of produce. Often no space in the plant is suitable for processing fruits and vegetables. For these reasons patrons have heretofore been encouraged to do their processing at home.

Whether fruits and vegetables should be processed in the plant depends on whether the plant is in town or in the country and on such local conditions as size of town, relative proportion of rural and urban patrons, crops produced, and facilities in the home for processing. Patrons who freeze small quantities of a few products, like strawberries, corn, and beans or peas from a garden, often prefer to do the processing at home when the crops are at the peak of condition or when time permits. Those who buy their produce for freezing in wholesale units and farmers or gardeners with relatively large quantities prefer to process at the plant or have the plant staff do the job. Two advantages in having a room for processing at the plant are that the work can be done under supervision and the managment can take advantage of market conditions for buying and processing produce for patrons and for sale locally. With some crops and under certain circumstances, the locker plants can compete with commercial freezers, even though the processing is done largely by hand.

The ideal locker plant provides adequately equipped preparation rooms and encourages patrons to bring their products and prepare and pack them under the immediate supervision of the operator. Neither room nor equipment need be elaborate, but the operator should be competent to advise on procedures and to warn against packing poorly graded, overmature, and unsuitable material. Controversies as to responsibility for unsatisfactory results will be largely avoided if the operator of the plant has seen the raw material and the methods of preparation and approved or disapproved them.

Certain items are indispensable in any preparation room. If meats and poultry and fruits and vegetables are being handled, separate or partitioned preparation rooms should be provided, each with outside doors for entrance of material and disposal of refuse. The rooms should have ample space for work, good light, natural and artificial, sanitary walls and work tables, an ample supply of good water, hot and cold, and steam. Deep and shallow sinks for washing and enamel-lined tanks for making up brine and sirup are indispensable. Other essential equipment includes scales, heavily enameled pans, buckets, measuring vessels, and paring and trimming knives.

The processing equipment needed in a locker plant for the initial preparation of fruits and vegetables depends on the crops grown in the community. Regardless of crop, though, a few items have general use—pea and bean shellers, green bean cutters, corn cutters, and peeling machines for vegetables and for fruits. Some have been developed for small-scale operations. Others are available only as large commercial machines.

A small pea and bean sheller of the viner type has been improved by agricultural engineers of the Department of Agriculture and the University of Georgia. The new machine has been used successfully for shelling handpicked peas, lima beans, and field peas (cowpeas) for freezing.

There is at least one commercial bean cutter that may be used on beans, rhubarb, and asparagus. However, a combination green bean snipper and cutter is needed for locker-plant use.

Development work in adapting commercial whole-grain and cream-type corn cutters for locker plants is in progress by commercial, State, and Federal agencies. Corn is customarily removed from the cob with knives or hand cutters for freezing in locker plants.

Lye and steam peelers are generally home-made, although as least one firm offers them for sale. Some plants have one of each and others only one type, depending on the nature of the product to be peeled. Small mechanical peelers, either hand- or motor-operated, are available for apples.

Steam-jacketed kettles and retorts are frequently used for blanching. An experimental machine developed by agricultural engineers of the University of Georgia for combining the operations of washing, blanching, and cooling has given satisfactory results on lima beans, field peas, green beans, and ear corn. The product is tumbled slowly and continuously in the machine. Water is sprayed on for washing, followed by steam from the same nozzles for blanching, and then water for cooling. The product is ready for packaging when removed from the machine.

A satisfactory and inexpensive home-made combination washer, blancher, and cooler is a large, heavily constructed wooden chamber equipped with a tightly fitting door and supplied with perforated pipes for admitting steam and water and a trapped outlet to the sewer for drainage. Material to be treated is spread on trays, which are supported on cleats attached to the sides of the chamber.

A SERIES OF FIVE 20-gallon tinned sheet-steel kettles has been successfully used by agricultural engineers of the Department, in cooperation with the Michigan Agricultural Experiment Station, for washing, blanching, and cooling vegetables. The product is held in tinned wire-mesh containers while in the water. The containers are large enough to hold 10-pound lots of most vegetables.

One kettle is used for washing, one for blanching, and three for cooling. Running water is supplied to the kettles for washing and cooling. It is kept flowing continuously throughout the operation. The overflow is discharged through an outlet near the top of each kettle. That arrangement keeps each kettle filled with fresh, cold water. The water in the blanching kettle is heated by a gas burner or by steam, and provision is made for emptying, cleaning, and refilling it with water. The source of heat is sufficiently powerful to bring the water to boiling within a minute or two after it has been cooled by a fresh charge of product.

In operation, a charge of product is placed in the wire-mesh container in the first kettle and washed by moving it up and down in the water. When it is clean, the material is dumped from the basket into a similar basket submerged in the blanching kettle, and the basket is moved up and down to separate the product and bring all parts into contact with the blanching water. From the blancher the product is dumped into a submerged basket in the first cold-water kettle for chilling and again agitated to separate and bring into contact with the water. As the water becomes warm, the basket is moved from the first to the second and then to the third of the cooling kettles. It remains in the last one until the contents have reached the temperature of the cooling water. The product is then drained and dumped into pans for packaging.

AMONG the packaging materials the plant should maintain for sale to patrons are various types and sizes of fiber cartons and inner liners, laminated plastic and plastic film bags, and tin cans. Closing and sealing equipment for handling them should be on hand. The plant operator or supervisor should be familiar with the uses and limitations of the various types of containers and packaging materials and should advise patrons as to the best types for the products that are being packed. The sale of such materials provides a minor source of income and protects patrons from unsatisfactory results that may arise from poor or unsuitable packaging.

The primary requirements for the successful operation of a locker plant include refrigerating machinery that is adequate to provide the temperatures needed at peak load, with a wide margin of safety, and is operated by a competent person; ample floor space for preparation and processing; and the machines and accessory equipment needed for handling the various products. When those requirements have been met, satisfactory results depend largely on the qualifications of the individual chosen to supervise reception of material and its preparation, packing, and freezing. He must have a personality and manner that begets confidence and willingness to accept his suggestions and instructions, as a considerable part of his work, especially at the outset, will be educational in character. Many patrons of a newly established locker plant may have inadequate knowledge of procedures, and that he must supply. He must know the best techniques of preparation and packing of the various products. In the case of fruits and vegetables he must know a lot about the raw materials— about the varieties grown in the area and of their suitability for freezing preservation.

He must also know the stage of development or ripeness at which the different vegetables and fruits are of highest quality. His qualifications may be summed up by saying that he must know what constitutes high quality in raw materials, when to harvest, and how to handle and pack each of them in order to maintain high quality in the finished product.

The best preparation for rendering service of this character would be a course in food technology in one of the institutions now offering such courses. The next best would be to work for at least a season, preferably two, in an established, successful plant located in the same general area, meanwhile studying the textbooks on freezing of foods and the bulletins on locker-plant operation issued by the Department of Agriculture and the State experiment stations. When the plant is opened for business, the operator should have a file of publications for reference and also a supply of publications of his own or a neighboring State for distribution to his patrons. It cannot be too strongly emphasized that such advisory and educational service does much more than create customer good will; it provides insurance against consumer dissatisfaction. The plant that does not give advisory service and exercise supervision over the material placed in it is without protection against claims that poor results were due to faulty operation of the plant when they were actually caused by use of inferior or unsuitable varieties, overmaturity or undermaturity, improper methods of preparing and packaging, or a combination of all of these.

THE VARIETIES of fruits and vegetables available for freezing in any locker plant will be those most generally grown in the area because they have been found to be well adapted to conditions, fairly productive, and of satisfactory quality for fresh use and possibly for canning. But the fact that a variety is of good quality for those purposes does not give assurance that it is equally good for freezing, as many such varieties make inferior frozen products. The fact that certain varieties are extensively used in commercial freezing does not always indicate that they are best for home use, as factors other than high quality (especially adaptation to mechanical harvesting and preparation) play an important part in determining the varieties commercially used.

No general list of varieties of fruits and vegetables that are best for freezing in all parts of the United States can be given here, for several reasons. Only a few varieties of fruits and vegetables are adapted to a wide range of soils and climatic conditions, and therefore grow well and produce material of good quality over large areas of the country. Most varieties are adapted to a fairly narrow range of conditions under which they develop best quality. As a consequence, each producing district has a group of varieties best adapted to its conditions and differing somewhat from that of any other area. The lists of varieties for widely separated districts, such as the Pacific Northwest, the Plains States, and the Atlantic coast, differ greatly. To be of value, any list of recommended varieties must be regional.

A good deal of information of this sort is available. Many State agricultural experiment stations have conducted studies on the suitability for home and locker freezing of the varieties of fruits and vegetables most generally grown in their respective States and have published their results. The publications give lists of varieties found most satisfactory in their respective areas.

Varieties of fruits and vegetables that are widely grown and have been found satisfactory in their freezing quality wherever grown over their range, and some that are less widely grown but have given good products wherever tested in the districts in which they are being grown, are listed here. Many vegetable breeders are concentrating their efforts on the production of new varieties especially adapted to freezing, and such new varieties are being offered by seedsmen every year. Many of these will undoubtedly be found superior to those now in use. Consequently any list of varieties now used will be largely obsolete in a few years. The progressive locker-plant operator will recognize it as a part of his job to keep himself and his patrons informed as to new and better varieties.

FRUITS

Apples: Jonathan, Winesap, Yellow Newtown, Stayman Winesap, Golden Delicious, York Imperial, Stark, Rome Beauty, Grimes Golden; and, in New England, New York, and Pennsylvania, Baldwin, Northern Spy, and McIntosh.

Peaches: Halehaven, South Haven, J. H. Hale, Early Elberta, Rio Oso Gem, Golden Globe, Veteran, Valiant; and, for pie stock, Elberta.

Strawberries: Blakemore, Premier, Progressive, Senator Dunlap, Fairfax, Dorset, Shasta, Sierra, Catskill, Midland, Tennessee Beauty, Rockhill; and, in Pacific Northwest, Marshall, Improved Oregon, and Brightmore.

Raspberries, red: Latham, Chief, Cuthbert, Viking, Taylor; and, in Pacific Northwest, Takoma, Lloyd George, and Newburgh.

Raspberries, black: Cumberland, Black Pearl, Bristol, and New Logan.

Raspberries, purple: Columbian, Sodus.

Blackberries and dewberries: Boysenberries, Youngberries, Eldorado, Early Harvest, Brainerd, wild blackberries; and, in Pacific Northwest, Olympic, Oregon Evergreen, and Lucretia.

Cherries, red sour: Montmorency, Early Richmond, English Morello, Schmidt.

Cherries, sweet: Bing, Lambert, Windsor, Napoleon (Royal Anne), Deacon.

VEGETABLES

Asparagus: Mary Washington, Martha Washington.

Beans, lima: Fordhook, Concentrated Fordhook, Fordhook 242, Premier, Burpee Improved Bush, Baby Fordhook, Triumph, Early Baby Potato, King of the Garden (pole).

Beans, green snap: Asgrow Stringless Green Pod, Burpee Stringless Green Pod, Giant Stringless Green Pod, Tendergreen, U. S. Refugee No. 5, Kentucky Wonder (pole), Blue Lake (pole).

Beans, wax: Round Pod Kidney Wax, Keeney's Stringless Kidney Wax, Pencil Pod Black Wax, Golden Wax, Sure Crop.

Corn, cut, yellow: Golden Cross Bantam, Tendergold, Bantam Evergreen, Carmelcross, Seneca Golden, Seneca Dawn, Golden Country Gentleman, Early Aristogold Bantam.

Corn, cut, white: Silver Cross Bantam, Narrow Grain Evergreen, Country Gentleman.

Cauliflower: Early Snowball, White Mountain, Perfection, Super Snowball, Forbes, Danish Giant.

Carrots: Chantenay Red Cored, Nantes, Danvers Half Long, Imperator, Tendersweet, Improved Coreless.

Broccoli: Calabrese (Italian Green Sprouting), Freezers Sprouting Green.

Kale: Dwarf Green Scotch, Dwarf Blue Scotch.

Peas: Thomas Laxton, Dark Podded Thomas Laxton, Glacier, Laxtons Progress, Little Marvel, Improved Gradus, Stratagem, Laxtonian, Worlds Record, Alderman, Lincoln.

Rhubarb: Ruby, McDonald, Canada Red, Valentine, Linnaeus.

Spinach: King of Denmark, Long Standing Bloomsdale, Nobel, Old Dominion, Viking, Improved Thick Leaved Viroflay, Victoria.

WHATEVER THE MATERIAL to be packed, some thought must be given beforehand to laying out the work so that it may be done rapidly and efficiently. This is highly important because prompt preparation and packing of most materials within a few hours after harvest is essential to a good product. Asparagus fast loses flavor and becomes tough and fibrous. Sweet corn rapidly decreases in sweetness and flavor and increases in starchiness after harvest, especially at room temperature. Peas, green beans, and lima beans lose in quality when held after picking, as do soft fruits and berries. No more of any of these products should be harvested than can be prepared and frozen on the same day, unless the surplus can be promptly cooled to 32° to 40° F. and held at that temperature until processed.

Most commercial frozen products are packed dry, that is, without brine or sirup. If sugar is added to such fruits as berries or peaches, it is added dry. In freezing most products for home use, one has a choice between dry and liquid pack, as the containers used will be liquid-tight and the additional weight of added liquid is not a factor requiring consideration, as it is in commercial frozen products.

In freezing fruits, it is advisable to pack in sirup, using a quantity sufficient to fill interspaces and completely cover the fruit. This prevents contact with air and consequent darkening before freezing and during thawing. In a number of fruits there is somewhat better preservation of flavor than in dry packs. Fruits having little juice and berries frozen whole should be packed in sirup. The same effect may be obtained with berries by slicing or crushing them and adding sugar to the juice to form sirup to cover. Many people believe that the blending of sugar from the sirup with the fruit gives an improvement in flavor over that of a dry pack to which sugar is added at the time it is eaten.

Experts disagree as to the comparative merits of dry versus brine packing of vegetables. The increasing popularity of a long list of commercially frozen vegetables which are dry-packed is conclusive evidence that there is no great loss of quality from dry packing. Dry and brine packs of some products are absolutely indistinguishable in color, texture, and flavor after cooking. A slight superiority in flavor is claimed for brine packs of others, probably as a result of more uniform blending of the salt with the product.

The important steps in preparing and packing fruits and vegetables most commonly frozen are given in the accompanying tables. Steps common to preparation of all materials, not given in the tables, are:

1. Select uniformly ripe material, rejecting overmature, undermature, badly blemished, bruised, or partially decayed units. It is much better to discard any material not in prime condition than to include it at the expense of lowered quality of the pack.

2. Wash thoroughly in repeated changes of water with as vigorous agitation as the product will stand, and discard units, such as berries or green beans, that retain visible dirt. Scrub vegetables with a brush, cutting off tips or portions that cannot be cleaned. Separate leaf vegetables and spray thoroughly from a faucet or nozzle to loosen and remove adhering sand or dirt. Inspect closely and discard portions carrying aphids or other small insects, insect larvae, or egg masses.

3. Make up brine and sirup in advance and cool thoroughly before use.

4. Have an ample supply of containers ready in advance. Cartons should be opened and liner bags set in place ready for filling. Tin cans should be washed and lined up for filling. Glass jars are not recommended; if used, however, they should be sterilized, with rubbers and tops set in place to protect from dirt until needed.

5. Speed at all stages of packing is essential, no less in transfer of packed and sealed packages to the freezer than at earlier stages. On no account allow packed material to accumulate for several hours before transferring it to the freezer.

J. S. CALDWELL *was for 31 years a senior physiologist and is now a collaborator in the division of fruit and vegetable crops and diseases in the Bureau of Plant Industry, Soils, and Agricultural Engineering. He is associate professor of food technology in the University of Maryland. He has spent many years in research on varietal adaptability of fruit and vegetable varieties to canning, drying, and freezing and on factors determining high quality for those purposes.*

W. M. HURST *is a senior agricultural engineer in the Bureau of Plant Industry, Soils, and Agricultural Engineering. He is in charge of the Bureau's engineering work in studies of the processing of farm products in rural areas.*

HAROLD D. WHITE *is research associate professor, Department of Agricultural Engineering, University of Georgia. He is a graduate of the University of Georgia and has a master's degree in agricultural engineering from Iowa State College.*

Procedure in freezing vegetables

Vegetable	Preparation	Scalding	Packing medium	Container
Asparagus	Sort into larger and smaller stalks; cut to container length or into 1-inch pieces.	Small stalks, 3 minutes, large, 4 minutes, in steam or boiling water; cool thoroughly.	2 percent brine or dry	Airtight carton; enameled can.
Beans, green or wax	Snip; cut to 1- to 1½-inch lengths.	Younger beans, 2 minutes, older, 3 minutes, in steam or boiling water; cool quickly.	...do...	Airtight carton; plain tin can; laminated bag if packed dry.
Beans, lima	Shell; sort out shrunken and whitened beans.	Small beans, 2–3 minutes, large, 4–5 minutes; cool quickly.	...do...	Do.
Broccoli	Select young heads; cut off large leaves and stalks; soak heads in 3 percent brine 1 hour; split heads lengthwise into slices.	4–5 minutes; cool quickly.	2 percent brine	Airtight carton; plain tin can.
Carrots	Scrape; slice transversely or cut into dice.	Slices, 4–5 minutes; dice, 3 minutes.	2 percent brine or dry	Do.
Cauliflower	Prepare as for cooking, cutting into 1-inch cubes; immerse in 2 percent brine 20–30 minutes.	4–5 minutes in boiling water; 6–8 minutes in steam.	Dry or (preferably) 2 percent brine.	Airtight carton; plain tin can; laminated bag if packed dry.
Corn, cut	Husk, trim, brush to remove silks; scald; cut whole-grain or cream style (freezing on cob not recommended).	5–10 minutes in boiling water or steam; cool thoroughly.	Whole kernel, dry or (preferably) 2 percent brine with 4–6 percent sugar added, cream style, sweetened brine.	Enameled tin can; airtight carton; laminated bag if packed dry.
Kale, mustard or turnip greens, swiss chard.	Use young, tender leaves; trim off large stems; wash thoroughly.	4 minutes in boiling water; stir to prevent matting; cool thoroughly; drain.	Dry	Laminated bag; plain can; airtight carton.
Peas	Shell; sort out shriveled, overmature, and very immature peas; wash thoroughly.	2 minutes in boiling water; 3 minutes at 190° F.	Dry or 2 percent brine	Plain can; airtight carton.
Spinach	Use young, tender leaves; discard stalks, developing flower heads, yellowish lower leaves.	2 minutes in boiling water; stir to prevent matting; cool thoroughly; drain.	Dry	Do.

Procedure in freezing fruits

Fruit	Preparation	Packing medium	Container
Apples...............	Peel, core, cut into slices ¼ inch thick; drop into 2 percent brine as cut; scald 2 minutes in boiling water or steam.	Sugar, 1 part by weight to 6 of apples; or enough 30 percent sirup to cover.	Carton with sealable, airtight cellophane or moisture-resistant inner bag; enameled tin can (glass not recommended).
Peaches...............	Peel, halve, slice ¼ inch thick for dessert use, or into sixths or eighths for pie stock; place in dilute citric acid, 1 teaspoon to 1 gallon water, for 2 minutes.	Sugar, 1 part by weight to 3 or 4 of fruit; or 40 percent sirup to cover. Pie stock, 1 part sugar to 5 of fruit; or 30 percent sirup to cover. Ascorbic acid may be added to sirup, 3 teaspoons per gallon.	Carton with sealable, airtight inner bag; plain tin can.
Strawberries............	Cap, wash, drain; may be packed whole, sliced, or crushed.	If whole, 40 or 50 percent sirup. If sliced or crushed, 1 part by weight sugar to 4 of fruit.	Airtight carton; enameled can.
Raspberries (red, black, or purple), blackberries, and dewberries.	Cap, wash, drain; pack whole............	40 or 50 percent sirup...............	Do.
Blueberries............	Wash, drain...............	Sugar, 1 part by weight to 5 of berries....	Do.
Cherries, sour............	Pit, fill immediately into package; cover with sirup.	50 percent sirup (sugar pack not recommended).	Do.
Cherries, sweet............	....do...............	30 or 40 percent sirup (sugar pack not recommended).	Do.
Rhubarb...............	Cut into 1-inch pieces, split larger stalks..	40 percent sirup; or sugar, 1 part by weight to 3 of rhubarb.	Do.

SUGAR, HONEY, AND MAPLE

The Production and Use of Sugarcane

L. F. Martin

Sugarcane and sugar beets have long reigned supreme as providers of sugar, an essential energy food. Sugarcane furnishes almost three-fourths of the world's supply. Many plants contain sucrose, but from none can it be produced as abundantly and cheaply in a highly purified form as from sugarcane. Besides the sugar, cane yields fiber, a mixture of some sucrose with other sugars in molasses, an industrially important acid, and a valuable wax. These are being recovered in some places and applied profitably in making useful byproducts.

Sugar itself intrigues chemists more and more as the cheapest and most abundant pure organic chemical available to industry. Its use in plastics and other synthetic chemicals is developing. Research is pointing the way to improvements in growing and processing the crop and to new applications and greater returns from utilization of every part of the cane.

Sugarcane can excel all other plants as a converter of the sun's energy and the carbon dioxide and water of the air into energy food and fiber. All around the world, wherever soil conditions and semitropical or subtropical climate combine to favor its growth, sugarcane has established itself as a major crop. From its homeland in India it traveled east and west until it reached the West Indies with Columbus. Thence it came to the French colony of Louisiana and later to Florida. We are concerned primarily with the industry in those two areas and in Hawaii and Puerto Rico.

The United States, with its high standard of living, is the world's largest consumer of sugar, but we grow only a small proportion of our total requirements. Unlike many other major commodities, sugar is not produced in surplus on American soil. In normal times there is no difficulty in obtaining the extra quantities from abroad, but in every crisis domestic production has been taxed to the utmost to meet our minimum requirements.

THE DOMESTIC cane-sugar industry is experiencing one of those recurrent periods of readjustments that have marked its progress during more than 150 years and have necessitated continuous effort in surmounting obstacles, technical and economic. Facing new situations and problems is no new experience to men in this industry. It met one challenge in the 1920's, when, having adjusted itself to the return to normalcy after the First World War, mosaic disease nearly destroyed it. Disaster was averted by the introduction of resistant varieties of sugarcane from the East Indies, which was followed by a program of breeding improved canes still more resistant to the disease. We expect that the present challenge will also bring forth major improvements in production and processing.

Today a major concern is the conversion to mechanical harvesting, a goal toward which there had been a gradual evolution but which was abruptly forced upon the industry almost completely by the scarcity of labor during the Second World War. There is general agreement as to the desirability of handling the crop mechanically, but the mechanization effected since 1945 has posed problems requiring ingenuity and intensive research for solution.

If the 1950 costs of producing the crop are to be justified, every substance of value, as well as every ounce of sugar, must be extracted. That has called for reappraisal of the entire process of grinding and manufacture into sugar and molasses, and for revaluing every fraction of the cane for application in producing useful byproducts.

THE PROCESS of producing pure white crystalline sugar from cane is almost invariably carried out in two stages—recovery of crude or raw sugar and its refining. Both are essentially simple, traditional procedures. Innovations have increased efficiency, reduced costs, and improved every step of the operations.

To produce raw sugar, the cane is crushed in a series of roller mills, with the addition of water between crushings. The added water serves to dissolve more of the sugar, which is pressed out in other mills. In that way as much sugar as possible is extracted. The somewhat diluted juice thus obtained is thoroughly mixed and a measured amount of lime is added. The lime combines principally with phosphate in the juice and, by altering its acidity, forms a precipitate when it is heated, which removes many impurities. After adjusting the amount of lime and heating to the boiling point, the juice is passed to large vessels arranged to hasten the settling of the precipitated impurities, which are drawn from the bottom while clear juice passes from the top. In most modern mills, the sludge of impurities goes to continuous filters and is washed with water, so that a maximum proportion of the sugar trapped in it is recovered and returned with the clear juice to the evaporators.

Finally, the juice is evaporated to a sirup. That is done under vacuum to prevent darkening and decomposition, which would result from the high temperatures necessary if open kettles were still used as in earlier days. The raw sugar can be crystallized from the concentrated sirup in vacuum vessels heated by steam. Molasses is thrown out of the mass of crystals by spinning in centrifugal machines, from which the brown raw sugar is then discharged.

In some factories the crude product goes on to the refining process. More commonly, however, the raw sugar is shipped to large central refineries, which have much greater operating capacity than most sugar mills. It is redissolved at the refinery. The sirup is clarified. Impurities are filtered out. The color is removed by carbon, most commonly bone char, or bone black. The heated sirup is passed through towers charged with the decolorizing bone char; the sirup, now water-white, goes to evaporators and vacuum pans much like those of the raw-sugar factory. It is concentrated and white sugar is crystallized and separated from the sirup in centrifugals. After drying in large rotary driers, in which the sugar crystals are poured through a stream of filtered and heated air, the product is screened and packaged.

Every step in the process requires precise technical control and depends on the latest innovations of chemical and engineering science.

The most difficult step is the clarification, in which lime is added and conditions are adjusted to effect the removal of plant coloring matter and other impurities as completely and rapidly as possible. The success of subsequent operations in crystallizing the sugar and the yield obtained depend almost entirely on the effectiveness of the clarification. Sugarcane of different varieties and grown and harvested under different conditions is not uniform, and the juice varies in composition and quality as grinding proceeds through the harvesting season. Control of the clarification process must be adjusted continually to meet varying requirements.

AFTER RECOVERING from the mosaic epidemic of the 1920's, the Louisiana cane-sugar industry has been a dynamic one. Before 1926, practically the entire crop consisted of two varieties of cane, Louisiana purple and D–74, obtained from Demarara. They were extremely susceptible to mosaic, and within about 3 years had to be replaced completely by the P. O. J. (initials of the name of the East Java Experiment Station) canes from Java. New varieties have been released on an average of about one a year—24 since 1924. Consequently, between 1929 and 1939, nearly all the P. O. J. canes were displaced by varieties from Coimbatore, India, designated as "Co." varieties. The Co. canes, in turn, have been almost completely replaced by varieties from the Department's breeding station at Canal Point, Fla. They now occupy about 85 percent of the total cane acreage in Louisiana. Indications are that they will be displaced by other improved and more resistant varieties in the coming decade.

Changes in varieties meant changes in milling practices. Differences in physical and chemical properties introduced new difficulties. The P. O. J. cane was much harder than the older varieties it replaced and required cutting and thorough shredding before it could be handled by the mills. Differences in chemical composition raised a problem, especially during clarification. Depending on the composition of the canes, the juices of some varieties are much more rapidly and completely clarified than others. As few mills grind cane of only one variety, and composition is affected also by soil and growing conditions, the composition of the juice being treated varies from day to day and, at times, from hour to hour. Undesirable changes in composition

and quality of juice almost invariably result from delay in grinding the cane after cutting, and the entire operation of a factory may be affected and yields lowered when stale cane is received.

For better control of the operation of removing impurities, two improvements have been almost universally adopted in sugar mills. One is the installation of modern equipment which automatically controls the addition of lime so that the juice is adjusted uniformly and accurately to the exact degree of acidity desired. Before the perfection of practical instruments for the purpose, the liming had been an art that depended on the judgment and skill of the operator, aided by a chemical determination of the acidity which could not be made rapidly and frequently enough to guarantee uniform liming.

The second improvement, adopted more to save labor, was the substitution of continuous filters for the filter presses used to collect the sediment discharged from the clarifiers and wash it free of sugar. The settlings are passed to a trough, from which the coagulated impurities, or muds, are collected on a rotating drum by suction and washed, after which they are removed from the drum by a scraper blade and returned to the fields as fertilizer.

THE MANPOWER shortage during the Second World War forced the rapid adoption of the best available machinery for harvesting the crop in order to meet the critical demand for sugar. Within 5 years the industry in Louisiana was converted almost 90 percent to mechanical harvesting. Rapid strides have been made in improving cutting and loading equipment. Each year since 1940 has seen the introduction of better models.

The rapid introduction of mechanical harvesting methods led to problems in factory operation. Besides including more of the top leaves than is desirable, the machines did not remove side leaves. When weather permitted, the side leaves were removed by burning. Loading machines for collecting the piles of cane after burning took up more soil and field trash than ever came in on hand-cut cane. Often greater delays occurred in getting cane to the mill after mechanical harvesting. All this meant greater changes in composition in a shorter period than the changes that followed the gradual replacement of old with new varieties. Difficulties were experienced in clarifying the juice; factory operations had to slow down or stop; and the yields of sugar per ton of cane dropped in almost exact proportion to the percentage of cane harvested mechanically.

With experience and the adaptation of factory practices to the new conditions, the situation is being remedied. At the same time, improvements continue to be made in harvesting and loading equipment, and experience in their use is improving the cleanness and quality of cane delivered to the mills.

CHEMICAL RESEARCH helped. The composition of separate parts of the cane plant—tops, side leaves, and trash—was determined. Now we know which parts contribute undesirable impurities. The information makes it possible to give particular attention to eliminating the most objectionable part of the trash.

The research also established the extent of the losses that resulted from a delay of more than 24 to 48 hours in grinding the cane, especially cane that has been burned to remove the side leaves. This knowledge stimulated greater efforts to organize harvesting operations so as to eliminate excessive laying up of cane either in the field or in factory piles.

As an emergency measure under extremely bad processing conditions, the settling of the precipitated impurities in clarification can be accelerated by adding calcium carbonate, the cheapest form of which is finely ground oyster shells readily available in the Louisiana sugar-producing area. The addition of oyster-shell flour makes it possible to maintain reasonable grinding capacities when rain precludes burning off the trash and bringing in fresh cane, and when factory operations would otherwise be seriously slowed down or stopped.

BECAUSE IT WAS long the practice to burn the bagasse to supply the steam required for factory operation and to distribute the muds removed in clarification on the cane fields as fertilizer, the sugar industry has had no expensive waste-disposal problem.

In one way it was fortunate that the factories produced no bothersome wastes, but at the same time the industry was rather tardy in recognizing the potentialities of its byproducts.

The first uses for the materials other than the sugar and molasses were developed on a commercial scale just before the First World War, and their commercial value was established after its end. One development was the manufacture of insulating wallboard from bagasse fiber. It became a flourishing industry in Louisiana and was soon followed by the establishment of other commercial products from bagasse for use as a mulch and poultry litter. Just before the Second World War, success attended the manufacture of a molding plastic from bagasse; the development has become firmly established.

Another development is extracting sugarcane wax. It was carried out in South Africa in 1916 on a large scale from the clarification mud, or press cake. The wax was produced there for about 10 years until competition from low-priced natural waxes stopped its manufacture. The scarcity of hard waxes during the Second World War caused a revival of the industry in Cuba. Advances in engineering practices and in development of more suitable solvents for extraction during the intervening years provide a better foundation for the current venture.

Research has added to our knowledge of the composition of the wax and the substances extracted with it. Improvements in the methods of separating the desirable hard wax from dark and soft impurities permit more efficient refining. The process is being carried out now in Louisiana on crude wax imported from Cuba. Depending on labor costs, cane wax may become a valuable byproduct of the domestic crop. Research on new uses and wider applications should provide expanding market outlets. It is estimated that about 4 million pounds of the wax are potentially available every year in Louisiana.

FIBER IS another product from sugarcane. The Louisiana mills ground a little more than 5.25 million tons of cane to produce almost 750 million pounds of raw sugar in 1948. At the same time more than 3 billion pounds of bagasse accumulated; it contained more than 1.5 billion pounds of dry fiber. Much of it went into insulating board, plastic, mulches, and litter, but large quantities were burned to generate the steam for operating some mills.

A part of the fiber is a high-grade cellulose, but some of it is lower-grade cellulose and pith, which must be removed if the cellulose is to be usable for paper or as pulp for making synthetic fiber. We have investigated a number of processes for effecting this purification, but none of them is cheap enough to provide bagasse cellulose at a price competitive with that from wood and other low-cost sources.

Recent experiments on new pulping processes promise to bring nearer to realization the dream of paper production and possibly still more valuable applications of cellulose from bagasse. Progress has been made in reducing the cost of processes for separating bagasse into fractions, one high in high-grade cellulose and the other containing the low-grade materials and pith. The future of the operations depends largely on the success of research directed toward finding uses for the lower-grade materials or the chemical products derived from them during the pulping operations.

NEXT IN QUANTITY after bagasse and sugar is the molasses produced, principally as blackstrap. Relatively limited amounts are marketed as high-grade edible sirups. The tonnage of molasses may amount to more than half as much as that of the raw sugar. In 1948 in Louisiana, 220 thousand tons of molasses was obtained in the production of 370 thousand tons of sugar. The molasses contained 114 million pounds of sugar, which did not crystallize, partly because of the presence of more than 100 million pounds of other more soluble simple sugars.

During emergencies such as the last war, when alcohol in huge quantities was needed to make synthetic rubber, molasses is a valuable byproduct. Practically all of its sugar content, of both sucrose and the simpler sugars, is available for fermentation into alcohol.

The other principal use of molasses is in feedstuffs, into which goes most of the domestic molasses.

Several other products, such as citric and lactic acids, obtained by fermentation might be manufactured from cane molasses, but the blackstrap production of Louisiana alone would more than suffice to meet present domestic needs. On the other hand, we have an almost endless list of chemicals that might be derived or synthesized from the sugars in molasses. Uses for some of them are being sought. Research is being directed toward the chemical conversion and utilization of the sugar which constitutes the principal value of blackstrap molasses.

ONE NEW BYPRODUCT established since the close of the Second World War is aconitic acid, an organic acid that cannot be produced by fermentation of the molasses, but is present in Louisiana sugarcane blackstrap. Formed normally as a constituent of the cane, aconitic acid accounts for a large part of the acidity of the natural juice. Its presence in cane juice and molasses has been known for almost 75 years, but until comparatively recently we knew of no large-scale use for it. Now its value has been established in making plastics. Chemicals derived from the acid are effective in giving desired properties for molding to important transparent plastic materials. Other chemicals derived from it are used for wetting agents in making emulsions and in cleaning compounds.

With commercial uses in sight, research was intensified to determine the amounts of the acid present and to find simple and effective ways for separating it in the form of a salt that could be crystallized and collected by centrifuging. At the time the process was launched commercially, the war was still in progress and molasses was a critical material. The simple, continuous process evolved could be applied at an intermediate stage in the course of sugar manufacture without any loss of molasses or sugar. It has proved equally effective in separating the salt of aconitic acid from blackstrap molasses, so that production of the byproduct can be extended beyond the end of the grinding season.

Complete separation of the acid from molasses is not possible by the simple process operated under the limitation that no sugar or molasses be lost. Under peacetime conditions surpluses of low-priced molasses usually develop, and more efficient methods of recovery that need not fit into the sugar-manufacturing operation can be used. In late 1950, the price of molasses again went up sharply; in such periods the simple process, which conserves the molasses, is best.

An estimated 10 million pounds of aconitic acid is present in the blackstrap from a Louisiana cane crop such as that of 1948. Perfection of effective commercial methods for recovering and refining substantially all of it will add one more substantial byproduct to a growing list.

The amounts of materials other than sugar produced by our cane-sugar industry are so large that no single byproduct can use up any one of them. Much research is devoted to the subject, but I think we could well explore many other possibilities of chemical conversion and utilization of molasses and bagasse in order to create uses for substantially all of the materials obtainable from sugarcane at levels that will bring increased revenue to processors and growers.

SUGAR ITSELF is put to a wide variety of industrial uses. It is an ingredient of such things as hair tonics, shoe polishes, photographic materials, and explosives. It is used in tanning leather and silvering mirrors and in adhesives and core binders for casting metals. About 60 million pounds a year is used in compounding prescriptions and pharmaceuticals. It serves as the starting material for the synthesis of vitamin B_2. Sugar mixed with soil is reported to prevent damping off of conifer seedlings. Sugar is used in formulating a variety of insecticides. By reacting sugar as completely as possible with the anhydride of acetic acid, it is converted to an insoluble, intensely bitter substance that has found application in denaturing alcohol and as a plasticizer in some types of plastics.

Recent research by the Department of Agriculture, in cooperation with the Sugar Research Foundation, has developed methods of making another derivative, which is insoluble in water but soluble in organic solvents and suitable for making into protective coating materials. The product, known as allyl sucrose, takes its place with a similar derivative of starch among the promising protective coating materials now available to industry.

More than 10 thousand derivatives of sugar or the readily obtainable halves of the sugar molecule—dextrose and fructose—have been prepared and described by organic chemists. More than half of the derivatives can be obtained directly, or through intermediate steps, from ordinary sugar. Research workers are exploring every possible useful application of the substances and their properties. The first great era of synthetic chemistry was based on the discovery of the almost limitless possibilities of obtaining useful derivatives from coal tar. In more recent times the petroleum age has brought even more products. But coal and petroleum are irreplaceable raw materials. Sugar takes its place with cellulose and starch in the big three of the carbohydrates, which provide a renewable source of raw material for chemical synthesis, industrial uses, and food. I think it is almost certain that industry will increase its utilization of carbohydrates and that sugar will steadily become more important as we advance in the carbohydrate age.

Industrial food uses of sugar continue to consume far greater quantities than are used in nonfood industries. The largest industrial food use is in commercial baking and candy making. Large quantities are also used in canning and preserving, in curing meats, and in ice cream and carbonated beverages. The candy industry alone uses more than 1.3 billion pounds a year, in combination with other products of agriculture, to make a total of nearly 3 billion pounds of candy. Because the industry is such a good customer of agriculture, the Department cooperates with the National Confectioners' Association in research on candy as a phase of its work on sugar. The investigations are aimed at finding better

ways to employ sugar in candies in which a still wider variety of agricultural products are incorporated. Experiments have been conducted with many new ingredients in all types of candy, and methods have been developed for improving formulas and methods of manufacture, and also for enhancing the keeping quality of the candies.

L. F. MARTIN *was born in New Orleans and is a descendant of early Louisiana settlers, members of whose families have been associated with the sugar industry there for five generations. He has degrees from Tulane University and the University of Illinois. Before joining the Department of Agriculture in 1936, he was a research associate at Tulane University, where he conducted research on problems of organic chemistry. He joined the staff of the engineering and development division of the Southern Regional Research Laboratory upon its establishment in 1939, and conducted pilot-plant research on sweetpotato starch, oilseed processing, and the recovery of natural rubber from goldenrod during the war years. In 1944 he became head of the agricultural chemical research division.*

PEDRO FAGES, a Spanish explorer, wrote in his diary of 1775 that Indians of the Santa Clara Valley were pressing vegetables and concentrating the juice to make sugar. We do not know whether the raw material was sugar beets. In reviewing a translation of the diary, Henry Dahlberg, research director of Great Western Sugar Co., noted that the Indians used a vegetable and not wild fruit. He has also observed two different types of annual wild sugar beet now growing in California. If Fages' notes can be clarified, it might be concluded that sugar was made routinely in America at least 25 years before sugar was produced in quantity from beets in Europe.—*Harry S. Owens, Western Regional Research Laboratory.*

Developments in Handling Sugar Beets

Myron Stout, S. W. McBirney, Charles A. Fort

Recent developments in harvesting, storing, and processing sugar beets have greatly increased the efficiency of domestic production of sugar, our largest single item of imported food.

Mechanical harvesting is finally replacing hand methods, which have remained much the same ever since the industry was introduced into the United States about 80 years ago. Even the change from horses to tractors for harvesting and from the horse-drawn wagons to motor trucks for hauling did not greatly alter hand topping and loading methods. Before 1943 (when about 135 harvesters were built and used), not more than 15 or 20 machines were in commercial use, and they were experimental. The first machines for loading windrows of hand-topped sugar beets, many of them made by small manufacturers and local shops, elevated beets from a windrow into a truck driven alongside the loader. Their use for hand-topped beets may be a passing phase. To meet the need for more complete elimination of hand labor, sugar-beet harvesters are used. Some commercial harvesters leave the beets windrowed in the field, and for them windrow loaders will still be necessary. But equipment is favored that puts beets directly into trucks or trailers, rather than windrows.

From 1943 until 1948 the number of machines built each year was roughly double the number built the preceding year. The percentage of the crop mechanically harvested also was roughly twice that of the previous year until 1948, when about half the acreage was harvested mechanically. In 1949, when 54 percent was machine-harvested, the further increase was small, partly because of bad harvest conditions in some sections. In 1949 about 1,900 harvesters were sold and 9,100 were in use. Most of the larger growers now have harvesters.

Mechanization of the harvest has been more rapid in California than in other sections, because of the development of a harvester particularly suited to conditions there—large-scale operations, favorable weather during harvest, and a longer harvest season. In 1949, about 73 percent of the sugar-beet acreage in California was machine-harvested; more than 60 percent in Idaho, Washington, Oregon, and Utah; nearly 49 percent in the eastern slope of the Rocky Mountain area, including irrigated areas of Kansas, Texas, Nebraska, and the Dakotas; nearly 40 percent in the Minnesota-Iowa area; and about 35 percent in Michigan-Ohio.

Most of the harvesters in use today do a complete job. They dig the beets and put them, topped and ready for storage or processing, into trucks or trailers in one pass through the field. Some machines drop the beets in windrows, which are loaded with a separate machine. One type tops the beets in the ground, then digs them and separates out the soil. Another type digs the beets first and tops them in the machine. Some machines are tractor-mounted; others are pulled. Most are 1-row machines, but 2-row machines are more common on California's large fields. The harvesters travel 2¼ to 3½ miles an hour or more. The 1-row machines harvest 2½ to 3 or more acres a day and usually average 50 to 75 acres a season. Some harvest more than 100 acres. The 2-row machines harvest about 5 acres a day and, with the long harvest season in California, average about 250 acres a season. Some harvest more than 500 acres.

A new development in mechanical harvesting came into use in 1947 in Idaho. It is the beater-topper, which beats off, chops up, and scatters the stems and leaves of the beets. It has one or two beater shafts, which carry rubber flails. The beater is mounted under a hood, crosswise to the beet rows, and is driven at 600 to 800 revolutions a minute, either by a power take-off from the tractor or by an auxiliary engine. It is necessary to cut a thin slice of crown from the beets to improve storing and processing properties. Equipment to do that has been developed. The beater-topped beets are usually dug by multiple-row diggers, which lift the beets and soil to a bed of kicker rolls. The rolls remove the loose soil before the beets are elevated to a truck or trailer. The machine is best suited for friable soils, where no clods or wet lumps of soil come up with the beets. A disadvantage is that the tops and crowns are lost for stock feed.

Mechanization of the beet harvest has brought large savings in labor requirements and costs. The savings over hand harvest depend on the yield, the previous methods of hand harvest, the machine, the depreciation period, seasonal use of the machine, and the size and efficiency of operations. The savings in both man labor and cost increase rapidly as yields increase. And, as with all machinery, more days of use during the season spread the overhead cost over more acres, reducing the cost of harvest per acre. Average harvest-labor requirements have been 30 to 35 man-hours an acre for hand harvest; they average 6 to 7 hours for machine harvest. The saving by mechanization usually ranges from 20 to 30 man-hours an acre. The cost saving by mechanizing the harvest, taking all costs into consideration, probably aver-

ages about 15 dollars an acre. As more than half of the 900,000-acre crop in the United States in 1950 was harvested by machine, the saving to beet growers was more than 7 million dollars.

Sugar beets are grown principally in temperate climates, where the growing season may be from 5 to 8 months. The longer growing seasons generally produce higher yields. The harvest has to be finished before wet weather makes the work difficult or freezing weather damages the crop. The extractable sugar per acre sometimes increases more than 25 percent during the last month of a short growing season, but the late increase is usually less in areas with longer growing seasons. Economic crop production, therefore, requires that maximum advantage be taken of the growing season and that the beets be harvested when high yield and quality are attained.

The fixed costs of factories for processing sugar beets are necessarily high. Estimates based on 1948–49 costs are that a factory capable of processing 2,800 tons of beets a day will cost about 7 million dollars and will require approximately 150 thousand dollars a year for maintenance. Obviously, only a large yearly volume can insure profitable operation, and the operating period of a factory must be extended far beyond the ideal harvest season that would give maximum economy of crop production. Between the opposing economic factors of reduced yield and quality by prolonged harvest and highcost of factory capacity for direct processing lies the possibility of storing the crop harvested at the best time until it can be processed by a factory that can operate long enough to make its expenses and some profit.

THE BREEDING OF IMPROVED varieties of biennial sugar beets has produced a superior type for storage. Roots have been stored from one season until the next in order to produce seed the second year. The roots that did not store well were eliminated from seed production. Losses of sugar do occur in beets that are stored, however. We therefore have three economic factors to consider—cost of crop production, factory capacity, and storage losses.

About 3 million tons of beets are stored each year from 3 weeks to 3 months. An equal amount is stored from 1 to 3 weeks before processing. Normal storage amounts to from 120 million to more than 200 million tondays. Normal losses range from about 0.2 pound to more than 1 pound of sugar a ton a day of storage. Rapid spoilage frequently develops in storage piles. Sometimes losses amount to as much as 5 pounds a ton a day, or to complete loss in a few weeks if the beets are not quickly processed. Removal of the hazards of storage is the primary problem of commercial-storage improvement.

Storage losses result from two general causes: Through the normal process of respiration of the living tissues of the beet, whereby oxygen is absorbed, stored food, principally sugar, is used up, and carbon dioxide, water, and energy as heat are given off; by spoilage through the action of invading organisms, principally certain species of fungi.

Both factors must be considered in attempts to improve commercial storage, because some conditions may reduce loss from one cause and increase loss from the other. Many factors influence losses from respiration and spoilage. Several investigators have agreed that each increase of 15° to 18° F. doubles the rate of respiration, but they have failed to agree on the respiration rate at a given temperature, indicating that other factors also caused large differences.

Studies of some of the other factors showed that partly dried or wilted beets respired and also spoiled more rapidly than fresh, crisp beets. Beets that were topped high respired more rapidly, but were less subject to spoilage than low-topped beets. High-topped beets also yielded more sugar to the acre. Low-

ered oxygen concentration in the storage atmosphere reduced respiration, but increased spoilage, especially if the oxygen concentration was below 5 percent. Increased carbon dioxide concentration (up to 5 percent studied) reduced both respiration and spoilage.

Beets grown in a cool climate respired much more rapidly at a given temperature than those grown in a warmer climate. Broken beets and beets severed into top and bottom halves and stored together respired and spoiled more rapidly than whole beets. The top halves of severed beets, when stored separately, respired more rapidly, but the bottom halves were more subject to spoilage.

Healthy beets stand relatively rough treatment in harvesting, handling, and piling without an appreciable increase in respiration or spoilage. Treatment of beets with disinfectants or fungicides has had little effect on respiration and usually has increased spoilage. Treatment with methyl ester of naphthaleneacetic acid, which is used to prevent sprouting of potatoes, nearly doubled the respiration rate and increased the inversion of sucrose. The chemical apparently reduced top growth, but increased the development of small rootlets on the beets.

One variety of beets respired and also spoiled more rapidly than another variety grown and tested under the same conditions. Breeding improved varieties for storage, therefore, appears promising. Beets that were deficient in phosphorus spoiled more rapidly than those given enough. Boron-deficient beets developed heart rot in the growing crop even before storage and continued to spoil during storage. Unbalanced nutrition, therefore, may be expected to affect storage adversely. Research has indicated that any treatment that seriously interferes with the normal functioning of the living tissues of the beets adversely affects storage and that healthy beets have a strong resistance to invasion by most fungi.

Losses are the lowest when healthy, freshly harvested, clean beets are immediately stored at the lowest temperature possible without freezing, in a storage environment that produces little drying and no persistent moisture on their surfaces and is ventilated only enough to control temperature, eliminate respiratory moisture, and maintain adequate amounts of oxygen in the atmosphere. Low temperature seems to be the most important single factor in keeping losses down.

ECONOMICAL METHODS of storing and recovering the beets for processing have largely determined commercial storage methods. Beets must be washed before processing. Soaking for a few minutes during transportation to the factory greatly reduces the task of washing and removing small stones and trash. Many beets stored at the factory yard, therefore, are stored over concrete flumes. When the flume covers are removed, the beets drop into water and are carried to the washers. Such storage has sometimes resulted in heavy spoilage losses, usually caused by water in the flumes, especially warm water, which evaporates, rises through the pile, and condenses on the beets. If kept dry, the flumes provide a means of introducing cool air for ventilating the piled beets.

The development of efficient heavy machinery for receiving truckloads of beets, cleaning and piling them, and recovering them from the piles has helped relieve the problem of rapid delivery and recovery for processing.

One large piler can handle truckloads at the rate of one a minute. The beets are dumped from either side into a hopper, from which they are conveyed up into a large piler and tumbled over kicker-type rolls or screens to remove dirt and trash. The dirt and trash are returned to the truck that delivered the beets. The beets are then borne over an oscillating-boom conveyor to the top of the pile. All the beets are delivered along the top edge, from which they tumble down to form the slopes of the growing pile. Piles are usually 16 to 22 feet high and 110 to

130 feet wide at the base. As the pile grows, the piling machinery is moved back to extend the pile to 1,000 feet or sometimes more. A pile 20 feet high, 130 feet wide at the base, and 1,000 feet long contains about 45,000 tons. It is not unusual to see 75,000 tons of beets piled at one receiving station.

Storage difficulties usually develop just below the top edges or shoulders of the piles. Dirt or trash that is not eliminated by the cleaning equipment concentrates a few feet from the top of the pile, where, because more beets are delivered on the shoulders, the concentration of dirt and trash is greatest.

A PILE OF BEETS contains 60 percent beets and 40 percent air spaces. If the spaces are filled with dirt or trash, natural ventilation is restricted, and the respiratory heat and moisture do not escape. A 50,000-ton pile of beets at 41° F. gives off as much heat every 24 hours as is produced by burning nearly 2 tons of coal. At 77°, the heat evolved is equivalent to that produced by burning 10 tons of coal. The heat is produced by converting sugar into carbon dioxide and water. It is important that ventilation is not restricted so that the heat can escape without further increasing the temperature of the beets. Otherwise, a cycle of increased respiration that further increases temperature and again increases respiration results. Partly spoiled beets are difficult and expensive to process.

There is little resistance to air movement in a pile of clean beets. In a series of tests, beets caused an increase of only $\frac{1}{8}$-inch static water pressure when 150 cubic feet per minute of air was forced through an experimental column of beets 24 feet high and 3 feet wide at an average velocity of 58 feet a minute. The heat and moisture transfer to the air stream was rapid. Relative humidity of the air increased nearly to the saturation point after passing through 8 feet of beets at an average velocity of 22 feet a minute.

The natural draft in a pile of clean beets is rapid. When the beets are warmer than the outside air, the air movement is in through the sides and out the top of the pile. When the temperature difference is reversed, the direction of the air flow is reversed. This natural breathing, if it is not restricted, tends to keep the temperature of the pile near the mean air temperature. Enclosed storage would prevent the drainage of cold air from the pile and some drying and freezing, but would require other methods of piling and reclaiming the beets. It is possible that such complete control of storage conditions may be found economically sound, especially in climates where unprotected piles suffer excessive damage from freezing. The sides of one large commercial pile were covered with heavy waterproof paper almost up to the shoulder. Beets under the paper did not freeze, even when the outside temperatures dropped to 0° F. Some freezing damage was sustained, however, in the top of the pile.

Beets on the surface of a pile usually suffer greater losses than those inside unless hot spots develop inside. Surface beets are dried out, are warmer from exposure to the sun, and are more exposed to freezing damage in cold weather. To reduce pile surface in relation to volume, storage piles are built as large as practical. Whitewashing the surface of the pile with a mixture of lime and waste lime cake from the factory reduces drying, keeps the beets cooler, and reduces losses in storage. On a bright day the white-coated beets may be 15° to 20° cooler than uncoated beets.

A practical way to reduce the temperature of the pile is by forced ventilation at night when the air is cool. During the harvest season, night temperatures are 15° to 35° lower than daytime temperatures. The higher relative humidity at night also causes less drying. In an early demonstration of forced ventilation, air ducts were placed in the bottom of an enclosure, and about 65 tons of beets were piled over them. Air was blown through the pile for several nights to lower the temperature from 60° to about 35°. The beets were in excellent condition after 77 days of storage, and showed losses of only about 0.1 pound of sugar in a ton a day. One company, which operates several factories in the East, used forced ventilation at night on nearly all the beets it stored in the 1949–50 season. Tests have shown that savings are greatest when conditions for normal storage are unfavorable. Under normal or good storage conditions, tests to date have shown that losses are usually reduced at least one-third by using forced ventilation.

Portable units have proved effective for reducing the temperature of hot spots in piles of sugar beets. Fairly large perforated pipes were forced into the pile, and air was forced through them into the hot spot until the temperature was under control.

ANOTHER FACTOR in storage is the condition of the beets as they are piled. Hand-harvesting methods invariably follow the practice of placing the lifted and topped beets in windrows in the field, then loading from the windrow into trucks by hand or machinery for delivery to the storage pile. Measurements have shown that on warm days the temperature of beets exposed to the sun may increase as much as 35° in less than 3 hours. That is enough to increase their respiration rate and heat output fourfold. The withering that occurs if they are left in the windrow very long makes them pack more tightly in the pile and increases their susceptibility to attack by fungi. The increased use of harvesting machinery, that delivers cool beets directly from soil to truck to pile, and improved piling equipment for the removal of soil and trash is doing much to reduce storage losses.

The improved methods that prevent temperature rise, freezing damage, or partial drying before storage also apply to beets transported by rail for several days before piling. Shortage of cars during harvest periods might delay delivery to the storage pile, but growers frequently continue harvesting. The result often is that harvested beets are left unprotected in the field. Immediate delivery to a pile for storage and shipment later to the factory for direct processing would reduce car shortages, improve storage, and establish good will among growers, processors, and railroad companies.

Delivery of frozen beets to the storage pile is being greatly reduced by the use of mechanical harvesters, except when the crop is frozen in the ground. When beets are frozen, they normally are delivered directly to the factory for immediate processing, because they spoil very rapidly when they thaw.

Beets that freeze on the unprotected sides of piles lose considerable sugar, but beets that are frozen and then covered with undamaged beets cause much greater losses. Frozen beets inside the piles do not dry out as they thaw, but exude infected juice and contaminate surrounding beets so that spoilage spreads rapidly. Methods for protecting the freshly formed face of the pile during cold nights until piling is resumed the next morning are being studied. Radiant heaters offer a solution to the problem. Automatic operation of heaters during danger periods will reduce the hazards, heating costs, and need for constant supervision.

The increasing use of more efficient harvesting machinery is expected to cut the harvest to a few weeks in most areas. Equipment will then be needed for receiving and piling the increased daily volume of beets. Improved storage of the promptly harvested crop to allow a longer operating period for the factory is one way to improve the economy of production.

THE FIRST moderately successful factory for beet sugar was put up in Prussia in 1802. Another was established in France in 1811. Attempts to manufacture beet sugar in the United States began in 1830, but none was reasonably successful until 1870. Now more than 80 high-capacity factories process more than 12 million tons of

beets annually and supply 20 to 25 percent of the sugar we consume.

Beet sugar is made by extracting the sugar from the beet by water and purifying the juice thus obtained to a degree that insures a finished sugar nearly chemically pure and equal to sugar from other sources. The washed beets, freed from trash and spoiled beets, are sliced into thin, V-shaped shreds, called cossettes. From them the sugar is extracted with moderately hot water in batteries of 14 or more cylindrical tanks. Fresh hot water enters the tank in which the cossettes are most nearly freed of sugar. The water passes through the other tanks until it leaves the system at the one just freshly filled. One tank of the series is always being emptied of the essentially sugar-free cossettes, now called pulp, while another is being filled with the freshly shredded beets. The resulting juice, the diffusion juice, contains about 12 percent dissolved solids, of which from 75 to 90 percent is sugar.

Besides the sugar, the juice carries all the other soluble substances from the beet root, such as minerals, proteins, pectins, and organic acids. The problem is to separate the sugar from the nonsugars and produce a commercial granulated white sugar that is at least 99.97 percent pure sucrose. Sucrose is the chemical name for common sugar, of which we consume more than 7 million tons annually. Sucrose is also the principal sugar of sugarcane, sorghum, and the sap of the maple tree.

Purification of the diffusion juice starts with the addition of lime until the juice is very alkaline, after which carbon dioxide is pumped into it. Both the lime (calcium oxide) and the carbon dioxide are produced at the factory by burning limestone. The carbonation of the juice neutralizes the lime. The resulting calcium carbonate separates as a flocculent solid, which removes much of the coloring matter and some of the nonsugars when it is filtered off. The light-colored, clear juice is slightly sulfured with sulfur dioxide and refiltered. Then it is concentrated to sirup in multiple evaporators. The sirup is filtered through a powdered mineral to remove the last trace of suspended impurities.

The filtered sirup is boiled under vacuum, to remove the remaining water, until microscopic sugar crystals form. Boiling is continued, with addition of fresh sirup, until the sugar crystals have grown to the desired size, and the entire mass is a thick mixture of solid sugar in the remaining sirup. The sugar is separated from the mixture by centrifuges, which have perforated outside walls that hold back the sugar but allow the liquids to pass off. In the centrifuge, the sugar is washed with hot water or steam until it is white and free from the impure sirup. The wet sugar is dried in huge rotary drums by filtered hot air. It is then ready for sacking and sale.

Because the sirup recovered from the centrifuge still contains some dissolved sugar, it is reboiled for another crop of crystalline sugar. The second batch, of poorer quality, is washed, redissolved in water, and returned to an earlier part of the process. Even after the second boiling, the sirup (which by now is very dark) contains crystallizable sugar; so a final boiling is made and the crystals are given a long time to grow in special equipment. The result is a low-grade sugar, which is dissolved in water and often is treated with vegetable carbon to lighten its color before it is returned to the juice that is just starting through the process.

The sirup from the final boiling is molasses. It contains sugar but it will not crystallize. Sometimes it is given a processing that removes the sugar as a chemical compound from which fairly pure sugar can be recovered and returned to an earlier part of the process. That is the so-called Steffen process. The waste from the process is nearly sugar-free, but it contains a complex mixture of nonsugar substances that have value, especially as a source of monosodium glutamate.

Two innovations in beet processing are outstanding.

The first is a continuous automatic process to replace the battery for diffusing the juice from the cossettes. It gets around one of the most laborious parts of the conventional process—filling and emptying the tanks of the battery. In the continuous battery, the shredded beets are fed onto a special carrier, which transports the cossettes through a series of 21 narrow tanks against the reverse flow of warm water. The tanks are enclosed and look like a single unit. About one-fifth of the factories had installed continuous diffusers by 1951. Besides saving work, the continuous diffuser gives a more complete extraction of sugar from the cossettes, the diffusion juice is more concentrated, and the pulp is better drained and ready for processing for stock feed.

The second innovation is the ion-exchange process, which removes practically all of the salts and many of the organic impurities from the juice before it is boiled and concentrated to a saturated sugar solution. The juice is merely percolated or forced through beds of the exchangers, which are of two types and are used in sequence.

The granular ion-exchange resins soon became saturated with the materials being removed, however, and have to be chemically revivified. The process produces a lower-ash sugar, but its great advantage is that the sugar can be more completely crystallized. The impurities in sirups made by the usual process actually keep some sugar from crystallizing. That is why molasses contains sugar and why molasses is produced in quantity. In the juices that have received ion-exchange treatment, nearly all the sugar can be crystallized and the yields of molasses are low. Several factories were using the process in 1951.

OTHER IMPROVEMENTS are being made constantly. The liming and carbonation of juices is more than just a haphazard mixing of the ingredients. It requires attentive control of alkalinity through chemical testing, as well as equipment that gives almost instantaneous and uniform mixing. For many decades that was done on a batch basis, a tank of juice at a time. In most factories it is now performed continuously and is controlled all the time by instruments that maintain the best conditions for removing impurities and color. The process notably reduces variations in processing conditions.

Multiple-effect evaporators have also been improved. Many are now equipped with control instruments so that the flow of juice and sirup from one evaporator to the next is regulated and stabilized. Sometimes an electric eye is used to give warning of excessive foaming in the evaporator.

The centrifugal and washing operations (which separate the sugar from the molasses or sirup) largely determine the quality of the sugar. The operations have been improved by the use of higher-speed centrifuges and a higher-temperature wash, both of which are now automatically controlled. Often water under pressure at 220° F. or higher is used for the washing, which gives effective cleaning of the sugar with less loss of sugar crystals.

Among other advances are improved rock catchers, trash removers, and washers for the beets, thickeners for settling the juice after carbonation, rotary vacuum filters to filter the sediments from carbonation, automatic controls on the sugar boiling, more efficient sugar driers, and up-to-date packaging and storage of sugar in bulk. The list could be longer, but it serves to show that the industry is keeping pace with modern engineering and scientific developments in order to reduce operating costs and losses and to improve the quality of sugar.

SEVERAL BYPRODUCTS come from the sugar beet; in fact, it is a two-crop industry. The harvested tops from an acre of beets plus the pulp that remains after extraction of sugar from the roots equals the stock-feeding value of the entire product from an average acre of corn. The tops are fed directly or after curing or ensiling. When properly cured, the total digestible nutrients of the tops are equivalent to alfalfa hay, pound for pound.

The pulp is fed wet in much of the western sugar-beet area. After temporary storage in huge open silos, it is used locally for fattening beef and lambs. In the East and far West the pulp is usually dried, with or without the addition of molasses. In this form it can be readily stored and shipped interstate. Because dried pulp is roughly 5 percent of the weight of the beets, the total potential domestic production of it would be over half a million tons annually. Beet pulp is known to be high in pectin, and a pilot plant in Wisconsin has started operations to recover the pectin for use in competition with fruit pectin.

Besides its use with dried pulp, beet molasses is also added to many mixed stock feeds and even is fed direct. That use is only for surpluses, as the molasses has become industrially important. It is used for the production of food yeast and citric, lactic, and gluconic acids and as an accessory in the fermentation processes that yield alcohols and acetone. Beet molasses is rich in the food substances and stimulants that favor rapid growth of micro-organisms and also supply the sugars for conversion into chemical products.

Glutamic acid occurs naturally in the beets and is accumulated in the molasses. Its recovery from the waste after desugaring molasses by the Steffen process has attained notable commercial importance. In factories in Ohio and California millions of pounds of monosodium glutamate are recovered and purified for use in foods.

MYRON STOUT *is a physiologist in the division of sugar plant investigations, Bureau of Plant Industry, Soils, and Agricultural Engineering.*

S. W. McBIRNEY *is an agricultural engineer in the division of farm machinery in the same Bureau.*

CHARLES A. FORT *is a chemist in the Bureau of Agricultural and Industrial Chemistry.*

Sources and

Values of

Honey

George P. Walton

A great number of flowering plants provide the nectars that bees gather, modify into honey, and store in combs. The nectars differ as the species of the plants differ. So honey, which is a natural, ready-made confection, is not a specific, uniform product. It varies from the pale-gold, mild-flavored honeys from fireweed and sweetclover to the strong-flavored, molasseslike honey from cultivated buckwheat.

To produce honey, the bee draws up the nectar from flowers and stores it in her honey sac while in the field. At the hive, the nectar is concentrated by the evaporation of water and deposited in open cells in comb. Here, more water is evaporated until, by the time the honey has become well ripened, the water content is only 18 percent or less. When the cell has been filled with ripened honey, it is sealed with a cap of wax. Such honey, with the cells in which it is contained, is called comb honey.

Section comb honey is capped comb honey in the thin wooden sections or frames in which it is produced. A section weighs 10 to 15 ounces, depending upon how well it is filled.

Extracted honey is liquid honey that has been separated from the uncrushed comb, usually by centrifugal force developed by whirling the uncapped (i. e., decapped) comb in an extractor. Liquid honey can be separated by gravity (by suspending macerated comb in a cotton jelly bag) or by pressing the honey out of the comb. Extracted honey is marketed in both liquid and crystallized forms.

Chunk honey, also called bulk-comb honey, packed chiefly in the Southeastern States, consists of pieces of comb honey surrounded by, or immersed in, liquid honey. Custom decrees that the weight of the comb honey shall equal not less than 40 percent of the total net weight. Some exception has been noted for packs in small-mouth jars, which do not readily admit that much comb.

Most of the honey of commerce is extracted. Extracting is done by the beekeeper, who strains the warm honey to remove particles of wax and other foreign matter. If it is to be stored or sold in bulk, the honey is usually transferred to 60-pound honey cans, much like the common rectangular 5-gallon oil can. Sometimes bulk honey is marketed in barrels.

The commercial floral-nectar types of honey, including natural blends, produced in this country number scarcely more than two score. Types produced in large quantities are few. Nearly 65 percent of our total honey crop is from the clovers and alfalfa. Contributions from the blossoms of lima beans, mesquite, and vetches raise the total from legumes to possibly 70 percent of the crop. Clover honeys and most of those from the other legumes have mild, pleasant flavors, and are comparatively light in color.

Honeys from orange and other citrus blossoms are produced in important volume, and, whether from California, Florida, or Texas, are prized because of their attractive flavor and aroma and pale to golden color. California sage honey and its natural blends are market favorites. Honey from tupelo, produced chiefly in swampy areas of Florida and Georgia, probably is our sweetest commercial honey and has a delicate, spicy flavor. Others prominent in the market are from basswood, buckwheat, cotton, and yellow-poplar, and a number of natural blends, such as those from wild berries and fall flowers.

Not all floral-nectar types of honey are suitable for the table. Several are unfit for food uses. Some, such as strong-flavored smartweed(*Polygonum* spp.) honey, have a restricted market, chiefly because of undesirable odor, which affects the flavor. A few, including mescal, bitterweed (*Helenium tenuifolium,* Nutt.), and chinquapin honeys, are unsalable in the natural state, the mescal because of its offensive odor, the other two because of intense bitterness. They are of use only as winter stores for the bees.

Even buckwheat honey—a favorite with many who have grown up with it, or have acquired a liking for its rich, strong flavor—is occasionally considered an inferior variety in the clover belt.

"Honeydew" honeys are not derived from floral nectar, but from various saccharine exudations, collected when nectar is scarce. They are characterized by a peculiar molasseslike or sorghumlike flavor and high dextrin content, and by having a dextrorotatory effect on polarized light, whereas floral honeys are levorotatory. They bear no relation to honeydew melon.

And, we must admit, a few honeys are actually poisonous. They are chiefly from species of *Kalmia, Rhododendron,* and *Andromeda* and from the yellow (false) jessamine. Fortunately, these seldom reach a market, because they are not ordinarily produced at a time or in sufficient quantities for harvesting and because of the vigilance of the beekeepers. At least one of these poisonous honeys was known to antiquity. L. F. Kebler (1896) cites a passage from the *Anabasis,* Book 4, in which Xenophon in his account of the retreat of the ten thousand in 400 B. C., described the disastrous but not fatal effects on his soldiers from eating honey produced in mountainous country south of the Black Sea. Scientists have concluded that the honey came from one or two species of *Rhododendron.*

THE ANNUAL WORLD production of honey is estimated at more than 800 million pounds. The 10 highest producers are believed to be the United States, the Union of Soviet Socialist Republics, Germany as of 1939, Spain, Canada, Australia, France, United Kingdom, Cuba, and Argentina. Poland, Mexico, and Turkey also produce a great deal of honey.

Production of honey in the United States has been mounting in recent years. It reached 233 million pounds in 1945, nearly 214 million in 1946, and more than 228 million in 1947, when the value (based on prices for "all honey" received by beekeepers) was more than 57 million dollars. The comparable valuation of the 1949 production of nearly 227 million pounds dropped to less than 35 million dollars. In 1945, allowing for imports and exports, more than 254 million pounds was available for consumption.

RECENT INCREASES in the annual production of honey in the United States have been due chiefly to expansion in the number of colonies of bees, which was stimulated by short supplies of sugar and comparatively good prices for honey. Also, increases in bee population were sought for better pollination of legumes grown for seed, many fruits, and some vegetables. But greater numbers of bees have provided more honey; also, since the end of the Second World War, ample supplies of sugar and other sweets have again become available. These developments contributed to a notable surplus of extracted honey (especially of the darker, stronger-flavored varieties) from the 1947 crop and a reported stock on hand in January 1948 of approximately 27 percent of the 1947 production. The reported stocks carried over into the calendar years 1949 and 1950 were even larger. Aware of the need to maintain our bee population at a high level for adequate pollination of seed crops and realizing that the beekeepers' compensation derives chiefly from the sale of the honey, the Department of Agriculture has undertaken a search for new market outlets for extracted honey.

We have no accurate statistics from the industry on the disposal of the annual honey crop. But reliable estimates place the normal consumption of extracted honey in the homes of this country at 45 to 50 percent of the total. About 15 percent more is directly consumed as section comb and bulk-comb honey. Much of the extracted honey is sold as a finely crystallized spread in cardboard containers.

The remaining 35 to 40 percent of the total crop, all of it extracted, is consumed in various food or other industries. This honey is marketed wholesale, chiefly in 60-pound cans. Nearly 25 percent, or about 50 million pounds a year, is used by the baking industry. Most of the remaining 10 to 15 percent is used in the manufacture of confectionery, ice cream, beverages, alcoholic liquors, honey-cured hams, fruit products, vinegars, and sirups. Some nonfood uses are in chewing tobacco, as a moisture-holding agent in cigarettes, and in cosmetics. Honey has been used as a heavy and incompressible fluid center for golf balls.

THE AVERAGE composition of definitely floral-nectar honey, based on Charles A. Browne's 78 analyses of 33 floral-nectar types, is: Moisture, 17.7 percent; total sugars, 76.4 percent (comprising levulose, 40.5 percent; dextrose, 34.0 percent; and sucrose, 1.9 percent); ash, 0.18 percent; dextrin, 1.5 percent; and total acid (as formic acid), 0.08 percent; leaving 4.1 percent undetermined. The ratio of levulose to dextrose is 1.16 to 1.

The analyses show extracted honey to be inherently a sirup of mixed sugars, for it is 92 to 98 percent sugars and water. As its chief sugars are levulose (also called fructose or fruit sugar)

and dextrose (grape sugar), with only comparatively small amounts of sucrose (ordinary table sugar), honey is sometimes referred to as essentially an invert sugar sirup. Invert sugar consists of levulose and dextrose in equal amounts.

But honey is far more than just a concentrated invert sugar sirup. Besides providing a variety of attractive flavors and 2 to 8 percent of substances other than sugars and water, true floral-nectar honeys contain appreciably more levulose than dextrose. Exceptions are infrequent and negligible. This preponderance of the levulose is marked in several commercial honeys (among them those from tupelo, black and purple sage, and fireweed) and is of practical significance. It accounts for the greater sweetening power of the sugars of average honey in comparison with either granulated sugar or invert sugar, and for the notable moisture-absorbing property of honey. Also, a high ratio of levulose to dextrose tends to prevent or at least to retard granulation, or sugaring, meaning the separation of crystals of dextrose hydrate from the liquid honey.

Its comparative sweetening power is of importance to the industrial user, when honey is to be used in other food products. Different results noted in comparing the sweetness of honey with that of sucrose in various products may be explained partly by the effect of other ingredients of the mixtures tested. For example, a particular honey may appear to have a higher relative sweetening power in a plain sirup or candy than in ice cream.

Honey has the following general values: One gallon of average honey contains slightly more than 9 pounds of total sugars. Theoretically, its sweetening power is equivalent to approximately 11.25 pounds of granulated sugar or to 1.67 gallons (measured volume) of this sugar. One pound of average honey has about the same sweetening power as 0.95 pound (15.25 ounces) of sugar. The energy value of 1 pound of this honey is 1,480 calories, while that of the same weight of sugar is 1,805 calories. The minor constituents of honey include: Ash, or mineral matter; dextrin, which is more gumlike than starch dextrins; acids; and substances for which the quantitative determination is difficult and which make up the undetermined fraction.

Because the ash seldom exceeds 0.25 percent, it brings only small proportions of calcium, potassium phosphate, and other mineral entities to the diet. Traces of iron, copper, and manganese have been found, generally more in the darker than in the lighter honeys. Citric, malic, formic, and acetic acids are present in small amounts, but are sufficiently ionized to add a pleasant sharpness, more or less noticeable in the taste. This sharpness is correlated with the active acidity, technically stated as the pH value. American honeys examined by H. A. Schuette and F. J. Schubert ranged in pH from 3.16 to 4.52, but usual values lay between 3.4 and 4.3. Low pH values correspond to high acid intensity; and the pH scale is logarithmic. Vinegars show pH values from 2.4 to 3.4; therefore, the most acid honeys have an active acidity equal to that of the less acid vinegars. Were it not for their contained sugars, they would taste as sour as some vinegars.

In the undetermined fraction are pigments, including chlorophylls; the enzymes invertase, diastase, and others; additional colloidal substances, made up largely of proteins; and small (sometimes negligible) amounts of vitamins of the B group and vitamin C.

Nutritionally, honey is not a noteworthy source of either vitamins or minerals. Most honeys have been found wholly deficient in vitamins A and D.

The colloidal material ranges from 0.8 percent in buckwheat honey to 0.1 percent or less in very light-colored honeys. Colloids add to the body and viscosity. They increase the tendency to scorch when the honey is heated, however, and they hinder filtration.

When extracted honey leaves the beekeeper, it should be clean and free from evidence of fermentation. Quite generally, the producers strain it, while warm, through cheesecloth or fine-mesh wire screens. A number of larger producers and some commercial packers filter at least part of their output by pressure. Honey that has been strained but not pressure-filtered has a slightly cloudy appearance because of such natural accompaniments as pollen, very fine particles of beeswax, and minute air bubbles.

Also, most of our extracted honeys granulate after standing, especially in a cool place. One of the simplest treatments for clarification is to allow the honey to settle and then draw off the clear middle portion. To produce a clarified honey that sparkles, and at the same time retard granulation, a process of simple pressure filtering was developed in the Department of Agriculture by H. S. Paine and R. E. Lothrop. The honey to be clarified is warmed and mixed with just enough of a suitable grade of diatomaceous earth (an inert filter aid) to permit filtration under moderate pressure, at an industrially practicable speed. Precoating of the filters is practiced, and after the filter cake is formed the amount of filter aid required may vary from none, for clear, light-bodied honeys, to as much as 0.5 percent of the weight of the honey, for darker, heavier types.

Besides such processing, producers and commercial packers try to keep their named honeys uniform in color and flavor. To do so, they commonly have to blend different floral types.

Granulation, or crystallizing of the dextrose, is one of the vexatious accompaniments of honey packing, particularly in the Northern States. The lower temperatures and the natural tendency to granulate of the predominant types of honey in those States increase the problem.

Granulation may be minimized by thoroughly heating the honey to dissolve all crystalline dextrose that might serve as nuclei for further crystallization, and by avoiding the introduction of fresh nuclei while bottling. But it should not be heated as high as 160° F. except for flash heating, or above 150° for more than an hour; otherwise the product may be impaired by an effect akin to scorching. Proper heating also tends to safeguard the product against fermentation.

When honey granulates spontaneously, the crystals of dextrose hydrate often are coarse or granular, but some unheated honeys—notably that from alfalfa in the West—crystallize after a time, with the production of very fine crystals of dextrose.

Honey that develops this semisolid but soft consistency has been so popular with consumers as a spread for bread that efforts have been made to produce it artificially by induced controlled crystallization of the dextrose. The products have been variously known as creamed honey, honey butter spread, crystallized honey spread, Dyce-processed honey, and so on.

At Cornell University, E. J. Dyce developed a commercial process of controlled crystallization. The licensing rights to it have been assigned to the Cornell Research Foundation. The process consists of heating the honey to 145° F. for 10 minutes or to 140° for 30 minutes to effect a "commercial sterilization" and to prevent subsequent fermentation; seeding the batch at about 75° with crystals of dextrose hydrate to hasten crystallization, because fineness of "grain" depends on rapid crystal formation; and cooling to about 57°, the best temperature for crystallization, and holding at that temperature for several days.

OTHER THAN in the home, the chief use of honey is in the bakery. Generally, the lighter-colored honeys are packed for home use, and bakeries and other industrial users get the darker ones of stronger flavor. Many bakers believe that the honey flavor of the darker sorts carries over into the baked goods better than that of mild, light ones.

Large quantities of honey are used in crushed-wheat and other specialty breads and in honey-graham crackers. Bread that has 6 percent or more of honey (based on weight of flour) is said to have a crust of improved color and flavor and of chewy texture; it also retains moisture better and does not get stale so soon. In such items as honey cakes and jumbles, for which higher proportions of honey are indicated, those desirable effects are more apparent. Distinctive flavor and aroma (determined by the type of honey used), "tenderness" of the crumb, and improvement with age are recognized benefits from the use of the larger proportions of honey. Fruit cakes for the holiday trade, intended to be kept for weeks or even months, and of unusually fine flavor and quality can be made with 18 to 24 pounds of honey to 100 pounds of flour.

In using honey in baking and in other cookery, allowance is made for its water content. One gallon (11.8 pounds) of average honey contains approximately 2 pounds 2 ounces, or 1 quart, of water.

HONEY HAS much to contribute to present-day candy making, but great care and skill are required to prevent scorching during the boiling of the candy. The right honeys add greatly to the flavor and quality of nougats and other chewy types. Originally, nougat was made with honey as the sole source of sugars, and manufacturers of fine candies are willing to pay the price for the kind of honey required. Before 1940, Grecian honey, produced from wildthyme bloom in the vicinity of Mount Hymettus, was imported by one of our makers of fine nougat.

Large quantities of ice cream are made with the milder honeys in areas where they are abundant. P. H. Tracy, H. A. Roehe, and F. P. Sanmann, at the University of Illinois Experiment Station, found that excellent ice creams with appealing flavors could be made by using up to 18 pounds of honey to 100 pounds of mix.

Wine can be made from honey. A red sweet wine, for ritualistic use, is made from buckwheat honey diluted with water. Mead, hydromel, metheglin, pyment, and cyser are variations of honey wine; their production goes back to the dawn of history. Press announcements in 1948 said that the mead, pyment, and cyser industry of England is being revived, but along modern scientific lines.

Vinegar can also be made from diluted honey, in a manner paralleling the making of cider vinegar from fermented apple juice. Some of the scientific aspects of the process were investigated by F. W. Fabian of the Michigan Agricultural Experiment Station. After diluting the honey with roughly 6 times its weight of water, the sirup (containing approximately 12 percent of honey solids) is heated to boiling. After it has cooled, there are added a small quantity of yeast-nutrient salts (1 ounce each of ammonium phosphate and potassium tartrate for every 150 pounds of solution) and a fermentation starter of pure yeast. The acetic acid (vinegar) production is assisted by the addition of mother of vinegar.

HONEY can be used as a flavorful source of sugars for preserving fruits, but ordinarily it is advisable to provide not more than one-half of the total sugar from this source. Research in the Department of Agriculture showed that, although the flavors of choice honeys and of many common fruits blend well, higher proportions of honey tend to mask more delicate fruit flavors. In making these products, it is advisable to concentrate the fruit or fruit-juice base, preferably in a vacuum pan, before adding the honey.

Bottled carbonated soft drinks can be made with honey modified by special processing. If untreated honeys are used in such beverages, they tend to become cloudy shortly after being made, and sediment may form. But sirups satisfactory for this purpose and for fountain uses can be prepared by removing colloidal substances and undesirable flavors and pasteurizing. The honey is diluted with water to approximately 60 percent solids content and warmed, and colloidal substances are precipitated by mixing with it a few tenths of 1 percent (based on the weight of honey) of colloidal bentonite clay (previously mixed with water to form a cream). After removing the colloids by pressure filtering, the clear sirup is bottled and heat-sterilized. The addition of some filter aid is required; and for strong, dark honeys, treatment with 1 percent or more of activated carbon to modify flavor and color is often desirable. Sweetclover and buckwheat sirups, with and without acidulation (to pH 3.0), are satisfactory sweeteners for a number of types of bottled soft drinks.

I have mentioned the use of honey in some chewing tobaccos. As a humectant agent in cigarettes, apparently a very small amount of honey in the tobacco serves to maintain the desired moisture content of the product.

Milk and honey combine excellently and supplement each other nutritionally. Surprisingly, however, few firms have thought to market such a product. Dr. F. W. Schlutz and associates, working in the pediatrics department of the University of Chicago Hospital, obtained favorable results with formulas in which honey supplied the sugars in the diet of infants. They found that the energy-giving sugars of honey quickly became available, but, unlike other rapidly assimilated sugars also tested, honey did not load the infants' blood with an excessive amount of sugar. With honey, the sugars available to the body rose to a moderately high point and were maintained at this desirable level for a longer time than with any other carbohydrate tested.

Technological obstacles, the difficulty of producing a shelf-stable product, provide the chief reasons why such combinations as honey-sweetened condensed milks and wheys have not been manufactured. Department of Agriculture researchers made condensed milks and wheys with honey in pilot-plant quantities. Canned modified milks for infants and spray-dried combinations of milk and honey and of skim milk and honey also have been produced by them. Their work has shown that sweetened condensed milks of excellent flavors and quality, when freshly made, can be made from choice honeys, but the canned products have tended to darken and thicken in a short time. In canned modified milks, high-quality honeys can provide an excellent source of 8 percent of available carbohydrates.

Spray-dried skim-milk and honey powders appear to hold great promise because of ease of handling and dispensing and excellent flavor. Because they can be made with different ratios of honey solids to milk solids, and possess high concentration and convenient form, they should find use in baking and in confectionery. Producers of ready-mixed cakes and similar dry mixes would doubtless have included honey in certain formulas if a dehydrated honey powder had been commercially available. A skim-milk (or milk) and honey powder with a ratio of honey solids to milk solids of 40 to 60 or 50 to 50 should serve well for such use. The compositions of two spray-dried skim-milk and honey powders, having 20 to 80 and 42 to 58 ratios of honey solids to milk solids, and of one 20-to-80 whole-milk and honey powder are shown in the accompanying table. The second of these powders, containing more than 21 percent of skim-milk proteins and nearly 69 percent of sugars, of which 39 percent are honey sugars, should prove of interest and value to confectioners, bakers, and manufacturers of ready mixes and similar foodstuffs.

Because of the deleterious effects of oxygen in the air, such precautions as gas-pack (packing in an atmosphere of nitrogen) or vacuum-pack canning should be observed in packing dried whole-milk and honey powders. These precautions are practiced in the commercial canning of the ordinary dried

Composition of spray-dried milk and honey powders [1]

	Skim-milk and honey powders	Whole-milk and honey powder
	Percent	Percent	Percent
Moisture	3.2	1.6	2.5
Total solids	96.8	98.4	97.5
From honey	19.4	41.3	19.5
From milk	77.4	57.1	78.0
Butterfat	.8	.6	20.0
Milk proteins	28.6	21.3	21.4
Sugars, total [2]	60.3	68.8	50.4
Lactose	41.7	29.7	31.6
Levulose	9.2	20.5	9.3
Dextrose	8.9	16.7	9.0
Sucrose	.5	1.9	.5
Ash (mineral matter)	[3] 6.4	4.7	[3] 5.0
Undetermined	.7	3.0	.7

[1] In part calculated.

[2] Sweetening effect of the total sugars is calculated (in terms of pounds of sucrose per 100 pounds of product) for the 3 powders at 31, 55, and 29 pounds.

[3] Includes calcium carbonate added to the honey. PH values of the mixtures before drying were 6.2, 6.1, and 6.7.

whole milks, to avoid rancidity and tallowy flavor.

Spreads consisting of mixtures of heavy (dairy) cream and honey, and of creamery butter and honey have been manufactured from time to time. P. H. Tracy, at the University of Illinois, produced a satisfactory spread with 42 percent of honey and 58 percent of heavy cream. A product containing upward of 20 percent sweet-cream butter mixed with mild-flavored honey appears to have been well received. Honey and peanut-butter mixtures when freshly prepared make a tasty and nutritious spread. The products, however, require special processing to retard development of off-flavor.

HONEYS FROM smartweed, varieties of eucalyptus, horsemint, and some blends of autumn flowers, although wholesome and, with the exception of eucalyptus, produced in substantial volume, do not have satisfactory marketability because of objectionable flavor or odor. The demand for buckwheat honey is affected by its strong flavor and dark color.

Treatments to improve unattractive honeys have been developed in Australia and New Zealand and by W. W. Somerford and others in the United States. A feature common to most such processes is to treat the heated diluted honey with activated carbon. That serves to lighten the color and to remove some flavor.

In 1948 the heavy carry-over of the 1947 crop of honey, including millions of pounds of types hard to market, posed a serious economic problem to the beekeeping industry. On the recommendation of representatives of the industry, the Department of Agriculture set up a project, under the Research and Marketing Act, at the Eastern Regional Research Laboratory to develop industrially applicable processes to modify the less marketable honeys so as to make them acceptable primarily to bakers.

Two types of processing were offered at the completion, in 1950, of one phase of the research. Diluting the honey, adding a few tenths of 1 percent of bentonite clay to the honey solution heated to 150° F., agitating for 20 to 30 minutes, pressure-filtering with the help of filter aid, and reconcentrating under vacuum to honey density improve the flavor and color of honeys from buckwheat, fall flowers, and horsemint for bakery use and retain a desirable honey flavor. The products may be standardized as to moisture content, acidity, and flavor for a specified use in food industries.

The second process offered deflavors the honey completely. The diluted honey is treated with a few hundredths of 1 percent of calcium hydroxide to adjust the acidity of the sirup to pH 4.3 to facilitate the precipitation of honey colloids. It is then heated with a suitable activated carbon in proportions varying with different honeys from less than 1 to 3 percent for 30

minutes and pressure-filtered. The density may be reconstituted under vacuum. The product is a bland, light-colored sirup of honey sugars, with little if any of the original flavor, even when made from smartweed honey, whose objectionable flavor components are very difficult to remove. Reconcentration of the filtered sirup requires the evaporation of upwards of 21 pounds of water to 100 pounds of the sirup. Since few small honey packers are equipped for such an operation, it apparently would be more practical for them to heat-sterilize and can the filtered sirups and market them for use by bakers or in confectionery or ice creams.

Suitably modified honey sirups could provide a new source of wholesome sweetness of attractive flavor for use as fountain sirups, in the bakery, and for bottled beverages.

To one who fully appreciates the delicate flavors and ethereal fragrance of honey newly ripened from wholesome floral sources, no man-made confection equals honey in the comb. The greatest appeal of honey is its taste, which comprises far more than sweetness plus the aroma of flowers. Piquant tartness stemming from its natural acids enhances the flavor and is an important taste component. The full body of well-ripened honey, which conveys a sense of smoothness and substance to the tongue, also plays a part in the sensation of a satisfying taste effect.

As a confection, comb honey appeals to those persons who esteem moderation. The great sweetness and palpable body and concentration quickly satisfy the normal appetite for food sugars. A little goes a long way.

GEORGE P. WALTON *joined the Department of Agriculture in 1907 and was in charge of the honey section in the Eastern Regional Research Laboratory from April 1948 until his retirement at the end of December 1949. He has done research in honey since 1939. He holds degrees from George Washington University.*

Crops From the Maple Trees

C. O. Willits

Maple sirup, cream, sugar, and candies all come from the sap of the hard maple tree (*Acer saccharum*), the black maple (*A. nigrum*), and the red maple (*A. rubrum*). Those trees grow from North Carolina and Missouri north to the Great Lakes and along the St. Lawrence River in Canada. The commercial maple area extends westward from the New England States to Minnesota and southward to Kentucky, an area that includes the 10 States that produce most of the crops and the States in which the maple industry is of importance in some localities. It is entirely a North American industry. It is a farm industry. It is unique among all farm enterprises because maple sap, a dilute sugar solution, is the only farm commodity that is unmarketable until it has been processed on the farm.

How long sugar has been made from the sap of maple trees no one knows. The earliest explorers found the Indians making maple sugar for their own use, even producing it in sufficient amounts for trade in some sections, especially along the St. Lawrence. Accounts dating from 1634 show that maple sirup and sugar are among the oldest of American farm products.

Typical is an excerpt from a letter written in 1648: "I have enclosed you some sugar of the first boiling got from the juice of the wounded maple. Mr. Ashton, Secretary to the Royal Society, presented it to me. It was sent from Canada where the natives prepare it from said juice, eight pints yielding commonly a pound of sugar. The Indians have practiced it time out of mind; the French began to refine it and turn it to much advantage."

Perhaps it is this history, wrapped in romance, that makes us associate the production of maple sirup with old-fashioned methods. Most of us, when we think of making maple sirup, think of it as we do of quilting bees—just another old-fashioned, backwoods social highlight of the long hard winters. Seldom do we think of the equipment used as anything at all modern. Instead, our artists have fixed in our minds that maple sirup must be made in a big black iron kettle hung over an open fire, with the whole family participating. In reality, it is a far cry from the old open kettle to the present-day, flue-type evaporators. But even these and the methods of processing sap to sirup are much the same as they have been for the past 50 to 100 years. It would shock some people to be told that maple products can be produced by modern, streamlined methods, upon which research has recently started.

Emphasis has been less on improvement of processing and more on protection of the industry by preventing the sale of adulterated products. The need for this protection has not passed; under present conditions of high prices and insufficient supply, adulteration has again become a problem of the industry.

MAPLE PRODUCTS, essentially a forest or woodland crop, come mostly from mountain or hill country, where the acreage of tillable soil is limited. The nature of the place of origin is one of the reasons why maple products are an important cash crop. Processing usually is done in March and April, when most other farm activities are at their slowest and income at its lowest. The income, whether a small or a large part of the total, often is the fraction that spells success or failure to the farm.

THE ACTUAL income from maple sirup and sugar is difficult to estimate, because the season, type of equipment, and cost of labor and wood fuel vary from farm to farm. However, a measure of the profit to the farmer is his hourly income. J. A. Cope, of Cornell University, in a survey of 20 farms in 1947, learned that the farmer got from $0.56 to $3.78 (with an average of $2.08) for each hour of work. The figures were calculated from the total returns, minus all other costs except those for labor. The total return was based on an average price of $4.78 a gallon of sirup. The fixed costs, equipment, trees, and so forth represented only 38 percent of the total cost. According to H. R. Moore and others of Ohio, producers in that State earned as much as $3.51 an hour while making sirup.

From 1945 to 1950, approximately 70 percent of the maple crop was sold in retail trade. Any estimate of the direct sales is difficult to make, because records kept by the farmer-producer are not generally available. In 1944 and earlier, most of the maple crop went into the wholesale trade, so we have an accurate record of the crop. For that year, which was fairly typical, production amounted to 565,000 pounds of sugar and 2,612,000 gallons of sirup, valued at more than 8 million dollars. Were this figure based only on the sugar (sucrose) content, it would have been worth no more than 2 million dollars. The differential of 6 million dollars was due mainly to the premium price which the commodity commands because of its unique flavor and partly to the high cost of farm processing.

MAPLE SAP is essentially a dilute solution of sugar in water. Its sugar content averages 2 to 3 percent. The sap may contain less than 1 percent and as much as 9 percent, as typified by sap from a few trees at the New York, Vermont, and New Hampshire Agricultural Experiment Stations. It takes 86 gallons of a 1-percent-sugar maple sap to produce 1 gallon of sirup. Given the percentage of sugar in any particular maple sap, the number of gallons required to yield a gallon of sirup can be calculated merely by dividing 86 by the percentage of sugar in the sap. That is known as the rule of 86. Thus, a 3-percent-sugar sap requires less than 29 gallons for a gallon of sirup. It is plain, then, that it would be desirable to have for maple sirup production only trees that yield sap with 4 percent or more of sugar and to cull the trees that yield sap of low sugar content.

RESEARCH WORKERS at the Vermont Agricultural Experiment Station have begun a study to find the causes for the high concentrations of sugar in the sap from some few sugar maples. Already they have demonstrated that this sweetness is characteristic of the few trees that consistently yield sap high in sugar year after year. They hope to develop trees of increased sirup-producing capacity by vegetative propagation of selected, proved trees or by the development of a better tree through hybridization. Should it become possible to have available stocks of maple trees that are rapid growers and that will produce large volumes of sap rich in sugar, the cost of production would be reduced materially and the quality of the sirup would be improved. At present, it takes more than 20 years for an orchard of wild seedling transplants of uncertain sap yields to come into production.

The processing of maple sap to sirup or sugar involves the evaporation of large volumes of water, perhaps the most costly of all industrial operations. The concentration of sap must be done so that the maple flavor is retained without the development of off-flavors.

For reasons of economics it would be desirable to process sap in centrally located evaporating plants, each serving a large area. That is done in a few places, but the plan is usually impractical because of the inaccessibility of the sugar bush, the cost of transportation of large volumes of sap, and the danger of spoilage. One way to avoid some of the difficulties is to concentrate the sap partly and ship the concentrate to a vacuum evaporating plant for finishing off. According to Orval Polzin, superintendent of the Antigo Milk Products Cooperative, such a plan was inaugurated at Antigo, Wis. The cost of the method may be too high unless the evaporating unit employed is part of an existing industry.

In any case, until an economically feasible method of centralized concentration is developed, the sap will be processed on the producing farm. For this, new equipment that is efficient and simple in design and inexpensive enough to justify its purchase for use only a few weeks a year is urgently needed.

MAPLE SIRUP contains about 35 percent water and about 65 percent solids.

Of the solids, the sucrose accounts for about 92 percent; reducing sugars as invert, 5.5 percent; and ash, 1 percent. The undetermined constituents that make up the remaining 1.5 percent are proteinaceous material (proteins, amino acids, and polypeptides), organic acids, and phenolic compounds. The accompanying table gives the analyses of five samples of sirup, which represent the four classified and the one unclassified grades. The samples were produced in the same grove under identical conditions.

They can be compared to the maximum and minimum analytical values typical of sirups produced in the United States and Canada.

The analyses show nothing to justify the luxury prices of maple products, except the 1.5 percent of undetermined constituents. It is in this fraction that we must surely find the flavor, which alone justifies the cost. Until more is known about this substance, little can

Analysis of different grades of maple sirups produced in 1947 from one sugar grove (in percentages)

Grade	Moisture	Invert sugar	Sucrose	Ash
Fancy...........	32.8	0.89	65.07	0.70
No. 1...........	32.6	1.52	62.90	.68
No. 2...........	31.5	2.05	64.35	.66
No. 3...........	32.5	1.72	65.51	.77
Unclassified.....	32.7	4.86	59.83	.68

Analysis of 481 pure maple samples from the United States and Canada (in percentages)

	Moisture	Invert sugar	Sucrose	Ash
Minimum.......	24.85	0	47.20	0.46
Maximum.......	48.14	11.01	70.46	1.06
Average........	34.22	1.47	62.57	.66

be done toward improving processing practices and processing equipment, or the development of new uses for maple products. For that reason, the major effort of a current research program is directed toward a better knowledge of the substances that are either directly or indirectly responsible for the maple flavor.

Already we have strong evidence that the flavor does not exist as such in the sap as it comes from the tree, but is developed by what happens to the sap after it leaves the tree, namely heating. The amount of the flavoring material, or the amounts of the substances that make up the material, are extremely small. They account for less than 0.1 percent of the weight of the sirup. We know that the flavoring material is of a complex nature, and so the task of isolating and identifying it at best will not be simple. Fortunately, the past few years have brought the development of the new analytical tools, which will help reveal this unknown quantity.

So FAR, the work has supported a theory that flavor is due to nonenzymatic browning, a chemical reaction set up by heat between certain of the components of maple sap which include amino acids, organic acids, and reducing sugars. This would indicate

Color development by heat in sirups produced by concentration of maple sap under reduced pressure

Heating period (minutes)	Optical density [1] at 450 millimicrons and —						
	25° C.	60° C.	70° C.	80° C.	90° C.	100° C.	103° C.
0	0.148	0.148	0.148	0.148	0.148	0.148	0.148
15					.153	.187	.192
30				.155	.180	.260	.280
45					.247		.364
60			.149	.158	.351	.417	
120		.148	.155	.192	.629	.733	.745

[1] Measured by a 1-centimeter cell.

that in the development of maple flavor there is an accompanying development of a yellow-red (brown) color. We have been able to produce maple sirup through low-temperature vacuum evaporation that is essentially free of color and flavor. The use of even lower temperatures and freeze-drying has produced a colorless and tasteless sirup.

In following the development of maple flavor, we have tried to establish the conditions, temperature, and time of heating that contribute to a maximum yield. In doing so, we have followed step by step the development of color, which apparently is associated with flavor. The colorless sirup obtained by low-temperature distillation was used as the starting material. Color was developed in the sirup by heat under controlled conditions of temperature and time. The amount of color developed was measured precisely with a spectrophotometer. The results, given in the table above, show that color begins to be produced at a reasonable rate at about 80° C. (176° F.). The rate of color development becomes pronounced at temperatures above 90° C. (194° F.). The time of heating is of great importance, because the amount of color formed at any one temperature increases directly with time.

The developed color (nonenzymatic browning) is without doubt closely associated with and parallel to the development of flavor. Because there is no known means of measuring accu-

rately differences in flavor levels, the associated color does provide something that can be measured. The color of maple sirup is of great importance because it designated the commercial grade of the sirup, providing it meets the requirements for density and has no off-flavors.

With present-day practices of using open-pan evaporators, the temperature at which the sap is boiled (evaporated) cannot be varied. The only other variable, which also affects the color and which can be controlled, is the time of heating. Therefore, for any given type of evaporating equipment, the producer has little control over the kind of sirups, the grades, that he will produce. His final product, exclusive of fermentation, depends almost entirely on the sugar content of the sap.

As I mentioned before, to make sirup from 1-percent-sugar sap, 86 gallons of water must be evaporated, while only 29 gallons have to be evaporated from a 3-percent-sugar sap. Assuming that evaporation rates are the same in both instances, we see that the 1-percent sap will have to be heated nearly three times as long as the 3-percent sap. We would therefore rightly suspect that sirup made from the 1-percent-sugar sap will be the darker. For example, some producers who normally make only the higher grade (light-color) sirups, in 1948 made sirups of low grade (dark color), using the same equipment and following the same practices. Any improvement in technique that will produce the same grade of sirup throughout the season, regardless of the sugar concentration of the sap, would be an aid to the industry. We hope that such an improvement will result from our studies on the development of flavor and color.

The farmer-producer always has the problem of making his finished sirup of just the right density—that is, of the correct sugar concentration. That means that the sirup must be removed from the evaporator at just the right instant; otherwise it will be too light in weight or too high in sugar content. The desired density of the finished sirup is set by law, which recognizes that below a definite sugar concentration spoilage is likely and that above the concentration sugar will crystallize out of the solution.

THE PRODUCER determines when the boiling sirup has reached the proper density by use of a thermometer, a hydrothermometer, or a hydrometer. All are more satisfactory when sirup is made in single batches than they are for measuring the sirup end product of a continuous process, the procedure most widely used. In the latter case, only the thermometer is satisfactory. The boiling point of the sirup of the proper weight a gallon and of standard density is 7° F. above the boiling point of water or dilute (0- to 3-percent-sugar) sap. This exact elevation of the boiling point makes the thermometer an accurate instrument for following the progress of the evaporation and determining when the sirup is finished and ready for drawing from the evaporator.

The use of the hydrometer for determining the completion of the evaporation process is unsound because it involves measurements that are subject to error. The measurements are the exact level at which the hydrometer floats in the hot sirup and the exact temperature of the hot sirup when the hydrometer is read. The failure of sirup for the wholesale trade to meet the standard density set by Federal and State agencies causes a substantial loss to the producer, because light sirup is marked down in price and heavy sirup yields a smaller volume. The producers need equipment that will tell them exactly when they can draw off the finished sirup at the proper density in a continuous process.

MAPLE SIRUP IS more than something to eat only on pancakes. Many producers extend their incomes by processing their sirup into spreads of fondantlike consistency, which are known as maple cream or maple butter, and into candy or sugar. Those items are the only ones manufactured by the commercial processors and, along with sirup, are insufficient to support the industry in adverse years.

None of the products can be used readily in established food recipes by industry or the housewife—too much of them is needed to get the desired flavor, and the accompanying large amounts of sugar and water upset the ratio of the other ingredients in the recipes. The housewife or food manufacturer therefore must experiment with their old recipes or undertake to use new and unfamiliar ones. New maple products designed for particular needs would help to overcome the objections.

WE HAVE SUCCEEDED in developing a new process which intensifies manyfold the flavor of maple sirup and sugar. The product may fill the need for a full-bodied maple flavor that can be added with little danger of throwing current food recipes out of balance. Its immediate use will be to provide a sirup that because of its high, true flavor is suitable for making blended maple sirup. It is inexpensive. It has opened vast new markets for an old product.

C. O. WILLITS, *a native of South Dakota, holds degrees from Huron College and Cornell University. Before he took charge of the analytical chemical section of the Eastern Regional Research Laboratory in 1940, he taught chemistry in Westminster College in Utah and conducted research at the New York State Agricultural Experiment Station.*

WE CREDIT Étienne de Boré with being the first to succeed in producing granulated sugar on his plantation, which stood on the site of the present Audubon Park in New Orleans. His achievement in 1795 marks the establishment of the domestic cane-sugar industry.

The early planters had little chemical science to guide them in their efforts to expand their infant industry. Considering the state of scientific and technical knowledge at that time, their progress was indeed remarkable. They discovered and contributed to science and technology much of the knowledge they required.

Valcour Aime is notable for his invaluable journals, in which he kept detailed records of the many experiments he performed.

Day by day his journals note the effects of weather, fair and foul, on the growth and harvesting of the cane. They record the yields he obtained by novel methods of clarifying and evaporating the juice and granulating the sugar. Despite losses from floods, droughts, freezes, and hurricanes, he persisted courageously for four decades, from 1820 to 1860, in pioneering and making his experience available to other planters. It was during that period that the industry grew to maturity.

Aime eagerly tried every new device that became available for carrying out the various steps of the manufacturing process, often at great personal expense. He traveled and sent agents abroad to learn everything possible that might assist the industry. He introduced scientific methods as they were developed and brought to his attention. In 1850 he imported a polariscope for determining the sugar content of the juices, very soon after the invention of the instrument in France. Aime even considered the possibilities of other crops as sources of sugar. In August 1833, his journal records an experiment in which "one hundred and thirty-seven watermelons gave forty-six gallons of juice which, being evaporated, gave only three gallons of thick syrup."

The Howard vacuum pan, which was invented in 1813 and had been in use in sugar refineries, was adopted by manufacturers of raw sugar in Louisiana as early as 1832.

The vacuum pan was used only for the final crystallization or granulation of the sugar. More important for the evaporation of large volumes of juice were the scientific principles of multiple-effect evaporation and their practical application, which were achievements of the Louisiana industry. Credit for this basic invention goes to Norbert Rillieux, a Louisiana student at the École Centrale in Paris in 1832. The following year he brought his idea home. With the support of Theodore Packwood, a progressive planter, it was successfully developed and widely adopted.—*L. F. Martin, Southern Regional Research Laboratory.*

The Sugar We Get From Milk

C. H. Fisher

Milk sugar, or lactose, is one of the naturally occurring sugars. It differs from sucrose, dextrose (or glucose), and other natural sugars in several respects. It is less sweet. It dissolves slowly in water. The amount that can be dissolved is smaller.

Lactose is present in the milk of all mammals to the extent of 2 to 8.5 percent; it is uniquely the sugar of the animal kingdom. Nutritionally it is highly important; because it is in milk, it is consumed in larger quantities than any other sugar except sucrose.

The cow's milk produced annually in the United States contains approximately 6 billion pounds of lactose. Because only a relatively small proportion of it is separated, however, its production in purified crystalline form is far below that of crystalline sucrose and dextrose.

Lactose was isolated and first understood as a separate milk component by the physiologist Fabritius Bartolettus in 1633. Some time later commercial production of lactose was started in Switzerland. For many years that country produced the only sizable quantities, but before the close of the nineteenth century most of the world's supply was made in the United States near St. Charles, Ill. Probably an even greater proportion of the world's current lactose production is in this country.

The quantity of lactose produced annually in the United States increased gradually until it became constant at about 7 million pounds during the several years preceding the development of penicillin. After workers in the Northern Regional Research Laboratory found that lactose is the best sugar for penicillin substrates, the need for this sugar increased at such a rate that production trebled in a few years. As penicillin became more and more important the manufacture of lactose went up from 7.6 million pounds in 1943 to 23 million pounds in 1946.

Lactose is utilized industrially in several ways. It can be used as such; that is, as the purified solid sugar. Lactose can be used also as it occurs in whole milk and in dairy byproducts, such as skim milk, buttermilk, and whey. Lactose can be converted chemically into various derivatives, such as lactose esters and ethers, which have potential industrial importance. A fourth method comprises degrading the large lactose molecule—by heat, chemical agents, or microbiological organisms and agents—into smaller molecules. Most of the smaller molecules thus produced are chemicals of actual or potential usefulness.

Lactose was important during the Second World War. It was a valuable ingredient of vanilla and chocolate tablets and other concentrated foods distributed to the Armed Forces in all parts of the world. It was an important fuel in pyrotechnics; because it burns slowly and deepens the color of signals, it was used in various military and distress signals and in target identification candles.

WHEY, AN INEXPENSIVE DAIRY BY-PRODUCT containing lactose as the principal organic constituent, is the best source of lactose.

About 10 billion pounds of whey is

produced annually in the United States. Approximately 9 billion pounds of whey is obtained as a byproduct in the manufacture of whole-milk cheese; 1 billion pounds is obtained similarly from cottage, pot, and bakers' cheese. A lesser quantity, 600 million pounds, of whey accompanies the production of casein. Casein whey is important, however, because it was the sole source of lactose in this country until about 1944.

The 10 billion pounds of whey produced each year contains about 500 million pounds of lactose. Because only about 4 percent of that lactose is actually separated and refined, there is plenty of whey for the manufacture of much larger quantities of the sugar. Other important constituents in the 10 billion pounds of whey are 50 million pounds of protein, 40 million pounds of nonprotein nitrogenous matter, 30 million pounds of fat, and 12,000 pounds of riboflavin (vitamin B_2).

Much of the whey is produced at widely scattered points; hence not all of it is available under conditions suitable for economic processing and utilization. Considerable quantities of it, however, are available in production centers under favorable conditions. In addition, at many centers of production, skim milk or whey could be concentrated and transported to nearby manufacturing areas at relatively low cost. In the manufacturing centers, where whey is obtained in volume, the utilization and disposal of this perishable and biologically active material present a problem.

Some types of whey are better than others for making lactose. For precipitating casein to obtain casein whey, either hydrochloric (muriatic) acid or sulfuric acid can be used. The casein whey produced with sulfuric acid is objectionable because of the difficulty of removing certain metal sulfates that impart cloudiness to the lactose solutions. Self-soured casein whey also is not a suitable raw material for making lactose because a considerable quantity of the lactose has been converted by fermentation into lactic acid. The

Properties of common sugars

Sugar	Melting point ° C.	Solubility at 25° C. Parts per 100 parts water	Sweetness Percent
α-Lactose.....	202	[1] 21.6	27
β-Lactose.....	252	[1] 21.6	>27
Sucrose.......	160–186	211.4	100
Glucose.......	146	82	50–60
Levulose......	102–104	....	100–150
Galactose.....	167	68.3	....
Maltose.......	102–103	108	60

[1] Equilibrium mixture of α- and β-lactose.

same is true to a less extent for cottage-cheese whey. Muriatic casein whey is largely free of the objections, and so is considered a desirable raw material for making lactose.

Several methods have been developed for recovering lactose from muriatic casein whey. In one of them the whey is heated to boiling in iron tanks with live steam. Lime is added during the heating until the acidity is about 0.5 percent or the pH value is 6.2. The coagulum is allowed to settle and the clear whey is evaporated in a multiple-effect evaporator to a concentration of 30 percent lactose or 20° Baumé. After being passed through a filter press, the sirup is concentrated further to about 40° Baumé by evaporation. The hot mass is dropped into crystallizing vats, where it is cooled and agitated slowly. The solid lactose thus obtained is freed from mother liquor by centrifugation and then washed with cold water. A second crop of crystals can be obtained by concentrating the mother liquor. The wet crude lactose should be either refined or dried promptly to prevent spoilage.

The recovery of crude lactose is usually 3 to 3.5 pounds per 100 pounds of whey. Further crystallization is required to produce refined, or United States Pharmacopoeia, lactose, the yield of which is 2.5 to 3 pounds per 100 pounds of whey. The less costly lactose of crude or technical grade is satisfactory for many purposes. At one time manufacturers usually attempted to obtain the maximum yield. Some manufacturers now find it profitable to make only partial recovery of about 2.5 pounds and to use the remaining mother liquor to make poultry feed.

The increased demands for lactose imposed in 1944 by the penicillin development were met principally by increasing production from cheese whey. Lactose can be made from cheese whey by concentrating it in a vacuum evaporator to 55 to 60 percent content of solids, cooling the concentrate with occasional stirring in a vat, centrifuging to separate the solid lactose, washing with cold water, and drying.

Cheese whey ordinarily must be gathered from several cheese factories; and, unless properly handled, it often ferments. So procurement is more costly, and the average yield is lower than that from casein whey.

The three grades of commercial lactose are crude, technical, and refined. The refined lactose is a white, odorless powder, at least 99.7 percent pure, as determined by the polariscope. The crude and refined grades sold for about 16 and 26 cents a pound, respectively, in December 1949. As sucrose and dextrose are usually available at less than 8 cents a pound, lactose is at a disadvantage for applications that can be met equally well by the other sugars.

Because β-lactose is more soluble than α-lactose, the normal form, and gives the impression of being sweeter, β-lactose is in demand for some uses. To meet the demand, methods for making β-lactose have been studied. Drying lactose solutions by the spray-drying process produces a mixture of the two forms in approximately the equilibrium ratio of 1.65 parts beta to 1 part alpha. The product dissolves much more rapidly than α-lactose, but it is hygroscopic and has poor wetting properties. The product made by drying lactose solutions on a drum drier contains as much as 90 percent of β-lactose if the most favorable drying conditions are used. Such a product has good wetting properties and is less

hygroscopic than the spray-dried product and slightly more soluble initially than pure β-lactose. Other methods for making β-lactose have been developed, and its production in purified form has become an established industrial operation.

MUCH ATTENTION has been directed toward the mother liquor, or molasses, from lactose production to achieve maximum utilization of the byproducts. Early observations revealed that the material possesses marked growth-promoting properties that are accentuated by the addition of traces of crude rice polishings. At the time of the observations, vitamins were differentiated merely as fat-soluble or water-soluble. The evolution of vitamin technology gradually disclosed that lactose molasses contains numerous water-soluble vitamins, mainly riboflavin. Methods for the commercial recovery of natural crystalline riboflavin from this product were perfected about 1935, and for a short time this crystalline material was the only pure riboflavin commercially available. The natural product, however, did not long enjoy this status because of the persistence of research chemists, who rapidly synthesized riboflavin and initiated its mass production.

The byproducts of lactose manufacture, which contain valuable vitamins, minerals, and other food factors, are generally concentrated and used in poultry and animal feeds.

CHEMICALLY, lactose is called 4-d-glucose-β-d-galactopyranoside. It is a compound that has several hydroxyl groups, an acetal group, and a reactive hemiacetal or aldehyde group. Its chemical reactions are those that would be expected from a material having these functional groups. The normal form of lactose is the readily crystallizable α-hydrate; the β-form is more soluble than the α-form. Like other sugars, lactose dissolved in water has the characteristic of rotating plane-polarized light.

Lactose can be hydrolyzed with acids or enzymically with lactase, but not with maltase. The hydrolysis products are two other sugars, glucose and galactose, in equal parts. Glucose, made from starch, is an industrial product of great importance, but galactose has not yet been made commercially.

Having a reactive hemiacetal or aldehyde group, lactose is a reducing sugar. The reaction product of lactose and hydrogen cyanide is the corresponding aldehyde cyanohydrin. Lactobionic acid can be made from lactose by fermentation or by chemical oxidation of the aldehyde group. More extensive oxidation of lactose yields mucic and saccharic acids.

Both d-glucosan and d-galactosan have been made by the pyrolytic distillation of lactose. Depending on the conditions used, hydrogenation of lactose yields propylene glycol, hexanetriol, dulcitol, sorbitol, lactitol, and similar compounds. Various esters and ethers of lactose have been prepared.

Like many other sugars, lactose is a good substrate for microbiological processes and hence can be used to make various chemicals by fermentation. Of the many substances obtainable from lactose by fermentation, those that have been produced in moderate or high yields are lactic, citric, acetic, propionic, and butyric acids, ethanol, butanol, acetyl methyl carbinol, and riboflavin.

Lactose cannot compete with sucrose and dextrose as a sweetening agent because of its low solubility, hardness, dryness, and bland taste, and the slowness with which its crystals dissolve on the tongue. Although those properties have precluded the large-scale use of lactose as a sweetening agent, they have made possible its successful application in other fields. For example, the low degree of sweetness is essential in certain pharmaceuticals and special foods.

Prior to the commercial production of penicillin in 1944, more lactose was consumed in food preparations for infants, invalids, and the elderly than for any other purpose. Physicians pre-scribed it to make the lactose content of infant food comparable with that of human milk.

The pharmaceutical industry has always provided one of the principal outlets for lactose. Hospitals, dispensaries, and pharmacists need lactose for filling prescriptions. Tablets and pills must weigh at least 1 grain and powders 2 grains, regardless of the weight of the active ingredients. Lactose is usually selected to meet these weight standards because it is innocuous, soluble, odorless, and, in small quantities, virtually tasteless. Lactose may be used also as a coating on pills or tablets to mask the taste.

A comparatively large quantity of lactose is used in making compressed tablets and vitamin capsules, in which it serves largely as a vehicle. Lactose is good for that use because it blends well with other ingredients, does not absorb atmospheric moisture quickly, minimizes the disintegration of tablets in shipment, and prevents stickiness at high temperatures. Those characteristics accounted also for an important wartime demand, under Army and Navy contracts, for lactose to be used in vanilla and chocolate tablets and in ration packets distributed to the Armed Forces in all parts of the world, particularly in the hot humid areas of the Pacific.

As lactose in milk is the sugar selected by Nature for feeding infants, one might expect that lactose would be beneficial nutritionally. Although its specific nutritional advantages are not well understood, the general importance of lactose as a food is universally recognized. Lactose, unless fed in excessive quantities, accelerates growth in young animals better than other common sugars. It favors the production of riboflavin and vitamin B_6 in the intestine of the rat.

Certain lactose-rich whey products, such as plain condensed, sweetened condensed, or dried whey, may be used to make some candies, including fudge, caramel, and taffy. These lactose-rich products are particularly suitable for making fudge, because the lactose, by crystallizing, contributes to the desired texture.

Lactose, a complex condensation product of the sugars glucose and galactose, is more slowly broken down and utilized biologically than other common sugars. This slow rate of degradation and biological utilization may be important in several respects. For example, it has been suggested that the slow absorption of lactose may be a factor in the retention of glycogen, or animal starch, in the liver and muscles. There is evidence also that milk sugar increases the utilization of calcium and phosphorus, particularly in the young.

Whether or not the low rates of absorption and metabolism of lactose are important generally in biological processes, its superiority as a raw material in making penicillin by fermentation is undoubtedly due to slow metabolism. As the fermentation proceeds the alkalinity of the culture medium increases to a point where penicillium mold ceases to grow. Lactose is used as the acid-forming sugar in the medium to prevent excessive alkalinity. It is preferred for this purpose because it is utilized slowly by the organism and its effect is prolonged.

The development of penicillin has played a greater part than any other single factor in expanding the manufacture and consumption of lactose. Instead of the usual annual requirement of 6 to 7 million pounds, the lactose industry in 1944 was confronted with a need for 12 to 14 million pounds. The need was met largely by increasing production of lactose from cheese whey. New plants were built, existing facilities were improved and expanded, and refining was utilized more efficiently. Time was required to gear production to meet the greater demand. In the interim, with some minor exceptions, the entire milk-sugar supply was placed under allocation under War Food Order 95, effective on April 1, 1944. Through excellent cooperation between Government and industry, pro-

duction to meet the new requirements was increased in 5 months, and it was feasible to suspend the allocation on September 1, 1944. The allocation was completely terminated a year later.

Largely as the result of penicillin manufacture, the estimated total production of lactose increased from 7.6 million pounds in 1943 to 13.3 million pounds in 1944, 18.8 million pounds in 1945, 23 million pounds in 1946, and 21 million pounds in 1947. Improvements have been made in penicillin manufacture during the past several years, so that less lactose is required. This probably was partly responsible for the drop in total production of lactose in 1948 to 17 million pounds. Lactose has proved superior to the cheaper sugars in making penicillin, and the use of crude lactose, which is relatively inexpensive, has been found feasible for the purpose. The need for penicillin, therefore, should keep the production of lactose at a high level for a long time.

WORKERS AT THE Eastern Regional Research Laboratory have shown that unsaturated esters and ethers of sugars, such as glucose methacrylate and sucrose and glycoside allyl ethers, can be used in making plastics and protective coatings. Lactose is more expensive than certain competing sugars, and therefore there is no good reason for believing that this potential outlet for it will prove important commercially.

An ester of lactose, the octanitrate, is an explosive, but this explosive has not proved important commercially. Calcium lactobionate-calcium bromide, made by electrolytic oxidation, is reputed to have particular merits as a sedative and for the alleviation of certain nervous disorders.

The production of mucic acid and saccharic acid from lactose on a pilot-plant scale was initiated in 1948. These two polyhydroxy dibasic acids undoubtedly can be used to make plasticizers, plastics, and other useful products. Probably the eventual commercial success of the acids will be determined largely by economic rather than chemical factors.

Many other uses for lactose, such as silvering mirrors, preserving latex and oil cake, and giving a frosty appearance to certain bottled liqueurs, have been recorded, but these are of negligible commercial importance.

BECAUSE LACTOSE as it is found in whey is much cheaper than in its solid, crystalline form, the utilization of lactose in whey is attractive economically. Although not suitable for the applications now met by solid lactose, lactose as it exists in whey can be utilized efficiently to make certain other materials by fermentation. Utilization by fermentation comprises transforming the lactose microbiologically into useful products, followed by recovery of the products from the fermented whey solution.

The chief factors that determine whether whey can be used economically for a commercial fermentation are the existence of an organism that will convert lactose efficiently into the desired product and the cost of whey in comparison with that of other carbohydrate materials, such as blackstrap molasses and starch hydrolyzates. Certain vitamins in whey give it an advantage in some instances.

Of the many substances obtainable from whey by fermentation, those that may be produced in yields sufficient to warrant consideration for commercial production are lactic, citric, propionic, and butyric acids, ethanol, butanol, acetyl methyl carbinol, and riboflavin. The only fermentation products now being manufactured from whey in the United States are lactic acid, ethanol, vinegar, riboflavin, butanol, and acetone.

Lactic acid is produced commercially from whey with a mixed culture of a lactobacillus and a mycoderm. The process is efficient because the yield is more than 0.9 pound of lactic acid for each pound of lactose.

The principal uses of lactic acid are in the leather industry, where it is employed to delime hides, and in foods and beverages. The function of lactic acid in food products is to give an acid taste to materials such as sherbets, fruit preparations, confections, pickles, and carbonated beverages. It is used also in bakery products, fruit pectin, mayonnaise, cheese manufacture, and various other food preparations (in brine of green olives, pickles, and sauerkraut, in preserves, jams, and jellies, fruit essences and extracts), and as a food preservative. It is used also for acidulating worts in brewing and for preventing growth of *Clostridium butyricum* in yeast manufacture.

Lactic acid is used in the production of phenolic resins, in cheese manufacture, instead of tartar bath in dyeing, as mordant in printing woolen goods, as solvent for water-soluble dyes, as reducer of chromic oxide in mordanting wool, and as flux for soft solder. Calcium lactate is employed in baking powder, foods, and pharmaceuticals to introduce calcium for nutrition. Sodium lactate is useful in industry because of its viscosity in solution and its ability to absorb and hold atmospheric moisture. Sodium lactate solutions have been substituted for glycerol in textile printing and in paper making. Because it corrects acidosis, yet does not produce alkalosis, it is sometimes used to overcome indigestion. It acts as a buffer in preventing undesirable reactions and decomposition of certain drugs in the alimentary tract. By a relatively new process, copper lactate can be used to electroplate almost any desired color. Iron lactate furnishes iron in nutrition. Various metal lactates have found use as mordants.

Lactic acid, a versatile chemical by virtue of its two functional groups, can be converted into various products of actual or potential industrial importance. These include solvents, plasticizers, alkyd resins, low-pressure laminating resins of the allyl type, vinyl polymers and copolymers, humectants, insect repellents, and acrylic esters. The acrylic esters can be transformed by polymerization or copolymerization into polymeric plasticizers, rigid plastics, and elastomers. The acrylic elastomers Lactoprene EV and Hycar PA are superior to most rubbers in resistance to deterioration caused by heat, oxidation, light, ozone, mineral oils, and repeated flexing.

Ethyl alcohol can be made from whey in 84 to 90 percent of the theoretical yield, by yeasts such as *Torula cremoris*. The protein, spent yeast, and distillation residues are suitable for feed. In making spirit vinegar from whey alcohol, the dilute alcohol is allowed to trickle over beech shavings or birch twigs impregnated with the acetic acid organism. Passage of air through the vinegar converter accelerates the fermentation.

The riboflavin content of whey can be increased by fermentation with *Clostridium acetobutylicum*. A yield of at least 30 micrograms of riboflavin per gram of whey can be obtained. About 30 percent of the lactose is converted during the fermentation into alcohols and acetone. Butanol, which is sufficiently valuable for recovery by distillation, comprises two-thirds of these compounds.

Butanol and acetone are in great demand as industrial chemicals and intermediates for making many commercial products, including esters of great value as solvents and plasticizers.

Of all the possible methods of utilizing lactose industrially, fermentation is one of the more attractive. Fermentation utilizes lactose in its cheapest form and converts it into versatile chemicals, which, in turn, can be transformed into a multitude of useful materials.

Just as the present industry based on lactose was created largely by research, so will research bring new discoveries and design the future of the industry. Already chemistry has pointed the way to the transformation of lactose into adhesives, explosives, fibers, plastics, protective coatings, rubbers, solvents, plasticizers, pharmaceuticals, and similar products. But this is only the beginning. It now remains to improve known methods and materials, fit old products into new uses, and find new procedures and products. In particular, the chemist must accumulate much more information on lactose, find a way to lower its cost, and ascertain how its unique properties can be used to advantage and in spite of competition from cheaper sugars. The attainment of these goals will greatly enhance the value of lactose, give this sugar of animal origin its rightful position as a fundamental raw material, and provide the basis for the maximum utilization of lactose-rich dairy byproducts.

C. H. FISHER, *director of the Southern Regional Research Laboratory and formerly head of the carbohydrate division of the Eastern Regional Research Laboratory, has worked in Federal research laboratories since 1935. During the past decade, he has been primarily interested in developing new methods for utilizing carbohydrates as raw materials in making useful chemicals, plastics, and rubber substances.*

Composition of whole milk, skim milk, and whey

Constituent	Whole milk	Skim milk	Whey
Water	87.10-87.75	90.25-90.48	93.15-93.40
Fat	3.40- 3.90	.10- .20	.24- .35
Casein and albumin (protein)	3.20- 3.55	3.55- 4.00	.85- 1.00
Lactose	4.60- 5.10	4.70- 5.25	4.80- 5.09
Ash	.70- .75	.75- .80	.49- .65

CROPS OF THE FIELD

Cereal Grains as Food and Feed

Kenneth R. Majors

Most of the world's population depends directly on the annual harvest of cereal grains for its basic food staples. The needs of the great numbers of domestic livestock and poultry add a secondary value to the cereals as a source of feed. The vast acreage planted to cereal grains in relation to that of other crops reflects their essentiality as food and feed.

The cereal grains, all members of the grass family, are grown for their edible starchy seeds. Most prominent members of the group are corn, rice, wheat, barley, oats, rye, grain sorghums, and millet. Among them are several of the world's leading crops. Buckwheat is not a true member of the grass family, but it is often classed with cereal grains because of its similarity in chemical composition and use.

The origins of some of the more important cereal grains are obscure. More than one had its cultural beginning before recorded history. The development of cereal grains, probably more than any other factor, permitted the earliest tribes to change from nomadic life to more settled existence. They learned that cultivation of cereal grains provided more food with less effort than did any other crop. No other offered such security of subsistence. In addition, grain could be easily stored to provide food between harvests. Certain it is that the saving in time needed to provide their food essentials left them with more leisure to learn new arts and crafts.

Major parts of the world's population subsist mainly on wheat and rice. The importance of wheat in the basic food economy of the United States and the other advanced countries is well known. As a country develops from a totally agrarian mode of life to a diversified existence, consumption of wheat as food increases accordingly. The use of wheat as a feed grain varies from year to year, depending on supply and market prices.

In other parts of the globe, rice is equally essential to the fundamental food habits of another large segment of the world's population. Those who depend almost entirely on rice for their subsistence live in the poorer and more thickly populated areas of the rice-growing regions.

Inhabitants of many countries, because of climate or other factors, must depend mainly on corn, rye, barley, or one of the lesser grains for their main food staple. That is especially true of the underprivileged classes of such countries.

Corn, sometimes termed the backbone of American agriculture, owes its importance to its principal use as feed. It provides livestock and poultry feeders in the United States with well over half of all their feed grain. Some 85 to 90 percent of the crop is used in that way. Consequently about 75 percent of the corn crop never leaves the farm on which it is produced. Since the Second World War, corn utilized in industrial processes accounts for about one-third of that grain sold off the farm. Most of the rest goes to feeders and to the mixed-feeds industry. Thus, an important cereal grain, while not being consumed directly as human food, is converted on a big scale to other forms of food for humans.

Also used as feed grains are oats, barley, grain sorghums, wheat, rye, millet, and buckwheat. In localities where corn is not grown, we find one or more of them in a leading role as a feed grain, depending on which is suited to the climate and economics of the region.

Most of the cereal grains, except rice, which enter the world commerce grow on the prairies and plains of the United States and Canada, on the pampas of Argentina, in the Russian Ukraine and nearby countries, and in the grain belt of Australia.

WHEAT, grown on more of the world's acreage than any other crop, is adaptable to a wide range of soils and climate and can be grown extensively throughout the world, except in the Tropics. Barley perhaps is the only other grain with the same degree of climatic adaptability. In general, the main wheat belt lies between latitudes of 30° to 55° in the North Temperate Zone and 25° to 40° in the South Temperate Zone, where the annual rainfall averages between 12 and 45 inches.

In the United States, five classes of wheat are commonly grown—hard red spring, soft red winter, hard red winter, durum, and white.

Winter wheats are sown in the fall for harvesting the following summer. They have an earlier start over wheats planted in the spring, and can be harvested earlier. They yield more than spring wheats wherever they can survive the winter.

North Dakota, South Dakota, Minnesota, and Montana, which supply most of our hard red spring wheats, are so far north that winters are too rigorous for winter wheats, except in limited areas.

Hard red winter wheats are grown on more acres than are any of the other classes. These wheats are produced in about two-thirds of the Great Plains States and in parts of Idaho, Washington, and Oregon. Kansas, Nebraska, Oklahoma, and Texas lead.

Durum wheats can be grown in much the same areas of the United States as the hard red spring wheats, but most of the production is in North Dakota.

A humid climate is favorable for the soft red winter wheats, which are grown more in the eastern part of the United States, from the east coast west to the hard red winter wheat belt. Ohio is one of the leading producers. Some is also grown in the Pacific Northwest.

White wheats are produced in some parts of New York, Michigan, and Ontario, and to a greater extent in the Pacific Northwest and California.

Rice, on a world basis, follows wheat and corn in acreage. Only potatoes and wheat exceed rice in quantities produced, and wheat has but a very narrow margin of advantage.

Rice is produced in warm, humid regions in tropical or semitropical climates, and where fresh water is available or where topography and soil types are suitable for irrigation. An abundance of water is required at certain seasons, because rice plants must be submerged in 4 to 6 inches of water during most of the growing period. One type, upland rice, is grown like the other cereal grains without a flooding period. Because rice produces high acre yields, it is grown as the principal food in the densely populated areas of the Orient. About 95 percent of the rice is produced in Asia and nearby islands.

Before the Second World War, most of the rice entering world trade was grown in Burma, Siam, and French Indochina. The surplus exported from that area in 1947 was only one-fourth the prewar volume. Arkansas, Texas, Louisiana, and California are the rice-growing areas of the United States.

Corn is grown in many areas because

it is adapted to a wide range of environments. The main producers are the temperate regions that have a rainfall greater than 8 to 10 inches in summer. It is also produced on irrigated land. It is the most important New World crop grown in the Old World; large acreages in the Danube basin are in corn. In the United States, corn ranks first in acreage, which is heavily concentrated in the Corn Belt, from the Dakotas, Nebraska, and Kansas on the west to Ohio on the east. From that region, in average years, comes almost half of the world's supply of corn. The principal type grown there is dent, which accounts for more than 90 percent of our production. Flint is the other main type. Yellow and white varieties of both types are grown. The yellow predominate.

Grain sorghums can stand more heat and drought than the other common cereal grains. They are grown in hot and semiarid regions world-wide. Sorghums are important crops in Africa and Asia and are grown also in the United States, Argentina, Australia, and southern Europe. In many of the poorer sections of those regions, they are used as food. In the United States, grain sorghums are grown in the southern Great Plains, in places too hot and dry for good corn yields. There, large numbers of livestock are raised, and the crop takes the place of corn in feeds, because it nearly equals corn in feeding value and is cheaper than the corn that must be shipped in.

Oats are grown in most of the temperate regions, and are adapted to cool, moist climates. Oats can grow under less suitable conditions than some other crops, and are raised in much of the Corn Belt in rotations with corn and clover. A large part of the oat crop in the United States is sown in much the same areas as spring wheats. Next to rye, oats have the lowest soil requirements among the cereal grains. Oats constitute one of the principal feed grains in the United States and other countries. In quantities produced for the world, the oat crop ranks next to corn, wheat, and rice in the cereal group.

Rye, grown in much the same areas as wheat the world over, will survive severer winters and produce larger yields of grain on soils of low fertility than any other cereal crop. It is grown principally in temperate and cool regions, not only because of its greater winter hardiness, but because it ripens earliest of all the small grains. Rye is produced on sandy soils and in regions just north of the areas where winter wheat is hardy. Most rye is sown in the fall. Some spring varieties are planted. It is a major food crop only in the more populated sections where wheat is not the principal bread grain. In the United States, a small amount of rye flour is used for bread.

Barley is cultivated in all the temperate regions, mainly in the spring-wheat areas. A diversity of types, however, permits the planting of barley in many widely varying places. Although not winter-hardy, most varieties grow best in cool, moist climates. A great deal of barley is grown in the Dakotas, California, Minnesota, Colorado, Montana, and Idaho. Barley is used as a main food grain in some countries, but its principal use is as a feed grain. In the United States and a number of other countries, barley is used both as a feed and as a source of malt.

Buckwheat is grown largely in Europe and North America. It is particularly adapted to nonproductive lands. In good soils it is less productive than the other grain crops. Sometimes it is used for food, but most of it is fed to livestock.

Millet is grown in semiarid regions, principally for livestock and poultry feed. In sections of Asia, Africa, and Europe, it is used as food for mankind.

ON A RELATIVE BASIS, the world's combined production of cereal grains does not vary greatly from year to year. Shortages of certain crops in some areas are often balanced by above-average production elsewhere. The areas of production, all through the world, have climatic conditions that by and large are fairly average, although in localities the conditions in some years might deviate considerably from the averages for those areas. From 1930 to 1945, the average yearly production of cereal grains for the world was approximately 634 million tons. The maximum range in production levels during those years was from about 694 million tons in 1938 to about 565 million tons in 1934—which is approximately 9.5 percent above the average for the period and 10.9 percent below the average, respectively.

FACTORS that can affect favorably the world supply of cereal grains are improvements in crop production. Small improvements applied to the vast acreages devoted to cereal crops will add up to many bushels. Through active plant-breeding programs, hardier strains of plants are being developed to reduce losses in yields from disease and insects, thus increasing significantly the yields per acre. For some plants, the aim is to increase winter hardiness, resistance to heat and drought, or greater food value. For some, geneticists seek a higher content of particular constituents—for example, oil in corn and niacin in grain sorghums.

Widespread use of hybrid seed in the production of corn in our Corn Belt, which started around 1933, can be expected to continue. Large further increases there, above the present use of hybrids, are doubtful, however, because in many localities it has reached almost 100 percent. Corn producers in the South did not start to use hybrid seed as soon, but the trend there is rapidly moving upward. Extension of hybrids in foreign countries could increase substantially the yields there, too.

Greater production also should follow the extension of knowledge of the chemistry and physics of soils and fertilizers and their relationships to plants. Significantly larger harvests in the United States have come with improvements in the construction and design of farm machinery; if other countries make or buy more machinery, their production levels should rise also. Higher yields may also result from the use of insecticides and sprays and the wider use of chemicals in weed control, especially in small grains that cannot be cultivated because of broadcast planting.

Much of the loss of stored grains caused by improper storage methods may some day be eliminated when the natural processes that grains undergo during storage are better understood. Prevention of internal heat in stored grains when their moisture content is too high, with the accompanying mold and heat damage, would add many thousands of bushels a year to the better grades of grain suitable for food consumption. Better methods of protection against insects and rodents would likewise conserve thousands of bushels of stored grain each year.

THE AVERAGE WORLD PRODUCTION of the cereal grains remains very close to the normal world demand. As far as climate and other influences permit, the world tries to raise enough grain to feed itself and its livestock and poultry, but does not attempt to produce much beyond its basic needs.

The demand for the cereal grains for food and feed remains about the same year by year. The demand for grains as a staple food is so universal that local surpluses, caused by overproduction or by disturbances in the affairs of countries, are scarcely felt against the huge demand for food grain in the rest of the world.

One factor, however, is working to change the basic demand of the world for grains and other foodstuffs. That is the ever-increasing population. As the world's population increases, at an estimated rate of 1 percent each year, the need for more food grain and for feed grain to produce the meat, eggs, milk, and other animal products goes up accordingly. Furthermore, some years hence, when more of the world's heavily populated but impoverished areas are gradually brought within range of more efficient distribution facilities, those people will begin to use, more and more, their share of the world's produce. Grains will be the first to feel the increased demand. It can be assumed, however, that for a time, at least, the world's cereal-grain production, with increasing yields resulting from improved agricultural methods and equipment, and the opening up of new lands to cultivation, will keep pace with demand.

The per capita consumption of the various grains for food is a barometer of actual demand and an economic indicator of a sort. This is seen in the long-time trend of grain use as food, which seems to follow a pattern. The poorer or more remote countries usually consume as food the cereal grains that normally are used as feed grains in the more advanced countries. As the backward areas progress, wheat gradually becomes the main cereal foodstuff. From that stage, the development is normally toward eating more meat, dairy products, eggs, fruits, and vegetables.

As the quantities of meat and other select foods increase in the diet, the quantities consumed of wheat and other grains are smaller. Beyond a certain point, however, the tendency to change to the meat diet is strictly regulated by supply and demand. As it takes about 10 pounds of grain to produce 1 pound of meat, the load on grain production facilities to provide feed for livestock, which gives back only about one-tenth in food, becomes more and more prohibitive. When meat becomes too costly because of weakened feed supplies, the demand for cereal grains in the human diet returns, until a new balance is struck between supply and demand.

Because wheat and corn are critically important commodities in this country, small variations in over-all supply often cause large fluctuations in open-market prices. In the United States, the ease of transportation of the grains and the efficient marketing system of the grain trade do much to eliminate large price differentials between low-production and high-production areas. Only if the total supply of grains in the country is high or low compared to the average annual supply and demand, do open-market prices show major fluctuations. Through commodity exchanges in strategic cities, factors of supply and demand work rapidly in the grain trade. Prices are up-to-the-minute indicators, theoretically, of the current balance between these factors.

Prices must drop rapidly when real surpluses develop in major grains. Grain is of little use as food when consumer demand has been fully met. Grain processors cannot continue to buy when they have provided for their future business, except at much reduced prices so that the storage costs can be met. When the demand for a grain as food disappears, the only outlets for utilization are for feeds and for raw material for industrial purposes—neither of which offers a market price as high as the price the grain would bring as food.

Conversely, when grain supplies are too short to meet normal food demands, prices rise because of competition for the grain that is available. Mills and other processors must procure grains to keep their mills or plants in operation so as to provide their trade with food and other products. Idle plants and lack of merchandise for customers both are about as disastrous from a profit-and-loss standpoint as are overloaded warehouses and lack of a market during a period of grain surplus.

Attempts to alleviate the effects of overproduction of the principal grains (and other critical crops) have been made by the Federal Government in its price-support program. Money received by the farmer from support prices in the time of surpluses is intended to protect him from taking the entire loss of the price drop caused by factors which are operating on a national scale. This tends to keep him solvent as a producer of grain so that full production can be expected of him the following year.

Because of their nonperishable nature when sound and dry, surplus grains can be stored easily. Of all types of primary food materials, grains are the most easily carried over. Practically all other crops require processing or treatment to preserve them for future use. In normal times, it is desirable that moderate grain surpluses be carried over from one year to the next. This carryover enables equalization, to a fair degree, of fluctuations in year-to-year supplies of grains and forestalls drastic price changes that would occur when supplies of grain from one year are exhausted before the new harvest is in.

Cereal grains are interchangeable to some extent for different uses and are, therefore, mutually competitive. They can substitute for one another in a number of food and nonfood uses. In their use as feeds they are almost completely interchangeable. That allows more latitude within which available grain supplies can satisfy a series of demands.

As raw materials in major processing industries, however, grains are not always so interchangeable. Technology of a particular process often requires a specific combination of chemical and physical characteristics in the raw material, which can be met fully by only one type of grain.

In cultivation of cereal crops it is the seed, or grain, that is sought as the valuable portion of the plant. Because the true cereal grains are all seeds of members of the grass family, they are closely related to one another in their general physical and chemical structure, although there are many variations in size and shape of the kernels, even in varieties of one type of grain.

The cereal grains are essentially a starchy crop, although they may also contain substantial quantities of protein and oil. Structurally, all grains are composed of three main parts: Endosperm, which contains the starch portion and a large part of the protein; germ, or embryo, which contains most of the oil, considerable protein, and a large amount of minerals; and pericarp, or seed coat. The pericarp, also called bran, consists mainly of cellulose and hemicellulose, with some lignin and protein.

Relative proportions of the three components vary among the different grains, the largest variation being in the size of the germ. In corn the germ is about 12 percent of the whole kernel. In grain sorghums the proportion is somewhat lower. In smaller grains, the proportion of germ to the whole kernel drops to around 3.5 percent or lower. Variations in germ size are quite large among different varieties of corn.

The universal reliance on one or more of the cereal grains as a primary food material is not just happenstance. They contain the main food essentials for the human and animal body, although they are deficient in vitamins.

Starch, the major constituent in cereal grains, breaks down in the digestive tract into simpler and more easily digested sugars to supply the body with its primary source of energy.

Protein, the second largest constituent, provides factors for body building and maintenance. Cereal grains vary in amino acid content, and not all essential amino acids are present in adequate amounts. Knowledge of amino acid content of various materials is applied in planning improved diets or feeds so as to provide a complete series of essential amino acids. Some thought is being given by plant breeders to the improvement of the nutritive value of protein in this respect in cereal grains.

Cereal grains contain varying percentages of oil. Although the amount present never constitutes a large part of the whole material, the oil furnishes additional calories. Grain oils, including wheat-germ oil, contain small amounts of certain regulatory chemicals, including vitamins, which are valuable adjuncts to the diet.

Cereal grains do not meet all of the vitamin and mineral requirements of an adequate food or feed. Most grains contain considerable amounts of thiamine, riboflavin, niacin, and pantothenic acid, as well as some vitamin E. Yellow corn differs from white corn and the rest of the grains in that it contains provitamin A, a precursor to vitamin A. Calcium, an element important in nutrition, is generally low in cereal grains. Recognition of these deficiencies in vitamins and minerals has aided the correction of diets by proper combinations and additions to food and feed materials.

Fibrous material is present in all grain, principally in the bran coat. The value of the crude fiber in the diet, except as bulk, is thought to be very slight. However, much of the vitamin content of the grain, as well as nutritionally important minerals, are often located in the seed coat. This is a factor to be reckoned with, notably in milling wheat and rice.

It is these chemical constituents—the carbohydrates, proteins, oils, vitamins, and minerals—that are of primary interest to chemists concerned with the utilization of cereal grains as food and feed. The processes employed in the production of food and feeds from grains must not alter seriously the nutritional properties of the material.

Cereal grains are not often used as human food without some preparation to convert them to a more edible or digestible form. Application of modern grain-processing methods gives us a great variety of flours, baking mixes, meals, breakfast foods, macaroni, spaghetti, and many other products made wholly or chiefly from cereals.

Direct use of cereal grains for animal and poultry feeds accounts for a large share of the entire grain consumption. Considerable quantities of feeds derived from commercial processes that utilize cereal grains as raw materials, however, find their way back to the feedlot as supplements. Almost all processes making use of cereal grains send some portion of the raw material back into commercial channels as feeds.

All grain-processing methods depend on the chemical properties and structural characteristics of the grain kernel. Dry millers, wet millers, brewers, distillers, manufacturers of semolina products, and cereal-food producers are concerned with these factors. Many of them first isolate the three main chemical components—starch, protein, and oil. Normally, the separation methods used are based primarily on the physical properties of the components. Chemical characteristics of the separated materials are then utilized if modification of the initial materials is desired.

Milling of wheat into bread and pastry flours is by far the largest commercial activity that utilizes cereal grains in this country. In the United States during four postwar years, 1946 to 1949, an average of 273,387,000 100-pound sacks of wheat flour was produced annually. In 1948, 2,160 flour mills were operating, with a total 24-hour capacity of 1,334,480 sacks. This, compared to the 2,571 mills operating in 1945, with a capacity of 1,349,700 sacks per 24-hour period, illustrates a continuance of the long and gradual decline in the number of American flour mills as the smaller operators give way to the larger mills.

Flours derived from hard red spring and hard red winter wheats make the best "light breads." Soft red winter and soft white wheats produce soft flours, which are better for making pastries, cookies, and crackers.

The milling process separates the flour portion of the wheat kernel from the germ, bran, and most of the harder portions of the endosperm. The wheat is cracked and put through a series of increasingly closer milling rolls, reducing the material to a fine flour. Between various stages of milling, sifters and bolters take out the germ, bran, and the granular particles that do not produce good flour. In normal milling practice, about 72 percent of the wheat kernel is utilized in producing the best grade of bread flour, called family patent flour. To produce flours of lower quality, more of the kernel is included. The remainder is used mainly as feedstuffs.

The germ fraction is sometimes separated and the oil removed from it for special uses. The germ oil cake goes back into feeds. When all of the wheat kernel (except about half of the bran) remains in the flour, whole-wheat flour is the product. Graham flour contains all parts of the kernel, but is more coarsely ground than regular flour.

Milling of rye for bread flours involves smaller volumes of grain than the wheat-flour output. The average annual consumption of rye for production of rye flour is about 4,870,000 bushels, which is equivalent to about 2,156,000 100-pound sacks.

CORN is dry milled by one of two methods. The old process produces a corn meal that is essentially the ground whole corn. In larger mills, about 5 percent of coarser particles are removed from the product. Although the presence of the germ in corn meal shortens the shelf life of the product, its inclusion enhances the nutritive value and flavor of the fresh product. The oil in the germ becomes rancid in time, making the meal unsuitable for food.

The new process resembles the wheat-milling operation. The corn is passed through a series of cracking and reducing rolls. Sieves and sifters separate the floury endosperm, corneous endosperm, germ, and hull. Oil is removed from the germ fraction and is used as cooking or salad oil. The byproducts, germ cake and hulls, are used in feed supplements. The corneous endosperm fraction produces hominy grits, or corn grits, and coarse meal. Grits are used as a breakfast food or in puddings and cakes. The floury endosperm fraction produces fine meal and corn flour. The flour is used for baking and as a binder in sausage making. In the United States, about 63.5 million bushels of corn is utilized annually for the production of corn meal and related products.

The wet milling of corn provides a variety of products for food and nonfood uses. In the process, which utilizes 114 million bushels of corn annually, the starch and the protein- and oil-rich fractions are separated while the corn is wet. Shelled corn is steeped for 30 to 48 hours in water to which sulfur dioxide has been added. The softened kernels are then coarsely ground. The loosened hulls and germs are removed. The germ fraction is separated from the hulls by flotation. The rest of the material is then ground more finely to a milky slurry. The remaining bits of bran are screened out. Left are the principal constituents, starch and gluten (the protein fraction).

The starch is separated by passing the slurry at a regulated rate down a long, narrow table set at a gentle slope. The starch, the denser fraction, settles out on the table. The lighter gluten stays suspended in the slurry and passes over the lower end of the table, where it is collected and concentrated to be used in protein supplement feeds. A newer method of separating starch from gluten is by means of a centrifuge.

Oil is removed from the germ fraction by pressing or by solvent extraction and is marketed for use predominantly as a salad or cooking oil. The oil cake, along with the hulls and the gluten concentrate, goes into feeds.

Steep liquor, which results from the steeping process, contains most of the mineral constituents from the corn and other soluble nutritive factors. It is evaporated down and added to the other feed byproducts to enhance their feed value. Corn steep liquor has a special use as one of the nutrients on which penicillin-producing molds are fed in the commercial production of that antibiotic.

The raw starch produced in the wet-milling process is a versatile material. By means of mild, graded hydrolysis it can be modified into a series of products, many of which are used for food. Cornstarch, corn sirup, and corn sugar are some of the products in this group.

Grain sorghums are becoming important as a raw material in the wet-milling industry. Certain modifications in the process required by the differences in germ size have been made. Collection of a carnaubalike wax from the seed coat of this grain during processing may become an important and profitable operation.

RELATED particularly to the feed industry are the brewing and distilling industries. Fermentation processes produce beverages from one or more of the cereal grains. Both industries produce large quantities of cereal-grain byproducts, which are valuable as feeds. The beverages, although produced for human consumption, are not usually classified as foods.

Brewers and distillers use corn and barley (for malt) chiefly as their raw materials. They employ various other grains for special purposes, or when the supply of corn is short.

In the brewing industry, the corn is ground and boiled in water. Ground malt (prepared from sprouted barley) is made into a mash with warm water. This is added to the corn mash, which has been cooled to about 145° F., to saccharify the starch into soluble, fermentable sugars. The liquor drained from the mash (called wort) is boiled with hops. Hops are filtered off, and yeast is added to the cooled liquor for the fermentation process. The yeast and other solids are filtered off after the fermentation has reached a certain stage, and the beverage, after carbonation, is packaged.

The spent grains from the mashing step, after being dried, are called brewers' dried grains. This material contains practically all the protein and other nutrients present in the original grain, except the starch and sugars. It is sold as a protein concentrate feed.

The fermentation process used in the distilling industry (to produce whisky and neutral spirits) is essentially the same as that used by the brewers, except that yeast is added directly to the mash of malt and cooked grain. Addition of hops is omitted.

After the fermentation is completed, the beverage is distilled off from the mash. The distillate goes through an other distillation step and then is stored in charred barrels to age. After a period of aging, the alcoholic content of the whisky is adjusted by addition of distilled water. The whisky is then ready for bottling. The spent grains left as residue from the first distillation contain (in addition to residual nutrients from the grains) proteinaceous yeast cells and numerous other nutritive factors elaborated by the yeast during the fermentation process. This material is valuable as a feed. The thin stillage is screened from the larger particles of spent grain. The stillage, when dried, is known as dried distillers' solubles. The coarser fraction, when dried, becomes distillers' dried grains. Both are marketed as feeds.

Semolina, from which macaroni, spaghetti, vermicelli, and similar materials are produced, is made from durum wheats. Especially hard wheats like durums are required so that the products will hold together when cooked. Durum wheats are milled so that most of the endosperm remains in much coarser condition, often called granulars. The fine, floury part of the endosperm, called semolina flour, is obtained as a byproduct. Semolina flour, representing 16 to 20 percent of the whole wheat grain, is not suitable for the manufacture of macaroni or related products. Formerly this residue found ready market in Italy and neighboring countries, but this trade has dropped off. New food or nonfood uses are being sought for the material.

In the production of macaroni, spaghetti, and vermicelli, the semolina is made into a heavy and plastic dough, and is extruded under heavy pressure through the appropriate metal die. Proper lengths of the extruded material are cut off and dried. Bran and germ fractions resulting from the milling of durum wheats go into feeds as in regular wheat-milling practices.

Puffed breakfast cereals are produced by heating grain or cooked dough in a closed chamber and then suddenly releasing the aqueous vapor pressure (from the moisture in the grain or dough, or from steam introduced into the chamber). Suddenly expanding steam or other gases explode the material to several times its original volume. To produce the flaked breakfast foods, moist grain or grain particles are cooked and passed through flaking rolls. The flakes are dried and toasted to the right crispness and color. Some breakfast foods are made by passing cooked grains through shredding rolls and baking them.

As long as the ready market for protein concentrates and feed supplements remains, the major outlets for byproducts of processes using cereal grains will necessarily be for feeds. The feed market will lose some of the hold it now has on the byproducts only when uses are developed for certain constituents in the byproducts that will command high enough prices to justify costs of extraction and any loss in nutritional value in the residual material as feed.

The future of cereal grains as food cannot be questioned. The position of this group of agricultural commodities in the food habits throughout the world insures its continued importance into the far distant future. Any changes are most likely to be in the manner or form in which the cereal grains reach the table, either through new and improved foods or through more complete utilization of all the invaluable constituents.

KENNETH R. MAJORS *is technical assistant to the director of the Northern Regional Research Laboratory. He was formerly acting head of the commodity development division of that Laboratory. He holds degrees in chemistry from the University of Nebraska and the University of Illinois. He joined the Department in 1936 as a member of the United States Regional Soybean Industrial Products Laboratory.*

THE GERMANS during the Second World War demonstrated that it is possible to produce a synthetic food of high calorific value from nonbiological and even inorganic materials. In 1938 a plant in Witten, Germany, started operations to use the soft, waxy paraffin byproducts from the Fischer-Tropsch process for synthesizing petroleum oils from carbon monoxide and hydrogen. The plant cost the equivalent of more than 5 million dollars. When operating at full capacity, it produced annually 31,000 tons of fatty acids from 40,000 tons of paraffin waxes. About 5 percent of the fatty acids were actually used for the production of edible fats. The rest went into soap and other industrial products.

In the first step of the process, the waxy byproduct, or a mixture of hydrocarbons from petroleum or coal, was placed in an aluminum vessel, a catalyst consisting of a 0.2-percent solution of potassium permanganate was added, and the entire mixture was heated to 230° F. while air was bubbled through it. The waxes oxidized, or burned, partially to yield the desired fatty acids.

To avoid the formation of undesirable byproducts, the reaction was stopped after 30 percent of fatty acids had been produced. These were separated and the original material was reprocessed.

The crude fatty acids first were purified to remove all accompanying original hydrocarbons and then fractionated, because only 55 percent of the purified product was suitable for use in fats. However, the residual fractions had other industrial uses.

In the final step, the fats were made by chemically combining the selected fatty acids with glycerin, which was obtained by fermenting sugar solutions.— *R. O. Feuge, Southern Regional Research Laboratory.*

New Products From an Old Crop

T. R. Stanton

To the values that men have always ascribed to oats have been added new products and uses. Furfural, made from oat hulls, has become a valuable solvent and chemical intermediate for refining mineral and vegetable oils. The use of oat flour as an antioxidant or stabilizer in food products is increasing rapidly. Other promising products are still in the pilot-plant stage. From the large research organizations set up by processors we can expect even better cereal products and byproducts.

Oatmeal, or rolled oats, ranks high among breakfast cereals in the United States and many European countries. It is relatively cheap and rich in protein, fat, vitamin B_1, and such minerals as phosphorus and iron.

It contains approximately 18 percent protein, 6 percent fat, 70 percent carbohydrates, and 2 percent ash, compared to 11, 2, 80, and 2 percent, respectively, of those constituents in whole-wheat cereals used as breakfast foods. Oatmeal excels in percentage of protein and fat. It has about 1,750 calories to the pound; whole-wheat cereals have about 1,680 calories.

Oatmeal, as steel-cut or Scotch oats, was first packaged for the market in glass jars by Ferdinand Schumacher of Akron, Ohio, in 1854. Later it was packed and shipped in wooden barrels to the local grocer, who weighed and sold it by the pound. The whole groat (kernel) or cut pieces of the groat (granulated oats) apparently were not flaked or rolled until late in the nineteenth century. The term "rolled oats" then replaced the term "oatmeal" to some extent, and for reasons of sanitation and better merchandizing the product was packed in small cardboard cartons.

The original rolled oats formed comparatively thick flakes. Each flake was rolled from a single oat groat (a kernel with all the hulls removed). A quicker-cooking flake is thinner; it is rolled from groats cut into about three pieces. Still quicker-cooking flakes, relatively new on the market, are rolled very thin. All three have the same food value.

IN THE MILLING of oatmeal, the oats are cleaned, dried, and toasted to make the hulls more brittle so they can be removed more easily by the hulling stones. The toasting also develops a good flavor in the groat, which is carried to the final product. The next step is the separation of the oat grains into grades, or sizes, on the basis of length and diameter. The processes of hulling, separation of the unhulled oats from the groats, steaming, cutting, rolling the groats into flakes, and packaging follow in order.

Milling percentage, or extraction, varies rather widely, depending almost entirely on the quality of the grain. The heavier, plumper, and cleaner commercial oats give the highest extraction of rolled oats. The skill of the millwrights in dressing and adjusting the hulling stones, as well as in operating numerous accessory machines, contributes much to the yield and quality of rolled oats.

About 13.5 bushels, or 432 pounds, of medium-good to excellent oats produce a barrel of high-grade rolled oats. The standard barrel for rolled oats or oat groats is 180 pounds; for ground oatmeal of steel-cut oats it is 196 pounds. Following the distribution of improved disease-resistant varieties with higher test or bushel weight, a higher milling yield of rolled oats is being obtained. Certain new varieties, such as Clinton, Benton, and Bonda, with large groats and relatively thin hulls, are outstanding in milling value.

Food products might be made from oats gathered in the milk stage if a method could be developed for extracting the milk. The active nutritive principle found in coconut milk and corn in the milk stage might also be found in the developing oat groat.

OAT FLOUR contains an antioxidant that is used to preserve the quality by delaying the development of rancidity in fat-containing foods. It is used in several ways: Thoroughly mixed or infused with lard, margarine, and peanut butter; dusted or coated on potato chips or salted nuts; in the coating of paper or other containers of foodstuffs, such as lard, bacon, and coffee.

As much as 10 percent of oat flour may be coated on or incorporated in paper of various types.

Special grades of oat flour are marketed under the name Avenex for use as a preservative of food products. Avenex also is used as an antioxidant or stabilizer in the preservation of milk, ice cream, other dairy products, fish fillets, fish oils, other fishery products, meat and meat products, candies, powdered egg yolk, peanut butter, piecrust mixes, and doughnut flours. Cereal extracts protect the flavor of butter and retard the development of oxidized and tallowy off-flavors.

During the Second World War, oat flour was included in special candy bars used in an Army emergency ration to keep them from freezing or melting in storage, in transit, or on the battlefield.

Oat gum, a fraction of the oat grain, has excellent possibilities for use as a stabilizer in ice cream. It imparts a desirable texture to the mix and to the finished ice cream. It also has antioxidant properties and retards oxidation of ice cream in storage. Oat gum compares favorably with other stabilizers, such as gelatin, gels made from psyllium seed, and alginates made from seaweeds, for ice-cream mixes and finished ice cream. It also improves the keeping qualities of pork products.

The total consumption of oats for the manufacture of antioxidants and stabilizers is relatively small, despite the numerous uses.

OATMEAL HAS BEEN USED separately or with soaps for reducing skin blemishes and alleviating rashes and sunburns. Although we cannot confirm these assumed beneficial effects, the belief has long prevailed that oatmeal has some virtue as a skin conditioner. A good many soaps contain oatmeal. Oat flour has marked power as a detergent or cleansing agent.

The oat gum mentioned earlier is used as a mild detergent. It is put into the bath water to treat certain skin diseases—a replacement for the oatmeal bag of our grandmother's day.

OAT HULLS, in the diet of poultry, serve chiefly as a preventive against slip tendons and also for the development of feathering. They contain a dietary corrective property that checks cannibalism and feather picking in chickens. Oat hulls also are rich in manganese. Thus oats are a popular ingredient in poultry rations. About as much oat grain is now fed to domestic fowls as was fed to horses in the days before the automobile and tractor.

FURFURAL is the most important product made from oat hulls, a by-product of the milling of rolled oats. About 4 percent of our national crop of oats goes into the making of rolled oats and oat flours. Thus 50,000,000 bushels, or 800,000 tons, of oats yield approximately 27 percent, or 210,000 tons, of oat hulls. About 235 bushels of oats, weighing 32 pounds to the bushel, produce a ton of oat hulls, or 200 pounds of furfural.

The most important uses for furfural are in oil refining, the purification of wood rosin, and the production of synthetic resins such as bakelite.

A few pharmaceutical products have been synthesized from furan resins, which are made from oat hulls. These include Furmethide, a quatenary ammonium furan compound (furfuryltrimethylammonium iodide), Furacin—(5-nitrofurfuralsemicarbazone), an antiseptic and possible supplement for penicillin or streptomycin, and other products that may serve as substitutes for novocain and sulfanilamide. Furan compounds have a wide variety of possible medical applications.

Each threshed grain of oats bears two integuments (hulls), the lemma and palea, which enclose the groat. In processing rolled oats, the hulls are removed by milling stones. Oat hulls have little feed value. They are poor in actual nutrients and low in digestibility. Ground oat hulls, however, have some nutritive value in mixed feeds. They contain about 4 percent protein, 1.5 percent fat, 29 percent fiber, 52 percent nitrogen-free extract, and 6 percent ash.

Oat hulls are rich in pentosans, from which furfural is derived. Before the manufacture of furfural, the hulls were used only for fuel or packing. In making furfural, the oat hulls are subjected to destructive distillation—that is, they are pressure-cooked with weak acids. After that comes a complicated purification process. Furfural (furfuraldehyde) is a high-boiling, tan, transparent liquid, with a faint bitter-almond odor, closely related to formaldehyde. Furfural can be made from cornstalks and corncobs, bagasse, rice hulls, and many other waste products, but few of them give as high yields of furfural as do oat hulls. Corncobs are the only present source of furfural other than oat hulls.

According to Fredus N. Peters, Jr., vice president of Research Laboratories, furfural was first manufactured commercially in the Cedar Rapids, Iowa, plant of the Quaker Oats Co. It was developed by H. J. Brownlee and Carl S. Miner. The first drum of furfural was shipped in 1922, the first railroad tank car in 1927. In 1947 furfural was shipped in a tank steamer.

Early uses of furfural were as a fungicide for seed treatment, a preservative for glue, a fumigant for poultry houses, a repellent for screwworm flies, and an embalming fluid. It also was used as a paint and varnish remover, for control of slime deposits in water supplies, as a remover of carbon from gasoline motors, and as a fungicide in the form of hydrofuramide to control the infection known as athlete's foot. It likewise was used early as a solvent for plastics.

Since 1936, the use of furfural has gone up spectacularly, especially as a selective solvent in petroleum and vegetable-oil refining, and in the manufacture of furan resins. One of the most recent uses for furfural has been for chemical intermediates, such as furan, tetrahydrofurfurylalcohol, methyltetrahydrofuran, and dihydropyrn.

According to H. H. Gross, of the Texaco Development Corp., of New York, the furfural-refining process licensed by his firm is one of the most widely used processes in the world for processing lubricating oils. In 1948, 20 furfural-refining units had been installed and 13 others were under contract for construction. The units can handle 60 to 6,000 barrels of charge oil a day. The furfural-refining process also is used for refining gas oils to produce premium grades of Diesel fuel of improved cetane number and heating oils with improved burning properties.

The use of furfural as a raw material for the manufacture of adiponitrile, a nylon intermediate, was announced in 1947. Dr. Oliver W. Cass, research supervisor of the Niagara Falls laboratories of the E. I. du Pont de Nemours & Co., described the making of nylon and nylon yarns thus: ". . . A most exacting and complicated processing, which includes reactions of furfural with steam, gases, and various other chemicals. The result is adiponitrile. This is further processed into hexamethylene diamine . . . and then reacted with adipic acid to produce nylon 'salt,' which looks like table salt. . . ." To facilitate its handling, the "salt" is dissolved in water and transported in tank cars to plants for further processing. It is then spun into yarn for clothing and flaked for plastics.

In recent years, oats have been clipped in the early, succulent-growth stages—3 to 4 weeks after the plants emerge—for processing into highly nutritive "green-grass products" as feed for animals and pellets for man. Those products are high in chlorophyll, protein, vitamins (particularly carotene and vitamin K), and other desirable food elements. They are available on the market. Wheat, barley, and rye have proved as good as, or even better than, oats for clipping under most conditions. The rye grasses are superior to any of the cereals because they recover more quickly after clipping. Consequently, the utilization of oats for this purpose has been limited.

T. R. STANTON *is senior agronomist in charge of oat investigations in the division of cereal crops and diseases, Bureau of Plant Industry, Soils, and Agricultural Engineering. He is a graduate of the University of Maryland. In recognition of his work in improving oats, through the development of better disease-resistant varieties with better agronomic and milling characteristics, he received the honorary degree of doctor of agriculture from Iowa State College in 1945.*

HOME DRYING OF FRUITS is a simple and practical method of preservation which consists in the removal of moisture by heat and air circulation. This results in the concentration of the fruit ingredients and prevents spoilage in storage.

The drying may be accomplished by sun drying or with the use of artificial heat. The former has limitations because it depends on weather conditions. The latter is more practical because the drying is under control.

The kitchen oven makes a simple, convenient drier. The only additional equipment required are drying trays and a thermometer.

After preparation, the ripe, sound sliced fruit is spread evenly on wooden slat trays or cloth-covered wooden frames and placed in the oven, which is adjusted so that the top tray is about 150° F. The oven door should be propped open several inches at the top to permit rapid drying. The drying period extends over a period of 6 to 12 hours, depending upon the oven, product, etc. Twelve pounds of sliced fruit (1 peck) such as apples, peaches, or pears will usually dry down to 1½ pounds of dry material, which will fill three pint jars. Glass jars are excellent containers because they may be tightly sealed against moisture gain or loss and insect infestation. The jars should be stored in a cool place.

Color and flavor are sometimes impaired during drying unless the fruit is previously treated with sulfur fumes, steamed, or dipped in salt water. For detailed information on processing, construction of home-made cabinet driers, and other details, see U. S. D. A. Farmers' Bulletins Numbers 984 and 1918 or AWI–59. If copies are not in print, they may be read in comprehensive city or university libraries.—*William Rabak, Western Regional Research Laboratory.*

Concentrates and Meals of Alfalfa

George H. Brother,
C. W. Murray,
Francis P. Griffiths

Alfalfa, the leading forage crop in the United States, accounts for about a third of the annual hay crop of 100 million tons and is grown on a fifth of the 75 million acres used for hay production. The 15 million acres in alfalfa are principally in the Midwest and far West. Michigan and California have more than a million acres each. Nebraska, Minnesota, Kansas, Wisconsin, Idaho, Montana, and Iowa have about 700,000 acres each.

Dehydrated alfalfa and ground alfalfa hay are important constituents of mixed feeds. The development of mixed feeds (feeds made up of a number of components, such as grain, soybean meal, ground alfalfa, and meat scraps, each contributing specifically to the value of the whole) began about 1900.

The chief feed value of alfalfa is in the leaves. When hay is made from alfalfa, a part of the leaves is lost by drying, shattering, and handling. If the hay is rained on in the field, leaching causes serious losses.

Carotene, one of the important feed elements in fresh alfalfa, is partially destroyed if hay is field-cured. The loss may amount to 50 to 80 percent of the total carotene present in the green plant. How to prevent the losses and enhance the values of alfalfa are matters that engage the attention of many agencies concerned with farm problems.

Artificial drying of alfalfa as a means of conserving valuable feed elements was investigated, and by 1930 was in use on a commercial scale. Since 1945, about a million tons of ground sun-cured alfalfa hay—sun-cured alfalfa meal—with a value of approximately 50 million dollars has been produced each year. About 2 percent of the total alfalfa crop goes into the production of dehydrated meal.

Dehydration of alfalfa is now essentially a farm industry. To produce meal high in carotene and protein, the plants must be cut at the right stage of growth, and the dehydrators must be as near the fields as possible. Every hour that elapses between the time of cutting and the drying means greater loss in carotene.

For efficient operation, the dehydrator must be assured a steady flow of cut alfalfa for as many months of the year as possible. California, with its longer growing season, has an advantage over many States in that respect. In regions like southern California and Arizona, where alfalfa is cut the year around, dehydration can be expected to develop further and faster, if marketing costs can be cut. Of the problems that remain, the chief ones are the better utilization of the fiber; the preservation of the carotene in storage; and the isolation, identification, and elimination of the factors that limit its usefulness in feeds for poultry.

Alfalfa usually is cut and chopped in the field. Its moisture content is 78 to 82 percent. It is hauled promptly in trucks to the dehydrator, less than 10 miles away, where it is dumped into a hopper and fed to the large, rotating drum drier, in which the air is heated to about 1,700° F. A balance is maintained between the heat input and the moisture in the forage. The temperature of the dried material as it emerges is kept between 250° and 300° to prevent scorching. In most installations, three passes through the dehydrator reduce the moisture content to about 8 percent. The dried material is put through a hammer mill and bagged for shipment or storage. The capacity of a dehydrating unit is about a ton of meal an hour.

Some alfalfa meal is compressed under high pressure to produce pellets as a means to reduce bulk and eliminate dust.

Alfalfa varies in composition according to stage of growth of the plant. Higher protein, carotene, ash, and ether extract (fats and fat complexes) and lower fiber values are obtained from plants harvested while they are immature. For the best meal, the alfalfa usually is cut in the prebloom to the one-tenth bloom stage.

Standard alfalfa meal is graded and sold on the basis of 13, 15, or 17 percent protein. It should contain less than 33, 30, or 27 percent crude fiber, respectively. Alfalfa leaf meal averages more than 20 percent protein and contains not more than 18 percent fiber. Alfalfa meal contains about one and a half times more protein than grains like corn and wheat, and about half as much nitrogen-free extract (carbohydrates). Alfalfa protein supplies such essential amino acids as arginine, lysine, threonine, and tryptophane.

Also important nutritionally are the vitamins. Intensive feeding, as practiced in the poultry industry, requires adequate amounts of vitamins so that the feed can be effectively utilized for maximum growth. Good dehydrated alfalfa meal contains 200 to 300 parts per million of carotene (provitamin A) at the time of dehydration. It is particularly rich in the dietary factors supplied by green forage or good pasture. The leaf meal also is a good source of riboflavin, vitamin E, choline, folic acid, pantothenic acid, and vitamin K.

We do not know exactly how much of these and other biologically active agents are present nor how stable they are during dehydration and storage.

Vitamin C is present in good quantity in fresh green alfalfa, but it is largely lost during processing and storage.

In some sections where corn and other grains are not produced locally, the protein contribution of alfalfa meal would be more valuable in poultry feeds if we could find a way to remove limitations of the amount that can be fed effectively. The digestive tracts of young poultry cannot utilize fibrous feeds as do those of ruminants, like cattle and sheep; consequently, the fiber in most alfalfa meals is lost.

In the processing of alfalfa through dehydrators, a low-fiber meal can easily be had from leaves and young stems alone by a simple screening operation. Such meals, which are produced commercially, are high-grade feed concentrates, but often they are not profitable because the stems screened out are useful, at most, for low-priced stock feeds. The true leaf meal (the term "leaf meal" as used in the trade represents a meal from young alfalfa plants) often does not command a price differential high enough to permit competition with standard alfalfa meals.

Work has been done on the development of low-fiber feed concentrates by processing fresh alfalfa through rolls or screw extruders to press out the juice. The juice sometimes is drumdried to produce a concentrate; the stems have enough nutrients left in them for good cattle fodder.

The problem considered most urgent by men in the alfalfa-dehydration industry now is the stabilization of carotene. Alfalfa meal is added to many feeds principally for its carotene content; feed dealers, therefore, would like to buy meal of a guaranteed carotene content. Only limited guarantees have been possible, because carotene is lost steadily when meal is stored at room temperature; the higher the temperature, the more rapid the loss.

The loss can be retarded by storage at a low temperature. The meal is being used increasingly, but storage adds to its cost. Storage under inert gas (by replacing the air with nitrogen or other oxygen-free gas) has given good results, and at least one industrial concern has installed large silos for gas storage of alfalfa meal. Gas storage, however, suffers from the same disadvantage as cold storage; when the artificial conditions are removed, the loss of carotene again occurs.

Work is being done on the use of antioxidants as stabilizers for carotene. More than 100 organic compounds known to have the property of retarding the oxidative degradation of rubber, gasoline, and fats due to oxygen have been tested for their efficiency in stabilizing carotene in alfalfa meal.

Several have shown promise when used at the rate of one-eighth of 1 percent with respect to the dry meal. The results indicate retention of about 65 percent of the carotene, compared to about 25 percent in alfalfa meal that is not treated, when the meal is stored for 2 weeks at 149° F. If meal is stored at room temperature for 6 months, about 70 percent of the carotene is retained when efficient antioxidants are used. Before they are used commercially, however, extensive tests are needed to verify that they are not poisonous. A patent on the use of diphenylparaphenylenediamine has been issued to a commercial concern; that antioxidant is permitted in concentrations of 0.015 percent. A vegetable oil may be used as a carrier for the antioxidant. At the rate of 1 percent of the alfalfa meal, it reduces the dustiness of the final product and enhances its food value and appearance.

More information also is needed on the mechanism by which carotene is destroyed and the relationship of carotene and the other constituents. For example, vitamins C and E are natural antioxidants—are they destroyed before or after the carotene? What part, if any, do the lipids play in the destruction of carotene? Alfalfa is complex. Its stability is affected by every treatment to which it is subjected. We have to know more about the plant before farmers can realize its full value.

A determination of the total carotene in alfalfa does not give an accurate picture of the nutritive value of the product. In fresh alfalfa, β-carotene (the form in which this chemical is found in alfalfa) occurs almost entirely in three forms, about 86 percent all *trans*, 6 percent neo beta B, and 8 percent neo beta U. Dehydration causes a loss of all *trans* and a corresponding increase of the other two forms. The relative biological value as provitamin A of the three forms, when assayed by means of rats and chicks, has been shown to be 100, 53, and 38, respectively. Because the proportion of each varies according to the treatment the meal has received, that biological variation should not be overlooked in evaluating carotene in alfalfa used for feeds.

Synthetic vitamin A is now commercially available. As its price goes down—and that is happening—the importance of alfalfa as a source of carotene will drop and the other components will be of greater moment in the further use of alfalfa meal as an ingredient of feeds.

For the preparation of protein concentrates and for the study of other constituents in alfalfa, separation of the juice from the fresh plant is frequently desirable. A satisfactory method for obtaining the juice is to press the fresh alfalfa plants between steel rolls, as we mentioned earlier. The juice is a thick, deep-green liquid, which contains about 10 percent solids.

Some of the known constituents of alfalfa are: Chlorophyll, the green coloring pigment in plants; xanthophyll, one of the yellow coloring materials in plants; carotene; riboflavin (vitamin B_2); thiamine (vitamin B_1); ascorbic acid (vitamin C); tocopherol (vitamin E); proteins; mineral salts; some fats and waxes; and sugars.

We have indications that unidentified growth-regulating substances also are present. Several of the investigators learned that feeding dehydrated alfalfa to chicks in proportions of 10 to 20 percent of the ration retarded their growth. Note well, however, that feed-

Composition of alfalfa fractions obtained by pressing [1]

Fraction	Pro- tein [2]	Crude fiber	Total sugar	Ash
	Percent	Percent	Percent	Percent
Fresh alfalfa......	28.1	23.1	5.3	9.3
Roll juice........	41.7	.....	13.1	16.7
Hydraulic juice..	39.0	.....	15.8	18.1
Hydraulic bagasse	20.5	34.4	1.7	5.7

[1] All figures are on a moisture-free basis.
[2] Calculated by multiplying percentage of nitrogen by 6.25.

ing at the usual level of about 5 percent does not retard growth. S. Lepkovsky and D. Peterson, of the University of California, discovered that the saponins in alfalfa may be responsible for the ill effect. Saponins are water-soluble compounds found in many legumes. Cholesterol is known to have the property of combining with most saponins to form insoluble and therefore inactive products.

In experiments, the addition of cholesterol to alfalfa largely nullified the growth-inhibiting action.

Alkaloids, especially stachydrine, are present in small amounts, but their effects in feeds have not been shown.

Several investigators have noted the presence of growth-promoting substances in alfalfa. The presence of vitamin B_{12} (commonly known as the antipernicious anemia factor) has been reported. Vitamin B_{12} is recognized as an essential component of the animal diet. Feeding tests have disclosed that chicks require 10 to 20 milligrams of B_{12} per ton of mixed feed for best growth. Current assays by different workers vary considerably in the amount of B_{12} reported in alfalfa but indicate that the vitamin probably is present to the extent of 10 to 20 milligrams per ton.

Complexes known as ribo-nucleic acids are found in alfalfa. From laboratory tests we infer that they are nutritionally important. The acids occur in plants and animals and are important constituents of all cells. They comprise phosphoric acid, sugar, and organic bases called pyrimidines and purines. No adequate amount of the acids of sufficient purity has been available for nutritional study; researchers have yet to evaluate their place in the feeding of farm animals.

Present in alfalfa, as in other plants, are complex chemical compounds known as sterols. Sterols derived from soybeans are used to produce some sex hormones. Corticosterone ("Compound E"), which has curative properties in cases of rheumatoid arthritis, is derived from animal sterols. Extraction and characterization of sterols from alfalfa have not progressed to the point where definite applications can be indicated, but further research with these important compounds seems to us to be well justified.

All in all, however, alfalfa will continue to be important chiefly as forage and hay and as an ingredient of feed for farm animals. It is a multiple-purpose crop—it is used for pasture or forage, cut for hay, or dehydrated for meal and industrial processing. Research is adding to the list of its nutritionally important ingredients and to our knowledge of their physiological functions. The information will give a basis for making more effective use of the valuable proteins, carbohydrates, and growth-promoting substances in alfalfa.

GEORGE H. BROTHER has been a chemist in the Bureau of Agricultural and Industrial Chemistry since 1937, at the United States Regional Soybean Industrial Products Laboratory and the Western Regional Research Laboratory, where he is now in charge of the protein division.

C. W. MURRAY has been a chemist with the Department of Agriculture since 1930, in the Bureau of Agricultural and Industrial Chemistry and the Bureau of Entomology and Plant Quarantine.

FRANCIS P. GRIFFITHS joined the staff of the Western Laboratory in 1947 as special assistant to the director.

Industrial Uses for Grain Sorghum

John H. Martin,
M. M. MacMasters

Grain sorghum, which is harvested for grain on about 6½ million acres in the United States, exemplifies our success in putting old products to new uses. Right in the region where sorghum is grown, sorghum starch now is used as an ingredient of drilling muds for oil wells.

The average production of grain sorghum in recent years has been 120 million bushels. It is grown chiefly in the drier sections of Texas, Oklahoma, Kansas, and adjacent States.

Before the Second World War, it was used largely for feed. Since 1945, American-grown grain sorghum has found wide use as food for people in India and other war-stricken countries. People of southern Europe, who were unaccustomed to eating grain sorghum, nevertheless consumed a great deal of our crop as flour that was blended with wheat flour before shipment. A common blend was one part of sorghum flour to four of wheat flour.

Because grain sorghum had been regarded as a feed crop, it received little attention, until recently, from industrial processors or from the research laboratories.

Grain sorghum has long been a potential source of industrial raw material. It contains more protein (11.5 to 16.5 percent) than does the corn grain. The protein and oil from grain sorghum should find uses similar to those from corn. The starch content of grain sorghum (63 to 73 percent) is about the same as that of corn, and the starch is like cornstarch in general.

Waxy varieties of grain sorghum have been used for special food delicacies in China for several centuries. Natives of Africa have made beer from grain sorghum since prehistoric times. Varieties with a brown or red seed coat or subcoat are used for making the native beers, because the tanninlike substances in colored grains supply the bitterness that in European and American beers is derived from hops. African natives reserve the palatable white and yellow varieties for food.

Grain sorghum nearly always is cheaper than corn on the open market. The heavy-producing area in the Southwest, particularly along the Gulf Coast, is favored by transportation advantages in reaching important domestic and foreign seaboard markets, as compared with corn from the central Corn Belt. Products from grain sorghum should be able to replace sugars, oils, starches, and waxes that have been shipped into the South and Southwest from other areas. Large amounts of those products are regularly imported. Industrial utilization of grain sorghum should permit the crop to replace some of the wheat and cotton which must seek foreign markets when they are in oversupply. Research on grain sorghum thus helps producers of other crops.

With the outbreak of the Second World War, several new and improved dwarf varieties of grain sorghum came into extensive production. The scarcity of labor forced some cotton growers to shift to sorghum, which had become a profitable mechanized crop. The mobile brigade of custom combines moved into the area to harvest the grain, because the number of local combines was inadequate for the large acreage. At about the same time the southwestern corn borer advanced eastward to devastate the corn crop of the southern Great Plains States, and much of the corn in central and western Kansas was replaced by the new resistant combine grain sorghums. Processing plants that depended on corn from the region sought a new raw material. Shortage of corn on the cash market during and after the war caused industrial users of corn to seek additional sources of supply. Eyes turned toward grain sorghum.

The investigation of grain sorghum as a possible source of industrial material was begun at the Iowa Agricultural Experiment Station about 1936. Shortly thereafter the Kansas Agricultural Experiment Station took up the problem. Intensive research financed by the Corn Products Refining Co. was begun at the company's laboratories and at the Midwest Research Institute in Kansas City, Mo. Additional research was conducted by the General Foods Corp., the Kansas and Nebraska Agricultural Experiment Stations, the Northern Regional Research Laboratory, and various distillers and brewers. Sorghum breeders of the Bureau of Plant Industry, Soils, and Agricultural Engineering cooperated with the State agricultural experiment stations of Nebraska, Kansas, Oklahoma, and Texas in expanding their activities. The experiment stations received support from industrial concerns for this new work. Varieties better suited to industrial processing were needed.

It was necessary to develop modifications of wet- and dry-milling methods that would be adapted to grain sorghum. That was done first in the laboratory and then in a pilot plant. Finally, large-scale milling of grain sorghum was carried out in a corn wet mill. New varieties were analyzed to determine their chemical properties. The suitability of grain sorghum products for various purposes had to be determined. Possible markets for the products were explored. Byproduct protein feeds were tested for palatability and nutritive value.

Research at the Kansas Agricultural Experiment Station revealed that the seed coat of grain sorghum contains a wax that is similar to carnauba wax, which is extracted from the leaves of the carnauba palm of the Tropics and is used for making polishes for furniture and shoes, carbon paper, sealing wax, electrical insulators, and other products. One ton of sorghum grain yields 5 pounds or more of a wax which may replace much of the imported carnauba wax. The wax is present in the seed coat of all varieties, whether or not the endosperm contains the waxy starch. The possibility of obtaining wax as a byproduct tends to offset the disadvantage of the lower oil content in grain sorghum, as compared to corn.

Sorghum breeders had developed several dwarf disease-resistant varieties now widely cultivated. More recently they developed several new white-seeded, combine-type varieties of kafir and milo, which can be processed at a lower cost than can the colored varieties. Some of the white-seeded grain sorghums, including the Cody waxy variety, are entirely free from pigments that stain the starch. White-seeded varieties also yield more palatable gluten feeds than are obtained from deeply colored varieties.

Combined research efforts brought quick results. Grain sorghum was accepted as a source of grain alcohol and some 30 million pounds was used for that purpose in 1942. The alcohol industries in 1945 used more than 2 billion pounds, nearly half of which went into industrial alcohol. Smaller quantities have been used since that time. However, some 560 million pounds was used by the distilling and malt-beverage industries in 1946. The manufacture of butyl alcohol from grain sorghum was begun in 1944. Butyl alcohol, when combined with certain organic acids, forms butyl esters, which are used as lacquer solvents and in the manufacture of 2,4–D weed killers.

As much as 32 million pounds of waxy grain sorghum was used in a year for making a substitute for a fast-cooking "tapioca," a product not available during the war.

A factory for processing 6 to 7 million bushels annually began operations in 1949 in Corpus Christi, Tex. This large, modern plant of the Corn Products Refining Co. manufactures dextrose, starch, edible oil, and gluten feeds by a wet process like the one widely used in making the same products from corn. Several innovations in equipment and operation were incorporated in the new plant.

WHEN INDUSTRY uses a new crop, special problems often arise. In this case, one difficulty was that farmers often harvest grain sorghum while it still has a high content of moisture in order to avoid losses from lodged stalks. Damp grain will not keep in storage; hence the company was confronted with the problem of drying the sorghum. Experience with corn had shown that improper drying would affect the milling properties of the grain adversely. A cooperative project was therefore set up by the Corn Products Refining Co. and the Northern Laboratory to determine the best conditions for drying grain sorghums to be used for wet milling. Facilities for drying grain sorghum in the Corpus Christi area have since been built.

A dry-milling plant was established in 1950 at Dodge City, Kans., to manufacture flour and livestock feeds from grain sorghum. The flour is used in making gypsum lath or wallboard. The industry is the outgrowth of experiments conducted by the Kansas Agricultural Experiment Station in cooperation with the Kansas Industrial Commission. New types of equipment for hulling and cracking the grain were tested in a pilot plant operated by Dodge City Industries, Inc., Dodge City, Kans.

Thus, in devising industrial uses for grain sorghum, the crop from 500,000 to 2,500,000 acres already has found a new outlet, and further expansion is probable.

Products of grain sorghum have many possible uses.

The grits obtained from the endosperm can be used in brewing, just as corn grits and broken rice are now used.

Until methods of milling that permitted a satisfactory separation of the germ from the endosperm were developed in 1947, sorghum grits were too high in oil for the best use in fermentation industries. Most of the oil of the grain is in the germ. The oil is suitable for salad oils.

The starch from grain sorghum can be used for food products, adhesives, and sizing for paper and fabrics.

Another use is in drilling muds. Drilling muds, which are mixtures of starch and added materials and water, are circulated through the bit during the drilling of oil wells. The muds remove the cuttings rapidly from the well, lubricate and cool the drill, and seal the walls so as to retard the entrance of water. A ton or more of starch is used in each new oil well.

The practical separation of grain sorghum starch into its two component fractions, amylose and amylopectin, if it could be accomplished, would greatly enlarge industrial outlets. Amylose, the straight-chain component, comprises 22 to 24 percent of the ordinary, nonwaxy sorghum starch. The material seems to be suitable for making plastic films and fibers similar to those made from cellulose acetate. The branch-chain component, amylopectin, is the type that constitutes the entire endosperm starch of waxy grain varieties.

Glucose sirup and dextrose sugar, made by acid hydrolysis of starch, are better known as corn sirup and corn sugar, because in this country they are commonly made from cornstarch. They find a wide use in canned fruits, sirups, confections, sweet baked goods, and other foods. We expect that similar outlets will be found for the products of sorghum starch. Dextrose from grain sorghum is identical with that from corn. The proteins from grain sorghum probably will be used largely as gluten feeds, but they have possibilities as food adjuncts and as paint ingredients.

JOHN H. MARTIN *has been a research agronomist in the division of cereal crops and diseases, Bureau of Plant Industry, Soils, and Agricultural Engineering, since 1914. He has had charge of grain sorghum investigations in the Bureau since 1925. He has a doctor's degree from the University of Minnesota.*

M. M. MACMASTERS *obtained her graduate degrees in chemistry at the University of Massachusetts and spent 5 years, chiefly in research on starch pastes and gels, at the Illinois Agricultural Experiment Station. In 1940 she joined the staff of the starch and dextrose division of the Northern Regional Research Laboratory, where she is in charge of research on the structure and chemistry of cereal grains and the properties of starch granules.*

IN OUR DESIRE to develop nonfood, industrial uses for farm crops, we sometimes overlook their natural and more important uses.

Compared to their life-saving value as food, all the millions that rice and soybeans have brought to industry were as nothing to a young American and his wife during their third year of internment by the Japanese in the Philippines.

In 1944 the Japanese began a systematic starvation of the several thousand Americans interned in Philippine camps. Some, who had borrowed money from Filipinos not interned, were able to buy food in various ways inside the camp. Others, not so fortunate, were provided for by the camp officers.

In late 1943 and early 1944 the Japanese gave the Americans a high-moisture soybean residue, from which almost all oil and protein had been extracted. The stuff was commonly used as slop for swine; to the internees it was life itself. They used it in soups, mush, and baked or fried dishes. Whole soybeans, when they could be had, were soaked for 12 hours or more and then boiled. Whenever Japanese trucks hauled soybeans in or out of camp, the internees picked up the spillage, burned it slightly, bottled it, and ate the beans at night when hunger prevented sleep. Toward the end of 1944, soybeans, with or without worms, were selling for 12 to 15 dollars a pound. The transactions were made in American money, diamonds, pearls, watches—any article that attracted the Japanese soldier could be traded for food.

Rice followed the same price pattern. Rice, as it was cooked in the camp, was often a watery mass, called lugao. But most internees considered it much better than dry rice, because the bulk made it seem like more food. Individuals would cook "extra" rice with such fillers as palm roots, leaves, pigweed, and any other pulpy green material that had proved edible. Sweetpotato tops, when available, were a favorite. One man once found in the garbage a quart can of rice that had fermented. This he and his wife dried and ground to powder, mixed with a little water, and baked as a flatcake. They shared it; it had an excellent cheeselike flavor.

I was that American internee, and I shall remember that rice flatcake fondly to my dying day—which, indeed, it delayed. And still, although my work now deals with the chemistry and physics of rice and soybeans, they are first food to me, and are among my favorite dishes, no matter how they are prepared.— *William A. Wellborn, Southern Regional Research Laboratory.*

Making Pellets of Forage Sorghum

A. F. Swanson

As the American pioneers well knew, forage sorghum is a basic feed for livestock in most of the Great Plains.

The forage sorghums, along with barbed-wire fence and windmills, did much to stabilize the livestock industry at the time of the great migration into the territory west of the Missouri River and south of the Kansas-Nebraska line. It was a time of conflict. Cattlemen, who believed in the free range, fought it out with the settlers who, coming to possess the land, brought in fencing, windmills, and stable crops. Forage sorghum was one of the stable crops—although, strangely, the earliest settlers used it for molasses. Within a decade, the pioneers discovered its value as cured fodder, as hay to supplement native grasses, and as a winter reserve against bad weather. Sorghum was the cushion that absorbed shocks in the first days of strife and adjustments to the climate, soil, and ways of farming, all different from those in the East.

An expanded use came with the introduction of silos, a movement that gained impetus after 1900. Forage sorghum is a good crop to ensile; sorghum silage, used with a supplement such as cottonseed cake, remains today a basic feed in the Sorghum Belt of the United States.

About 10 years ago came the idea of dehydrating the forage sorghums with the equipment that was used for dehydrating alfalfa. Paul Johnson, of Independence, Kans., is said to be one of the first to dehydrate sorghum. He processed 35 acres of Atlas sorgo on his farm in 1940 and fed the product to his dairy herd with apparent success. He mixed the dehydrated sorghum meal experimentally with molasses in proportions of 20, 30, 40, and 60 percent. He reported that the 30-percent mixture seemed to be the best, as it absorbed all of the molasses and produced a dry feed that was neither sticky nor inclined to pack in the bags. He also found that the 40- and 60-percent mixtures were sticky and wet, but the molasses did not seep through the sacks.

John Vanier, of Salina, Kans., began dehydrating sorghum in 1946. He used dehydrators that he had for processing alfalfa. Besides a milling company, he owned a dairy and ranch, where livestock was available for feeding trials. Chemical analyses were made in the laboratory of his firm.

In the course of the experimentation, he added more proteins, molasses, and other ingredients in proper proportions to the dehydrated meal, which was then made into pellets.

Federal and State research on the use of dehydrated sorghum has been limited. Unpublished data from digestibility trials by the Kansas Agricultural Experiment Station indicate that the nutrient value of dehydrated sorghum meal compares favorably with that of silage or fodder made from the crop.

Sorghum breeders at the several experiment stations in Kansas have cooperated in selecting and testing a number of high-yielding varieties that have a high content of sugar. Some limitations in dehydrating sorghum partly offset the advantages, and some uncertainty exists as to costs of using prepared feeds in which dehydrated sorghum meal is a base, in comparison with those of feeding sorghums in the form of fodder, silage, and hay, and supplemented with cottonseed cake. Even so, because of the ease and convenience of using it, dehydrated sorghum holds promise as a supplement to the more bulky feeds on farms. It has been favorably received, and the supply has not been equal to the demand.

PROCESSING a growing sorghum crop into pellets is a specialized operation. Field cutters, to reduce the standing crop to green silage, and large trucks, to bring the material to the dehydrator, are required. Up to that point, the operation is the same as for ensiling the crop. When it is to be dehydrated, the green silage is quickly unloaded and passed through huge drums, in which high temperatures and air movement reduce the moisture to 10 percent or less. It takes about 5 minutes from the time of unloading the green silage until the dried product reaches the discharge end of the processing plant, either as a dry, somewhat coarse and bulky meal, or in the form of pellets, if a pelleting machine is used. In a later operation, more protein, molasses, and other ingredients are added to the product, which is repelleted and then sacked. To save one operation, the extra nutrients may be added while the crop is passing through the plant. The pellets can be made in various sizes, but usually they are one-half inch or less in thickness.

One limitation on dehydrating sorghum is the distance from the fields to the processing plant, a factor that limits its general use on farms far from a dehydrating plant. Also, dehydration can hardly be carried out economically unless cheap natural gas is available for fuel. In Kansas, natural gas is readily available from a supply distributed from the western end of the State.

For efficiency, the sorghum should be grown near centers of alfalfa production and dehydrators. The two crops greatly extend the seasonal use of the dehydrating plants. Usually the first alfalfa is ready for processing in late May or early June. The earliest sorghum is ready in August. Growing varieties with a range in maturity makes it possible to extend the season for dehydrating it into October—or even later, if the crop is in the shock. The best time, however, to start dehydrating sorghum is when the grain has just entered the hard dough stage, when the stalks are highest in sugar. The whole plant, including the stem, leaves, and head, is dehydrated.

The cost of processing a ton of dehydrated sorghum, from the time the cut fodder leaves the field until it is made into meal or pellets, is only slightly higher than that of making an equivalent amount of sorghum dry matter into silage. A little more than 4 tons of silage is about equal to 1 ton of dehydrated sorghum in dry matter.

When sorghum is dehydrated, nothing is added that the crop did not have while growing. Nearly all the nutrients are retained in the dry product. The process eliminates certain losses that occur when the forage is cured and fed as fodder, or when it is converted into silage. Dehydrated sorghum pellets are easy to handle, store, and transport. The low moisture content makes the product highly resistant to insect damage.

Dehydrated sorghum has a sweet, pleasant taste and odor and an attractive appearance. The pellets are dried down to 8 to 10 percent moisture. They contain 75 to 85 percent total carbohydrates, 3.5 to 6 percent protein, and 2 to 2.5 percent fats. The total sugar content ranges from 25 to 35 percent for dehydrated sorghum, compared to 12 to 20 percent on the basis of green weight in the field.

Sorghum pellets are nutritious and palatable to cattle and hogs. They are particularly valuable when they are supplemented with other feeds. As the protein content of sorghum is relatively low, the general practice is to increase the protein equivalent from 12 to 17 percent or more, depending on the age and type of livestock to be fed. Alfalfa meal, soybean meal, and a limited amount of urea are used. Other ingredients, such as calcium carbonate (from limestone), steamed bonemeal, and iodized salt, are included. Dehydrated sorghum meal before it is pelleted is an excellent carrier of blackstrap molasses. Molasses adds flavor to the pellets.

The feeding of dehydrated sorghum enriched with protein and mineral supplements differs from the conventional practice of using either sorghum silage or sorghum bundle feed with 1 to 2 pounds of cottonseed cake or its equivalent in other protein supplements.

Most of the forage varieties now available are satisfactory for dehydration, although a range of early to late varieties is desirable to lengthen the season. Ellis, Atlas, Collier, and Sourless are Kansas-grown varieties that range from early to late maturity.

As a rule, the lower the seed yield of a forage variety, the higher will be the sugar content of the stems. The darkseeded forage sorghums with small panicles usually run highest in sugar, particularly if they mature late. The white-seeded varieties make a more attractive pellet and are more likely to be free from a bitter taste. Varieties of forage sorghum differ in amounts of total sugars in the stem and in the ratio of dextrose and levulose (reducing sugars) to sucrose (cane sugar). A good example from the 1948 crop is that of Kansas Collier, in which the stems showed 12.95 percent of dextrose and levulose to 29.40 percent of sucrose. Ellis has shown 26.10 percent of dextrose and levulose to 12.50 percent of sucrose. The ratio of dextrose and levulose to sucrose is fairly constant from year to year for a given variety. The leaves contain less sugar than the stems. The amount of total sugars in the green crops varies from year to year, depending on the rainfall and growing conditions.

From the standpoint of livestock feeds, the various forms of sugar have no special advantage over starch as found in the grain, except possibly some effect on palatability. Through selection, however, differences in sugar characteristics have been developed among the varieties. Some that rank highest in sugar are highest in total acre tonnage, but require a long growing season.

Ellis, a new early maturing sorgo released by the Fort Hays Branch Experiment Station at Hays, Kans., in 1948, has been found satisfactory for early dehydration. Ellis carries a high sugar content and has a white, palatable seed that is high in niacin. Its leaves are free from red blotching and have a bright appearance. It has fed out well in the bundle feed and silage.

Axtell and Atlas, two other whiteseeded varieties of mid-early to late maturity, are suitable for dehydrating, but their sugar content may be reduced when a heavy seed crop has been produced under droughty conditions.

Selected strains of Kansas Collier and Kansas Sourless, which mature late and yield a heavy tonnage under favorable growing conditions, are among the highest in total sugars. With a heavy rainfall and a long growing season, they can be expected to analyze from 25 to 35 percent of total sugars when dehydrated and from 12 to 20 percent on a green field weight. A green weight of 25 or more tons to the acre of forage sorghum is possible under the best growing conditions; a range of 12 to 20 tons is a good average.

The dehydrated sorghum pellets have been considered as a source of alcohol, sirup, and crystalline sugar by several industrial laboratories. In the manufacture of sirup or crystalline sugar, the diffusion method of extracting the sugars from the pellets is a possibility. That would eliminate the starches, waxes, and minerals to a much greater degree than when the juices are pressed from the fresh stalks in a sorghum roller mill.

Peter Collier, of the Department of Agriculture, almost succeeded in making crystalline sugar commercially in the 1880's. Because of mechanical difficulties his investigations had no practical result. He did not have our modern machinery to harvest the green crop efficiently and to preserve the material so that extraction could be extended. However, his general methods are now being studied by at least one sugar company.

Sorghum pellets to which nothing is added may have industrial possibilities, which are being explored now. Regardless of industrial possibilities, as this article goes to press, the use of sorghum pellets in prepared feeds continues unabated in ever-increasing tonnage. There is every reason to believe that the new method has ushered in an improved concept of utilizing a roughage feed never dreamed of 50 years ago.

A. F. SWANSON, *agronomist in the division of cereal crops and diseases, Bureau of Plant Industry, Soils, and Agricultural Engineering, has been engaged in cooperative research on sorghum at Hays, Kans., since 1919. He originated and put into production such varieties as Club Kafir, Early Kalo, Midland, Norkan, Ellis, and Cody. Cody was used as an emergency source of glutinous starch during the Second World War, when the root starches were cut off from the Dutch East Indies through enemy action. He has conducted palatability tests with sorghum and has extensively studied the utilization of the crop as fodder and silage and as a supplement to fall-sown wheat when used as winter pasture. Mr. Swanson also has originated varieties of sorghum whose grain is high in niacin.*

WE HAVE NO written account of the earliest uses of the flax plant. Primitive man left no yearbooks. But the Stone Age man did leave a record of another kind. Carefully cleaned bundles of flax fibers have been discovered among the remains left by the Swiss lake dwellers. These people made cords and ropes from flax for use in fishing, trapping, and navigation. Their skill and efficiency in processing the fibers and making useful products from them amaze us even today. Some 2,000 to 3,000 years later, from about 3000 B. C., inhabitants of Mesopotamia, Assyria, and Egypt cultivated flax extensively. Much of their production was consumed as linen cloth, to them a very important textile. In Egypt, linen was the only fabric priests were permitted wear.

Probably the most important ancient use of flaxseed, other than for planting, was as food. The Greeks and Romans included flaxseed in their diet. Even today Abyssinians are said to eat the seed roasted. Medicinal uses also existed, but they became fewer and fewer, and generally have been discontinued, except in veterinary medicine.

The first written description of a practical method for extraction of oil from the seed was in the twelfth century. That coincides with the appearance of linseed oil in paint or varnish in the eleventh or twelfth century. Perhaps the oil was known previously; it may have been used as a food or as a salve.

Throughout the ensuing years, although growing flax for its fiber has continued, industrial development in paints and varnishes and related fields has been so extensive that flax is more important in our economy for the oil in its seed than for the fiber in its stem. Another factor contributing to the decline in importance of fiber flax was the development of cotton, whose fiber is more adaptable to modern high-speed spinning and weaving.—*Howard M. Teeter, Northern Regional Research Laboratory.*

Fermented Soy Foods and Sauce

Lewis B. Lockwood,
Allan K. Smith

Soybeans, in the form of soy sauce and soybean cheese, paste, sprouts, milk, and curd, have been an important source of protein in the diet of the Chinese and Japanese for centuries. In Asia the whole bean is not ordinarily eaten. The people favor mostly fermented soy products or other modifications—sprouts, curd, or milk—in which the characteristic flavor and shape of the beans are lost. Only soy sauce and monosodium glutamate have found much favor in Western countries.

Asiatic people live largely on a vegetable diet. It is estimated that in China meat and eggs make up less than 3 percent of the food of the peasants, compared to 21 percent among Americans. About 95 percent of the protein eaten is of vegetable origin. Much of it comes from soybeans, which form about 20 percent of the basic diet in Northern China.

Soy sauce, *shoyu* in Japanese, is the most popular use made of the soybean. It is a dark-brown liquid, very salty and sharp in flavor. Its odor suggests cooked beef. It accentuates the flavor of vegetables and meat. Sweetening and thickening agents and spices may be added to give the sauce variety in flavor.

Soybean paste is a semisolid, mushy food. Its flavor is like that of soy sauce. In Japan it is known as miso. It is used as a relish for rice, in soups, and to add flavor to vegetables.

Soybean cheeses of the Orient are solid or semisolid. They are made by fermenting the soybean curd. Soybean cheeses are unlike American and European cheeses in flavor and appearance; it is too bad that the name cheese has been applied to them. Some of the soybean cheeses have a flavor resembling soy sauce. Others are quite different. Many are too salty for the American taste.

The Chinese made soy sauce in ancient times as a household industry. Descriptions of the process are found in books written more than 1,500 years ago. It has remained largely a family art; even now some manufacturers point with pride to the fact that their factories have been operated as family enterprises for five centuries.

Soy sauce is manufactured by two basic processes. One involves a fermentation technique and the other a chemical method. A third procedure, which is thought to have some advantages, is a combination of the two. The third method is still in the developmental stage. The products of the different methods differ somewhat in taste and odor; the fermentation product is the most acceptable. Sometimes the products of two basic processes are blended.

The fermentation method is a mixed fermentation by three micro-organisms: A mold, *Aspergillus oryzae;* a bacterium, *Lactobacillus delbruckii;* and a yeast, *Zygosaccharomyces soja, Z. major,* or a yeast closely related to *Hansenula anomala.* In the traditional Chinese method, the manufacturer adds a prepared mold culture, a koji, to the soybeans, but relies on chance inoculation for the bacterium and yeast. Modern methods include the use of pure-culture inocula of all the micro-organisms needed in the fermentation.

The materials are soybeans, wheat or other starchy grains or flour, and salt. First, the beans are washed and then soaked in water for 12 to 24 hours, depending on the temperature or season of the year. Longer soaking is needed in winter or when the temperature is low. The soaking finished, the beans are drained of excess water and cooked with steam under 10 pounds pressure. The cooking period covers several hours.

The second step includes the addition of soft wheat, which has been cleaned, roasted, and cracked or very coarsely ground. It is mixed with the cooked soybeans in the ratio of about 3 pounds of wheat (initial weight) to 10 pounds of cooked soybeans (initial weight).

In the third step, the mixture of beans and wheat is inoculated with a culture of one or more strains of the mold *Aspergillus oryzae*. The inoculation cultures are made by growing the mold on steamed polished rice. An ounce of rice will make enough koji to inoculate 10 pounds of the soybean-parched wheat mash. In modern factories, cultures of the necessary yeast and bacteria are added at this point. A good yeast growth before the mold growth becomes apparent is believed to result in a sauce of superior quality. In some modern plants the order of adding the micro-organisms is changed; the yeast is added to the steamed beans about a day before mixing them with the parched wheat, and the yeast starts to grow before the mold gets under way. The procedure is said to give very good results.

After inoculation, the mash is spread in a layer 3 inches deep in wooden trays or baskets about 4 inches deep. The trays are stacked so that air will circulate freely over the beans. During the fermentation stage, the mold grows throughout the mash and gives off considerable heat. The temperature of the material may reach 40° C. (104° F.) or higher, if it is not controlled. This phase of the process lasts about 3 days. A thin white surface growth of mold appears, and turns yellowish as spore formation begins. The brine fermentation, or second phase of the

fermentation process, is then started. If it is started too soon, the supply of the mold enzymes, which are responsible for certain necessary chemical reactions, will be inadequate. If the start is delayed too long, many spores will cover the surface of the beans and may contribute undesirable flavors to the sauce.

This molded soybean-wheat mash is placed in deep vessels and barely covered with brine made with 22-percent salt solution. In the old Chinese factories, 50-gallon earthenware vessels are used. These are set in the open and are covered only during rain. Many of the old Chinese manufacturers believe that sunlight, even moonlight, affects the flavor of the sauce.

The beans are stirred daily for the first few weeks, then weekly until the end of the fermentation period. In modern Japanese and Chinese factories the aging process is carried out in concrete vats of about 5,000-gallon capacity. Air is blown through the bean mash to stir and mix it every 2 or 3 days in the beginning, but after several weeks the material is aerated for 30 minutes once a week. Gas is given off during the first 2 weeks of the brine fermentation.

After 3 months—preferably after a year or longer—the mash is pressed to remove the liquid. This is considered the best grade of soy sauce. A second grade is made by suspending the press cake in 18- to 20-percent brine and pressing. A third (occasionally a fourth, or even a fifth) grade is prepared by further extraction of the press cake in like manner. Each extraction gives a product of weaker flavor and hence of less commercial value than the preceding one. The sauces are pasteurized at about 65° C. (149° F.). If higher pasteurization temperatures are used, a cloudy sauce results because of the precipitation of partly degraded proteins. Alum is then added as a flocculating agent, and the sauce is filtered.

The salt content of the sauce, 18 to 20 percent, prevents the growth of most micro-organisms. Sodium salicylate or β-naphthol may be added as preservative, but that is not necessary if the salt content is high enough. Cloves, cinnamon, nutmegs, pepper, ginger, and other spices enhance the flavor and are believed to prevent spoilage. They are added only to the lower-grade products. Caramel may be added to darken the sauce. Licorice or maltose may be added to sweeten it.

The chemical changes in the production of soy sauce are complex and interrelated. Wheat serves as a carbohydrate source for the growth of the micro-organisms. The mold undoubtedly supplies the enzymes necessary to convert the starch to sugar, which, in turn, is acted upon by all three micro-organisms. The mold and yeast produce some alcohol from the sugar. The bacteria produce lactic acid and other organic acids. Esters, such as ethyl acetate, are also formed by interaction of the alcohols and organic acid. They account for much of the aroma and flavor of the sauce. Other important flavor constituents are amino acids or salts of amino acids. Monosodium glutamate is the most important of these. The amino acids are produced by enzymatic decomposition of the proteins of the soybeans and wheat. Most of the protein degradation and carbohydrate fermentation occurs during the first 2 weeks of the brine fermentation. After this time, the flavor matures by very slow reactions, which involve the formation of esters and the splitting of dextrins.

The chemical composition of soy sauce with a specific gravity, at 15° C., of 1.19 to 1.20 is (in parts per 1,000 parts of soy sauce) : Total solids, 250; sodium chloride, 130 to 150; total nitrogen, 6 to 13; protein nitrogen, 0.8; amino nitrogen, 3 to 6; volatile acids (as acetic), 8.0 to 40.0; nonvolatile acids (as lactic), 50; sugar (as glucose), 20 to 70; and dextrin, 8.

IN THE MANUFACTURE OF SOY SAUCE by the chemical method, soybean meal is first extracted with water, which has been adjusted with acid to the isoelectric point of the protein in the meal. The isoelectric wash removes soluble carbohydrates and nitrogen compounds and raises the protein content of the meal above 65 percent. The meal is then cooked with 17 percent hydrochloric acid under a steam pressure of 30 pounds to the square inch for 15 to 18 hours to reduce the protein to amino acids. In place of the soybean meal, soybean-protein curd may be used as the starting material, and constant-boiling hydrochloric acid used in the cooking process. After hydrolysis of the protein, the acid is neutralized with sodium hydroxide or sodium carbonate, and the resultant solution is marketed as chemical soy sauce. Sometimes, after incomplete neutralization, a crop of crystals of monosodium glutamate is removed. The remaining amino acids are neutralized, and the concentration is adjusted to a suitable amino-nitrogen content. Such a sauce is poorer in glutamic acid but richer in other amino acids.

In the soy sauce prepared by the chemical method, the protein hydrolysis is more complete than in the fermented product. The chemically produced material is essentially a solution of salt and amino acids. Some of the flavor and odor constituents of the fermented sauce (such as peptides, alcohols, esters, and nonnitrogenous organic acids) are not found in the chemically manufactured sauce.

Recent attempts to combine the convenience, economy, and speed of the chemical method with the desirable flavor characteristics obtained by the fermentation process involve the partial hydrolysis by acid treatment, followed by neutralization of the acid. The material is then fermented for about a month by the organisms used in the fermentation method.

Miso is the most important soybean food product of Japan. It is prepared in three varieties—white, red, and black. Soybeans, wheat or wheat flour, and rice are used to make white miso in the proportions of 2: 1: 1. The soybeans are soaked in water about 20 hours, drained, and cooked for 2 hours in a pressure cooker under 10 pounds steam pressure. Soybean meal can be substituted for the soybeans. When wheat flour is used it is made into a dough with water, and baker's yeast is added. The dough is allowed to rise for a day. It is then molded into loaves about 2 inches square, and steamed for 1 hour at atmospheric pressure. Polished rice is soaked 2 hours in water, drained, and steamed in a collander. The loaves of dough are broken and mixed thoroughly with the steamed rice and soybeans. The mixture is inoculated with a rice culture of soy-sauce mold, *Aspergillus oryzae*. Shallow pans are filled with the paste to a depth of 2 inches, and left at room temperature until the surface is covered with a white mold growth. If the mold growth continues until green spores are formed, the miso will be of poor quality. The moldy paste is put in a deep vessel, and 7 volumes of salt water added for each 10 volumes of miso paste. The brine contains 7 ounces of salt per gallon. The fermentation time in the salt mash will vary from 1 to 4 weeks, depending on the temperature. At the end of the fermentation period, the mash is steamed and is ready for use without further treatment. The salt content of miso is much lower than that of soy sauce. Consequently, miso is much more subject to spoilage by microorganisms. The paste is usually consumed within a month or two after manufacture. Spices are commonly added to miso shortly before it is served.

Red miso is made from a combination of soybeans with rice and wheat or barley, but the relative quantity of soybeans is greater in the red miso than in the white. More salt is also used in its preparation.

Black miso is made entirely from soybeans. The brine-fermentation stage of the process is 1 to 3 years, although an inferior-quality product may be prepared in a 2- to 3-month brine fermentation. The salt content of black miso approximates that of soy sauce.

Protein hydrolysis in miso manufacture is less complete than in soy-sauce preparation. The protein content of miso is about 15 percent. The moisture content is about 50 percent.

Soybean cheeses are made by fermenting the curd obtained from soybean milk. To make the curd, the soybeans are soaked in water 6 or 7 hours in summer, or up to 24 hours in winter. If the soaking period is too long, a good, firm curd will not be formed later in the process. The raw, soaked beans are ground with cold water, then pressed to remove the milk. More water may be added to complete the protein extraction. Ordinarily, about 10 pounds of water is used for each pound of soybeans. The curd is usually precipitated from the milk, which has been heated almost to the boiling point, by the addition of calcium or magnesium sulfates. The type of salt, the hydrogen-ion concentration, and the temperature of the milk at the time of precipitation markedly influence the physical properties and taste of the curd. Too much magnesium sulfate results in a bitter curd, and the bitterness is retained in the finished cheese. This may be observed to a lesser extent when other divalent ions are used as precipitating agents. The curd is pressed to a consistency suitable for cutting into small cubes.

Sufu is a light-gray soft cheese made by the fermentation of cubes of curd 1 to 1½ inches thick. The cubes are dipped in dry salt, placed in a shallow pan, and inoculated with a culture of the mold *Mucor sufu*. After 3 days at a temperature of about 25° C. (77° F.), they are covered with a white mold growth, which turns gray by the fifth day as sporangia are formed. If the curd is too wet or too dense, an ammoniacal odor may be noticed at this time. Such curds make cheese of inferior quality. When the mold completely covers the cubes and has started to turn gray, the moldy curd is immersed in brine, to which a culture of wine yeast has been added. The final salt content should be 12 to 15 percent.

The brine fermentation is continued in a sealed vessel for 3 or 4 months.

Red sufu is a red cheese. It is prepared in much the way that sufu is, except that the curd cubes and red rice are placed in alternate layers in deep vessels when the brine fermentation is started. The red rice is a Chinese product made by growing the mold *Monascus ruber* in the grains of polished white rice until the entire grain is permeated with the coloring matter. The red rice contributes a pleasant taste and aroma to the red sufu cheese.

Chee-fan is a brownish soft cheese made from soy-milk curd cut into cubes about one-half inch square. The curd obtained from 70 parts of soybeans is salted with 20 parts of salt, the cubes are inoculated with the *Mucor*, and a week is allowed for mold development. Both the *Mucor* and a blue *Aspergillus* appear to play a part in this fermentation. The week-old moldy cubes are covered with Shaohing wine, and a rice or wheat-flour culture of the mold and wine yeast is added. The cheese is allowed to age in wine in an earthernware vessel for about a year. Shaohing wine is a yellow wine made from rice.

Tsue-fan is prepared in the same manner as chee-fan, except that the quantity of curd is greater in proportion to the salt and wine than in chee-fan. The cubes are about one-half inch on each side. They are boiled in water, cooled, and partly dried before inoculation or salting. This cheese is aged in rice wine for 6 months.

Hon-fan is a red cheese prepared like red sufu, except that the cheese is aged in soy sauce instead of brine.

The principal flavor constituents of the soy cheese are a combination of the amino acids derived by the hydrolysis of protein and fats. The red rice and its fermentation products, along with the rice wine, contribute sugars, esters, alcohols, and organic acids to the flavor and odor of these foods.

IN THE United States, soy sauce is manufactured by both the fermentative and chemical methods. Sauce blended from the products of both processes has been marketed. Soy sauce is the principal constituent of the popular meat sauces of the Worcestershire type. The use of soy sauce without added condiments is not popular in this country except in the so-called Chinese foods. The recent introduction on a broad scale into American markets of monosodium glutamate as a seasoning agent indicates the wide field for expansion of the soy-sauce market in the food industries.

LEWIS B. LOCKWOOD, *a native of Indiana, joined the Department of Agriculture in 1931. From 1940 until his resignation in July 1950, he conducted research on bacterial oxidations and organic acid production at the Northern Regional Research Laboratory.*

ALLAN K. SMITH *received his doctor's degree in chemistry in 1926 from Columbia University. He is senior chemist at the Northern Laboratory, where he is in charge of the protein properties, isolation, and food use section. Dr. Smith has worked in the Department of Agriculture since 1937.*

THE FARM BOY of a half century ago was familiar with the custom of occasionally washing or rinsing with oatmeal water the inside of the glazed clay jug in which he carried fresh water from the well to the harvest hands in the fields. It was believed that the water in which oatmeal had been soaked had some cleansing or purifying quality that kept the jug sweet and clean. Now we find oat flour used in foods, on food packages, and on women's skin, all for the purpose of preserving sweetness.—*T. R. Stanton, Bureau of Plant Industry, Soils, and Agricultural Engineering.*

News of Rice, An Ancient Staple

Ernest B. Kester,
Jenkin W. Jones

For hundreds of years rice has been a staple article of diet in many parts of the world. It is a major part of the daily fare of millions of people. We mean the familiar milled white rice, which is marketed and eaten in many populous countries. It is nourishing, but it is deficient in B vitamins and minerals.

Brown, or husked, rice contains more minerals, proteins, and vitamins than milled rice, but milled rice is more attractive in appearance, requires less time to cook, and is easier to digest. Also, it keeps much better in storage than does brown or undermilled rice, which soon become rancid in hot, humid climates, where most of the world's crop of rice is produced and consumed.

The Asiatic methods of rice storage and milling, based on ages of experience, are fundamentally sound. Much of the rough rice produced in Asia is stored after threshing and milled only as needed for local use. A mortar and pestle operated by hand or mechanically are extensively used for milling. With this primitive equipment, parts of the bran layer and germ of the kernel are left on the milled rice. Hence, the product is more nutritious than machine-milled rice. Much of the rice consumed in Asia is therefore undermilled, but in the larger cities and in some rural communities the use of machine-milled rice has increased. Beriberi, a deficiency disease, is apt to occur among people whose major food is machine-milled rice, which lacks thiamine.

Man has continually searched for ways of improving rice by transforming it into a more attractive food, and legion are the recipes for cooking rice with condiments and other foods to enhance its appeal and nutritional value. In the United States, we consume only 5 to 6 pounds of rice a person a year, compared to 200 pounds in the Orient. The American housewife uses it as an occasional substitute for potatoes, a side dish, the basis for a pudding, or an addition to soups. She does not usually rely on rice to any great extent in the daily diet of her family.

The large rice-producing areas of the United States are in Arkansas, California, Louisiana and Texas. Each of those States raises at least 20 percent of the total crop, which in 1950 was about 2 million tons.

Varieties of rice in the South and in the West are chosen for their adaptability to the soils and climate of each area. In the South, long-grain and medium-grain varieties predominate; but in California, almost the entire acreage is devoted to the Japan or Pearl rice, a short-grain type.

LET US LOOK at a whole grain of rice and see how it is constructed and what happens to it in milling. On the outside is the hull, a fairly rigid but loosely adhering protective covering, which constitutes about 20 percent of the grain and contains 20 percent of ash, mostly silica. Beneath the hull is the brown rice, which owes its color to layers of bran, or pericarp. The bran is rich in oil, protein, mineral salts, and vitamins. If it is not removed, the rice turns rancid. The bran is therefore rubbed off in special machines, and with it goes the embryo or germ. This is the costliest part of rice milling, because 20 to 30 percent of the kernels are broken and must be separated and sold at a discount. The different grades of broken rice are called second head, screenings, and brewer's rice, depending on the sizes.

Inside the outer brown bran layer is a finer, lighter-colored layer like the outside bran in composition. It is called polish and is also taken off. The bran and polish together constitute about 10 percent of the original brown rice and contain about 85 percent of the oil, 10 percent of the protein, 80 percent of the thiamine, 70 percent of the mineral matter and crude fiber, 50 percent of the riboflavin, and 65 percent of the niacin.

What is left is the highly milled white rice of commerce, which is 90 to 94 percent starch and 6 to 10 percent protein. It contains very small amounts of vitamins and minerals.

At our present low rate of rice consumption, however, the detrimental effect of overmilling on the human diet is a debatable point.

By a process of parboiling before the hull is removed, most of the B-vitamin content of rough rice is retained in milled rice.

How is rice parboiled? The variations in that treatment are many, but essentially it is performed as follows. Rough (unhulled) rice is steeped in warm or hot water, then drained, steamed (usually under pressure), dried, hulled, and milled in the usual way. Milling causes very little breakage, especially if steaming is done under pressure and the rice is carefully dried. The finished rice has a light, sometimes a very light, brown color. It is translucent because of the partial cooking and gelatinization of the starch.

In most of India, Burma, Ceylon, the Malayan Peninsula, and in British Guiana, the parboiling of rice before milling has been practiced for generations. In those areas, this form of rice is eaten almost exclusively. Its acceptance

has not been so favorable in China. Originally, the natives of those other lands used a short boiling to make the hulls easier to remove, but in time they learned that they were healthier from eating parboiled rice instead of raw rice. The incidence of beriberi is indeed low in areas where parboiled rice is consumed. Chemical examination shows that parboiled rice contains much more of the antiberiberi vitamin (as well as other nutrients) than does highly milled white rice. The reason is that much of the vitamin content and mineral salts are driven or infused from the bran and germ into the endosperm by this treatment. Most of the oil remains in the bran, which is removed in milling.

Results of studies on the effect of parboiling on the milling and cooking quality of American rice, reported in 1935, in general bore out the claims made of the benefits of the process in Asia. Advantages of properly parboiled rice are higher mill yields of head rice (whole kernels), better retention of vitamins, improved cooking quality, resistance to insects, and suitability for use in canned products. Those advantages are of prime importance to rice millers, dealers, and consumers.

Much work has been done in evaluating different parboiling procedures in the University of Arkansas, University of California, and the Bureau of Plant Industry, Soils, and Agricultural Engineering. What is desired in parboiled rice, or aimed at in technical studies, is a maximum infusion of vitamins and other nutrients from the bran and germ into the endosperm, a uniform and pleasing appearance of the rice grains, superior cooking qualities, minimum loss from breakage during milling, and a reasonably long storage life. Cooking without disintegration or formation of a pasty mass is a prime consideration. Modern methods of parboiling have attained many of the goals, but, as in most food processing, the road to improvement never reaches an end.

In the United States, parboiling has been modernized and adapted to large-scale manufacture. At least three plants are in operation that make converted, Malekized, or processed rice, although this long-known treatment of an age-old cereal was not introduced to our country until the Second World War. Indeed, the critical shortage of rice when Asiatic imports were shut off prompted the development here.

American parboiled rice was in great demand by our Armed Forces during the war. The sterilization it receives from the steam treatment under pressure helps preserve it against spoilage and insect infestations. It is an excellent ingredient of canned soups because the grains do not go to pieces under steam pressure. The housewife can cook parboiled rice more satisfactorily than raw rice without the bother of rinsing or steaming it. The grains do not readily become sticky and adhere to one another during cooking, and their brownish color becomes considerably lighter as cooking proceeds.

Parboiled rice has disadvantages, however. It lacks the perfect whiteness of well-milled raw rice, which by long association has become identified in people's minds with purity and cleanliness. Some nutrients are lost in the steeping liquors. In one mill, the liquors are recycled from batch to batch, but ultimately they become so highly colored that they must be discarded. Parboiled milled rice is costlier than raw milled rice. The oil in parboiled rice is more susceptible to rancidification than is oil of white rice, even though the amount is very small.

Nutritionally, however, the treated rice is superior to well-milled white rice. Let us compare data for three of the B vitamins in white and parboiled rice. Brown rice is included to show the maximum that could be attained if all the vitamins were captured in the parboiling. The figures are for micrograms per gram.

White rice	Thiamine	Riboflavin	Niacin
(milled)	0.60	0.25	18.1
Brown rice	3.69	.50	53.8
Parboiled rice			
(milled)	2.57	.36	39.8

It must be understood that some variation may be observed in different samples, depending on varieties and the method of parboiling used, but the figures are at least illustrative.

ARTIFICIAL ENRICHMENT with mineral salts and synthetic vitamins also improves milled white rice. In the method currently used, batches of completely milled rice are fortified very heavily with strong solutions of vitamins and minerals applied layerwise. Each layer is dried and protected from abrasion with a light soluble coating. The enriched rice is then blended with untreated rice in the proportions of about 1 to 200. The mixture is so uniform in appearance that without chemical tests it is almost impossible to distinguish the enriched from the unenriched grains.

A large-scale try-out of the product has been started in Bataan Province, Philippine Islands, where incidence of beriberi was high (1,500 cases among 12,000 natives examined). Of the B vitamins, only thiamine and niacin are being used in the fortification. Riboflavin is omitted because of its color, which might prevent general acceptance of the rice by the islanders. Natives of seven municipalities in Bataan are being fed the fortified rice; those in five others, for comparison, are being fed only plain milled rice. After 9 months of this experiment, a marked decline in mortality, as well as incidence of the disease, had taken place where the fortified rice was used.

The outcome of the study, which is being conducted jointly by the United States Public Health Service, the Philippine Department of Health, and the Williams-Waterman Fund of New York, will undoubtedly have a bearing on future remedial measures for nutritional problems in other parts of the Orient where vitamin B deficiency is prevalent.

OLD AND NEW FORMS of rice now on our retail markets include the following:

Puffed Rice, a familiar breakfast food, was patented in 1902. It is literally a "food shot from guns," in that the rice is treated with steam under pressure in a special type of bomb. The container is suddenly vented at the end, and the release of the pressures causes the grains to expand to about 10 times their normal size.

Flaked Rice is well cooked, mixed with sirups and other flavoring materials, rolled into thin flakes, and toasted in an oven.

Peeled Rice is brown rice with part of the bran removed.

Rice Krispies are oven-popped with sugar, salt, and malt flavoring. Vitamin B_1, niacin amide, and iron are added.

Precooked rice is also called Minute Rice. White rice is about 60 percent cooked, then dried at 300° to 400° F. in air stream.

Ready-to-Eat Rice is a precooked rice put up in cans without preliminary drying.

Cream of Rice is an uncooked granulated rice cereal.

Rice Curls, a snack food, was invented by Robert L. Roberts, of the Western Regional Research Laboratory. The curls are made from whole or broken grades of rice. The rice is ground to a coarse grit, made into a paste with boiling water, and extruded in strings into hot oil. After about 3 minutes at 400° F., the curls are crisp and golden brown. They can be flavored with salt, cheese, onion, garlic, celery, smoked salt, or combinations of them. They can be made into a confection. Most people seem to prefer plain salt with a little sodium glutamate added to bring out the flavor.

Expanded rice is another development of the Western Laboratory. It is made by deep-fat frying of parboiled rice or by heating it in a current of hot air. Parboiling is a necessary preliminary step. The "expanded" product is crisp, porous, and tasty.

Wild rice is a native plant and is not the ancestor of the cultivated rice of commerce. It grows throughout the eastern half of the United States and adjoining parts of Canada, but is more abundant in central and northern Minnesota than in other sections. In Minnesota, wild rice supplies autumn feed for waterfowl. Indians harvest the grain for food and also for sale in packaged form in retail markets. The wild rice gathered has never exceeded 800 tons in 1 year.

Cultivated wild rice is planted in water 1 to 3 feet deep. The seed germinates in May or June. In early July, the stalks emerge. By late August or September, the rice has matured. Harvesting is done by poling flat-bottom boats through the stands and knocking the grains into the boat. It is then parched by rotating it in a steel barrel over a low fire. Later it is threshed in another barrel equipped with revolving paddles.

IF THEY ARE NOT MIXED with hulls, the bran and polish, when fresh and handled under sanitary conditions, should be fit for human consumption and should make excellent additions to special cooking flours, breakfast cereals, and waffle and pancake mixes. In some areas, particularly California and the Southern States where rice mills are located, a high-grade edible oil is extracted from rice bran. The oil resembles cottonseed and peanut oils in general characteristics and is quite stable by itself, that is, out of contact with the bran. The deoiled bran is a nutritious stock feed and is preferred by many users to untreated bran, because it no longer turns rancid.

A GREAT DEAL of research on rice is under way in laboratories of the Department of Agriculture. At the Southern Regional Research Laboratory, A. M. Altschul and his staff are trying to find improved methods for the preservation of rough rice in storage. K. S. Markley is studying rice-bran oil, its extraction and refining.

Because many houswives do not have the time or patience to cook rice properly, the researchers have developed frozen cooked rice, which can be stored for months without loss of quality. Indeed, the product seems to be slightly improved as a result of freezing. They are developing a dry-packaged rice that can be made ready for the table by merely adding hot water. They also have found several ways to prevent acid formation in brown rice. One is by blanching rough rice with steam. Another is by extracting part of the oil with light petroleum solvents. Others involve control of temperature and moisture.

Dr. Helen L. Hanson, also of the Western Laboratory, has made a white sauce from a variety of so-called waxy rice, Mochi-Gome. This new sauce does not "break" or separate when frozen and thawed. White sauce and gravy made from other flours tested separate and give an undesirable, though harmless, curdled appearance. Heretofore, the main use for this type of rice has been in the preparation of Japanese ceremonial foods.

Elsewhere, research on rice is also being pursued vigorously. M. C. Kik, at the University of Arkansas, has undertaken studies of the nutritive value of rice and rice byproducts, including their content of vitamins and amino acids. E. A. Fieger and Virginia Rice Williams, at Louisiana State University, are likewise engaged in nutrition work, and are investigating improved packaging methods for brown rice that will prevent deterioration during storage. Walter Kempner, at Duke University, has started tests to find out whether a rice diet will relieve high blood pressure. The agricultural experiment stations of Texas, Arkansas, Louisiana, and California, in cooperation with the Department, are developing new varieties and improved strains of rice. The drying of rough rice is also receiving much attention at the experiment stations. Research in rice milling has been started at Stuttgart, Ark., by the Arkansas Institute of Science and Technology.

The aims of those who direct research on rice in laboratories are products with better quality and more nutritive value, greater economy and simplicity in milling, new outlets for byproducts, and new and attractive forms in which rice can be consumed. A development to be desired is to get better standards for foods and lower food costs for the small wage earner. Rice will probably never attain the position of wheat and corn in American diets, but it is a useful, healthful, and versatile cereal, made more so by day-to-day advances in technical knowledge.

ERNEST B. KESTER *is a graduate of the University of Minnesota and Northwestern University. He has been engaged in research on fats and oils at the Western Regional Research Laboratory since 1939, and is now in charge of studies on the utilization of rice.*

JENKIN W. JONES *has had many years of experience in rice breeding and production as senior agronomist at the Biggs, Calif., Rice Field Station of the Department of Agriculture and at Beltsville, Md., where he is now principal agronomist. He is a graduate of Utah College and holds an advanced degree from the University of California.*

ALFALFA has been an important forage crop since earliest history. The observations of the Greeks and Romans are as true today as they were when Columella wrote in A. D. 60: ". . . . But of all the legumes, alfalfa is the best, because, when once it is sown it lasts 10 years; because it can be mowed four times, and even six times, a year; because it improves the soil; because all lean cattle grow fat by feeding upon it; because it is a remedy for sick beasts; because a jugerum (two-thirds of an acre) will feed three horses plentifully for a year."—*Francis P. Griffiths, Western Regional Research Laboratory.*

Opportunities

To Grow Our

Own Rubber

Irvin C. Feustel,
Frederick E. Clark

After Pearl Harbor, the Japanese got control of the sources of about 90 percent of our natural rubber. Had it not been for remarkable achievements in the production of synthetic rubber, the consequences would have been most serious.

Our dependence on a limited area in the Far East for nearly all our natural rubber had long been a matter of concern. Attempts to establish plantations of Hevea rubbertrees (*Hevea brasiliensis*) in Mexico were made as early as 1910. The Firestone Rubber Co. started plantings of these trees in Liberia about 1925. The Ford Motor Co. made plantings in 1928 in Brazil. In 1935, the Goodyear Tire & Rubber Co. entered on a similar venture in Panama and later in Costa Rica. However, the production of tree rubber in the Western Hemisphere has been seriously curtailed by the South American leaf blight. Adequate methods for control of the leaf blight are essential for success in establishing large plantations.

The United States is unsuited climatically to the growth of both the Hevea and the Castilloa rubbertrees (*Castilla elastica*), although attempts have been made by the Department of Agriculture to grow the rubbertrees in Florida. Some of the trees were able to survive, but they did not produce enough latex to be profitable.

Consumption of natural rubber in the United States rose gradually to 775,000 long tons in 1941. In 1945, consumption dropped to 105,429 tons. The production of synthetic rubber was very small before 1943, but climbed steadily to a peak of 761,699 tons in 1946. In 1947, the use of natural and of synthetic rubbers was practically the same. Since then the proportion of natural rubber consumed has increased. The trend in 1950, however, was again toward a sharp increase in synthetic-rubber consumption because of unsettled international conditions. The use of reclaimed rubber, including natural and synthetic, has been fairly constant—around 200,000 to 300,000 tons—for the past 10 years. Our total consumption of new natural and synthetic rubbers is presently about half of the world total. Approximately 70 percent of the rubber used in the United States goes into tires.

Confronted by a critical shortage of rubber in 1942, the 77th Congress passed Public Law 473, which directed the Department of Agriculture to plant 75,000 acres of guayule, a rubber-yielding shrub, to carry out cultural and processing research, and to construct and operate mills for the extraction of the rubber. The program was called the Emergency Rubber Project.

Workers in the Intercontinental Rubber Co., which had produced rubber from wild guayule shrubs in Mexico since 1905 and from cultivated guayule shrubs in California since 1925, had proved that guayule would grow in limited areas in California, Arizona, and Texas. The company had also selected a supply of seed from high-yielding strains developed by the late W. B. McCallum, chief botanist of the company. The Government bought the entire United States holdings of the Intercontinental Rubber Co., with headquarters at Salinas, Calif., in order to obtain the benefit of the existing

Rubber hydrocarbon content of domestic rubber-bearing plants

Common name	Rubber content [1]	Portion of plant richest in rubber
	Percent	
Guayule............	7–20	Bark.
Kok-saghyz.........	5–10	Roots.
Cryptostegia........	2–4	Leaves.
Goldenrod..........	4–7	Do.
Milkweed...........	2–5	Do.
Pingue.............	1–2	Bark.
Rabbitbrush........	1–2	Do.

[1] Rubber content as reported in the literature. Selected to represent as nearly pure rubber hydrocarbon as possible.

rubber-producing facilities for the Emergency Rubber Project. These included nurseries, plantations, a small assay laboratory, a mill for processing the shrubs, research files, and patents.

The Forest Service was charged with the administration of the project and with responsibility for large-scale cultural and processing operations. The Bureau of Plant Industry, Soils, and Agricultural Engineering was designated to conduct research, within its usual field of endeavor, on all phases of plant production. The Bureau of Agricultural and Industrial Chemistry was called on to improve the existing process for recovering rubber from guayule and to develop methods of extracting it from other domestic plants. The Bureau of Entomology and Plant Quarantine, the Weather Bureau, the Soil Conservation Service, the Agricultural Adjustment Administration, State experiment stations, and universities also participated in the program.

Most of the authorized plantings were in California, the first near Salinas. At one time plans were developed to plant 400,000 acres of guayule, principally in California and Texas. To avoid competition with food production, however, only 32,000 acres were actually under cultivation at the end of the Second World War. Improvements were made in the Salinas mill, and another mill was erected at Bakersfield.

About 1,400 tons of rubber was produced from Texas wild shrubs and California cultivated shrubs before Congress ordered the liquidation of the Emergency Rubber Project at the close of the war. Much effort went into research and development designed to improve cultural practices and the steps involved in the extraction of rubber. Wild shrubs in Mexico supplied about 7,000 tons of rubber a year during the war, thus greatly depleting that country's reserves. Because of the shortage of water for irrigation, the outlook for cultivated guayule shrubs there is not good. Mexico apparently cannot be counted on to supply much guayule rubber for some years.

It was assumed that the need for the domestic production of natural rubber would end with the war. But a postwar appraisal showed that, despite advances in the technology of synthetic elastomers, a big part of the Nation's civilian and military needs could be met only by natural rubber. Because of the uncertainty of a constant supply of plantation rubber from the Far East, it seemed advisable to establish a small but sound and readily expandable source of natural rubber within the United States.

GUAYULE and other domestic plants can provide our strategic natural-rubber reserves if their economic production can be assured. Indications are that economic production may be accomplished through further improvements in culture and processing. Guayule particularly has promise of being a valuable supplementary crop in several Southwestern States that are marginal for other cultivated crops because of drought.

Shortly after the close of the Emergency Rubber Project, the Office of Naval Research and the Stanford Research Institute entered a contract to provide funds and facilities for renewed activity. Long-range, fundamental studies on guayule and other rubber-bearing plants were envisaged. Research on the genetics and physiology of guayule plants was initiated in October 1946, under the leadership of Stanford Research Institute. A study of the biochemistry of rubber formation was subcontracted to the California Institute of Technology. A similar arrangement was made with Oregon State College to plant kok-saghyz for seed production. On August 1, 1947, after termination of the contract between the Office of Naval Research and Stanford Research Institute, Congress authorized and appropriated funds, under the Strategic and Critical Materials Stockpiling Act, for continuation of the program under the Department of Agriculture. These funds established the Natural Rubber Research Station at Salinas, Calif. The program was expanded to include research on rubber extraction and processing.

• Research on crop production, genetics, and related activities is assigned to the Bureau of Plant Industry, Soils, and Agricultural Engineering; research on the development of new or improved methods for extraction and processing of rubber to the Bureau of Agricultural and Industrial Chemistry.

Guayule now appears to be the most practical rubber-producing plant that can be grown in the United States. Kok-saghyz (the Russian dandelion) is regarded as the second-best prospect. Research on other plants, among them cryptostegia (a rubbervine native to Madagascar), goldenrod, milkweed, pingue, and rabbitbrush, has given less promising results. Hundreds of other plants in the United States contain rubber, but in too small amounts to be of practical interest.

GUAYULE (*Parthenium argentatum*) was known to the early Indians in Mexico. It was first noted scientifically in 1852 near Escondido Creek, Tex., by J. M. Bigelow, a physician attached to a Mexican boundary survey. Guayule was first described botanically by Professor Asa Gray of Harvard some years later. Public attention was drawn to guayule rubber, apparently for the first time, by an exhibition at the Centennial Exposition in Philadelphia in 1876. Production of rubber from native wild plants began in Mexico in 1902. The Texas Rubber Co. began operations at Marathon, Tex., in 1909. About 9,000 tons of guayule rubber was imported from Mexico in 1910—one-fifth of the total rubber consumption of the United States at that time.

Guayule is a semidesert shrub, which somewhat resembles the sagebrush. It grows wild in north-central Mexico and in the adjacent Big Bend section of Texas. It prefers a well-drained, light soil. As indicated by its natural range, the plant needs a mild climate, although it has survived temperatures of 5° F. or below.

Guayule resists drought and will grow with a rainfall of only 10 to 15 inches a year. It responds readily to more favorable conditions of moisture.

The guayule plant may live for 30 years or longer. It probably accumulates rubber during most of its lifetime. The deposition of rubber, however, appears to be greatly stimulated by conditions that interrupt growth of the plant periodically, such as low temperatures or drought. If moisture and temperature are conducive to growth during most or all of the year, a large plant with little rubber results. Under domestication, the economical peak of rubber production is reached during early maturity. The recommended cropping period is about 4 years on irrigated land and 5 or 6 years on non-irrigated land. Yields range from 900 to 1,500 pounds of crude rubber to the acre.

Rubber in guayule is present in the form of latex. Unlike latex in Hevea rubbertrees, which is in the canals, it is in the cells of the plant. Each rubber-bearing cell must be ruptured to free the rubber.

THE PROCESS FOR EXTRACTION of rubber from guayule used by the Intercontinental Rubber Co. was adopted by the Emergency Rubber Project. The whole shrub was harvested with a machine that cut the roots 4 to 6 inches below the surface. After a short curing period in the field, the material was baled and transported to the mill, where it underwent a long period of partial drying. The drying, or conditioning as it was commonly called, completely coagulated the latex in the plant cells, an essential step in preparation for milling. Following the conditioning treatment, the material was parboiled and passed through a revolving screen to remove the leaves. It was then cut or chopped and passed through a series of corrugated crushing rolls, which reduced it to a finely shredded condition. The material then was mixed with a fixed proportion of water and fed into the first of a continuous series of tubular pebble mills, which were lined with silica bricks and partly filled with smooth flint pebbles. The plant material was ground in the pebble mills and the separated particles of rubber were agglomerated into "worms." After completion of pebble milling, the material was discharged into a flotation tank, where most of the plant material—the bagasse—sank, and the rubber "worms" floated.

The rubber, along with light cork or corklike material, was skimmed from the surface of the flotation tank and given a hot-water pressure treatment in a specially constructed pressure vessel called a paila. The remaining plant material, thus waterlogged, was separated from the rubber by a second flotation. The rubber was treated with antioxidant, then dried and pressed into bales for shipment to rubber manufacturers.

Research under the Emergency Rubber Project led to significant improvements in several steps in the time-honored pebble-mill extraction process. For example, hammer mills replaced knife cutters or chopping equipment in preparing shrubs for milling. An efficient, continuously operating, high-pressure hydraulic unit for waterlogging cork replaced the low-pressure, slow-acting, batch-type pailas. The flotation of rubber "worms," the manner

of adding antioxidant, and the drying of the crude rubber were also improved.

Because the pebble mill is cumbersome and inefficient, other types of equipment were tested in an effort to make a basic improvement in the extraction process. Attrition mills, paper-pulp beaters, and jordans were tried. Only the jordan was superior to the pebble mill. Preliminary work was conducted on the solvent deresination of shrubs before milling to obtain a crude rubber with a minimum of resin. The results were most encouraging in that the crude rubber gave vulcanizates with exceptionally high tensile strength.

Experimental work conducted on the extraction of rubber in latex form indicated that a dilute latex obtained by cutting guayule shrubs when freshly harvested and milling them in water could be concentrated to 35 to 50 percent solids by centrifugation. This process remains to be perfected and its economical feasibility to be demonstrated, but the physical properties of the latex rubber thus obtained were shown to be excellent.

GUAYULE RUBBER is chemically identical with Hevea rubber because each is a *cis* polymer of isoprene, as shown by X-ray and infrared absorption studies. However, the molecular weight of the guayule rubber appears to be lower and its content of resins and insoluble matter higher.

Crude pebble-milled guayule rubber averages approximately 70 percent rubber hydrocarbon, 20 percent resins, and 10 percent acetone-benzene insoluble. Hevea rubber is about 93 percent hydrocarbon, with only 4 to 5 percent resins, and 2 to 3 percent protein. Crude guayule rubber is not only less pure, but it is more variable in composition and inferior in aging qualities or storage life. Comparatively rapid deterioration of guayule rubber during storage is believed to be due to a combination of factors, including the absence of natural antioxidants, lower molecular weight, action of resins as oxygen carriers, and the presence of larger amounts of copper and manganese, which act as oxidation catalysts. Aging of vulcanized guayule rubber, however, is not greatly different from that of Hevea.

Guayule rubber was particularly useful during the war for constructing the inner swelling layer of airplane fuel-tank cells as a protection against loss of fuel following puncture of the tank by bullets. Guayule rubber also added tack and other desirable properties when blended with GR–S, but was not used much for that purpose because of lack of supply. Usefulness was also shown for fabrication of footwear, hoses, belting, and other items, where tack and adhesiveness to fabric are important.

Recent work at the Natural Rubber Research Station has shown that the purification of guayule rubber (removal of resins and reduction of insolubles) holds promise of producing a rubber of uniformly high quality that will be essentially equivalent to Hevea rubber in most physical characteristics. Deresination (solvent extraction) of the shrub before milling offers one approach to such quality improvement. The process yields, as a byproduct, resin, which has potential value as a source of organic chemicals and which might help support the cost of deresination.

It has been demonstrated that the conventional conditioning treatment of guayule shrubs is harmful to rubber quality, and that this step may be eliminated by a new technique applied to freshly harvested shrubs. The direct processing of fresh shrubs improves crude rubber in both uniformity and quality, because it prevents degradation that results from conditioning the material under unavoidably variable climatic and storage conditions. Milling the fresh shrubs yields more rubber, based on the percentage originally present in the growing plants, and the crude rubber obtained has a lower content of insoluble impurities. This man-

ner of processing promises also to reduce labor and shrub handling costs in factory operation.

Recovery of the rubber in latex form constitutes still another possibility of quality improvement, because guayule latex rubber is relatively low in resin and is essentially free from insoluble material.

PLANT BREEDING offers a promising means for increasing the productiveness of guayule. This field of research is being actively pursued by the Bureau of Plant Industry, Soils, and Agricultural Engineering. It is interesting that the sugar beet in the wild state contained only 5 to 7 percent sugar, and now—through plant improvement—it contains 16 to 18 percent sugar. The roots also have increased greatly in size. Similarly, rubber production of the Hevea rubbertree has been more than doubled through research. Great differences have been found in percentages of rubber among guayule plants. It has also been found possible to cross the quayule shrub with related species that are almost treelike in growth. An outstanding example is the cross between guayule and *Parthenium stramonium*. Such hybrids are more vigorous than guayule. Although at the present stage of development the hybrids do not contain quite so high a percentage of rubber as guayule, their greater growth and vigor make possible a total increase of 40 to 50 percent in rubber production per acre. Another promising feature in breeding guayule is that when a desirable hybrid is found it can immediately be fixed, so that it breeds true and reproduces itself by seed indefinitely. That is possible in guayule because of the plant's peculiar method of reproduction—that is, production of seed without fertilization by pollen.

OF THE RUSSIAN DANDELIONS, the leader is *Taraxacum kok-saghyz*, which was discovered in Russia in 1929 in the Tien Shan Mountains near the Chinese border during an investigation of the possibilities of producing natural rubber in Russia. The Russians rapidly developed the source in the belief that kok-saghyz combined the essential qualities of adaptation to conditions in northern latitudes and the possibilities of improvement into a satisfactory cultivated plant. Other less well known species of Russian dandelion that have promise as potential rubber producers are *Taraxacum megalorhizon* (krimsaghyz) and *Scorzonera tau-saghyz* (tau-saghyz).

Soon after Pearl Harbor the United States started negotiations with Russia to obtain kok-saghyz seed. In May 1942, two sacks of seed were flown to this country and experiments were immediately begun by the Department of Agriculture. More than 60 indicator plantings were established in various parts of the United States through cooperation with State agricultural experiment stations. More than 600 acres of kok-saghyz were planted, largely in Michigan and Minnesota.

Analyses of typical one-season kok-saghyz plants made at the Eastern Regional Research Laboratory showed that more than 90 percent of the rubber is in the form of latex in interconnecting ducts in the root. The remainder is in the crown and leaves of the plant, which constitute about 25 percent of the total dry weight. Individual roots with 23 percent of rubber hydrocarbon, on the dry-weight basis, have been noted, but most of the roots contained 5 to 10 percent.

The variability in the rubber content is testimony to the nonuniformity of the seed stock supplied this country, and suggests the possibility of attaining a higher and more uniform rubber content through an intensive program of research on selection and breeding of kok-saghyz.

A process of extracting rubber from kok-saghyz was developed by the Eastern Laboratory. The dried roots are run countercurrently through hot water that contains a little soda ash to leach out carbohydrates and soften the roots. The leached roots, representing only about 55 percent of the original dried weight, are given a short pebble milling in water to disperse the softened plant tissue and to roll together the fine filaments of rubber. Approximately 65 percent of the remaining solids is eliminated upon dilution of the milled slurry and passage over a vibrating screen, which leaves a residue composed largely of rubber and adhering root skins. A second short pebble milling with water disengages the root skins from the rubber. The rubber is then separated from the plant debris by flotation and final washing on a vibrating screen. The rubber, centrifuged to remove excess water, is mixed with an antioxidant and dried. Analyses gave the following averages: Rubber hydrocarbon, 80.5 percent; benzene-insoluble material, 12.5 percent; and acetone-soluble material (by difference), 7.0 percent. The benzene-insoluble material can be reduced to 5 percent or less by additional pebble-mill scrubbing, but the material is not so objectionable as it is in the guayule rubber.

Enough kok-saghyz rubber was produced to permit the fabrication of experimental passenger-car and truck tires by commercial manufacturers. The results of road tests, as judged by experts in the rubber industry, indicated that kok-saghyz rubber was superior to GR–S and approached plantation rubber in physical characteristics. Thus there is no doubt of the high quality of kok-saghyz rubber.

Nevertheless, it became apparent in 1944 that kok-saghyz could not contribute enough rubber for emergency war requirements because of the necessity of extensive plant-yield improvements by selection and breeding. So, processing research was discontinued.

Because the Russian dandelions can produce rubber in 15 months or less and can be grown in most areas of the United States, they hold promise as domestic sources of rubber.

Cryptostegia plants (*Cryptostegia grandiflora* and *C. madagascariensis*), leafy tropical vines native to Madagascar, have long been known to contain rubber. Experiments have shown that they will grow and reproduce in Florida.

Rubber is found in every part of the plant (except the woody portions of the stem and root), but it is concentrated in the leaves. Approximately 10 to 15 percent of the total rubber in the mature leaf also occurs in latex ducts, but the remainder, 85 to 90 percent of the leaf rubber, is imbedded in individual chlorenchyma cells.

The unusual way most of the rubber occurs—in the form of globules entrapped in protoplasts and surrounded by cell walls—accounts for the difficulties experienced in the extraction of rubber from cryptostegia. The cell rubber is not directly available by tapping the latex system and has not been satisfactorily recovered by pebble milling. The cell walls can be fractured by pebble milling, but the rubber-bearing globules are not readily freed from the protoplasts and are thereby prevented from agglomerating into "worms" separable by flotation. Solvent extraction is also unsatisfactory because it gives poor yields, even after prolonged extraction, unless the leaves receive an extensive preliminary chemical or fermentation treatment.

The cell rubber obtained by a caustic cook-creaming process was relatively soft, had a low molecular weight, and contained approximately 30 to 45 percent resins. Solvent-extracted rubber, which contained both cell and duct rubber, was much purer, but only slightly better in quality, than the solvent-extracted cell rubber alone. However, the latex rubber of cryptostegia appears to have physical properties roughly comparable to those of Hevea latex rubber.

Harvesting rubber from cryptostegia cultivated in Mexico and Central and South America has been done mainly by periodic tapping or clipping of the long, nearly leafless stems, or whips, of the plant. A few drops of latex are obtained from each stem in this way. It has been estimated that an ambitious

native could collect a pound of rubber a day by the method.

In 1942, the Government, through cooperation with the Société Haitiano-Americaine de Développement Agricole, established a large cryptostegia plantation in Haiti to aid the war effort. Difficulties in tapping, however, and the fact that not enough rubber could be produced in time to meet emergency requirements resulted in abandonment of this project. The vines are not regarded as an economical producer of rubber.

THOMAS EDISON became interested in domestic sources of natural rubber during his later years. Of the many plants he investigated, goldenrod attracted the most attention and has been the subject of continued study. The fact that it can be harvested annually by mechanical methods and that it will grow in nearly any climate contributed to its attractiveness as a possible rubber producer. It has been shown that the rubber of goldenrod (*Solidago* genus) is confined to the leaves.

The Southern Laboratory undertook an intensive investigation during the Second World War on the extraction of rubber from goldenrod. The percentage of rubber in the dried leaves was found to vary from 4 to 7. The acetone-extractable resins were generally present in quantities 2.5 to 3 times that of the rubber. The method of rubber extraction, as developed on a pilot-plant scale at the Southern Laboratory, consisted of a preliminary extraction with acetone to remove most of the resinous material. An extraction with benzene and evaporation of the benzene to obtain the rubber followed. Enough rubber was prepared to make various commercial articles. Performance tests indicated that bicycle tires of goldenrod rubber were superior to tires of prewar grade or those made from reclaimed rubber.

The relatively high cost of the process required for the extraction of goldenrod rubber, the extremely low molecular weight (which necessitates a partial vulcanization before the rubber can be satisfactorily processed), and related factors make goldenrod a relatively unattractive source of rubber.

Other domestic rubbers include those from milkweed (*Asclepias syriaca*), pingue (*Actinea richardsoni*), and rabbitbrush (*Chrysothamnus nauseosus*). They were studied as potential rubber sources during the Second World War, but do not look promising for several reasons. The stands are scattered and collection is difficult. The percentage of rubber is low, and the ratio of resin to rubber is usually high. Extraction is difficult, and yield is low. The rubber is of low molecular weight and inferior quality.

The Natural Rubber Research Station, at Salinas, Calif., has the responsibility of developing a domestic source of natural rubber for national security purposes. This is of vital significance in relation to the stockpiling of natural rubber from the Far East. If it is shown to be possible and practicable to produce domestic natural rubber of good quality in quantity in 1 to 3 or 4 years, it will obviously not be necessary to maintain as large a stockpile of natural rubber as would otherwise be required.

Guayule is receiving major attention because of its greater immediate promise of high yields and low-cost production. The Russian dandelions are also being investigated in view of their ability to produce a crop of rubber in a shorter time.

One possibility of having guayule rubber available in the event of an emergency is through the establishment of a reserve supply of living rubber by seeding unused or wild lands where guayule is adapted. Plants, once established, are hardy and may live 30 or more years. They could be harvested whenever it became necessary to extract the rubber. Much experimentation remains to be done, however, in order to determine the ability of guayule to flourish competitively with other plants growing in wild areas. The comparative vigor of different varieties and hybrids of guayule, and the effects of different soil and climatic conditions, must also be investigated before wild-land planting becomes practicable.

Another possibility for producing guayule is to establish it as an economic farm crop. In southwest Texas, for example, there are vast areas of marginal dry lands which might be adapted to guayule culture. Guayule lends itself readily to large-scale mechanized farming. Improvement in the rubber-producing ability of guayule, together with the development of more efficient processes for extracting the rubber, might make guayule a profitable crop in selected areas of the Southwest. The establishment of guayule as an economic farm crop which could readily be expanded to meet emergency needs for rubber is believed to be the best ultimate solution to this vital part of the defense problem.

The objectives of the current research program are, therefore, aimed at lowering producing costs, increasing yields, increasing efficiency in recovery of available rubber, improving the quality and uniformity of the rubber obtained, and developing uses for by-products. The objectives are actually no different, except in detail, from those for any other agricultural crop produced for industrial utilization.

IRVIN C. FEUSTEL *has been employed as a chemist in the Department of Agriculture since 1926. He has investigated problems in the fields of soil organic matter, fruit- and vegetable-waste utilization, and production of yeast and antibiotics. He is head of the natural-rubber extraction and processing investigations of the Bureau of Agricultural and Industrial Chemistry at the Natural Rubber Research Station in California.*

FREDERICK E. CLARK *is in charge of the analytical and physical testing section at the Natural Rubber Research Station. He has been associated with the Bureau of Agricultural and Industrial Chemistry since 1942, with the exception of two years which he spent with Battelle Memorial Institute.*

FIBERS FROM COTTON

The Utilization of American Cotton

Robert B. Evans

To tell of cotton one has to use big figures and big statements.

Cotton is man's main reliance for clothing and other textiles. It enters into the daily life of more of the world's peoples than any other product except salt.

Practically the entire cotton crop is used as raw material for manufacturing, and that industry is one of the largest industries in the United States and the most important based on an agricultural commodity.

Our modern machine age had its beginnings in the efforts during the eighteenth century to spin and weave cotton mechanically. During the past 200 years, the history of western Europe, the Orient, and America has been shaped to a great extent by the ability of countries to produce the fiber and process it, and by their need for using it.

Cotton became King Cotton when Eli Whitney invented the cotton gin in 1783. The gin, which pulls the cotton fibers off the cottonseed, did away with the tedious hand-separating job required until then. Cotton production in the United States immediately began the upward march that made this country the main source of the world's supply. Production climbed from 4,184 500-pound gross bales in 1791 to 10.3 million bales in 1900. It averaged 12.5 million bales annually in 1910 to 1919, 13.1 million bales in 1920 to 1929, 13.2 million bales in 1930 to 1939, and 12 million bales in 1940 to 1949. The 1949 crop of 16.1 million bales, the fourth largest in history, was followed in 1950 by one of only 9.9 million bales.

World production of cotton reached its peak just before the Second World War. The 1935 to 1939 annual average was 31.7 million 500-pound gross bales, of which 18.6 million bales was grown outside the United States. The world total declined to a low of 21.1 million bales in 1945, but went up to 31.2 million bales in 1949. Of the 1949 total, the United States produced 16.1 million bales; India and Pakistan, 3.3 million bales; the Soviet Union, 2.7 million bales; China, 1.7 million bales; Egypt, 1.7 million bales; Brazil, 1.6 million bales; and Mexico, 1.0 million bales. Some 40 other countries grew the remaining 3.1 million bales.

The world output of 31.2 million bales in 1949 weighed 7.5 million net tons. Spun and woven into fabric, that would be enough to make 19 million miles of 40-inch-wide sheeting, or enough to provide nine shirts or house dresses, or three sheets, for every person in the world.

COTTON is to textiles what iron is to metals. Although there are perhaps 700 plants that have been used by man for fibers, only a few have proved suitable, in qualities and cost, for large-scale economic development. Cotton is the giant among them. It alone accounted for more than half the 25.5-billion-pound world production of the principal textile fibers in 1949. There are

377

two reasons for cotton's hold on world fiber markets: Cotton has an excellent all-around combination of properties that makes it technologically suitable for a wide range of clothing, household, and industrial products. It can be grown in large quantities at relatively low costs. The end uses of other textile fibers are more or less specialized, but there are few end uses in the entire textile field where cotton is not a factor.

Other fibers, in order of quantities produced, are jute, rayon, wool, the hard fibers, flax, hemp, nylon, and silk. Jute, grown in Pakistan and India and used throughout the world mainly for bags and bagging, accounted for 12 percent of the world's production of fiber in 1949. Wool, used for clothing, upholstery, blankets, carpets, and similar articles, accounted for another 9 percent of the total. Rayon, used mostly in clothing but with some household and industrial uses, accounted for 11 percent. World production of rayon climbed rapidly from 457 million pounds in 1930 to a peak of 2,817 million pounds in 1941, with most of the increase in Germany, Japan, and Italy. It declined during the Second World War to a low of 1,398 million pounds in 1945, but since then has been reviving rapidly and was up to 2,690 million pounds in 1949. Hard fibers— abacá (Manila), sisal, and henequen— are used almost entirely for cordage and twine. Flax, once the most important vegetable fiber, is used mostly for household linens and clothing. Hemp is used mainly for cordage, twine, and bags. Silk, the most expensive fiber in common use, has given way somewhat to rayon and nylon. Nylon is growing rapidly in importance, first for women's hosiery, and now for many other things, but the total production was still relatively small in 1950.

Also, there is a limited production of other new man-made fibers, such as glass fiber; Saran, Vinyon, Orlon, and Dynel made of synthetic resins; and Vicara and Ardil, made of corn protein and peanut protein, respectively. Asbestos, the only important natural mineral fiber, is used for such products as brake linings, pump packings, and fire-resistant clothing. A matter of interest, more than economics, is the use of metal yarns, raffia, thin strips of bamboo, leather, and many other materials by hand weavers and fabric designers.

COTTON IS AS IMPORTANT as a farm crop as it is as a textile fiber. It is grown on 1.2 million of our 5.9 million farms. Except from 1945 to 1947, when wheat outranked it, cotton has been the most important cash crop of the entire United States. In 1949 it returned to farmers a total income of 2.6 billion dollars. For more than a century it has been the South's dominant agricultural commodity. This single crop was the source of more than half of the South's cash farm income in 1929, and 36 percent of it in 1949. Even in California, far west of the traditional Cotton Belt, cotton brought in more dollars than any other crop in 1947, 1948, and 1949—more even than oranges and grapes. That does not mean that cotton is as valuable a source of income as livestock, or as important a crop as corn, the bulk of which is fed to livestock. Cotton's contribution to farm income is particularly significant because cotton lint is not used for food or feed, and thus does not compete with other crops for those markets. Its market is not bounded by the human or animal stomach; it is our most important farm crop from an industrial standpoint.

In its raw state cotton cannot meet the needs of man. It must first pass through a series of processing and marketing steps.

The first step in its progress from plantation to mill is its transportation by wagon or truck to one of the 8,000-odd active cotton gins scattered through the Cotton Belt. Here the lint fibers are torn from the seed, compressed, and baled. Lint cotton and cottonseed follow different processing and utilization paths from the gin. For every pound of lint cotton produced, there is an output of 1.7 pounds of cottonseed, which moves into a wide range of food, feed, and industrial products. Cottonseed by itself is the United States' eighth most important cash crop, with receipts totaling 256 million dollars in 1949, compared with 2,380 million dollars for cotton.

After cotton has been ginned, it enters a marketing system which grades, classifies, compresses, stores, insures, transports, finances, and delivers it in even-running uniform lots to the cotton mill. These tasks involve the efforts of large numbers of people, but they are performed so efficiently that the total price spread between farm and mill for cotton grown near Abilene, Tex., and delivered in South Carolina was 2.8 cents a pound in October 1950. Cotton may follow many marketing routes between farm and mill, but the dominant pattern is: Producer to local buyer; local buyer to cotton market; market to mill through mill buyer, or to foreign importer.

AT THE TEXTILE MILL, cotton begins its processing in an industry that calls for more big figures and big statements. The industry accomplishes the stupendous task of ordering into a usable arrangement the 90 million to 340 million fibers present in every pound of cotton, each one of which is different from all the others. The fibers vary in softness, color, luster, and other properties, depending on their variety, where they were grown, the care taken in picking and ginning, and other factors. They range in strength from 60,-000 to 120,000 pounds to the square inch, compared with 50,000 to 80,000 pounds to the square inch for steel wire. If they were increased a thousand times in size they would appear as collapsed, flattened tubes ranging from ⅓ inch in diameter and 200 feet in length, to 1⅓ inches in diameter and 40 feet in length, with some 18 to 36 twists every 10 feet.

Three principal operations are involved in cotton manufacture: The fiber is processed into yarn and the yarn into fabric; the cotton goods are bleached, dyed, and finished; the finished goods are cut up and sewed into end-use products. This is the dominant pattern, but there are many variations.

Some cotton yarn is made into knit goods, and some cotton goods are not bleached, dyed, or finished. In England, yarn is usually manufactured in mills that do not weave. In the United States, most fabric is made in integrated mills. A trend has grown in the textile industry during the past few years toward integrating all manufacturing processes under single organizations, but most cotton goods still pass through two or more ownerships in their manufacture.

Raw cotton is converted into yarn and fabric by some 1,200 mills, which in October of 1948 employed some 525,000 workers. The industry has 90,542 carding machines, where the cotton (after it has been opened and formed into a roll or lap) is brushed out into a thin mistlike sheet, then shaped into a round rope called a sliver. If intended for particularly fine goods, the sliver goes to one of the industry's 7,067 combing machines, where the short fibers are combed out. Whether or not this sliver is combed, it next goes through a series of intermediate operations, which draw it finer and finer into thick roving, suitable for spinning. The industry has some 3,825,000 slubber, intermediate, speeder, and jack spindles for the operations.

In the spinning process, the cotton strand, or roving, is drawn out still farther, the necessary twist is inserted, and the product, now yarn, is wound on bobbins. A total of 20,758,000 spindles were active on cotton in October of 1950. After two or more preparatory processes, the yarn is woven into fabric on one of the 366,584 looms used for cotton goods in the United States.

COTTON MILLING was a pioneer industry of the United States. Like many others, it was first centered in New England, where it continued to expand until the First World War, reaching its maximum cotton consumption in 1917 and its maximum active spindleage in

1921. Since then, the equipment in New England has dwindled as obsolete machinery has been junked under pressure of competition from the South and as the amount needed to meet the Nation's textile requirements has declined because of increasing efficiency and longer hours of operation.

The South had a few cotton mills before the Civil War, but the real growth in manufacturing there began after 1880. By 1905, southern mills were using more cotton than the mills in New England, and after 1925 the South had more spindles in operation. The southern textile industry became concentrated in the foothill areas of North Carolina, South Carolina, Georgia, and Alabama. An estimated 63 percent of the country's cotton-spinning activity is within 200 miles of Clinton in South Carolina. Probably the key reason for the movement of the industry thère was the availability of an abundant labor supply. The cotton-textile industry requires a high proportion of unskilled labor, which was available in the South from the farm population and because of the lack of opportunities in other industries.

By moving south, the cotton mills came closer to their raw-material supply, but for many years now the supply in their immediate areas has been inadequate and they have had to look farther west. Because they are on one of the main rail routes between the more westerly cotton-growing States and the population centers of the Eastern Seaboard, the southern mills have been at no disadvantage in this regard.

Mills in cotton-growing States used 91 percent of the total cotton consumed in the United States during the year that ended July 31, 1950, compared with 7 percent in New England and 2 percent elsewhere. New England's proportion of the country's cotton spindles declined from 52 percent in 1920 to 19 percent in October 1950, while the percentage in the cotton-growing States climbed from 43 to 79.

More than 92 percent of the total cotton consumption is by cotton mills.

The rest goes to manufacturers of knit goods, processors of rayon and silk, makers of woolen and worsted goods, and other industries.

Of the cotton going through cotton mills, the gross waste loss is 12 percent in making carded goods and 28 percent in making combed goods. Much of this waste, however, is thrown back into the hopper to make the same or different goods. All but 7 percent of the raw cotton, it is estimated, is eventually used in textiles. Most of the rest goes into battings, felts, toy stuffings, oil filters, and other nontextiles.

To classify, handle, and steer cotton waste to its best use, a substantial trade has grown up. Just as packing houses are said to use all but the pig's squeal, so cotton mills put practically all their waste to good use, throwing out very little on the dump heap. All cotton mills, of course, try to keep as much cotton as possible from falling into the classification of waste.

Returning to the main stream of cotton utilization, roughly 93 pounds of cotton yarn was produced in 1947 from every 100 pounds net of raw cotton consumed. Of this yarn, about 6 percent went into thread, twine, tire cord, and crochet yarns, 84 percent into woven fabrics, and about 8 percent into knit goods. About 2 percent was exported.

ONE POUND OF COTTON goes a long way in the cotton-manufacturing industry. It is enough to produce from 2 to 6 square yards of the goods used for shirts and house dresses and even 15 or more square yards of tobacco cloth or cheesecloth. The industry converts the huge quantities of cotton it uses into enormous quantities of fabrics, as well as the other products I have mentioned. The output of the 10 principal groups of cotton broad-woven goods, exclusive of tire fabrics, totaled 8,287 million yards in 1939, 11,108 million yards in 1942, 9,646 million yards in 1948, and 8,512 million yards in 1949. These groups are subdivided into about 140 types of cotton fabrics and again into many hundreds of diversified constructions.

Cotton duck, the heaviest kind of cotton goods, is one of the 10 main groups of cotton textiles. It is used for awnings and tents, among other things, and is much needed in time of war. Narrow sheetings and similiar goods are medium to heavy fabrics used for bags, pocketings and shoe linings, tickings, diapers, coated fabrics, and bookbindings. Next come the print-cloth yarn goods, a group of mediumweight and lightweight fabrics, including print cloth, bandage cloth, tobacco cloth, cheesecloth, and carded broadcloth. Colored yarn goods include fabrics like ginghams, seersuckers, and denims, which are made of yarns that have been dyed before weaving. Wide cotton fabrics consist mostly of bed sheetings and other wide sheetings for industrial use.

Fine cotton goods differ from the others in that they are made at least partly of yarns that have been combed as well as carded. They include broadcloths for shirts, handkerchief fabrics, lawns and organdies for dresses, typewriter ribbons, and tracing cloth. Napped fabrics include flannels, moleskins and suedes, blankets, and the headlinings for car interiors. Towels and towelings need no explanation. Specialties and other fabrics include bedspread, drapery, and tapestry fabrics, luggage fabrics, corduroys, and plushes.

Besides the many woven fabrics, cotton yarns also are made into a wide variety of knit goods. They reach the consumer largely in the form of underwear, polo shirts, gloves, sweat shirts, hosiery, mosquito netting, and meat coverings.

To make the wide range of cotton goods, the industry uses a wide variety of raw cottons. Unless you have studied cotton, all cotton may look alike to you. Actually, however, there are wide differences in degree of whiteness, amount and kind of trash, fiber fineness, staple length, basic fiber strength, cohesive ability, and other properties, which greatly affect the suitability for different types of end products. Cotton mills are sensitive to these differences, so much so that in October 1950, they were paying 55.7 cents for cotton having a staple length of $1\frac{1}{4}$ inches, as compared with 42.8 cents a pound for the same grade of cotton having a staple length of 1 inch.

Why do not cotton farmers grow more long-staple cotton? In recent years the average staple length of American cotton of the upland type has increased, but, because of some law of nature, the growing of long staples is usually accompanied by a lower acre yield, so that most American growers have found it more profitable to stick to medium-staple cottons.

Nearly 98 percent of the cotton used by mills in the United States is American cotton of the upland type, which is medium in staple length (mainly from $1\frac{3}{16}$ to $1\frac{1}{8}$ inches) and of medium fineness. For towelings, ginghams, denims, bag fabrics, and other carded fabrics, mills use mostly cotton that is Middling to Low Middling in grade and $\frac{7}{8}$ to $1\frac{1}{32}$ inches in staple. For tire cord, Middling and Strict Low Middling cottons of 1- to $1\frac{1}{16}$-inch staple have been employed. Knitting yarns require cotton of medium to high grades, because they must be relatively free of imperfections. Long-staple cottons, $1\frac{1}{16}$ inches and longer, are usually spun into combed yarn; the shorter, into carded yarns. Very long staple, high-grade upland cotton finds it way into thread and fine combed fabrics, such as broadcloth and shirtings, lawns and organdies, and airplane and balloon fabrics.

DESPITE THE HUGE PRODUCTION of cotton in the United States, there are some requirements for which mills have had to look outside the country. For instance, they used 100,000 bales of Egyptian cotton and 15,000 bales of Peruvian cotton during the year that ended July 31, 1950, because of the shortage of domestic cotton having staple lengths of $1\frac{7}{16}$ to $1\frac{9}{16}$ inches.

These cottons, like long-staple uplands grown in the United States, were used for sewing thread and fine combed fabrics. Before the First World War, 100,000 bales of sea-island, the finest of all cottons, with staple lengths of 1½ to 2 inches, was grown along the coast of Georgia, South Carolina, and Florida but, because of the boll weevil, very little of this cotton is now grown there. In Arizona, Texas, and New Mexico, production of the American Egyptian cotton having a staple length of 1⅜ to 1⁹⁄₁₆ inches climbed to 92,561 bales in 1920 and again to 73,808 bales in 1942. Only 4,000 bales was grown in 1949, but production climbed to 59,300 bales in 1950, when this cotton, unlike the upland crop, was not under acreage controls.

American mills also use about 100,000 bales annually of short-harsh cotton from India. This very coarse cotton, less than ¾ inch in staple length, is used for blankets, mattresses, upholstery, filters, and the like. No cotton of this type is produced here.

Except for about 7 percent (which is woven from dyed yarns), cotton cloth is grayish as it comes off the loom and hard to the touch, with occasional fragments of leaf, seed, or other materials that have survived the manufacturing process. The 7 percent of colored-yarn goods and another 23 percent of gray goods are used as they come from the loom. The gray goods go into products like bags, laminated plastics, belting, and tobacco cloth, where appearance is secondary. The other 70 percent of cotton goods undergo one or more of the chemical processes of bleaching, dyeing, and finishing. About half of the goods are bleached and finished white; another one-fourth are plain-dyed and finished; and the rest are printed with various designs and finished.

Many cotton mills have their own finishing departments, but most cotton goods are finished by independent concerns on a contract or commission basis. The 600 finishing plants in the United States employed 92,000 workers at the beginning of 1949. Cotton was the

major fabric processed, but rayon and wool were produced also. This industry is mainly in New England, the Middle Atlantic States, and the Carolinas. The present trend is toward greater concentration in the South. The treatments applied to cotton fabrics by the finishing industry include: Singeing, to eliminate loose threads; bleaching, to make cotton white; mercerization, to add luster and make possible brighter dyeing; dyeing, to impart color; printing, to put designs on the fabric; preshrinking, to keep the fabric from shrinking when laundered; and the application of synthetic resins, to wrinkleproof and to increase wear. By the application of these processes, cotton goods are further specialized and adapted to specific end uses.

THE FINAL MANUFACTURING OPERATION in making a usable textile product sometimes takes place in the textile mill. Such articles as knitted outerwear and underwear, hosiery, sheets, towels, bedspreads, and blankets are usually sent directly from the textile mills to wholesalers or retailers. Most end-use cotton products, however, are made by the cutting trades, which cut and sew the fabrics into shirts, dresses, and many other items. Rough estimates indicate that in a usual peacetime year, 40 to 50 percent of the cotton fabrics goes to cutters, 20 to 30 percent to shoe manufacturers, bookbinders, and makers of similar products, and 20 percent to household consumers as piece goods. The remaining 5 to 10 percent is exported, or sold to such buyers as hospitals and hotels.

Fabricated clothing and household products, as well as piece goods for household use, traditionally have moved to the ultimate consumer by the usual wholesaler-to-retailer-to-consumer route, but more and more frequently in the last 25 years they have been sold directly from the manufacturer to the retailer.

Of the dollar the consumer paid before the Second World War for apparel and household goods made of cotton, it has been estimated that 7.5 cents went to the farmer, 0.7 cent to the ginner, 2.1 cents to the cotton merchant, railroad, and warehouseman, 17.2 cents to the cotton mill, 4.2 cents to the dyer and finisher, 30.9 cents to the manufacturer of the goods, 4.9 cents to the wholesaler, and 32.5 cents to the retailer.

For many industrial cotton goods sold in large unit quantities direct to the user, the farmer's percentage of the consumer's dollar is somewhat higher because of lower marketing costs. It is believed that the division of the consumer's dollar was about the same in 1950 as before the war, although cotton fabrics averaged more than three times higher in price.

Farmers often wonder why they receive so little of the final price and whether the charges made by the processors and marketers between him and the consumer are not excessive.

It should be pointed out that much must be done to raw cotton before it is suitable for meeting human needs, and that the various in-between manufacturing and merchandising steps are characterized by as intense a competition as will be found in any section of the American economy. There is room for gains in efficiency in these steps, of course, but the gains are likely to be small and occasional, rather than large and frequent.

About 42 percent of the cotton used in the United States goes into clothing uses, about 22 percent into household uses, and about 36 percent into industrial uses.

Shirts, the most important single end-use product in 1949, accounted for only 6.7 percent of the total consumption, but the 534,330 bales used for that purpose represented a return to farmers that year of about 83 million dollars and was more cotton than was grown in 1950 in all of South Carolina or Tennessee. Sheets, the second most important, accounted for 5.6 percent of the total consumption. Bags were third, with 5.1 percent of the total. Consumption of cotton in tires, formerly the most important single use of cotton, declined from 701,090 bales in 1948 to 383,570 bales in 1949 as a result of competition from rayon.

We each used 25.7 pounds of cotton a year in 1905 and 48.8 pounds a year in 1935 to 1939. Consumption per person jumped to an all-time peak of 40.2 pounds in 1942, because of our wartime need for uniforms and other fighting equipment, but declined thereafter to 24 pounds in 1949. In 1950, however, it jumped to 30 pounds as a result of a recovery in business activity and increased demand for textiles arising from the Korean crisis.

Despite competition from other fibers, cotton met about 60 percent of our textile requirements in each decade from 1890 to 1940. During the past 15 years or so, however, cotton has been losing important markets to rayon and paper, and faces greatly intensified competition from them in the future. It also faces competition from nylon and other man-made fibers, which have appeared in quantity since the end of the Second World War. The full effect of competition from these markets was not fully felt during the years immediately following the war because of the huge demand for textiles of all sorts. By 1948, however, cotton's share in the textile-fiber consumption had dropped to 57 percent, compared with 65 percent in 1940 to 1945, and 61 percent in 1930 to 1939.

RAYON—one of America's greatest success stories—undoubtedly is cotton's most potent competitor. Production started in 1911, and there have been very few years since that production did not show a large gain over the previous year. The greatest advance has been during the past few years, with consumption increasing from the equivalent in quantity of 1 million bales of cotton in 1939 to the equivalent of about 3 million bales in 1950. This expansion is the result largely of a steady improvement in quality, coupled with a downward trend in price.

At first rayon was a weak, sleazy fiber, but during the past 20 years, thanks to research, it has been greatly improved in appearance, drape, softness, wrinkle resistance, colorfastness, and washability. Poor strength was one of the difficult problems that the rayon industry had to conquer to make rayon a usable fiber. By 1937, rayon had enough strength for many clothing and household uses, but it was still barred from many industrial and other uses dominated by cotton, where strength is important.

Two developments are directly associated with three-fourths of the large production increase since 1939—rayon staple fiber and high-tenacity rayon.

Until about 1936, practically all rayon was in the form of continuous-filament yarn. Then rayon staple fiber, or rayon cut into short fibers, appeared, and ever since it has been increasing rapidly in importance. This development had a dual effect. It opened the door to the vast cotton-spinning industry as a potential user of rayon and, at the same time, gave this industry for the first time an alternate raw material. By using rayon staple it is possible to make fabrics entirely different from those that can be made from continuous rayon yarn—fabrics that frequently resemble very closely standard cotton and wool. In 1950, consumption of rayon staple in the United States—most of it in cotton mills—totaled the equivalent of more than 800,000 bales of cotton.

With the introduction of high-tenacity rayon—a type 80-percent stronger than the ordinary viscose type used in clothing—rayon cords and fabrics equal in dry strength to cotton cords and fabrics became possible. Production of high-tenacity rayon was expanded tremendously during the Second World War for use in tires; by 1949 it had reached the equivalent of about 650,000 bales of cotton and comprised 29 percent of the total rayon production. Before the war, practically all tire cord was made of cotton, but in 1949 rayon had captured nearly two-thirds of the market. Because of a tremendous increase in tire production, cotton tire-cord production, nevertheless, was at record-breaking levels in 1946 to 1948. There was a sharp decline, however, in 1949.

From 1920 to 1940, the history of rayon was one of continued reduction in price. In 1940, however, it cost cotton mills only 11.1 cents for a pound of cotton*(Middling $^{15}\!/_{16}$), as compared with 22.3 cents for a comparable quantity of rayon staple fiber. This difference in favor of cotton was wiped out during the war, and in November 1950 cotton cost the mills 45.3 cents a pound, as compared with 32.9 cents for a comparable quantity of rayon staple fiber. Thus the competitive potential of the rayon industry at the beginning of 1951 was much stronger than prewar, as a result of gains in the quality of its products and a price situation that had changed greatly in its favor.

Until about 1935, rayon, or synthetic fiber made of cellulose, was the only manufactured fiber in commercial production in the United States. Since then, several other synthetic fibers, including nylon, glass fiber, Saran, Vinyon, casein fiber, and corn-protein fiber, have been introduced.

The combined consumption of those fibers rose from 4.5 million pounds in 1940 to around 90 million pounds in 1949, the latter equal to, only about 200,000 bales of cotton, but already greatly in excess of the consumption of silk or flax in this country. Some of these fibers possess admirable qualities for textile use; others appear to be suited only for special purposes. All are priced considerably higher than either cotton or rayon, but prices can be expected to decline somewhat as technical progress is made.

Another important competitor of cotton is paper, which competes directly in such products as bags, towels, handkerchiefs and napkins, window shades, plastics, twine, and draperies. Consumption of cotton in bags, formerly its second most important use, climbed from 548,000 bales in 1940 to an all-time peak of 820,000 bales in 1943, because of wartime demand and an acute shortage of burlap. But it declined to 383,000 bales in 1948, despite an increased total market for bags. In the meantime, the output of paper for shipping sacks increased from 195,000 tons in 1940 to 667,000 tons in 1948.

Over the years, paper bags have become better and better adapted to users' requirements as a result of an aggressive research program. In addition, paper bags benefited from a lower and lower price relative to that of cotton. Paper bags always have had a lower first cost than cotton bags, but they are nearly worthless after being used once, while cotton bags frequently make several trips or may eventually wind up as someone's house dress or dish towel. After allowing for their second-hand value, cotton bags had a slight advantage in cost over paper bags before the war, were at a decided disadvantage in 1947 and 1948, and regained a slight advantage in 1949. As a result of this, and an extensive campaign to emphasize how second-hand cotton bags can be used again for other purposes, use of cotton bags went up slightly in 1949 while use of paper bags declined.

IN THE LIGHT OF MORE intense competition from synthetic fibers and paper, it is obvious that a real fight must be made on behalf of cotton if its markets are to be maintained on the scale to which the American farmer has been accustomed. Yet there is no reason to view the future pessimistically.

Markets go to the product that offers the consumer the most for his money, quality and price considered. The improvements in quality made by the competitors have been accomplished through continued, large-scale research programs. The same weapon can be used on behalf of cotton, but it must be used on a scale commensurate with cotton's importance if it is to succeed. Total expenditures for research on cotton, from the farm to the end product,

were not more than 4 million dollars in 1948; for rayon (only about one-third to one-fourth as important quantitatively) they may have run as high as 10 million dollars. The cotton industry, however, in 1951 was taking strong action to keep from losing its market through lack of research.

A SECOND primary factor in cotton's outlook has to do with price. At present the cotton industry is well into its greatest revolution since the invention of the cotton gin. Mechanized cotton production, together with the greatly increased acre yields, means that cotton will be produced at a much lower cost in terms of human effort in the future than it has been in the past. In fact, it appears that cotton can be grown at a far lower cost than seems to be possible, at least yet, for the production of any man-made fiber. For most textile markets, price is a factor of great importance. It is extremely significant, then, that, from all appearances, cotton can undersell its synthetic competitors, if the industry wants to. At the same time, although cotton cannot compete with paper products in lower first cost, it can compete in many markets on the basis of net cost for service rendered.

STILL ANOTHER primary factor has to do with the clothing habits of the American people. The type of clothing we wear was designed for warmth, being brought over by our ancestors from western Europe, where summer temperatures are much milder than they are in most of the United States. At present there is a strong trend toward greater use of lighter, more open sports-type apparel, for which cotton is particularly well adapted.

THUS FAR WE HAVE dealt with the domestic market. Until about 1935 more American cotton was exported than was used in this country, but thereafter our average annual exports declined rapidly from 7.2 million bales a year in 1930 to 1934 to 5.3 million bales in 1935 to 1939 and 1.4 million bales in 1940 to 1944. Traditionally, our exports of cotton went to such highly industrialized nations as Great Britain, Germany, and France, and more recently to Japan. During the decade that ended with the Second World War, Germany and Japan became the largest producers of rayon in the world, in an attempt to free themselves of the necessity of using American cotton, which required dollar exchange. At the same time, Great Britain and France made strong efforts to grow cotton in their colonies, so as not to use any more American exchange than necessary. This decade also saw Brazil emerge as an important cotton-growing nation.

WITH a rapidly growing world population, there is no question that a need exists for all the cotton that can be produced both in the United States and elsewhere. Per capita consumption of cotton in 1948 was 3.3 pounds in Asia, 2.4 pounds in Africa, 6.2 pounds in Latin America, and 7.5 pounds in Europe, compared to 28 pounds in the United States. The key to the future of American exportation of cotton is the matter of paying for it. The outlook here depends in part on world recovery, on the willingness of the United States to open its doors to foreign goods in return payment, and on how well cotton can compete with our industrial products for the foreign buyer's American exchange. The effect of postwar recovery in other countries and of Marshall Plan aid is seen in the increase of United States exports from 2.0 million bales during the 12 months beginning August 1947 to 5.8 million for the same period beginning August 1949.

One untoward factor in the outlook is the fact that countries like Brazil, Argentina, and India are becoming self-sufficient in providing their own cotton goods from their own cotton, when formerly they bought heavily from Great Britain and Japan, both large users of American cotton. At the same time exports for these countries

have declined and production of cotton outside the United States in 1950 was still less than prewar.

Another factor is the rapidly rising world production of rayon. The recent construction in England of the largest plant under one roof in all Europe to make nylon, which is based on coal and which thus will not require foreign exchange, is significant.

When the United States entered the Second World War, it had on hand carryover stocks equal to an entire year's production. This extra supply served us well, for cotton was called upon to supply around 83 percent of our military needs for textiles, as compared with 11 percent for wool, and 6 percent for rayon. Although one-third of the entire consumption of cotton went into military uses during the war, there was sufficient cotton to take good care of the civilian needs.

A combination of reduced acreage, poor crop yields, and increased domestic consumption bids fair to bring domestic carryover stocks in 1951 down to the equivalent of only 3 or 4 months' consumption, despite the fact that exports for the 1950–51 cotton season have been placed under control. The heavy demand for cotton in the face of reduced supplies has been reflected by the highest prices for cotton since the Civil War. The 1951 situation emphasized again the great importance of cotton for meeting both civilian and military requirements.

ROBERT B. EVANS, *a native of Salt Lake City, has degrees in economics from the University of Utah and American University. He was on the staff of the cotton utilization section of the Bureau of Agricultural Economics from 1937 to 1940, when he joined the staff of the Southern Regional Research Laboratory, where he later served as special assistant to the director. He was in charge of commodity and industry studies. He became executive secretary of the International Cotton Advisory Committee, of which the United States Government is a member, in 1949.*

What Cotton Has; What It Needs

Walter M. Scott

Because the most particular buyer in the world today is undoubtedly the American housewife, her selection of textile materials provides an index to the esteem in which cotton is held.

A survey by the Department of Agriculture in 1947 disclosed that women prefer cotton in 11 out of 16 important ready-made apparel and household uses.

Their choice of cotton for the 11 uses was beyond question. For every woman who favored some other material, 29 preferred cotton for house dresses, 24 for anklets, 10 for aprons, 7 for bedspreads, 6 for dish towels and pajamas, 4 for curtains, 3 for part-wool blankets, and 2 for nightgowns, raincoats, and tablecloths. The women also placed cotton on a par with any other material for the ready-made summer street dresses. Women who made their own clothes chose cotton by an overwhelming majority—43 to 1 for house dresses and nearly 2 to 1 for summer street dresses.

The products considered in the survey for which most women ranked cotton lower than other materials were winter street dresses, hosiery, slips, and short-sleeved blouses.

Such a reputation among homemakers alone would be good evidence of the ability of cotton to meet modern standards of performance. But industry provides further evidence. The number of industrial uses for cotton runs into the hundreds, and the choice of cotton is overwhelming in many instances—industrial thread, awnings, tents and tarpaulins, industrial hoses, bags, and upholstery felts. Large quantities of cotton also go into protective coverings or insulation for electrical wires.

The reason for such a preference, which now has endured for centuries, is simple. Cotton can give the products made from it many desirable characteristics. Cotton is versatile. Some of its qualities can be successfully duplicated, but the incorporation of all of its desirable traits in any one synthetic fiber has proved impossible so far. Its variety of desirable properties extends the number of products for which it is suitable; the combination of many useful qualities in a single item is also possible. Synthetic fibers, as a rule, must sacrifice some valuable characteristics to obtain adequacy in others.

Cotton is tractable; it can be modified chemically. Many of the qualities in which cotton naturally is superior to other fibers thus can be enhanced, and other qualities for which cotton is not noted can be changed as needed for highly satisfactory end uses.

End use means the form in which a product reaches the ultimate user. If this be the yardstick by which cotton is evaluated, homemakers' reasons for preferring cotton for many uses and for disliking it for some other uses are significant. Therefore, in the survey I mentioned, women were asked why they did or did not choose cotton.

High on their list of reasons for preferring cotton were its good wearing qualities, its launderability, and its appearance after laundering. For some household articles, such as towels, they particularly liked the absorbent ability of cotton and its lack of shedding or linting. In curtains, they said, it was less likely than other materials to deteriorate in the sunlight. Their chief objections to cotton were when certain aspects of appearance were dominant.

The scientist makes another kind of appraisal, a separate evaluation of each aspect of quality—wearability, appearance, and what happens to a fabric in the washing machine.

Launderability includes a quick rate of drying, colorfastness, dimensional stability, and other qualities. Appearance is the sum of such aspects as crease resistance, luster, drape, and color. Some of these individual components overlap; for one instance, high tensile strength, a requirement of long-wearing qualities, also influences washability.

Perhaps the leading virtue of cotton is its high tensile strength—its ability to resist tearing or breaking when it is under stress. The scientist defines tensile strength as the breaking strength of a material expressed in force per unit of cross-sectional area of the original specimen. By such measurement, the strength of cotton is roughly equivalent to that of structural steel. Strength gives cotton an advantage in many uses, including women's foundation garments, thread, upholstery materials, warp yarns for carpet backs, bags, and twine.

A remarkable feature of the tensile strength of cotton is that it becomes appreciably stronger when it is wet. Most other fibers lose strength when they absorb moisture. Some lose more than half of their original strength. The advantage to cotton is obvious, because fabrics frequently are exposed to water (in awnings, raincoats, bath cloths, and towels) and to dampness from perspiration in clothing. The ability of cotton materials to stand up under many washings is largely due to their high strength when wet.

Another good quality of cotton fabric is dimensional stability—resistance to permanent change in its length or width. High dimensional stability makes for minimum shrinkage and loss of shape during washing and is essential in practically all household articles and clothing, as well as in many industrial products. Cotton can be stabilized by mechanical means alone, so that washing will not shrink it more than 1 percent in either direction.

Rayons, on the other hand, are difficult to stabilize by mechanical means, and chemical treatments to improve their dimensional stability frequently sacrifice strength and other desirable properties.

Cotton resists abrasion, or friction with other materials. It surpasses wool, silk, and rayon in that quality, which is particularly important in children's play suits, men's shirts and work clothes, everyday dresses, and all outdoor garments in which serviceability is a major consideration. It is an essential quality in shoelaces, bags, thread, beltings, and many other items subject to rubbing against other materials in use. During the Second World War, soldiers crawling over logs, along the ground, or through brush barricades, and squeezing through narrow passages, between brick walls, and the like, gave cotton garments a tremendous test for abrasion resistance—and cotton played its part with outstanding efficiency.

Cotton is the principal fiber used where absorption is a basic requirement. Combining the inherent ability to dry quickly with a tremendous capacity and rate for taking up and holding water, it is naturally superior to many other fabrics in humid climates, where human comfort depends on clothing that will rapidly absorb perspiration and as rapidly permit its evaporation. Furthermore, a method of chemical treatment has been developed that increases the normal absorbency—so essential in dish towels, bath towels, handkerchiefs, diapers, and socks.

When service requirements involve protection from water rather than water absorbency, cotton fabrics also are suitable. They are amenable to water-repellency and waterproofing treatments. Various types of finishes, some of which retain their effectiveness against water after several launderings or dry cleanings, are used commercially on cotton goods. Besides, cotton fibers tend to swell when they are wet and thus to seal the fabric against the penetration of water. Although the swelling is not quite so great in cotton as in rayon, the characteristic, combined with the increase in its strength in the presence of moisture, has made cotton desirable for fabrics such as those adopted by the Army for protective outer garments for the field. These fabrics are made from tightly constructed cottons, which have a soft-twisted filling for quick swelling on contact with water.

Water-repellent cotton fabrics also find extensive application in awnings, tents, and truck and boat covers, and in many other places where people or property need protection from rain.

A characteristic that makes cotton especially suitable for industrial use—tire cord, machinery belts, twine—is its long flex life. Cotton survives repeated bending over a longer period of time than most other fibers.

Because of its superior ability to make contact with resins and rubber, cotton long kept a major part of most textile markets where that property is important, such as oilcloth and other coated fabrics, laminated plastics made with fabric, tire cord, and beltings.

SUCH AN ARRAY of excellent properties enabled cotton for many years to hold many end-use markets without challenge. Recently, however, tremendous efforts to improve competing materials have made all who grow, manufacture, or use cotton aware of its shortcomings, as well as its virtues. Cotton lacks inherent qualities needed for some specific uses. Also, it is becoming increasingly obvious that the superiority of the most desirable properties is relative; even those properties might lose their importance if synthetic fibers are improved further. Some of them are mentioned in this over-all introductory article and discussed in further detail in the articles that follow.

A study of major end-use markets made for a subcommittee of the House Committee on Agriculture in 1947 indicated that improvement is needed in 31 quality characteristics of cotton, including many in which it is now admittedly superior to other fibers. A 10-percent increase in the consumption of cotton might be achieved by improving some of the qualities.

Particularly in need of improvement if cotton is to achieve and maintain a strong foothold in the women's apparel market are properties that affect appearance—draping, resiliency, crease resistance, and luster, factors that are important in the creation of fashionable clothes. Indeed, many stylists pass over cotton because it does not fit smoothly or hang gracefully, is easily mussed, and lacks the silklike sheen many women prefer for dress-up occasions. We hope that cotton will one day overcome those deficiencies. For instance, industry reported developments in 1948 in the field of resin treatments to produce wrinkle resistance in cotton.

New resins have been made available to the textile industry in commercial quantities, and cotton finishers are applying them to certain types of dress goods with satisfactory results. The treatments are expected to increase markedly the popularity of cotton for summer dresses and suits.

Another factor is color. The colors that can be obtained on cotton depend on the dyeing properties of the fiber. Cotton outdoes its competitors in the acceptance of fast dyes, and thus has advantages over other fibers, but the very nature of cotton makes for certain limitations in getting specific color effects that are particularly desirable from the standpoint of fashion. For example, dyeing characteristics restrict the production of cotton materials in colors as lively as may be obtained on silk, or as warm and restful as may be given wool and some synthetic fibers.

For more than 50 years, scientists the world over have been trying to modify cotton to enable it to take wool dyes by the introduction of nitrogen. Several processes have been developed on a laboratory scale, but none has proved entirely practical for commercial application. Now, however, an improved method for the introduction of nitrogen into cotton, on which the Southern Regional Research Laboratory was granted a patent in January 1949, indicates progress. Cotton fabrics processed by this method—a chemical treatment called aminization—take dye in darker shades and the colors are faster to washing than on untreated fabrics.

Besides improving the dyeing properties of cotton, aminization permits the addition of organic chemicals to give cotton improved water repellency, rot resistance, or other new qualities needed for specific uses. One particularly interesting property of aminized cotton fabric is its ion-exchange ability. For instance, it can take traces of minerals out of water. Although too expensive for this particular use at present, aminized fabric does appear to have some advantages for use in laboratories and perhaps in certain types of industrial purification processes—in the production of antibiotics, for example.

One basic objection to cotton for dressy clothes has been its lack of permanent stiffness. Cotton materials quickly lose their crisp, fresh appearance and must be starched each time they are laundered. Starching involves extra work and additional laundering cost. Also, some types of fabric constructions do not hold starch well; after a brief period of use, they become wilted and limp. Once crispness is lost, soiling is rapid—and cotton soils easily even under the best conditions. Starch manufacturers, as well as cotton-fabric processors, are interested in overcoming these difficulties. Interest has been considerable in the past year or two in attempts to develop and market products for imparting lasting crispness to cotton materials. Successful products of this type should greatly strengthen the competitive position of cotton in suits, blouses, and some dresses, and in household items such as curtains and draperies.

Lack of sheerness—the property that gives materials a thin, transparent appearance—has proved a disadvantage to cotton in products like hosiery and fine lingerie. For, although cotton yarns can be spun and woven into very thin fabrics, the cost of producing them is high. Improved elasticity also is needed to make cotton competitive with other materials in hosiery and in such other knit goods as bathing suits, sweaters, and underwear.

COTTON has been kept out of some uses almost entirely because its fabrics cannot be given adequate, permanent warmth-retention properties. But the problem is not primarily to make a warm cotton fabric. That is relatively easy, because cotton fiber is outstanding in its values as an insulating material. The problem is rather to make a warm fabric that looks attractive and will not lose its functional values on repeated washing. For example, a cotton blanket when new is as warm as a blanket made of any other fiber. With use and laundering, however, it loses its fluffiness and, consequently, its warmth. A practical method of retaining the heat-insulating properties of cotton in apparel and household articles would mean substantial gains in markets for fall and winter coats and sportswear, as well as blankets.

At one time cotton held a major part of the market for linings, but it has lost those end uses because of deficiencies in slipperiness and resistance to clinging, which enable one material to slide over another with little friction. Lack of slipperiness in cotton is also a reason for its unpopularity for women's undergarments and light-weight dresses.

THOSE EXAMPLES of its needs are enough to emphasize the potential end uses that cotton is losing and to direct attention to the grave threat of a decline in existing uses unless this natural fiber keeps abreast of synthetic fibers, in which improvements are constantly being made.

An example of the need for research on the utilization of cotton is tire cord, once the largest outlet for cotton. No question of cotton's inherent suitability for cord, especially for use in tires for passenger cars and tractors and light trucks. Cotton has a high flex life, strength, and resistance to heat and to abrasion; tire fabrics of cotton have good adhesive qualities.

Nevertheless, most of the market for tire cord has shifted to rayon, partly because of improvements in the quality of rayon cord, but largely on the basis of relative cost. Obviously, then, a combination of maximum quality and minimum cost is needed to maintain the position of cotton in tire-cord fabrics, where it must keep pace with rayon on a cost as well as a technical basis.

Research has greatly increased the usefulness of cotton in some fields. The investigations under way at the Southern Laboratory are of two kinds: A search for ways to overcome the weaknesses of cotton and a search for ways to enhance the qualities in which it is inherently outstanding. Both are aimed at improving the suitability and attractiveness of cotton for specific purposes.

Typical of such research is the study of mildew resistance. Cotton fabrics rot in warm, damp climates. Many preventive measures have been tried, but the most effective so far is a process of acetylation, by which the cellulose in fiber, yarn, or cloth is converted to a partial acetate, a material highly unpalatable to the rot-producing organisms. The change is brought about by treatment with a simple substance, acetic acid, the acid of vinegar, which does not harm the cotton. The treated textiles, colorless, odorless, and nontoxic, look and feel like ordinary cotton materials.

Workers at the Southern Laboratory have made extensive tests, some in cooperation with industrial organizations, to determine the usefulness of partial acetylation in expanding the consumption of cotton. In one test, bags used to hold the chemicals in home water-softening systems were partially acet-ylated. They were used a year with no loss in strength and no sign of attack by micro-organisms, although the untreated cotton bags for the same purpose sometimes last only a month or two. In another test, partly acetylated twines, cords, and gill nets for fishing were exposed in river and ocean waters for 4 months, with little or no loss in strength. Some were still usable after 6 or 8 months—against a useful life of less than 1 month for ordinary untreated cotton fish nets under the same conditions.

Other suggested uses for partially acetylated cotton textiles are as fabrics for seedbed covers and similar outdoor products, bags for fruits and vegetables, thread for shoes and other leather merchandise, fabric for uses in the control of floods and soil erosion, and many other materials subjected to conditions that cause mildew or rotting.

Partial acetylation also gives cotton superior resistance to degradation under intense heat. In tests made in 1949 by the Southern Laboratory in cooperation with commercial laundries in Mobile and New Orleans, the useful life of laundry press covers was at least tripled by partial acetylation. Treated covers were still good after use for 3 or 4 weeks—ordinary ones wear out in 1 week.

An illustration of research to improve a quality in which cotton already is better than other fibers is the study of weather resistance. Despite inherent strength, the life of cotton can be cut by exposure to the sun's rays over long periods. A product in which extended exposure to sunlight is required is the cloth used for shading some types of tobacco during growth. Farmers use a light, open-weave cotton fabric for the purpose. Ordinarily the material lasts only a season, and the cost is excessive. But a treatment that precipitates an inorganic yellow pigment, lead chromate, into the fabric has been found to prolong greatly the useful life of the cloth. The pigment screens out the rays of the sun that are responsible for the deterioration of the exposed cloth, and thus slows up their damaging effect. Material so treated lost only about a third as much strength as untreated material in the 1948 season in Florida. The same material used the following season was not completely worn out, so that it may be possible to re-use it during a third season—untreated cotton can be expected to last only one season.

THE TREND OF RESEARCH on cotton, and its present status, can be shown by a review of projects which have been considered by the Cotton Advisory Committee since its formation in 1948. The committee is composed of a group of specialists from the cotton industry, whose function is to advise the Department of Agriculture on its research program. The specialists listed 82 projects on which research is needed, either because existing studies are inadequate or because no investigations have been initiated. Twenty-five projects deal with fiber properties, 7 with yarn and fabric properties, 28 with new and improved cotton products, 10 with processing methods and machinery, and 12 with test methods and equipment. The Southern Laboratory has worked on more than two-thirds of the projects since 1949.

Some of the research is basic. Methods like X-ray diffraction in photomicroscopy are used to explore the invisible inner structure of cotton fiber, both in its natural form and after various stages of processing. Modern equipment—calorimeters, viscometers, and the like—measure precisely heat, moisture, fluidity, and other conditions that affect the performance of cotton. The newest testing devices are employed for measuring strength, fineness, length, and other physical properties of fiber, yarn, and fabric.

Knowledge obtained by such techniques is the foundation for the research that eventually leads to the practical development of more efficient processing methods and to new and improved products. One result of research combining fundamental investigations with processing studies was the development in 1949 of a new kind of water-resistant cotton fabric. Basic investigations revealed that certain types of cotton, when spun into yarn and woven into cloth, prevent the passage of water better than others. Processing studies led to the development of a special loom attachment, which permits an extra-dense weave. The water resistance of the fabric is thus improved.

Other investigations at the Southern Laboratory are conducted in the chemical-finishing pilot plant, where equipment for small-scale processing of cotton cloth through the major finishing steps—scouring, bleaching, dyeing, chemical treatment, drying, and stretching—is available. It was here that a successful chemical treatment, developed in cooperation with the Bureau of Entomology and Plant Quarantine, was first applied to flour bags to prevent the penetration of insects.

Cotton-utilization studies also have an important place in the programs of many other research agencies, public and private. Some of the organizations, working under contracts supervised by the Southern Laboratory, are performing research recommended by the Cotton Advisory Committee.

At the University of North Carolina, in Raleigh, studies were undertaken to find a way to prevent the formation of neps—the little tangled knots of fibers which prevent a smooth, evenly colored surface—in the production of cotton fabrics.

The Lowell Textile Institute, in Lowell, Mass., is trying to improve cotton for the warp yarns of carpets, a highly specialized use that requires high strength and dimensional stability at prices competitive with those of rayon.

The University of Tennessee, in Knoxville, began work on an improved machine for determining rapidly and accurately the tensile strength of cotton fibers.

The National Bureau of Standards, in Washington, D. C., started an investigation of a method for determining the infrared absorption or reflection characteristics of cotton cellulose. Such a method will be valuable in studying the effect on cotton of various degrading influences, such as light, heat, and air oxidation.

Men at the Institute of Textile Technology, in Charlottesville, Va., undertook to find a way to lessen the tendency of cotton fabrics to soil. A study to improve the luster, or sheen, of cotton fabrics has been begun by the Harris Research Laboratories, in Washington, D. C.

Another kind of research, under way in the Bureau of Human Nutrition and Home Economics, is providing information about the present use of cotton in homes. One project is directed at obtaining facts on how cotton fabrics of known composition and construction meet the needs of families—how long different types of fabrics wear under conditions of actual use, how they withstand abrasion or rubbing, how they launder, and how much they shrink or stretch when washed or dry-

cleaned. Another project seeks information on inventories held by families, annual purchases, prices paid, and other factors affecting family utilization of cotton clothing and household articles. Data obtained in the studies will be used in planning future research.

WALTER M. SCOTT *was director of the Southern Regional Research Laboratory from 1945 to 1950. He assumed the post on his release from active duty in the Armed Forces, in which he was chief of the technical division of the Chemical Warfare Service in the European theater. From 1939 until the outbreak of the war, he was head of the Laboratory's cotton chemical-finishing division. In 1950 he became assistant chief of the Bureau of Agricultural and Industrial Chemistry. Before he entered Government service, Dr. Scott worked for many years in industrial research organizations, specializing in problems connected with the dyeing, printing, and finishing of cotton, silk, wool, and rayon fibers and fabrics, and in color specification.*

MORE THAN 9 billion yards of cotton cloth was produced in this country in 1948—a huge ribbon that would run back and forth between the earth and the moon 21 times.

Tests show that cotton canvas awnings can keep as much as 75 percent of the sun's heat from passing through windows.

Cotton awnings, popular everywhere today, date from 63 B. C., when wealthy citizens in Rome watched the Apollinarian games shaded by awnings.

The world's longest single conveyor belt, made of 50,941 pounds of cotton, 152,798 pounds of rubber, and 39,754 pounds of steel, was installed near Morgantown, W. Va. It hauls coal from the washery near a mine through a tunnel in an adjacent hill to a tipple on the Monongahela River for loading into barges. It measures 10,900 feet from the center of the head to the center of the tail pulley.

Cotton that has been stored more than 80 years has been found to be in excellent condition for fabrication into cloth.—*Charles L. Sens, Southern Regional Research Laboratory; excerpts from the periodical Textile Age.*

Fibers in a Different Light

Ines V. de Gruy, Mary L. Rollins

Not long ago the scope of textile microscopy was limited to the study of natural fibers. Now it has broadened to include examination of the many new synthetic fibers. Thus, the microscopist helps the buyer, who knows little about what has been done to a piece of cloth and scarcely realizes how much research goes into the selection of a particular cotton for a specified use.

One of the most important uses of the microscope in textiles is to identify fibers. The problem of distinguishing different types of fibers in a yarn or fabric is a common one in both research and trade. It is often surprising how many different fibers may be revealed in a single yarn said to be composed of only one type. For example, in yarns claimed to be 100 percent wool, the microscope has shown rayon and cotton fibers mixed in as adulterants.

Several approaches may be used in the identification of fibers in an unknown sample. Staining methods are the most common, the color reaction being based on the chemical character of the fiber. For example, to distinguish between fibers of viscose rayon and acetate rayon, staining with Congo red is employed. The stain produces an intense red color in viscose rayon but does not affect acetate rayon. The stains and procedures for applying them are similar to those used in clinical biology in the study of disease organisms, and for the identification of fibers in the pulp and paper industries.

Characteristic markings and shapes also furnish clues to the identity of fibers. The distinctions show up well in cross sections of the fibers, because a beam of light passing through a thin slice of a bundle of fibers under the microscope reveals significant details not apparent in the whole fiber. For that reason, the cross-sectioning technique is probably the most valuable method for fiber identification. A simple tool for sectioning textile fibers is the hand microtome developed by J. I. Hardy of the Bureau of Animal Industry. The device, about the size of a microscope slide, consists of two metal plates fitting together to hold the sample in a slot. An auxiliary plunger for propelling the bundle of fibers is attached by means of a small screw, and cross sections about 4 microns thick are cut with a razor blade. These thin slices are examined under the microscope at magnifications from 100 to 500 for the study of the fiber characteristics.

EACH of the natural fibers has a distinctive cross-sectional shape. Cotton fibers resemble kidney beans; flax fibers are polygonal and show a small dot or line for the central canal. Other vegetable fibers whose outside edges are sharp, straight lines include jute, sisal, abacá, tula, palma, and hemp, but the number of sides of the polygonal cross section and the shapes of the central canal openings are different.

Another characteristic peculiar to some of these vegetable fibers is their occurrence in fibrovascular bundles, which also have distinctive shapes, depending on the types of plant stems from which they come. Among the animal fibers, cross sections of wool are round or oval and vary considerably in size. Silk fibers, extruded in pairs by the silkworm, are regular, and usually somewhat triangular in shape.

Of the synthetic fibers, the commonest are the many rayons manufactured commercially from regenerated or modified cellulose. These fibers have characteristic shapes and markings by which the microscopist learns to recognize them in unknown samples. The cross sections of viscose filaments are irregular in both size and shape and have serrated edges, while cuprammonium rayon filaments are small and almost round. Acetate fibers are irregularly lobed and appear fused; Fortisan, a very fine saponified acetate, is scalloped.

Protein synthetics derived from agricultural products—soybean, peanut, casein, egg, and zein fibers—are not so easily distinguishable in cross-sectional size and shape, although they have different physical properties.

Nylon and Vinyon are examples of synthetics of purely chemical origin. Nylon filaments are round and regular; Vinyon filaments are flat and peanut-shaped.

To GET A BETTER UNDERSTANDING of the complexities of the microscopist's study of fibers, let us consider the small cotton fiber as it comes from the boll.

When the flower opens, the cotton fibers, which are single cells, begin to be produced on the surface of the seed. There may be as many as 10,000 fibers to the seed—better than a quarter of a million to the boll. In the unopened boll, the fiber attains its maximum length in 16 or 17 days. At this stage, the lumen, or central canal, of the fiber is large and filled with fluids from the living protoplasm of the cell. Subsequently, the lumen becomes progressively smaller as the cell wall thickens by deposition of a layer of cellulose each day. When the boll opens at the end of the growing period, the fiber dries and the cell, no longer distended by plant juices, collapses into a shriveled, twisted, flattened tube, often more ribbonlike than cylindrical, and as much as 4,000 times longer than wide.

Cross sections of the fibers from any one seed show that the thickness of the cell wall varies considerably from fiber to fiber. Fibers that for some reason or other did not attain full growth have collapsed into flat, transparent ribbons, which in cross section are thin-walled and often curiously curled and misshapen. These underdeveloped fibers are said to be immature. Occasionally a sample of cotton will show a few thin-walled fibers, which failed to collapse on drying, so that in cross section they look like doughnuts. The normal fibers, having completed their growth, are so nearly filled with cellulose that when they dry their cross sections are oval to circular, or have collapsed to bean-shaped contours. These thick-walled fibers are called mature.

It is one of the chores of the microscopist to compare cotton samples with respect to maturity and to detect any departure from the expected varietal characteristics. The extent of cell-wall development is an inherited characteristic of cotton fibers, but maturity is even more affected by such environmental factors as soil fertility, fluctuations of rainfall and temperature during the growing period, and the time of harvest. Normal commercial cottons of better than average grade contain less than 25 percent immature fiber, while frost-killed samples can be as much as 60 percent immature. These facts may often be deduced from microscopical examinations. Such information is invaluable in manufacturing where the strength of yarns is affected by the fibers from which they are made.

THE LENGTH and fineness of the fiber denote the growth group or species to which it belongs. Sea-island and Egyptian cottons are extremely fine and long; upland varieties are characteristically much shorter and often much coarser; Asiatics are extremely coarse and short. It is impossible to identify the variety of an unknown cotton sample by microscopic examination, but experience teaches the microscopist certain distinguishing features by which particular varieties may sometimes be spotted. For instance, S×P cotton (a commercial variety bred by crossing an American and an Egyptian variety), besides being fine, often shows in cross section one or two fibers containing an amber-colored deposit in the lumen. Stoneville cotton has fibers whose cross sections have greater length than breadth, while Rowden fiber sections are conspicuously round.

Useful as the cross-sectioning technique is, it reveals almost nothing of the internal structure of the fiber. By more specialized methods, which involve swelling of the cellulose by chemicals, microscopists have investigated the morphology of the cotton fiber to obtain a better understanding of its "architecture." An over-all knowledge of the inherent structure of cotton often helps the chemist to predict the result of a treatment before he applies it; if he is familiar with the basic fiber properties and reactions, he will have some idea of the reason why a process does or does not work.

Many questions remain unanswered, but agreement has been reached regarding the fundamental concepts of the gross or broad microscopic structure of the cotton fiber. No microscopist questions the existence of three major parts—the primary wall, the secondary wall, and the lumen. Opinions differ, however, on details of the chemical composition and physical structure of the parts.

When the fibers are treated on a microscope slide with such reagents as cuprammonium hydroxide, sulfuric acid, phosphoric acid, or trimethylbenzylammonium hydroxide, all of which are solvents for cellulose, swelling of the fiber before it dissolves shows clearly its structural details. When the fiber is completely immersed in the liquid, it begins to twist and turn on itself, and the primary wall, which encases the fiber, is ruptured by the swelling pressure of the cellulose in the secondary wall beneath it.

The primary wall breaks, often into a spiral pattern, and peels back to form constricting collars or bands. The "ballooning" thus produced is characteristic, and is similar in appearance to bead necklaces in which the "beads" are separated by constricted parts of the primary wall. In the balloons may be seen the laminated structure of the secondary wall, whose layers indicate the age of the fiber. During swelling, the lumen wall reacts in much the same way as does the primary wall, both being much more resistant to attack than the secondary wall.

The cellulose of the primary wall is made up of a network of branching fibrils of cellulose, thought to spiral about the fiber at an angle of approximately 70° to the fiber axis. In addition, it contains both wax and pectin.

The secondary wall is almost pure cellulose, believed to be deposited in alternate compact and porous layers; these are made up of branching fibrils, which spiral at an angle of approximately 30° to the fiber axis. Between the primary and secondary walls is a thin layer often referred to as the "winding," because it is seen as a coarse spiral thread wrapped around the fiber after the primary wall peels off during swelling.

The lumen contains the protoplasmic residue, which is composed for the most part of coagulated proteins. The pattern of fiber structure revealed by swelling techniques contributes information useful in interpreting the results of chemical treatment.

As a research tool, the microscope provides a means of comparing treated fibers, yarns, and fabrics with untreated specimens for a rapid evaluation of experimental results during the development of laboratory methods for the modification of cotton.

While there are well-established procedures for the more routine phases of such work, new research developments make continuing demands on the ingenuity of the microscopist. Whether it is the chemist's objective to impregnate a cloth completely or just to force compound to penetrate the edge of a yarn, microscopical techniques, both old and new, are applied in the study of the results.

To the textile chemist, mercerization is a process in which cotton yarn or cloth is treated under tension with sodium hydroxide. As a result, the fibers swell and become smooth and lustrous. Immature fibers do not mercerize normally. Present as thin, nearly untwisted ribbons before mercerization, they become highly convoluted in the solution and remain so. Well-developed fibers, on the other hand, when fully mercerized appear as clear, smooth rods, with little twist and no convolutions. In cross section they are virtually round with tightly closed lumens. Microscopical examination will show how many of the fibers in any sample have been affected and approximately to what extent.

One method of making fabrics more resistant to rotting is by acetylation of the cellulose. To show under the microscope whether or not any of the methods used is successful, an acetate stain is applied to the cloth before the yarns are withdrawn and cross-sectioned. The acetylated fibers in the yarn will take the stain and appear blurred in outline, but the untreated fibers will remain white and distinct.

Another treatment applied to cotton fibers to change their properties by changing their chemical composition is partial carboxymethylation, which may find commercial application in the manufacture of absorbent materials. While they are in the dry state, the treated fibers look the same as untreated cotton; if they are mounted in water and examined under the microscope, they swell somewhat as does raw cotton mounted in cuprammonium hydroxide. Only a little of the internal structure is visible, however, because the fibers give the appearance of being fused and solid. Fibers that have been subjected to the treatment but that have not been affected by it are not changed by water.

Some treatments are used to modify cotton by changing the physical characteristics of the fabric without altering the chemical structure of the cellulose. Resin impregnation of fabrics to render them crease-resistant is a process of this type that has reached commercial production. The methods of applying the resins are varied, as are the results. To assist the chemist in detecting the degree of penetration, the microscopist soaks the sample in a resin stain, which will be attracted to all areas in the yarn where the impregnant has entered, but will not color the untreated cellulose. In this way the location of the resin may be seen with little difficulty.

Kiton Pure Blue V, a wool dye, is readily absorbed both by urea and by melamine formaldehyde resins, but differences are noted in intensity of color for the two, the melamine taking a slightly darker stain. The cloth is soaked in the dye and dried, and a yarn is selected for cross-sectioning. If the section shows the stain around (but not in) the fiber walls, it is concluded that the resin has penetrated the yarn but has been deposited on the outside of the fibers only. If, on the other hand, the fiber walls are uniformly colored and the interfiber spaces in the yarn are clear, deposition of the resin in the cellulose may be assumed. If the latter is the case, good crease resistance is achieved. Thus the chemist may decide from the microscopical examination which method of treatment he wishes to use for the desired effect.

A similar technique has been employed in a study of the use of sweet-potato starch as a sizing for cotton fabrics. Iodine applied to the section colors the starch blue black. In a yarn taken from a starch-sized fabric, the starch is easily discernible from the fibers in the yarn.

Rubber adhesion is of interest in studies of the behavior of dipped cords in an automobile tire. It is not difficult to determine the extent of penetration of black rubber stock into a cord because of the sharp contrast between the rubber and the fibers. The problem arises when colorless latex is the material used; then staining is necessary to show the exact location of the dipping compound.

In connection with studies on cotton cords, a series of rayon cords dipped in latex under varying degrees of tension was investigated. The trial-and-error approach was used until a suitable procedure was found. The method finally chosen is a simple process, which involves soaking the sample overnight in Calcogas red and cross-sectioning; an aqueous solution of polyvinyl alcohol is used for the embedding material instead of the special collodion usually employed. A cross section of the cord dipped in latex without tension showed penetration into the center of the cord; in the same cord dipped under 150-gram tension latex was observed mainly on the outside. Now that a suitable method has been developed, the problem of finding out where the latex is located in a cotton cord will be easily solved.

THE FIBER MICROSCOPIST is also of service to the textile engineer. The mill man is interested in the physical characteristics of cotton yarns—their shapes and the number and position of fibers in them. The system used for designating the size of cotton yarn gives a figure representing the number of 840-yard lengths in a pound. For example, a 21s yarn denotes 21 × 840, or 17,640 yards of yarn to the pound. In a pound of 80s yarn there are 67,200 yards. If the yarn number is small, the yardage in the pound is also small. In this case, the microscope will show a cross section with a large periphery and a great many individual fibers. Yarn number is, therefore, an important factor in the processing of cotton to be used in fabrics, threads, and cords.

The cross-sectional technique is useful in microscopical studies of yarn sizes. Under the microscope the cross section shows the fibers in each yarn of a series. It is sometimes necessary to study the relationships of the plies one to the other in a yarn, although a plied

yarn is more difficult to section than a single yarn because there is the possibility of slippage where the yarns meet. Yarns are also studied longitudinally under the microscope to observe the lay of the fibers in the yarn, and to measure the angle of twist of the plies.

The sectioning of fabrics requires the greatest skill because warp and filling must be sliced without distortion, the one in cross-sectional and the other in longitudinal direction. Then, for a clear picture of both views of the yarns of the fabric, the directions must be reversed. Using such sections, the mill man is able to study the construction of the weave, the spaces between the yarns, and the angle at which the yarns intersect in the fabric.

Microscopical investigations of cord construction, size, and twist are useful in processing research for the improvement of cotton tire cord. For this work, a special modification of the Hardy device is used. The sample is placed in a circular opening and surrounded by filaments of some alien fiber to fill the empty spaces and prevent distortion of the cord in slicing. In cross section, it is possible to see the construction of the plies and the changes that occur in fiber alinement as a result of stretching, twisting, and so on. Before stretching, a cord shows in cross-sectional view spaces in the loosely constructed yarns as well as fibers lying horizontally at the interstices of the plies. After stretching, the cord is smaller in diameter, spaces are eliminated, and where the yarns meet few fibers appear in longitudinal view, the loose fibers having been straightened in the direction of cord axis. Such stretching increases the tensile strength of the cord.

INES V. DE GRUY *is a native of New Orleans and a graduate of Ursuline College in that city. She joined the staff of the Southern Regional Research Laboratory in 1943 and is now fiber microscopist in the cotton fiber division.*

MARY L. ROLLINS *is in charge of the microscopical properties section of*

the cotton fiber division in the South-
ern Laboratory. A native of Texas,
reared on the Mississippi Gulf Coast,
Miss Rollins is a graduate of Newcomb
College, Tulane University, in New
Orleans, and George Washington Uni-

versity. Before joining the Laboratory,
she served as a fiber technologist in the
National Bureau of Standards, in
Washington, D. C., and specialized in
the microscopical identification of tex-
tile and paper fibers.

RESEARCH CAN PRODUCE many valuable things; yet scientific investigations are often delayed, or even put aside, because the means of determining the value of a product are not readily available. To keep this from happening, it is necessary to plan methods and means of evaluation, as well as the course of investigation.

A good example of how to avoid delay in determining the value of a new treatment is the test to determine improvement in the resistance of cotton materials to rotting and mildewing developed at the Southern Regional Research Laboratory. If an untreated cotton sandbag will last several months in service, it is apparent that many months will be required for testing a treatment of the fabric to improve its resistance to rotting. If the treatment is many times more effective, the testing time could run into years. A much faster test is necessary.

Accordingly, the Laboratory devised rapid tests for the evaluation of cottons treated to make them mildew- and rot-resistant. The most severe is the soil-burial test. The micro-organisms that produce mildew and cause rotting are ever present in air and soil. Their number, or activity, is held in check normally by such conditions as lack of moisture or nourishment. By deliberately making conditions favorable for their growth, their activity can be greatly increased.

By setting up conditions known to be most conducive to the growth of cotton-destroying micro-organisms, then, the time for testing cotton treated in various ways can be greatly reduced. A sample of untreated cotton exposed to the most severe condition is reduced to half strength in 3 days and completely destroyed in 7 days. A sample of cotton that lasts a week in the soil-burial test without serious loss of strength may last a year in ordinary service. A better preserved cotton that stands up for 6 or 8 weeks in the test may last a year under really severe conditions of exposure. Testing in a soil bed teeming with destructive micro-organisms cuts the time required to a small fraction of that required for an actual service test.

At the Southern Laboratory the rapid soil-burial test used in the development of rot- and mildew-resistant treatments for cotton is conducted in sliding trays like drawers (8 inches deep) inside a cabinet with provisions for keeping the temperature between 85° and 90° F. In the trays is composted soil—30 to 40 percent well-rotted leaf mold, 30 to 40 percent dry manure, and about 20 percent lake sand. The moisture content of the compost is kept at 25 to 30 percent of its dry weight. Samples are usually buried horizontally at least 1 inch below the surface. The activity of the compost is checked frequently by burying control samples, which should lose all their strength within a week.—*Albert S. Cooper, Jr., Southern Regional Research Laboratory.*

902722°—51——27

The Scientist Looks at Cotton

James N. Grant

Cottons grown in the different parts of the world vary in color, maturity, size, length, and strength of fibers. Soil, climate, and the species of cotton cause the variations.

Fibers may be short and coarse, as in the Asiatic varieties. They may be long and fine, as in Egyptian and sea-island varieties. They may be intermediate in length and size, as in the American upland varieties, which constitute the great bulk of cotton produced in the United States.

This diversity and the demand on textile products to meet definite requirements in specific uses necessitate the classification of cotton by quality.

The conception of quality depends somewhat on individual interests. In the trade, the cotton classer judges quality by what he can see with his eyes or feel with his hands. The textile-mill superintendent thinks of quality in terms of fibers that meet requirements of his special product. The consumer judges quality by the appearance or serviceability of the product manufactured from the cotton.

In the laboratory, the textile technologist thinks of quality in terms of the chemical or physical properties of the fibers and the potentialities of those properties in putting out superior products. Because the chemical composition of most cotton fibers is nearly the same, quality is usually defined in terms of the physical properties of the fibers— length, strength, fineness, maturity, or color.

Qualities of raw cotton fibers evaluated in commercial classification are identified under such terms as staple length, character, and grade. The values assigned according to accepted scales of measurements or specified terms of description determine the relative market worth of the cotton and denote its useful attributes.

Of the many physical properties of cotton fibers, staple length is the only one assigned a concrete value in commercial classification. To the cotton classer, staple length represents the length of only a typical part of fibers he has segregated and straightened between his thumb and forefinger. From the several thousand fibers in his hands he estimates the staple length of a cotton. Uniformity in making this selection requires great skill. Evaluation is made by comparison with official standards provided for three types of cottons—American upland, American Egyptian, and sea-island. Official standards of length for American upland are available in 20 intervals over the range from ¾ to 1½ inches. American Egyptian and sea-island have 4 intervals over the range from 1½ to 1¾ inches, with provision for estimating beyond the official standards. The length evaluation is the basis for international classification of cotton for export and import. Such a selection is reasonable, because length often imparts fundamental information on other properties of the fiber, such as strength and fineness. The general tendency, for instance, is for long fibers to be very fine, with high tensile strength. The uses of fibers depend upon these basic properties.

Character of cotton fiber is based on strength, fineness, maturity, elasticity, and many other inherent physical properties, together with uniformity of fiber-length distribution. Some terms that designate character are weak, strong, soft, wasty, perished, irregular, and normal—depending on the deviation from the normal cotton. Character terms are relative rather than absolute as compared to staple length, but they provide essential information where strength, dyeing qualities, or spinning properties of the fibers are the critical factors.

Evaluations of cotton fiber under grade are associated with the history of the fiber from opening of the boll until packing in the bale. Grade combines a visual classification of the color, the amount of foreign substances entangled in the fibers before and during harvest, and the evenness with which the fibers were ginned. Long exposure to intense sunlight produces changes in color and gloss. Stalks, hulls, leaves, or other foreign material entangled in the fibers may increase cleaning damage and cost before processing. High moisture content of seed cotton at the gin, as well as improperly operated ginning equipment, can result in gin damage or cause the fibers to be left in small matted tufts.

THE THREE GENERAL classifications are satisfactory in the evaluation of cotton for purchase or selection for general uses. But that type of information is of little use to breeders, who desire specific values for many physical properties of their cottons, or to manufacturers, who require correlation of physical properties of fibers with product performance. Definite values for individual fiber characteristics, such as strength, fineness, surface characteristics, maturity, and length uniformity, as well as detailed knowledge of chemical structure of the fiber, are essential to an understanding of the mechanical behavior of cotton. The characteristics determine durability, appearance, dyeing properties, and other qualities of interest to consumers.

The desire for specific values indicative of fiber-length distribution in a sample to replace dependence on judgment from visual examination has resulted in the development of several instruments for the purpose. Mechanical separation of fibers into groups of $\frac{1}{8}$-inch intervals is more time-consuming than optically scanning the fibers in a beam of light, but results from the mechanical method give more detailed information. Both methods are extensively used in breeding programs, in which knowledge of lengths of individual fibers and the distributions of the fibers by length is helpful in predicting the demand for a new variety. Length of individual fibers in samples of cotton range from a small part of an inch to more than the staple length. The greater part by weight is always less than the designated length. Individual fibers in varieties of American upland cottons often exceed 2 inches and in sea-island $3\frac{1}{2}$ inches, but the number ever attaining these unusual lengths is small. Cottons with the higher proportion of fibers of the same length group have better manufacturing characteristics—the breakage due to long fibers is lessened. Experience indicates that an increase in lengths of fibers of the same weight fineness (weight of cellulose per inch of fiber), without change in strength, increases the strength of yarns by reducing the number of discontinuities between fiber ends, and that interspacing short fibers with longer ones increases yarn size without proportionally increasing its strength or durability. Extremely long fibers, however, add to processing difficulty because they have a greater tendency toward neppiness and are more difficult to separate and parallelize on textile machinery without breakage of individual fibers.

Although an increase in fiber length is often associated with an increase in yarn strength (through the fact that use is made of a higher proportion of the fiber strength corresponding to the greater length), it is the inherent strength of the fiber that is fundamental to strength in a yarn or manufactured product.

The inherent strength of the fiber depends on the deposition of spiral layers of cellulose in the cell wall during the growth of the fiber. The angle of these spiral layers of cellulose with the fiber axis, determined from X-ray patterns of masses of fibers, is closely associated with fiber strength.

Individual fiber strengths range from $\frac{1}{400}$ to $\frac{1}{30}$ pound; the average is about $\frac{1}{100}$ pound. When fibers are tested in small compressed bundles, however, their bundle tensile strengths range between 50,000 and 100,000 pounds to the square inch, the higher strength being commensurate with the tensile strength of steel. American upland varieties produce fibers intermediate in this range, with strength averaging about 78,000 pounds to the square inch.

The three common mechanical methods for determining strength are round-bundle, flat-bundle, and individual-fiber breaking load. In the round-bundle test, comparison of cottons is based on the strength per unit of the cross-sectional area of the bundle, expressed as pounds per square inch. From the flat-bundle method, the ratio of breaking load to weight of fiber tested furnishes essentially the same information as the round-bundle test but in less time. Neither of these methods gives the fundamental knowledge of elastic properties or variation between fibers obtained in the individual-fiber method.

As a complement of strength, the elastic properties of cotton fibers (determined on the individual fiber) influence their usefulness. The individual fiber elongates rapidly when load (less than $\frac{1}{1000}$ pound) is first applied, because of its natural twists and convolutions and the kinks that result from the condition of the fiber in the boll. After the rapid initial elongation, the fiber elongates very slowly and finally breaks. At break, the length increase may be as much as 6 to 10 percent. If the load is removed before break, only a fractional part of the elongation is recovered. Strength and elongation of cotton fiber depend in general upon the variety of the plant and growth conditions. The longer fibers in a variety usually have greater strength and elongation.

In contrast to elongation and recovery, which are considered in a direction parallel to the fiber axis, such properties as flexibility and brittleness are judged by ability of the cotton fiber to bend in directions perpendicular to the axis. Performance tests on the textile product indicate that the flexibility of cotton fiber is satisfactory and superior to that of other natural cellulosic textile fibers. However, this evaluation is a composite with other fiber properties and fabric construction.

Closely associated with other properties, but undesirable in a textile fiber, is the lack of resilience, or inability of the cotton fiber to recover rapidly from deformation, such as bending or compression.

The sizes of fibers are difficult to determine if the fiber diameter is taken as the measure, because shapes of dry fibers are highly irregular. The cross-sectional shapes assumed by fibers on exposure to the air depend on the thickness of the cellulose wall. Thick-walled fibers remain almost circular. Thin-walled fibers are approximately elliptical. Internal stresses within the walls cause the fibers to twist. The twisting produces convolutions. Such variations make fiber diameter unreliable as a measure of size.

Instead of diameter, the weight of cellulose per inch of fiber, called weight fineness, is generally accepted as a good measure of cellulose content, closely associated with size. The range in weight fineness of commercial cotton extends from 2.5 micrograms per inch in sea-island to 8.8 micrograms per inch in Asiatic varieties. American upland cottons range from 3.2 to 6.0 micrograms per inch. Special varieties, such as S×P, or United States sea-island, have weight fineness as low as 3.0 micrograms per inch, while varieties of Chinese cotton show values up to 11 micrograms per inch. A rapid approximation of weight fineness can be obtained from instruments that measure the resistance to air flow. This measure is more accurately one of fiber surface, because passage of air between fibers depends on both the fiber shape and the cross-sectional perimeter.

Textile fibers, natural or synthetic, differ in many physical and mechanical properties. Length and size of hemp, jute, and ramie fibers depend partly upon the separation of cells in the retting process, whereas the cotton fiber is a single cell. In contrast, synthetic fibers are extruded to the size and cut to the length desired by the manufacturer.

The relative thickness of the cell wall as compared to total fiber diameter when a fiber is swollen in sodium hydroxide is generally accepted as an expression of the maturity of the fiber. Cottons with total wall thickness more or less than half the diameter of the swollen fiber are arbitrarily referred to as mature and immature, respectively. Cell-wall thickness influences such properties of the fiber as strength, elongation, and absorption of dyes. The usual evaluation of fiber maturity has depended on microscopical examination of a fiber swollen with sodium hydroxide, or of its color when the fiber is viewed through polarizing crystals in the microscope. A newer test for maturity is based on the different reactions of mature and immature fibers to a mixture of a green and a red dye; those with thick walls dye shades of red and those with thin walls dye green shades.

THE RANGES in strength and elastic properties overlap for natural and synthetic fibers. Jute fiber has a cross section 10 times the size of that of the cotton fiber, but its tensile strength per unit of weight fineness is the same as that of cotton. Flax, hemp, and ramie, also larger in cross section than cotton, have strengths almost twice that of cotton, but their elongation under load is far less. Silk filaments, 30 percent smaller than cotton fibers, have 40 per-cent more tensile strength and about 300 percent greater elongation, with larger relative recovery when the load is removed. Wool fiber, recognized as an inherently weak fiber, with a tensile strength about half that of cotton, increases in length as much as 34 percent before breaking and has excellent recovery of length. Protein fibers are weaker than wool and have comparable elongation at break, but show little recovery at the high elongations. In general, stretched rayon has elongation comparable with that of cotton and with a higher strength. Unstretched rayons, however, have lower strength, with higher elongation and poor recovery from loading.

Synthetic fibers have a much wider range of property differences, depending on the materials used and the mechanical or chemical treatment given the fiber.

NYLON FILAMENT, slightly weaker than ramie, the strongest of the natural fibers, has strength and excellent elongation and recovery after loading, exceeding even that of silk. Such composite properties have made nylon filament in demand for products like parachute cords and hosiery.

Textile fibers differ in flexibility, that is, their ability to bend repeatedly without breaking. Glass fiber, as an extreme, is very brittle. The bast fibers are less brittle. Cotton is considered to have better flexibility properties than bast fibers, as reflected by the behavior of its manufactured products. The flexibility of synthetic fibers is as good as that of cotton and in some fibers is far superior to that of the cotton fiber.

Natural and synthetic fibers respond differently to changes in temperature and moisture. Most natural fibers, notably ramie and cotton, increase in strength with increase in moisture, while synthetic fibers usually decrease in strength with increase in moisture. Natural fibers lose strength with a rise in temperature; synthetic fibers vary in their response to temperature.

Wool, nylon, and silk are superior to cotton in their ability to absorb energy, or work, because they have excellent elongation and good recovery.

The properties of textiles are of immediate interest to the manufacturer and the user. The characteristics of any product depend upon the basic fiber properties and the interaction of the properties in the geometrical structure of the fabric containing large aggregates of fibers. Many of the properties have been evaluated only in the yarn stage.

Differences in physical properties of cotton fibers are recognized in their selection for many textile products. Fibers used in tire cord must be strong and flexible to withstand the strains and bends of the tire as it hits obstacles in its path. Color in these fibers is of secondary importance, because they are concealed in layers of rubber.

Fibers made into a mattress or a rug must have sufficient resilience to recover from bends or other deformations while in use, a property more pronounced in the coarse fibers.

Size, strength, and color are important qualities of the cotton fibers used in fine fabrics, because they add to durability and appearance of the finished products. Immature, or thin-walled, cotton fibers are generally avoided by the manufacturers because they forewarn of processing difficulties. Their strengths are usually insufficient to withstand the mechanical processes of separation and straightening to produce uniform fine yarns without significant decrease in length. These fibers, manufactured into fine yarns produce irregularities in strength and cross-sectional area because of small mats of entangled fibers, called neps. Neps dye to lighter shades of color than does the rest of the yarn.

The thin-walled fibers are especially suitable for the manufacture of products, like fire hose, in which color is unimportant and fine yarns are not required, but in which, rather, fibers that have natural swelling capacity to close the interstices between yarns and fibers are essential to prevent leakage. Many intricate cotton fabrics are constructed from yarns designed to overcome the undesirable elastic properties of the fibers both in extension and compression. An analysis of elastic properties of fibers in these fabrics is often complicated with superimposed properties, such as staple length, twist in the singles yarn, twist in the plied yarns, and weave of the fabric.

Coarser fabrics can be produced from average cotton that has acceptable strength and good spinning characteristics. Most domestic fabrics require cottons with physical properties within the range found in our American upland varieties; special fabrics must be produced from imported cottons or those produced at a higher cost per pound. The demand for cotton with long, strong, and fine fibers is greater than can be met by domestic production. To meet it, quantities of Egyptian cottons are imported each year.

The practice of evaluating the fiber qualities in terms of service of the manufactured products has prevented many properties from being recognized, because processing and fabrication of yarns introduce variables that sometimes overbalance the property under test. The textile technologist is working to meet the needs of the breeder for information on quality characteristics of cottons by developing precise methods and equipment to measure and evaluate properties of textile fibers during stages of processing and product performance.

JAMES N. GRANT *is a native of North Carolina and a graduate of Duke University. He joined the staff of the research and testing division of the cotton branch, Production and Marketing Administration, in 1937, to perform research on physical properties of cotton fibers and devise rapid methods for measuring those properties. He transferred to similar work with the Southern Regional Research Laboratory in 1942.*

Chemically Modified Cotton

J. David Reid, James D. Dean

For all its usefulness, cotton cannot compete with other fibers in certain respects. It is not so flame-resistant, soil-resistant, or resilient as wool. It resists mildewing and rotting less well than cellulose acetate rayon. It is weaker and less elastic than silk or nylon. It is less water-absorbent than flax or ramie.

Plant breeders and growers have made some changes in the qualities of the cotton fiber, but its essential composition remains unchanged. It is the chemist's task to modify the cotton to make it more suitable for a particular use. Like many synthetic fibers, cotton fiber must be tailor-made for its job.

Chemical modification of cotton is sometimes difficult. Cotton is so sensitive to many chemical treatments that the fiber may lose strength. Occasionally, fiber characteristics are markedly changed by modifications so slight as to be almost undetected by analytical methods; again, the modification required to change qualities to the desired extent is great.

By chemical modification of cotton is meant the transformation of all or part of its cellulosic material into another chemical compound, which retains the fibrous character of the cotton. This modification differs from the chemical modification of purified cellulose made from cotton linters, wood, or fibrous agricultural wastes to obtain a chemical compound that can be dissolved and then spun or cast into materials like rayon or transparent sheeting. Chemical modification of cotton is also in contrast to that type of cloth finishing in which an inert finishing agent is added physically, rather than chemically, to a fabric.

We have to understand the nature of cellulose in order to bring about the precise degree of modification demanded for a special use.

Cellulose resembles alcohols and sugars in chemical structure—indeed, it is composed of long chains of glucose residues layered together. Much of the fundamental chemistry of cellulose remains to be explored, however. A great deal of chemical work has been done in practical research (to obtain cotton with certain desirable characteristics) and in fundamental research (to determine the nature of the changes). Often the fundamental work precedes the practical. Fundamental research involves a search for truth, often with no immediate practical application in mind. It is concerned with such things as molecular structure, methods of carrying out reactions, and instruments or methods for complex measurements—in general, with problems not necessarily of monetary value. Fortunately, once such truths become evident, practical use may be made of many of them. Practical research alone, without insight into reaction mechanisms, is likely to be extremely limited in scope—almost "trial and error" work. Fundamental work points the way to a wider scope; it is generally true that fundamental research leads to broader applications of a method or to entirely new uses.

THE REACTION OF CELLULOSE with formaldehyde is interesting because the addition of amounts as small as a few tenths of 1 percent changes the fibers greatly. The reaction has limited practical application now, but it encourages the chemist to continue his search for reactions that may yield fibers of greater usefulness.

The formaldehyde-treated fibers become more brittle, will not dye with many of the direct cotton dyes, and will not dissolve in cuprammonium hydroxide solution. Those properties indicate the possible formation of cross-linked methylene ethers of the cellulose—apparently the formaldehyde has linked together the long chains that make up the cotton fiber. If the fiber is visualized as being made up of tiny glucose residues and the relative sizes of building units to fiber are calculated, only about 0.05 percent of the units are on the surface of an ideally uniform fiber. A. C. Walker, of the Bell Telephone Laboratories, however, has estimated that to cover the many internal surfaces between the fibrils making up the fiber about 1 percent of water would be required to form a monomolecular film. Apparently, in the case of formaldehyde, it is only necessary to change those readily available surface units to change greatly the characteristics of the fiber.

Formaldehyde alone is not of great practical importance as a treating agent for textiles, but resins formed by condensing melamine or urea with formaldehyde have been widely used in cloth finishing; an estimated 40 million pounds was used in 1949. The process involves the application of a water solution or emulsion of the material to the fabric, followed by polymerization, or insolubilization, in place, with heat. This type of finish, originated by an English concern, is used to make cloth creaseproof or wrinkleproof. Another commercial concern has modified this method to give a "permanently glazed" chintz by using the resin and following it by friction calendering, or pressing, to obtain the glaze.

For apparel fabrics, the treatments have so far proved more applicable to rayon and wool than to cotton; cotton loses some tensile strength after treatment. The technique of resin application to fabrics, however, is being steadily improved. The simple melamine, for example, is being replaced by a more effective methylated methylol compound, and a thermoplastic vinyl resin is being combined with the formaldehyde condensates to give stronger creaseproof cotton products. The first objective of such research is the production of cotton apparel fabrics that resist creasing and wrinkling. Present progress indicates the near availability of resin-finished goods having a resilience that will not be removed by laundering.

Chemists differ as to whether the changes in fabric properties caused by the action of the resins are physical or chemical. Filling the vacant spaces in the fiber with the insoluble resin undoubtedly makes a great deal of difference in its properties, and many maintain that that is the whole story. On the other hand, because formaldehyde alone has such a great effect, it is possible that the formaldehyde component of the resin reacts with the cellulose to change its character. In this field of study, the practical developments have far outdistanced the fundamental theoretical work. Full understanding of the physical and chemical effects of such resin applications to cotton should be followed by the appearance of cool summer-wear cotton suiting that is the equal of wool in nonsoiling and wrinkle-free properties.

W. O. KENYON, of the Eastman Kodak Research Laboratories, in 1936, observed that gaseous nitrogen dioxide would oxidize cotton to a product that retained its fibrous form and a reasonable amount of tensile strength, although it was soluble in weak alkaline solutions. It would even disintegrate in 1 percent sodium bicarbonate solution because of the presence of carboxyl groups in the cellulose chain. This apparent fault was turned to advantage by other workers, who found that the material could be absorbed by the body and could be implanted in body tissues to avoid adhesions. As a dressing for wounds it could carry thrombin, a natural blood-coagulating agent, and was itself able to prevent the flow of blood. The material now is manufactured and sold as a medical specialty. It is often packed into a wound and left there. The body absorbs it in 7 to 20 days.

The characteristic solubility of the oxidized cellulose fiber in alkalies has been utilized in studies on the structure of the cotton fiber by microscopists of the Department of Agriculture, who found that the gaseous oxidation made the fiber capable of solution but that it did not destroy the physical form. As the fiber swelled and successive layers dissolved under the microscope, it was possible to study the details of its structure.

FLAMEPROOFED CLOTH is generally understood to mean a cloth that will not transmit flame across its surface after the igniting source has been removed. Flameproofed cloth is important in wartime. It has been less used in peacetime, although serious accidents to children, fire in public gathering places, and similar accidents draw attention to the dangers of such materials as flammable play clothes and draperies. Restrictive legislation is increasing with regard to flammable fabrics, particularly those used as draperies in public places.

Flameproofing · is often done by home methods, but such treatment is generally temporary in that it is removed by laundering. The cloth is saturated with solutions of certain water-soluble salts and then dried. One recommended method uses 7 parts of borax to 3 parts of boric acid, the whole diluted with 64 parts of water. In 1946 a more permanent type was developed at the Department of Agriculture by two chemists, Kenneth S. Campbell and Jack E. Sands. The fabric is padded with an emulsion incorporating a chlorinated hydrocarbon wax, a water-soluble urea-formalde-hyde resin, and antimony oxide, and cured at a high temperature. Because of the technique and equipment necessary, the treatment is suitable for commercial application alone.

Only two of the known methods of commercial flameproofing are considered to be chemical modifications of the cellulose. One of the methods uses a complex mixture of titanium and antimony chloride compounds.

When it is soaked in a solution of the mixture and then made alkaline and washed, cloth becomes resistant to burning. The resistance remains through numerous launderings. In this case, practical application has preceded theoretical knowledge. It remains for fundamental research to determine whether a compound of cellulose has been formed and, if so, what further variations and applications of the method may be made.

The second method of commercial flameproofing is known to modify chemically the cellulose of the cotton fiber. The process involves esterification—a process of combination—of the cellulose with phosphoric acid. Although treatment with strong acids generally causes a great loss of strength in cotton cloth, the industry has developed a method that ingeniously avoids much of this degradation. Cloth is impregnated with a solution of the urea salt of phosphoric acid, dried, then heated for a few minutes between 300° and 350° F. The high temperature causes esterification and at the same time breaks down the urea to give ammonia, which counteracts the degradative effect of the acid and simultaneously forms the ammonium salt of the newly formed cellulose phosphate. An average substitution of about 1 phosphate group in each 6 of the glucose anhydride groups of which the cotton fiber is composed gives a satisfactory protective action when the material is in the form of the ammonium salt.

The phosphorylated cellulose ester as such is fairly stable toward hydrolysis, but unfortunately ion-exchange occurs during laundering and reduces the flameproofing effect. That is, the ammonia portion of the material is replaced by the sodium of the soap or the calcium of hard water, and the flameproofness is reduced. That is a reasonable result, because sodium and calcium phosphates are not flameproofing agents, while ammonium phosphate works very well. To be effective for flameproofing, acid salts have to decompose to yield free acid groups at flame temperatures or below. The acid presumably has caused the cellulose to decompose, not to volatile inflammable gases, but rather to less flammable products, perhaps even to carbon and water, and in that manner has produced flameproofing. The ammonium content can be returned to the phosphorylated cellulose by re-treatment with ammonia; other treatments also may tend to fix the ammonia content. Research workers have studied methods of phosphorylating cellulose and have examined the constitution of the resulting compounds. The ion-exchange property has been utilized by J. F. Jurgens, J. D. Reid, and J. D. Guthrie, of the Department of Agriculture. They have developed the use of phosphorylated cotton as a cation-exchange material. In the laboratory, phosphorylated cloth is useful in this capacity, and has been employed to obtain salt-free protein materials.

THE SODIUM SALT of carboxymethyl cellulose is completely soluble in water if the degree of substitution is at least 1 carboxymethyl group for each 2 glucose units. Solubility declines as the substitution becomes less. This fact has been used to advantage at the Southern Regional Research Laboratory by J. David Reid and G. C. Daul, who reasoned that partial carboxymethylation would give quickly swellable cotton fibers, depending on the amount of substitution. On this premise, they prepared several modified cottons that contained various amounts of substitution (about 1 carboxymethyl per 5 to 40 glucose units). They impregnated the cotton with the required amount of monochloroacetic acid and then treated it with strong sodium hydroxide for about 30 minutes. The process did not greatly affect the tensile strength, appearance, or feel of the cotton, but did make it highly water-absorbent and quickly swellable. The highly absorbent material is promising for toweling and similar uses. A patent assigned to the Secretary of Agriculture has been granted on the new type of material.

In a further modification of the same process, Reid and Daul prepared cotton yarns that were more highly substituted. The yarns have the interesting property of disintegrating or dissolving in water. The disappearing yarns offer possibilities for use as scaffolding yarns in novelty fabrics and for use in knitting processes where it is desirable that connecting yarns be eliminated in the finished article.

Another method of etherification, a British process announced in 1940, modifies cotton fabrics chemically in a way that makes possible the production of several striking finishes. If the cotton material is first activated by impregnation with caustic soda and then treated with ethylene oxide dissolved in carbon tetrachloride, its hand and appearance change markedly. By varying the concentrations of the treating agents, finishes can be secured that range from a linenlike to a parchmentized appearance without much loss of fabric strength. When cloth that has been energetically treated in this manner is dampened and calendered, a highly transparent fabric is produced.

ALTHOUGH A NUMBER of beautiful and permanent dyes have been developed for cotton, direct dyeing of cotton cloth has never been so satisfactory as the dyeing of wool. Wool has dyed better because the amino groups present in the protein of which the wool is composed adsorb or react with the dyes to give a wide range of shade and color with good stability. In the effort to utilize wool dyes with cotton, attempts have been made for many years to "animalize" the cotton; that is, introduce amino groups into the cellulose molecule to attract the wool dye.

A number of such methods have been evolved, but most of them are hard to carry out on a commercial scale. A more promising method was developed by J. D. Guthrie, of the Department of Agriculture, in 1948. The use of methyl or ethyl sulfate to form stable ethers with cellulose has long been known, and the process is used commercially. By the use of aminoethyl sulfuric acid, which is commercially available, Guthrie was able to ethylate the cotton cellulose to a small extent without much loss in strength or change in physical characteristics. The method consists in impregnating the cloth with a strongly alkaline solution of the aminoethyl sulfuric acid and drying at a temperature high enough to drive off the water fairly rapidly. Variations in the treating conditions give cloth with different nitrogen contents, but one containing only 0.3 percent nitrogen will dye with many direct wool dyes. The cloth may be used for ion-exchange purposes in the same way as the phosphorylated cloth just described. The method of producing the aminoethoxy cellulose material has been patented and the patent assigned to the Secretary of Agriculture.

Chemical modification of cotton may also be used to produce entirely different dyeing effects. An example, which has been employed commercially is known as immunized cotton. It is a partly esterified cotton, which does not dye with the ordinary cotton substantive or direct dyeing colors, and can thus be used for novel effects. In the process, the bleached cotton yarn or fabric is first treated with a concentrated alcoholic solution of caustic soda to form a sodium compound of cellulose. It is then reacted at a high temperature with a solution of toluene-p-sulfonyl chloride. By this reaction part of the cellulose is converted into a toluene-p-sulfonyl ester, and

a modified cotton product almost unchanged in strength and appearance, but extremely resistant to cotton dyes, results.

THE ROTPROOFING of cotton is a thorny problem for the chemist. It is, of course, a blessing that nature has provided for removal of cellulosic wastes by micro-organisms, which continually transform such wastes into food and finally into carbon dioxide and water. Unfortunately, the organisms make no distinction between wastes and tarpaulins, fish nets, tentage, awnings, tobacco shade cloth, and others.

One way to modify cotton to prevent rotting is by partial acetylation. The cellulose molecule is so changed that micro-organisms find it difficult to attack, and little or no rotting occurs. Like partial acetylation, both the chemical methods of flameproofing previously described also inhibit rotting of cotton cloth. Workers in the Department of Agriculture have found that both the carboxymethylated cotton and the aminoethoxy cellulose described previously will react with some metallic salts, such as mercury salts, to fix the metal firmly in the cloth and thus prevent microbiological degradation. These methods of preventing the rotting of cotton cloth offer promise, particularly if the chemical modification of the cellulose also serves some other useful purpose, such as flameproofing in the case of phosphorylation.

The modifications we have described and the others they exemplify offer limitless opportunities for improving the usefulness of cotton for specific purposes. Every new treatment produces what is essentially a new fiber, which differs from the original cotton and from all other fibers. Each, also, has a double usefulness—its own practical utility and the value of proving that much more can be done to create new and better fabrics.

J. DAVID REID *is a chemist in charge of the chemical properties section at the Southern Regional Research Labo-*

ratory. Dr. Reid did his undergraduate work at Washington State College and came to the Department in 1930. He has since worked in the field of agricultural chemistry, first at the Color and Farm Waste Laboratory in Washington, D. C., then with the Agricultural Byproducts Laboratory in Ames, Iowa, and since 1940 with the Southern Laboratory.

JAMES D. DEAN *worked for more than 20 years as chemist, purchasing agent, and plant superintendent for several textile companies. In 1941 he joined the standardization branch of the Office of the Quartermaster General in Washington, and a year later transferred to the Southern Laboratory, where he is in charge of the cotton chemical processing division.*

FABRICS HAVE been bleached to remove impurities since the earliest times. Pliny, in the first century A. D., referred to the use of ashes of plants for bleaching. But little is known of the process of bleaching before the seventeenth century, when the Dutch in Haarlem acquired a reputation for skill in bleaching linen.

The district had unlimited quantities of pure water and an abundance of buttermilk to furnish lactic acid, a bleaching agent. The process took weeks or even months. After steeping in warm water, the goods were washed, rinsed, wrung, and dried. Then came the first treatment in a bath of potash, the recipe for which was the real secret of the whole process. The grass-bleach followed. During the treatment, the cloth was held in place on the grass and never allowed to dry. Sometimes the alternating treatments of potash and grassing were repeated 20 times to obtain the desired whiteness. After another warm bath, the cloth was subjected to the action of the acid contained in fermented buttermilk—a process lasting from 6 to 8 days. A third rinsing was followed by a soaping on long tables, more rinsing, and finally drying in the wind and sun.

Bleaching flourished in Haarlem until the middle of the eighteenth century. Chemists then introduced pure chemicals—an alkali and sulfuric acid—and quick-acting chlorine compounds in place of exposure for long periods on the bleaching greens. Thus started the modern bleaching industry.

The prejudice against lime for bleaching, on the grounds that it injured the material, was finally overcome, as well as a prejudice against the use of a dilute sulfuric acid instead of a buttermilk sour. James Ferguson, of Belfast, in 1764 experimented with lime in bleaching. Francis Home, of Edinburgh, introduced the sulfuric acid sour in 1750, thereby reducing the length of the process from 7 or 8 months to 4 months. Claude Berthollet suggested using chlorine as a whitening agent. A great obstacle to its use, the noxious fumes, was overcome when Berthollet found that the gas could be dissolved in solutions of alkaline hydroxides. In 1799 Charles Tennant, of Glasgow, patented the manufacture of bleaching powder by the use of lime and chlorine.

Chemists have continued to introduce new products as kier "assistants" and "wetting" agents, and engineers have developed new machines for speeding the processes. Today, two general procedures are used—the caustic soda kier boil, with either hypochlorite bleach or peroxide kier bleach, and the continuous peroxide bleach. The complete process in a modern continuous bleach takes only 2 or 3 hours.—*Rita M. Kraemer, Southern Regional Research Laboratory.*

How To Keep Dry Under Cotton

J. David Reid,
Charles F. Goldthwait

Cotton fabrics are the basis for many kinds of raincoats—the once-popular oilskins, yellow slickers, and heavy rubber coats, and some of the newer plastic garments. Fabrics of those types resist water because of their construction; they are watertight but also airtight, so that the wearer may be almost as wet from sweat as he would be from rain without the coat. In attempts to improve cotton for water resistance, therefore, technicians have tried to develop fabrics that are porous to air but impermeable to water.

Cotton in the boll is not easily wet by the rain, because a tiny bit of wax on the surface of each fiber repels water and keeps the boll from becoming waterlogged and heavy, dragging on the ground, and meeting an untimely end through mildew and rot.

But this natural wax is not usually allowed to stay in the fiber after the cotton has been made into cloth. Without the wax, cotton becomes hydrophilic—it shows a strong affinity for water and absorbs it readily. That trait is good in toweling, but far otherwise in products where resistance to water is essential. What is wanted is a means of making cotton hydrophobic—that is, water-repellent.

Since 1870 or so, that has been possible through the application of water-repellent chemicals to the cotton fabrics. For a decade, Department of Agriculture chemists have been working on another possibility for developing water-resistant cotton—by utilization of the swelling effect of wet cotton to prevent the passage of water. Cotton fabrics of this type are called self-sealing.

Water-repellent fabrics and self-sealing fabrics represent two classes of water-resistant cotton. We consider them in the pages that follow.

WATER-REPELLENT COTTON is fabric in which the individual fibers have been treated with a chemical which (like the natural wax in the growing fiber) repels water and causes it to collect in drops on the surface and run off instead of penetrating the yarns. Water-repellent fabrics are understood to be permeable to air because the spaces between the fibers have not been affected.

Chemical treatments that produce water repellency have been known since the late 1870's. Many, though, are not permanent; they are called re-treatable water repellents, for the fabric must be re-treated after each laundering or dry cleaning to be serviceable again. At first, the treatment was generally accomplished by dipping the cloth in a solution of soaplike emulsion, such as sodium ammonium stearate, drying it, and then passing it through a second solution of an aluminum salt, usually aluminum acetate, and washing. The metallic soap deposited on the cloth gave good water repellency. Later, a one-bath treatment was developed; the cloth was dipped in a single emulsion and dried. The effect was the same.

Much work has also been done to develop a durable treatment, one in which the water repellency is not removed by laundering or dry cleaning. To do that, two principal methods are theoretically available to the research worker. The first involves a reaction of the water-repellent material with the cellulose of the cotton fiber to yield a stable compound that will remain during laundering. The second method consists of allowing small molecules of a water-repellent material to penetrate the fiber and there polymerize to larger molecules—too large to escape when the cloth is cleaned.

That a tremendous amount of research has been conducted on the problem is indicated by the fact that by 1950 scientists had published 332 reports on the strictly chemical methods of imparting water repellency.

UNTIL LATE in the 1930's, the commercial development of a durable water-repellent treatment seemed almost impossible. Around 1937, however, such compounds as the alkoxymethyl pyridinium chlorides used earlier to give special finishes to cloth were modified by a British concern to give water repellency and were patented. The success of the compounds initiated the investigation of many pyridinium and other quaternary nitrogen compounds in this connection. The compounds, applied to cloth at high temperatures, broke down and were assumed to be reacting either with themselves or with the cellulose to give the water-repellent finish. The finish is remarkably resistant to laundering and dry cleaning, in that the major portion of it is not removed from the cloth. But the detergents used in the cleaning tend to stay in the cloth and neutralize the water-repellent effect. Careful rinsing and hot pressing will restore the repellency, but such aftertreatment is sometimes so difficult that the durable treatment loses much of its advantage over other treatments.

Although this type of treatment is used commercially in several forms, the mechanism of reaction is not well known. F. V. Davis made a substantial contribution to our knowledge of the reaction of one of these compounds, stearamidomethyl pyridinium chloride, with cotton. Working with English commercial materials, he found evidence from which he tentatively concluded that, when the application was less than 1 percent, the compound reacted entirely with cellulose to form a stearamidomethyl ether of cellulose. For applications between 1 and 2 percent there was formed some methylol stearamide in loose association with the cloth in addition to the cellulose ether.

In contrast to the extensive practical work done on producing water-repellent compounds for textiles, surprisingly little has been done on the theoretical side. Workers in the Department of Agriculture have started investigating the theory of water repellency. For that they needed a method sensitive enough to determine slight differences in the effectiveness of different water repellents. Many instruments are available for determining the value of cloth for use in raincoats, but, because rain is a moving thing, most of the methods involve dynamic tests and thus are unsuitable for classifying slight differences between compounds or in methods of applying one compound to a standard cloth. H. A. Schuyten and others devised an apparatus for the more precise measurements. The method is simple. Wetting agents enable water to wet even a water-repellent cloth—they lower the surface tension of water so that it no longer forms drops, which roll off the surface, but tends to sink in and wet the fabric. Starting with these facts, technicians devised a test in which the cloth is tilted at an angle of 45° and the solution is determined which will just wet it thoroughly instead of running off as pure water does. An electrical rather than a visual means is used to determine when the cloth is wet. The surface tensions of the various solutions are known, so the determination is called the surface-tension index of the fabric. The lower surface tension denotes the better repellency.

With the instrument, the investigators hope to determine the efficiency of applications, the comparative value of various compounds, and the effect of cleaning or other aftertreatments of treated fabrics to give eventually the ideal durable water-repellent fabric.

A COTTON FABRIC, suitably constructed, can approach watertightness through sealing itself by swelling as it becomes wet. The principle is the same as that of soaking up or swelling a dried-out wooden boat or bucket to stop leaking, except that instead of large cracks there are millions of minute spaces to be closed.

The idea of self-sealing of swelling-type fabrics is also conveniently illustrated by the linen fire hose, made without a rubber lining, long a common sight on shipboard and in the corridors of public buildings, where it is kept ready for emergency use. When the water is first turned on, the hose leaks badly for a few minutes; then the leakage all but stops, because the fibers have swollen to fill the minute air spaces in the cloth. The result is that the hose can transmit water effectively. The slight leakage that remains is desirable to keep the hose from burning.

The principle utilized in the linen hose has been applied also in a few other types of linen goods, such as tents, water bags, and canvas covers. But the principle was not successful with cotton until recently, when ways were found in England to make satisfactory unlined cotton hose and lightweight cotton fabrics. Work is in progress to apply the self-sealing idea to ordinary-weight cotton fabrics—some intended for clothing and others for sleeping-bag covers, tarpaulins, tents, farm fabrics, and similar uses.

That method of approaching a high degree of waterproofness is obviously quite distinct from methods of imparting water repellency through chemicals, although treatments of the repellent type may sometimes be used in addition to the self-sealing effect. The property of resisting the passage of water by swelling (with or without the aid of repellents) will be called for convenience water resistance, even though the opposite—wetting—is required initially for swelling to occur.

The first research by the Department of Agriculture on the water-resistant cotton fabrics of the swelling type was undertaken at the Southern Regional Research Laboratory during the Second World War to produce an unlined (rubberless) fire hose from cotton instead of linen to meet an expected shortage of linen.

At the time of the work, 1942, manufacturers of fire hose stated that many attempts had been made in all sorts of ways to manufacture such hose from cotton but without success.

You can get an idea of the problem by considering fibers and yarns of linen and cotton. Linen consists of relatively long, smooth, straight fibers of low elongation, readily laid parallel, and spun with low twist (small twist angle and little spirality) into strong yarn of low elongation. Such properties favor the tight packing of fibers in yarns as well as of the yarns in the hose structure and assure low stretchability of the hose walls, with a minimum tendency to expand and leak under pressure.

Untreated cotton fibers tend to make a less favorable type of yarn structure for the particular purpose. Cotton yarns are not so compact as linen yarns and tend to hold more air when made into a fabric, so that there is more space to fill. With more air space, there is necessarily less fiber within a given volume of fabric to swell and fill the space; and, to complicate matters, the natural cotton fiber has less swelling capacity than the linen fiber. Finally, the cotton yarns and fabric have more inclination to stretch—with the result that the fabric expands under pressure, allowing the yarns to move apart slightly and cause even more leakage.

Briefly, then, the problem in making an unlined cotton fire hose or the swelling-type cotton cloth for other purposes is to make the fibers pack more tightly in the yarn and the yarns more tightly in the fabric, or to do anything else that will have the effect of reducing the space to be filled.

After the research had been in progress for some time, it was announced that Dr. F. T. Peirce, of the Shirley Institute of the British Cotton Industry Research Association, had solved the problem of the cotton hose. His method, which was described in a British patent and later in an American patent, consisted essentially in using a long-staple Egyptian cotton in a combed, plied yarn of low twist, mercerized at high tension. That procedure favors the making of a good hose; it means that the fibers lie closely parallel in a compact yarn, which can be tightly woven into a hose wall with much less interfiber and interyarn air space than usual. The mercerization also supposedly imparted a somewhat greater swelling capacity to the cotton.

Such hose was apparently not actually used to any great extent in England during the war because the linen supply was maintained, but it was ready in case of need.

The procedure of the British patent, though, did not solve the problem of the cotton fire hose for American conditions. The relatively small amount of Egyptian and other long-staple cotton available was all being used in articles of higher priority than unlined fire hose. Mercerization and other means of consolidating yarns from American cotton had in fact already been tried but found inadequate for adapting the yarns to the manufacture of fire hose. Something radically different was required. Before the British solution appeared, this part of the problem had been solved at the Southern Laboratory by introducing into the yarn a supplementary swellable material that would not dissolve in water. While the treatment was used at first on yarn already somewhat improved by mercerizing, this extra operation has since been found unnecessary.

THE SWELLABLE MATERIAL most satisfactory so far is commercial hydroxyethyl cellulose, which makes up with caustic soda and water to a paste that can be applied to yarn by dipping, and squeezing between rollers, like a wringer. After the caustic is washed out and the yarn dried, the yarn will have become more compact, and will remain so, from the adhesive effect of the added cellulose derivative.

The woven yarn carries this additional material into the fabric as a permanent part of the structure, where it not only fills a small percentage of the space, but, when wet, aids in closing the fabric by swelling into some of the most critical remaining space, in the very center of the fabric.

The treatment was so successful that a fire hose made in that way from ordinary cotton yarns conducted water under regular working pressure without undue leakage.

During this development, a technique called the orifice method had been used to test yarns for fire hose. Briefly, a measured and weighed amount of yarn is drawn into a hole in a brass fixture which can be submitted to water pressure. The amount that seeps through the yarn is measured, and its volume affords a relative measure of the closing capacity of the yarn under test. For example, when cotton yarn treated as we have described closed the orifice to just the same extent as an equal amount of linen yarn, it behaved like linen when woven into a fire hose.

When working with yarns from different cottons, however, it was found that some cottons (in the natural state, except for the spinning) had more closing effect than others in the orifice. These better-closing cottons had large amounts of thin-walled, commonly called immature, fibers. For example, cotton of 40 percent maturity (60 percent thin-walled fibers) had better closing capacity in the orifice than cotton of 83 percent maturity (only 17 percent thin-walled fibers).

This appeared to be promising knowledge for the selection of cottons in making lighter-weight self-sealing fabrics, in which there was great interest for the Armed Forces and for civilian purposes. Thus interest was

ransferred from fire hose, a fabric in-
ended to keep water from leaking out,
o fabrics intended to keep water from
eaking in.

The development of the British fire
nose from cotton was followed by fine
ightweight fabrics made the same way
(apparently now without merceriza-
ion), under the name of Ventile Cloth,
for use in water-resistant clothing.
While a similar development in this
country on the basis of Egyptian cotton
would be rather limited in scope, the
observation that some American cottons had better closing capacity than
others suggested the use of the cottons
in the development of light or medium
goods of the self-sealing, swelling type.

Mainly because of its acceptance by
the British, but also because it is used
in some of the best linen fire hose, the
oxford weave has been accepted as a
suitable construction for comparing the
effectiveness of experimental fabrics
representing different cottons, different
treatments of the yarn before weaving,
and different finishing operations afterward.

First to be made were fabrics approximating an army oxford, woven
from combed yarns of the Acala 1517
variety of cotton without warp sizing,
all with plied warp and with plied or
equivalent singles filling. The fabrics
were made from gray yarns, for controls; from yarn mercerized before
weaving; and from gray yarn with
hydroxyethyl cellulose added to both
warp and filling before weaving. These
quite different yarns were woven into
fabrics of such closely similar construction that advantages due to mercerization and the superiority of the fabric
with added swellable material seem
unmistakable in laboratory tests.

Among the tests are simple special
techniques, which use water-repellency
apparatus and are intended to show the
effects of swelling independently of
repellency or water-shedding properties. The effect of repellency is eliminated by thoroughly prewetting the
fabric by boiling in distilled water for
5 to 10 minutes, and then soaking up

to an hour in cold water to allow opportunity to swell. The tests must not
be confused with service tests, because
the object is to test only the one variable, swelling—or, perhaps more correctly, closing capacity. In one of the
tests, the wet fabric was submitted to a
low head of water and the leakage during 5 minutes was measured. In
another, the wet fabric was showered
with water under controlled conditions
and the amount that penetrated the
wet cloth in 20 minutes was measured.

The decreases in leakage are in the
same order and of roughly the same
relative magnitudes as would be predicted from the tests on the yarn. The
piece with added swellable material is
better than the one improved by mercerization only, and this fact leaves little question that it would have the
highest water resistance in a group of
strictly comparable fabrics, under conditions allowing maximum swelling,
and might prove very effective in practical use.

The next fabrics were made each
from a different cotton to check the
idea that thin-walled fiber should be
more efficient for self-sealing in a fabric than thick-walled fiber.

The two cottons used were those we
mentioned, with 60 and 17 percent of
thin-walled fibers, respectively. Because they were of too short staple to
comb, they were carded, spun into plied
yarns, and made into 13-ounce fabrics
in the oxford weave, with no warp
sizing. The two fabrics were remarkably close together in construction and
weight, considering the great initial
difference between the cottons, but
they gave different results in the two
types of laboratory tests. Both tests (on
preswollen gray fabrics) showed that
immature cotton should make a much
more effective self-sealing fabric.

VARIOUS EXPERIMENTS seem to
prove that factors other than swelling
contribute to the differences between
the closing effects of different cottons
in the orifice test and that similar factors influence fabric performance. Not

Effects of treatment and maturity of fibers on closing capacity of cotton yarns and cloths

Material tested	Seepage through yarn in orifice (10 minutes)	Leakage through preswollen cloth under—	
		25-centimeter head of water (5 minutes)	Shower of water (20 minutes)
	Milliliters	Milliliters	Milliliters
Plain gray goods.....................................	6.48	731	66.3
Yarn mercerized before weaving.......................	2.23	168	9.2
Unmercerized yarn with swelling agent added before weaving..	.75	81	.6
Immature fibers (40 percent maturity)................	.96	196	5.0
Mature fibers (83 percent maturity)..................	11.80	1,675	140.0

Effects of tightness of weave and maturity of fibers on closing capacity of cotton cloths

Kind of weave and maturity of cotton	Filling picks per inch	Leakage through preswollen cloth under—	
		86-centimeter head of water (5 minutes)	Shower of water (20 minutes)
	Number	Milliliters	Milliliters
Plain weave, 74 percent maturity..................	54	381.75	11.60
	60	67.25	.13
	68	1.72	..00
	71	.00	.00
Oxford weave, 85 percent maturity..................	53	364.00	2.80
	68	7.90	.00
Oxford weave, 64 percent maturity..................	52	90.00	.20
	68	.05	.00

only have painstaking microscopic investigations failed to detect any great differences in the amount of swelling in water of thick- and thin-walled cottons, but liquids that do not swell cotton do not flow at the same rate through them in the orifice. These observations indicate that the differences in closing capacity must depend somewhat on differences in the capillary systems within the orifice and, similarly, within the cloth.

Such systems can easily be shown to differ appreciably. Average fiber weights per inch of two cottons tested were in the ratio of almost 2 to 1— which means that the cloth made from the immature cotton contained nearly twice as many fibers per unit of weight or area of cloth; also that it had about twice as much superficial fiber surface. Then, very roughly, there were twice as many interstices between the fibers, and each of these capillaries was only half as large as in the piece made from mature cotton. As far as mere flow is concerned, the differences might be expected to have influence, such as reflected in air permeability. Actually, the ratio in tests of air permeability on the two cottons was not far from 2 to 1.

It is not safe to draw final conclusions on such complex phenomena as water resistance and such complicated structures as water-resistant fabrics from so few sample materials. Additional pairs of thick- and thin-walled (mature and immature) cottons have been made into fabrics for further tests.

An important improvement has also been introduced into some of the experimental fabrics. We would expect that the weaving of fabrics even tighter than those discussed so far would improve water resistance. But since no more threads could be put in through ordinary loom adjustments, a special attachment was devised to crowd in more filling threads (picks) to the inch. Filling picks were added up to 25 or 30 percent—enough to make the fabric as a whole 5 to 10 percent tighter. That may prove to be an important improvement in this type of goods. Representative results, with pickages from 52 to 54 taken as representing normal constructions for these goods, show clearly the great decreases in leakage through the swollen fabrics with the increase in the number of filling picks. These tighter fabrics are promising, especially with the cottons of lower maturities.

The results also bring out the possibility of distinguishing between the water-resisting properties of cottons with relatively small differences in maturity when made into sufficiently tight fabrics. The leakages decrease in the same order as the maturities; for 68 picks the leakages for cottons of 85, 74, and 64 percent maturities were 7.9, 1.72, and 0.05 milliliters. This bears out the idea that decrease in maturity, even within the range of values found in commercial cottons, favors self-sealing by swelling.

WHILE IT IS TO BE EXPECTED that the heavier, canvas-type goods will not need finishing in the usual textile sense, except possibly the addition of fungicides, some water-resistant goods of the self-sealing type will require the usual finishing. The more important steps are some form of purification or boiling off with alkali, sometimes mercerization (in the piece), dyeing, and application of a durable water repellent.

Although the fully finished fabrics may respond well to tests for water repellency, they have invariably lost after finishing some of their capacity

for closing by swelling. Because the loss has occurred under many conditions, it is important to determine what causes it. That is one of the main problems still under investigation.

It follows from a consideration of the various phases of the work that any extensive application of American cottons for water-resistant fabrics depends upon gaining a little here and a little there to take advantage of favorable factors whose importance has now been established and to avoid unfavorable ones.

While one type of weave, the oxford, has been employed in most of the work, a few samples have already shown that plain weaves of suitable design may be even more effective.

Mercerization of the yarn contributes to the efficiency of water-resistant fabrics, but it is questionable whether it is worth while with American cottons, in addition to the other possible improvements.

In summary, there are three main ways of improving swelling-type fabrics, applied singly or in combination: Selection of cotton of better closing capacity, whether due to fineness, thin-wall structure, or, possibly, greater swelling; addition of a swellable material; and weaving of a more dense fabric by the addition of more picks to the inch.

Any fabric for use as clothing ought to be permeable to air and water vapor. It is not yet possible, however, to make a cloth that will be completely water-repellent and remain dry and repellent indefinitely. The best alternative seems to be a fabric that will shed water by repellency rather than by means of an impervious coating, and will then swell to impede further the passage of water as a second line of defense after the repellency effect breaks down. The wetting-through of such a fabric in order to make it effective is less objectionable in clothing than the continued passage of water through more pervious fabrics into wool and other garments underneath with continual increase in wetness and weight.

Research, in general, on water repellency has been leaning recently toward the use of two layers of treated fabric as being much more effective than a single layer. Obviously, if the ultimate conclusions favor two layers, it may quite possibly be found that one layer should be water-repellent and the other consist of the swelling-type cloth.

While the fabrics that have been described are not to be regarded as representing completed practical developments, it can be seen that we are well on the way toward helping to make cotton more nearly waterproof and that this research promises cotton fabrics with improved resistance to penetration by water for various uses. It indicates particularly wider extension of the use of outdoor fabrics for protection from water through improvement in quality at little if any increase in unit cost.

Also, the lower air and water permeability, obtained by using the fine immature cotton, with the tight weave, suggests the possibility of special filter cloths for gases, liquids, and possibly for other uses where control of permeability is desired.

The development promises also better outlets for immature, late-season, and other underdeveloped cottons, which are inferior and, at present, of somewhat limited use.

J. DAVID REID *is a chemist in the cotton fiber research division at the Southern Regional Research Laboratory. Dr. Reid did his undergraduate work at Washington State College and came to the Department in 1930. He has worked in the field of agricultural chemistry continuously since that time, first at the Color and Farm Waste Laboratory in Washington, then with the Agricultural Byproducts Laboratory in Ames, Iowa. Since 1940 he has been with the Laboratory in New Orleans.*

CHARLES F. GOLDTHWAIT *joined the Southern Laboratory in 1941. He is in charge of the modified finishing section in which is conducted a varied program of research on cotton. Upon his graduation in chemistry at Worcester Polytechnic Institute, with honors and election to Sigma Xi, Mr. Goldthwait took charge of the laboratory for a group of mills manufacturing and finishing cotton, as well as woolen, worsted, and union goods. He continued until 1924 his direct connection with textile manufacturers in charge of laboratory and production in making textiles from seed flax, and in the processing of cotton yarn—mercerizing, bleaching, and dyeing. Then, following a short period on rayon and silk, he joined Mellon Institute of Industrial Research, working there for nearly 15 years on research on cotton.*

A COTTON YARN recently submitted for microscopical study at the Southern Regional Research Laboratory was from a head band said to have been taken from a Peruvian Indian grave of a pre-Incan civilization. It is interesting to note that as long as 800 or 900 years ago two different types of cotton were being used together to make specialty cloths. The two-ply yarn in one direction of the fabric was of a fine-fibered cotton similar in cross section to some of our present Acala varieties. The singles yarn, which was woven in the opposite direction, however, was made of a cotton as coarse as any Asiatic type. It was mixed with a red-dyed Alpaca wool fiber for decorative effect. Perhaps in the field of utilization of cotton there is not much new to learn.—*Mary L. Rollins, Southern Regional Research Laboratory.*

Measuring the Absorbency of Cotton

Edmund M. Buras, Jr.

Water absorbency is a quality of great importance in cotton materials. It is desirable in underclothing, washcloths, diapers, towels, napkins, gauze, and bandage materials, but it can be troublesome during processing. If it varies from place to place in the same roll of cloth, printing will not be uniform and the shades in dyeing will differ. Cotton is one of the best known absorbent materials, yet the manner in which absorption takes place and its measurement has been largely a matter of speculation. Absorbency tests employed thus far are considered inadequate, because usually they answer only indefinitely the questions of most importance—how fast and how much?

One of the earliest tests that gave more satisfactory answers to the questions was perfected by P. Larose in 1938. He measured rates of absorption by weighing pieces of toweling before and after placing them in contact with a wet earthenware plate for varying intervals. The test was laborious in comparison with more popular test methods, but it enabled him to answer the question "how fast?" with great exactness and represented the first step toward the precise test so universally needed.

Eleven years later, James H. Kettering got around the tedious operation of weighing by adding to the apparatus that Larose used a calibrated side arm as a source of water for the porous plate. This permitted the more convenient operation of timing the passage of water past marks on the supply tube. Kettering's method was successfully used for evaluating the effects of bleaching operations on the absorbency of print cloth.

Several mathematical developments, together with further modifications of the apparatus, have provided means of evaluating the forces involved and have led to a new understanding of water absorption and a reasonable theory of how it progresses. The improved test is based on the use of automatic devices that indicate continuously the rate of the passage of water through the porous plate and also the total amount taken up by a fabric sample, which has been pressed on the plate by means of a bag containing fine lead shot. The apparatus can be assembled from glassware readily available in any scientific laboratory and meets the requirements, so common in the testing of textiles, of wetting a fabric or other absorbent material quickly from one side while it is under pressure, and permitting measurement of rates and amounts of absorption by different fabrics in a readily understandable manner.

UNDER ordinary conditions, when a fabric is pressed against a wet surface, it first gets wet only at the points where the yarns cross, where the fabric is thickest. At these cross-over points, the water is drawn into the bundle of fibers making up a single yarn, filling the spaces among the fibers in the bundle rapidly. Because of the small volume of the spaces, however, the observed rate of absorption is still quite small. As absorption continues among the yarn fibers, the fibers surrounding the spaces between the yarns become wet and those spaces, too, fill by capillary action. This marks the beginning of an appreciable flow. These different phases of absorption may be taking place at the same time in different parts of the cloth.

The improvement in absorbency of a fabric upon laundering is readily measured by the new test.

In a series of test fabrics, the initial rates of absorption and total absorptions before laundering varied by more than 2 to 1. Repeated home launderings, about 20, improved both the rate of absorption and the total absorption, the rates being improved more than 10 to 1. More important is that the differences among the samples were evened out, so that after laundering they all behaved almost alike. Larose noted the same effect upon comparing undyed samples with the same materials dyed by different procedures. Samples which initially varied as much as 6 to 1 also behaved alike after laundering.

This shows that home laundering, besides its usually considered cleansing action, is another mechanical treatment, which redistributes the yarns and

fibers more uniformly throughout the fabric. So for a given type of weave, fabrics containing the same amount of cotton become practically identical absorbers upon continued laundering.

Because laundering reduces the size of the larger spaces and increases the size of the smaller ones, there is less waiting of the larger capillary spaces on the filling of the smaller ones. With all tending to act simultaneously, the delay is less and the initial rate of absorption is greater. Whether or not total absorption changes with laundering depends upon the type of weave of the fabric. In a very open fabric, some spaces are at first too large to fill completely, whereas after laundering they are small enough to fill. If the fabric is laundered enough times to even up the spaces, further laundering will give no more improvement in total absorption.

EDMUND M. BURAS, *a chemist in the Southern Regional Research Laboratory, went on active duty in the United States Navy in 1950.*

CHINESE WOMEN'S, and men's, long hair once was sold to exporting firms, which compressed it into small bales and shipped it to textile mills in various parts of the world for making press cloths, used in the extraction of oil-bearing materials. Even in 1940, in the middle of hostilities in the Orient, Japanese textile mills sent letters to American textile mills informing them that because of the "restoration of peace and order" in China, only the Japanese had human-hair press cloth available for immediate shipment.

The lack of normal supplies of human hair in countries outside Japanese-controlled territories actually was beneficial to industrial users. It stimulated American research workers to use their ingenuity in a search for some material with qualities comparable to those of human hair. As a result, nylon press cloth has been introduced as a probable replacement for human hair. Synthetic fibers, glass fibers, and woven metal wire also have a possible future in making press cloth.—*William A. Wellborn, Southern Regional Research Laboratory.*

Acetylation To Make a New Textile

Charles F. Goldthwait

Cotton can be modified by reaction of its major constituent, cellulose, to change some of its properties without changing its fibrous nature and its strength. To all appearances it still is cotton, but it may virtually be a new fiber and may find new uses. It may also better meet the requirements of older uses.

Partial acetylation is an example of esterification and consists in the introduction of acetyl groups throughout the cellulose of the cotton to replace an equivalent part of its hydroxyl groups. The partial acetylation of cotton was performed in 1901 by two British chemists, C. F. Cross and E. J. Bevan.

Cotton contains about 30 percent of hydroxyl groups, and it is evident that the number replaced in a particular reaction will determine the degree of modification and the attendant changes in properties. Because we might thus have a great number of different acetylated cottons, it will be most convenient if one is singled out for discussion—the one corresponding to approximately one-third of complete acetylation. Earlier research had already shown that this degree of acetylation, corresponding to approximately the composition of a monoacetate, imparted properties that promised to give the acetylated cotton unusual commercial value for specific purposes.

Such acetylated cotton absorbs only about half as much moisture from the atmosphere as ordinary untreated cotton—a property that favors its use for electrical insulation. It also swells less when wet and should find use when a cotton-type textile has to maintain its weight, length, and width unchanged under varying weather conditions. Such acetylated cotton has acquired the ability to color with acetate rayon dyes and lost its capacity for coloring with most of the direct cotton dyes, so that it resists many of them and remains undyed. Partially acetylated cotton is also said to bond better than ordinary cotton with plastics, such as cellulose acetate, into laminated sheets or boards; the products are said to be less susceptible to swelling and distortion when exposed to high humidity or water, because of the lower moisture-absorbing capacity of the modified cotton.

Partially acetylated cotton resists rotting during long immersion in sea water and when it is buried in the ground. It withstands heat better than ordinary cotton. For example, tires made with acetylated cord have been patented for heavy duty, where unusual heating in service is encountered. Acetylated cotton does not melt under a hot iron, as acetate rayon does, and has a higher decomposition temperature, characteristics that contribute to its suitability for electrical insulation as well as to its heat resistance. We at the Southern Regional Research Laboratory have given most attention to the preparation and testing of partially acetylated cotton for the utilization of two properties, resistance to rotting and resistance to heat.

Because a modified cotton with those useful properties had apparently never been developed in the United States beyond the pilot-plant stage and was not on the market, it was necessary first to devise methods for preparing it in small amounts for preliminary testing and then in larger amounts for more conclusive evaluation. A convenient apparatus for the first purpose is a vertical tube with connections through a stainless-steel pump to a large bottle, which contains the reaction mixture set in ice water. The tube is connected also to the water line and sink for washing after the completion of the acetylation reaction. The cloth—unbleached or bleached or otherwise purified—is rolled up with a net or fabric of glass yarn, the purpose of which is to separate the layers of rolled cloth so that all its parts will be reached by the mixture.

The usual acetylation procedure is essentially the one that is described in A. C. Thaysen's British patents and intended particularly to impart resistance to mildew and rot. The first step is to presoak the cotton in glacial acetic acid. That is done most simply overnight in the reaction tube. The acetylating mixture usually comprises about 25 percent by volume of acetic anhydride, about 75 percent of glacial acetic acid, and an amount of perchloric acid equivalent to 0.15 percent of the mixture. The precooled mixture is circulated upward or downward through the cloth and back to the bottle of cooled stock solution. The reaction proceeds at about 18° C. for 1½ hours to reach approximately the usually desired 21 to 22 percent acetyl. Other degrees of acetylation can be obtained by varying the time.

Following the reaction, the tube is drained of the acetylation mixture and filled with water; the cloth is washed a little by circulating water through it. Washing can be completed outside the tube; to assure complete removal of acidity, the cloth is finally rinsed in dilute ammonia and again in water. After drying, preferably at 100° to 110° C., the cloth is ready for chemical analysis and testing.

The degree of acetylation is determined by chemical analysis. The quality of the product, however, depends also on factors other than the acetyl content. A special technique of testing by dyeing has been worked out at the Southern Laboratory to check uniformity. The material to be tested is dyed in a bath that contains a yellow dye, which colors partially acetylated cotton but does not dye or stain ordinary cotton, and a blue dye, which colors ordinary cotton but does not stain well-acetylated cotton. If the acetylation is uniform but not sufficient to permit yellow dyeing, the samples will be more or less green. If the acetylation is incomplete—because the reaction mixture could not penetrate a heavy piece of duck, for example— yarns raveled from it and dyed will have blue and yellow areas corresponding to their positions in the original piece. Such dyeings show clearly that chemical analysis alone may not reflect the quality of the product. Even though the acetyl content may seem adequate, small unacetylated areas, if present, would not have the properties of the acetylated material and could cause fabric failure, for example, by being less rot-resistant than the properly modified cotton.

The need for more extensive studies of the uses of acetylated cloth led to the adaptation of a commercial dye jig to the process. With washing on the jig and with textile driers available, the process is conducted in much the same way as in the laboratory apparatus, except that the operator moves the cloth through the solution instead of moving the solution through the cloth. To acetylate up to 150 yards, the cloth is rolled at low tension on a narrow stainless-steel tube and set in a stainless-steel tank to soak overnight in glacial acetic acid. The cloth is then transferred to the jig and run back and forth from one roller to another for the necessary length of time, washed completely, and finally removed for drying. It usually takes 60 to 90 minutes to reach 21 to 22 percent acetyl, with a mixture containing 25 percent of acetic anhydride and 0.15 percent of the catalyst, perchloric acid.

To prepare larger amounts of acetylated yarn, a stainless-steel package-yarn dyeing machine (6 to 10 pounds capacity) has been used.

These batch methods employ conventional machinery that required but little adaptation to the new use. While the batch processes may constitute pilot-plant steps toward production in instances where cost is not too great a limitation, continuous processes are desirable. We have shown that cotton can be acetylated by continuous processes and we are developing equipment.

THE ACETYLATED PRODUCTS look like the untreated cotton and have the same general textile properties, except in chemical behavior and dyeing. The acetylated materials are actually heavier for each unit of length or area and may have a stiffer or firmer texture. Cords representing large gains in strength over unacetylated cords have been prepared by manipulation of acetylated yarns, but, generally speaking, acetylated materials retain about their full strength per strand of yarn or per unit strip of cloth.

A fabric well protected from rotting by acetylation may be of lower strength and still give much better service than fabrics that are initially stronger but not so well protected. For instance, take one untreated cotton fabric; another treated with a fungicide, such as copper naphthenate and having the same breaking strength as the untreated piece; and a third piece partially acetylated, but with only 80 percent of the strength of the others. All are to be tested by burial in the soil. If the untreated cloth loses all of its strength in a week or 10 days (the common experience), a fabric containing 1 percent of copper present as naphthenate will lose 80 percent of its strength in 6 weeks, but a properly acetylated fabric will hold its original strength for a much longer time. So the modified cotton can start with lower strength but still give much longer service.

Partially acetylated cotton differs from acetate rayon that it retains its strength or gains slightly when wet with water, whereas acetate rayon loses strength when wet. Furthermore, twines and cords of acetylated cotton have the same strengths as those of untreated cotton when broken with knots in the test pieces. These factors are important for the possible use of such material in fish nets.

Amount of moisture absorbed from the atmosphere—regain—was found to be low, roughly one-half that of ordinary cotton. The low regain would contribute to the electrical properties required of yarn for insulation. It is said that the British Cotopa, a partially acetylated cotton equivalent to the monoacetate, was used for electrical insulation in the Tropics during the war because of its electrical properties, as well as for its resistance to microbiological rotting. At the Southern Laboratory, we have acetylated yarn for winding wire and cloth for use in varnished electrical fabrics and insulating tape.

We have started work on fabrics for use with plastics. Acetylated airplane fabric showed better adhesion and tautening with the applied dope. Cellulose acetate laminates employing partially acetylated cotton (28 percent acetyl) absorbed less water than those made up with ordinary cotton and so should have better dimensional stability.

The heat resistance of partially acetylated cotton is typified by its much greater retention of strength, in comparison with untreated cotton, when heated in an ordinary laboratory oven at a high temperature for a relatively long period. Acetylated cotton cords and threads have retained at least twice as much strength as ordinary cotton after heating for 2 or 3 weeks at 275° to 320° F. (135° to 160° C.), the results varying somewhat from one material to another. Cords made from acetylated cotton would thus be promising for use in driving or conveyor belts that are subject to unusual heating. Partially acetylated cotton cloth used as covers for pads in laundry presses lasted three or four times as long as similar covers of untreated cotton. Such heat resistance is possibly due to the substitution of acetyl groups for the more readily oxidizable hydroxyl groups. In that way, the amount of damaging oxidation that occurs at high temperatures in the presence of air is reduced.

Ever since textiles have been in use there has been need for a treatment that will make the fabric withstand mildew and rot, but cause no discoloration, odor, stickiness, or toxicity. Adding a fungicide—the most common method for protecting cotton goods against micro-organisms—makes it practically impossible to avoid one or more of these objectionable features. It is more logical to prevent mildewing and rotting by making the cotton unavailable to the micro-organisms. Partial acetylation seems to accomplish this object, and, when properly prepared, acetyl derivatives of cellulose are highly resistant to rotting. Because the modified cotton does not have the disagreeable properties of the fungicide-treated cottons, it is perfectly safe for such uses as bags for food.

Since rot-resistant fabrics are especially for outdoor use, the tests employed have usually been burial in soil or exposure outdoors in contact with the ground. In preliminary pure-culture tests, samples with low percentages of acetyl, up to 16 percent, retained 87 to 100 percent of their strength after untreated controls had lost nearly all their strength. Such preservation for 1 or 2 weeks of any cotton would be considered good, but the usual acetylated materials will meet the much more severe test of prolonged soil burial, and this method of testing seems preferable, because the aim is the highest possible degree of rot resistance.

The resistance to be expected follows generally the percentage of acetyl, but no strict correlation has been established. A few excellent results have been obtained at values of 15 to 16.5 percent; good results are usual at 21 to 22 percent; and exceptionally high resistance at 25 to 30 percent acetyl. Treated cotton that retains approximately full strength after burial for 6 weeks in soil that completely rots ordinary cotton in a week is considered highly resistant and seems to be adequate for many purposes. That, however, is a short time for a partially acetylated cotton; many samples have remained in the ground for months with slight or no loss of strength. In some of the long-time tests, acetylated sewing thread and other acetylated cotton materials have retained up to 90 percent of their strength for a full year in test beds so active as to completely rot untreated cotton in a week or two.

As the preservation of sandbags was a vital subject during the early part of the research on acetylation, bags made from acetylated cotton cloth and thread were exposed in small piles on the ground to the severe microbiological and weathering conditions peculiar to New Orleans. A bag with cloth of nearly 30 percent acetyl remained intact on the ground under another bag for two full years and still had strength enough to remain in service for a much longer time. The edges of the bag were exposed to weathering as well as to microbiological infection. Another bag with much lower acetyl content also survived the 2-year test. Thus, one of the earlier objectives—the 2-year sandbag—was rather easily attained.

Acetylated cotton twines and netting are being found promising for fishing gear.

C. Dorée, in 1920, was probably the first to show that partially acetylated cotton resists the micro-organisms that normally cause rapid rotting of ordinary cotton when immersed in sea water. In tests at Duxbury, Mass., our acetylated fish-net twine retained 65 percent strength after immersion for 3 months in sea water. During the same exposure, netting acetylated in the piece with the knots already in it retained 84 percent of its strength. The control twine and net were almost entirely gone long before.

In tests in a North Carolina coastal river and in neighboring ocean water, unprotected nets and twines were entirely without strength before the end of the first month when the first set of samples was removed. One of the acetylated twines retained 84 percent strength after 8 months.

Exposure to weathering cannot be sharply distinguished in most climates from simultaneous exposure to infection and degradation by micro-organisms. In very humid places, biological destruction may occur much faster than that due to the photochemical action of sunlight. It seems that acetylated cotton should be more weather-resistant than untreated cotton because of the protection from oxidation due to the blocking of the hydroxyl groups. For the same reason, if high temperature in the sun contributes to the effects of weather, partially acetylated cotton should be better than untreated cotton. A number of the tests have shown approximately equal weather resistance for comparative materials. Others have shown definitely better resistance. In some outstanding exceptions, partial acetates have shown unusual resistance to weather. The top of sandbags in a group out in the weather for 2 years varied in retention of strength from 35 to 100 percent.

The demonstrated resistance to rotting would seem to render this relatively new modified cotton suitable for use in the Tropics, but the possibility exists that some organism or other will attack it. We have heard that at least one such organism decomposes acetate, probably rayon or the plastic, but it obviously has not been present in soils of New Orleans or other places from which test results have been reported. It is true, of course, that if nutrients are present, mildew can grow—or appear to grow—on acetylated cotton, but such growths do not weaken the material.

To sum up, resistance with little or no loss of strength for months has been shown by partially acetylated cotton when buried in active soil, while untreated fabrics fail in a few days, and those with ordinary preservatives fail in just a few weeks. The high resistance to biological rotting predicted by earlier experiments with acetylated cotton has been verified over and over again at the Southern Laboratory.

Cotton finishers will no doubt consider the production cost of partially acetylated cotton goods high in comparison with that of their ordinary processes. The cost would not necessarily be excessive, however, in view of the longer life of the modified goods.

A partially acetylated cotton article that lasts several times as long as one made from untreated cotton will not cost nearly so much in proportion when the value of the added service is counted. For example, partially acetylated bags used in household water-softening systems will easily last several times as long as untreated bags. The value of partially acetylated cotton appears equally clear for fabricated articles where cotton is a relatively small but very important, if not vital, part; here partial acetylation may greatly extend service life, thus adding value in much higher proportion than the increased cost.

Large indirect economies would also be possible if wartime items like sandbags could be made from partially acetylated cotton. A fabric with such extra life would require few if any replacements and so lead to important savings of invaluable materials, time, and space—that is, savings in raw materials and their transportation, in production capacity of cotton mills, and in transportation of the manufactured goods, especially ocean shipments, with all the incidental handling and rehandling up to the point of use.

CHARLES F. GOLDTHWAIT *has been in charge of the modified finishing section at the Southern Regional Research Laboratory in New Orleans since 1941.*

Cotton consumed and active cotton spindles at end of year in the United States, by sections, 1900–50

| | Cotton consumed | | | | | Active cotton spindles | | | | |
| | United States | | Percent consumed by— | | | United States | | Percent of U. S. total in— | | |
Year ending July 31	Quantity consumed	Percent of total	Cotton growing States	New England States	All other States	Number	Percent of total	Cotton-growing States	New England States	All other States
	1,000 bales	Percent	Percent	Percent	Percent	Million spindles	Percent	Percent	Percent	Percent
1900........	3,873	100	39	49	12	19.5	100	22	68	10
1910........	46,22	100	48	43	9	28.3	100	37	56	7
1920........	6,420	100	56	37	7	35.5	100	43	52	5
1930........	6,106	100	78	19	3	31.2	100	60	36	4
1940........	7,784	100	85	12	3	23.6	100	75	22	3
1948........	9,347	100	88	10	2	21.3	100	79	19	2
1949........	7,795	100	90	8	2	19.1	100	82	16	2
1950.........	8,851	100	91	7	2	20.5	100	81	17	2

Compiled from Cotton Production and Distribution, Bulletin 186, and earlier reports, Bureau of the Census.

BEFORE THE Second World War, people realized that the supply of cotton linters for making guncotton, the nitrocellulose used to fire the big Navy guns, would be very scant in a shooting war. At that time we had a surplus of the long cotton fibers—and what more natural than to use these to make guncotton? The problem was not so simple, however. Chemists found that the long fibers became roped together during purification and tied up the processing machines. Other problems existed, but all were solved—except for the length of the fibers. Finally, a machine was developed at the Southern Regional Research Laboratory to cut the cotton to the lengths desired. The machine could eat up about 350 pounds of cotton a minute, but then the problem of feeding it arose. We had to design new machinery capable of tearing a mass of cotton apart and furnishing it in a thin, even sheet to the cutting discs. That problem also was solved.

The exigencies of the war never forced us to make nitrocellulose from our reserve supply of cotton, but the research developed several interesting sidelines.

First of all, one of the chemists, who was checking the quality of the cut cotton for the manufacture of nitrocellulose, found that the 40 to 60 hours of washing usually given the finished product was not necessary if a little cold ammonia water was added to the wash water after just a few hours.

The most important sideline, from the farmer's viewpoint, is that the new machinery for tearing the bale cotton apart and making it into a thin sheet is being modified at the Southern Laboratory for handling machine-picked cotton. Cotton of that type costs less than hand-picked cotton to grow, but it contains more trash and foreign matter. This drop in quality is reflected in the lower price paid to the farmer because the mill finds the trashy cotton harder to handle. But the modified feeder now being developed has provided a cheaper method of opening cotton and can put the cotton into such condition that it may perhaps be cleaned more easily.—*J. David Reid, Southern Regional Research Laboratory.*

New Values in Mercerizing Cotton

Charles F. Goldthwait

Mercerization gives cotton a high luster, makes it easier to dye, and produces brighter and fuller shades. Although it tends also to increase strength, it is essentially a process to improve the appearance of cotton.

Mercerization under somewhat unusual and controlled conditions can bring out properties in cotton not yet developed to any extent commercially. Some of these—greater retention of high strength under conditions of dryness, improved resistance to high temperature or long heating, increased flex life, and unusual elastic properties, for example—will better adapt cotton for knitted and woven goods in which such properties are especially important.

Two types of cotton products, each developed far enough so that patents have been granted, exemplify the new possibilities of mercerization. One of them utilizes the added heat resistance of treated yarn; it is illustrated by its application in tire cord. The other utilizes the special elastic properties of treated cloth, illustrated by a semielastic surgical gauze.

The process of mercerization was discovered about a hundred years ago by John Mercer when he was filtering a caustic soda solution through cotton cloth. He observed that the cloth shrank and puckered and acquired a closed, or fulled, appearance. His idea that he had a fulled cotton came from a similarity to the hardening, or felting, of some wool goods by fulling. Mercer obtained a patent, but he could not follow up his invention because caustic soda had not then been made commercially. There have since been numerous efforts to make a woollike cotton by such processes; and, while there has been no great success, the possibility is still intriguing. About 40 years later the method of producing luster as an effect of tension was disclosed in a patent issued to Horace Lowe. Mercer never saw any of the lustrous cotton because it was not made until 25 years after his death.

While the cotton-finishing trade has associated the term "mercerization" almost exclusively with luster, the name has come into general use as meaning any kind of treatment of cotton with caustic strong enough to swell or shrink it—a good enough usage, because that was the original meaning before luster was first observed.

The distinctive feature of ordinary mercerization is the application of tension to keep the cotton from shrinking. Caustic alkali causes cotton fibers to swell greatly if unrestrained and to shrink in length. If the alkali-swollen and shrunken fibers are constituent parts of yarn or cloth, the swelling causes the structures to shrink, too. But if the material is stretched back to its original dimensions by tension, the fibers become smooth; if the alkali is washed out while the material is still under tension, the fibers become lustrous.

The effect is also about the same if the yarn or cloth is held at its original length and prevented from shrinking during the treatment. The swelling of the restrained fibers develops high tension within the goods, and they are actually mercerized with tension, although no stretching force is applied.

Mercerization without tension—

that is, with more or less shrinkage—has been known longest. Although relatively little has been done with it in a practical way, it has possibilities that seem not to be appreciated fully. Cotton mercerized without tension differs from cotton as ordinarily mercerized (with tension) in that it has no appreciable added luster and undergoes no noticeable net change of strength, although it yields a much darker color than ordinary mercerized cotton when the two are dyed at the same time in the same bath. Yarn and cloth mercerized without tension may also assume new properties or may display old properties to a greater degree if the yarn and fabric are suitably selected for the treatment and the process is properly carried out.

THE MAIN CLUE leading to the study of mercerized cotton for greater heat resistance was the claim that rayon tire cord is more resistant to heat than cotton cord. Because the usual regenerated type of rayon consists of mercerized cellulose (the same type of cellulose that results from the mercerization of cotton), it was natural to test the heat resistance of the latter. Two other discoveries had claimed heat resistance for mercerized cotton, but presented rather indefinite evidence because their data had to do with breaking while dry after a moderate amount of heating, rather than with severe tests to heat.

Because the main interest at the time was tire cord, most of the work was done on yarn and cord. It was found that several changes from the ordinary yarn-mercerizing procedure would improve the strength when the yarns, or the cords made from them, were evaluated by heat tests intended to predict the behavior of the cords in tire service. Specifically, low yarn twist favors a high degree of swelling and complete mercerization; for best results the yarn must be allowed to shrink while in the caustic soda. Finally, traces of acid must not be present.

In any mercerization it is difficult to remove the caustic soda by simple washing with water, so the last of the caustic is frequently removed by treating the goods with dilute sulfuric acid. The acid, in turn, is difficult to wash out; if ordinary raw (gray) cotton is being mercerized, the "souring" with acid means that some of the noncellulose constituents (usually considered impurities) are left in the cotton as insoluble, or difficultly soluble, acids. The acids apparently derive from the consecutive actions of the caustic and the sulfuric acid. Consequently, the use of acid is avoided, either by thorough washing or by using a small amount of sodium bicarbonate, which will neutralize either acid or alkali, so that there will be no acid residues in the yarn to cause degradation during tests or while in service.

The effects of mercerization and of variations in the process are shown by the results of tests for strength after heating for 15 days at 130° C. (266° F.) in an oven with air present, in comparison with similar unmercerized samples. Mercerized yarn neutralized with sulfuric acid retained 46 percent of its strength; that neutralized with sodium bicarbonate, 59 percent; and that neutralized with various alkalies, 58 to 70 percent. Untreated gray yarn retained 45 percent and 41 to 45 percent when small amounts of alkali were present.

The specially mercerized yarn, if neutralized with sulfuric acid, had no greater heat resistance than the ordinary gray yarn. Various treatments with alkalies, which left small amounts in the yarn, made no improvement in the unmercerized, but caused appreciably better retention of strength in the mercerized.

Although the type of test made on yarn—heating with full exposure to the atmosphere—is of less interest for tire cord, which is used tightly enclosed in rubber with relatively little chance for oxidation by the air, similar tests were made on the tire cord, subject to interpretation for other uses. Two commercial-type unmercerized cotton tire cords retained 51 to 62 percent strength, while the special mercerized cord retained 70 percent, after the 15 days of heating. The mercerized cord still had half its strength after 32 days, while the regular-type cords were down to 40 percent. The mercerized cord thus had one-fourth to one-third greater strength after exposure to heat, an increase which might be very significant for some uses of cord, as for reinforcement for conveyor or driving belts subject to unusual exposure to heat.

To make the best heat-resistant cord prepared so far from mercerized cotton, the singles yarn has been mercerized while being allowed to shrink freely by about 15 percent. At that point it is sufficiently slack to be drawn back 5 or 10 percent to recover part of its original length without any real stretch, the natural objection to the shrinkage being nearly overcome. The moderate pulling-back here, plus the usual tensions in subsequent winding and plying into cord, results in the recovery of the larger proportion of the loss of length in the original shrinking.

If the yarn starts with a low to moderate twist, preferably about the minimum with which it can be spun efficiently, and is finished without any free acidity, it will be most suitable for making a heat-resisting cord. For tire cord the yarn is given an intermediate plying and is then plied again to the full size required; the cord is submitted to some form of wet stretching to make it smaller in diameter, more compact, and stronger.

Tires, especially tires in heavy truck and bus service, frequently run very hot, sometimes up to the temperature of boiling water or higher. A cord, consequently, should be strong to withstand the air pressure in the tire and road shocks. It should retain its strength to withstand those forces while it is hot. It must also withstand an almost infinite amount of flexing as the tire flattens and recovers its shape continuously while running in contact with the road.

Because the cord embedded in a rubber tire tends to dry out and stay dry while running, cords are tested dry as a better basis of comparison than when containing their natural moisture. The usual result has been that the mercerized cord has normal strength and retains its full strength when dried, while comparative unmercerized cords drop at least 5 or 10 percent. But the improvement is still more striking when cords are heated quickly (within 5 minutes) and tested hot. At 130° C. (266° F.)—a somewhat higher temperature than that reached in most tires, but lower than those reached under extreme conditions—the mercerized cord drops 15 or 20 percent in strength, while the unmercerized cord loses 30 or 35 percent, almost twice as much.

The real test for tires is in running, but before that the cord is submitted to preliminary tests—fatigue or flex tests—to help select the best cords before making the more expensive and time-consuming tests under service conditions. On the Karrer-Grant flexing machine, developed at the Southern Laboratory, striking results were obtained with cords at 120° C. (248° F.). Ordinary cotton cord withstood 3,006 flexures; commercially mercerized cord, 3,143; cord with special mercerizing but with the usual acid treatment, 5,159; and specially mercerized cord without the acid treatment, 8,124. The specially mercerized cord withstood far more flexing than the unmercerized or the ordinary commercially mercerized. The cord made without the use of acid was better yet.

During the research, attempts have been made to obtain the same results in some simpler manner, but, despite many mercerizings and many tests on both yarn and cord, the best heat resistance has been obtained by the method I indicated. The process was granted a patent.

When the fibers in cotton cloth swell during mercerization without tension, they do not swell lengthwise, but outwardly in every other direction. Because the fibers are spiral structures, they tend to shorten as they increase in diameter. Similarly, since the yarn of which they are constituents is twisted so that the fibers spiral within it, it also tends to shrink in length as the fibers swell in diameter. Finally, when the yarns in a piece of cloth tend to become greater in diameter as they shrink, they need to be longer in order to crimp over each other in the cloth. Because so many factors tend to make them shorter instead of longer, the whole piece of cloth shrinks.

After the caustic soda is washed out and the cloth has dried (if it has not been pulled or stretched too much during the operations while wet) it will be stretchy, because the structure will be loose and open after the swelling has gone down with the removal of the caustic. When a piece of surgical gauze is treated in that way, it is left with numerous crimps and kinks. If it is stretched moderately, it will come back elastically to approximately its original size as crimps and kinks tend to return to their original positions. If it is allowed to shrink in only one direction and restrained from shrinking the other way of the piece, the gauze is converted into a fabric with a high degree of stretchability and of considerable true elasticity in the one direction and relatively little in the other. Such fabrics should find special uses. A patent has been obtained on this type of product.

A similar product, which, however, has stretchability and elastic recovery in both directions, has aroused interest for use as a semielastic gauze bandage. It also has been patented. A number of physicians and surgeons have tried it, and 30,000 unit strips were used in a test at the United States Naval Hospital in New Orleans during the war. It was reported consistently as meeting needs that other bandages do not.

This type of cotton bandage can be readily made on a small scale by allowing bleached 20 × 12 surgical gauze to shrink completely in 20 percent caustic soda, draining and washing with a few changes of water, and then neutralizing with dilute acetic acid, washing a little more, and spreading out to dry, all without stretching the gauze.

It can then be readily cut up in strips—for trial as bandage, after sterilizing.

Among the properties that make the bandage successful is its moderate amount of stretch or give while it is being applied, so that it can be made to exert moderate pressure. Its stretchability and elastic properties make the bandage somewhat self-fitting and self-tightening. The high degree of crimping in the fabric gives it a nonslip surface, so that it stays in place readily, rather than tending to slip or loosen.

Those who have used the bandage professionally report its superior ability "to conform to the contours of the body and to remain in place—ideal for securing splints of all types." For example, it is satisfactory for binding plaster splints and does not add appreciable weight to them. It is unusually suitable for pressure dressings, including those for burns, varicosities, and skin grafts. The bandage is especially useful about joints, because it will stay in place without slipping, it will exert pressure even after moderate swelling has subsided, and its elasticity and clinging power enable it to stay in place even when a patient is encouraged to use a bandaged joint. While it was available to the Naval Hospital in New Orleans it supplanted all other bandages for securing dressings about freshly operated joints. Some surgeons at the hospital found it particularly useful for head bandages.

The study of applications of semielastic fabrics prepared by mercerization has been limited so far to their uses as bandages. Such fabrics, however, are suggested for consideration where there is need for conformability to moderately irregular surfaces, for any use where a large amount of irrecoverable stretch is desirable (to take up some sort of shock in an emergency, for instance), and for a material in which low true elasticity is needed.

CHARLES F. GOLDTHWAIT *is in charge of the section of the Southern Regional Research Laboratory that deals with modified finishing of cotton.*

Dyeing Cotton To Test Its Fibers

Charles F. Goldthwait

The dyes that are used to decorate cotton with different colors and with printed patterns can sometimes be employed as tests to detect chemical or physical changes in cotton or differences among cotton fibers. Thus a new dyeing test that depends upon physical differences distinguishes thin-walled from thick-walled cotton fibers. It has been used to help determine the quality of cotton at all stages from the growing boll to piece goods ready for dyeing in the finishing plant.

Because the dyed colors differ with the wall thicknesses of the fibers, they must really depend upon the mode of growth of the fibers. The cotton fiber is a tubular seed hair, a single plant cell, which grows normally by a steady secondary thickening inward of the cell wall, after a thin primary wall has grown to the full length of the fiber. The well-thickened fibers are called mature. Those with but little secondary thickening are called immature. Hence, the terms "mature" and "thick-walled" will be used interchangeably, and also "immature" and "thin-walled," since this is the common usage, although it is not a question of maturity in a true physiological sense.

The new test is a simple, direct dyeing of any number of cotton samples at a time, with two quite different commercial dyestuffs, a red and a green, used together in the same dye bath. Certain pecularities of the dyes and of the two types of cotton—the thick- and the thin-walled—work together to cause a pronounced differential effect.

Loose cotton samples are enclosed in gauze bags or placed between sheets of gauze with seams sewn through, so that each sample is in a separate compartment. If possible, the samples that are to be compared at one time are dyed all at once, 3 grams of each being a convenient amount. The gauze with the samples is weighed and entered into a boiling dye bath made up of 40 times the weight of cotton and containing 1.2 percent Diphenyl Fast Red 5BL Supra I (Geigy) and 2.8 percent Chlorantine Fast Green BLL (Ciba), calculated on the weight of all the cotton, samples plus gauze.

After dyeing for 15 minutes at the boil, the cotton is lifted out, and 2½ percent of its weight of pure sodium chloride is stirred into the bath. The cotton is reentered for 15 minutes, then lifted again, and a second portion of 2½ percent sodium chloride is added. The dyeing proceeds at the boil for 45 minutes, when the cotton is lifted, drained, and washed in two changes of cold distilled water in the proportion of 50 parts to 1 of cotton. After excess water is squeezed out, the dyeings are dipped into vigorously boiling water (50 to 1) for 30 seconds, with stirring. Then they are lifted, drained, and washed with cold water as before. The hot washing, really a differential stripping, is not in accordance with usual direct dyeing practice. It removes excess red dye but relatively little green, and so eliminates grayness and results in more clearly defined colors, especially in a clearer green. After the final wringing, the dyeings are removed from the gauze bags and allowed to dry in the open air or with moderate heat. Mature cotton in its natural state will have colored to a pronounced red. Thin-walled, or immature, cotton will be usually a distinct green.

If a better idea of the resultant color is desired than can be obtained from simple inspection of the usual dyeing, the fibers may be blended by carding. But in a simple and more effective method the samples are cut to a near powder in a Wiley mill, and the cotton is stirred into water containing a little adhesive and filtered with suction in a coarse fritted disc funnel to form a pad. The pad is removed by applying compressed air to the stem of the funnel or blowing into it. The colors of a series of the pads can be easily compared.

People have known for many years that immature cotton does not dye normally, but no dye test has been described for clearly distinguishing thin-walled fibers.

When a mill wrote to the Southern Regional Research Laboratory for help with respect to "bad-dyeing" cotton, which was causing trouble in dyeing and manufacturing and was creating factory seconds in the finished goods, I remembered a red-green dye combination that we found very sensitive to variations in cotton. Tried on "good-" and "bad-dyeing" samples from the mill, it showed a pronounced differential effect. Microscopists observed that the difference in the dyeing effect corresponded to the difference in wall thickness; the novelty of the new dye test was at once apparent, and it was soon developed to its present form.

Many other dye combinations were tried. Some showed differential effects with mature and immature cotton, but none was so satisfactory as the original red and green.

THE DIFFERENTIAL DYE FORMULA has been applied in many ways to cotton—and also, incidentally, to other cellulose fibers, including rayon of different kinds, ramie, wood pulp, and cotton linters. Some of its applications are in large-scale use.

The possible applications of the test to cotton begin at an early stage of growth in the boll, where it can demonstrate visually the progressive development of the lint on the seed. When the fibers have acquired their full length but have not begun the secondary thickening, they dye green in the test. After some of the thickening has taken place, they dye red. When a systematic sampling was made of unopened bolls of different ages, there was a regular increase in the proportion of red-dyeing fibers until—in a boll that opened naturally—nearly all dyed red. The test seems to indicate that thickening does not necessarily take place uniformly from end to end of the fiber. There may be green-dyeing base portions and sometimes green-dyeing tip ends, with indications that these thin-walled ends may become normally thickened later. From the test we may also be able to learn more about the way cotton grows.

The test can also be made to show that there is a submicroscopic structural change, besides the well-known deswelling and changes of shape in cotton fibers when they dry as the boll opens. If a lock of cotton taken from a boll picked before opening naturally is dyed without previous drying, the fibers will dye green, even though almost fully developed. But if a lock from the same boll is dried and then dyed, the fibers will color red, to a degree that depends upon the number of fibers with secondary thickening. Clearly, the wall thickness and all other fiber characteristics from lock to lock in a given normal cotton boll are about the same. Hence the great difference in dyeing before and after drying (from the original boll) must arise from some change in the cellulose of the cotton fiber.

The test can be applied to cotton while it is still on the seed from a boll which has opened naturally to show the relative amounts and locations of underdeveloped fibers. They are likely to be present on one end of the seed, readily seen as small tufts of green-dyed fibers, with all the rest red. Under some conditions of growth, there may be larger tufts or some other distribution of the green-dyed fibers. The test was employed by O. J. Hunt in experimental work in the department of agronomy at Louisiana State University, where "the differential-dyeing technique gave a very accurate and consistent evaluation of fiber maturity" and "should be of practical value to the cotton breeder." Differential dyeings can also help, in the selection of cotton fibers while still on the seeds for studies of fiber properties.

Similarly, the dyeings have been used extensively for the selection of fibers from ginned cotton for studying the properties of thick- and thin-walled fibers.

The exact relationship between the green-dyeing of all the fibers in the original undried condition in the boll and that of the ordinary dry, thin-walled fibers is not yet entirely clear. The differential dyeing gives the impression that all fibers grow in the green-dyeing state, which is retained until the boll opens, but that certain of the thin-walled fibers remain in that state or in some similar condition— even upon drying, when the normally thickened fibers have become red-dyeing. It seems probable that a high degree of porosity in the originally wet fibers in the boll is lost when they are dried, and not restored in the dye bath, while a corresponding porosity in the thin-walled fibers is retained, or restored by swelling in the dye bath, enabling them still to dye green.

EXCESSIVE AMOUNTS of immature fiber in cotton for manufacture may cause a number of difficulties. Thin-walled fibers, especially those with practically no secondary wall thickening, give rise to the very small tangled clumps, or neps, which cause difficulties, such as an undue number of breaks in yarn during manufacture, and defects which frequently show up as unsightly white specks in finished colored goods. When the amounts of unrecognized immature fibers are large

enough, there are frequently other difficulties in the dyeing and spinning processes. The result sometimes is a high proportion of factory seconds, because of stripes or bars across a piece of cloth meant to be uniformly dyed.

The differential dyeing gives at once a means of observing the relative amounts of immature, or green-dyed, fibers in a cotton sample. Often the nep-forming fibers can be seen in small, glazed sheets, brighter than the other immature fibers, but not dyed quite so dark a green.

The cotton trade is greeting the test as a simple and practical method for checking the character of cotton, because samples from bales containing excessive amounts of thin-walled cotton have not been readily identifiable. Several brokers are installing this qualitative test in their laboratories to help avoid shipping immature cotton to mills, which would have trouble with it. Checking every bale is especially important because even one or two bales containing excessive amounts of immature or neppy cotton can contaminate a whole blend of perhaps dozens of bales.

While some dealers in cotton are trying to forestall trouble before the cotton reaches the mill, mills themselves are making systematic differential-dyeing tests of part or all of their cotton supply. One company is making dyeings at the rate of at least 50 samples at a time, for routine checking of its cotton as an aid in selection for specific purposes before it enters production. Working on a still larger scale, another company has used differential dyeing to select bales of cotton for chambrays, where neps again may be especially objectionable as pronounced white specks of surprising prominence.

A simple procedure has been worked out to dye up to 500 samples at once, representing 500 separate bales of cotton. Each sample, bearing a part of the bale ticket for identification, is put into a small gauze bag. All samples then are put in a net laundry bag, which is placed in a small raw-stock dyeing machine. The machine is packed with extra raw cotton to prevent channeling. Dyeing is done by the differential formula, adapted to this purpose. The samples are rinsed, whizzed, dried, and laid out for inspection. Experience tells us that too green a dye in any of the samples is evidence of a higher proportion of immature fibers and of a tendency toward an abnormal number of neps. The bales that correspond to such samples are diverted to some use where neps are not so serious.

In these last few applications, the interests of both seller and user of cotton are involved. Both could utilize the same tests, just as they employ the same techniques for estimating grade and staple. Cotton men with whom the matter has been discussed agree that a differential dyeing ought to tell things that a classer does not see readily in working with ordinary raw stock. As evidence, this whole research started from the purchasing of cotton that was about 40 percent mature and was mixed with cotton about 80 percent mature. The cottons were accepted as Middling and as Low to Strict Low Middling; although they obviously were different, they were not considered too different and went into the same blend. The result was the bad-dyeing cotton problem, which would not have arisen if the new dyeing technique had been available and had been utilized in checking the classers' samples from the bales before assigning them to mill lots.

That mill learned to reject the highly immature bales, and its production consequently increased. Such a screening can be readily made by differential dyeing; a classer who handled his ordinary white cotton in his usual way could undoubtedly learn to tell much more about the cotton if he had differential dyeings to go along with his regular samples. Not only could he reject the worst bales; if he were experienced in observing the dyed cottons, he could draw conclusions regarding their character as well as the properties covered in the usual estimates of grade and staple.

The test promises to be useful in another way in cotton manufacture. If samples of the processed cotton and of corresponding waste from different steps in manufacturing are dyed, it is possible to follow the blending-in of the immature fibers and check final uniformity. It is apparently possible also to determine something of the nature of the waste. In a few trials on samples from the experimental manufacturing unit of the Southern Laboratory, there was no observable tendency to remove in carding any greater proportion of immature fibers than was left in the carded cotton. In combing, however, a somewhat larger proportion of immature cotton was removed. The observations indicate what can be done. They are not to be taken as necessarily representative for all cottons or for all conditions of manufacture. However, the method seems worth trying for comparing the running of different cotton and possibly for comparing different machine settings to obtain more efficient production and better quality.

Other applications to yarn and piece goods may be to correct specific faults and difficulties—or they may be embodied in routine testing. The test serves well to show up mixed yarn, including that in cotton piece goods—in one case, streaks in a warp pile fabric.

Similarly, a pronounced change in shade may occur at a seam joining two different lots as they go through a dyeing process. The differential dyeing can be used to predict whether the cottons in such lots are likely to dye differently and to cause serious trouble.

ALTHOUGH SOME APPLICATIONS of differential dyeing amount to estimates of maturity, there is need for a quantitative technique, preferably by a simple dyeing and inspection of the resulting color.

The over-all color obtained on almost any cotton sample will enable it to be placed correctly in a series of dyed samples in the order of percentage of maturity. So far, visual observation has seemed adequate if the fibers are cut up and made into pads as I have suggested, but the color may also be estimated by optical measurements.

While the results have already been suitable for mill use, numerous difficulties have been encountered in the development of the test as a quantitative method. Recognized difficulties lie in the reproduction of dyed shades with such a two-color combination (especially when different cottons are being dyed nearly every time) and in the influence of exposure of open bolls in the field to weather, which can alter the ultimate dyed shades. Factors of unknown nature also have caused anomalous results from time to time, as compared with the results of conventional maturity determinations.

However, the point should be made that the results from dyeings need not check with maturity determinations, and the colors obtained may eventually prove to be even more useful than maturity figures. In support of this possibility, the dyeing is made on a larger sample and includes the full lengths of all the fibers; it is not merely an estimate of the relative wall thicknesses at their midportions.

While the real need is for the rapid method based on a simple observation or measurement of color, it has been necessary to make many regular maturity counts, and the occasion was taken to try the method first used by O. J. Hunt—counting the numbers of red and green cross sections in differentially dyed samples.

The method, as it was adapted at the Southern Laboratory for ordinary samples of cotton, consists in dyeing, sampling for the microscope, cross-sectioning, and counting the red and green fibers in a total of 1,200. Although it is a microscopical method not too greatly different from those ordinarily used (which employ either swelling by caustic soda or viewing by polarized light), operators who have used all three prefer the colored cross-section method. One reason is that there are no questionable fibers, all being easily placed as green or red. A possible additional advantage is that it is based on cross sections of natural fibers just as they are, rather than on fibers distorted by a high degree of swelling, or on somewhat uncertain optical effects.

While differential dyeing generally follows wall thickness or maturity, as commonly understood, it is almost certainly not actually due to wall thickness or to maturity in a more strictly physiological sense. The same general effects are obtainable with cotton fibers, which are seed hairs, with ramie bast fibers, and with man-made rayon. Hence it seems clear that the differential dyeing depends upon fine-structural features of cellulose which are not peculiar to cotton. This view is supported by the observations on dyeing cotton wet from the boll as already described. The properties of the two dyes used also enter into the picture. Whatever the complete explanation, most of the applications to cotton—whether in growing, trading, or manufacture—are associated with effects having to do with so-called maturity or immaturity.

In sum, the detection and estimation of immaturity in cotton are of special importance at all stages—from the growing cotton, where immaturity originates, to the finished goods, where it may lower the value of the product.

CHARLES F. GOLDTHWAIT *was graduated in chemistry from Worcester Polytechnic Institute. For several years he was in charge of a laboratory that served a group of textile mills. He gained wide experience with woolen, worsted, and union goods, the processes of mercerizing, bleaching, and dyeing, the manufacture of textiles from seed flax, and rayon and silk. Later he joined the Mellon Institute of Industrial Research, and worked there for nearly 15 years on research on the processing of cotton. Since 1941 he has been in charge of a varied program of research on cotton in the Southern Regional Research Laboratory.*

Effect of Light on Cotton Textiles

P. James Fynn, James D. Dean

To the chemist, light is something more than just the absence of darkness. It is a form of energy that can change the physical and chemical nature of substances.

Light consists of a group of electromagnetic radiations capable of stimulating the eye. It is a small portion of a wide range of radiations that include radio and radar waves, diathermy waves, ultraviolet rays, and X-rays.

When the radiations are arranged in a progressive order of their wavelengths, the array is referred to as a spectrum. The visible spectrum begins at the long-wavelength end with red and passes through the rainbow colors to violet at the short-wavelength end, each color having a progressively shorter wavelength. When all of the visible wavelengths stimulate the eye at once, the effect is perceived as white light. We use the word light to include also invisible radiations immediately adjoining the visible spectrum, the infrared at one end and the ultraviolet at the other.

Radiation absorbed by substances increases the energy content of their molecules and so may cause changes, the nature of which depends upon the kind of radiation absorbed. Thus, long-wavelength radiation, when absorbed, increases the average speed of molecular movements and so raises the temperature of the absorbing material. Short-wavelength radiation may cause displacement of electrons in the atoms composing each molecule of the absorbing substance and activate it so that it becomes chemically unstable. A chemical change resulting from this absorption of radiation is known as a photochemical reaction.

VARIOUS WORKERS who have studied the photochemical reaction of cotton have shown that the most important effect of light is an activation of the cotton cellulose. It accelerates enormously the reaction of cotton cellulose with oxygen of the atmosphere.

We do not know when the discovery was made that light has a harmful effect on cotton textiles. About the middle of the nineteenth century, manufacturers of curtain and casement cloth noticed that the materials lost more strength in the parts directly exposed to light than in the shaded folds. Probably the systematic investigation of photochemical action on cotton was fostered in the latter part of that century by Georges Witz, vice president of the Société Industrielle de Rouen, who published results of some original studies on oxidized cellulose. That in itself would be of academic interest only, were the oxidation of cellulose not accompanied by changes in the strength and appearance of the cotton. Because of the importance of such characteristics to the users of cotton textiles, it is of practical interest. During the First World War the harmful effect of light on textiles became a military problem. The Second World War stimulated further research on the mechanism of deterioration and the development of protective treatments.

Many scientists now are engaged in research to evaluate and solve the problem of photochemical degradation of cotton. Basic to this research is an understanding of the chemical nature of cellulose, of which cotton is almost entirely composed.

Cellulose is a polymer substance: Its chemical structure consists of a simple molecular pattern that is repeated many times. The patterns are joined like links of a chain into long, thread-like molecules. The chainlike structure gives cotton its fibrous qualities. Light attacks the cellulose at the points of linkage and thus shortens the average chain length. Although photochemical degradation, until it is well advanced, docs not alter the feel or appearance of the cellulose, it reduces the strength and finally causes the loss of all fibrous properties.

To approach logically a study of the destruction of cotton by light, one has to know something of the quality and quantity of the light.

Because the quality of light depends on wavelength, an evaluation of the effect on cotton samples requires selection and control of the wavelengths. That is accomplished in several ways: (1) By selecting a light source that radiates its energy in narrow bands of wavelengths, as does the mercury arc; (2) by using conjunctively a wavelength selector, such as a spectrometer, and a light source that radiates all wavelengths of the light spectrum (known as a continuous source); (3) by using a continuous source and shutting out all but the desired portion of the spectrum with colored-glass filtering screens.

None of the methods is perfect. In the first, the kind of light available is limited to the particular wavelengths characteristic of the source. The second gives the greatest selection and purity of radiation, but it is limited because of the very small area illuminated by the selected radiation and because of the feebleness of the beam obtained with even the most powerful sources. The third is limited by the nature of glass color filters, which either transmit efficiently broad and often overlapping spectral bands or transmit inefficiently the required narrow and exclusive spectral bands.

The amount of light falling on the cotton can be measured accurately by several devices. Bolometers, thermopiles, pyrheliometers, and radiometers operate on the principle of the conversion into heat of all radiation falling on an especially prepared surface. The resulting thermal effects can be measured accurately by a change in electric current or potential, the expansion of mercury in a glass tube, or the increase in velocity or torsion of a suspended, rotating vane. Actinometers depend on measuring the chemical change in a system that reacts in proportion to the total amount of light it receives. Photoelectric cells of various kinds either generate or conduct an electric current proportional to the amount of light falling upon the sensitive surface.

After one has subjected samples of cotton to the action of known quantities of light of selected quality, he can measure the photochemical effects by several means. The most direct method, but not the most sensitive, is to compare the tensile strength of the cotton before and after exposure, as determined by a machine that registers the force necessary to break the material by pulling. Because of the inherent variability of the mechanical properties of cotton, even the most carefully determined strength measurements cannot be precisely duplicated. Because of its directness, speed, and simplicity, however, the breaking-strength method is widely used.

A more sensitive index of photochemical damage is in the measurement of the viscosity of a solution of the exposed cotton. Cuprammonium hydroxide solution, a solvent made from ammonia, water, and copper, will convert cotton into a clear solution. Solutions thus made with undegraded cotton are thick, viscous liquids, because the long, threadlike molecules of cellulose move with difficulty past one another when the liquid flows. Badly degraded cotton, whose chainlike molecules are broken and fragmented by photochemical reaction, however, produces a thin, watery solution.

Cotton in various stages of degradation yields solutions with all gradations of viscosity between that of cotton with a high degree of polymerization and that of seriously damaged cotton with a low degree of polymerization. For example, data obtained by exposing cotton to the action of sunlight for progressive periods up to 3 months gave viscosity indices of 0.07, 0.04, and 0.03 poise (unexposed control, 0.37 poise), which indicates an average molecular chain length in each instance of 1000, 600, and 430 polymer units (unexposed control, 2250). By way of comparison, the results were approximated by 30 hours of exposure to radiation from either the carbon-arc or mercury-arc lamp, two sources of artificial light.

OTHER MEASURES of the photochemical damage to cotton by exposure to light depend on detecting and following the chemical changes produced by irradiation. One of these, the copper-number method, measures the ability of the cotton to reduce the copper in a copper salt solution from the high- to the low-valence form. The reducing power of the cotton cellulose depends on the reaction of the terminal group of atoms at the end of each chainlike cellulose molecule. It is obviously greater when many short-chain molecules, rather than few long-chain molecules, compose a given sample.

Another method of following the chemical change produced in cotton by radiation is the methylene-blue test, which depends on the affinity of the basic dyestuff methylene blue for oxidized cellulose, the cotton absorbing more of the dye as the oxidation proceeds.

Still another method requires a closed system, so that analyses can be made of the sample and its surrounding atmosphere before and after irradiation to detect evidence of oxidative reaction.

These methods, developed by many investigators, have contributed to a growing body of information on the problem of the deterioration.

According to the accepted theory of photochemistry that higher energies are associated with the shorter wavelengths of light, the ultraviolet light should be expected to be the most damaging to cotton. That has been shown by the rapid degradation of cellulose exposed to light rich in ultraviolet, such as the light from mercury- and carbon-arc lamps. Although the proportionately greater effect of ultraviolet light made it customary to disregard the effects of other parts of the spectrum, it was our thought that light from other parts of the spectrum might not be insignificant. This prompted us to investigate the spectral distribution of the cotton-degrading radiation in sunlight.

For the investigations, we used a special cabinet in which samples of cotton fabric were exposed to sunlight and protected from rain, wind, and dust. The samples were arranged so that each was irradiated solely with the sunlight transmitted by one of six glass color filters, which divided the light spectrum into five sections, the sixth being transparent equally to all wavelengths. Special automatic devices recorded the cumulative quantities of solar energy received by each sample beneath its respective filter. Sample temperatures were kept nearly constant by the circulation of water of controlled temperature through broad-surfaced metal cells on which the samples were mounted. The cabinet used solar radiation with maximum efficiency by turning automatically to follow the course of the sun. During the 8 months of the exposure, portions of the samples were withdrawn periodically.

Although the ultraviolet portion of the sunlight demonstrated the highest degrading efficiency, the damaging influence of sunlight was not limited to the shorter wavelengths of light. Even at a lower degrading efficiency, energy of longer wavelength than ultraviolet light was definitely effective. This was noticeable probably by reason of its greater abundance in sunlight, which, when it reaches the earth's surface, has less than 3 percent of ultraviolet. It may be that the effectiveness of the ultraviolet light is further reduced by an antagonistic action of longer wavelengths. Scattered evidence reported by various workers supports the view that the presence of longer wavelengths of light mixed with the ultraviolet light lessens the photochemical effectiveness. Evidence of this nature was obtained in experiments in which samples exposed under a blue filter suffered more degradation than others exposed under a clear filter and more than some samples which were exposed with no filter at all.

The relative effectiveness of light from various parts of the spectrum probably depends more upon the amount of light absorbed than upon the differences in its energy content. It is well known that certain dyestuffs make cellulose more sensitive to light. In a study of the increased degrading effect of light caused by dyes, Dr. Gerard S. Egerton, of the College of Technology, Manchester, England, offers an explanation of the oxidative reactions to which the photochemical degradation of cotton cellulose is due.

He states that undyed cotton is photochemically activated by absorption of light energy in the ultraviolet section but that cotton dyed with certain "active" dyes is activated by energy which the dye absorbs from the visible region of the spectrum. The actual oxidation is accomplished by a volatile oxidizing agent, probably hydrogen peroxide, formed at the cellulose surface. In substantiation of this idea is offered the evidence from an experiment in which a set of alternate dyed and undyed yarns, strung closely together but not touching, was exposed in a small enclosed chamber. The undyed yarns were definitely more degraded when exposed near the dyed yarns than when exposed away from them. In all instances, the presence of both oxygen and moisture was necessary to produce degradation.

The results seem to reduce to relatively simple terms the action of light upon cotton—but the problem is probably more complex. At the Institute of Paper Chemistry, in Appleton, Wis., Robert A. Stillings and Robert J. Van Nostrand found evidence that radiation alters or activates cellulose in some way, even in the absence of oxygen and water vapor, so that the cellulose can be oxidized subsequently by the atmosphere in the absence of radiation.

TEXTILES ARE RARELY EXPOSED to light isolated from other factors of deterioration. Light is usually a part of weather, and light-protective treatments of textiles must be directed also against rain, micro-organisms, and atmospheric contaminants.

Finishes that afford cotton materials protection from the weather have long been known, but they are usually waxy, tarry, and sticky, and rob the fabric of practically all textile properties. Research continues for a finish closer to the ideal, which would seal the fibers against moisture, screen the fabric from the deleterious action of light, and inhibit biological growths, without being injurious to the user. Furthermore, we need a protective finish that would be permanent, with no adverse or objectionable effect upon the weight, strength, appearance, body, and hand of the fabric. It should also be simple and inexpensive to apply.

One approach to the ideal treatment has been the attempt to modify chemically the molecular structure of the cellulose and still retain the textile qualities of the original fibers. Such chemical modification is generally effected by adding on groups of atoms at the reactive points that characterize each link of the cellulose chain. The new groups occupy or block those reactive points and render them inactive. One such modification is had by partial acetylation, a treatment long known in theory but just recently developed along practical lines by the Department of Agriculture. Cotton treated by the process, which does not distinguishably alter the appearance or feel of the material, has been successful for a number of uses in which unmodified cotton has failed.

The increasing development of plastics or synthetic resins offers many possibilities for their use in protective treatments for textiles. In many places, experiments are in progress on the utilization of resins for fabric finishes. We have tried urea and melamine formaldehyde resins as experimental protective finishes. Textile qualities have not been impaired seriously, and fabrics treated with some of the finishes have resisted sunlight and weather for a year without loss of strength, although untreated material exposed similarly lost half its original strength.

It is easy to see that progress in research on these finishes is delayed by the necessity of subjecting all experimental treatments to protracted outdoor service tests for sometimes as much as a year. Rapid exposure methods that we could carry on in the laboratory would be a great help.

Many attempts have been made to develop such faster methods. For testing the protective treatments of cotton cloth, use has been made of the susceptibility of cellulose to the very short wavelength ultraviolet radiations produced by the carbon-arc lamp. In fact, a treated fabric that would require a year of exposure to natural sunlight in order to show a strength loss of but 15 or 20 percent could be broken down completely in a week by radiation from that source. The results obtained by such artificially accelerated means will be of little practical value unless they duplicate with reasonable accuracy the results of exposure to natural sunlight.

An illustration is found in the results that we obtained from a series of 20 experimental finishes on cotton duck exposed to sunlight and weather for a year. We subjected identically finished samples to an accelerated laboratory test that made use of light from a carbon-arc lamp. In each instance, the protective finish was evaluated as poor, good, or excellent on the results of the test. Fourteen out of twenty of the finishes were rated the same by both exposure methods—a degree of correlation of 70 percent between the natural and the laboratory tests. The results do not justify complete reliance on accelerated methods to screen good treatments from poor, but they show promise that the method may develop into a reliable timesaver.

P. JAMES FYNN, *a graduate of Tulane University, has been engaged since 1944 in work on the accelerated aging of cotton textiles and on finishes for protecting cotton textiles from the action of light and weather. In 1949 he joined J. C. Penney Co., Inc., where he is assistant to the director of research and testing laboratories.*

JAMES D. DEAN, *after graduation from Brown University, was employed as a chemist in a New England cotton-finishing plant. He remained in the industry more than 20 years, serving with several companies as chemist, purchasing agent, and plant superintendent. In 1942 he joined the Southern Regional Research Laboratory, where he heads the cotton chemical processing division.*

A POUND of cotton has about 90 million fibers. A bale of cotton has a gross weight of about 500 pounds. Some cottons grow on small trees. The entire cotton fiber is a single tubelike cell. No other vegetable fiber has the spirallike form of cotton fiber. The natural colors of cotton are brown, green, cream, and white. The length of the cotton fiber may be from 1,000 to 3,000 times its diameter. The tensile strength of cotton approximates the tensile strength of steel. Cotton is produced on six continents. The cotton fiber is the most-used vegetable textile fiber.—*James N. Grant, Southern Regional Research Laboratory.*

Problems of Machine Picking

Ralph A. Rusca,
Charles A. Bennett

Power machines have lowered the cost of producing cotton, but they have also created new problems at the gin and the textile mill.

Machine-picked cotton contains extra moisture from the spindles and considerably more than the usual 5 to 15 percent of trash present in hand-picked cotton; particularly bothersome is leaf material, one of the most difficult types of trash to remove.

The additional moisture and trash in machine-harvested cotton frequently complicate ginning and raise the costs of textile manufacture by calling for extra cleaning steps at the mill. Yet the industry recognizes that mechanical harvesting is an essential step in the mechanization of cotton production to reduce over-all costs to levels comparable with those of synthetic textile fibers.

The actual percentage of the total American cotton crop picked by machines is small. The National Cotton Council put it at 16 percent for the 1950 crop. On the basis of a total crop of nearly 10 million bales, that means that about 1.6 million bales of machine-picked cotton were available. The significant fact is that this number is an increase of 75 percent over the 1949 estimate. The limiting factor in mechanical harvesting has been not so much the unwillingness of cotton farmers to use mechanized equipment as it has been the lack of machines. With availability of machines and mechanical improvements a certainty, machine-picked cotton is bound to be reckoned with more and more as time goes on.

MACHINES USED to harvest cotton are of two general types—spindle pickers and strippers. Varying designs of each are on the market.

The present spindle picker was evolved from a machine believed to have been first patented in 1850. Today's models are high-wheeled motorized vehicles, which straddle the cotton row during picking. The revolving spindle is designed to remove the cotton from the boll with a minimum of entanglement with the plant. Operation of this type of picker has recently been improved by application of chemical wetting-agent solutions to the spindles—to reduce the amount of moisture transferred from the spindles to the fibers below the amount transferred by former methods, which used large quantities of water alone.

The mechanical stripper in common use operates on a principle whose first application to harvesting was recorded in 1871. The original design was a large boxlike body, or sled, which was pulled along the row so that the cotton plants extended through finger-type projections in front. Modern units have the fingers mounted separately on the side of a tractor, with a built-in conveying system to discharge the cotton into a trailer, which the tractor pulls. The stripper, in contrast to the spindle picker, removes everything from the plant but the upright stalk and heavier branches.

The efficiency of either type of machine is affected by cultural practices. With strippers, varietal characteristics are especially important. Spindle pickers are satisfactory for harvesting a wider range of cotton varieties than strippers, but because the strippers cost less they tend to be used even where the varieties grown make them unsuitable.

THE COTTON that the farmer brings to the gin continues to belong to him. His acre yield will be calculated from the amount of lint actually ginned. The quality of the baled cotton will determine the price he will receive. During just the few minutes it takes to gin a bale of cotton, the marketable values of the lint can be vitally affected. From the farmer's standpoint, therefore, poor ginning of his crop may nullify any advantages he has had in producing it.

The specific problems in any locality in ginning mechanically harvested cotton arise from many variable factors—regional production, variety of cotton, skill of labor, type of machine used in the harvest, and other conditions that contribute to the market qualities and end uses of the cotton.

An example of variables in regional production: Objectionable growths of grass are seldom found in cotton fields of the Southwest, where varieties of shorter staple length are grown and more mechanical strippers than spindle pickers are employed for harvesting. But in the Central and Southeastern States, where the cottons have somewhat longer fibers and spindle pickers are more popular and feasible, it is more likely that grass will tangle with the fibers and so increase the difficulties of cleaning at the gin.

Many farming practices that affect the efficiency of mechanical harvesting—the cotton variety, the method of picking—correspondingly affect the efficiency of ginning. The manner of transporting and the nature of storage before ginning also make special demands upon ginning facilities.

The purpose of ginning was once only to separate the seeds from the cotton fibers, but the process has been expanded through the years to include the service of improving the quality of the ginned lint. More recently, additional cleaning steps have been introduced to meet the requirements of mechanically harvested cottons.

Gin operations today begin with storage of seed cotton, when necessary, on the premises or at the gin. Thereafter they proceed in this order: Drying the seed cotton; screening out the smaller particles of trash; extracting pieces of foreign matter too large to be screened out (sticks, stems, leaves, and hulls); feeding the cotton into individual gin stands; the ginning proper (separating the fiber from the seed by the saws); conveying the fibers by air to the press box; and, finally, packaging, or baling, the fiber. The ginned seed is usually conveyed to a seed-storage house or returned directly to the farmer's wagon or truck.

A recent development to which the Department's Cotton Ginning Laboratory has contributed is a lint-cleaning process introduced between the gin stand and the press condenser. As much as half a grade in quality has been gained by the extra cleaning at this point. Several ginning-machinery manufacturers now sell lint cleaners to cotton gins, and more than 2.5 million bales have been handled to date through them, seasons 1948–49–50.

Bulk storing of seed cotton on farms or at gins is particularly necessary in mechanical harvesting, where the speed of gathering exceeds that of ginning. Older forms of storage seldom benefit cotton after a week, especially moist cottons from mechanical harvestings. The Department is conducting research to develop better methods of handling mechanically harvested cottons in storage, with the thought that the storage period may be turned into an asset for the industry.

A new system under study is based on drying and cleaning the seed cotton before storage, and then, if necessary, drawing air through a series of bins in which the cotton is stored. With this arrangement, the cotton can be processed and aerated on its way in or out of storage or after it is in the bins.

More than a problem in storage of seed cotton, excessive moisture hinders cleaning and ginning, for it impedes the removal of foreign matter and causes rough preparation and fiber damage by the gin stands. A moisture content in fiber of 5 percent or below for cleaning and 7 to 10 percent for ginning is desired. To accomplish that, the Department's drying process has been adopted almost universally. Basically, it consists of conveying the seed cotton pneumatically through a vertical drier in which heated air travels about twice as fast as the cotton. The blast of hot air dries out and fluffs the cotton. For cotton that requires drying, air temperatures as high as 260° F. have not seriously affected the fiber or yarn strength, but the fibers have shortened somewhat. Loss in length may ultimately be regained through restoration of moisture at the gin or during after-ginning storage of the baled cotton, but generally the farmer will have been penalized unless approved drying processes are used, because his cotton usually is sold soon after it leaves the gin.

The developments indicate that although the cotton ginner is progressively solving some of the new problems introduced by machine picking, further improvements in gin processes are needed to handle the more trash-filled and moister cotton if the farmer is to derive full benefit from the many advantages of machine harvesting.

THE COTTON TEXTILE INDUSTRY, on its part, too, has watched with interest the rapidly expanding use of mechanical methods of harvesting cotton. The industry is interested in evaluating the problems it will face in processing the cottons. But the coming of mechanization to cotton farms is so recent that research workers have done little more than try to determine the scope of the problems the new development will bring.

Mechanically stripped cotton that has been ginned at plants in the High Plains of Texas with adequate cleaning equipment does not give undue trouble in the textile mill, but only a few gins elsewhere are equipped to handle stripped cotton. Inadequately cleaned cotton has an excess of fine leaf material, referred to as pepper trash, that requires rather severe handling before spinning.

The situation with respect to spindle-picked cotton is somewhat different, for most of the large gins are now equipped to clean it properly.

In 1945–46, the spindle-picked lint cotton seen by mill buyers frequently had roped and twisted masses of fiber and green stains from plant juices. Even with the more modern practice of defoliation before spindle picking, some green leaf may remain to tangle in the fiber. Its removal is almost impossible without excessive loss of lint. Mills have also complained of a peculiar dull cast in spindle-picked cotton that they attribute to fine dust and trash particles, to overdrying of the seed cotton during ginning, or to insect infestation.

The Department of Agriculture and individual mills have investigated the difficulties to be anticipated. The investigators used cottons of medium staple lengths, with an average difference of one grade between paired samples from hand-picked and spindle-picked bales. They found that the latter had about 15 percent more picker and card waste, 3 to 13 percent more neps, somewhat less spinning efficiency (based on ends down per 1,000 spindle hours of operation), and slightly inferior yarn appearance. On the other hand, the yarn strength of the machine-picked lint was slightly higher. Evidently trash and moisture contents are higher in spindle pickings.

The textile mills, of course, cannot economically use mechanically harvested cottons if they cost more to process than hand-picked cottons. And, should the mills become prejudiced against mechanical harvesting, the trend may be toward planting the shorter-staple varieties, which can be cleaned more easily. The farmer, ginner, and textile manufacturer want to avoid those difficulties.

One hopeful approach to a solution lies in the development of machines that are specifically designed for cleaning mechanically picked cottons and that can be used in the production line with existing mill cleaning equipment. The Department's research on how to obtain best results with machine-picked cottons at the textile mill has therefore included the development of new and improved cleaners. The significance of improvements in cleaning during the initial steps of manufacture is obvious to anyone who realizes that in the manufacture of textiles nothing is added to the raw material from the opening of the bale through the woven fabric, except starch sizing, which is applied to help the yarn through the weaving process. Any improvement in the first stages of processing is cumulative through subsequent stages.

A machine developed at the Southern Regional Research Laboratory for opening and fluffing up the lint from bales of mechanically harvested cotton—to put it in the best condition for cleaning—is representative of the type of new machinery needed for the manufacture of quality products from machine-picked cotton.

The opener, a simple machine, consists essentially of several steel-toothed cylinders mounted one above the other. The lint cotton is fed on a flat conveyor belt into the machine, where it forms a rapidly revolving soft roll between flat metal sides. Small tufts of cotton are pulled out of the roll by the cylinder teeth and are removed on the rear side by revolving brushes. The cylinders reject hard objects, such as bale tie buckles. The opener separates the large masses of cotton into finely divided tufts, similar to the lint before it was densely packed in the bale at the gin. The fluffiness of the open cotton permits more adequate cleaning in the usual processes that follow.

The new opener causes no damage to the fibers, even when the same lot of cotton is passed through it several times. Careful measurements of the length of lint cotton processed through conventional textile opening and picking machinery showed the cotton from the finisher lap had a classer's length of 1.05 inches, an average length of 0.87 inch, and a variability of 28.5 percent. The same cotton put through the new opener and then through the same standard processes showed results of 1.05 inches, 0.87 inch, and 28.4 percent, respectively.

RALPH A. RUSCA *has done research on cotton production, fiber, ginning, and textile manufacture since 1933. He has written a number of articles on those subjects. He is now senior cotton technologist in charge of research on developing new cotton textile machinery and methods at the Southern Regional Research Laboratory.*

CHARLES A. BENNETT *is principal agricultural engineer in the Department's Cotton Ginning Laboratory at Stoneville, Miss. He has conducted cotton-drying and ginning investigations for the Department since 1926 and now is in charge of cotton-ginning investigations at Stoneville and Mesilla Park, N. Mex.*

ORIGINALLY DOCK MEANT anything cut off, such as a tail. Later came the current word dockage, meaning something not wanted or useless. Weed seeds, other grains, sand, cinders, ashes, stones, cobs, hulls, pieces of metal, rodent excreta, pieces of insects, and moisture account for the dockage of grains. Dockage, therefore, is a word associated with poor quality. The dry matter or dry substances give grain its real value industrially and on the farm. Discounts for grades of grains are applied because dockage reduces the amount of usable material. Industry, like an animal on the farm, has a bad time trying to make something out of the dockage.—*Robert L. Zipf, Northern Regional Research Laboratory.*

Better Ways To Handle the Bale

Charles L. Sens

By the time a bale of cotton hits the concrete floor of the opening room in a textile mill, it has run a ruthless gauntlet. Saws at the gin have separated the lint from the seed and removed some sand and plant trash. Covered with burlap or cotton bagging and girded with steel bands, the bale has undergone repeated compression, none of which is a gentle operation. At each exchange of ownership in its trade route, the bale is knifed to give up a sample. Its wrapping no longer looks the same. With the many cut places, or burlap patches, and tags, it resembles anything but a unit possessing potential beauty. Yet the down-soft contents must find their way into fine and sheer articles of wearing apparel, as well as into rugged materials for heavy industrial uses.

In this day and time, manufacturing usually is closely associated with assembly lines. But cotton processing consists of many interrelated steps, each of which is performed by human hands, often without the help of automatic machinery.

To get a better idea of this course, go with me into a typical cotton textile mill. A far different sight now meets the eye that observes a hundred or more bales of snow-white cotton, wrappings removed.

Cotton at this stage is a mass of tangled fibers of varied lengths. It contains motes, sand, particles of leaf and stalk of the cotton plant, and some seed fragments.

Its route to the spinning frame or weaving loom is long and involved. The mass of matted lumps of fibers, sometimes as compact as a board, is progressively reduced, first to small tufts and then to separate fibers. Although all the cotton in a bale may be white, it needs blending, for cotton in a single bale usually differs in character, grade, and staple length. Blending cotton is comparable to mixing paint, where a better consistency is obtained by thoroughly compounding a hundred gallons in one container than by duplicating the process in a hundred 1-gallon vessels.

To fluff the tightly matted fibers, to blend or mix the cotton for a more even consistency throughout, and to clean the cotton, a series of vigorous operations is employed. Batteries of hoppers with spiked lifting aprons and regulated air currents convey the crude cotton to revolving beaters. Under these are adjustable grid bars or perforated screens. The foreign matter is thrown through these openings into waste-collecting areas beneath each beater.

The cotton does not have to be cleaned to the same extent for all end products. But highly efficient cleaning and preparation methods are required for fine goods that are to receive special finishes, and to insure the unbroken swift passage of thread through the eye of a needle in knitting or sewing. The same cleaning is essential for cotton materials that must hold up under severe mechanical uses, such as hose or outdoor conveyor belts.

Loose and partly cleaned, the cotton is drawn by air to what is called picking, a textile term, not to be confused with harvesting. Picking is an intermediate step in cleaning. Cleaning, however, is not its only purpose. Of equal importance is that by this operation the loose mass of cotton is delivered in a predetermined form, and becomes a continuous roll of certain length and weight. The product is called a lap. For example, it may be upwards of 50 yards long and 40 inches wide, weighing generally 12½ to 14 ounces to the yard. In the picking process, blades or pins on the surface of a horizontal and fast-revolving beater remove small quantities of cotton at each blow by picking, or plucking, upon a fringe of cotton as it is delivered from between two fluted steel feed rolls.

Picking machines are much alike in principle, but vary in detail. Most of them have two or three sections. Each section generally has a control unit that regulates the transfer of cotton to feed rolls. A fast revolving beater moves forward small quantities of cotton in rapid succession. Again we find adjustable grid-bar openings beneath each beater. Through these vents is thrown more trash, in the form of motes and broken leaf particles. Aiding the beater is a stream of air, the volume of which in 1 minute is approximately equal to that filling a room 15 feet long, 12 feet wide, and 8 feet high. To avoid a turbulence like that which results when a big bag of feathers is dumped in a windstorm, the air is separated from the cotton by two revolving and converging cagelike cylinders. The cylinders not only perform this trick, but also begin to condense the fluffy, downy material. Finally, the cotton moves through a set of heavy steel rolls, which press and form the lap, or roll, of cotton, which now can be handled by hand, on a truck or by some automatic system.

The reader who asks, "What is so wonderful about this invention?" might note that one-process picking is not an invention. It is a development—the result of 15 years of experiment and research. To move cotton·by an air stream through a duct or on a trough conveyor is no more difficult than carrying your hat in your hand. But to clean cotton thoroughly without damage to the fibers is a job yet to be completed. To place minute quantities of cotton at the rate of from 300 to 500 pounds every hour, with homogeneous distribution, upon moving surfaces of specified areas, and to do so economically, is a problem now engaging the talents of many engineers and scientists. This stream of cotton-laden air is moving at velocities of more than 3,000 feet a minute. Because cotton fibers are so volatile in an air current and so subtle as to lodge on the surface of glass, they defy control.

Before 1915, most processors had to use two and sometimes three picking operations. The cotton was poorly blended, insufficiently cleaned, and unevenly supplied to the first picking machine. The laps were removed by hand from the delivery end of each machine and placed on the feed end of the next one. Development of a one-process system, or a continuous picking operation, has done away in many instances with as much as one-half of the manual labor. Two of the several reasons why a virtually automatic procedure became possible are: First, compartments were supplied within the machines for a regulated storage of cotton; second, automatic devices to control the flow of cotton were developed. The result was a decided improvement in the uniformity of feed to the last, or finisher, section.

The economies and better preparation resulting from improved precleaning and the benefits of better regulation for uniformity of feed and delivery do not end at the picker. They carry forward and are reflected in all subsequent processes.

ONE EXAMPLE is at the carding machine, where the 40-inch-wide lap is reduced to a soft, ropelike strand of cotton, called a sliver. This unit is measured in, say, 50 to 60 grains a yard. The card formerly was expected to do more than its share of cleaning—to the detriment of quality. But constant improvement in the early stages of cotton preparation, with respect to the removal of heavier trash particles and to the better separation of the cotton fibers, enables the card to improve upon its cleaning task in its specialized sense. Further investigation doubtless will disclose that the card is better able to perform such other functions as fiber blending, and that a superior sliver, whose fibers are more favorably arranged, can be produced. Obviously, this would influence the adaptation for the next significant step, which is drawing, based on the principle of roll drafting, by which the fibers are drawn parallel to one another.

Still other benefits have been obtained. Bearing directly on lower costs, the improvements have shortened operations by doing away with one entire step of drawing and roving. The process of roving has changed slowly. And as we proceed from a bulky strand of cotton to a roving (smaller in diameter and many more yards to the ounce or pound) just enough twist must be inserted to give the unit sufficient strength for normal handling, such as winding.

Roving and spinning are essentially drafting processes in which the bulk or diameter of the loosely twisted strand of cotton is successively reduced, or drafted, by sliding the individual fibers along one another to produce yarn. It is accomplished by maintaining the proper ratio of progressively increasing surface speeds of each following pair of rolls or aprons (small endless bands) binding the fibers.

Since the invention of drafting, textile men have constantly been trying to reduce costs by increasing the draft in every process. The early system of drafting used three pairs of rolls, defining two drafting zones. The first zone, between the back and middle pairs of rolls, served as the break-draft zone to "unlock" the fibers; the second, between the middle and front pairs, served to thin down the bulk of fibers to the extent of the draft performed. For example, the first zone operated, say, at 1.5 and the second or extended

zone at 8, the product being the total draft of 12. This system had its limitations. Having only two zones, the second draft zone for greater elongation was incapable of uniformly stretching out the bulk of mixed length of fibers. The shorter fibers reacted in waves between the nips of pairs of rolls; unevenness resulted because of thick and thin portions of the slightly twisted small strands of cotton. Even with more uniform length of fibers, the spreading tendency of the ribbons of fibers could not be kept within the bounds of the main body of the loose cotton strand. The result was yarn of inferior quality.

There are several types of high-draft systems. They perform the same function and can be considered as a whole.

While the 3-roll system of drafting gave a maximum total draft of 12, the improved, or high-draft, system is capable of 30—with as high as 50 appearing evident. The mechanical stretching of these smaller strands of cotton, consisting of long and short fibers, is now attained by an appropriate combination of aprons or narrow bands and rolls. These devices have their surface speeds in proper ratios with one another. This drafting assembly allows the fibers to be held gently and to yield under proper tensions. The fibers are then drawn forward by the pressure of the aprons and rolls. The spacing or setting between the nip of the front rolls and the delivery nip of the aprons is within the staple length of practically all fibers. In the usual commercial, so-called 1-inch cotton, the fibers vary greatly. Although the predominant number of fibers are close to 1 inch in length, there may be appreciable quantities of fibers varying in length from $1\frac{1}{8}$ inch to $\frac{1}{4}$ inch. Besides length, such properties as fineness, strength, spirability, wall thickness, elasticity, and moisture content may complicate any drafting system in the attainment of uniformity in yarns.

Although the principle of high, or long, drafting—names synonymous with many trade names in use today— introduced obvious improvements, applications were not widely realized until 1918, 50 years after its invention. The new draft system permitted the elimination of one roving process; but, like many advances, the improved system demanded concessions on the part of mill operators. Because of the greater number of exposed parts, more frequent cleaning was necessary and the machinery was more expensive. These objectionable features are fast being corrected.

Nearly two-thirds of the spinning spindles were equipped with the new system in 1951. In fact, in textile-machinery circles, the high-draft spinning equipment is considered standard and the old 3-roll system special.

The cotton-manufacturing industry processed 50 percent more cotton in 1946 to 1947 than in 1922 to 1923, with 42 percent fewer spindles.

Much of the change came because the industry generally switched from single-shift to 2-shift and even 3-shift operation. Some of the step-up was due to cheaper and heavier fabrics. Further analysis of data for the two postwar periods, however, shows that credit goes also to improvements that permitted higher spindle speeds or lower number of turns to the inch in the yarn, or both. These peculiarities of the textile industry, which mean more yards of output without an increase in the speed of the spindles, are manufacturing facts. Thus the quantity of yarn produced by each spindle increased greatly. In 1946 to 1947 only 22.6 spindle hours were required to spin 1 pound of cotton; in 1922 to 1923, 31.9 spindle hours were required. Granted that heavier yarns and fabrics accounted for some of the increase in efficiency of output of the spindles, better equipment and improved techniques unquestionably contributed greatly to the gain.

The yarn direct from the spinning frame cannot be processed economically at the warper. The automatic high-speed spooler has accelerated the transfer of yarn from a spinning bobbin to a package of greater continuous length for subsequent use. The spooler is a type of winding machine on which units of yarn of individual lengths are made continuous for greater yardage and wound on packages specially adapted for use in the creel of a subsequent machine. The real value of the radical improvement in this new type of spooler is that it prepares by winding units of yarn with precision and high speed. These units are especially adapted to feeding a companion process, high-speed warping.

The process of warping is the winding on a large spool, called a beam, yarn from large supply packages mounted in a creel. As many as 600 threads, uniformly arranged and with equal tension, are drawn rapidly to form the warp beam, in such number as to be an increment of the total required in the fabric to be woven, and also to accumulate the supply of yarn for the slasher, thence to the loom.

The old-style warper unwound yarn from spools at a maximum rate of less than 100 yards a minute; the modern warper, which embodies many automatic and sensitively operating features, attains 900 yards a minute. Amazingly, this high-speed, continuous operation and the mass production depend on a minute element—one end of a thread. If a single end breaks, a threaded drop wire makes electric contact and immediately the stop-motion control actuates a magnetic brake to stop the machine before the loose end has been covered by the winding. Direction of air currents prevents the accumulation of fine lint, which can cause an end to break or otherwise give rise to a defect in the product at this stage. At higher operating speeds, air friction alone provides sufficient tension to assure a compact and smooth warper beam.

In addition, a control that permits the machine to be set for a predetermined yardage helps supervision. One such improved warper can perform the work of six old-style machines. The intricacies of the unit do not increase operating costs in proportion to the increased output. The better warps can more readily be sized, or starch-treated, so that weaving becomes even more efficient. With the new machine, broken warp threads and knots are fewer because less tension and strain are put on the yarn. The elasticity in the yarn is retained to a greater extent. Fewer kinks occur. The looms can produce more cloth of better quality and at lower cost. Even yarn inventory costs are reduced.

STRENGTH OF YARN is a relative term. A yarn designated as having high tensile strength still requires a temporary coating, or sizing, such as with starch, so that it will have protection against the chafing action caused by the several surfaces with which the yarn comes in contact during weaving.

The slasher is the machine on which a sheet of parallel strands of yarn from the warper is sized and then dried, normally to a moisture content of at least 7 or 8 percent. Sizing consists of passing the yarns through an open vat, or size box, which contains a starch solution, and then between cushioned squeeze rolls for removal of excess coating. The solution has in it also a small quantity of gum and softener to give the yarn greater elasticity and pliability.

For more than a century, the steam-cylinder, or contact, method was employed in drying the size-treated warp yarns. The parallel strands of yarn in the sheet were threaded around revolving cylinders so as to obtain the maximum metal-yarn contact surface. Two general types of slashers were used. One had 2 cylinders, 5 and 7 feet in diameter; the other had 5 to 9 cylinders, generally 23 or 30 inches in diameter. The steam pressure applied was under 10 pounds, and the temperature ranged from 180° to 230° F.

Although through the years auxiliary equipment (such as controls for size level and temperature, and steam pressure and temperature) has been developed and applied to improve this method, it still has shortcomings.

In 1930 came an improved type of slasher, based on the conventional machine. It had such added features as variable-speed control governed by a constant-moisture regulator. At best, however, it did not meet the increased production needs; more general use was made of supplementary devices, and finally the design was changed.

The use of radiant heat from infrared drying lamps or gas-fired burners, employed as initial or preheating measures, speeded up slasher production, sometimes doubling it, without impairing the quality of the warps.

The direct application of heat, the most efficient method of drying sized warps, eliminated the elaborate equipment needed to provide steam for the drying cylinders and made working conditions much better.

One successful unit of the direct-fired type of warp drier is an insulated housing containing two high-temperature blowers, with a combined capacity of about 10,000 cubic feet a minute. Heat to the drier is furnished by a series of gas-type burners, which fire through the wall of the machine into the blower suction chamber. The burners operate high or low in a regulated response to the demand of a thermometer controller, which regulates at any desired point between 200° and 400° F. The drying medium—the inert products of combustion and superheated vapor, which have great attraction for water—is reheated and driven through a drying chamber 25 times a minute. Such reducing atmosphere eliminates oxidation, which occurs when heated air is used for drying. A little air enters with the burner flames and is drawn through openings.

The sheet of starch-sized yarns is drawn through the circulating hot-air chamber. Fluted rolls are arranged to serpentine the yarn in the passage and subject it to this atmosphere, according to the drying requirements. The yarn, held in suspension between the rolls of minimum contact, passes between a series of baffles, which vary the velocity of the drying gases.

In an emergency, safety and operating controls shut off the main burners and mechanical features, including those designed to prevent burning of the warp. At the same time enough heat is supplied to maintain a temperature that will preserve the quality of the product.

The improved method of drying cotton with direct firing gives 20 percent stronger yarns with preserved elasticity, and the even coating and roundness of the threads are unimpaired. Air-dried yarns feel much softer than contact-dried yarns. Other advantages are the effect of the movement of air on the uniformity of the product and the rate of drying.

Under development by the company that produced the one just described is a drier capable of treating a wider range of yarns. Much finer yarns, as well as the coarsest, are being processed under mill operating conditions. The production rate is nearly double that of the conventional can or cylinder-type slasher.

These improvements, together with the recent practice of increasing the continuous yardage supply of the warp as much as threefold in order to lessen the loom-stoppage intervals, directly reflect an increased efficiency in weaving, which is nearly always the most expensive process in textile manufacturing.

The principle of weaving on a loom is that of operating two series of yarns so that they interlace in a definite manner to form a fabric. One series, the warp, is a sheet of the required number of yarns, which are slowly drawn forward under regulated tension. The yarns in the second series—the filling yarns, or weft—pass singly and at right angle through the warp yarns. The warp threads are supplied from the beam, a large spool placed back of the loom and containing several hundred to a few thousand parallel strands of yarn. The filling yarns are supplied on bobbins in the shuttle, which passes between the alternate warp yarns as they are successively raised and lowered.

The chief motions in weaving are: The shedding motion, which separates the warp ends to form a shed or opening, according to the pattern of the fabric; the picking motion, which passes the shuttle and inserts the crosswise lay of the filling or binder; and the beating-up motion, which beats into place or strikes each pick of filling spent by the passage of the shuttle. These, with several auxiliary motions, call for a complicated mechanism, with many operating parts, principally of cast and malleable iron, some of wood and leather, and a few of rubber.

The loom, an ingenious machine, has been in use for many years, and it has been improved constantly. Improvements since 1940 have increased the speed and production of the modern loom more than 15 percent. But there has been no change in the fly-shuttle principle of weaving. To supersede it, any machine or method to weave a fabric better than the present product must indeed be revolutionary in design and operation. There have been some practical modifications, however.

One such, a loom, developed beyond the laboratory stage and placed in industry for practical testing under competitive conditions, is of precision construction, with its motions made positive. Many parts and former practices have been eliminated; metal parts have replaced practically all wooden ones. A drastic change has been in the method of inserting the filling. In place of the conventional shuttle and the bobbin of filling yarn is a small yarn-carrier shuttle, which grips and inserts a section of filling. The fabric edge, or selvage formation, is a tuck-in, or overlap, of the single filling yarn. The filling supply package is a stationary cone containing usually thousands of yards of yarn. The yarn is passed through devices that ensure proper tension and prevent mechanical yarn defects. The pick, or inserted yarn, is cut at both edges and is slightly longer than the width of the cloth. The small extensions are folded into the selvage by a tucking needle. Although the filling yarn is inserted only from one side and the carrier shuttle returns empty for a repeat course, speeds upward of 240 picks a minute are common on light fabrics as wide as 110 inches—more than twice the speed of the conventional loom.

The machine-tool design of this loom, with the absence of many conventional parts, has eliminated much vibration and reduced noise. And because eye-level superstructure is not used on it, lighting is more effective, providing for better visibility and better supervision.

THE DEVELOPMENT of fabrics from loose fibers, rather than yarns, promises products that will give cotton new outlets. These novel products conceivably could find uses where paper is not suitable and also uses in which they would be more appropriate than woven fabrics.

Early in the nineteenth century an American patent was granted for grouping cotton cards to produce "webs" preparatory to treatment with a starch solution. The demand for the product was not great at that time. Since 1940, however, research has been offering to the textile industry a low-cost way of making nonwoven materials for specific uses.

Several methods are employed. A typical one produces a thin web, or sheet, of fibers on the carding machine. These fibers are in single or multiple layers and are randomly alined to give greater strength in the longitudinal direction. Such lightweight and low-priced fabrics meet mainly the need for absorbing qualities in products like facial tissues, bibs, table mats, dusting and polishing cloths, surgical dressings, and napkins. They can absorb 10 to 15 times their own weights of water.

Attractive effects in laminated webs of fibers alined in one direction are obtained by the deposition of narrow lines of starch or other bonding agent at right angles to the warp line or direction of the fibers. The effect is that of a decorative filling. The binder line may be white, tinted, or highly colored. Decorative and colorful printing or glazed patterns can be added.

In another method, used to give a more serviceable product, the fibers are parallelized, laminated, and cross-laid to impart strength in more than one direction. They may be bonded and made repellent to stain, water-resistant, or flame-resistant.

In a third method, the fibers are alined, cross-laid, and plasticized with a bonding agent. Some of these products are stronger than woven fabrics of equal weight—possible because the inherent strength of the fibers is made use of in a way not possible in weaving.

Originally, the webs, or sheets, were made on conventional cotton textile cards, with complementary equipment for collecting, folding, and spraying with bonding agents. Specially designed production machines now are used for laminating and cross-laying multiple sheets, for applying resins or other bonding agents, and for curing them.

Most fabrics just off the loom require a special cleaning or purification treatment before they are ready for use. No matter how carefully cotton is cleaned during its manufacture, the woven fabric contains some bits of leaf, seed hull, and the like, as well as small amounts of oil or sizing left after spinning and weaving. Also present are the natural noncellulosic constituents of cotton, including wax and pectins. Such impurities are removed from the fabric by bleaching, a chemical process.

Up to the time of the Second World War, the common method of bleaching was a caustic kier boil, followed by either a hypochlorite or a peroxide bleach. It embraced usually 12 or 13 separate operations, including intermediate washings and final drying. It took 3 or 4 days. A new method of continuous (in contrast to batch) bleaching, developed commercially a few years ago, has cut processing time to less than 10 hours. But it has some limitations—it does not treat medium and heavier fabrics perfectly. It is, however, adaptable to lighter fabrics, such as print cloths, in which a slight variation in whiteness may be covered by the colored patterns.

In the continuous process, essentially the same steps are followed as in the batch process and in much the same sequence. The steps are: Singeing the fabric to remove the fuzzy surface; steaming to facilitate removal of the starch sizing by the caustic soda treatment; washing; another steam passage; hydrogen peroxide J-box bleaching; another washing; and drying.

Two methods of passing the cloth are in use in both processes. One, the chain passage, mechanically routes the cloth from one process to another in the bleaching by drawing it in unbroken lengths through porcelain rings mounted near the ceiling. The second passes the open (full) width of the cloth, as in dyeing piece goods.

In continuous processes, the significant departures from the conventional are in the use of higher-priced, but more effective, chemicals and in the equipment.

The use of hydrogen peroxide solutions to replace calcium or sodium hypochlorite is more expensive, but their quicker reactions offset the extra cost, and they do less harm to the fabrics.

The principal difference in equipment is in the use of two 3,000-pound-capacity J-boxes as containers for the chemicals, in contrast to six 4-ton-capacity kiers, or pressure-type metal vats, in which the material was formerly boiled out and subsequently bleached. Each step in the batch process took several hours. The continuous-process equipment costs more. The initial cost and the upkeep of controls to regulate all operations are factors to be considered.

Edward S. Pierce estimates these savings by use of continuous-bleaching processes: 25 percent in floor space; 40 percent in labor costs; and 75 percent in steam consumption. The capacity of the vessels for the caustic and the bleach treatments also has been cut from 24 to 3 tons, and the time to bleach has been reduced from several days to a few hours. In addition, there is less handling of the product and less mechanical damage.

Cotton used to be bought chiefly, if not solely, on the classer's judgment of staple length, grade, and an undefined item called character. Present-day buying of cotton involves the consideration of other recently recognized properties, such as fiber length, the estimated proportion of spinnable fiber and waste, and fiber fineness, maturity, and strength. It is already possible to obtain a valuation of its spinning properties by pilot-plant operation. The techniques resolve themselves, finally, into lot labeling or variety identification of lots and bales, whose known properties influence processing and adaptability for specific end uses.

CHARLES L. SENS *has been a cotton technologist at the Southern Regional Research Laboratory since 1941. He attended the University of Texas and the Georgia School of Technology, where he specialized in textile engineering. He has had experience in textile mills in Tallassee, Ala., LaGrange, Ga., and Baltimore.*

COTTONSEED HULLS, which often are discarded as wastes in pressing cottonseed oil or making cottonseed meal, form a good mulch in flower and vegetable gardens. A layer of hulls 2 or 3 inches thick on rose beds, applied in early spring, makes an insulating mantle that keeps the overwintered, soil-borne blackspot inoculum from reaching the newly developed foliage. As with other organic mulches, a thick layer of cottonseed hulls prevents the rapid drying and packing of the soil from heavy rains and helps to keep down weeds.—*H. R. Rosen, Department of Plant Pathology, College of Agriculture, University of Arkansas.*

CMC Makes Cleaner Cotton

Winston B. Strickland

Wherever washday Monday is a tradition and cleanliness is a virtue, news will be welcomed of a simple washtub treatment for cotton goods that speeds soil removal in the tub and leaves a soil-resistant finish.

Because resistance to soiling is so important in many uses of cotton, the Agricultural Research Administration of the Department of Agriculture accepted the responsibility and authorized the expenditure of funds in a Research and Marketing contract research project at the Institute of Textile Technology, Charlottesville, Va., to study the problem.

The treatment developed there consists merely of adding to the water each time the goods are washed a solution of a commercially available compound, carboxymethyl cellulose, known as CMC. The solution coats the fibers and yarns in the fabric with a film much like that caused by starch. In ordinary amounts, CMC does not noticeably stiffen the cloth, although when it is used in larger amounts it gives stiffening if desired. The film protects the fabrics in use from a great deal of the dirt and grease that would otherwise be deposited. During the next washing it dissolves and acts to suspend the soil particles in the soapy water so that they cannot be redeposited. Thus it acts as a detergent aid. The treatment has no adverse effects on the wearing quality of the fabric.

Also, CMC, by almost completely removing dirt, eliminates the need of bleaching in home laundering and reduces the amount of bleach required in commercial laundries. Since the usual chlorine bleach shortens the service life of cotton materials, CMC-rinsed articles give extra wear.

White clothes rinsed in CMC keep their whiteness and colored goods come out brighter and do not "bleed" and discolor white things in the wash.

Some CMC-rinsed materials can be ironed in less time. CMC also washes out underarm perspiration odors, increases resistance to creasing and mussing, and removes iron stains.

CMC has long been sold on the wholesale market. Several detergents on the market contain a small amount of CMC (0.5 percent) as a detergent aid. During the Second World War, the inclusion of CMC in soap powder was mandatory in some parts of Europe, as a means of conserving fats. CMC is also regularly used as a thickener for pastes in textile printing, as a sizing agent, and in similar uses.

In their preliminary investigations, scientists at the Institute of Textile Technology learned that soil particles are trapped in the irregularities of the fiber surfaces and between the fibers and yarns in cotton fabrics. They discovered this by examining, under the microscope, short-length cotton fibers soiled with lampblack. They found that when a small amount of dirt or grease was already attached, a second deposit adhered more easily, because there tended to be a build-up of soil particles at vulnerable points.

CMC smooths the fiber surface by coating over the irregularities—to insulate or block them—so that soil particles, while the article is in use, cannot find a lodging place. It suspends the soil particles in the wash water, so that

453

they cannot, after removal, be redeposited on the cloth.

To TEST its effectiveness, the treatment was applied to strips of purified and bleached cotton cloth, and the strips were immersed in a CMC solution, passed through squeeze rolls, and dried. The samples were then soiled artificially by dipping into a dispersion of carbon black, and the amount of carbon black needed in the bath to soil the sample was measured. The determination was made by measurements of the whiteness judged by a reflectance method. A reflectometer is an instrument in which a beam of light is directed upon a material and the amount of light it reflects measured. Magnesium oxide has a high degree of whiteness—its reflectance reading is 100 percent—and it was selected as the standard in the reflectance tests. The untreated bleached cloth, when compared to magnesium oxide, has a reflectance reading of about 85 percent. Samples treated with only 0.5 to 1 percent CMC required almost three times as much carbon black as untreated cloth for both to show a reflectance of 25 percent.

A very dilute solution of CMC can be added to the wash during the last rinse to give an antisoil finish that will remain on the article until the next wash to help in soil removal. A much stronger solution can be applied as a sizing instead of starch.

CMC comes in powder form, and before it is added to the water in the machine it must be mixed with water, with the help, say, of an ordinary kitchen food mixer, or by adding boiling water to the proper amount of CMC and allowing the mixture to continue boiling for 5 to 10 minutes.

For convenience, a large quantity of a stock solution can be mixed and kept for several days' use by heating a gallon of water almost to the boil and stirring in 7 ounces of technical grade CMC powder as rapidly as possible. Stirring is continued for 5 to 10 minutes longer, or until a uniform, smooth, sirupy solution is obtained. This makes a 4-percent concentration of pure CMC.

To impart the nonstiffening soil-resistant finish in the home type of washing machine of average capacity (8 gallons), 3 cupfuls of the stock solution is sufficient. In use as a size, good results will be obtained with 2 to 4 cupfuls of the stock solution.

Mrs. W. L. R., who supervises the laundering of articles used in tourist cabins, tried out CMC in the suds operation—she used 2 cups of the stock solution with one-half cup of her regular soap, in place of the 1½ cups which she generally used. She found that pillowcases, sheets, bath towels, washrags, and aprons, even though some had become quite gray, when rinsed in CMC all cleared to a beautiful white, without either bleach or alkali.

Two commercial laundries, after several uses of 1 quart of the 4-percent stock solution for each 100 pounds of clothes, added to the wash wheel after most of the sour-blue water had been emptied, reported a definite increase in the visible whiteness of the washed articles.

Nevertheless, the applications of CMC require further research: What is the place of alkali in detergency when CMC is added to the detergent? What can be learned about the action of CMC in causing clothes to resist the deposition of iron oxide from contaminated water and the effect of the hardness of water on the use of CMC? How does the CMC treatment affect dyeing properties of cotton? Can CMC be modified by other chemicals to control the film-forming properties in such a way as to make the treatment perform as a superior finish? What is the proper ratio of CMC to the usual commercial soaps or to synthetic detergents to obtain the highest detergency efficiency?

WINSTON B. STRICKLAND, *a former member of the staff of the Bureau of Agricultural and Industrial Chemistry, is technical sales representative of a commercial firm. He lives in Charlotte, N. C.*

NATURAL AND MAN-MADE FIBERS

Tests To Help You Know Textiles

Ruby K. Worner

When you judge cloth or any other textile product, your eyes and hands can tell you a lot about it from the way it looks and feels, but they cannot tell you how it will wear or whether it will require special care to give satisfaction. To know what to look for and what to expect, you need to know something of the fibers and the processes used to make textiles. Even when you are a textile expert, though, your predictions may not be right if you depend solely on your knowledge, as sometimes you must in over-the-counter buying, for many properties of the finished product are not revealed until that product is subjected to service or laboratory tests. Fortunately, tests of both types are available to aid in the production and certification of textiles of quality. Not everyone can apply the tests, but everyone can benefit from an understanding of textile properties and of how technologists and producers test them.

When you choose a textile, you usually know the general type of product you require and some of the special properties—strength, the colorfastness, launderability, and so on—that are essential for your purpose. The textile manufacturer, to furnish you such a product with assurance, must know which fiber or fibers, which thread, or fabric, or other construction, and which finish to use. Most producers maintain testing laboratories in their mills and finishing plants to help them check quality from the fiber through the finished material.

If a special product is needed, technologists are called in to determine, in terms of measurable properties, the specific characteristics needed, and also the manufacturing details to achieve them. For instance, say a technologist decides that a jacket to be used for hunting should be windproof, water-resistant, light in weight, and durable. He finds from laboratory correlations of service and manufacturing requirements that those needs can be met by a lightweight, closely woven cotton poplin with an efficient water-repellent finish.

But the laboratory tests, so useful in determining specific properties of textiles, are made under reproducible, controlled conditions, and so are often limited. In actual use, textiles meet unpredictable conditions so diverse and complex that it has generally been impossible to simulate all of them in the laboratory. The ultimate test of products, especially new ones, is their behavior in use, and service tests should therefore supplement laboratory evaluations.

Similarly, judgment of a laboratory test should be based on the agreement between its answers and those found in service. To illustrate: Many different laboratory machines have been developed to test resistance to abrasion and wear, but little has been known of how well the results with them agreed with behavior of the textile in use. During the war, the Army needed methods for predicting accurately how materials would wear in service. Because its technical laboratories could not supply the information, the Army designed and constructed a combat course at Camp Lee, Va., for testing military clothing and equipment under simulated battle conditions. Then it called upon the textile division at the Massachusetts Institute of Technology and the Fabric Research Laboratories to determine the relationship between the combat-course and laboratory abrasion tests. On the basis of the results, it was possible to select laboratory procedures that could help predict wear.

Certain large groups of consumers also make use of laboratory tests. Government, railroad, and institutional purchase departments apply them, usually in their own laboratories, to check deliveries for conformance with specifications.

Organizations whose business it is to protect the public often require laboratory tests to aid them in detecting misrepresentation and violations of trade-practice rulings. For instance, the Federal Trade Commission needs accurate methods for identifying, analyzing, and evaluating textiles to insure correct labeling or certification. The Customs Bureau and the Interstate Commerce Commission require methods for identifying textile products in connection with duty and tariff rates.

IN TEXTILE TESTING, wherever possible, standard atmospheric conditions and standard procedures and equipment are used. In that way, results by different investigators and on different instruments can be compared and their significance understood. Much past effort is practically worthless for guiding technologists today because the information published on the materials used or the details of test conditions was insufficient.

Especially in tests of physical properties, atmospheric conditions influence results. For example, the amount of invisible water in the fiber (in the trade usually called moisture regain) depends mostly on the relative humidity and temperature of the surrounding atmosphere—to a lesser degree on the previous history of the fiber. In buying and selling on the basis of weight, moisture regain is important and transactions are often made on an oven-dry weight basis. Because of differences in moisture regain, some textiles are stiff on sunshiny days and limp on damp days. Moisture regain also affects the strength of fibers. Cotton and most other vegetable fibers tend to be stronger wet than dry, while the rayons, the man-made protein fibers, and fibers of animal origin, such as wool, tend to be weaker. Therefore, to furnish uniform conditions, practically all testing laboratories maintain rooms with a relative humidity of 65 percent at 70° F., the generally accepted standard condition.

Testing equipment and procedures must be known if results are to be understood. Consider breaking strength. Breaking-strength testers of many types and ranges provide facilities for testing from single fibers that break almost on handling to heavy ropes that require many thousands of pounds to rupture. Types of machines and procedures are selected with reference to the material and the purpose for which it is being tested.

A measure of breaking strength has little significance unless the test method is given. For fabrics, mention must be made as to whether the break was a grab break—in which the action of grabbing the fabric between the fingers of two hands and pulling to break is imitated—or whether it was a strip break—where a strip of the fabric raveled to a width usually of 1 inch is broken. Grab tests usually give higher values than strip tests because the yarns alongside those caught in the fabric jaws give "fabric assistance." The time required to make the break after the pulling starts also affects the result.

In the same way, measurements of breaking strength on different types of instruments may have different meanings. The common breaking-strength testers for yarns, cords, and fabrics operate on one of two principles, the pendulum or the inclined-plane principle. In the pendulum type, the jaws move at a fixed rate of speed, usually 12 inches a minute, so that a stretchy textile breaks much more slowly than one with little stretch. With the inclined-plane type, the load is applied at a definite rate, so that, regardless of stretch, different textiles can be broken in approximately the same length of time. Because the rate at which the load is applied may affect the results—a higher strength usually being indicated when the load is applied rapidly than when it is applied slowly—different values may be obtained from the two types of machines or even from two machines of the same type but of different capacities.

In all tests of breaking strength, the capacity of the machine, the type of jaws and the distance between them, and the size and shape of the test specimen may affect results. Each should be specified.

FIBERS ARE THE building blocks of all textile structures. For their best use, their chemical nature must be known. They can be cellulosic, protein, inorganic, or resinous—corresponding to the old kingdoms of plant, animal, and mineral, and to the newer chemical kingdom. On the basis of these classifications, much of their behavior with chemical agents in processing and in use can be predicted and explained.

Cellulosic fibers, illustrated best by cotton, are characterized by resistance to alkalies, which makes them excellent choices for the wash fabrics used in work clothing, sheets, and children's play clothes. Protein fibers, of which wool is the most familiar, are sensitive to alkalies and require special precautions throughout their processing and in laundering. They have the advantage of resistance to mildew, but the disadvantage of sensitivity to insect damage.

Many natural characteristics of fibers can be changed by chemical finishing—cotton can be made resistant to mildew and wool to moths and other insects.

The physical properties of the fibers are reflected in yarn and fabric structures. Fineness and length determine spinning properties. For example, the longer and finer the cotton fibers, the finer and more uniform (in general) will be the yarns made from them.

Consumers can see or feel the pliability or the stiffness, the softness or the hardness, the stretchiness, limpness, compactness, roughness, slipperiness, and the warmth or coolness of textile fibers. The corresponding physical properties, measurable in the laboratory, are flexibility, compressibility, extensibility, resilience, density, surface contour, surface friction, and thermal character.

Also important in textile fibers for many industrial uses are the mechanical properties, for they largely account for responses to forces like pulling, compressing, or twisting. Strength, stiffness, elasticity, resilience, and toughness are the basic qualities that determine those properties.

WHEN YOU RELY only on feel and looks, a textile that looked good for a particular purpose may prove unsatisfactory in use. Failure may be shown later in a variety of ways, such as fading from sunlight or laundering, shrinkage when caught in the rain, pulling at the seams, or a tear or break in the fabric. All these imperceptible deficiencies could have been predicted from laboratory tests.

Laboratory tests of serviceability are available for a great many of the outstanding characteristics of textiles, including strength, colorfastness, launderability, air permeability, absorbency, and resistance to water, mildew, fire, and insects. Other qualities—warmth and resistance to wear, for example—are important, but no standard tests for them are yet available.

Strength is the most often determined property of textiles from raw to finished product. Elongation, which is a measure of the stretch in a fabric when pulled, probably comes second in importance. It may be determined at the same time as the breaking strength.

The ultimate breaking strength of a textile tells the quality, but is not necessarily a measure of serviceability. Window curtains and many other household textiles, as well as some clothing fabrics, require only moderate strength. Some fibers, like glass, have a relatively high breaking strength but have limited uses, partly because of little stretch, or give, and brittleness. Ramie, which has been widely publicized for its strength, also suffers from brittleness. In pulleys, sash cords, and certain industrial fabrics, flexibility may be more important to service life than strength. Moreover, in service, textiles are seldom strained to the breaking point, but are often subjected to lower stresses, which occur repeatedly or over a long period. Technologists today appreciate the value of studying the stress-strain behavior (relation between load and elongation) of industrial textiles, such as tire cord and parachute belts, for service life often depends on their ability, under strain, to stretch and absorb energy, and, under relaxation, to release this energy and to resist fatigue—that is, loss of elasticity on being stressed repeatedly or beyond their elastic limit.

Strength tests are useful for determining damage in processing or under conditions of use, for they measure total damage whether produced by chemical, mechanical, or biological agencies. In testing cotton and other cellulosic fibers, fluidity is often used in conjunction with strength as a measure of the amount of chemical damage. The fluidity test is based on the fact that solutions of chemically degraded cellulose in cuprammonium hydroxide are more fluid than comparable solutions of undegraded cellulose. At the Southern Regional Research Laboratory, this relation between strength and fluidity has been used to evaluate finishes for cotton duck, awnings, and tobacco shade cloth intended for use in warm, humid climates where protection from both sunlight and fungi is needed.

Bursting strength, or "pop," tests imitate the bursting out at the elbow or knee or a burst in a feed or flour bag. Such failures occur when the fabric cannot withstand severe local pressure. In one type of bursting test, a steel ball is forced through the fabric; in another type, pressure is applied to the fabric through a rubber diaphragm, which is blown up like a balloon by increasing the pressure on the glycerin beneath it. With either method, the pressure in pounds required to burst through the fabric under prescribed conditions is determined.

Tearing strength is determined by measuring the force required to start or continue a tear in a fabric. For this we use a regular tensile machine, which operates in such a way that the average load required to continue the tear is observed directly or by means of an autographic recording device.

Colorfastness is an important requirement wherever color is part of the finished textile. This property is the ability of a color to resist fading, running, or bleeding when subjected to conditions of everyday use. A color that is fast to certain agencies may not be fast to others; for instance, fastness to light is no assurance of fastness to laundering, and vice versa.

The American Association of Textile Chemists and Colorists has developed many of the recognized procedures for testing colorfastness to light, weather, commercial laundering and domestic washing, dry cleaning, perspiration, rubbing or crocking, acids, alkalies, bleaching, atmospheric-gas fading (for fibers of cellulose acetate), and some processing conditions. In the tests, conditions are controlled to reproduce effects obtained in service.

Little special equipment would be required to set up qualitative tests using the same principles, so that a consumer could try out materials under his own conditions of use. For example, tests of colorfastness to light can be made outdoors. The specimens are placed under glass (to protect from rain) and are inclined at an angle of 45° from the horizontal, facing south, in an open place. The exposures are made on sunny days from April 1 to October 1 from 9 a. m. to 3 p. m. The more common method of test is in the laboratory with a Fade-Ometer. To simulate the action of the sun, this machine uses a carbon arc enclosed in a heat-resistant glass globe around which the sample rotates. Such a machine can operate 24 hours a day without hourly or seasonal variations in light intensity.

Likewise, colorfastness to the total weather, as well as to light alone, can be tested either by outdoor exposures (similar to outdoor light exposures except no glass cover is used) or in machines. The machines imitate the action of light and rain by means of an ultraviolet-light source and water sprays. Because of the variable and complex factors involved, outdoor tests made at different times do not necessarily yield comparable results. On the other hand, the indoor tests are limited in their ability to duplicate service conditions.

To test the ability of fabrics to withstand laundering and dry cleaning—two properties essential for clothing and household textiles—standard procedures related to home and commercial practices have been set up. Effects are determined by testing such pertinent properties as colorfastness, resistance to shrinkage and stretching (as shown by maintenance of original dimensions and shape), and retention of finish. Resistance to steam and heat under conditions met in pressing and ironing is also determined.

The Launder-Ometer used in the tests for colorfastness consists essentially of a temperature-controlled water bath and a revolving specimen holder, which accommodates as many as 20 small jars, each serving as an individual washing machine. A small

specimen with a piece of white cloth sewed to it (to detect any bleeding of the color) is placed in a jar containing soap solution, alone or in combination with soda ash and bleach. The closed jar is fastened in place in the machine and agitated at a temperature determined by the severity of the test desired. The same machine, without the water bath, can be used for testing colorfastness to dry cleaning by replacing the soap solution with cleaning fluid and using room temperature.

Water absorption is of first consideration for such materials as towels, absorbent cotton, surgical dressings, and humidifying wicks. The rate at which water is taken up can be observed by noting how fast a drop is absorbed, or how fast water climbs up a fabric when dipped perpendicularly into a beaker of water, or wets and sinks when dropped onto the surface. The amount absorbed, important for some uses, can be determined by weighing the specimen before and after the test.

At the opposite end of the scale from absorbency is water resistance, an indispensable service requirement of rainwear, tents, awnings, cover cloths, and similar industrial fabrics. A great deal of attention has been given to its evaluation with reference, on the one hand, to the ability of textiles to repel water and so resist getting wet, and, on the other, to their ability to resist penetration of water.

Three types of tests are commonly used for evaluating water resistance: Spray or sprinkling tests, to simulate the action of rain; hydrostatic-pressure tests, to determine the height of a column of water that can be supported by the fabric before leakage occurs; and immersion or absorption tests, to determine the efficiency of the repellent.

The simple spray test is widely used for evaluating water repellency, but it is not adequate for predicting the resistance of a fabric to the passage of rain. It provides essentially for spraying a fixed quantity of water from a height of 6 inches onto the test specimen, which is mounted at a 45° angle on an embroidery hoop, and noting whether and to what extent the surface of the fabric is wetted.

In rainwear, resistance to leakage is essential. Spray or sprinkling testers used for evaluating this property are the rain tester of the American Association of Textile Chemists and Colorists, the drop-penetration tester, and the Bundesmann water-repellency tester.

The rain tester is designed to simulate different intensities of rainfall from a gentle shower to a heavy downpour. The intensity is controlled by the height of the column of water above the sample. The height at which leakage occurs is noted and the amount of water penetrating the test specimen within a specified time is calculated by determining the increase in weight of a blotter placed behind it.

The drop-penetration tester consists principally of a drop-forming device with a frame to support the test specimen 68 inches below it. The time required for a definite amount of water to leak through the fabric is determined.

The Bundesmann machine (used as a standard in Great Britain) provides a shower representative of a heavy downpour. Four specimens, fastened onto individual cups, are subjected to the action of wiper arms on the underside while they rotate under the shower. The wipers simulate the rubbing and flexing action on the inside of a garment while being worn. The leakage through the specimen in a fixed time is measured, and the amount of water absorbed is determined by weighing.

The hydrostatic-pressure test is largely a measure of the openings between the interstices of the fabric and so is especially useful for detecting pinholes in proofed fabrics. It has also been helpful in studying the water-resistant properties of the swelling-type fabrics. Its values are not necessarily related to serviceability of rainwear, however. For example, the newer type of rainwear—which is designed to "breathe"—may show up poorly in this test and yet be satisfactory in service.

Air permeability is a necessary feature of fabrics for some uses, such as parachutes and hygienic clothing. Its determination is also useful for evaluating uniformity in fabric structures and in application of coatings. It is generally measured in terms of cubic feet of air that pass in a minute through a square foot of fabric at a stated pressure drop across the fabric.

Mildew and rot cause trouble in warm, humid climates. Standard methods for testing resistance to attack by micro-organisms have been set up and are applicable to all types and kinds of textile materials. Two procedures are given. One, for materials to be used or stored in a damp, warm atmosphere but out of contact with damp soil, provides for exposing the test specimen to attack by prescribed test organisms (fungi) under standardized conditions and determining its loss in strength after a definite period of time. The other, for materials expected to be in contact with damp soil for a long time, is similar in execution, except that specimens are buried in beds of damp soil having high microbial activity.

INDUSTRIAL FABRICS, such as canvas for theater scenery, awnings, duck, tarpaulins, and tentage, often must be fire-resistant. The standard test for fire resistance of treated fabrics provides conditions for exposing the specimen briefly to a flame, removing it, and measuring duration of flaming and length of char.

Tests for flame resistance of untreated textiles have received considerable attention in recent years. Work is still in progress on the development of a satisfactory tester for classifying fabrics as safe or hazardous, according to their rate of burning.

Wool and similar fibers are especially sensitive to attack by carpet beetles, moths, and other insect pests. To evaluate the effectiveness of insect-protective treatments, the American Association of Textile Chemists and Colorists, the American Society for Testing Materials, the National Association of Insecticide and Disinfectant Manufacturers, and the National Retail Dry Goods Association have cooperated in developing procedures for exposing test specimens to insect attack. The present method includes details for rearing and handling the test insects so that they will be sufficiently active and hungry.

Conditions of wear cannot be reproduced in a test procedure, for, like weather, they are unpredictable and are never twice the same. Wear is usually the result of a number of destructive forces, working individually or collectively and in varying degrees. There are instances of success in developing wear tests for products with specific end uses. An example is the carpet-wear testing machine, which simulates the action of walking on a carpet and cleaning it with a vacuum cleaner. Another is the hosiery-flex tester, which imitates the action of repeatedly bending the knee while wearing a stocking. Both testers are achievements of the National Bureau of Standards. More recently, the Philadelphia Quartermaster Depot has developed a "universal wear tester," which provides means for evaluating plane or flat abrasion, abrasion on edges, folds, and projections (for example, cuff- and collar-edge wear), and abrasion by flexing and bending.

Because the problems involved in wear are so complex, usually the best way has been to direct efforts toward determining and measuring the individual factors. Resistance to abrasion, or rubbing, is most closely associated with the effects of wear. A number of machines that produce rubbing actions of several types are in fairly wide use; but there is as yet no one generally accepted method of test.

To insure satisfactory service from clothing and household textiles, a number of other complex qualities are often necessary. These are the properties related to hand and appearance—crease resistance, drape, pliability, luster—which you readily assess, qualitatively, with your hands and eyes, but which present difficulties when quantitative measures are required. Although testers have been developed to give quantitative values for many of these properties, the results often have limited meaning because they do not necesssarily correlate with actual service.

For crease resistance, probably no more useful test has yet been devised than simply crumpling the fabric by hand and observing how rapidly, if at all, the creases fall out. Draping characteristics can be measured with a drapemeter, which simulates the effect of a fabric hanging in use. The pliability of a fabric may be tested with the planoflex, an instrument that measures the angle through which a fabric may be distorted in its own plane without producing wrinkles in its surface. Luster and gloss can be measured by one of several reflectance or gloss meters. The ability of one fabric to slide over another, which indicates its slipperiness or resistance to clinging, can be rated by the friction meter. This property is important for lining fabrics and women's slips. Flexural characteristics, including ease of bending and stiffness, are related to crease resistance and can be measured with the flexometer—an instrument that measures the amount of work done in bending a fabric and the amount recovered on unbending. Softness or hardness of a textile, as indicated by squeezing it, can be evaluated in terms of compressibility by means of the compressometer. This instrument measures the change in thickness with increase of pressure and recovery of thickness on releasing the pressure.

In the selection of textiles for winter and Arctic wear, a measure of their thermal-insulating value, or warmth, is often needed. Many testers have been developed to evaluate this and related properties. While most of them give useful information, none has received general acceptance as a standard.

Comparative tests to date indicate that thickness is as useful a diagnostic as any one of the more elaborate devices so far developed for predicting relative warmth of textiles.

To DEFINE A TEXTILE completely, one has to know its fiber composition and its yarn and fabric structure, as well as the characteristics of the finished product as a whole. Methods of analysis are available for identifying the fiber and evaluating its quality, for determining the details of yarn, cord, and fabric structures, and for ascertaining the nature of the finish.

Fiber identification is most readily and accurately made by microscopic examination, using special staining and sectioning techniques. The different fibers have distinctive cross sections that help identify them. Identifications are sometimes difficult even with the microscope, however, because of chemical modification or mechanical damage to the fiber. Simple burning tests are informative, although their evidence is not conclusive. If, for example, you ignite slowly threads, or yarns, of known fiber composition, you will observe that cotton, rayon, and other cellulose fibers burn readily, with an odor of burning paper, and leave little or no ash. The protein fibers, such as silk and wool, burn slowly, with an odor like burning feathers, and leave a soft, easily powdered bead as ash. Acetate fibers give off an acrid odor and leave a hard bead as ash. Nylon burns with an odor of string beans and leaves a glasslike bead as ash. So-called universal stains, which are helpful in differentiating between some of the more common fibers, also are available. In the analysis of finished products, each component must be examined, because admixture of fibers before spinning or the use of different yarns in the warp and filling is not uncommon, "effect" threads are sometimes added for decoration, and occasionally a ply yarn is composed of singles of different fiber composition.

Although the identity of a fiber throws light on its chemical and physical nature, it does not define its quality, for that varies among different samples of like fibers because of differences in their previous history. Tables of fiber properties show some of the ranges to be expected in such properties as fineness, length, and strength, which are of particular interest from the textile viewpoint. Chemical differences that affect behavior in wet processing and in service are also found. Consequently, analysis of certain fiber properties is an important part of laboratory testing to insure quality control in production.

Yarns are analyzed with reference to the number of plies, the amount of twist, and the yarn number, which is a measure of the linear weight. Dissection readily shows whether the yarn is made up of a single strand or of two or more strands twisted together—the former construction gives a single yarn and the latter a plied yarn. Twist is expressed as the number of turns to the inch and is measured directly with a twist counter, which counts the turns as it unwinds the yarns.

For determining yarn numbers, two general systems are in use: The direct system, which expresses them in terms of weight per unit length; and the indirect system, which expresses them in reverse terms—namely, length per unit weight. Practically every fiber has its own unit of length and consequently its own system. This has led to much confusion, especially when yarns of different fiber composition are to be compared. An attempt is now being made to obtain general acceptance of a universal system, called the "grex," which is a direct decimal system, applicable to fibers as well as yarns, in which all yarn numbers are expressed as the weight in grams of 10,000 meters (10,936 yards). Its values are not greatly different from those in the denier system, which uses 9,000 meters instead of 10,000.

Cords differ from yarns in that two or more plied yarns are twisted together to make a cord. Methods of analyses are similar, except that they must be extended to cover the cord as well as the single and ply constructions. The gage, or thickness, is often measured by laying four cords side by side under the pressure foot of a standard fabric-thickness gage.

In the analysis of fabrics by visual inspection and by dissection, the method of interlacing—whether the fabric is woven, knit, or felted—and the pattern are determined. In woven fabrics, the thread count is the number of warp and of filling yarns to the inch. A magnifying glass mounted above a scale with a movable pointer facilitates counting. Other devices are based on diffraction and electronic-eye principles, but their usefulness for closely woven and high-count fabrics—where help is especially needed—seems limited. The weight of fabrics is expressed preferably in ounces per square yard, so that fabrics can be compared regardless of width. Ounces per linear yard and yards per pound of cloth are also used.

The finish may be described simply on the basis of its appearance—color, luster, and texture. It may also be described, nonspecifically, with reference to its function, or, specifically, by naming the chemical treatment or chemicals responsible for it. Color can be described in terms of standard color charts—that of the Textile Color Card Association is the most used for this purpose in the textile field. Identification of finishing materials and dyes usually involves complex chemical analyses far beyond the scope of this discussion.

Service tests, which evaluate behavior under conditions of use, are the final measure of satisfaction-giving qualities, for it is only through them that the synergistic (combined) effect of the various factors involved in use can be determined. Service tests can also aid in setting up performance requirements for quality standards—a subject of increasing interest in consumer groups. As an illustration, extensive observations were made on actual wear in sheets, the results of which have played a part in setting up a consumer standard for sheeting by the American Standards Association. Similar specifications can be developed for other commodities to furnish a basis for labeling products with information directly helpful to the consumer.

Service tests are not practical for most evaluations, for they have a number of disadvantages. They are time-consuming and are carried out under conditions that are not reproducible from one test to another, which means that neither are results reproducible. Also, because personal factors enter into the keeping of records, precise evaluation of performance is difficult, if not impossible.

Probably the greatest value of service tests is their contribution to the development and improvement of laboratory tests that correlate with results obtained under use conditions.

The resulting laboratory tests have the great advantage for general application that they can be standardized and that results obtained by them can be interpreted in terms of serviceability. Producers, sellers, and consumers can then meet with a common understanding of their needs.

RUBY K. WORNER *is in charge of the textile testing section of the Southern Regional Research Laboratory. Previously she was a member of the textiles and clothing division of the Bureau of Human Nutrition and Home Economics and of the textile section of the National Bureau of Standards. Dr. Worner is a graduate of the University of Chicago.*

MORE THAN 2 million yards of cotton fabric is used each year to make coffee-urn bags.

The English first used cotton to make candlewicks.

Some Fibers

From the

Proteins

Thomas L. McMeekin,
Robert F. Peterson,
Sam R. Hoover

The twentieth century brought a new era in the production of fibers. Chemistry gave us artificial fibers, the rayons, from the cellulose of wood, to supplement such natural fibers as wool, silk, cotton, and flax, which come from animals or plants. Pioneer work started also on making fibers from proteins—vegetable proteins, which are concentrated in the leaves and seeds of plants, and animal proteins, casein, gelatin, hair, and feathers, which are byproducts and are almost entirely protein. Because cellulose is more abundant and cheaper, artificial fibers from wood have had a greater development than fibers from the proteins. Tremendous amounts of proteins are available for industrial use, however.

The first commercial protein fiber was developed from casein by Antonio Ferretti in Italy in 1935. An American factory made a similar commercial staple fiber from casein and sold it under the trade name of Aralac. Between 1940 and 1947, it manufactured 5 million to 10 million pounds of Aralac annually. The factory changed ownership in 1947 and was converted to the manufacture of a fiber from the corn protein, zein, which is sold under the name of Vicara. A large-diameter casein fiber now is produced commercially for use in automobile air filters and as a padding material in furniture.

It is of economic importance to agriculture that industry make use of the proteins from surplus and waste agricultural products in the most efficient way. One way is to make artificial fibers, each according to its particular properties. The properties that make the natural protein fibers, such as wool, so valuable derive from their internal structure. They are made up of flexible chains of amino acids, which are tied together to make a strong and elastic fiber. Cloth woven from them springs back into shape after it is stretched. Strength and elasticity allow blankets to remain thick and warm for many years and permit a good worsted suit to retain its shape, come heat or high water.

The same amino acid chains make up the industrial proteins. It is a challenge to the chemist to arrange them in a fibrous form and thus produce a new and valuable product. Not that he can make a new fiber just like wool or silk; each protein has its own chemical characteristics. What these are, and how they can be used or altered, is a different problem with each protein.

Every new possibility is being studied and tested. The kind and amount of the different amino acids in the chains, the length of the chains, and the chemical reactions by which they can be tied together, all are being measured in the laboratory. The way we do it and the processes for making the fibers are reviewed here.

CASEIN, the principal protein of milk, is essentially the same as cottage cheese. It is a relatively pure protein and is available commercially in large amounts. Its conversion into fibers offers a means of utilizing skim milk from butter making. The properties and therefore the uses of casein fiber can be varied by the methods of manufacture.

Casein for making fibers must have

a high degree of purity. It should be light in color, easily soluble in alkali, and free from nonprotein materials. The preparation of a suitable spinning solution is the first stage in the production. The casein is dissolved in water that contains about 2 percent by weight of alkali to make a viscous solution with 20 to 25 percent protein. If too much alkali is used, the casein is broken down by the excess alkali and the fiber is inferior.

The next step is to pump the filtered casein solution by a metering pump through a platinum-gold alloy disc, or spinneret, which has thousands of fine, accurately placed, and uniform holes. Each hole is usually 0.004 inch in diameter—that is, 250 of them measure an inch. The solution, streaming from the holes of the spinneret, is immersed in water that contains an acid. The acid neutralizes the alkali used to dissolve the casein. The small, continuous fibers are then stretched, treated in various solutions, and collected by the spinning machinery.

The tensile strength of the yarn is enhanced by stretching the fiber while it is being tanned with aluminum salts and formaldehyde. It is stretched by passing it over rollers, each of which is driven at a higher speed than the preceding one. The action of the hardening baths can be accelerated by heating, and the fiber can then be stretched much more than at low temperatures. The strength of the fiber can be almost doubled by stretching. The standard casein fiber has a dry strength of 16,000 pounds to the square inch and a wet strength of 8,000 pounds. By carrying out the stretching and hardening over a longer period, the dry strength can be raised to 20,000 pounds and the wet strength to 10,000 pounds to the square inch.

A further treatment is needed in order to make the fiber resist the boiling bath commonly used in dyeing wool. Aralac was made resistant to boiling by acetylation with acetic anhydride in naphtha; another promising, inexpensive method involves heating the fiber in the presence of acid and formaldehyde.

Usually the fibers are cut into short lengths and spun in a blend with cotton, wool, or rayon. To the cellulosic fibers the casein fibers impart warmth, crease resistance, and resiliency. Recently we developed a laboratory-scale process for making a continuous-filament all-casein yarn, which has superior resiliency, softness, and dyeing properties. It should have the same type of uses as filament rayon and should be used in woven fabrics.

THE DEVELOPMENT of a domestic source of supply of artificial fiber of the size and properties of horsehair and hog bristle is of strategic importance and economic value because these fibers are largely imported from the Orient and become critical when trade relations are disturbed. About 6 million pounds of pig bristle and 4 million pounds of horsehair are imported annually. It is unlikely that an adequate domestic supply of coarse animal hair can be developed to replace imported hair, because the method of dressing animal hair involves much hand labor. A number of synthetic fibers are available for development to meet the demand for large fibers. Their properties and cost will determine their possibilities in this field.

In our laboratory we have developed a method of making a unique and low-cost casein fiber, or bristle, of the size of pig bristle and horsehair. The method differs in principle from the one described for making the textile fiber from casein. Fibers are made by extruding isoelectric casein, which contains 30 to 40 percent of its weight of water, at a temperature just below the boiling point, through a suitable die into air. After extrusion, the fiber is strengthened and made more durable by stretching and treating with either formaldehyde or benzoquinone. It is then dried on a large drum. Making casein fiber by extrusion differs from the previously described method for making textile fiber from casein in that the casein is not dissolved in alkali and precipitated in the fibrous form by spinning into acid. However, the fibers made by the two methods have similar fundamental properties. The extrusion method for making casein fiber is particularly advantageous in making a thick fiber. It is also simpler and less expensive.

Casein bristle is fairly durable under ordinary conditions. It has good flexibility, resilience, and resistance to abrasives and organic solvents. It is three-fourths as strong as horsehair or hog bristle under ordinary atmospheric conditions. Immersion in water for several hours, however, reduces the strength of casein bristle to one-fourth that of natural bristle.

Commercial production of casein bristle has just begun. It has been found to be particularly useful in the coiled form where its outstanding resilience is utilized. At present it is being used in automobile carburetor filters. Another promising use for the coiled fiber is in padding material for furniture, which offers a large and profitable outlet. The straight fiber may go into paint brushes for use with oil-base paint and into dusting brushes. Stiff cloth made with casein bristle woven with cotton thread has unique properties and is useful as a stiffening material in the clothing industry. It is expected that the uses for casein bristle will multiply as it becomes more available commercially.

A PROMISING woollike fiber is made from peanut protein.

Six steps enter into its manufacture: Shelling the peanuts; flaking the peanut kernels; extracting the oil from the flaked kernels by petroleum hydrocarbons at low temperatures; separating the protein from the solvent-extracted flakes or peanut meal; preparing a protein solution; and extruding the protein solution to form the fiber.

In a typical process, the purified peanut protein is dissolved in a solution of caustic soda to yield a thick, molasses-like mass. Other chemicals are added to effect the desired changes in the protein molecules. Then the solution is filtered to remove all undissolved particles. The solution is comparable to the protein solution formed by the silkworm within its body.

When peanut-protein solutions are extruded into air, they do not coagulate. Consequently, they have to be extruded into some chemical solution that will coagulate the protein. One of the most commonly used solutions contains sulfuric acid and sodium sulfate. After the plasticlike fiber has been formed in the solution, it is withdrawn in a threadlike form, stretched, and reacted with other chemicals, such as sodium chloride and formaldehyde. The fiber may be left in the threadlike form and dried for use, or it may be cut into staple lengths approximating the normal lengths of wool.

Peanut-protein fiber is the color of light cream in its natural state and has a soft handle and warmth, like wool. The fiber can be dyed with wool dyes. It has about 80 percent of the strength of wool. It can be stretched without breaking almost as much as wool.

Woven textile fabrics composed of blends of peanut-protein fiber and rayon or wool are used in suitings, linings for coats, and blankets. Two concerns in the United States have made the fiber in the pilot plant and have begun further work on the production of the fiber.

THOMAS L. McMEEKIN *is head of the protein division in the Eastern Regional Research Laboratory. He is a graduate of Clemson Agricultural College, Tulane University, and the University of Chicago.*

ROBERT F. PETERSON *is a chemist in the same division. He received his doctorate in chemistry from the University of Maryland.*

SAM R. HOOVER *has done chemical research in the Bureau of Agricultural and Industrial Chemistry since 1931. He received his training in Davis and Elkins College, and George Washington and Georgetown Universities.*

A New Fiber From Corn Kernels

C. Bradford Croston

From the corn kernel we now get a fiber that combines good qualities of cotton and wool. Fabrics made from it are durable, warm, and washable.

The starting material is zein, a relatively pure protein that is separated from the starch, oil, and other parts of the seed. It looks like discolored flour and is converted to fiber by complicated processes. The method, developed at the Northern Regional Research Laboratory, was announced late in 1945 and was so successful that it was in commercial operation in 1948.

Zein is isolated from corn-gluten meal, a byproduct of starch refineries, by alcoholic extraction. It is marketed as a dry, yellowish powder, which can be stored for long periods without appreciable change. It is soluble in the usual prolamine solvents, such as aqueous alcohols, ketones, and organic acids, and in alkaline solutions at a pH range of 11.5 to 12.5. Because of its unique properties, zein also is in demand for other industrial uses—in varnishes, plastics, and adhesives, for instance.

Fiber can be spun from zein solutions by either dry- or wet-spinning techniques. The dry-spinning method is copied from the spider or silkworm and is like the process used to make acetate rayons. The spinning dope is a clear, thick solution of material in a volatile solvent, such as alcohol or acetone. It is pumped through extremely small holes punched in the bottom of a metal cup called a spinneret. The spinneret is held at the top of a column of hot air; as the fine stream of spinning dope from each hole falls through the column, the solvent evaporates, leaving solid filaments, or fibers, which are collected at the bottom.

The wet-spinning process is like the one used for making viscose rayon. The spinneret is held below the surface of a water bath, which usually contains acids for solidifying the spinning dope as it comes through the holes in the spinneret. The solidified filaments are gathered together as a wet tow, which is processed on reels and in baths before being dried.

Theoretically, zein fiber can be spun from volatile solutions by either method. Patents cover processes for both, but there have been no successful commercial applications of them.

A more recent process developed at the Northern Laboratory has been more successful. Its operation was on only a small scale but was continuous, rather than batch. The basic principles are used commercially. A wet-spinning process, it uses alkaline dispersions (solutions) of zein as the spinning dope. Strengthening and hardening treatments of the newly formed filaments are necessary before they become suitable textile fibers.

Alkaline spinning dispersions consist primarily of about 1 part alkali, 50 parts zein, and 330 parts water. The alkali (sodium hydroxide) is necessary to make the zein dissolve in the water. Other substances may be added to the mixture for various reasons—for example, oils to soften the fiber, or a chemical, such as urea or alcohol, to hasten denaturation, the physical change necessary for satisfactory spinning.

The dispersions are easily prepared

469

if a few precautions are observed. The dry zein is first mixed in about three-fourths of the water, which preferably is precooled. If the temperature of the mixture rises much above normal room temperature, we get a doughy mass, which is difficult to work. The alkali and urea dissolved in the remaining water are then slowly added to the mixture, which is stirred until a clear, uniform dispersion results. Enough alkali must be present to bring the final pH up to near 12.0; an excess of alkali causes the zein to come back out of solution if the pH goes above 12.5.

Good spinning dispersions are essential for good fibers. There must be no undissolved particles or air bubbles in the dispersions. Anything that momentarily interrupts the flow of dope through the spinneret holes causes unsightly, detrimental breaks in the fiber. The best spinneret action is obtainable by using spinning dopes of relatively high viscosity, like thick molasses. The high viscosities result either from using high concentrations of zein or from aging dispersions of lower concentration. A convenient method is to prepare dispersions of low protein concentration, which readily pass through filters and from which the air readily rises. Then, while aging in the presence of denaturing agents, the viscosity gradually increases to the desired value.

When the dispersion has attained suitable spinning characteristics, it is forced by a metering pump through the holes of the spinneret into the acid coagulating bath. A satisfactory bath consists of 87 percent water, 5 percent sulfuric acid, 3 percent acetic acid, and 5 percent zinc sulfate.

The size and number of holes in spinnerets vary, depending on the desired size of filament and the ultimate use of the fiber. A spinneret containing about 40 holes is ordinarily used to make continuous-filament yarn. One with as many as 12,000 holes is used to make another type that is ultimately cut into short pieces before being carded and twisted into yarn. All the filaments from one spinneret are pulled out of the coagulating bath in the form of a rope, called tow, by passing over a revolving reel. The tow then runs continuously over reels and through treating baths until at the end it is separable into the dry, finished fibers.

The freshly coagulated filaments are tender and weak and must undergo special treatments to form useful fibers. The three essential treatments are a mild cure with formaldehyde, a high stretch in hot water, and a stronger formaldehyde cure of the stretched fiber.

The first formaldehyde cure is carried out on the slack fiber in a bath immediately following the coagulating bath, or the two baths may be combined. The first cure is important in toughening the fiber so that it will withstand subsequent handling. It is also important for imparting strength to the fiber. The formaldehyde probably ties the zein molecules together, so that the ensuing hot-water stretch is effective in orienting the molecules into a desirable fibrous pattern. The stretched fibers are strong, but have rubbery characteristics; that is, when the tension is released, the wet fibers return to their unstretched length. A drying of the elongated fibers temporarily stabilizes their length, but whenever the fibers again come in contact with water, the shrinkage occurs. The shrinkage, especially in hot water, prohibits the use of the fiber at this stage in textiles and other applications.

The second formaldehyde cure is applied to the stretched fiber. Its purpose is to stabilize permanently the fiber against shrinkage. The role of the formaldehyde is to form bridges, or cross-bonds, between the protein molecules, thereby holding them in an oriented state. It is desirable to form cross-bonds that are resistant to the boiling acid used for dyeing wool.

This second formaldehyde cure is conducted either in a water solution while holding the wet stretched fiber at constant length or in a nonaqueous system on dry fiber. When the curing is in an aqueous formaldehyde system, the most stable bonds are formed in solutions that contain a high concentration of hydrochloric or sulfuric acid. The nonaqueous cure consists of formaldehyde or a formaldehyde-yielding agent and a strong acid in an organic solvent, such as toluene or Stoddard's solvent. The treating temperature is about 212° F. The dry fiber does not shrink appreciably during treatment, even when left loose in the mixture. The cure is rapid and effective in producing a fiber stable to boiling acid.

An acetylating treatment with acetic anhydride has been used to good advantage on the fiber. It is applied between the two formaldehyde cures. It is not effective in preventing shrinkage, but improves such properties as water resistance, color, affinity for dyes, and softness of the fiber.

After it has been given its first formaldehyde cure, stretched to just short of breaking, and dried, zein fiber is exceptionally strong, wet or dry. The second formaldehyde cure eliminates the undesirable shrinkage, but does so at a sacrifice in strength of the fiber—especially when the wet cure is used. The stabilized fiber, however, is still as strong as wool, and, because it is proteinaceous, it has the desirable woollike properties of water absorption and resilience. Resilience involves the degree and rate of recovery after a distorting force has been applied. These properties are the main contributors to the wrinkle-resisting and crease-retaining character and to the warmth of wool fabrics. Zein fibers are flexible, although they contain no plasticizer, which might change with age or be washed out in laundering. They also have acceptable extensibilities, a good feel, and dye nicely with a variety of dyes.

The fiber, like all other protein fibers, is expensive in comparison with cellulosic fibers like cotton or rayon. On the other hand, it is cheaper than wool. It can meet competition with our other good fibers because of its unique combination of properties.

Anticipated uses for the fiber are in woven and knitted fabrics in which it will be used alone or blended with other fibers; in felts as a partial replacement of fur; and in brushes, in which bristle stiffness is gained by a larger size of filament.

Commercial production of zein fiber is actually in its infancy, although many years of research have gone into the making of fibers from proteins such as from peanut, milk, soybean, and corn. The Virginia-Carolina Chemical Corp. of Richmond, Va., began an investigation of high polymers from protein bases in 1939. Through the basic work done at the Northern Regional Research Laboratory, they investigated zein fiber and found it to be most suitable for a new textile-fiber development. As a result, Vicara came into commercial production in 1948.

It is known as the "fiber that improves the blend." It adds suppleness and draping qualities to rayon, warmth and absorptiveness to nylon, and softness to wool.

The blending, yarn spinning, and weaving are easily carried out in conventional machinery. It is readily dyed by most known methods and, because of its combined acid and alkali resistance, withstands better than other fibers, all textile processings. It burns slowly and is inherently moth- and mildew-resistant. When used alone or blended with other washable fibers, it is readily washed without any special precautions.

Zein fiber is a made-to-order "wool." The quality of the product is uniform and the fineness or coarseness of the fiber can be controlled to best fit the purpose at hand. Other properties can be controlled to enhance its ability to stand alone or to improve the blend. Fabrics made from it are as warm as wool, yet nonitching and launderable.

C. BRADFORD CROSTON *has been a chemist in the oil and protein division of the Northern Regional Research Laboratory since 1943. He holds degrees from the University of Missouri and the University of Minnesota.*

Progress With Long Vegetable Fibers

Mills H. Byrom

Most of the long, hard vegetable fibers, such as henequen, sisal, and abacá, come from tropical lands, where climate favors their growth, cheap labor is plentiful, and cultural problems are simple. Other long vegetable fibers, like jute, flax, and hemp, are produced in the temperate zones, but mostly outside the United States.

These fibers are the raw materials of rope, binder twine, burlap, and related products. Despite the importance of these products in peace and war, and despite its varied climate, fertile soils, and great capacity for agricultural production, the United States has never attempted to produce any of them in quantities equal to its needs.

India has supplied jute for burlap, bagging, carpets, and similar products. From Mexico, Cuba, and Africa we get henequen and sisal for binder twine, wrapping twine, and other cordage products. Nearly all of the abacá used for the better grades of rope and cordage is imported from the Philippines.

Because of increased needs and almost complete dependence on foreign countries for their production, an acute shortage of fibers developed in this country early in the Second World War. The Government spent millions of dollars to encourage the production of hemp, a soft fiber, to supplement the supplies of abacá, a hard fiber, when the Philippines were occupied.

The Government also subsidized the production of abacá in Central America with some success, but at costs much above prewar prices. Conditions in the Orient, where the largest amounts of abacá and jute have been produced, are such that adequate future supplies of the fibers from that source appear doubtful.

Some of the long fibers useful for special purposes can be produced in the United States. The research program under way aims to seek out the useful fibers suitable for production in this country, to develop equipment for producing them, and to determine the feasibility of establishing new industries to handle and process them. Other points are the urgent need for a fiber to fill an essential need, the adaptability of the plant and its fiber to mechanical production, and the extent of the probable market. Fibers produced here might supplement scant supplies from abroad.

THE FIRST FIBER selected for investigation was sansevieria, which grows half-wild in Florida. It contains fiber thought to be a good substitute for abacá for marine rope and cordage.

As the work on sansevieria progressed, we found that many of the basic principles governing its production apply also to production of other long fibers, especially ramie and kenaf, both of which are soft bast fibers. Ramie has potential uses in textiles and in paper making. Kenaf may be a substitute for jute in making sugar bags, twine, burlap, and such.

Sansevieria, commonly called the snake plant, is a member of the lily family. It is perennial and will completely cover the ground in which it is planted. More than 80 species are known that are native to Asia and Africa. The plant has been transplanted to most of the tropical and semitropical areas of the world and has become naturalized quickly.

As a war measure to relieve an acute shortage of cordage fiber, the Department of Agriculture and the Florida Agricultural Experiment Station in 1943 established a fiber research project 4 miles west of Boynton, Fla., and planted 10 acres to several varieties of sansevieria. Studies of all agronomic and engineering phases of propagating, growing, and processing were planned. The investigations have shown that if production is to be mechanized completely, cultural machinery (planters, cultivators, and harvesters) and processing machinery (decorticators, driers, and other specialized equipment) must be developed.

Of the several methods of obtaining planting stock, leaf cuttings set in nursery beds have given the most satisfactory plants for fiber production. In propagation by this method, strong mature leaves are cut in sections 6 inches long and are planted every 4 inches in rows spaced 12 inches apart. In 6 to 9 months, each leaf piece produces from 3 to 6 plants ready for transplanting to the open field.

Machinery has been developed that will make the cuttings and mark the ends to be placed in the ground, plant the cuttings in the nursery row, and transplant the plants in the field. A crew of five men can set 50,000 leaf cuttings or plants in an 8-hour day.

Weeds and grass must be controlled until the planting is well established. Occasional cutting or pulling of large weeds in the fields and weeding of the turn rows and ditches also are generally necessary during the later period of growth. Some of the new weed-killing sprays and the flame weeder may be effective for controlling weeds in the crop.

The problem of developing a satisfactory harvester for sansevieria is more complicated than that of developing planting and cultivating machinery. Recent tests indicate, however, that the leaves can be cut with the regular cutter bar and sickle of a mowing machine if minor adjustments are made. If harvested by this method, at least 2 inches of the lower end of the leaf will be left as stubble. Because the lower part of the leaf contains a comparatively high percentage of fiber of good quality, it is desirable to devise a cutter that will follow the contour of the ground and thus eliminate this loss. A rotary-type cutter is being studied as one possible answer to this difficulty. Modifications of the gathering and binding devices used on harvesters designed for other crops should work satisfactorily with sansevieria.

Sansevieria may be held in the field in a growing condition for a period of years, apparently with little deterioration of fiber quality or quantity. This is in marked contrast to the growing habits of other long fibers, either hard or soft. The cycle of production from leaf cutting to harvest for fiber production is 3 years.

The value of sansevieria fiber has long been recognized, but it has never been produced in commercial quantities because of the difficulties of mechanical decortication, resulting from lack of uniformity of fiber content in the leaves, as well as lack of suitable decorticating machinery. (Decortication is the process of separating the fiber from the outer covering, pulp, and other foreign material of the leaf.) Therefore, there is need for breeding or selecting a strain of sansevieria that will have a uniform fiber content in all the leaves, and also for further improvement in decorticating machinery, especially in the gripping chains that hold the leaves while decortication takes place.

Most of the attempts to decorticate sansevieria have been made with the raspador-type machine designed for sisal and henequen, both of which have tougher leaves than sansevieria. However, as this type of machine has simplicity, large capacity, and long life, it was selected as the basic machine for research in decortication, even though it is wasteful of fiber.

The decorticating mechanism of the raspador machine consists of a series of knives on a rotating wheel operating against a stationary bed plate. Clearance on the entering side is wide, and the knives have a beating action on the material. The clearance decreases as the material passes across the face of the wheel and the action of the knives changes gradually from beating to scraping. Floods of water in the decorticating wheel help to remove loose bark, pulp, and plant juice.

Two such wheels are mounted on opposite sides of offset gripping devices. The material to be decorticated is fed into the forward pair of gripping devices and carried through the first decorticating wheel. The fiber from this operation is caught by the rear gripping device and the leaf is carried through the other wheel, thus completing the decorticating process.

Improvement in the shape of the decorticating knife, proper speed of the decorticating wheel, and proper clearance between the knife and bed plate have given clean decortication. The fiber yield of Florida-grown leaves has averaged about 2.5 percent. Results of decortication tests show that 75 to 90 percent of the yield can be recovered as clean, dry fiber, suitable for the manufacture of marine cordage, the higher yields resulting from the use of improved adjustments.

A burnishing machine has been developed for further cleaning the decorticated fiber after it has dried. This machine parallels the fibers and removes pulp and other foreign material.

Extensive tests have been carried on to determine the basic principles governing the artificial drying of fibers. The investigations have been successful to the extent that it now appears possible to dry wet fiber adequately without bringing the temperature to a point high enough to injure it. As a result of the tests, a three-stage drier has been built. The first stage uses circulating air having high humidity and relatively low temperature. The second stage uses air having high temperature and low humidity. The air in the third stage has low humidity and low temperature.

In the first stage, the fiber is heated to drying temperature, but, because of the high humidity of the air, no actual loss of moisture takes place. This is termed the heating stage. In the second stage, the conditions of the fiber and the air favor rapid drying. This is termed the drying stage. Conditions in the third stage are set up to cool the fiber, thus closing the pores and equalizing any wet spots that exist. This is termed the cooling and equalizing stage. Indications are that this type of drying will give maximum production with no damage to the fiber.

The high quality of the American-grown sansevieria fiber has been indicated in spinning tests by the American Manufacturing Co., of Brooklyn, and by the Boston Navy Yard. In both series of tests, sansevieria processed satisfactorily on ordinary rope-making machinery. Rope made of sansevieria fiber was better than that made from American hemp or sisal, and 90 percent as strong as that made from abacá.

The research has progressed to the extent of demonstrating that sansevieria can be mechanically decorticated, that it can be grown in southern Florida, and that it is a good substitute for abacá. As the world figure for annual yields of hard fiber is approximately 1,200 pounds to the acre, sansevieria, having yielded more than 3,200 pounds to the acre where it grows wild, has demonstrated a potential production capacity in Florida that justifies more complete investigation. Under average field conditions, it would be reasonable to expect that yields might average somewhat lower than yields obtained in test plots.

RAMIE has had a romantic history that dates from the days of the Pharaohs. It has qualities that make it a first-class industrial and textile fiber. It is naturally a delicate white, with the soft brilliance of silk. Although its physical properties may have been overrated, a number of them are superior.

Federal procurement agencies became interested in ramie during the Second World War, when it appeared that large quantities would be needed by the Navy for stern-tube packing and many other products.

Ramie is a perennial from the Orient. The stalks grow 6 to 8 feet high, are about one-half inch in diameter, and are straight and nonbranching. A cluster of large, hairy, heart-shaped leaves grows on the top 12 inches of the plant. The fiber, borne between the bark and the woody core, is imbedded in a series of gummy pectin compounds.

A growing period of about 60 days is required to mature the fiber. In Florida, average yields of green material of 10 to 12 tons to the acre a cutting and three cuttings a year have been obtained under good management and on the better muck soils. The annual fiber yields were 2,000 pounds an acre or higher. Such yields, obviously, are better than would be expected on less fertile soils or during unfavorable seasons.

The characteristics of ramie make it readily adaptable to mechanization. The machinery needed to produce fiber ready for the spinner can be grouped as cultivating, harvesting, decorticating, degumming, and drying.

The quickest and best method of establishing a stand of plants in a new planting is through the use of root pieces 3 to 5 inches long. To obtain the cuttings, root clumps in an established field are plowed out and run through a rotary cutting head that has a suitable feed mechanism. The root pieces can be dropped by hand, but a transplanter is better where large areas are involved. After the first year, in good stands, little cultivation is needed in the Florida muck soils. Ramie is a heavy feeder and requires a well-planned fertilizing program. Thus far, insect pests and diseases have troubled it very little.

No harvesting machinery has been designed especially for ramie, but several reaper-type harvesters built for other crops can be adapted. The wartime hemp cutter has been combined with the hemp pick-up binder to make a complete cutting and binding machine. This unit is serving the purpose, but needs improvement for greater efficiency. Research is in progress to develop a harvester that will be better suited to ramie than any of the machines now available.

A number of lightweight portable machines that decorticate by beating, scraping, brushing, or wiping (or combinations of them) have been patented for use on ramie. Some of them produce fiber of acceptable quality, but none has been widely used, mainly because of their small capacity. A definite need exists for a lightweight, inexpensive, portable decorticator suitable for use on small acreages. Research on a machine of this type has been started.

Several of the portable machines have been built to decorticate the stalks after they have been dried. In south Florida, however, the frequent rains and high humidity during the harvest season make this impossible. All large-scale decorticate is done on freshly cut stalks.

The raspador machine used on sansevieria has been adapted to ramie and is producing fiber of a satisfactory quantity and quality. It needs further improvement, however.

The fundamental principles governing the artificial drying of sansevieria fiber also apply to ramie, with slight modifications. The pilot drier constructed for sansevieria is expected to be satisfactory for drying any long vegetable fiber.

Until quite recently, manufacturers thought they would have to degum their own fiber in order to get the uniformity needed for spinning. The grower was satisfied with this arrangement as it relieved him of the responsibility and expense of setting up and maintaining a chemical operation that was entirely out of his line. Lately many potential users of ramie have refused to buy undegummed fiber, but have expressed a willingness to buy large quantities of degummed material if a dependable source of supply could be found. The situation has caused many growers to consider adding a degumming plant to their facilities.

Degumming is the process by which the insoluble gums and pectins are dissolved or made water-soluble, thus freeing the embedded fibers. Two principal systems are being considered by Florida growers. One employs a series of open cooks at atmospheric pressure. The other is a closed system operating under steam pressure. Sodium hydroxide is the principal degumming agent in both systems. Recent improvement in the chemical formulas and their application has resulted in better fiber.

Several byproducts can be obtained from the ramie plant. The most promising ones are leaf meal for stock feed and chlorophyll, carotene, and other extracts from the leaves. The waste fiber and shives from the decorticating operation make high-grade paper. There should be a demand for the pectins in the gums if they can be separated and purified economically.

Public and private agencies interested in the establishment of a ramie industry in the United States, working in close cooperation, have made substantial progress.

KENAF, an annual, is like ramie in that it is a bast fiber. It has stalks 8 to 10 feet high and about one-half inch in diameter. The fiber is quite different from ramie fiber, being more nearly of the quality of jute, and is used for the same purposes. The fiber matures before the plant produces seed; hence, there must be a separate planting for seed production.

The rice combine has been found satisfactory for harvesting and threshing the seed on Cuba and El Salvador. Plantings for fiber production can be made with an ordinary small grain drill. Plantings for seed production should be in rows spaced farther apart and can be made by stopping up seed tubes on a grain drill until the desired row spacing is obtained.

The kenaf plant contains about 6 percent fiber, and acre yields of fiber in Florida have compared favorably with jute yields in India.

The harvesting, decorticating, and drying equipment developed for ramie works equally well on kenaf, but the fiber is brittle and the presence of plant residue in the fiber makes it unsatisfactory for spinning on available machinery. In order to produce a fiber acceptable to the manufacturer, the decorticated material will have to be water-retted or treated chemically to remove the foreign material and to soften the fiber.

Investigations have started to determine whether it is more economical to ribbon the stalks and water-ret the ribbons or to decorticate the fiber and treat it chemically.

Ribboning, if perfected, can be done with a light portable machine. The burnishing machine, already mentioned, has given excellent results in ribboning kenaf stalks. Used in conjunction with neoprene-rubber squeeze rolls, it has given good results in cleaning the retted ribbons.

Pond, or uncontrolled, retting of the ribbons has given a poor-quality fiber, which lacks uniformity, strength, and color. If the fiber is to be retted, it appears that retting conditions must be controlled.

Chemical treatment offers a solution to the problem of uniformity and has the advantage of continuous-line production of fiber from stalk to bale.

MILLS H. BYROM, *agricultural engineer in the Bureau of Plant Industry, Soils, and Agricultural Engineering, has been in charge of the Bureau's special fiber-processing work since its beginning in 1943. He was graduated from the Agricultural and Mechanical College of Texas in mechanical engineering and engaged in teaching and research work at that institution from 1928 until 1942.*

Angora, the Long-Haired Rabbit

Ethel H. Dolnick,
Thora M. Plitt Hardy

The wool of the Angora rabbit is valued for its length, softness, luster, and fineness. It is often combined with cotton, rayon, silk, and sheep's wool in an amount equal to approximately 25 percent of the total blend. Such a mixture will impart the desirable characteristics of soft "handle" and luster to the finished fabric.

The use of Angora wool as a specialty fiber is subject to fashion cycles, as are most specialty fibers. They are in vogue for a time, disappear from the market a while, and are rediscovered as something entirely new.

One may gain appreciation of the lightness and warmth of Angora rabbit wool by handling even a small sample. If the sample is teased apart, two main types of fibers can be recognized. The underfur fibers, the finer ones, constitute the main mass of the sample. They measure approximately 14 microns in diameter; 21 microns is the average diameter of fine wool from sheep. The remaining fibers, or guard hairs, make up about 5 percent of the total number of fibers in the sample. They are much thicker and measure about 90 microns in diameter.

GUARD HAIRS present in Angora rabbit wool at the time of spinning will produce a fuzziness in the cloth, which sometimes is fashionable. They can be eliminated by blowing the wool, before spinning, in a small tower or in a confined area; the underfur fibers are lighter and will collect at a higher level than the guard hairs.

For spinning, the wool should be of uniform texture and of fairly long staple. Angora rabbit wool has a tendency to "fly"—acquire static electricity in spinning—but that can be reduced by spinning in a room where humidity is controlled, or by dampening the fibers and cutting down the speed of the machinery.

Very fine wool is used to make Angora sweaters and underwear. The wool usually preferred for the purpose is obtained from the English variety of Angora rabbit. Most of the Angora rabbits raised in the United States are descendants of the types developed in France and England. French stock is bred for the coarser wool.

In knitting or weaving a cloth containing sheep's wool and Angora rabbit wool, the diameter of both types of wool fibers should be about the same. In such a combination, the wool obtained from the French variety may be preferred, because it more nearly approximates the diameter of the fine wool from sheep, with which it is usually blended. Coarse Angora wool is also used for socks, mittens, scarves, and heavy sweaters.

For hand spinning, plucked wool is more popular, because the fibers are longer and have a more even staple; a more uniform yarn is obtainable with the longer fibers. Some users believe that the taper of the fiber at the tip end and the slight thickening at the root end into a bulb, or brushlike structure, increase the spinning quality of plucked wool. Most Angora wool harvested by shearing or clipping shows cut ends.

MILLS DYE the yarn or the cloth in the familiar pastel shades and in the darker colors. The dye must be in a more concentrated form than that used for sheep's wool, because Angora wool absorbs more of it. Sometimes dyes are used that will affect only one of the fiber components, such as sheep's wool or cotton, while the rabbit fiber remains white. An attractive novelty cloth is thus produced.

The commercial use of Angora rabbit wool depends upon its availability in large quantities and upon current demand. For handicraft purposes, the wool may be accumulated and used as the needs arise. The wool is often spun on an old-fashioned spinning wheel in much the same way as sheep's wool is spun, but it is not necessary to wash or card the Angora wool before spinning. The carding treatment combs and straightens the individual fibers in sheep's wool. Angora rabbit wool is spun directly after plucking or shearing.

Small, electrically operated spinners with variable-speed controls, originally designed for use by disabled veterans, are now on the market. Angora rabbit trade journals tell where to buy these machines; instructions for their operation are available from the manufacturers. The spinners are easy to work.

Public interest in handicrafts has risen in recent years. Information on classes in arts and crafts can be had by writing to the departments of education of the various States. Connecticut, Massachusetts, New Hampshire, Vermont, Georgia, New Mexico, and North Carolina are among the States in which such classes have been organized. Public libraries also list local handicraft schools.

The raising of Angora rabbits is a comparatively new cottage industry that has been developing slowly since 1900. It received its main impetus during the Second World War, when imports were limited.

Angora rabbit wool is harvested every 10 or 12 weeks. Personal preference largely determines the choice of the method, whether it be by clipping, plucking, or shearing. Commercial grading is based on length of fibers.

The longest and most desirable fibers come from the back and sides of the animal. They are 2½ to 3 inches long, grade No. 1, and bring the highest prices. The wool from the belly grades as No. 3, if it is less than 1½ inches long, or as No. 2, if it is longer. Matted wool is placed in grade No. 4. Soiled wool is grade No. 5 and the lowest in value. Matting is found in some Angora rabbits and not in others. The cause for matting is not known; the type of cells in the cuticle, the outside layer of the fiber, may have some bearing on it.

The average yield of wool from an Angora rabbit is about 12 or more ounces a year. The total amount of wool obtained by any one of the harvest methods will be practically the same over the period of a year, but a greater proportion of No. 1 wool may be obtained by plucking. If a rabbit is to be plucked, an examination of the fur at frequent intervals is necessary in order to get the longest fibers when they will pluck with ease, that is, at the time the animal is in molt. Animals in molt are identified by the presence of loose, shedding hairs.

In full coat an Angora rabbit looks like so much fluff. The fibers stand out loosely over the body and give a rounded appearance to the animal. On the whole, the rabbits are gentle and easy to care for. The kind and quantity of feed, the frequency of feeding, and the breeding and management practices are discussed in Farmers' Bulletin No. 1730.

ETHEL H. DOLNICK *is a microanalyst in the Bureau of Animal Industry. She has been conducting investigations on the characteristics of North American commercial furs at Beltsville, Md., since 1943.*

THORA M. PLITT HARDY, *a graduate of Barnard College and the University of Chicago, was in charge of the fur fiber laboratory in the Bureau of Animal Industry from 1938 to 1948, when she joined the Production and Marketing Administration.*

Durable, Cheap Furs From Lambskins

John I. Hardy

Mouton meets the need for a durable fur that can be worn every day and on special occasions. It is attractive and inexpensive. It can be worn in the city or country or on the campus.

A chemical process straightens the curly fleece of yearling lambskins to produce mouton. In one method of manufacture, the dried skins are softened in a vat of warm water in which the heat is controlled. The skins are then washed and treated so that partial hydrolysis sets in. The wool protein is softened and amino groups are freed. Plasticizing agents are now ready to act on the fibers to make them pliable. The crimpy fibers are straightened by brushing and set permanently through the application of heat and pressure. The fibers are then dyed. One popular shade simulates beaver, but mouton can be dyed any color.

The production of mouton was stimulated by its use as a lining for aviators' coats in the Second World War. In order to meet that demand skins of older sheep were also used. They make good mouton, but the leather is thicker and heavier and not too desirable for coats.

In view of the large number of lambs born each year, the supply of raw material seems almost limitless. The normal annual production of shearlings from domestic sheep is between 2 million and 3 million. Imports run as high as 4 million.

So much has been written about mouton and the simplicity of producing it that many persons mistakenly believe every yearling lambskin can be used. Trade estimates for 1947 were that about 2 million pounds of lambskin pelts were processed into mouton. It may at times be necessary to examine 15 or 20 mouton skins before a choice one is found. The less desirable skins can be used for such purposes as bedroom slippers and coat linings. The requirements for good mouton coats are exacting, and there is need for better-quality skins.

For good mouton production, the processor selects pelts having wool grading as fine as 60's, 62's, or 64's, standard numerical wool grades. Pelts having coarse wool are not satisfactory for mouton production. The numerical grades for wool are the same as what is sometimes referred to as the count system for worsted yarn. Wool grading 60's is of the fineness that will produce 60 hanks of single yarn per pound of clean wool. In this case one hank measures 560 yards. Therefore, one clean pound of 60's wool will spin 33,600 yards of single yarn. Wool of 70's and 80's spinning count, which is exceedingly fine, may offer difficulties in manufacture because it tends to mat and the fibers do not straighten sufficiently.

WITH THE IDEA of helping the industry produce still better mouton and of helping sheepmen obtain a greater return for their lambskins, the Bureau of Animal Industry, with the cooperation of the Ohio Agricultural Experiment Station, investigated the quality of various moutons with new and improved methods of testing. The Ohio station produced and furnished the lambskins to the processing plant, and the Bureau tested the finished skins. A study was made of the fiber-fineness distribution, the density of fur, the weight of the finished mouton, the thickness of the skin, and the straightening properties of the fibers. Considerable variations were found in those qualities, even in sheep of the same breeding.

To determine the fiber-fineness distribution, tufts of fibers were taken from the finished skins at various locations, such as the shoulder, side, thigh, and back. The fibers were cross-sectioned, their fineness was measured in microns, and their variabilities of fineness were noted.

For the density measurements, 1- by 2-centimeter skin samples were removed, with fibers attached, and inserted in a cross-sectioning device. A standard was set up to furnish a measure of relative density of the fibers. That is, the wool fibers of the samples were cut to a length of 1.17 millimeters just above the skin surface on the 1- by 2-centimeter sections, and those fibers were weighed on a microbalance.

A special micrometer was used to measure the thickness of the skin on several areas from which the fibers had

been carefully removed. The individual fibers were then projected onto a screen in order to get some information on the degree to which the fibers had been straightened.

Mouton has often reached such a high degree of perfection that it is impossible for many to distinguish between it and much more expensive furs. It is truly amazing when one realizes that mouton, admired for its attractiveness and beauty, is produced from a pelt with a curly fleece, having from 10 to 20 crimps to the inch. Mouton is durable when properly made and excels in many ways—the fibers stay straight, are resistant to moisture, and may be readily cleaned.

JOHN I. HARDY *has been director of research on animal fibers in the Bureau of Animal Industry since 1923. He has conducted research on fur fibers, wool blends, the relation of nutrition to production of hides and wools, and tests for wool fineness and shrinkage. Dr. Hardy has degrees from Rhode Island State College, the University of Tennessee, and the University of Missouri.*

OUT ON THE ranches of the Southwest and Pacific Northwest an unusual use is made of the mane and tail hair of the horse and the switch of the cow's tail.

The cowboys make hair ropes, called mecates, to be used as reins for rawhide hackamores on the noses of young cow horses being broken and trained. The idea came down from the Spanish vaqueros of the region. Hair that has been cleaned, dried, and shaken out in a fluffy pile is fed out in a strand by one cowboy while the strand is twisted into long lengths by another. A hooked nail, or something similar, held in a carpenter's brace is often used to do the twisting. Two single strands are usually twisted together into a double strand. Two double strands are then twisted together, making a total of four strands in the finished rope. When the ends are securely tied the strands will not ravel out.

Strands of different colors, natural or dyed, can be twisted together to make a variegated pattern. I once made some snow-white mecates from hair bobbed from the tails of several hundred white-faced Hereford cows. The tails had been bobbed to show the cows had been vaccinated. Cows' tail hair makes a soft rope. Horse mane is intermediate and horsetail hair makes a very stiff, heavy mecate. The size of rope can be regulated by the amount of hair fed into the single strands in the beginning.—*Orman S. Weaver, Soil Conservation Service, Yakima, Wash.*

Feathers as a Source of Fibers

Harold P. Lundgren

Feathers have often been suggested as raw materials for synthetic fibers. They are fibrous in structure. They are tough. They are practically pure protein, which is the stuff from which other fibers—wool, silk, and hair—are made. The chief interest in feathers lies in their availability—an estimated 120 million pounds a year, which are mostly wasted, mainly because suitable ways are lacking for converting them into useful products.

The main difficulty in handling feathers has been their insolubility in common solvents. That is typical of the keratins, the class of proteins that make up the protective covering of animals—wool, hair, and skin—as well as the feathers on birds. Actually, that property would be desirable if the material were in the form of a usable fiber, but the feathers have to be in solution, or at least in a highly swollen condition, in order to extrude the fibers.

Feathers can be dissolved in strong caustic solutions, but that treatment is so harsh that the final units, the threadlike molecules, are broken into small pieces. As a result, anything that resembles a true fiber cannot be made from such material—the extruded thread, when dried, simply crumbles to a dust.

We have to find a less drastic treatment. That has been a major research problem, one that we have not yet solved completely.

In his search for appropriate agents and conditions for handling feathers, the chemist has learned that the characteristic inertness of feathers is chiefly the manifestation of certain chemical cross-links, or bonds, that tie the long, threadlike molecules into the natural, netlike structure.

Such hooking together of threadlike molecules occurs in other proteins, too, but in feathers the interaction is firmer. From his knowledge of the nature of these cross-links, the chemist can choose specific chemical agents that selectively sever them without destroying the other bonds that connect the atoms into long threads. In other words, the chemist, in tearing apart the feather, seeks to preserve the natural threadlike units, for they are the building blocks required to make synthetic fibers.

The long molecular chains can be separated by use of water solutions of a mixture of a salt (sodium bisulfite) and a detergent, one type of which is made from kerosene and sulfuric acid. The mixture of sodium bisulfite and detergent, acts simultaneously on the feathers to break the sulfur bonds, as well as salt bonds and hydrogen bonds, all of which help to stabilize the natural network. This reacting mixture is mild compared to caustic soda, which breaks the cross-links of the fiber network and the long chains. As soon as the bisulfite and detergent mixture acts, the molecules come apart and dissolve in the water solution.

The dissolved threadlike molecules, however, are not just feather protein alone. Some of the detergent molecules have attached themselves chemically edgewise to them.

That union, which is a rather loose one, has proved of special advantage for the manipulation of the feather material into fibers. The attached detergent helps to unfold the flexible, coiled-up, threadlike molecules. In that way, the molecules are lined up more readily when the solutions are forced through the tiny openings of the spinning nozzle. The alinement of the molecules is easily detected by special optical methods.

When the sirupy stream of lined-up molecules oozing through the spinning nozzle strikes a precipitating solution of salt, the feather molecules immediately congeal to form a fiber—they begin to form a new net structure. The newly formed fiber is highly elastic and weak. Extensive network formation, or rehooking of the protein molecules, is necessary before the fiber acquires appreciable strength, but that is not possible until the detergent molecules are removed. The detergent (which by now has served its purpose as an agent to help separate the protein molecules and then to keep them apart and straightened out until fiber formation has begun) is in the way and prevents extensive interaction. It can be removed by washing the fibers with solutions of acetone in water. This solvent combination breaks the rather loose union between the detergent and feather protein, and the solvent then extracts the detergent. The fiber is left as essentially pure protein. When the extracted fiber is stretched, the chains interact further, with corresponding increase in strength of the fiber.

A METHOD OF PREPARING BRISTLES from feathers, developed at the Western Regional Research Laboratory, is based on a new method for recovery of keratin. Instead of using synthetic detergents, we employ a simplified process having mixtures of alcohol and water as the solvent. When feathers are heated with this mixture at suitably high temperatures, about 70 percent of the protein dissolves. It is easily recovered as a dry powder. Bristles can be made by moistening the powder with the solvent and extruding the material at high temperatures through small openings.

The highly stretched keratin fibers from feathers are comparatively strong when dry—even stronger than wool. They also have a true fiber structure like wool, as revealed by X-ray pictures. But they suffer from a weakness that is characteristic of synthetic fibers made from proteins; they lack the resistance to water that is desired for a good textile fiber. The weakness can be overcome somewhat by treatment with chemical curing agents, such as formaldehyde and acetic anhydride, but in no case has it been possible to bring the wet strength up to more than half of the dry value. We have been unable to achieve the degree of cross-bonding of the chains found in the original feather.

Another limiting property of the fibers made from feathers is their low elasticity. They are not so elastic as the fibers made from casein and zein. But the keratin fibers do exhibit at least one unique characteristic—a close resemblance to hair. That characteristic suggests possible application of them for such comparatively minor purposes as mannequin wigs and as a component of various decorative fabrics. Such fabrics have potential use as suiting interlinings or oil filters.

A further disadvantage of the keratin fibers is their color. Feather pigments are intimately associated with the protein and are not removed in the processing. In consequence, the fibers carry the color of the feathers used, and the output of general-purpose fibers is limited to white feathers.

The biggest problem ahead is to cut the relatively high cost of the process. The need to extract and recover the detergent makes that procedure somewhat more costly than the methods adequate for casein and zein. Unless we can find easier ways to carry out the operations, the only use of the fibers is most likely to be in specialty items like brush bristles, wigs, insulation, and decoration. For the time being, then, technicians are acquiring more information on the molecular structure of the fibers and new methods for stabilizing the fibers toward water. It may yet be practical to use feathers for making a general-purpose fiber.

HAROLD P. LUNDGREN *is in charge of the wool section of the protein division, Western Regional Research Laboratory. He joined the Laboratory in 1941; previously, he was a research associate in the University of Wisconsin and a post-doctorate research fellow in the University of Upsala, Sweden. Dr. Lundgren is a graduate of North Dakota State College and the University of Minnesota.*

THE AMOUNT of water in any biological material may soon be measured by push-button electronic methods. Electrical methods for the determination of moisture are widely used because of their speed and because they do not alter the specimen being measured. Oven methods, by contrast, are time-consuming and alter biological substances so profoundly as to render them unfit for further use.

A new instrument to extend the range of electrical methods is being perfected. Existing instruments are inaccurate or fail entirely if the material under test contains more than about 20 percent water. As biological materials may consist of 90 percent water or more, application of electrical methods is limited.

The new instrument makes use of one of the most recent findings of nuclear physics. In 1946, physicists at Harvard University and Stanford University independently developed methods for measuring the magnetic energy absorbed by the nuclei of certain atoms in liquids and solids. Previously that had been done only for gases and vapors. The work at Harvard and Stanford showed that if water is placed in a magnetic field, the hydrogen nuclei in the water can absorb radio waves of a specific frequency, much as a radio receiver accepts only the waves from the station to which it is tuned. Tuning for the hydrogen nuclei is accomplished by adjusting the strength of the magnetic field to which they are subjected.

The ability of the hydrogen nuclei to absorb radio-frequency (rf) energy is utilized in the instrument which is being developed at the Western Regional Research Laboratory to measure the water content of agricultural materials. The instrument contains electronic circuits arranged to measure the rf energy absorbed by the hydrogen nuclei in a specimen of a water-containing substance. Allowance is made for the energy absorbed by the hydrogen nuclei in the non-aqueous components of the specimen by means of calibration measurements on the materials for which the instrument is intended. The calibrations become a part of the instrument and serve to relate the amount of energy absorbed to the moisture content of the material. Once the instrument is calibrated, the moisture content of a specimen containing an unknown amount of water can be found in the few minutes required to prepare the sample and read the instrument.

Preliminary trials on fruits and vegetables show that this new method can be used over the entire range of moisture encountered in natural or modified biological systems.—*T. M. Shaw, Western Regional Research Laboratory.*

Processing of Fiber Flax in Oregon

Jesse E. Harmond

Fiber flax is processed in the United States only in the Willamette Valley of Oregon. Flax plantings there have varied from 18,000 acres in 1942 to about 1,000 acres in 1950. The 1942 crop yielded 2,000 tons of line fiber, which is about a third of the quantity imported each year. Nearly 6,000 tons of unmanufactured flax fiber and 35 million dollars' worth of manufactured linen were imported into the United States in 1948.

The future of the Oregon industry depends largely on the ability of American farmers and processors to mechanize their operations so that high-grade fiber can be supplied at a price that will make competition possible with European flax fiber, which is produced with low-cost labor.

The United States Department of Agriculture, the Oregon Agricultural Experiment Station, and the fiber-flax industry have been working cooperatively on processing problems since 1938. New techniques and machines have been developed to reduce costs of production and processing and at the same time preserve the inherent good quality of fiber.

LINEN is a textile of great antiquity. Linen that was manufactured 10,000 years ago by the neolithic lake dwellers has been found in Switzerland. Flax was one of the first crops grown in the New World by the Pilgrims at Plymouth and by the early settlers at Jamestown. Nearly every farmhouse had a spinning wheel, and women were skilled in the art of spinning linen and woolen yarns. Homespun cloth was the chief textile of Colonial days. Flax growing and processing increased in the United States until Eli Whitney invented the cotton gin in 1793. The flax processors, unable to compete with the lower-cost cotton production, were forced to close their plants.

Flax is grown commercially for seed and for fiber. The varieties grown for seed are generally short plants with many lateral branches. Fiber from the seed varieties is often coarse and harsh and is not well suited for textiles. The varieties grown for fiber have fewer lateral branches and reach a greater height than seed flax. The fiber is finer, longer, and softer than that in seed flax. The seed from fiber flax is as valuable for oil and meal as that from seed flax.

Production of high-grade fiber flax calls for a cool, moist growing season, a requirement that has somewhat restricted the areas where the crop can be successfully grown.

The commercial processing of fiber flax in the United States has been largely confined to Michigan and Oregon. In Michigan, the industry ended with the beginning of the First World War. The present industry in Oregon began in 1915, when the State legislature appropriated $50,000 to the Oregon Penitentiary to erect a processing plant, which is still in operation.

Three cooperative processing plants were established jointly by the State of Oregon, the Works Progress Administration, and growers' cooperatives in 1936. Ten more were built with Federal, State, and private capital from 1941 to 1943, bringing the total to 14. The number of active processing plants dropped to four in 1950 because of the decline in prices of domestic fiber, competition from cheaper imported European fiber, failure of the industry to establish grade standards, lack of orderly marketing procedures, and high prices paid for competitive crops.

FLAX PROCESSING comprises six major steps: Pulling, or harvesting; deseeding, or separation of seed from straw; retting, or partial rotting, to loosen the fiber from the rest of the plant; drying, or removal of the retting water from the straw; scutching, or separation of the long line fiber from the rest of the plant; and hackling, or combing, to make the long fibers parallel and remove the short tangled fibers.

Fiber flax is usually planted from February 15 to April 15. It is pulled and delivered to the processing plants in July and August. A small part of the straw is deseeded as it is delivered; the rest is deseeded by January. Retting and drying are ordinarily done from June to October of the following year. Scutching and hackling are done from October to May. The processing operations cover from 18 months to 2 years from the time the straw is pulled until the fiber is ready for the market.

FLAX PLANTS grown for fiber are pulled by hand or by machine. Reapers, sometimes used, cut the flax straw from 3 to 7 inches above the ground. As the line fiber runs the full length of the straw, a good deal of valuable fiber is left in the field to rot when the crop is harvested by cutting.

A skilled workman can hand pull an acre of flax in 68 hours. The tractor-drawn Willamette puller with two men can do it in far less time.

Mechanical pullers thus far developed often scuff, or crush, the straw where it is gripped in the pulling mechanism and cause the fiber to over-ret and weaken at the damaged points during retting.

Uneven bundles produced in pulling cause seed losses in the deseeding and straw losses in the processing operations. The unevenness results in a lower yield of line fiber; it increases the proportion of tangled fiber, which is called flax tow, and causes the discharge of fiber with uneven ends from the scutching machine.

Many patents have been granted on flax pullers, but only four or five have been developed to the stage where they are used commercially. The slowness in adapting mechanical pullers has been attributed to an abundance of cheap labor in the flax areas and the small plantings of flax on each farm. The shortage of labor after the First World War stimulated the development and use of flax pullers.

A MAJOR PROBLEM confronting the industry at the beginning of the project was how to remove the seed from the flax stems without damaging the straw.

Devices for deseeding fiber flax already patented include a hand-operated ripple, one of the earliest devices. Ripple deseeding is still practiced to some extent in Egypt. The bundle of flax is spread and the seed ends are drawn manually through stationary metal combs. The seed balls are pulled off and collected on a sheet. This ancient method requires 18 to 20 man-hours per ton of pulled flax.

In 1938, when the research project was begun, the Oregon industry used the whipper deseeder, which consists of two smooth rollers revolving inward and pressed together by springs. The seed-bearing part of the straw is passed three or four times between the rollers, which crush the seed balls and liberate the seed. A crew of 10 men can deseed a ton of flax in an hour with the whipper machine.

An automatic rotary-comb deseeder, which facilitates straight-line operation, was developed by specialists on the research project. It has been widely adopted in Oregon.

One of the new deseeders, with auxiliary automatic conveying, butting, and tying apparatus, was installed at the Mount Angel flax plant in 1948. Four men can operate it. One unloads from the wagon to the deseeder table; one cuts the string and places the bundles on the straw conveyor; one receives the bundles from an elevator and stacks them on the wagon; and the fourth operates the threshing machine and sacks the seed.

The capacity of the improved machine has been limited to the ability of the operators to feed it. Four men can deseed 3 tons of pulled straw an hour.

FLAX FIBERS are in the cambium layer of the plant, where they are cemented together and to the other parts of the stem by pectins. To prepare it for fiber separation, the straw is subjected to a retting, or rotting, process. Retting is a bacteriological fermentation; micro-organisms decompose the pectins and loosen the bond between the fiber and other parts of the plant, so that the woody portions can be broken and the fiber removed.

There are two methods of retting—dew retting and water retting. In dew retting, the flax is spread on the ground, where it is exposed repeatedly to heavy dew. The pectins are slowly broken down by the action of mold fungus, so that the fiber is loosened from the remainder of the plant.

Oregon water-retting tanks, of the open-top type, are approximately 40 feet long, 16 feet wide, and 7 feet deep. About 8 tons of deseeded straw is packed, two layers deep, in an upright position in the tanks. The tanks are then filled with warm water and maintained at from 85° to 95° F. for 4 to 6 days, when retting is complete.

Flax straw is held beneath the surface of the water by means of the retting-tank cover, a removable lattice supported by heavy timbers. Nearly 100 separate wooden parts constitute the tank cover. Their installation or removal formerly required the services of 3 men for approximately 45 minutes. The wooden pieces become wet and slimy from contact with the retting water and partly rotted flax. They have an offensive odor, and their removal is laborious and disagreeable.

A mechanical device now makes it possible to fasten the many tank-cover parts together and handle them as a single unit. The operation takes 3 to 5 minutes.

Under the existing methods of flax handling, retted flax straw is dried only in the summer. The wet straw from the large concrete retting tanks is transferred to the field by truck. The strings are cut, and each bundle of retted flax is set up in the form of a wigwam to field-dry. The flax is manually removed from the field after drying and fed to a small mobile binder, which ties the bundle again and leaves it on the drying field. The bundles are loaded on a truck with pitchforks and transported to a storage shed.

A self-propelled machine, developed on the project, mechanically removes the dried wigwams from the field, binds them into bundles with one tie string, and conveys them to a trailing wagon. Three men operate the machine—one, a ground man, sets up wigwams that have been blown over; one operates the machine and guides the bundle; the third receives the bundles from the elevator and stacks them on the wagon.

SCUTCHING, the separation of the fiber from the remainder of the plant, is the next major operation. The condition in which the bundles are received from the field binder directly affects the amount of labor involved in spreading and feeding the flax straw into the scutcher and the percentage of cleaned line fiber discharged by the scutching machine.

The object of scutching is to extract the fiber, loosened during retting, from the remainder of the plant. All methods of scutching are based on two straw treatments. The first is to crush and break the woody central portion of the stem into small pieces, called shives. Next, the straw is held tightly near one end while the free end is subjected to a beating and scraping action to complete the separation of the long fiber from the woody portion.

Research to improve scutching machines has attempted either to increase the amount of long fiber extracted from the straw or to reduce the amount of hand labor involved, without damaging the fiber.

Various types of machines have been developed, but the turbine scutcher, which facilitates straight-line operation, is the most widely used.

An experimental scutching machine of the turbine type has been developed. It extracts 2 percent more line fiber and cleans it more thoroughly than the commercial machines do.

THE FLAX LINE fiber from the scutching machine is usually hackled, or combed, by hand to grade it and prepare it for the spinner. Hackling is done by manually drawing the scutched fiber over a series of coarse and fine pins to straighten or parallel it and to remove short, tangled fiber. The addition of combs to the scutcher blades cuts in half the time required to hackle and dress the fiber.

Fiber removed during the scutching operation falls into the refuse-removal system, where it is mixed with weeds and shives. It is called flax tow.

A large proportion of the foreign material can be separated from the tow by a shaker. Further processing is required to remove shives before the material is suited for use as upholstery tow or for yarn spinning.

Before a combination tow drier and cleaner was developed in 1941, so much dirty tow had accumulated that it filled the available storage space and was being burned for fuel in some plants. With the new tow drier and cleaner, processing plants can clean the tow fiber and render it suitable for making upholstery padding and coarse yarns. The development has transformed a waste material into a valuable byproduct, which now brings 160 to 240 dollars a ton.

The abundant supply of cleaned flax-tow attracted the attention of the California Cotton Mills Co. Members of this organization formed Oregon Flax Textiles, which put up a large flax-tow spinning and weaving plant in Salem, Oreg. It manufactures woven flax rugs and braided linen rugs. The company plans to double its capacity. Coarse yarns and wool-and-flax rugs are among its new items. The rug has a woven flax base and a tufted wool surface. It is an attractive, long-wearing floor covering.

The establishment of the State flax industry in 1915 provided a ready supply of raw flax fiber. This stimulated interest in flax manufacturing and led to the erection of two line-fiber spinning mills in 1925 at Salem, Oreg. Together, the physical plants are valued at 1.5 million dollars.

One of the mills, the Miles Linen Co., manufactures shoe thread, fish netting, sack and mattress twine, and weaving yarns.

The other, the Salem Linen Mills, produces chiefly sack twine, twine used in furniture construction, and colored linen twine for military use and fire hose.

Both mills operated at near full capacity in 1950. Salem Linen Mills operates principally on fast-color yarns to meet the demand of hand-loom weavers. With the increased availability of required yarns, the number of private looms has grown to about 15,-000 in Oregon and California. Besides affording an interesting hobby, this growing trend toward hand weaving is providing individuals with an economical method of obtaining a particular type of linen product desired.

Oregon fiber flax possesses qualities which enable it to surpass imported fiber. However, any advantages gained from superior quality are lost through a lack of segregation of qualities. This is a direct result of the conspicuous lack of standards or grades in the flax industry. Thus, a high-quality fiber may be produced which will sell only with difficulty, as it is baled with fiber of high, medium, or low quality.

Since there are no established and enforced quality specifications, the compliance with which would assure a satisfactory fiber, spinning mills use the Oregon fiber only to blend with the graded and more uniform imported fiber to give added strength. The flax industry stands ready to capitalize on its superior product once the fiber is graded in accordance with its spinning qualities.

THE PROGRESS MADE in the mechanical processing of flax since 1940 has been more rapid than in any other period in history. The several machines mentioned here have improved the flax preparation and reduced the processing costs.

While the progress in mechanization has been significant, there is need for the development of new equipment and techniques in bulk handling of flax straw, in artificial drying of retted straw, and in quality control during the production and processing.

JESSE E. HARMOND, *an agricultural engineer in the Bureau of Plant Industry, Soils, and Agricultural Engineering, has been research engineer in charge of the fiber-flax processing investigation at Corvallis, Oreg., since 1945. Previously, he was in charge of the Department's Compression of Dehydrated Foods Laboratory, at the Beltsville Research Center, research engineer at the Cotton Ginning Laboratory in Stoneville, Miss., and engineer for the United States Engineering Department's concrete casting plant in Greenville, Miss. He is a native of Mississippi.*

IN THE EARLY days of the cottonseed-crushing industry, most mills operated only during the 4-month harvesting season and remained idle the rest of the year. The mills thrived, nevertheless, because labor was cheap and poor roads kept the mills isolated, so that there was little competition.

When the industry expanded and new highways made long-distance transportation easier, keen competition for cottonseed sprang up. Mills became larger and more efficient, so they could operate over a longer crushing season. Competition and large-scale operation forced many mills out of business.

But the operation continues to be a seasonal one and competition in buying remains keen, particularly in short-crop years, since each miller strives to obtain his maximum requirements for the season. Thus, the market for cottonseed is largely a seller's market.

Why do many of the mills operate only a few months of the year? For one thing, the cotton crop must be picked before wet weather sets in. Otherwise the lint will be damaged, and few mills can store cottonseed over a long season. Another reason is the great demand for cottonseed meal as stock feed in winter. How can mills operate profitably while remaining idle the greater part of the year? Mainly because their hydraulic-pressing equipment is relatively inexpensive to install, so that overhead or fixed expenses are lower. Also, the labor costs for hydraulic pressing, though rather high, are eliminated when the mill shuts down.—*E. L. D'Aquin, E. A. Gastrock, and O. L. Brekke, Bureau of Agricultural and Industrial Chemistry.*

The Future for Domestic Wool

Harold P. Lundgren,
Kenneth J. Palmer

The United States produced 426,-200,000 pounds of wool in 1939 and only 258,600,000 pounds in 1949. There are several reasons for the decline, but they do not alter the seriousness of the situation, especially in a time when we are faced with a growing demand for wool for our national defense.

During the past decade our production of wool has been increasingly threatened by the continuing development of synthetic fibers, which are the result of intensive research aimed to meet new demands, new fashions, and lower costs. By contrast, the costs of producing and processing wool have gone steadily up, and comparatively little progress has been made in streamlining the traditional rule-of-thumb procedures. For example, the wage cost of producing a wool textile fabric in 1950 was approximately double what it was in 1941.

We want to keep our wool industry vigorous because wool is essential to our national health and security; the Armed Forces consider wool a strategic and essential material. Domestic wool production, even in peacetime, has never been equal to consumption. Normally we produce only from one-fourth to one-third of our total requirements. To meet any emergency we should produce at least two-thirds of our normal requirements of apparel wool.

The problems before us are: How are we to develop the wool industry to keep pace with developments in other industries? How make sheep production and the marketing and processing of wool more efficient? How improve the quality of domestic wools and the spinnability of the medium grades to satisfy the increasing demand for worsted yarns? Can we find ways to impart new properties to wool to increase its usefulness?

Although wool meets many demands in quality (notably its warmth, excellent resilience, and felting power), it has a number of weaknesses. Its lack of resistance to hot water and its vulnerability to micro-organisms and moths are well known. Its instability to alkalies, acids, and steam used in processing is encountered by the textile processor. From the chemical point of view, these weaknesses are the evidence that wool is itself a reactive chemical substance. The acids, alkalies, and steam react chemically with the wool structure to result in harshness, reduced wearlife, and lower strength of the fiber. But wool can be improved and its processes streamlined. It is entirely possible—through investigation of the chemical nature of wool, including its stability to chemical environments and its reactions with the host of new chemical agents—to find a means of stabilizing wool to deleterious environments and to impart new properties of practical significance. Such developments would provide the basis on which to convert present empirical methods in the wool industry to efficient modern practice.

Working together to find the answers are the Production and Marketing Administration and the Agricultural Research Administration, of the Department of Agriculture, and several State agricultural experiment stations. An example of the cooperative work on wool is a project for improving the spinning qualities of the medium grades, which is supported by the Department of Agriculture and carried out by the Textile Research Institute in Princeton, N. J. The American Wool Council, the International Wool Secretariat, and wool growers here and abroad also sponsor the investigations. The Forstmann Woolen Company is under subcontract to process the wools for the project. The Western Regional Research Laboratory assists in mechanical and microscopic characterization of the wools. Scientists of the Bureau of Human Nutrition and Home Economics study the properties of the fabrics made from the wools.

To THE CHEMIST, wool is an assemblage of molecules admirably suited for particular purposes. Because of its unique architectural design, wool is strong and yields to stress in a desirable manner. Basically, its molecular properties determine all its characteristics—moisture-absorbing property, felting behavior, affinity for dyes, draping qualities, and luster. Because wool can be modified chemically, the chemist disagrees with those who maintain that wool, being a product of nature, cannot be improved. It is true that wool possesses certain features, such as felting property, which the chemist has failed to reproduce in synthetics.

The application of chemistry to wool begins on the farm. The presence or absence of certain minerals can profoundly affect the quality of wool. A copper deficiency in the diet of sheep makes the wool stiff and steely and a cobalt deficiency also makes it markedly abnormal. The soil in certain areas, northern Wisconsin, for example, is deficient in cobalt. In some areas, as around Bakersfield in California, there is too much molybdenum in the soil and forage. An excess of that mineral in the diet of sheep causes the wool to lose its natural crimp. The wool from black sheep turns white when the diet contains too much molybdenum.

Alternate high and low amounts of molybdenum in the diet give corresponding white- and black-ribbed wool.

The chemical environment can also affect wool quality directly. Sheep that are kept in regions rich in alkali yield an inferior "alkalied wool," which is practically worthless. Sunlight, particularly in humid regions, can cause photochemical damage to the exposed tips of wool. Wool that is so damaged often takes dyes unevenly. Fortunately, chemists have learned to overcome the fault somewhat by treating the wool before dyeing.

Among the several unknowns of wool is why wools from Australia tend to be whiter after cleaning than do domestic wools. The problem is receiving increasing attention because of the greater use of light and pastel shades in fabrics.

The effects of a sheep's diet and environment on the quality of its wool are being studied at several State agricultural experiment stations and the Bureau of Animal Industry. The goal is practical information that will help the grower determine which feeds, environment, and breeds of sheep in specific areas will produce wools of maximum quality.

SEVERAL PROCESSES that involve chemical principles come between the shipping of wool and the time it is ready as a fabric. One of the first is the removal of contaminating grease, dirt, dried sweat, fecal matter, dried urine, and burs. Contaminants constitute 40 to 70 percent of the total weight. The farmer who sells his wool is paid on the basis of the yield of clean, scoured wool. What happens later may appear to be of little concern to him. Actually it is important to him that the costs of scouring and the other steps be reduced so that wool may better meet the competition of other fibers.

The chemist sees several possibilities for reducing scouring costs. First is the recovery of potentially valuable chemical constituents from the wool grease.

A second is to make more efficient the process, which for ages past has been largely done in the same manner—by washing the wool with water mixtures of soap and soda. A small quantity of wool in this country is scoured by the more expensive method of extraction by solvents. This method has the advantage of easy recovery of the potentially valuable constituents of grease. However, chemists now are finding it possible to recover economically the grease from the soap liquors.

Chemical research is also throwing new light on the action of soaps. New types of soap and other detergents, with more efficient washing power for specific purposes, are being discovered. Just why soda makes the washing by soap so much more effective is being studied. Actually soda is undesirable to the extent that it is alkaline and, unless used with caution, has a deleterious effect on the quality of wool. To streamline the soap-soda method, chemists at the Western Regional Research Laboratory are studying the mechanism of the action of soap and soda in cleaning wool. One outcome of the research is the finding that certain nonalkaline agents are effective—so effective, in fact, that scouring can be accomplished with only the natural soap present in the wool contaminants. These soaplike constituents are the dried perspiration, the so-called suint, which comprises as much as 30 to 40 percent of the contaminating impurities. It has been recognized for a long time that these suint salts might be effective for scouring. Europeans have used a process in which clarified water extracts of grease wool are used for grease removal. The process is not efficient.

The Chinese found that the recovery of grease by the water extracts is greatly improved when pig dung or urine is added. Recent laboratory findings support that discovery. The scouring efficiency of the neutral soaps in the suint is markedly improved when small quantities of certain chemicals, such as ordinary alcohols, are present,

together with small quantities of table salt.

The findings are still on a laboratory scale and must be tested commercially before their practical value can be determined. No doubt they will be significant in the further improvement of the wool-scouring procedure. The ultimate aim of the research is the development of methods to give the best overall economy of scouring and recovery of valuable grease constituents, without damaging the wool fiber too much.

Wool undergoes many manipulations in processing. One of the most critical is spinning and preparation for spinning. Offhand, we might not expect chemical principles to be involved in such mechanical processes as carding and spinning, but when we look more closely into the matter we find that they are.

The characteristics of wool—its toughness, its spinnability—depend ultimately on its structure, both the large structural units that we can see under the microscope and the molecular structure of those units. When we look at wool under an ordinary microscope we find that the surface has scales not unlike the shingles on a roof. The scales are about 4/100,000 of an inch thick and overlap one another in irregular fashion. Because the exposed edges of the scales point in one direction, the frictional resistance to rubbing differs in the two directions along the fiber. This difference in frictional behavior accounts to a large degree for wool's unique felting property.

Under much higher magnifications, as under an electron microscope, the scales themselves appear to be covered by an exceedingly thin membrane, called the epicuticle. The epicuticular layer might have an important role in the dyeing of wool by limiting the rates of dye penetration.

Beneath the scales is another membranous layer. This layer surrounds the cortex which makes up the bulk of the fiber. The cortex consists of elongated cells, the so-called spindle cells, which are approximately 4/1,000 of an inch long and about one-tenth as wide as they are long. The spindle cells are simply bundles of long, thin fibrils bonded together with a cementing material that is believed to have the same chemical composition as the rest of the wool constituents in the cortex.

Some wool fibers have an inside core of porous structure, the medulla, but it appears to have a minor effect on the physical and chemical behavior of wool. The response of wool to stretching is conditioned by the slippage of the scales and spindle cells, past one another, and ultimately by the slippage of the molecules comprising them.

The molecules in each unit are a particular kind of protein, called keratin, the type that is found in horn, feathers, and skin. A distinguishing feature of keratins is their relatively high proportion of sulfur. The molecules of all the keratins and, as a matter of fact, all proteins, are built of chains of atoms, the backbone of each chain being a repeating series of carbon and nitrogen atoms hooked together in such a manner as to give flexible joints. Because the chains are flexible, they can curl and uncurl when subjected to mechanical manipulation. But for the fact that the chains are tied together into networks, they would come apart. It is the function of the sulfur atoms to tie the chains together into networks, to give the tough materials that we find in horn, skin, feathers, and wool.

The protein chains have another characteristic. They are rather bulky. Attached laterally to the main chains are relatively large chemical groups, that interfere with ready curling and uncurling of the flexible chains. When wool is subjected to carding, combing, and spinning, the flexible networks of molecules are stretched, but, because these molecules are bulky as compared with the smooth molecular chains in rubber, the response in wool is slower than in rubber. Therefore it becomes necessary to consider time of response when dealing with manipulation of wool. It takes time to stretch wool; after wool has been stretched, it takes time for it to recover. Textile craftsmen have noted that the spinnability of wool benefits from delay periods between carding, combing, and spinning operations. If conditions of temperature and moisture for these responses were thoroughly understood, it might be possible to devise conditions for the spinning of coarser grades of wools into worsted yarns.

Under way is a study on the influence of delay periods at different temperatures and humidities between carding and spinning operations. Four special wools have been selected—a typical medium and a typical fine domestic wool, and corresponding grades of Australian wool. The processing is being done by a commercial wool manufacturer by standard commercial procedure. The studies on the fibers, roving, yarns, and fabrics at each stage of the processing are being made at the Textile Research Institute, the Western Laboratory, and the laboratories of the Bureau of Animal Industry and the Bureau of Human Nutrition and Home Economics.

The sequence of wool manipulations after spinning starts with the setting. Unless the fibers of the yarn are set the residual strains which have not relaxed will tend to curl the yarn. The yarn is alive, so to speak.

Setting is accomplished by a short treatment in hot water or steam, which permits the rapid relaxation of residual strains. The process is not entirely satisfactory. Undoubtedly the knowledge gained in the project on spinnability of wools will provide a basis for practical improvement of this step.

One of the important finishing processes after weaving is fulling, a treatment by which the wool fibers are made to felt in the fabric to give more desirable body and appearance to the material. Fulling consists of treating the fabric with warm soap solution under rather severe agitation for periods lasting up to many hours. The chemist sees opportunity for shortening the operation.

Another treatment of wool that is

often necessary is carbonization, which consists of the removal of traces of foreign matter, such as burs that have clung to the wool fibers throughout the processing. Sometimes the carbonizing treatment is done before spinning, but frequently it is left until after weaving. It is especially severe; the wool is treated with hot concentrated sulfuric acid for short periods. The acid attacks the foreign material before it does the wool and causes the cellulosic material to char—hence the term carbonizing. The charred material is readily dusted off. The process is costly and is likely to harm the fiber. Milder and more economical procedures need to be developed.

The potentialities for a chemical modification are illustrated in the case of propiolactone reaction with wool. That chemical agent has recently become available commercially. The Western Regional Research Laboratory has included it among some 100 different agents in a preliminary survey of effects of selected modification treatments on wool. The modification with propiolactone imparts a marked improvement in the ability of wool to felt. Not only does the propiolactone fiber felt significantly more rapidly than does the untreated wool, but the felts are more dense and require considerably greater force to tear apart. Those laboratory findings have been confirmed by mill tests under commercial felting conditions.

The modification with propiolactone is a rather simple process. The propiolactone may be dissolved in an organic solvent, such as carbon tetrachloride. The wool is merely soaked in this solution at room temperature for about 48 hours. Laboratory tests indicate that direct modification with vapors of the propriolactone might be feasible. Aside from the increased ability to felt, the modified fiber will be found to be whiter in color, itself a significant finding in view of the increasing demand for lighter wool for fabrics for pastel shades.

Although the results of the propio-lactone treatment appear promising, considerably more experimental study will be necessary before large-scale trials can be attempted. These trials are being planned and will be carried out with the cooperation of the felting industry as early as possible.

The significance of improved felting of wool to the industry is apparent when one considers that woolen cloth (which in 1947 had a total value of 620 million dollars) in fulling to give body is subjected to felting conditions. Moreover, commercial felt manufacture is also completely dependent on the felting properties of wool and is a slow procedure that requires hours of hammering. Strong sulfuric acid, the felting agent, causes expensive corrosion damage to equipment and necessitates costly means for subsequent removal of acid from the finished felt. Commercial felts are used widely for such purposes as thermal insulation, shock absorbents, mechanical filtration, gaskets, sound absorption, wick lubricants, and hats. Felt production was a 50-million-dollar industry in 1939.

The studies of propiolactone modification combined with investigation of the mechanical properties of the treated fibers provide an unusual opportunity for investigation of the mechanics of felting. With a better understanding of the mechanics of felting, the basis is laid for development of improved commercial practice. This, in turn, will reflect in reduced processing costs to help place wool in a better competitive position.

This illustration of the effects of propiolactone treatment may be duplicated with other modification treatments on other properties of wool—for example, improved shrink resistance, improved resistance to hot water, milder methods for dyeing and scouring, and improved methods for moth control.

New chemical agents appear on the market in increasing numbers. Many of them are potentially reactive with specific sites on the wool molecules.

Study of such reactions is being carried out at the Western Laboratory. Frequently agents will combine with wool to impart a desirable property, but sometimes the gain is obtained at the expense of some desirable property. For instance, improved flexibility is often accompanied by a loss in strength of the fiber.

Included in the investigations of chemical modification is the study of degradation of wool by heat, light, acids, fungi, alkalies, water, and mechanical abrasion. A complete understanding of how wool is degraded would put the chemist in a much better position to do something about its control.

HAROLD P. LUNDGREN *heads the wool section of the Western Regional Research Laboratory, where he has worked since 1941. Previously he was a research associate at the University of Wisconsin and a post-doctorate research fellow at the University of Upsala, Sweden. Dr. Lundgren is a graduate of North Dakota State College and the University of Minnesota.*

KENNETH J. PALMER, *a physicist, has been on the staff of the Western Laboratory since 1941. He has investigated extensively molecular structure by X-ray diffraction. Dr. Palmer is a graduate of the University of California and the California Institute of Technology.*

A NEW TYPE of synthetic rubber that shows outstanding resistance to heat has been developed by scientists at the Eastern Regional Research Laboratory. Called Lactoprene EV, the new rubberlike material is made by polymerization— the process whereby large molecules are built from small ones. The two chemicals used in the process are ethyl acrylate and chloroethyl vinyl ether, which can be obtained from carbohydrate raw materials, as well as from coal and petroleum. Lactoprene EV is vulcanized in much the same manner as is natural rubber. The vulcanized articles made from Lactoprene EV, unlike those made from natural rubber or other synthetic rubberlike materials, are remarkably resistant to deterioration when exposed to heat. They retain their rubbery characteristics even after being heated at 300° F. for more than 700 hours. Vulcanized Lactoprene EV also has excellent resistance to mineral oils, sunlight, and air. Because it is colorless, white products or products having pastel shades can be made from it.—*Edward M. Filachione, Eastern Regional Research Laboratory.*

A COLD PROCESS, which makes rubber less brittle and longer lasting than the hot-process product, has been developed by the synthetic-rubber industry. Tires can now be made with cold rubber; they have 30 percent more mileage efficiency than those made with the best grade of natural rubber.

What makes cold rubber of interest to farmers is that its manufacture depends in great measure upon the use of dextrose, the sugar obtained by acid hydrolysis of the starch separated from corn or wheat. The function of dextrose in the cold-rubber process is to speed up the chemical reactions that take place so slowly at the low temperatures used.

Before this novel use for corn sugar was discovered, it took several days to produce cold rubber, too long for the demands of wartime production. Now the process can be carried out in a matter of hours.—*C. L. Mehltretter, Northern Regional Research Laboratory.*

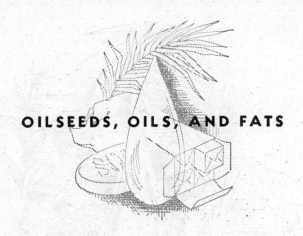

OILSEEDS, OILS, AND FATS

Oil Processing Through the Ages

K. S. Markley

What—it might be asked—do the chocolate coating of a candy bar, creamy white shortening, and a bar of soap have in common? They and a thousand more everyday products are made partly or entirely from fats and oils, which people in all times and climes have depended on for medicinals, cosmetics, lubricants, and illuminants.

The story of their development, told now in the light of the advances this generation has made in age-old processes, reveals how chemist and technologist have enhanced the value and broadened the market for farm products through increased efficiency and lower costs of processing, recovery of byproducts, and development of new products.

Probably the first fats used by man were of animal origin—tallows and greases—which were separated from other tissue simply by heating or boiling with water. Extraction of oil from fruits and seeds called for more vigorous treatment. As animal and vegetable oils were used from the time of the earliest records, methods for their separations must have been worked out before the dawn of history. The ancient Egyptians and Phoenicians used vegetable oils for food and for anointing their bodies, but not for illumination. The Egyptians used olive oil as a lubricant in moving large stones, statues, and building material. As early as 1400 B. C., Egyptian chariot wheels were lubricated with axle greases consisting of fat and lime. Earthen vessels predating the First Dynasty have been found which contained several pounds of oxidized palm oil. From the Egyptians and Phoenicians, knowledge of how to apply fats and oils spread to the Hebrews, and thence to the Greeks.

THE HEBREWS had oil mills powered by treads that usually were operated by prisoners. Pliny left the earliest description of an oil mill, which was used to crush olives. It resembled the ordinary edge runner, the stones being flat on the inner side and convex on the outer side. The Greeks and Romans are said to have employed screw presses similar to wine presses for recovering olive oil.

The wedge press was used in very early times in the Orient, particularly in China, where it is still operated. Another type of extractor, known as ghani, chekku, or kolhu, was developed long ago in India. It operates on the principle of a pestle rotating in a mortar and is often powered by bullocks. The mortar is generally made of wood, but in some parts of India may be made of granite. The ghani is still used in remote rural areas of India. The wedge press was revived in the seventeenth century as the Dutch stamper press powered by windmills.

Wedge, edge-runner, and screw presses were used in Europe for oilseed processing until the invention of the hydraulic press. Their efficiencies were

497

increased somewhat by precrushing and heating the seed in the presence of moisture, a practice in use today.

The development of the hydraulic press in 1795 made possible a marked increase in the recovery of oil. In its earliest form, this press was an adaptation of the wedge press, with hydraulic power substituted for that obtained by wedges and falling weights. By 1815, improved forms of the hydraulic press were introduced in France and Germany, where their use spread rapidly.

In the first hydraulic presses, bags of ground seed or meal were placed in a perforated metal cylinder surrounded by another metal cylinder. Pressure from a hydraulic ram pushed the bags upward against a fixed plate, squeezing out the oil from the seeds into the outer cylinder. The bags were a source of trouble and expense and were soon replaced by molded cakes wrapped in press cloths. A series of horizontal plates, between which the molded cakes could be placed and pressed, replaced the boxes that held the bags in the old presses. This press, commonly referred to as the plate or Anglo-American press, has been used in much of the world for processing many types of oilseeds. It has changed but slightly in the past 75 years.

A modification of the plate press, known as the cage press, was developed later, but, although relatively efficient, it is used much less widely than the plate press. Although the plate and cage presses made possible a much greater recovery of oil than was possible with the wedge press, the new presses still left 7 to 10 percent of oil in the cake.

The twentieth century brought a virtual revolution in the mechanical methods of processing oilseeds. An American invention, a machine for continuously pressing oil-bearing materials, was responsible. The new machine, still in use, is described in another chapter of this book (page 504).

The original continuous screw press, or expeller, was improved and built in increasingly larger capacities. The rise of the soybean-processing industry in the United States in the 1930's created a further demand for these presses. Efficiency, as well as capacity, increased until it became possible to process soybeans so as to reduce the residual oil content of the cake to 3.5 or 4.5 percent.

Oil technologists were not satisfied to leave even this amount of oil in the extracted cake, but efforts to reduce it appreciably below 3.5 percent by mechanical means were not successful. Other means therefore were sought to reduce the oil content of the cake or meal. This was eventually accomplished by extracting the seed with an organic solvent, or by pressing it to remove part of the oil and then extracting the cake with a solvent to remove the rest.

The first practical process for the solvent extraction of oil from oilseeds was developed by Jesse Fisher in Birmingham, England, in the 1840's, but no patent for the solvent extraction of fatty oils was granted in England until 1856. Since that time numerous patents have been granted in Europe and in the United States. Solvent extraction has been practiced on a fairly large scale in Europe since 1870. The first extractors were single-unit, unagitated, batch vessels. Soon multiple-unit, agitated, countercurrent extractors appeared. Many attempts were made to develop a continuous solvent-extraction process, and about 1920 Herrmann Bollman in Germany developed an extractor that was especially adapted to the recovery of oil from soybeans. This extractor and its operation are discussed in detail in the following chapter.

The development of the Bollman continuous extractor was followed by many other types. One of these, also developed in Germany—by Karl Hildebrandt—is a combination of two vertical enclosed screw conveyors connected at the bottom by a cross conveyor so that the whole forms a U. The previously rolled or flaked oilseed moves in one leg in the same direction s the flow of the solvent, and in the other leg in the opposite direction.

This type of continuous extractor was introduced in the United States for processing soybeans in 1934 and was followed very shortly by the Bollmann, or paternoster, extractor. Somewhat later, an extractor of American design—the rotating-plate, vertical gravity extractor—was introduced. It was followed by a modified type known as the stationary-place extractor.

These three types of extractors are used in all but a few solvent-extraction plants in the United States; the first two are used in most of the continuous-extraction plants in Europe.

The rapid adoption of continuous solvent extractors for processing soybeans resulted from the fact that such plants are almost completely automatic and yield a meal containing only 0.6 to 0.8 percent of oil, or a recovery of about 97 percent. These extractors, although ideal for removing the oil from soybeans, are not well suited for processing high-oil-content (40 to 60 percent) seeds. This difficulty was overcome in Europe by first reducing the oil of such seeds, by continuous screw presses or expellers, to 15 to 22 percent and recovering the remainder by solvent extraction. This combination of processes, known as forepressing and solvent extraction, was later introduced into South America and Canada, but it is practiced only on a limited scale in the United States even today. Its principal application in this country is to castor beans, olives, peanuts, and flaxseed. Early in 1950 this process was introduced into the cottonseed industry.

For many centuries improvements in the processes for recovering oils were exceedingly slow and only in the past 25 years has the amount of oil recovered nearly equaled that present in the seed. Little more can be done to increase the recovery of oil in the most efficiently operated plants and even the possibility that future developments may reduce the cost of this operation is limited. But we still have the problem of extending improved equipment and operation to many plants here and abroad which still process oilseeds by outmoded and inefficient methods.

FEW VEGETABLE OILS are used, in the United States at least, in the form in which they are extracted from the seed. Most of them are subjected to some type of refining to remove nonfat impurities, such as color bodies, odorous constituents, and any free fatty acids that may be present in the crude oil. Olive oil is an exception, because its use depends largely on its color and flavor.

The technology of processing oil is discussed in the chapters that follow.

The refining of fats and oils, which is essentially a chemical process, is carried out in fewer plants and on a much larger unit scale than is the extraction of the oil from the seed. For many years much secrecy prevailed in the industry, but that is now being dispelled through the introduction of standardized automatic processes and the application of well-known chemical reactions. Because crude fats and oils find little consumer acceptance, refining adds to the market value of the original product. However, refining is accomplished only at some loss of total volume of the original crude oil. The aim is to remove all of the impurities with the smallest possible loss of refined oil; that is, the operation should be accomplished as nearly as possible with only the "theoretical refining loss." This objective has been closely approached, but never entirely attained.

The refining process, like the production of crude oil, has evolved over many years. The earliest methods consisted simply of settling and filtering out the solid or gummy materials. Later, certain earths or clays were added before filtering to help remove solid impurities and also some of the pigments, thereby imparting a clear and bright appearance. One of the most important steps in the refining process consists in removing the free fatty acids naturally present in the oil.

Some oilseeds, especially if they are properly matured, harvested, and handled, yield oils with little free fatty acids, but oils extracted from other species or from immature, field-damaged, poorly stored, or improperly processed seeds or fruit may have from 10 to 50 percent of these acids. Oils with a high content of free fatty acids are difficult to refine or can be refined only with large losses of refined or neutral oil. Sometimes the amount of free fatty acids is so great the crude oil cannot be refined at all and is fit only for making soap.

Curiously, a knowledge of how to manufacture soap provided the basis for refining oils to remove free fatty acids. It is not known when the process of soap making was devised, but it certainly was a very long time ago. It is mentioned in the Bible and in the writings of Aristophanes and Plato. Pliny the Elder (A. D. 23–79) attributes the invention to the Gauls.

Heating with caustic soda (lye) or lime completely breaks down fats and oils (glycerides), forming the soaps of the fatty acids and liberating glycerol. If free fatty acids are already present in an oil they react directly with the alkali to form soaps. The early oil refiners took advantage of these facts to treat crude fats and oils with various alkaline materials under conditions where they would react primarily with the free fatty acids to form soaps, which were then removed by settling and separating the oil and washing it with water. Great skill is needed to bring about this reaction without breaking down some of the fat or oil into more free fatty acids, and also to separate the soap without loss of neutral or refined oil.

At first this operation was carried out crudely on a small scale, then on an increasingly larger scale, and finally on a very large scale, in kettles holding a tank car (60,000 pounds) of oil. It was entirely a batch operation, and, however skillfully done, appreciable quantities of neutral oil were lost.

The idea of making this process continuous was investigated at least as early as 1890 and was actually tried out commercially in 1893. The process, however, was soon abandoned. Not until 1923 was an improved process again tested on an extensive scale, and it too failed to be generally adopted. The first really successful continuous caustic refining process was developed in the 1930's. This process, or a modification of it, was rapidly and widely adopted in the United States.

Use of the new continuous refining processes has markedly reduced losses of neutral oil. With the most recent method the loss in refining some oils is only 1 to 2 percent greater than the "theoretical refining loss."

Soaps produced during the refining of crude oils by alkali neutralization of the free fatty acids present in the unrefined product carry with them other impurities and some of the refined oil itself. The mixture of these materials is called soap stock because of its use in the manufacture of soap. At one time refinery soap stock was used directly for making soap. Now, however, it is usually first converted to acidulated soap stock or to boiled-down soap stock. The latter product is actually a crude soap similar to that made before the day of high-quality soaps. It is prepared, as is regular or full-boiled soap, by heating the soap stock with lye and separating the soap by the addition of salt brine. After separating and washing the crude soap several times with salt brine it is boiled in a soap kettle to remove part of the water.

More modern practice converts the original soap stock to acidulated soap stock by adding sulfuric acid to the soap stock. The mixture of fatty acids and neutral oil is separated from the water and sold to the soap maker or the distiller of fatty acids.

For the manufacture of fatty acids, the raw soap stock is heated in the presence of water in closed vessels at a steam pressure of 100 to 150 pounds per square inch. The soap present in the raw or crude soap stock acts as a catalyst to break down all the neutral oil to fatty acids. After this reaction is completed the mixture is boiled with sulfuric acid to decompose the alkali soaps, and the free fatty acids are separated, washed, and dried.

Acidulated soap stock is treated in much the same way, except that a catalyst is added and a pressure of 350 to 400 pounds per square inch is used to break down the neutral oil and liberate the fatty acids.

The crude fatty acid mixture prepared from either raw soap stock or acidulated soap stock is now ready for distillation, which may be a batch or a continuous operation. In the batch method the distillation is carried out under vacuum, in cast-iron, direct-fired vessels at about 500° F. The crude fatty acids are added to the still until the purified acids coming from the still begin to be highly colored. The addition of crude acids is then stopped and the residue in the still is heated to a higher temperature than before to convert it to a black, tarry product called still pitch.

Still pitch is used in the manufacture of special paints and varnishes, asphalt tile and roofing materials, and insulation for electric wire requiring high resistance to moisture. The distilled fatty acids have many uses, principally in the manufacture of soap and soap products, but also in rubber compounding, in the manufacture of alkyd resins, and as lime-base greases.

The continuous process of distilling fatty acids is like the batch method, except that the crude stock is continuously fed into the upper part of a column still and the distilled fatty acids continuously pass out at the top and the residue at the bottom. The residue is accumulated and converted into pitch in a batch still. In the most modern method the fatty acids are separated not only from contaminating impurities, but also into different kinds of fatty acids. These separated, or fractionated, fatty acids are more valuable than the mixed acids. They serve as the starting material for the manufacture of fatty acid derivatives, which

are numerous and diverse both chemically and in their end uses. They include wetting and detergent agents, emulsifiers, flattening agents for paints, and plasticizers, as well as waterproofing, ore-flotation, and bonding agents, and germicides.

The production of fatty acids and still pitch from refinery soap stock is another example of the application of chemistry and technology to byproducts or waste products which once had little or no value.

A gummy mass of material called sludge, foots, or tank settlings separates out from certain crude oils on standing, especially in a moist state. This sludge readily separates out when the crude oil is treated with hot water or very dilute solutions of alkalies, such as sodium phosphate, and passed through a high-speed centrifuge. The water-washed, or degummed, oils can be refined more easily, and with much lower refining losses. This improvement results from the removal of a mixture of compounds collectively known as phosphatides, which are powerful emulsifying agents. When the phosphatides remain in the crude oil they produce emulsions of the water, soap stock, and neutral oil, which are difficult to separate and cause the loss of neutral or refined oil in the soap stock.

Crude soybean oil is especially high in phosphatides (2.5 to 3.0 percent). These compounds were first recovered in Hamburg, Germany, during the early development of the soybean-processing industry in that city. Originally they were separated merely to reduce the refining loss of soybean oil. Soon, however, they accumulated and became a serious disposal problem because of their tendency to putrefy.

When these crude phosphatides were purified they were found to possess a number of very useful properties, particularly an ability to lower the surface tension between oil and water. They were quickly put to use in the manufacture of emulsions and other products where it is essential to mix water and the fatty materials of many kinds.

The process of recovering phosphatides from crude oils is now called degumming, and the resultant oil is known as degummed crude oil. The degumming process as applied to soybean oil is in essence very simple and is generally carried out batchwise. Crude oil and hot water are mixed by stirring at high speed in a heated tank to hydrate the phosphatides. The mixture then flows to a high-speed degumming centrifuge, where the phosphatides are separated from the bulk of the water and water-soluble impurities. The phosphatides are sometimes bleached at this stage by running hydrogen peroxide or other bleaching agent into the bowl of the centrifuge.

After emerging from the centrifuge the phosphatides pass to a vacuum dehydrator, where the moisture is removed by heating to 150° to 160° F. under a very high vacuum. The operation usually requires 2 to 4 hours. The hot viscous phosphatides are clarified by recentrifuging in the clarifying centrifuge. The dehydrated and clarified phosphatides are spouted directly to the shipping containers, usually steel clamp-head drums.

The product, known in the trade as soybean lecithin, consists of about one-third soybean oil and two-thirds mixed phosphatides. It is the product which finds the greatest practical application. However, other grades are made. One, which has a very low oil content, is prepared by extracting the oil with acetone, in which the oil is soluble and the phosphatides insoluble. Others are made by mixing the deoiled phosphatides with another fat, for example cocoa butter, for use in the chocolate-coating industry.

Soybean and other lecithins are added to many products because of their interfacial modifying properties. Only very small quantities are required, usually a few tenths of one percent. Lecithin is added to nearly all oleomargarines as an antispattering agent; it prevents separation of the water into large droplets that form superheated steam and produce spattering during frying. In the presence of lecithin the water remains dispersed in minute droplets which evolve slowly in the form of steam without spattering. It also acts to prevent bleeding, or separation of droplets of water, on the outside surface of a print of margarine.

Another important use of lecithin is in chocolate coatings, where it reduces "bloom," or graying, which results from the separation of microscopic crystals of fat on the outside of the coating. It is also used in many fat-containing confections, such as fudge, nougat, and caramels, in ice cream, macaroni products, pharmaceuticals, and cosmetics, and in the paint, rubber, petroleum, leather, and textile industries.

Because of the tiny amount of lecithin needed to give the desired effect, the total consumption and, therefore, production is relatively small—about 8 million pounds annually in the United States from soybean oil and about a half million pounds from corn oil. In England and France, lecithin is produced principally from peanut oil, and in Germany, at the present time, from rapeseed oil. Small quantities are also produced in Denmark, Norway, and Japan. Potential production from soybean oil alone in the United States is more than 40 million pounds.

THE STEROLS are a complex group of compounds which the chemist calls cyclic alcohols. Their relatively large molecules are made up of four rings of carbon atoms, one or more attached side chains, and an alcohol group. These same complex rings are found in other natural products, notably the sex hormones. Sterols are present throughout the plant and animal kingdoms. In plants they are called phytosterols; in animals, zoösterols. In general, little is known yet of their biological function.

One of these sterols, known as stigmasterol, is found, together with several others, in soybean oil. This sterol became especially important in 1934, when Adolf Butenandt, and inlependently Fernholz, in Germany, announced the preparation of the female sex hormone, progesterone, from stigmasterol. Later, the male sex hormone, androsterone, was prepared from sistosterol, another sterol in soybean, cottonseed, and other vegetable oils. Many other hormones or hormone intermediates have been prepared from these two sterols and from cholesterol obtained from animals.

Sterols have also found applications as emulsion stabilizers in cosmetics, in paper sizing, and in printing pastes.

A variety of processes have been described for recovering sterols from crude soybean oil, soybean-oil foots, and deodorizer hot-well skimmings or scum. They are prepared principally from the two refinery waste products.

The tocopherol molecule, like the sterol molecule, is composed of rings of carbon atoms, with an alcohol group and one or more side chains. The condensed rings, however, are simpler than those of the sterols, and the side chains are very much longer. Four tocopherols have been found in one or another of the common vegetable oils. All of them exhibit vitamin E and antioxidant activities, which are inversely related. That is to say, the specific tocopherol, α-tocopherol, exhibits the greatest vitamin E activity and the lowest anti-

oxidant activity, whereas δ-tocopherol exhibits the maximum antioxidant and the lowest vitamin E activity.

The tocopherols are present in greatest concentration in refinery foots and deodorizer scum. They can be readily separated from vegetable oils by extreme high-vacuum, or molecular, distillation. This process is carried out commercially on a large scale for the recovery of both tocopherols and sterols. It is a highly specialized form of distillation, requiring special equipment. Consequently very few concerns recover these substances. Because of the limited consumption, present production of tocopherols is only a fraction of what it could easily be.

K. S. MARKLEY *holds degrees from George Washington University and The Johns Hopkins University. He heads the oil and oilseed division in the Southern Regional Research Laboratory. Dr. Markley has been engaged in plant-chemistry research for more than 30 years, more than half of which time he has devoted to research on fats, oils, and oilseeds. He has conducted various surveys of the fat and oil industries in the United States, Europe, and South and Central America, and is author or editor of 4 books and 70 articles on fats, oils, and related subjects.*

SOYBEANS were first processed in the United States with hydraulic presses about 1911. Those beans were importations from Manchuria. The earliest recorded crushing of American-grown soybeans was in a cottonseed-oil mill at Elizabeth City, N. C., in December 1915. The Chicago Heights Oil Manufacturing Co. processed small lots at intervals between 1917 and 1923, using both hydraulic and screw presses. In September 1922, the A. E. Staley Manufacturing Co. began operations in Decatur, Ill., in a mill that was equipped with screw presses designed for crushing soybeans. Today, four modern processing plants operate in Decatur, now known as the soybean capital of the world. Their combined capacity exceeds 100,000 bushels of soybeans a day, a large part of which is handled in solvent-extraction equipment. The four plants crush about half of the soybeans grown in Illinois, equivalent to a fifth of all of the soybeans processed in the United States. From 1924 to 1948, the production of soybeans increased forty-four-fold, and by 1950 the number of mills engaged in processing soybeans into oil and meal on a full-time basis had risen to 139.—*O. L. Brekke, Northern Regional Research Laboratory.*

Recovering

Oil and

Meal

E. L. D'Aquin, E. A. Gastrock,
O. L. Brekke

The three methods now in common use to recover oil and meal from oil-seeds are hydraulic pressing, screw pressing, and solvent extraction. The first two use pressure to remove the oil from the material. The third, as its name implies, employs a solvent to leach out or dissolve the oil, after which the mixture is separated. All the methods, alone or in combination, are used commercially on the many oil-bearing types of seeds, nuts, and beans that are grown throughout the world.

HYDRAULIC PRESSING, the earliest of the processes, is said to have originated in Europe in 1795. The hydraulic press, so named because it works on the principle of the hydraulic ram, operates like an ordinary machine-shop press. It was first used extensively in this country for processing linseed and cottonseed. Later it was used for soybeans; it is still the principal process for crushing cottonseed. Because it is a batch-type method that requires much hand labor, its use is declining in favor of the other methods, which are continuous, require much less labor, and recover the oil more completely. Different types of hydraulic presses are known as box presses, plate presses, cage presses, and pot presses.

THE CONTINUOUS SCREW PRESS is much like a household meat grinder in that it has a rotating screw to force the material under a very high pressure through a cagelike cylinder. The oil is squeezed out through narrow openings in the wall of the cylinder. The first successful continuous screw press was probably of American origin and was introduced about 50 years ago. Today the presses are used the world over to process every known type of oil-bearing material. In the United States they are used mainly for soybeans and flaxseed but also for cottonseed, copra, corn germ, tung nuts, and other oilseeds. American presses are unlike those in Europe, where the practice is to remove only part of the oil in order to procure a meal suitable for re-extraction with solvents or presses. In this country, continuous presses are designed to remove nearly all the oil in a single pass through the press by the use of a much higher pressure.

SOLVENT EXTRACTION originated as a batch process in Europe in 1870, and its use soon spread to the United States, where it is still employed for such materials as meat scraps, pine chips, garbage, and castor pomace.

Technological advances in Europe shortly after the First World War led to the development of continuous solvent-extraction systems, which proved excellent for processing soybeans to a very low oil content. As a result, the process was introduced in the United States for soybeans in the 1930's. Since then its use has increased tremendously to keep pace with our expansion in soybean production.

Despite its outstanding success with soybeans, solvent extraction has almost never proved fully satisfactory for directly extracting oil from other oilseeds. It is, however, satisfactory for indirect extraction of the other oils; that is, for application to the press residue obtained after mechanically pressing out the bulk of the oil. This is the general practice in Europe today.

American engineers, on the other hand, are experimenting with both methods, and already a number of plants have been erected for the solvent extraction of the oil from cottonseed, flaxseed, castor beans, corn germ, and rice bran.

Several mechanical operations are needed to prepare oilseeds before the oil can be removed. Cleaning to remove foreign matter comes first. Next the meats are separated from the hulls or shells. The meats are then reduced in size. The last step is usually a cooking operation, which conditions the material for extraction of the oil.

Actually, the procedure is not that simple. It varies for each oilseed and for each process. Moreover, every step in the sequence depends on how carefully the previous operation was carried out. In general, proper size reduction, moisture content, and cooking are requisites. All those factors must be integrated by experience and controlled if the best yields and quality of oil and meal are to be obtained.

First come storage and cleaning. Deliveries to the oil mill of soybeans and cottonseed are usually in bulk and by trucks or rail. Peanuts are handled in sacks. Unloading is done mainly by power shovels, pneumatic systems, and hydraulic lifts. Arrivals in excess of crushing requirements are placed in storage. Cottonseed is stored in seed houses of the Muskogee type. Silos and grain elevators are used for soybeans. Soybeans containing excess moisture are dried before storing. Cottonseed is not dried, but the houses are generally equipped with facilities for circulating air through the seeds to cool them if they heat up in storage.

Oilseeds contain miscellaneous foreign matter. Cottonseed, for example, contains bolls, twigs, stones, leaves, sand, and tramp metal—matter that must be removed by cleaning to prevent damage to the machines or costly shutdowns and to improve the quality of the oil and meal products.

Cleaning equipment varies from mill to mill. Shaker screens and rotary reels generally are used, along with air aspiration to remove the very light and the very heavy impurities. The most effective and versatile cleaners are the pneumatic-mechanical type, which employ both reciprocating shakers and air currents for making the various separations. Magnets are also used at one or more points to remove iron and steel.

Hulling and separating are next. Hulling follows cleaning for all but cottonseed, which must first be passed through delinting machines to remove most of the short fibers, or linters, left on after ginning. Because the oil content of hulls is very low, the hulls are broken off and separated before extraction—except tiny seeds like sesame and flaxseed, which are usually processed without this decortication. Hulls of medium-size seeds, like cottonseed, soybeans, and peanuts, are cracked or cut in disc or bar hullers or in attrition mills. Larger oilseeds, including palm kernels, tung nuts, and copra, are first broken up in hammer mills.

After cracking in the huller, the mixture of hulls and kernels is separated. The standard machines for the purpose are reciprocating and rotary screens equipped with air aspiration. Usually the hulls are removed as completely as possible, because their presence reduces the capacity of the extraction equipment and lowers the total yield of oil in pressing. Cottonseed is more difficult to separate than peanuts. Tung nuts are even harder to separate completely. Soybeans have only a thin skin coat, which sometimes is removed prior to solvent extraction.

After the hulls are removed, oilseed meats are reduced in size to facilitate flaking, cooking, and extraction of the oil. The general practice is to flatten them into thin flakes. The machine almost universally used is a vertical stand of five superimposed cylindrical rolls, between which the material is given four successive crushings as it passes from the top to the bottom. The flaking, cooking, and pressing are most effective when the meats are of proper moisture content and are rolled to uniform flakes 0.005 to 0.010 inch thick. The moisture content is a critical factor in flaking; the rolls will pulverize the meats if they are too dry. They will gum up on the roll surfaces if they are too wet.

When the oilseed is to be hydraulic-pressed, flaking is considered necessary. Cottonseed meats and corn germ may be flaked also for the continuous pressing, but soybeans, flaxseed, and peanuts are merely reduced in cracking rolls to grit-size particles. Flaking rolls are essential in preparing an oilseed for solvent extraction, because no other form of mill gives particles thin enough to permit ready extraction and allow percolation of the solvent without crumbling.

NEXT, THE OILSEED MEATS are subjected to some form of cooking or heat treatment. Not all the changes that take place in cooking are well understood, but cooking seems to coagulate the protein and to rupture the oil cells, a development that makes the oil more readily extractable. Careful control of cooking is essential in mechanical pressing, because both quality and yield of oil are affected by the conditions of moisture and temperature and duration of cooking.

For hydraulic pressing, the practice is to cook the flaked meats to a moisture content of 5 to 8 percent. For screw pressing, the material must be cooked until it is very dry (1 to 3 percent moisture). If the oil is to be solvent-extracted, the procedure is somewhat different, in that the meats are first given a moderate heat tempering. Flaking is the last step.

The cooked oilseed is ready for oil extraction by hydraulic pressing, continuous screw pressing, or solvent extraction.

A stack cooker is used for cooking flakes for hydraulic pressing. It is a vertical bank of three to six steam-jacketed kettles, stacked one above the other so that the meats are progressively cooked as they pass continuously through the kettles. Stirring blades facilitate heating. The typical modern procedure in cooking cottonseed meats is as follows. The flakes, preferably of 11 to 12 percent moisture content and 0.005 to 0.010 inch thick, are fed into the top kettle, where their temperature is brought up quickly to 180° to 190° F. Then the temperature is gradually raised as the material progresses for 80 to 120 minutes through the other kettles. In the last kettle the temperature is brought up to 225° to 235° F. and the moisture content down to 5 to 8 percent. If the final moisture content is too high or too low, the cooked material does not handle properly in the presses.

As they are discharged from the cooker, the hot, cooked meats are formed into uniform cakes in press cloths made of human hair and are charged by hand into the boxes of the press. The typical hydraulic press used for cottonseed consists of a heavy steel frame made up of four vertical steel columns fastened at the top and bottom to heavy iron blocks. The space within the columns is closely filled with a series of horizontal plates, which are hung from the top block. Each plate is suspended from the plate above it by linkages, which permit the entire assembly to be compressed by the upward motion of a hydraulic ram built into the bottom block. Most presses contain 15 openings or boxes, and the cooked material in the thick press cloths is inserted between the plates until the press is filled.

When all the boxes are filled, hydraulic pressure generated by a pump is applied to the ram. This forces the ram upward; that, in turn, slowly compresses the cake and causes the oil to flow through the cloths and down into the drip pan of the press. Effective operation requires that the pressure be applied at a carefully controlled rate. That is accomplished through the use of a change valve. The highest pressure to which the cake is subjected is about 1,800 pounds to the square inch.

The cake is held at the maximum pressure for 20 or 30 minutes to allow the oil to drain. Finally, the press is opened by releasing the ram pressure, and the cakes are removed by hand and delivered to a cake stripper, which removes the cloth for later use. The soft edges of the cakes are trimmed off. The trimmings are returned for re-pressing. The cakes are then fed to cake breakers and next to mills for grinding into meal. The oil is collected in tanks, where it is settled, to separate suspended matter, and then filtered. The capacity of a typical press depends on the drainage time. With drainage for 30 minutes, the average 15-box unit can handle in 24 hours the meats from about 10 tons of whole cottonseed. The final cake usually contains from 5 to 7 percent oil.

For processing peanuts and soybeans, the flaking, cooking, and pressing procedures are about the same as for cottonseed. For peanuts, however, because of their high oil content, a somewhat lower cooking temperature is used, and a slower rate of pressure application is required in pressing.

The hydraulic method of processing is not economical, mainly because of the large amount of hand labor required in the press room, nor is it efficient because of the large amount of oil left in the cake. Practically no hydraulic mills have been erected since 1925. The hydraulic-pressing industry since its very origin has not benefited materially from any constructive research toward the understanding and solution of its technical problems, and practically all operating techniques have evolved from "cut and try" approaches. Cooking, for example, has always been regarded as an art rather than a science and has been done by feel and smell. The situation has shown some improvement, however, as a result of experimental work done at southern universities since 1930, and there is now a better understanding of the reason for carrying out various operations by specific controlled methods.

The screw-type press utilizes a greater pressure than the hydraulic press, so that a somewhat larger amount of oil is recovered. The hot material is forced through a cylindrical steel cage and then through a small opening by means of a powerful rotating screw. An extremely high pressure is developed by restricting the discharge, and that causes the oil to be expelled through narrow slots around the chamber. The compressed cake is extruded through the small opening.

Two types of screw presses are in general use in this country. They operate on the same principle; both process the material in two successive stages, the first operating at a low pressure, and the second, or finishing stage, under a high pressure. Both machines are complete processing units in that they are equipped with the necessary heat-treating vessels in which the oilseed is conditioned before pressing.

Soybeans are first cracked or ground into small particles to facilitate heat penetration. They are then dried to the low moisture content best suited for pressing. The hot material is fed into a tempering vessel above the press, where it is held at a relatively high temperature to cook and toughen the protein and to equalize the moisture and temperature. The hot granulated material is then fed into the low-pressure barrel of the press, where it receives its first pressing to remove part of the oil. From there it is forced into the finishing barrel, where it is subjected to a pressure up to 12 tons to the square inch. The bulk of the remaining oil is squeezed out and escapes through the slots. The cake emerges as irregular-shaped fragments. It is very hot and dry, and must be sprayed with water to cool it and to increase its moisture content. The oil is passed over screens to remove meal particles, called foots, and is then filtered. The foots are continuously returned to the press.

The action of the screws raises the temperature of the material, so that some means must be provided to prevent burning or damage. One way is to cool the hot oil and to flush it continuously over the exterior of the barrels. Usually the cooling is controlled at a critical point at which the press operates at its maximum efficiency. To operate the machines most efficiently, uniform feed rate and a uniform composition of the material must be maintained.

In the United States, continuous presses are employed principally for processing soybeans, flaxseed, and copra. They are also used for cottonseed, corn germ, peanuts, and tung nuts. Most materials are dried to a moisture content of about 3 percent or less. The temperature required for best results varies somewhat with each oilseed. Recommended optimum temperatures are 275° to 290° F. for soybeans, 220° to 240° for cottonseed and peanuts, 220° for flaxseed, and 200° for copra. Continuous presses are generally operated as close as possible to their maximum rated pressure. The capacities of the large commercial units average 18 to 22 tons a day for soybeans, 22 to 24 tons for cottonseed, 15 tons for flaxseed, and 18 to 20 tons for copra. With well-operated equipment, the oil content in the cake usually is 4 to 6 percent for soybeans, flaxseed, and cottonseed.

The capacity of the continuous presses depends largely upon the oil content desired in the final cake. The machines can be readily operated at a 25- to 50-percent increase in throughput at only a relatively small sacrifice in oil separation. During the war emergency, oil millers were called on to speed up their machines to those capacities to handle larger volumes of oilseeds. For prepressing to remove the easily expelled oil from the material to be subsequently solvent-extracted, the machines are operated at higher screw speeds and at two to four times their normal capacity.

Continuous presses, although rapidly adopted by the soybean and flaxseed industries, have never been used extensively for cottonseed. The reason has been mainly that mill operators up to 1935 could not get as good an oil ex-

traction or an oil equal in quality to that obtained by hydraulic pressing. The situation has changed, however, as a result of improvements in performance efficiency and operating techniques, and, since 1940, more and more of these presses are being used for cottonseed. One practice now is to roll the meats and cook the flakes before drying, rather than to just crack and dry the meats. Perhaps the most significant recent improvement in press design has been the use of independent drives on each of the two screws. That permits utilization of both screws to best advantage and makes it possible to handle a wider variety of oil-bearing materials.

Solvent extraction for processing oilseeds leaves only 1 percent or less of oil in the cake, compared to 4 to 7 percent in mechanical pressing. That is its greatest advantage. The advantage perhaps stands out more clearly in the case of a seed like the soybean, which contains only 18 percent of oil. Here the yield of oil is about 95 percent for the solvent process and 76 percent for mechanical pressing.

Solvent extraction in this country is carried out mainly by the continuous process. The batch method is relatively inefficient and has had only limited application in processing oilseeds. The continuous process utilizes the principle of countercurrent flow of solvent and solids in the extraction apparatus. The oil-bearing material moves in one direction while being washed by solvent passing in the opposite direction. Thus, the solvent is used to better advantage than in batch extraction, and the oil is removed more effectively, because the flakes come in contact with purer and purer solvent as they progress through the extractor. In addition, the process is continuous and automatic in operation, a combination that saves labor, power, steam, and materials.

The continuous process is readily adaptable to extracting oil from low-oil-content seeds and press cake. Its principal use in the United States is for soybeans; 40 percent of the beans crushed from the 1948–49 crop were so processed.

Direct extraction of oil from oilseeds of higher oil content is more difficult. The reason is that flakes prepared from such seeds, unlike soybean flakes, tend to disintegrate into a powder known in the industry as fines. In that form their oil cannot be extracted thoroughly nor can they be handled successfully in continuous-type equipment. It has been the experience with continuous extraction in Europe that the high-oil-content seeds cannot be processed successfully unless they are first pressed to remove most of the oil. There appears to be some evidence to the contrary, however, and since 1947 several commercial installations have been erected in the United States to attempt direct extraction of oil from cottonseed, castor beans, peanuts, and flaxseed. Fore-pressing is also being investigated. The European contention is that a combination of the two methods is the best procedure for nearly all oilseeds. Among the advantages claimed are a lower residual oil content, more rapid extraction, increased capacity of the equipment, lower solvent requirement, and the practical elimination of fines.

Several types of continuous extractors are used commercially in this country. The early American designs were largely modifications of German equipment, but since 1938 American engineers have designed several entirely new types. Some designs employ screw conveyors. Others utilize a chain of baskets on the order of a bucket elevator. Others employ a single vertical column. Another type is a series of troughs equipped with paddle wheels.

The preferred solvent for extracting oil in this country, and the one used almost exclusively, is commercial hexane, a petroleum fraction similar to gasoline. It has many advantages, but it is flammable. The extraction plant must be designed with that in mind, and safety measures must be followed strictly to prevent explosions and fires.

The solvent-extraction process has one other advantage, which may some day prove very important. The meal is not damaged by excessive heat at any time in the process—so it is more suitable for industrial application in the manufacture of such products as fibers, adhesives, and sizes, and its use is not restricted to livestock feeds.

For the continuous solvent-extraction process, soybeans are first cleaned and their moisture content is adjusted to 10 to 11 percent. They are then passed through cracking rolls to be cut, with a minimum of crushing or powdering, into small grits-size particles. They are tempered by heating for 15 to 25 minutes to a temperature of 130° to 170° F., which makes them more plastic and equalizes their moisture content. The grits are rolled into flakes about 0.007 inch thick.

Flake preparation is considered the most critical step in the process. Great care is taken to have the final material in just the right condition so that it will give up its oil most readily, drain easily after extraction, and produce very few fines. The hot, tempered flakes are fed into the extractor. There they are treated with the hexane solvent for about an hour. Hot solvent is used to facilitate removal of the oil. Most extractors are designed to produce a residual meal of about 0.8 percent oil. The most popular extractor is the Bollman or basket-type.

The Bollman extractor has a number of baskets suspended on chains, which operate over sprocket wheels much like a bucket elevator. The baskets on the descending side are filled with flakes. As the baskets approach the top, on the ascending side, they are sprayed with fresh solvent. It percolates through the flakes, drips through the perforated bottom of the basket, and is redistributed onto the basket immediately below. The solution increases in oil concentration to 10 to 15 percent as it descends. It is known as half miscella. The half miscella is collected at the bottom of the tower, filtered, and sprayed onto the feed flakes in the descending side. This solution, much richer in oil, is called full miscella. It is collected in a sump below the baskets and is continuously pumped away to be evaporated. The baskets carrying the oil-free, or spent, flakes drain for a short distance. Then they are inverted and dumped into a hopper, which is emptied by screw conveyors that carry the flakes out of the extractor; 35 to 40 extraction baskets are fastened to the chains, and they make one complete revolution in 40 to 60 minutes. Many finely divided particles of meal that were suspended in the miscella are filtered out by the bed of flakes in each basket.

The flakes leaving the extractor contain 25 to 35 percent of solvent. It is removed and recovered by heating the wet residue as it passes through a series of jacketed, steam-heated driers. Indirect heat removes the greater part, but the last traces are removed usually in the final driers, where a little direct steam is injected into the meal. The vapors are passed through a scrubber, where particles of meal dust are removed by a spray of water or solvent. The dust-free vapors are then condensed into liquid and the condensate flows to a water-solvent separating vessel in which the solvent is separated from the water.

The raw extracted soybean flakes may be further processed into edible flour, paints, paper sizing, and other products that utilize their high protein content. Actually, most of the meal is sold for livestock and poultry feed, after first being subjected to a toasting process in which it is moistened and cooked at 220° to 230° F. for 45 to 90 minutes. The treatment enhances its feeding value and produces a brown color and a pleasant odor and flavor, which add to its palatability.

The oil-solvent mixture from the extraction apparatus contains 18 to 30 percent of oil and some fines, which are removed by filtration. Most of the solvent is recovered in evaporators or stills. The better solvent-removal systems are designed to evaporate the sol-

vent rapidly without overheating the oil, although temperatures of 240° to 250° F. for only a few minutes do not lower the quality of the oil.

The final traces of solvent are removed from the oil in a stripping column—a vertical tower filled with packing, bubble trays, or vertical tubes, which spread the oil into thin films as it flows downward. Steam is injected at the bottom and as it rises it strips the solvent from the oil. Sludge, or gummy material, known as gums, is usually present. It is removed by agitating with water and then separating the mixture. The degummed oil is suitable for industrial uses without further treatment. But for edible purposes it must be refined, bleached, and deodorized.

The outstanding success of solvent extraction for the soybeans stimulated its application to the other oilseeds. Several cooperative oil mills in Arkansas became interested, and in 1947 a plant with a capacity of 200 tons a day was erected for processing cottonseed directly. Two others of identical construction were built shortly afterwards, and two more large plants and several smaller plants employing different types of extractors have since been built.

The operators of these mills discovered that cottonseed is not so easy to process as soybeans. They met and overcame many operational difficulties before achieving relatively smooth performance of the equipment, and some problems remain unsolved. The over-all operation is said to be satisfactory, but more experience is needed. The plants are regarded in the industry as still in the development stage, and, during 1950, two of those processors converted from direct extraction to forepressing and have reported very satisfactory operation.

The principal processing difficulty has been the excessive formation of fines during the extraction. This has complicated the entire operation and has prevented efficient recovery of the oil. Another problem is that the meal produced when a petroleum solvent is used contains somewhat more of certain toxic substances than mechanically pressed meals and cannot be fed in as large amounts to hogs and poultry. The varying moisture content of cottonseed also introduces some operational troubles and makes it difficult to extract the oil efficiently.

In the process, as it was used for cottonseed by the cooperative mills in 1949, the meats are tempered and then flaked to a thickness of 0.010 to 0.012 inch. From that point on, the procedure is about the same as for soybeans, except that more fines are formed and, as a result, accessory equipment is needed to separate and return the fines to the process. Another difference is that cottonseed oil darkens more easily on heating, so that lower evaporating temperatures must be used.

Three solvent-extraction units for processing flaxseed were erected in Minnesota in 1948. All forepress the seed to a 15 to 20 percent oil content and process the press cake by the continuous solvent method. At least three plants forepressed corn germ in 1948. One used the batch method for extracting the oil from the press cake; the other two used continuous extraction. At least eight plants on the west coast have processed rice bran by batch extraction. Two plants using continuous extraction have gone into operation since 1947, one in California and the other in Texas.

MUCH INTEREST has been shown in the use of the solvent-extraction process for peanuts and for tung, sunflower, castor, copra, and other oilseeds. Plant-scale tests, with either batch or continuous equipment, have been made on practically all, but the results have not been considered satisfactory. Many improvements in extraction equipment and processing techniques have been made since 1934, however. Research and development work are under way, and promising results have been reported by some investigators using various alcohols as solvents. Among new

developments announced since 1944 is a pilot-plant-scale method originated at the Southern Regional Research Laboratory, by H. L. E. Vix and others, for separating the pigment glands from cottonseed. The glands contain the toxic materials present in cottonseed. Seventy percent of the meal obtained is practically free from hulls, oil, and other glands. The meal is highly nutritious and has a number of potential industrial and food uses.

Solvent-extraction equipment costs more to install, and the process costs more to operate than continuous pressing, but it is more profitable because it recovers so much more of the oil. R. L. Kenyon states that the initial outlay is a third to a half more, depending upon the capacity, and that the processing cost is 15 to 25 percent higher. Detailed cost-comparison data for processing soybeans by the two methods show that the increased return for the extra oil (1.8 pounds to the bushel) obtained by the solvent process may be many times the additional processing expense incurred.

Such facts prove that the solvent process has a definite financial advantage. One must realize, however, that the extent to which an oil mill can operate profitably regardless of the process used depends just as much upon a great number of other factors, all of which directly affect the manufacturing cost or the so-called gross operating margin. Among the factors are the size of the plant, the efficiency of operation, location of the mill with respect to raw-material supply and markets for products, availability of raw material at economical hauling distances for year-around operation, and adaptability of the equipment for processing oilseeds besides soybeans. Other important considerations are the gross cost of raw material, income realized on products, quality of the raw material, proximity of other mills that compete for raw material and markets, and operation of a mixed-feed mill for additional revenue.

One serious problem that confronts

all operators of oil mills is the fluctuation in price of the products after they have acquired sufficient raw material for the season's operation. The risk may be minimized by making forward sales of mill products at the time raw material is purchased and also by the use of futures markets. It is well known in the industry that a proper combination of these conditions operating to the advantage of the small operator can permit him to compete with the larger solvent processors. Oil mills falling in this category should presumably be among the last that will be forced out of business or have to convert to solvent extraction.

ALTHOUGH HYDRAULIC PRESSING has become obsolete in the soybean and flaxseed industries, it was used to process close to 80 percent of the cottonseed crushed in 1948. Compared to screw pressing, its main disadvantages are the higher labor requirements and the lower yield of oil. One continuous screw press does the same job as the cooker, several hydraulic presses, and the rest of the press-room equipment. The expense of press cloths is eliminated, processing conditions can be readily controlled, and relatively little labor is required as the operation is largely automatic.

Hydraulic pressing has the advantage over screw pressing of lower power and maintenance costs, but its main advantage is its lower capital investment. In fact, the relatively inexpensive type of equipment required, the availability of cheap and plentiful labor through the years, and the acceptable quality of the oil and meal products have been of vital importance in enabling cottonseed mills to operate profitably over a crushing season that averages only 3 to 4 months each year.

Continuous pressing has the advantage over solvent extraction of lower operating costs. Also, the continuous presses are more versatile. They can be used to process practically any oilseed that may become available. These advantages, however, do not offset the greater returns from the increased oil recovery by solvent extraction.

The theoretical advantages of the solvent process over mechanical pressing for cottonseed appear to be much the same as for soybeans.

Aside from the technological problems in the solvent-extraction process itself, a number of other factors deter its widespread adoption for cottonseed. Many oil millers believe that in order to realize fully the economies of the process, the installation must be of large capacity and the operation year-around (300 days). That requires an adequate supply of raw material within reasonable hauling distance of the mill. Thus the use of the process by the cottonseed industry would appear to be limited to a relatively few terminal locations, because the production of cottonseed is not so centralized as that of soybeans. The expense for large storage facilities is also a deterrent; so is the present inability of the industry to store wet cottonseed successfully over an extended period.

E. L. D'AQUIN was graduated from Tulane University, where he received the bachelor of engineering degree in chemical engineering. Before joining the staff of the Southern Regional Research Laboratory in 1941, he was employed by the Southern Cotton Oil Co.

E. A. GASTROCK is head of the engineering and development division of the Southern Laboratory. A graduate of Tulane University, he has had industrial experience in the hydrogenation of vegetable oil, in the manufacture of paint, varnish, and enamel, and in quality control and mill research on fibrous structural insulating board.

O. L. BREKKE is a member of the engineering and development division of the Northern Regional Research Laboratory. After graduation from the University of North Dakota as a chemical engineer, he worked for a petroleum research laboratory, and joined the Department in 1940 as a member of the United States Soybean Industrial Products Laboratory.

Fractionating Fats for New Products

R. O. Feuge

Salt and sugar and many other household staples are single compounds or mixtures of a few single compounds. Anyone who casually examines a fatty material like shortening might think that it, too, is a single compound or, at most, a mixture of only a few compounds. To all appearances it is quite simple. Shortening is usually a creamy white, homogeneous mass, nearly odorless and tasteless. It melts into a clear, almost colorless, oily liquid when it is warmed slightly.

But, actually, shortening is an extremely complex material. Like most other fatty compounds, it contains some ingredients that, when pure, remain hard and glasslike even in hot water, but it also contains ingredients that are liquid at temperatures as low as those of ice. Shortening melts completely when it is warmed only because the high-melting ingredients are dissolved by the lower-melting ingredients. Some of the fatty parts are so resistant to oxidation by air that they become rancid only after long periods; other parts can become rancid in a few hours if they are heated in air.

Shortening is a highly processed fat: It is a natural fat that has been treated to give it useful properties. Salad or cooking oils need much less processing to be ready for household use, but they are chemically just as complex as shortening. Both shortening and salad oils are obtained from fats or oils, which are in turn extracted from seeds, fruits, or animal tissue. Each such fat or oil is a complex mixture of simple fats, which the chemist calls triglycerides because they contain three fatty acid molecules attached to a single molecule of glycerin.

Naturally occurring fats and oils contain, in addition to a variety of triglycerides, up to 5 percent of such other substances as antioxidants, vitamins, pigments, free fatty acids, and resins. Some of these nonfat components have no special significance, but others have physiological or biological activity that makes them especially valuable—particularly after separation from the fat or oil. In still other instances, the minor components unfavorably affect the fat or oil for certain uses.

Crude fats and oils are generally not very useful in the form in which they are obtained from seeds, fruits, or other materials. They have to be subjected to many forms of processing to increase their utility. One is known as fractionation, which is any process whereby a complex natural product is separated into simpler products with properties and uses different from those of the original product. Among the methods of fractionation are distillation, which separates the low-boiling from the high-boiling portions; chilling, which freezes out the most easily solidified portion; and extraction with a solvent, which separates the most readily soluble portion, or fraction.

Some of the processes have long been used in industry. When candles were the principal source of artificial illumination, for example, the art of separating solid stearic acid from liquid oleic acid was developed. It was accomplished by chilling the mixture and pressing it to separate the liquid acid, or red oil, from the solid stearic acid. The solid acid was used for making candles. The red oil was sulfonated for use in the textile industry.

After the cottonseed-oil industry developed in this country and the demand grew for oils that would remain bright and clear when stored in the refrigerator, the process of winterization was developed.

The process involves slow chilling for 4 or 5 days, followed by filtering the chilled oil to remove a part of the high-melting fat, or glycerides, which it contains. Thereby the oil is made usable in salad dressings.

As the importance of vitamins became generally known, the recovery of the fat-soluble vitamins from fish, fish-liver, soybean, wheat-germ, and other oils assumed commercial importance. The oldest method of separating the vitamins was to saponify the fat or oil with caustic soda, extract the crude unsaponifiable material with an organic solvent, and then re-extract or distill the extracted material to concentrate the vitamins.

These older processes generally did not effect complete separation of one type of fatty product from another. Often the methods were tedious and required constant attention. Since about 1920, specialists have realized that the separation could probably be achieved more readily and efficiently by dissolving the fats and oils in organic solvents, from which relatively pure components would separate when the temperature of the solutions was changed. Such processes seemed attractive and technically intriguing, but before 1944 no very large plants were built to put them in operation. The obstacles were technical and economic—not to mention the age-old reluctance to adopt revolutionary processing methods. Research on the separation of fats and oils by means of solvents, that is, by so-called solvent fractionation, however, had advanced to a point where change seemed inevitable and several large solvent-separation plants were built. The impetus of the new processes and

plants, which are now in daily operation, and the improved products that thus became available established the desirability of other similar plants and processes.

THE VITAMINS and antioxidants in fats and oils are by far the most valuable nonfat constituents, weight for weight. The antioxidants—complex substances present in minute amounts—are important because they can prolong the shelf life and increase the resistance of fats and oils to rancidification. We do not know their exact chemical structure or the way they act to prevent rancidification.

In many vegetable oils, the tocopherols, which are considered to be vitamin E, are the most abundant of the fat-soluble vitamins. All four of the common tocopherols exhibit both vitamin E and antioxidant activity, though not in the same degree. Apparently the types that have the greatest antioxidant activity have the least vitamin E activity, and vice versa. Tocopherols occur to the extent of about 0.1 percent in cottonseed, soybean, corn, and rice-bran oils. Wheat-germ oil contains about 0.4 percent.

Palm oil contains a great deal of carotene, or provitamin A, which is changed into vitamin A in the liver of animals. Fish oils are rich in vitamins A and D. Some, indeed, contain as much as 7.5 percent of vitamin A.

When the amount of a vitamin in an oil is large enough, the oil can be sold directly as a vitamin preparation. Frequently, however, the vitamins are concentrated, either by the process I mentioned or by one known as molecular distillation.

EXPERIMENTS BY W. S. Singleton and A. E. Bailey at the Southern Regional Research Laboratory proved that tocopherols can be concentrated by fractional crystallization from solvents. The oil is simply mixed with a solvent and the solution cooled until most of the glycerides, or true fats, have solidified in the form of fine, white crystals. The separated crystals are then removed from the solution by filtration. The remaining solution, which contains the vitamins and the antioxidants, together with some fat, is warmed to evaporate the solvent.

When refined and bleached cottonseed oil that had a rather low tocopherol content, 0.05 percent, was mixed with 8 parts of acetone and chilled to a temperature of −76° F., the chemists got a concentrate that contained 5.4 percent of tocopherols. The separation was practically perfect, because all tocopherols were removed from the fat, or glyceride, portion by a single crystallization.

The separation, or fractionation, was even more efficient after the cottonseed oil was converted into a shorteninglike product by partial hydrogenation or hardening. By using the same ratio of acetone to oil and reducing the temperature to −98° F., the chemists prepared a concentrate that contained 29.6 percent of tocopherols, or 94 percent of all the tocopherols that were present in the original oil. When they reduced the temperature still further, they got a more potent concentrate, but the percentage of total tocopherols in the concentrate decreased. At −130° F., the concentrate contained 37.8 percent, but only 76 percent of the tocopherols originally present in the oil were separated. Similar results were obtained by research workers in the laboratories of the National Oil Products Company when they investigated the concentration of vitamins and antioxidants in wheat-germ, soybean, and fish-liver oils.

The technical feasibility of the process has been proved beyond any doubt.

With slight variations, it can be adapted to remove other minor nonfat constituents, such as waxes, pigments, and free fatty acids. Such processes can also be incorporated with other fractional-crystallization procedures (to be described later), thereby reducing the cost of separating the minor constituents from the natural fats and oils.

As for commercial applications, the fractional separation of fatty acids is the most successful of the several solvent-crystallization processes yet proposed. We can attribute this advance partly to the ease with which fatty acids solidify into large, well-formed, rigid crystals, and partly to the simplicity of the fatty acid mixtures as compared to the natural fats from which the acids are obtained by saponification.

Whenever a domestic fat is converted into fatty acids by one of the several processes of saponification, about 96 pounds of a mixture of acids are produced from each 100 pounds of fat. The physical and chemical characteristics of the resulting mixtures of fatty acids vary with the type of fat from which they were produced. Most domestic fats, however, consist principally of combinations of several, or all, of just five acids—palmitic, stearic, oleic, linoleic, and linolenic acids.

Interest in the separation of fatty acids into normally solid and normally liquid fractions was first evinced more than a century ago by candlemakers who were trying to improve the quality of their product. A fractional-crystallization process that does not employ solvents was developed and is still in common use, although it has never been improved much beyond its original efficiency. Until about 1947, practically all commercial stearic acid and red oil were manufactured by this method. It consists essentially of molding the mixed acids into slabs, cooling them, and forcing out the liquid fraction by mechanical pressing.

Effective separation of the solid and liquid portions requires that about 40 percent of the total acids in process be recycled; that is, the molding and pressing must be repeated two or three times. The large amount of hand labor required is another disadvantage. Also, the utilizable raw materials are limited because efficient operation demands that the ratio of palmitic to stearic acid in the original fatty acid mixture (feed stock) be in the neighborhood of 55 to 45.

Distillation was the only other fractionation method of recognized commercial utility before 1946. Distillation permits the separation of fatty acids according to their boiling points and usually works well when the acids to be separated are of appreciably different molecular weights. Unfortunately, several of the most common acids (stearic, oleic, linoleic, and linolenic) have molecules of approximately the same weight, and therefore cannot be fractionated readily by distillation.

J. B. Brown and his coworkers at Ohio State University were the first to show that practically any common fatty acid can be prepared in fairly pure form by fractional crystallization from solvents. These workers began publishing the results of their experimental work in 1937. Other investigators had used similar techniques on a few of the common acids, but had confined their activities almost entirely to the preparation of products for laboratory use. The development of commercial methods came later.

IN 1944, PROFESSOR BROWN patented a process for the preparation of highly unsaturated fatty acids for use in the manufacture of improved drying oils. He converted fish oils into a mixture of fatty acids, which he dissolved in petroleum naphtha. When the solution was cooled, the relatively nondrying portion separated as solid particles or crystals and was removed. When the remaining solution was cooled to a still lower temperature ($-75°$ F. and below) or the solvent was removed by evaporation, the rapid-drying fraction of the original oil was obtained.

W. S. Singleton and others at the Southern Laboratory in 1945 demonstrated that the solid and liquid acids from both hydrogenated and unhydrogenated cottonseed oil can be separated by fractional crystallization from solvents under conditions that are relatively simple and not too expensive for industrial operators. They found that when the fatty acids from cottonseed oil are mixed with acetone, in the ratio of 1 part to 4, and the solution cooled to $-5°$ F., the firm white crystals that separate from the solution consist entirely of the saturated, or normally solid, acids (melting points, $130°$ to $167°$ F.). All except 2 percent of the acids that remain in solution are oleic and linoleic acids, which have melting points of $61°$ and $23°$ F., respectively.

Similar results were had when petroleum naphtha was substituted for the acetone, provided the temperature was lowered further to compensate for the greater solubility of the solid acids in the hydrocarbon solvent. Other common solvents, such as methyl acetate, ethyl acetate, and methyl ethyl ketone, were also found to be suitable for this fractionation.

When the fatty acids obtained from hydrogenated cottonseed oil are used and the ratio of solvent to fatty acids is changed to 6 to 1, an equally pure low-melting fraction can be recovered from the mixed acids by solvent fractionation. In this case the saturated-acid fraction will contain appreciable amounts of high-melting iso-oleic acids, which are produced during hydrogenation of the liquid oil.

Daniel Swern and coworkers at the Eastern Regional Research Laboratory successfully applied similar methods to the preparation of oleic acid of high purity. The raw material they used was inedible grease, which had been partially hydrogenated to change all of the low-melting acids to oleic and stearic acids. When the mixed acids from the hydrogenated greases were subjected to fractional crystallization and the oleic acid fraction was distilled, a product of approximately 95 percent purity was obtained.

While some of that work was under way, research workers at Emery Industries, Inc., in Cincinnati, were developing their own version of the solvent-crystallization process. The company for many years had produced fatty acids by the old chilling and pressing process. The new solvent-crystallization process, which they introduced under the name Emersol process and first publicized in 1945, has since been adopted by various concerns in place of the old chilling and pressing method of producing oleic acid.

The process begins with the purification of the raw material, or feed stock, by distillation to remove color, odor, and other nonfatty acid material. The cleaned acids and the solvent, which is methyl alcohol containing a small amount of water, are automatically proportioned and mixed. From 1 to 3½ percent of fat may be added to promote the subsequent formation of easily washed crystals.

The fatty acid-solvent mixture is passed through a series of stainless-steel tubes, where it is cooled to about 10° F. Lowering the temperature causes the higher-melting acids to separate from the solution in the form of small solid particles. Regulating the rate at which the temperature is lowered controls the type of acids that settle out. When high-purity fractions are desired, the cooling is done in steps and the solids are removed between each step.

Separation of the solid acids and adhering solution, or slurry, is done by pumping the wet mass to a refrigerated room, where a rotating filter automatically picks it up, sucks out the liquid portion, washes the solid portion with solvent, and discharges each fraction separately.

BESIDES PRODUCING fatty acid fractions more cheaply than can be done by mechanical pressing, solvent-fractionation processes make possible the commercial production of various types of fatty acids in heretofore unobtainable purity.

In the manufacture of cosmetics and pharmaceutical preparations, fatty acids entirely free from unsaturated acids, like oleic and linoleic acids, can be employed to produce lotions, brushless shaving cream, cold cream, and other products that have a greatly reduced tendency to become discolored or develop off-odors. The oleic acid, on the other hand, can be combined with just the right amount of palmitic or other acid for conversion into household soaps of superior quality. Such soaps do not have to contain imported coconut oil.

Metallic soaps for use in the manufacture of lubricating greases can be prepared from fractionated fatty acids without the impurities detrimental to the performance of specialized greases. Other specialty products, such as soluble cutting oils, dry-cleaning soaps, leather penetrants, and plasticizers, can be prepared from fractionated fatty acids.

Purified unsaturated acids, such as linoleic and linolenic acids, which are obtainable by solvent fractionation, can be used in the manufacture of synthetic resins and other protective-coating compounds, which will form harder and more durable films.

UP TO THIS POINT, we have considered only the isolation of minor constituents in natural oils and the separation of mixtures of fatty acids. The third and most difficult type of fractionation is the separation of the natural fats (which, as I mentioned, are mixtures of triglycerides) into their chemically and physically distinct components.

Because every fat normally contains four to six different fatty acids, all natural fats contain many glycerides. As many as three chemically different fatty acids can combine in one molecule of a fat, and each fatty acid can occupy any one of three different positions in the molecule. Each different fatty acid and each different position occupied influences the property of the resulting fat. It can be shown mathematically that a mixture of 6 chemically different fatty acids can form 126 different kinds of triglycerides or different fat molecules. This type of distribution, usually referred to as random because it is fixed by the laws of chance, describes approximately the composition of certain processed fats.

However, natural fats seldom follow the pattern of random distribution of fatty acids in the glyceride molecules. Nature apparently directs or controls the distribution of the acids so that generally a natural fat tends to be less heterogenous, or simpler, with respect to the number of glycerides in the mixture. Nevertheless, the number of different glycerides in most natural fats is still relatively large.

A. E. Bailey at the Southern Laboratory conceived the idea that a commercial grade of winterized cottonseed oil could be prepared easily by solvent crystallization. Previous workers who used such a procedure had failed to get a quantitative separation of the complex glyceride mixtures existing in natural oils—even after the most patient and laborious crystallizations. Apparently it had not occurred to them that commercial separations of glycerides did not have to be quantitative in order to be highly useful.

Bailey and his coworkers found that a good winterized cottonseed oil could be produced by mixing refined oil and petroleum naphtha in a ratio of 1 to 1, cooling the solution to 2° F. for 7 hours, filtering off the solid particles that separated out of solution, and then evaporating off the petroleum naphtha. The procedure gave a yield of 77 percent of winterized oil; the conventional procedure gives·yields of 65 to 75 percent. Furthermore, the solvent process produced a superior winterized product, which did not cloud even when kept for 72 hours at 32° F. Ordinary winterized oils become cloudy after 5 to 15 hours at that temperature.

HOWEVER, THE MOST IMPORTANT features of the solvent-winterization process were the ease with which filtration was accomplished (10 to 100 times the conventional rate) and the short period of cooling required—7 hours compared to 3 to 6 days by the conventional process. When treated by the conventional method for winterizing cottonseed oil, peanut oil becomes a jellylike mass that cannot be filtered;

therefore, it has never been winterized by this process. By using conditions similar to those employed with cottonseed oil, however, the same workers winterized peanut oil in a yield of 80 percent.

The success of solvent winterization is due to several factors. The addition of petroleum naphtha makes a solution of high fluidity, which facilitates the orientation of molecules and permits well-formed crystals to be deposited with relative rapidity. After the crystals are formed, separation of the liquid oil-solvent solution from the crystals is effected much more readily and cleanly than is possible for oil alone.

Techniques similar to those used in winterizing cottonseed and peanut oils can probably be used to prepare superior or heretofore unknown products from other common fats and oils. Oleo oil, which is customarily prepared by slowly cooling beef fat to about 90° F. and then pressing out the liquid portion, should be obtainable in higher yields and better quality by solvent fractionation. It should be possible by solvent extraction to separate soybean oil into two fractions, one of which would be a better drying oil and the other a superior edible oil. Inedible tallow and fish oils now are fractionated in liquid propone solutions.

Partial-crystallization methods also can be applied with good results to modified fats. In further experiments, E. A. Kraemer and A. E. Bailey used hydrogenated cottonseed oil to make a product that is like cocoa butter.

COCOA BUTTER, an ingredient of many candies, is peculiar in that it resembles mutton tallow in fatty acid composition yet differs greatly in physical properties. Because of this difference, the one product is highly prized and expensive, but the other has little value for food. Mutton tallow is a waxy solid at body temperature, but cocoa butter is hard and brittle at ordinary temperatures and melts in the mouth with a pleasing and cooling sensation. The difference lies in the pattern in which the fatty acids are combined in the molecules of the two fats.

The artificial cocoa butter was prepared by hydrogenating cottonseed oil to create a sizable proportion of fat molecules almost identical with those in the natural product. The undesirable molecules were then removed by partial crystallization from petroleum naphtha (4 parts of naphtha to 1 of fat) at 35° F. The product, which separated from the solution on chilling, closely resembled natural cocoa butter in melting point, shortness of plastic range, consistency, and solidification behavior. The yield of finished product was rather law, only 28 percent, but the remaining product is useful as a hardening agent in shortening and similar products.

Audrey T. Gros and I extended the solvent-crystallization technique by applying it to the separation of mixtures of monoglycerides, diglycerides, and triglycerides, which are present in technical-grade monoglycerides. The technical product, which is made by heating glycerin and fat in the presence of a small amount of soap, contains only 30 to 60 percent of the desired monoglycerides. The other constituents are totally devoid of most of the valued properties of monoglycerides, and for many uses they merely act as expensive diluents.

BECAUSE MONOGLYCERIDES have physical properties so radically different from those of diglycerides and triglycerides, purification by fractional crystallization from solvents is a highly valuable process when applied to technical products made from highly hydrogenated cottonseed oil. When a technical grade monoglyceride—for example, one containing only 39 percent monoglycerides—was dissolved in commercial-grade ethyl alcohol and cooled to 86° F., the undesirable portion separated from the solution, but the monoglycerides remained in solution. The purity of the monoglycerides remaining in solution increased from 60 to 92 percent as the water content of

the alcohol increased from 0 to 35 percent. The lowest yield of monoglycerides obtained under those conditions was 74 percent.

Other solvents, like methyl alcohol, isopropyl alcohol, and acetone, behave like ethyl alcohol, provided the amount of water in the solvent is adjusted to the proper level. At the lower temperatures, where the high-purity products separate, isopropyl alcohol has the highest dissolving power for monoglycerides and is the best solvent where purification is to be effected with the least possible amount of solvent.

Monoglycerides are fatty, waxlike solids with alcohollike properties—one part of the molecule resembles an alcohol molecule, the other, a fat molecule. Most present uses for monoglycerides result from the ability of these compounds to act as emulsifying agents for oil-water mixtures. One of the major uses of high-purity monoglycerides is in the preparation of inedible oil-water emulsions where the oil to be emulsified is not a natural fat or is one of relatively low value. Monoglycerides emulsify mineral oils more easily than they do vegetable oils and fats.

Better cosmetic and pharmaceutical emulsions can be prepared with high-purity monoglycerides. Such products are also valuable as solvents for oil-soluble dyes to be dispersed in water and as soluble coatings for edible powders and salts which tend to take up moisture from the air.

The possibility of using highly purified monoglycerides as intermediates in the preparation of a variety of useful compounds has never been extensively explored because until very recently such products were not commercially available.

R. O. FEUGE, a native of Texas, received his degree in chemical engineering from the University of Texas in 1938. Since 1941 he has been a member of the technical staff of the Southern Regional Research Laboratory and has been engaged in research on the processing of fats and oils.

Vegetable Oils and Fats for Edible Use

R. O. Feuge

Crude edible vegetable oils are subjected to various types of processing for several reasons. One is consumer preference. Most people prefer to eat light-colored and bland oils. The preference stems partly from the apparently reasonable but incorrect assumption that only colorless, odorless, and tasteless oils and fats are pure. It is true that such products can be used without masking or detracting from the characteristic flavor and palatability of the foods to which they have been added. In the United States the only notable exception is olive oil, which is prized primarily because of its own odor, flavor, and color.

From the oil processor's standpoint, purification of crude oils is advantageous. Some consumers could be persuaded to accept a few oils having characteristic flavors and odors, but marketing a wide variety of oils of different origins is greatly facilitated by purifying practically all of them to the point where their origin is not evident to the senses.

Two factors besides preference and convenience are responsible for the existence of vegetable-oil refineries. A number of oils, including some of our most common and plentiful oils, are practically inedible in the crude state and must be processed to become edible. The supply of naturally liquid oils is greater than the supply of naturally semisolid, or plastic, fats, but the demand is just the reverse. Therefore, in order to supply the big demand for the scarce plastic fats, the abundant liquid oils have to be converted to semisolid fats of good quality.

Because of those requirements, a large and widely dispersed industry now converts crude oils from many sources into a variety of refined edible products. The industry may appear complex, but actually it consists of a number of more or less standardized operations, or unit processes—refining, bleaching, hydrogenating, winterizing, and deodorizing, which are combined and modified to meet special conditions. Nearly all edible vegetable oils are first subjected to refining and bleaching. Then they may be deodorized and go directly to consumers, or they may be processed further to yield either winterized oils or so-called hardened fats. Regardless of the kind and number of intermediate steps, deodorization is nearly always the final step in processing any edible fat of vegetable origin.

PURE FATS OR OILS comprise a mixture of fatty acids chemically combined to form what the chemist calls triglycerides. Refining is therefore concerned with the removal of undesirable nonglyceride components. In vegetable oils, the impurities normally consist of oil-soluble substances, which are extracted from the seed along with the oil, particles of meal, gummy substances, and degradation products of the oil itself. The amounts and kinds of the impurities depend mainly on the type and origin of the seed processed and the method of extraction. The undesirable constituents generally amount to less than 10 percent by weight of the crude oil—more often to only 3 to 5 percent.

The oldest and most important

method of refining vegetable oils for edible use consists in treating the crude oil with a solution of caustic soda. It looks like a simple process, but it involves complicated chemical and physical phenomena. The caustic soda reacts with the free fatty acids that are present in the crude oil to form soaps, which are insoluble in the oil and therefore tend to pass into the water phase where hydration (absorption of water) begins. However, the concentration of the remaining caustic soda in the water is so high that the soap is kept out or is thrown out of the water solution by a phenomenon called salting out.

THE RESULT of the different reactions is the transformation of the water, the caustic soda, and the soap into numerous minute, soft, gelatinous particles. Simultaneously the other nonfat substances—phosphatides, protein, protein-degradation products, and other gummy substances—are forced out of solution in the form of coarse particles suspended in the oil. Some of the caustic soda reacts with a portion of the fat or oil to form more soap and free glycerin. Almost as soon as the various types of particles are formed they begin to clump together, or coalesce. As the particles grow in size and gather in the color bodies and other collodial impurities, they also adsorb (occlude) some of the refined oil. The oil remaining after completion of the operation is much lighter in color and retains only traces of nonfat compounds.

In some of the older and smaller refineries, this treatment of crude oil with caustic soda is carried out in large open kettles. Generally, the kettles are cylindrical, have cone-shaped bottoms, and hold 60,000 pounds of oil apiece. Each kettle has a steam coil for heating the charge and a stirrer for mixing. Oils like cottonseed, soybean, and peanut are charged into the kettle at a temperature of about 70° F. After the bubbles of air have escaped from the oil, the stirrer is set for rapid mixing, and the caustic soda is added. A milklike emulsion forms immediately; as the mixing continues small particles of soap appear and start to grow. After a mixing period of 10 to 45 minutes, the surface of the mixture of oil and caustic solution gradually assumes a slightly granular texture because of the clumping together of soap particles. This is known as the pin break. Stirring is slowed down, and steam is turned into the heating coils to raise the temperature of the oil to about 140° F., at which point relatively large flakes of soft soap form. Heating and agitation are discontinued, and the mixture is allowed to separate into an upper layer of clear, refined oil and a lower layer of semisolid soap stock, called foots. The two layers are separated after cooling and hardening of the soap stock.

The refiner who employs the batch method generally uses enough caustic soda to neutralize the free fatty acids in the oil and provide an excess of 0.2 to 0.6 percent, based on the weight of the crude oil. The exact excess of caustic needed is the amount that will produce the desired color in the oil with the lowest refining loss. An excess of 0.2 percent is often sufficient for peanut oil, but cottonseed oil often requires 0.5 percent or more. The concentration of caustic soda ordinarily used for refining is 8.0 to 16.4 percent, which is determined and expressed on an arbitrary specific-gravity scale as degrees Baumé—in this case, 12° to 20° Baumé. The lower concentrations are used for the purer and more easily refined oils.

CONTINUOUS methods of refining vegetable oils with caustic soda have largely replaced the batch method in the United States. Continuous refining was first advocated in Europe in the 1890's. Only in the early 1930's, however, did the development in continuous centrifuges, proportioning pumps, and general mechanical equipment reach a point where the process became practical and economically feasible.

Continuous operation has the advantage of eliminating large and intermittently unused equipment in favor of smaller and continuously working apparatus. Also the amount of material actually being processed at any moment is relatively small, so that the process is flexible and responsive to the will of the operator. In the batch method, an error in judgment might necessitate re-refining a batch of 60,000 pounds of oil, but in the continuous method a similar error can be detected and corrected before an appreciable amount of oil is damaged. Another important advantage of continuous operation is that the over-all time of contact between oil and caustic soda is only 2 or 3 minutes, and the attack on the oil itself by the caustic soda consequently is kept to a minimum. The centrifugal force employed in separating the soap stock and oil is tremendously greater than the force of gravity, which acts during settling in the kettle process. Because the rate of separating the refined oil and soap stock is higher in centrifuging than in settling by gravity, the excess caustic soda has less time in which to attack the refined oil and thereby increase the refining loss.

In the continuous process, the oil and caustic soda solution (both at 75° to 85° F.) are delivered to separate measuring devices, which usually consist of a positive displacement-type pump for the oil and a synchronized adjustable metering pump for the caustic soda solution. After the proper proportions of the oil and caustic soda are measured by the respective pumps, the two streams are combined and discharged into a mixing chamber, where an emulsion is formed. After about a minute in the mixing chamber, the water-oil emulsion is forced into a tube-type heat exchanger, where hot water, or low-pressure steam, quickly heats the emulsion to 140° F. and causes it to break, or separate, into soap stock suspended in the oil. The oil and soap-stock mixture is now conveyed to a special, high-speed centrifuge, which separates the mixture and discharges two continuous streams, one consisting of refined oil that contains a small amount of soap stock and water, and the other consisting of a small amount of the semisolid soap stock. Normally, less than 3 minutes elapse from the time the crude oil enters the proportioning device until it emerges as refined oil.

The oil from the refining centrifuge can be settled, filtered, and stored. It is customary, however, to wash it almost immediately once or twice with 5 to 10 percent of hot water (180° F.). Washing is also carried out continuously by mixing the refined oil with hot water and centrifuging again to separate the soapy wash water and oil. The washed oil, containing about 0.5 percent of moisture, flows to an automatic vacuum-drier system, which is a vertical cylindrical tank in which a low pressure (1 to 2 inches of mercury) is maintained by steam-ejector pumps. The heated, wet oil is sprayed into this tank, where the water is evaporated, and the oil, which contains less than 0.1 percent of moisture, is removed at the bottom.

A modification of the continuous refining process was introduced about 1942. It is said to reduce the refining loss of an oil to nearly the theoretical minimum. The new process, known as the continuous soda ash process, subjects an oil to two separate refinings. In the first, a solution of soda ash (which is a much weaker alkali than caustic soda and, therefore, cannot attack the oil) removes most of the free fatty acids with which it can combine to form soaps. The second refining, which is carried out with caustic soda solution, removes the pigments and the remainder (about 0.1 percent) of the free fatty acids.

While most vegetable oils processed in the United States for edible use are refined by one of these three processes, or modifications of them, several other processes are used, too. The simplest of these is a water washing or degumming, which is referred to as refining by hydration. Warm, dilute solutions of weak alkalies or salts may be used, but as a rule only warm water is employed. Warm water reacts with some oil-soluble substances, such as phosphatides, proteins, and other gummy materials, to form relatively insoluble products, which can be separated from the oil by continuous centrifuging.

Water washing before alkali refining reduces the total refining loss of an oil, but that advantage probably is appreciable in only a few instances. Some oil is always lost during washing, and the washed oil may be more difficult to refine because of a greater tendency to form stable emulsions or emulsions that are hard to break. Crude soybean and corn oils are washed primarily to separate and recover the phosphatides. About 8 million pounds of soybean phosphatides, called lecithin in the trade, and a half million pounds of corn phosphatides are produced annually in the United States by this process.

Certain crude oils that contain minor amounts of impurities other than free fatty acids can be refined by a process known as steam refining. It is merely a high-temperature steam distillation under reduced pressure. The crude vegetable oil is heated to about 450° F. and maintained under a pressure of 0.25 inch of mercury or less while steam is passed through it. The steam strips the free fatty acids out of the oil. The process is used somewhat in Europe but not often in the United States.

Solvent refining has been developed so recently that only a few plants have been built to use it. By such a method, crude oils are treated with solvents that have the property of preferentially dissolving either the oil itself or the impurities in the oil. Each type of solvent finds use in one or another process based on the property of the solvent. For example, free fatty acids may be separated from crude oils by a mixture of water and isopropanol, an alcohol. In this mixture the fatty acids are relatively soluble and the oil relatively insoluble.

Another process of this type employs propane, a simple petroleum hydrocarbon. As propane is a gas at ordinary temperatures and atmospheric pressure, the process must be operated at a high pressure, at which the propane is liquid. Still another process, which involves both refining and fractionation of the oil, employs furfural.

BLEACHING is necessary to remove the color bodies, or pigments, not removed from crude oils during alkali refining. Pigments common to many vegetable oils include the carotenoids, which are red and yellow, and the chlorophyllides and pheophytin, which are green. In addition, refined oils contain degradation products of various colors and unknown character. Some oils may contain uncommon pigments; for example, gossypol, a yellow pigment, is found only in cottonseed oil.

The amount of any one pigment to be removed by bleaching is always small. For example, objectionably green oils may contain only 0.0002 percent of a chlorophyllide. Refined cottonseed oil usually contains only about 0.0003 percent of carotenoid. Crude palm oil has a relatively high content of those pigments, to which it owes its deep, orange-red color, but even its content of β-carotene is only 0.005 to 0.20 percent.

Bleaching is generally accomplished by the action of bleaching earths, or clays, or various forms of carbon. Those substances can adsorb on their surfaces the pigments that are dissolved in the oil. The exact manner by which this adsorption is brought about is not fully understood. However, it is known that in the bleaching process the amount of color bodies which are removed from the oil depends on the nature of the adsorbent used, its surface area, the concentration of the color bodies in the oil, and the temperature.

Almost any solid material that is chemically inert toward the oil can be used to adsorb the color bodies, provided that the solid material is in a state of subdivision fine enough to provide the necessary surface area. However, various economic factors limit the selection of adsorbents for bleaching oils to several types of clays and to activated carbon.

The earliest clay used in the bleaching of vegetable oils was fuller's earth, which occurs naturally in extensive deposits. The mineral is semiplastic when wet and rocklike when dry. The active adsorbing ingredient is a complex form of hydrous aluminum silicate. As mined, the mineral usually contains 40 to 60 percent of free moisture, and its preparation as an adsorbent consists in heating it to remove moisture and grinding it to a fine powder. Grinding does not produce the surface area required for adsorption, but merely makes it more accessible.

In recent years, fuller's earth largely has been supplanted by activated clays, which are more effective adsorbents. The clays are inactive as mined. High adsorbing power is imparted to them by treatment with strong mineral acids, after which they are rinsed with water and ground. Activated clays intended for removing the green pigments from vegetable oils are left slightly acidic after washing with water to remove most of the strong mineral acid.

Activated carbon, or charcoal, is the third type of adsorbent commonly used. It is effective in removing certain types of compounds, but it is expensive and it adsorbs large amounts of oil that are not removed from the spent carbon.

Oils are almost always bleached by batch methods in kettles with capacities of 15,000 to 35,000 pounds of oil. The kettles may be open, or they may be constructed so that the bleaching can be performed under a vacuum. In either case, they are equipped with steam coils for heating the charge and with agitators for intimately mixing the adsorbent and oil.

The oil to be bleached is pumped into the kettle and heated to slightly above 212° F. before the clay is added, usually in amounts ranging from 0.5 to 4.0 percent. Just enough clay is used to produce the desired degree of bleaching. If activated carbon is used, it is used in conjunction with the clay and in amounts of 5 to 10 percent of the amount of clay used. After addition of the adsorbent, the oil-solid mixture is agitated for 15 to 20 minutes. A longer contact period tends to darken the oil and partly defeat the purpose of the operation. At the end of the mixing period, the bleached oil and adsorbent are separated by filtration. If the bleaching was conducted under vacuum, the oil is cooled before filtering.

The plant process is controlled by laboratory refining and bleaching tests, designed to determine how much and what types of adsorbents are necessary to produce the desired color in the bleached oil. The amount of permissible color depends on the type and quality of the end product. For instance, oils to be made into high-grade creamy shortenings must be bleached to a very light color; oils intended for cooking purposes can be darker; and oils intended for use in mayonnaise and other salad dressings can be bright yellow. Whenever possible, oils having a minimum color before bleaching are selected for processing into light-colored products.

Determination of the color of vegetable oils is made by matching the color of the oil against a combination of standardized red and yellow glasses. The red glasses form a series of small increments of color increasing in intensity in accordance with a standard color scale. The yellow glasses form another series, but, because the eye is less sensitive to variations in yellow, the differences in the yellow glasses are many times greater than in the red glasses, and the oils need only fall within relatively wide limits.

AFTER REFINING AND BLEACHING, an oil may be further processed by any one of several procedures, depending on its final use. One is its separation into the higher (semisolid) and lower (liquid) melting fractions by crystallization. The object of such a process, called winterization or destearinization, is to produce salad oils that will remain liquid or "bright" in household refrigerators at 40° to 50° F. Oils that remain liquid at refrigerator temperatures are preferred by housewives for storage in the refrigerator. Manufacturers of mayonnaise and other salad dressings use these oils to prevent the emulsion from breaking and the separation of the oil and water ingredients on cooling.

An oil is considered to be adequately winterized if it will remain perfectly clear when kept at 32° F. for 5½ hours. Usually a commercially winterized oil will remain clear for 12 hours or longer. Both time and temperature must be specified, because crystals of fats grow very slowly in cold oils. It is possible for an oil stored at a low temperature to remain perfectly clear for several weeks but to solidify partially after storage for several months.

Cottonseed oil is practically the only vegetable oil now winterized on a large scale. Soybean and corn oils intended for use as salad oils are chilled and filtered to remove traces of wax, but that is not true winterization. Soybean, corn, sesame, and sunflower oils are natural salad oils and do not require winterization. Rice-bran oil is relatively easily winterized, but it is of minor importance because of its limited production. Peanut oil cannot be winterized by the ordinary method used for cottonseed oil because gelatinous and nonfilterable crystals are formed when it is chilled.

Winterization is a batch process, in which 40,000 pounds of oil may be treated at one time. The oil is pumped into long, narrow tanks in a refrigerated room, or into large, well-insulated metal tanks that contain cooling coils. In either case, the tanks are constructed so that no part of the oil is more than a few feet from a cooling surface. The cooling system is arranged so that a small temperature differential (usually 10° to 25° F.) can be maintained constantly between the cooling surface and the oil.

The temperature of the oil is re-duced to approximately 40° F. at a rate of about 0.5° F. an hour, which requires 2 or 3 days. At about 40° F., crystallization commences and releases heat, so that the temperature of the mass of oil rises 2° or 3° F., even though the rate of heat removal is kept constant. After a short time, the temperature of the oil starts to go down again; when it reaches a point slightly below that at which crystallization began, the oil is filtered in filter presses precooled to a temperature slightly below that of the oil. The yield of winterized cottonseed oil usually ranges between 65 and 75 percent.

The present winterization process is the least satisfactory of the processing operations. It is slow. Care must be taken during the chilling to produce the right type and quantity of crystals. Filtration is difficult. Improper handling of the chilled oil causes the soft crystals to break and makes the separation of the oil and crystalline material almost impossible.

Hardening, or hydrogenation, the process which converts naturally liquid oils into more valuable plastic fats, is widely employed. The techniques have advanced to the point where hydrogenated vegetable oils have characteristics superior to those of hog and beef fats, which they originally were meant to imitate. In fact, hydrogenation now permits processors to turn out a variety of plastic fats with desirable physical characteristics that are specified before the operation starts—tailor-made, so to speak. The characteristics might be controlled plasticity over definite temperature ranges, or complete and rapid melting at a specified temperature, or superior emulsifying properties.

Besides hardening, two incidental benefits are obtained: The color of the final product is lightened, and greater resistance to rancidification and other deteriorative processes during storage and use is imparted.

Chemically, hydrogenation is the addition of gaseous hydrogen to part of the carbon-to-carbon double bonds which form part of the molecule of liquid fats. The addition of hydrogen at the double bonds occurs rapidly only in the presence of a catalyst, a foreign substance which itself remains unchanged during the reaction and is removed from the fat after the hardening has been completed. Nickel and several other metals, with specially prepared surfaces, are effective catalysts. Generally, hydrogenation is accomplished by intimately mixing the finely divided metallic catalyst, hydrogen, and oil and heating the mixture at atmospheric or higher pressure.

The catalyst used in commercial hydrogenation to form plastic fats consists of finely divided nickel. The preparation of the nickel varies somewhat, and special substances may be added to increase its catalytic activity. The simplest form of nickel catalyst is made by suspending nickel formate in an oil, generally a vegetable oil of the type to be hydrogenated, and heating the mixture to about 300° F. At that temperature, the organic part of the nickel salt decomposes, with the formation of very finely divided metallic nickel. In another method of preparation, an aluminum-nickel alloy is decomposed with caustic soda solution, which dissolves the aluminum in the alloy and leaves the nickel in finely divided form. After all of the alkali and salt have been washed out, the nickel is suspended in oil and dried. It is then ready for use. In other methods, various compounds of nickel (such as nickel hydroxide or nickel carbonate) are precipitated on diatomaceous earth, the mixture is dried and ground, and the nickel compound is reduced at a high temperature with gaseous hydrogen, after which the finely divided nickel is added to the oil.

Commercial vegetable-oil hardening plants use tremendous quantities of pure hydrogen. Many manufacture their own hydrogen. Where electricity is cheap, hydrogen can be produced by electrolyzing a dilute solution of caustic soda. Oxygen is a byproduct of the process, and it is usually collected, compressed, and sold in steel cylinders.

The steam-iron process of manufacturing hydrogen is the one most widely used. In it, water gas is passed through a bed of hot iron ore. The water gas reduces the ore to metallic iron. Steam is passed through the reduced iron, reoxidizing the iron to iron oxide and liberating hydrogen through simultaneous reduction of the water (steam). The oxidation-reduction cycle is repeated over and over.

Other processes for producing hydrogen include the water-gas catalytic process and the hydrocarbon-reforming process. In the latter process, natural gas, or hydrocarbons from other sources, are cracked catalytically in the presence of steam to produce carbon dioxide and hydrogen. The carbon dioxide is separated from the hydrogen by chemical means. In the water-gas catalytic process, steam is passed over hot coke to produce a mixture of hydrogen and carbon monoxide. The carbon monoxide in the mixed gas is converted to carbon dioxide and hydrogen by another catalyzed reaction with steam.

All commercial hydrogenation of vegetable oils in the United States is carried out by the batch process in tall, gastight, cylindrical vessels known as converters. The converters, which have a capacity up to 30,000 pounds of oil, are equipped with heating and cooling coils, mechanical agitators or other mixing devices, and a device for distributing the incoming hydrogen through the oil.

The previously refined and bleached oil is mixed with a small amount of catalyst (0.05 to 0.50 percent nickel) and pumped into the converter. Then the free space above the oil is evacuated, agitation is started, and steam is introduced into the heating coils. When the desired temperature is reached (generally 200° to 400° F.), heating is stopped, and hydrogen is introduced and allowed to build up a pressure of 10 to 75 pounds per square inch above that of the atmosphere.

Hydrogenation is an exothermic reaction—that is, heat is generated in the catalyst-oil mixture as soon as the reaction commences. If the hydrogenation temperature is to be kept constant, the oil is cooled as the reaction proceeds. In some instances, the temperature of the oil is allowed to increase; if it reaches an unsafe level, hydrogenation is interrupted temporarily. When the desired degree of hardening has been attained, the flow of hydrogen is stopped, the charge is cooled, and the catalyst is removed from the oil by filtration.

The point at which hydrogenation is discontinued depends on the type of product desired. For instance, if an oil is intended for use in margarine, just enough hydrogen is added and conditions are employed to make a fat which is semisolid at room temperature but liquid at body temperature. For the production of shortenings, the oil may be hardened to lardlike consistency, or it may be hardened completely to a material which melts at 140° F. and is glasslike at room temperature. The completely hardened material is blended with unhardened oils to produce so-called compound types of shortenings.

The melting point of a liquid fat is very sensitive to the addition of hydrogen. The melting point of a simple fat that contains only triolein can be changed from 41° to 161° F. by the addition of only 0.68 percent of hydrogen, which is the amount required for complete saturation of all the carbon-to-carbon double bonds. A variety of intermediate melting points can be obtained by smaller additions of hydrogen.

In the production of a semisolid, or plastic, fat, the amount of hydrogen added is the first consideration, but also of importance are the conditions under which the hydrogenation is conducted. The temperature, hydrogen pressure, type of catalyst, concentration of catalyst, and degree of agitation of the charge all influence the manner in which hydrogen combines with the oil.

Deodorization is the last processing step in the production of edible vegetable oils before packaging them for

shipment to the consumer. Its primary purpose is to remove all undesirable odors and flavors. Several incidental benefits are had by deodorization. For example, it destroys any oxidation products present in the oil, thereby increasing the resistance of the oil to rancidification. Also, it removes traces of free fatty acids, which are themselves odorless and tasteless, but, if allowed to remain in the finished product, would lower the temperature at which the oil would begin to smoke when used in frying. Finally, it further reduces the color of the oil through decomposition of some of the pigments that remain after refining and bleaching.

Odors in processed, but undeodorized, fats and oils include those from the original crude oil, those resulting from breakdown of the oil itself, and those that develop during refining and bleaching. Refining and bleaching induce traces of strong, characteristic odors, particularly odors characteristic of the bleaching earth used. The quantity of odoriferous components to be removed from a properly processed oil is usually less than 0.1 percent. The chemical nature of the compounds is not completely known, but they include derivatives of the fatty acids, as well as aldehydes and hydrocarbons.

In deodorization, the oils are held under a vacuum and heated to temperatures that will drive out the odorous compounds without injuring the oil itself. Meanwhile, steam is blown through the oils to carry off the volatile compounds.

Deodorization is actually an application of low-pressure steam distillation, often employed to separate compounds of very low volatility from others having still lower or no volatility.

The physical laws governing this form of distillation make it possible to predict, among other things, that the time required to deodorize a batch of oil at a fixed temperature and steaming rate is directly proportional to the amount of oil being deodorized, directly proportional to the absolute pressure at which the operation is conducted, inversely proportional to the volatility of the pure odoriferous substances, and directly proportional to the logarithm of the ratio of initial to final concentration of the volatile substances in the oil.

Deodorization is usually carried out in a closed, insulated, vertical steel tank that holds 10,000 to 30,000 pounds of oil. The lower section of the tank is provided with a network of coils for introducing steam. The upper part is equipped with baffles to trap and return any oil droplets entrained by the vapor leaving the tank.

Equipment for producing the vacuum required for deodorization generally consists of multiple-stage steam ejectors connected to a barometric condenser. Such an apparatus is satisfactory for removing the condensable vapors and simultaneously keeping the pressure in the deodorizer below 0.12 pound per square inch absolute, which is a common and acceptable pressure in commercial deodorization.

Special equipment must be provided for heating and maintaining the required temperature of the oil. Steam is ordinarily not available at pressures high enough to provide the necessary temperatures (400° to 500° F.). In an early method the oil was continuously circulated between the deodorizer and a system of tubes heated by direct heat. In an improvement on the method, mineral oil is heated and circulated through coils in the deodorizer.

The most modern method, however, utilizes the hot vapors of a high-boiling mixture of two organic compounds. The vapors of this product, which is called Dowtherm, supply the necessary heat by condensing in the coils of the deodorizer.

Batch deodorizers have several undesirable features. The oil in the vessels is several feet deep, thus causing a pressure gradient through the oil so that not all of it is deodorized at the low pressure existing above the oil. Also, the oil must be kept at a high temperature for an undesirable length of time (1 to 6 hours) to complete the deodorization.

Continuous deodorizers, which avoid the defects inherent in batch deodorizers, have been developed. A countercurrent flow of oil and steam is achieved in them. The continuous units, which operate at the same temperatures and pressures as batch deodorizers, make use of a system of shallow trays. The oil is deodorized as it flows downward from one tray to the next while the steam travels upward through the thin layers of oil. The deodorized oil is collected at the bottom of the deodorizer and is continuously removed through a suitable trap. Meanwhile, an equal amount of undeodorized oil enters the top of the deodorizer.

R. O. FEUGE *is a member of the technical staff of the Southern Regional Research Laboratory.*

TEMPÉ, a staple food of the New Guinea Indonesians, is made by fermenting soybeans wrapped in banana leaves. A special kind of mold, a strain of *Rhizopus oryzae,* is used. During the Japanese occupation of New Guinea, the mold was lost. Without it, the natives would not eat the soybeans imported to feed them. The mold was returned to New Guinea by air mail from Surinam, after it was learned that Javanese laborers there were cultivating it.—*Lewis B. Lockwood, Northern Regional Research Laboratory.*

Tailor-Made Fats for Industry

R. O. Feuge

In the manufacture of erasers, an elastic, rubberlike material with just the right degree of crumbliness is needed. Technicians have found that the light-colored plastic formed when castor or rapeseed oil is treated with sulfur compounds meets the requirements perfectly.

Makers of high-grade linoleum also need a plastic ingredient, but their exacting requirements can be met only by the solid obtained when linseed oil or another suitable drying oil is allowed to react slowly with air while warm.

The textile industry uses a number of specially prepared oils. One such oil, used in finishing fabrics, must possess the usual properties of an oil, so that it makes the treated fabric attractive and soft—but at the same time it must be soluble in water, so that it can be applied, as well as removed, with water.

Thus, many fatty materials intended for industry are modified to give them special properties or the characteristics that better adapt them to the process or final product.

The new characteristics given them by chemists may be entirely different from their original, natural characteristics. Sometimes they are changed to resemble another natural product—for example, cottonseed oil is made into various plastic products, which could pass for tallow or other hard fats. Many special fats are prepared for industrial uses—uses so diversified and numerous that nobody has been able to list them all. Often the fats lose their identity during processing and conversion to finished products. In oil-modified plastics or finishes, for example, the fat disappears as such and is unrecognizable in the final product.

Let us consider here the types of tailor-made fats and oils that are manufactured in quantity—not necessarily just the compounds chemically identical with some of the constituents of a natural fat, but those that are derived from natural fats or oils and fall within the broad definition of an oil. We include fatty acids, fatty alcohols, and their monoesters, but not alkali and heavy-metal soaps.

The special fats most important from the standpoint of volume are the ones produced by catalytic hydrogenation of the carbon-to-carbon double bonds in the molecules of the fatty acid portion of the oil. This consists simply of the addition of hydrogen at the double bonds, or, as the chemist says, at the points of unsaturation. The reaction is called catalytic because it is enormously accelerated in the presence of certain metallic surfaces (usually nickel), which remain unchanged at the end of the reaction.

$$H-\underset{\substack{|\\H}}{C}=\underset{\substack{|\\H}}{C}-H \xrightarrow[\text{catalyst}]{\text{hydrogen}} H-\underset{\substack{|\\H}}{\overset{\substack{H\\|}}{C}}-\underset{\substack{|\\H}}{\overset{\substack{H\\|}}{C}}-H$$

Ethylene   Ethane

Here we have illustrated the hydrogenation reaction of a very simple molecule, that of ethylene, a well-known hydrocarbon. The ethylene molecule consists of two carbon atoms joined by a double bond and otherwise surrounded by hydrogen atoms, each of which is connected to a carbon atom by a single bond. The double bond enables the molecule to take up two more hydrogen atoms, so that the two carbon atoms will also be joined only by a single bond.

A natural fat molecule is made up of three long hydrocarbon chains attached to a molecule of glycerol to form a triglyceride. Any one or all of the long chains may contain one or more carbon-to-carbon double bonds, or so-called ethylenic linkages.

When one or more of these carbon-to-carbon double bonds is present in each of the three or even in two of the three long chains in the fat molecule, the product will be a liquid at room temperature; that is, it will have a low melting point. As the number of the carbon-to-carbon double bonds is reduced by the addition of hydrogen, the melting point will increase, and eventually, when enough of the double bonds disappear, the liquid oil will become a solid fat at room temperature.

The formula for a fat molecule—triglyceride—is shown in the accompanying diagram.

This particular fat molecule contains three different fatty acid residues, each with a different number of carbon-to-carbon double bonds. The formula shows how the various atoms are combined to form a molecule of a simple fat, or triglyceride, which in this case is called oleo-linoleo-linolenin, because it contains one residue each of oleic, linoleic, and linolenic acid. It is one of many triglycerides found in natural fats or oils, which are merely mixtures of such glycerides whose molecules contain different numbers and kinds of fatty acid residues. The C, H, and O represent carbon, hydrogen, and oxygen atoms. Arrows that point to the carbon-to-carbon double bonds have been added to facilitate subsequent discussion.

With the diagram before us, we can discuss the changes which a fat undergoes during hydrogenation. This triglyceride contains six carbon-to-carbon double bonds, any one or all of which may add hydrogen, with a resulting decrease in the number of such bonds

and a consequent change in properties. The change in properties is affected not only by the number of double bonds that are saturated with hydrogen, but also by the particular carbon-to-carbon bonds at which the addition occurs.

For example, if hydrogen is added at the carbon-to-carbon double bonds labeled 5 and 6, this portion of the molecule will look exactly like the oleic acid residue (at the top of the formula). If it is added at the position labeled 3, then the middle portion of the molecule will look like the oleic acid residue.

Complete hydrogenation of all the double bonds would convert all of the fatty acid residues to stearic acid residues and the resulting fat would be solid at room temperature. If the hydrogen is added at the double bond labeled 2, or only at the bond labeled 5, the resulting product would differ chemically and physically from any natural fat.

During hydrogenation, the hydrogen tends to add to the fat in a more or less specific manner. The carbon-to-carbon double bond farthest from the glycerin residue in the more reactive and is hydrogenated first. Also linolenic acid is much more reactive than linoleic acid, which in turn is more reactive than oleic acid. The relative reactivities, however, do not strictly control the actual addition of hydrogen. Some completely hydrogenated acid residues are formed simultaneously with the conversion of linolenic and linoleic acid residues to less highly unsaturated forms.

Investigations by A. E. Bailey and his coworkers in the Department of Agriculture showed that under selective conditions (conditions that favor the conversion of highly unsaturated acids to oleic acids but not oleic acids to stearic acid) the relative reactivities of the unsaturated acids toward hydrogen may be approximately represented by the following whole numbers: Oleic acid, 1; iso-oleic acid, 1; isolinoleic acid, 3; linoleic acid, 20; linolenic acid, 40. In nonselective

REPRESENTATION OF A SIMPLE FAT MOLECULE LIQUID AT ROOM TEMPERATURE hydrogenation, the ratio of reactivity of linoleic acid to that of oleic acid may be as low as 5, as compared with 20 or above under selective conditions.

The investigators also observed that, under commercially used conditions, the formation of completely saturated stearic acid is repressed, and the formation of iso-oleic acid is simultaneously favored, by increasing the temperature, increasing the concentration of the catalyst, decreasing the pressure of hydrogen, and decreasing the agitation. The nature of the nickel catalyst, as influenced by its method of preparation, was also found to have a marked effect on the composition of the hydrogenated product.

Margarine oil or fat produced from liquid vegetable oils is one illustration of an industrially important oil whose special characteristics are the result of carefully controlled hydrogenation.

The hydrogenated oils used in the manufacture of high-grade oleomargarine must possess physical characteristics almost identical with those of butterfat. An acceptable margarine oil must be a soft plastic at room temperature. The ratio of solid or crystalline fat to liquid oil in the mixture must be such that when the fat crystals are of the proper size and well dispersed, the mass will offer some resistance to deformation and separation of solid and liquid fats will be negligible. On the other hand, all the fat crystals must melt completely at body temperature; otherwise they will leave a pasty sensation in the mouth. For maximum palatability, however, the fat crystals must not melt too abruptly. Furthermore, to impart the necessary characteristics to margarine oil, the conditions of hydrogenation must be highly selective in order to suppress complete saturation of triglyceride molecules in favor of the formation of high-melting iso acids.

Commercial bakers employ special fats which are not ordinarily used by the housewife. Some closely resemble general-purpose shortenings. Others are quite different. These tailor-made fats usually must have specific physical properties. Biscuit and cracker fats, for instance, must resist rancidity and other forms of deterioration.

Likewise, fats used in the manufacture of puff- or Danish-type pastry and for coating candy must have special traits. Those for puff-type pastry must be processed so that at ordinary temperatures they become tough, waxy solids with good extensibility, essential for the flaky or laminated structure of the pastries.

Fats for coating candies must be relatively hard and nongreasy at ordinary temperatures. At the same time they must melt in the mouth—they must have a very short plastic range. Furthermore, the fats must not exhibit any change in crystalline structure, which would alter the appearance of the coatings or interfere with normal manufacturing processes.

The triglyceride structure of oils intended for use in soaps is not important, because the triglycerides are broken down by saponification and the component fatty acids are converted into alkali salts or soaps. Therefore, the properties of the component fatty acids, rather than the structure of the original oils, are important.

Domestic fats yield fatty acids that contain primarily 16 and 18 carbon atoms per molecule and make good soaps, provided the fats are hydrogenated to convert the linoleic, linolenic, and other highly unsaturated acids to less saturated acids. Highly unsaturated acids produce soft soaps of relatively poor stability and detergency. Conversion to normal oleic acid is preferred because sodium oleate has high detergent power and dissolves more easily than does the sodium salt of stearic acid, which is formed by complete hydrogenation.

If fats are subjected to the action of hydrogen in the presence of special catalysts (usually metallic chromites) and if high temperatures (400° to 750° F.) and very high pressures (1,500 to 3,000 pounds to the square inch) are employed, a type of hydrogenation occurs which is entirely different from the one I have just discussed. Instead of adding hydrogen at the carbon-to-carbon double bonds, this type of hydrogenation results in the addition of hydrogen to the oxygen in the molecule. It may be represented as follows:

$$\underset{\underset{H}{|}}{\overset{\overset{H}{|}}{H-C}}-O-\underset{}{\overset{\overset{O}{||}}{C}}-\overset{\overset{H}{|}}{C}- + 4H \longrightarrow \overset{\overset{H}{|}}{H-C}-OH + HO-\underset{\underset{H}{|}}{\overset{\overset{H}{|}}{C}}-\underset{\underset{H}{|}}{\overset{\overset{H}{|}}{C}}-$$

This formula represents the reaction of four atoms of hydrogen with one of the three ester groups in the triglyceride molecule shown previously. As before, the letters C, H, and O represent atoms of carbon, hydrogen, and oxygen, respectively. Actually, hydrogen reacts with all three of the ester groups in a triglyceride molecule. Complete reduction of a triglyceride molecule yields three molecules of fatty, or high-molecular-weight, alcohols. The free glycerol, which is formed simultaneously, is unstable under the conditions of the reaction and is converted to another product called propylene glycol.

The yield of these fatty alcohols that are obtained by hydrogenation may exceed 98 percent. Either the fats themselves or the free fatty acids or the monoesters that can be produced from them can be hydrogenated. Some hydrogen always reacts with the carbon-to-carbon double bonds in the unsaturated acid molecules while addition of hydrogen to the oxygen occurs.

Another method of preparing fatty alcohols is important commercially. A fat is hydrogenated with the aid of metallic sodium in the presence of a reducing alcohol. The reaction is complicated, and its details are not entirely known. The sodium-reduction method compares favorably with catalytic hydrogenation of saturated or hard fats because of the simplicity of the operation and the equipment employed. The process is carried out at atmospheric pressure and at temperatures usually below 212° F. In the production of fatty alcohols from un-

saturated oils, the sodium-reduction process is preferable, because it does not affect the carbon-to-carbon double bonds of the unsaturated fatty acid portions of the molecule.

Like the fatty acids, the alcohols derived from domestic fats contain principally 16 and 18 carbon atoms arranged in a chainlike fashion. Alcohols from some imported fats, such as coconut oil, may have carbon chains with as few as six carbon atoms. In all cases the alcohols possess lower melting and boiling points than the corresponding acids. The shorter-chain alcohols have sharp, pungent odors. Those of intermediate chain length have pleasant, rather fruity odors. The long-chain alcohols are odorless. All of them are oily when liquid and waxy when solid.

Fatty alcohols are used in the preparation of many products. The most important are synthetic waxes and detergents, emulsifiers, wetting-out agents, and other surface-active materials. The surface-active materials made from fatty alcohols are unaffected by hard water; at the same time they are structurally similar to soap. Besides their various industrial uses, they are used in shampoos, dentifrices, and quick-dissolving soaps. The exact type of alcohol required for a given application varies widely, and it is, therefore, customary to select the fat to be transformed into an alcohol on the basis of the intended use of the alcohol.

Natural oils containing unsaturated fatty acid residues in their molecules can be transformed into surface-active materials without being converted into soaps. That is done by treating certain oils with sulfuric acid, which will add to the carbon-to-carbon double bonds somewhat like hydrogen. The reaction may be depicted as follows:

$$-\overset{\overset{H}{|}}{C}=\overset{\overset{H}{|}}{C}- + \overset{O}{\underset{O}{\overset{OH}{\underset{OH}{S}}}} \longrightarrow -\underset{\underset{O-S-OH}{|}}{\overset{\overset{H}{|}}{C}}-\underset{\underset{H}{|}}{\overset{\overset{H}{|}}{C}}-$$

The reaction is generally referred to as sulfonation, but it is really a sulfation, although there may be a slight sulfonation at the same time. Both sulfated and sulfonated oil molecules are surface-active. The molecule of sulfuric acid, which is composed of one atom of sulfur, four of oxygen, and two of hydrogen, is water-soluble and imparts the surface-active properties to the oil.

In the manufacture of sulfated oils, it is necessary to cool the oil to a temperature that will just permit it to be stirred. Then 17 to 33 percent of strong sulfuric acid (approximately 93 percent) is slowly added. If the oil undergoing treatment is highly unsaturated (that is, its molecules contain many carbon-to-carbon double bonds) as, for example, most fish oils, the addition of acid may have to be interrupted to cool the mixture to 10° or 20° F. The oil-acid mixture is stirred and allowed to stand for several hours. A solution of sodium sulfate is then added, and the mixture is allowed to separate into two layers, after which most of the acid is withdrawn. The oily product that remains is treated with caustic soda, which neutralizes the free sulfuric acid and also substitutes a sodium atom for the hydrogen atom in the sulfuric acid molecule added to the carbon-to-carbon double bond.

The sulfated oil may be partly or completely miscible with water, depending on the degree of sulfation. The characteristics of the sulfated product vary greatly, according to the conditions under which the reaction is conducted. Besides the sulfated triglycerides, the finished product contains other products in varying amounts.

The surface activity of the best sulfated oils is not so great as that of some other surface-active materials, but they are useful for many purposes. For example, the textile industry uses large quantities of them in dyeing and as a lubricant in spinning and weaving cloth. In finishing leather, sulfated oils are used to force untreated oils into the hides after tanning. Sulfated tallow serves as a defoaming agent in the paper industry. Some cutting oils used in the metal-working industries are a mixture of sulfated oils, mineral oil, and water. Sulfated oils are also used in the petroleum industry for several purposes.

POLYMERIZATION, like sulfation and hydrogenation, is an addition reaction. It differs from sulfation in combining two similar molecules into one larger molecule, which in turn can combine with still other molecules to form a still larger molecule and so on until a very large molecule is obtained.

The reaction occurs by cross linking of carbon-to-carbon double bonds in the triglyceride molecules. Depending on the degree of polymerization, the final product can range from a substance of the consistency of castor oil to a solid. Oils of various degrees of polymerization are industrially useful. However, to be valuable, there is a further requirement: A number of the original carbon-to-carbon double bonds of the oil must remain in the molecules of the polymerized product.

Cross linking, which is essential to the formation of polymerized oils, can be brought about in several ways. Heat bodying is one of the oldest methods for accomplishing this end. Oils may be heat-bodied by placing them in kettles of 100- to 1,000-gallon capacity, blanketing with an inert gas or placing under vacuum, and heating while stirring. Under those conditions, one of the bonds of the carbon-to-carbon double bonds in a fatty acid residue detaches itself from the carbon atom in its own acid and attaches itself to a carbon atom of another molecule of fat or oil. This may occur with any one or any number of carbon-to-carbon double bonds. The exact manner by which this occurs is not known.

Both time and temperature influence the extent of heat bodying or heat polymerization. Temperatures commonly range between 450° and 625° F.—the greater the number of carbon-to-carbon double bonds originally present in the oil, the lower will be the required temperature. It has been established, for example, that the polymerization rates of linseed and dehydrated castor oils bodied in the neighborhood of 550° F. are approximately doubled for each 25° increase in temperature. The rate of heat polymerization is followed by viscosity measurements of samples withdrawn from time to time, and the heating is discontinued before the oil becomes semisolid or gels.

Cross linking may take place directly with a carbon atom of another molecule or through some other intermediate atom. The most common interconnecting substance is oxygen, which is usually introduced by heating the oil to about 250° F. and blowing air through it for several hours. In this case, the carbon atom in one molecule is joined to a carbon atom of another molecule with the oxygen between the two. These oxidized products, which are known as blown oils, usually acquire properties like those of heat-bodied oils. The two types of products are interchangeable for many purposes. Blown oils, however, are preferred for certain uses. Several commercially important fat products are prepared by adding oxygen to them under conditions other than those just mentioned. Sometimes the oil is partially burned; sometimes it is oxidized very slowly at low temperatures.

Sulfur and some of its compounds can act as interconnecting substances and are used in industrial processes for condensing unsaturated oils. Sulfur functions in much the same manner that oxygen does but is more reactive.

The principal use for polymerized oils is in paints and varnishes. For use in protective coatings, heat-bodied oils are superior to raw oils because they dry faster to tack-free films and form harder, more durable, and more attractive surfaces.

Blown oils made for use in protective coatings will produce films less resistant to wear and deterioration than those of comparable heat-bodied oils. Blown oils are surface-active and are often incorporated in paints to increase wetting of the pigments. They are used also in compounding various printing inks, which are chemically similar to varnishes.

Oils polymerized with the aid of sulfur and its compounds form a rubber-like material known as factice. Light-colored factices, produced by the action of sulfur monochloride on castor, rapeseed, and similar oils, are used in the manufacture of erasers and as a modifier for rubber. Brown factice, which is produced by the action of sulfur on oxidized oil, is used as a modifier in varnishes and linoleums, as well as in rubber.

Large quantities of specially oxidized and polymerized oils are used in making linoleum. The oils must be highly oxidized at a low temperature (below 120° F.) so that the products are crumbly solids. Oxidized oils are not converted directly into linoleum but are further reacted with resins, and the resulting thermoplastic mixture is cured before being used.

PARTIALLY POLYMERIZING the oil to be incorporated in paints and varnishes is the most important, but not the only, way in which the drying properties of the products can be improved. The structure of the individual molecules of the original oil can be changed so that polymerization will proceed rapidly. Advantages of a fast rate of polymerization are rapid initial set of paint films and rapid drying of the films to a tack-free state.

The process, as well as the chemical change involved, is known as isomerization. It consists in shifting the carbon-to-carbon double bonds along the carbon chains of oil molecules until they are attached to adjacent carbon atoms or, as the chemist says, until they are in a conjugated position. This shift of bonds can be represented as follows:

$$-\overset{H}{\underset{H}{C}}=\overset{H}{C}-\overset{H}{C}=\overset{H}{C}- \longrightarrow -\overset{H}{\underset{H}{C}}-\overset{H}{C}=\overset{H}{C}-\overset{H}{C}=\overset{H}{C}-$$

In commercial practice, oils are isomerized by first converting them into soaps and then heating the soaps with an excess of caustic soda. After isomerization the soaps are converted back into oil.

Since 1940, the chemist has sought catalysts that would directly isomerize an oil. Up to now, the most effective catalysts for the purpose include specially prepared metallic nickel, sulfur dioxide, and certain iodine compounds. The use of these compounds is still in the experimental stage, but we expect that it will be expanded to the commercial scale.

Because of the unique structure of the castor-oil molecule, conjugated double bonds can be introduced by a process not applicable to other oils. When castor oil is placed under vacuum and heated in the presence of a catalyst, it gives up a molecule of water. Removal of the water creates new double bonds in the molecule of castor oil. Part of these new double bonds are conjugated. The treated oil, known as dehydrated castor oil, is used in large quantities in making decorative and protective coatings.

The tailor-made fats considered so far are all produced by changes within the fatty acid portions of the oil molecules.

Because the properties of a fat or an oil are determined by the individual properties and proportions of the three fatty acid groups combined in the molecule, oils having different properties can be made by regrouping the fatty acids in the oil molecules, by removing some of them from the molecules, or by substituting other acid groups for some of those originally present.

Special properties can be imparted to them by replacing the glycerol portion of the oil molecule with other alcohols. Changes of this type are known as interesterifications.

Many variations of interesterification reactions are possible, and as the demand increases for special fat products, more and more of the reactions will be employed on a commercial scale. Several are now of commercial importance; others may soon be.

In 1927, C. van Loon, a Dutch chemist, was granted the first patent for regrouping or rearranging the three fatty acid groups found in each oil molecule. His process, which was apparently designed to produce improved margarine fats, consisted of heating the oil in contact with special catalysts. In this type of reaction, heating causes the fatty acid groups to rearrange themselves in a helter-skelter fashion among the oil molecules. High-melting portions of the fat or fat mixture disappear. Lower-melting forms replace them, and at the same time the lower-melting portions of the original fat are eliminated and are replaced with higher-melting materials. The net effect will be either a higher or lower melting point, depending on the proportion and original arrangement of the various fatty acids combined in the fat.

In 1948, a novel rearrangement process was described and patented by E. W. Eckey in this country. The process is the only one now known which can control to some degree the rearrangement of the fatty acid components of an oil. In previous processes the rearrangement was always random. Control of the rearrangement is made possible with a catalyst effective at low temperatures, so that the reaction can be carried out below 100° F. Under those conditions, the high-melting fatty acid groups, whenever they combine to form high-melting oil molecules, solidify and separate out of the solution in which the reaction takes place. It is said that controlled rearrangement makes possible the conversion of tallow into a material more satisfactory for shortening and that treatment of oils like coconut oil makes possible the production of confectioners' butters without hydrogenation.

The glycerol portion of a fat may be replaced with another alcohol, such as methanol (wood alcohol) or ethanol (grain alcohol), by interesterification.

Both alcohols can combine with only one fatty acid group; the resulting compounds therefore are called monoesters. The alcohol interchange is carried out very easily at atmospheric pressure in soap kettles at a temperature of 80° to 175° F. Absolute grain alcohol containing about 0.5 percent of caustic soda on a fat basis is added to the dry fat. The alcohol used is about one and a half times the theoretical amount required to complete the reaction. A rapid reaction begins as soon as the alcohol and fat are mixed, and after about an hour it is complete. The free gylcerol which is formed settles out.

The monoesters of fats are used in the manufacture of such products as plasticizers. Probably the greatest use is in the manufacture of soaps that can be manufactured from monoesters in a relatively short time and at comparatively low temperatures (below 200° F.). Also, if necessary, soaps which contain no water can easily be made.

The addition of glycerol to a fat is another commercially important variation of the interesterification reaction. Glycerol is the alcohol which forms a part of the molecules of natural fats. The object of combining a fat with additional glycerol is to remove one or two of the combined fatty acid groups from the natural fat molecules and combine them with the added glycerol to make synthetic fatty molecules. The reaction is brought about by mixing the fat and glycerol with about 0.1 percent of caustic soda (on a fat basis) and heating the mixture to 350° to 480° F. while agitating it under an inert atmosphere. The fatty acids simply distribute themselves among all the glycerol molecules available to them and in a manner that can be calculated by statistical methods. It is almost impossible for the end product of this reaction to contain more than about 60 percent of so-called monoglycerides, which are usually the end products desired. A monoglyceride is composed of one molecule of glycerol and one molecule of fatty acid. The products of the reaction are known as technical monoglycerides, although the content of monoglyceride may amount to less than half of the total material.

Technical monoglycerides can emulsify oil-water mixtures. They are edible and readily digestible—hence they are ideal additives to shortenings. Shortenings containing monoglycerides are usually referred to as high-ratio or superglycerinated. In addition, technical monoglycerides find extensive use in the manufacture of margarine, in which they also serve as emulsifying agents. The cosmetic industry uses them for the same purpose. Also, technical monoglycerides are produced as intermediates in the manufacture of resinlike varnishes.

R. O. FEUGE *conducts research on the processing of fats and oils at the Southern Regional Research Laboratory.*

DRIED SKIM MILK is an important contribution to health and economy. Skim milk contains two nutrients, calcium and riboflavin, which are likely to be low in many diets of the world. Our taste for butter has led to the separation of butterfat from milk and the use of the skim milk for animal feeding. That is unfortunate, because calcium and riboflavin can be obtained for animals from other acceptable sources. Skim milk is easily dried and keeps well. Dried skim milk is relatively cheap and combines well with other foods in cooking.—*Paul E. Howe, Bureau of Animal Industry.*

Animal Fats and Oils in Industry

Daniel Swern, Waldo C. Ault, A. J. Stirton

For a long time we have used inedible animal fats and oils and products made from them in a wide variety of industrial applications, many of which have been modified only a little since they were first developed.

But now the industry is entering an era of expansion and development, comparable to periods passed through by both the petroleum and coal-tar industries, in which emphasis is being placed on isolating and preparing chemically homogeneous substances.

This approach opens a tremendous field for fundamental and applied research and for the manufacture of many new products. Such a trend promises increased income to the farmer, industrialist, and wage earner, as well as many products to add to the public comfort and health.

As industrial raw materials, it is the inedible grades of animal fats and oils that are used almost exclusively. Inedible tallow and grease comprise about 90 percent of these materials, with pork fat and neatsfoot oil making up the rest. Factory consumption of inedible animal fats and oils in 1947 to 1950 was about 2 billion pounds a year.

Inedible tallow comes mostly from cattle and sheep as trimmings from meat-packing plants or as scrap fats obtained from meat trimmings in butcher shops or saved in the kitchen and sold to commercial renderers for processing. A large amount of inedible pork fat is marketed as grease, an average of about 5 pounds of grease being produced for each hog slaughtered. Other sources of grease are city garbage, waste fat from restaurants and hotels, and bones. When production of lard exceeds the demand, a part of this edible fat is diverted to grease.

Although grease is ordinarily considered to be hog fat, and tallow the fat of cattle and sheep, the commercial distinction between greases and tallows is made entirely on the basis of the titer (the temperature at which solidification occurs) of the fatty acids obtained from the fat. If the titer is below 40° C., the fat is a grease; above 40° C., the fat is a tallow.

Inedible tallows and greases are graded on the basis of color, content of free fatty acids, and general quality—flavor and odor. The important grades of tallow, in order of quality, are: Prime (Packers') Tallow, produced from the choicest inedible stock; Number One Tallow, the most widely used industrial grade; and Number Two Tallow. The important grades of grease are A White Grease, B White Grease, Yellow Grease, and Brown Grease.

For most uses, the materials have to be modified chemically. The only important exception is neatsfoot oil, which is prepared from the feet and shinbones of cattle and is used in lubricants and dressings for leather. Only 3 million to 4 million pounds of neatsfoot oil is produced annually, a relatively small percentage of the total quantity of inedible animal fats consumed by industry.

The most important outlet for inedible animal fats is in making soap, a chemical process that has been conducted for hundreds of years and for a long time was almost the only outlet for inedible animal fats. Soap accounts for about 80 percent of the inedible animal fats, or about 1.5 billion pounds (1943 to 1950), consumed in the United States annually. Saponification of fats with alkali yields glycerol as well as soap.

Some of the many uses of glycerol are in the preparation of explosives and synthetic resins, as a moistening agent, and in the food, cosmetic, and pharmaceutical industries.

Everybody uses soap because of its detergent properties. Soap is an excellent detergent in soft water and at an alkalinity greater than pH 8, but not in hard water. For use where water is hard, synthetic detergents, which are said to be equal or superior to soap, are now available, the result of intensive industrial research. The production and consumption of synthetic detergents have increased tremendously and will probably continue as new uses for these products, based on certain of their properties, are found.

The production and consumption of soap have remained substantially constant (1943 through 1949), despite the active competition from the newer detergents in a field that until recently was reserved almost exclusively for fat derivatives. The use of inedible fats in the preparation of synthetic detergents is increasing, but chemicals from petroleum and coal tar are still by far the most important source materials in synthetic-detergent manufacture. Production of synthetic detergents was about 300 million pounds in 1947, 500 million in 1948, 800 million in 1949, and about 1 billion in 1950.

Another important industrial outlet for inedible animal fats and oils is in the preparation of lubricants and lubricating greases, which account for somewhat less than 5 percent of the annual consumption, or approximately 100 million pounds.

Most of the remaining inedible animal fats and oils (10 to 15 percent of the total, or 200 million to 300 million pounds) go into the preparation of free fatty acids, of which about 50 percent are used in the preparation of stearic acid and red oil. The remainder are used in the preparation of soap (10 to 20 percent), lubricants and greases (about 10 percent), rubber, and miscellaneous products.

Minor applications for inedible animal fats and oils (5 percent of the total, or about 100 million pounds) are in the manufacture of synthetic detergents, leather, illuminating oils, cutting oils for metal-working operations, printing inks, and paints and varnishes.

Although most inedible animal fats and oils are converted by simple procedures to end products, which are then used up (soap, lubricants, greases), the fatty acids represent an intermediate stage in the consumption of inedible animal fats and oils, and find their way into a surprisingly wide variety of products.

FREE FATTY ACIDS obtained by hydrolysis of inedible tallow and grease consist of 40 to 50 percent saturated acids (mainly palmitic and stearic acids), as much as 10 percent polyunsaturated acids (mainly linoleic acid), and 40 to 45 percent of oleic acid, the monounsaturated acid. For many years this mixture was separated into solid and liquid fractions by pressing, to yield so-called stearic acid, originally employed in the preparation of candles, and red oil (or commercial oleic acid), originally considered to be of little value and occasionally discarded or burned.

Commercial stearic acid consists of about equal parts of stearic and palmitic acids and it is contaminated with unsaturated acids, depending on the number and efficiency of the pressing operations. Thus, the terms single-, double-, and triple-pressed grades of stearic acid were introduced, the last-named containing the smallest proportion of unsaturated acids, occasionally as little as 2 percent, and having the highest melting point and the best color, odor, and stability to oxidation.

Red oil, or commercial oleic acid, is a yellow to dark-brown liquid that contains 60 to 75 percent oleic acid. The remainder is saturated and polyunsaturated acids in about equal quantities. Because of this composition, the conventional analytical values for red oil agree with those calculated for pure oleic acid. Many investigators thus assumed that red oil was chemically homogeneous. As a result, a great deal of research with red oil, rather than purified oleic acid, as the starting material has led to erroneous conclusions. By redistillation, the color of commercial oleic acid can be improved, but, because the composition remains almost the same, its stability of color and odor and resistance to oxidation are only slightly improved. The residue from this and other distillation operations in the preparation of fatty acids is called fatty acid pitch, or stearine pitch. It is used in electrical-insulating and roofing materials and in other materials that require a product with pitchlike properties.

Separation of solid- and liquid-acid fractions by pressing is mainly a hand operation. The process is slow, and labor costs are high. Other disadvantages are limitations in the quantity of fatty acids that can be separated, excessive product losses due to handling, and cost of remelting, chilling, repressing, and recycling. About 1945, however, a commercial solvent-crystallization process, the Emersol process, was developed for the separation of the solid from the liquid acids. The process separates the acids efficiently and it is continuous. Operating costs are said to be only about 35 percent of those for pressing. The composition of the solid and liquid fractions is about the same as that obtained by pressing. Because the process is efficient, the iodine number of the solid-acid fraction can be easily reduced below the value usually obtained by conventional cold- and hot-pressing operations.

Despite this lack of chemical homogeneity, the fatty acid fractions obtained by pressing or crystallizing operations have a good industrial position. Their use is widespread and increasing. The use of fatty acids in organic synthesis, however, can be expected to increase greatly when pure individual fatty acids are available.

The most important use for stearic acid is in compounding rubber. About 15 million pounds were used in 1949, out of a total of about 50 million pounds of stearic acid consumed. Stearic acid is also used in cosmetics, ointments, and shaving creams and in other pharmaceutical and toilet preparations. As shown by the number of pounds used in 1949 (in parentheses), it was used largely in the form of soaps (6 million), lubricants and greases (4 million), chemicals (7 million), candles (3 million), paints, varnishes, and resins (1.5 million), metal-working operations (1 million), textiles (1.5 million), and many miscellaneous applications (11 million).

Approximately 45 million pounds of commercial oleic acid were consumed in 1949. About 16 million pounds of that amount went into liquid, or low-melting, soaps intended primarily for use in textile-scouring operations. Commercial oleic acid is also used as a textile lubricant (10 million pounds), in the manufacture of chemicals (8 million), in lubricants and greases (2.5 million), sulfonated oils (3 million), rubber (1.5 million), protective coatings (1 million), resins (1 million), metal-working operations (1.5 million), and many miscellaneous industrial applications.

The instability of color and odor of commercial oleic acid and the ease with which it forms gummy polymerization and oxidation products are serious drawbacks to many industrial uses. It has been impossible to eliminate the disadvantages by the use of inhibitors or antioxidants. The undesirable characteristics can be attributed to the high percentages of polyunsaturated acids in the commercial product, which oxidize and polymerize faster than oleic acid. Textiles lubricated with red oil and stored for long periods may burst into flame as a result of spontaneous combustion, caused by the evolution of heat during oxidation of the polyunsaturated acids. The gummy deposits formed on textiles lubricated with red oil cannot be removed by scouring and may cause uneven dyeing and unpleasant odors in the finished fabric.

Commercial oleic acid is not a good chemical intermediate, because the impurities, notably polyunsaturated acids, cause reactions to proceed inefficiently and result in low yields. It is difficult—sometimes impossible—to isolate a desired derivative in a pure state. Purified oleic acid is a much better intermediate from the dollar-and-cents standpoint. The polyunsaturated acids, which react much as oleic acid does, require the use of enough chemicals to react with all the unsaturated components present, because preferential reactions are usually not available.

The earliest procedure for separating the saturated and polyunsaturated acids from oleic acid consisted in fractional crystallization of the soaps of the mixed acids from organic solvents. With proper selection of soap and solvent, the oleic acid could be purified at convenient operating temperatures on a small laboratory scale, but such procedures were tedious and unsatisfactory on a larger scale. In general, procedures involving crystallization of soaps have been abandoned.

As the polyunsaturated acids are more soluble and the saturated acids are less soluble in organic solvents than oleic acid, procedures have been developed for the solvent crystallization of mixed fatty acids. The procedures are workable even on a large laboratory scale, but crystallization temperatures in the range of $-50°$ to $-70°$ C. are required. Those temperatures are not readily attainable industrially at present, and many engineering problems are introduced. Furthermore, the solvent action of the polyunsaturated acids on oleic acid causes loss of oleic acid with the polyunsaturated acids, and even interferes with separation of the saturated acids.

THE FIRST commercially feasible procedure for the preparation of purified oleic acid (oleic acid content 90 to 98 percent) was described in a preliminary report by Daniel Swern and John T. Scanlan, of the Eastern Regional Research Laboratory, in 1944. Complete details of this procedure were published in 1946; in 1948 a public service patent (U. S. 2,457,611, assigned to the Secretary of Agriculture) on this process was granted to Dr. Swern and Waldo C. Ault. Nonexclusive licenses to operate under the patent can be obtained without cost from the Secretary of Agriculture.

Inedible tallow or grease is the starting material. Most of the polyunsaturated acids (in the form of glycerides) are first converted to monounsaturated acids (in the form of glycerides) by selective hydrogenation. Hydrolysis of the selectively hydrogenated fat gives a fatty acid mixture, consisting mainly of saturated and monounsaturated acids. By solvent crystallization of the mixed acids at temperatures from $0°$ to $-20°$ C.—temperatures well within the operating range of present-day commercial practice—the solid acids precipitate and are easily separated by filtration. The solid acids, corresponding to the double-pressed grade, are obtained in good yield. Recovery of the solvent from the filtrate yields a residue consisting of 90 percent oleic acid, 1 to 3 percent polyunsaturated acids, and saturated acids. By fractional distillation, the oleic acid content can be raised to 98 percent. Pilot-plant and cost-evaluation studies indicate that the purified oleic acid should cost only slightly more than red oil. The process was placed in large-scale commercial operation in 1949.

Another development in the preparation of a purified grade of oleic acid is the process of Emery Industries, Inc. It consists in preferential polymerization of the polyunsaturated acids in red oil to a nonvolatile dimer, from which the more volatile oleic acid is separated by distillation. A basic difference between the preferential polymerization process and the selective-hydrogenation process is that in the former the starting material is red oil, which is a partially fractionated or purified product already, whereas in the latter the inedible fat is the starting material, and only one fractionation procedure to obtain purified oleic acid is employed.

Purified oleic acid can be used directly wherever stability in color and odor and high resistance to oxidation and polymerization are required, and as a chemical intermediate. The disadvantages caused by polyunsaturated acids are largely eliminated. In some applications, however, low melting point and resistance to solidification of the products (soaps, greases) are more important than chemical homogeneity, and for such uses, red oil, which usually has a lower melting point than purified oleic acid, will probably always be in demand. Some degree of chemical homogeneity is attained, however, even with the present commercial grades of fatty acids, as they are monobasic, long-chain aliphatic acids.

Because oleic acid contains two reactive functional groups, the carboxyl group and the carbon-to-carbon double bond, it undergoes numerous chemical reactions that yield potentially useful products. Reaction of the carboxyl group with appropriate reagents gives a wide variety of esters, amides, and salts (soaps). Alkyl esters of oleic acid can be used as plasticizers and textile lubricants, and alkenyl esters, such as the vinyl and chloroallyl, can be polymerized. The alkenyl esters can also be copolymerized with some commercially useful monomers, yielding copolymers ranging from glasses to rubbers. Because the long fatty chain is a part of the polymer molecule, modification in properties caused by the oleate is permanent. Generally, mechanical mixing of fatty derivatives with high-molecular-weight polymers is not satisfactory because the long-chain fatty compounds are not compatible with many industrially important polymers. Purified grades of oleic acid also show promise in the preparation of a synthetic, inedible substitute for olive oil.

Amides of oleic acid can be readily converted to products with useful wetting and detergent properties. Soaps of oleic acid are useful in the preparation of oxidation catalysts and high-quality, stable greases. Water-soluble soaps of oleic acid can be used as emulsifying agents in low-temperature polymerization reactions, because they neither inhibit the reaction nor precipitate. Selective hydrogenation of oleic acid, or reduction with sodium, yields oleyl alcohol, which undergoes a wide variety of interesting and useful reactions and is a good emulsifying agent.

Reaction of the double bond of oleic acid yields many products of potential and actual value, such as monohydroxystearic and dihydroxystearic acids, expoxystearic acids, arylstearic acids, and monobasic and dibasic acids by oxidative cleavage with oxygen. The preparation of those acids by cleavage of oleic acid with oxygen is one of the most important problems in the field of fats, because both fragments are immensely important in the preparation of plastics, plasticizers, and low-temperature lubricants, and as chemical intermediates. The epoxy and hydroxy acids are potentially useful intermediates in the preparation of plasticizers, wetting agents, and waxes; salts of the arylstearic acids are potentially useful addition agents to lubricants.

The carboxyl group of the saturated acids also undergoes the reactions discussed under oleic acid. The absence of the double bond, however, gives the molecule a stability that derivatives of of oleic acid do not have. Amides, particularly those of the saturated acids, are well-established industrial products and are used to make wetting agents, waxes, and water repellents, and as chemical intermediates.

It is often rash—but always exciting and challenging—to make predictions. The development that appears to hold the most promise for the large-scale consumption of inedible animal fats and oils is the preparation of chemically homogeneous substances and their derivatives.

Most of the present uses for inedible

animal fats and oils do not require chemical homogeneity—in fact, homogeneity may sometimes be a disadvantage. But where mixtures are employed to obtain certain average properties, substitute materials that are less expensive, more readily available, or superior are always appearing on the market.

Every organic compound has its own special chemical and physical properties, as well as properties common to all members of its homologous series. Thus, compounds having long-chain molecules are high-boiling, water-insoluble, and relatively nonvolatile and water-repellent. Some of them also have the property of lubricating and of modifying and lowering the solidification point of materials with which they are mixed. Furthermore, by chemical reaction, the long chain can be introduced into a wide variety of organic molecules, permanently imparting these characteristics to the final product.

DANIEL SWERN *was born in New York City and was educated at the Col-*

lege of the City of New York, Columbia University, and the University of Maryland. Dr. Swern has been a member of the staff of the Bureau of Agricultural and Industrial Chemistry since 1937, and is head of the oxidation products section of the oil and fat division at the Eastern Regional Research Laboratory.

WALDO C. AULT *was born on a farm in Ohio and was educated at Ohio State University, where he received the doctor's degree in 1934. After 7 years in industrial research, he joined the staff of the Northern Regional Research Laboratory. Later he transferred to the Eastern Laboratory, where he has since served as head of the oil and fat division.*

A. J. STIRTON *is a graduate of Wayne University, George Washington University, and the University of Maryland. He has been employed by the Department of Agriculture since 1930, and has carried out research on anthraquinone vat-dye intermediates and surface-active agents from oleic acid.*

Soybeans processed by solvent-extraction, screw-press, and hydraulic-press methods

Crop year	Methods						Total by years
	Screw press		Solvent extraction		Hydraulic		
	1,000 tons	Percent	1,000 tons	Percent	1,000 tons	Percent	1,000 tons
1936–37	423	68.4	82	13.2	114	18.4	619
1937–38	637	70.1	156	17.1	116	12.8	909
1938–39	967	72.2	214	16.0	158	11.8	1,339
1939–40	1,274	74.4	346	20.2	92	5.4	1,712
1940–41	1,426	74.2	444	23.1	52	2.7	1,922
1941–42	1,715	74.1	558	24.1	41	1.8	2,314
1942–43	2,531	63.2	654	16.3	819	20.5	4,004
1943–44	2,786	65.2	699	16.4	784	18.4	4,269
1944–45	3,246	70.5	919	20.0	437	9.5	4,602
1945–46	3,073	64.2	1,347	28.2	363	7.6	4,783
1946–47	3,262	63.9	1,357	26.6	488	9.5	5,107
1947–48	2,647	54.4	1,830	37.6	388	8.0	4,865
1948–49	3,048	55.3	2,186	39.6	281	5.1	5,515

Autoxidation of Fats and Oils

C. E. Swift, F. G. Dollear

Products that contain fats and oils turn rancid and deteriorate in other ways when they are exposed to air. The action, known as autoxidation, imparts disagreeable flavors and odors to fats and foods containing them. For a long time baffled investigators spent a vast amount of effort trying to find ways to prevent autoxidation. Specifically, the basic problem was the mechanism of autoxidation—how oxygen attacks a fat. On that point the investigators made several discoveries in 1943. They have developed moderately effective methods of preventing rancidification, and believe now that the solution of the problem is in sight.

It is important to prevent autoxidation because fat and fat-containing foods valued at several billion dollars are produced and marketed annually. The oil, meat, fishery, dairy, and bakery industries suffer serious losses from autoxidation of their products.

Rancidification was an important economic and military problem during the First and Second World Wars, although many modern scientific practices reduced the frequency of its occurrence. Measures that were moderately effective in preserving civilian foods availed little for food that had to be transported long distances and stored in unfavorable climates.

In different fats, and under different conditions, autoxidation produces tallowy, painty, burned, fishy, grassy, and other off-flavors and odors; the senses of taste and smell can detect autoxidative deterioration quite readily. Fats in the early stages of autoxidation are edible, but unpalatable. Thereafter the degree of unpalatability increases until the odor and flavor become so repulsive that the fat cannot be eaten.

Nutritional tests indicate that autoxidation reduces or destroys the food value of fats. For example, the vitamin E content of vegetable oils and the vitamin A content of fish oils are reduced, if not entirely destroyed, during autoxidation. Furthermore, the fatty acid components of fats that are most essential in the diet are the first to be attacked during autoxidation. Rancid fat in diets adversely affects the body's utilization of vitamins from other sources. Finally, there is some evidence that autoxidized fat may exert a toxic action.

NATURAL ANTIOXIDANTS, substances that tend to prevent autoxidation, are present in small amounts in most vegetable fats. Their importance has been realized for a very long time. For instance, the American Indians added oak-bark extracts to the fat of bears to keep the fat from spoiling. Some natural antioxidants have been isolated recently from the fats in which they occur and their chemical structures have been determined. A number of fats and oils contain the same natural antioxidant; some contain one not yet found in any other fat or oil. Fats and oils also differ very markedly in the amounts of natural antioxidants originally present in them.

The most common antioxidant is vitamin E, or tocopherol. Generally speaking, vegetable fats contain appreciable amounts of tocopherols, while animal fats contain them in very low concentrations. Sesame oil contains a unique antioxidant, called sesamol. Crude cottonseed oil contains a different antioxidant, gossypol.

BESIDES NATURAL antioxidants, fats and oils generally contain phosphatides, complex substances that sometimes act as an antioxidant and sometimes also enhance the activity of other antioxidants present. A substance which has practically no antioxidant activity, but which increases the activity of a true antioxidant, is called a synergist.

Unfortunately, both the antioxidants and synergists are sometimes partly or wholly removed from crude fats and oils during the refining process to which they must be subjected to rid them of objectionable coloring matter and flavorous or odorous constituents. A refined fat or oil may, therefore, require the addition of antioxidants to increase its stability.

When refining is carefully carried out, however, most of the natural antioxidant remains in the refined oil. Under such conditions, there may be no advantage in adding more antioxidant, for it has been found that there is an optimum concentration for these substances in any fat or oil. It is still possible, however, to add synergists to assist the natural antioxidants in protecting the fat. Sometimes, of course, it is advantageous to add both antioxidants and synergists.

The phosphatides and certain other compounds form effective synergist-antioxidant combinations with natural tocopherols. The manner in which synergists act to increase the activity of antioxidants has been investigated, but is not clearly understood. Phosphoric acid, which forms an effective synergist-antioxidant combination with tocopherol, apparently is capable of regenerating tocopherol that has been oxidized. It has been shown that tocopherols in the presence of a synergist are depleted at a retarded rate during autoxidation. One present theory assumes that the antioxidants are continuously regenerated at the expense of the synergists.

The tocopherols, which are only moderately active as compared with certain antioxidants, have some advantages. They impart no color, odor, or flavor to fats. During the autoxidation of fats that contain tocopherols, red substances, known as chroman-5, 6-quinones, are produced, but the color formed is usually not objectionable. Because the tocopherols are not soluble in water and are relatively stable to heat, they generally are carried over into finished food products, as, for example, baked goods, such as piecrust or cakes. Finally, the antioxygenic activity of a tocopherol may be greatly increased when any of a number of synergists is used to increase its activity. These properties indicate that the tocopherols are singularly well adapted to their role as natural antioxidants.

Several effective antioxidants and antioxidant combinations have been suggested for use in artificially stabilizing fats. Only a few are important. The addition of antioxidants to foods is subject to Federal regulations. Their acceptability must be established by toxicological and nutritional tests before their addition is permitted. A long time may elapse between the laboratory discovery and the commercial utilization of an antioxidant.

MANY INVESTIGATIONS of the effect of various antioxidants on fat stability have provided a great deal of information on the properties of antioxidants. Most compounds with appreciable antioxygenic activity belong to the phenols, a group of complex substances including the natural tocopherols—gum guaiac obtained from a tropical tree and nordihydroguaiaretic acid obtained from the creosotebush of the southwestern United States—and the synthetic substance known as hydroquinone.

Adding phenolic antioxidants to vegetable fats which already contain natural tocopherols improves the stability of the fat only slightly. On the other hand, addition of the phenolic antioxidants to fats naturally lacking in antioxidants, such as animal fats, improves stability appreciably. Moreover, a relatively large group of synergists can greatly enhance the antioxygenic activity of the phenolic antioxidants. The effective members of this group include citric, ascorbic, gallic, and phosphoric acids and the phosphatides, especially the commercial lecithins, such as the soybean, peanut, and rapeseed lecithins.

Propyl gallate, a chemical compound that acts synergistically with tocopherols, is particularly effective in vegetable fats. It is one of the few compounds that are both phenolic antioxidants and synergists. Animal fats and fish oils can be effectively stabilized by the addition of phenolic antioxidants, and even more effectively by synergist-antioxidant combinations. The antioxidants approved for use, subject to change and with certain limiting restrictions, are the tocopherols, gum guaiac, nordihydroguaiaretic acid, butylated hydroxyanisole, thiodipropionic acid, thiopropionic acid plus dilaurylthiodipropionate, and propyl gallate, also the lecithins, and citric and phosphoric acids, which are synergists. The addition of natural food substances is permissible, but generally only mildly effective.

There are several other effective antioxidants whose use in food products has not yet been approved. At the Eastern Regional Research Laboratory work has been done to improve the utility of gallic and ascorbic acids as antioxidants by converting them to esters, which are more soluble in fats than the acids themselves. One recently discovered phenolic antioxidant is norconidendrin, which was derived from the waste liquor from pulping western hemlock by workers at the Southern Laboratory. This compound has antioxygenic activity approximately equal to that of nordihydroguaiaretic acid.

IN PRESENT PRACTICE, autoxidation is prevented mainly by methods of handling, processing, and packaging fats and fat-containing foods. Care is taken to minimize exposure to light, heat, and air (oxygen) and contamination with metallic pro-oxidants, or promoters of autoxidation, such as copper and iron. These precautions call for attention to the design of equipment, to the materials from which the equipment is fabricated, to packaging materials, and to numerous other details. If suitable precautions are observed, many fats, particularly vegetable fats, are sufficiently stable for most uses without added antioxidants.

A large portion of commercially important liquid vegetable oils are hydrogenated, or hardened, to produce plastic fats like shortening and oleomargarine. Although the main objective of hydrogenation is to produce plastic fats, hydrogenated fats are generally many times more stable than the unhardened oils from which they are produced.

Lard and other animal fats are the main ones that require stabilization with antioxidants. Much of the lard marketed today is stabilized with approved antioxidant-synergist combinations selected from those we have mentioned.

An appreciable quantity of fat is marketed in the form of animal-vegetable fat combinations. The animal fat ingredients in such products are stabilized to a marked extent by the natural tocopherols present in the vegetable fats.

THE MECHANISM of autoxidation, or how fats become rancid, has held the interest of chemists for many years.

M. E. Chevreul, a French chemist, discovered a century ago that fats are compounds formed by the reaction of fatty acids and glycerol, or are, as the chemist says, glycerol esters of fatty acids. Scientists also learned that some fatty acids contain carbon-to-carbon double bonds ($>C=C<$) and are therefore chemically related to other compounds that undergo autoxidation.

In 1858, C. F. Schönbein, in Germany, proposed that these carbon-to-carbon double bonds are involved in the autoxidation of turpentine. The view that double bonds are involved in autoxidation was extended in 1897 by C. Engler and W. Wild, also in Germany. They suggested that autoxidation involves the addition of oxygen to the carbon-to-carbon double bonds of fats producing cyclic peroxides, which may be represented as follows:

$$>C=C< \; + \; O_2 \; \longrightarrow \; >\overset{\displaystyle O-O}{\overset{|\qquad|}{C-C}}<$$

double bond   oxygen   cyclic peroxide

That concept was generally accepted until recently; most investigators supposed that the reaction at carbon-to-carbon double bonds with atmospheric oxygen is a simple addition, analogous to reactions at such bonds with other chemical agents such as bromine and ozone. Also, this theory explained how, during autoxidation, oxygen is consumed, peroxide groups, or at least groups containing active oxygen, are formed, and the carbon-to-carbon double bonds disappear. Actually, these details applied only to the over-all reactions of autoxidation; it is now known that carbon-to-carbon double bonds do not disappear during the initial (or peroxide-forming) stage of autoxidation.

During the next 40 years, while the fundamental reactions of autoxidation remained a mystery except for that theory, scientists learned many useful facts. New data indicated that autoxidative reactions are autocatalytic; that is, they perpetuate themselves at a rate that depends on the amount of oxidation products present at any given instant. The scientists also found that certain substances possess pro-oxidant or antioxidant activity; that is, they accelerate or retard the rate of autoxidation of fats. They also found that fats spoil faster at higher temperatures and can be preserved for a long time if refrigerated. Chemists investigating the effect of light on fat deterioration found that exposure of fats to light, particularly ultraviolet light, promotes rancidity, and that for maximum stability a fat should be stored in the dark or in an opaque container.

Investigators also developed chemical methods for detecting autoxidation and for measuring the keeping quality, or stability, of fats and oils. They devised improved methods to prevent or retard autoxidation and isolated and identified from rancid fats and oils a number of products formed by autoxidation.

Alfred Rieche at the University of Leipzig and R. Criegee and coworkers, at the Chemical Institute of the Technical University at Karlsruhe, Germany, reported in 1937 and 1939 that the relatively simple hydrocarbon cyclohexene, and the related compounds containing carbon-to-carbon double bonds, form hydroperoxides during autoxidation. In those simple compounds a molecule of oxygen was presumed to add to the carbon atom nearest the double bond and between that carbon atom and the hydrogen atom already attached to it; that is, C–H in cyclohexene became C–O–O–H, the whole reaction being represented thus:

cyclohexene   oxygen   hydroperoxide of cyclohexene

E. H. Farmer and coworkers of the British Rubber Producers' Research Association in England, while studying the autoxidation of various substances with chemical structures related to those occurring in rubber, investigated the autoxidation of the methyl ester of oleic acid, one of the principal fatty acid constituents of fats. They reported in 1943 that the initial product formed during the autoxidation of methyl oleate is indeed a hydroperoxide, which they succeeded in isolating. They believed that the hydroperoxide group is attached to carbon atoms on either side of the carbon atoms possessing a double bond.

$$-\overset{\text{H}}{\underset{\text{H}}{\text{C}}}-\text{C}=\text{C}-\ +\ \text{O}_2\ \longrightarrow\ -\overset{\overset{\text{H}}{\underset{}{\text{O}}}}{\underset{\text{H}}{\text{O}}}\ \ -\text{C}-\text{C}=\text{C}-$$

segment of   oxygen   segment of
methyl oleate   hydroperoxide
showing double   of methyl
bond   oleate

Farmer's description of the isolation for the first time of a hydroperoxide of a fatty acid greatly stimulated investigations of autoxidation and invited reexamination of all of the phenomena of autoxidation. The fact that the autoxidation of methyl oleate occurs with the formation of hydroperoxide without destroying the carbon-to-carbon double bond was confirmed at the Southern Laboratory and in the laboratories of Prof. T. P. Hilditch at the University of Liverpool. Shortly afterwards, two of Farmer's associates, J. L. Bolland and H. P. Koch, and also S. Bergström, of the Nobel Institute at Stockholm, investigated the autoxidation of linoleic acid. This acid, which is also a constituent of many of the common fats and oils, such as cottonseed, soybean, and peanut, differs from oleic acid in having two carbon-to-carbon double bonds instead of one.

In that case, autoxidation occurs initially to form a hydroperoxide, but now one of the two carbon-to-carbon double bonds is shifted along the carbon chain to produce a different kind of linoleic acid. The different linoleic acid contains conjugated carbon-to-carbon double bonds; that is, the double bonds are attached to adjacent carbon atoms, instead of being separated by an intervening carbon atom without double bonds.

The two forms of double bonds can be represented thus:

$$-\text{CH}=\text{CH}-\text{CH}_2-\text{CH}=\text{CH}-$$

unconjugated carbon-to-carbon double bonds

$$-\text{CH}=\text{CH}-\text{CH}=\text{CH}-$$

conjugated carbon-to-carbon double bonds

But let us return to the autoxidation of linoleic acid. As we have stated, the oxidation of natural linoleic acid is accompanied by a shift of one of the carbon-to-carbon double bonds, with the formation of a hydroperoxide, which may be illustrated as follows:

$$-\overset{\text{H}}{\underset{\text{H}}{\text{C}}}-\text{C}=\text{C}-\overset{\text{H}}{\underset{\text{H}}{\text{C}}}-\text{C}=\text{C}-\ +\ \text{O}_2\ \longrightarrow$$

segment of linoleic acid   oxygen
showing two double bonds

$$-\overset{\text{H}}{\underset{\text{H}}{\text{C}}}-\overset{\overset{\text{H}}{\underset{}{\text{O}}}}{\underset{\text{H}}{\text{O}}}\ -\text{C}-\text{C}=\text{C}-\text{C}=\text{C}-$$

segment of hydroperoxide
of linoleic acid showing
conjugated double bonds

These observations all accorded with Farmer's concept of the way oxygen adds to the unsaturated fatty acids. Additional evidence was soon brought forward in other laboratories to substantiate Farmer's theory and today there appears little doubt that the initially formed products of autoxidation of the principal fatty acid components of fats are hydroperoxides whose structures are reasonably well established.

Having resolved the problem of the first step of the addition of oxygen in the autoxidation of fats, the next problem to be attacked was the fate of the hydroperoxide once it had been formed. It was well known that this compound is not in itself the cause of the off-flavor and off-odor of rancid fats.

As soon as chemists learned how to prepare and isolate the hydroperoxidized fatty acids from rancid or autoxidized fats and oils, it became possible to investigate the purified product itself. At the Southern Laboratory we found that this product continues to react with other substances that are parts of, or are present in, most fats and oils. The first discovery was that the hydroperoxide reacts with other substances containing one or more carbon-to-carbon double bonds. For example, the hydroperoxide of methyl oleate reacts with unoxidized oleic acid or methyl oleate to form oxido and dihydroxy acids or esters. This reaction may be illustrated as follows:

$$\begin{array}{c} \text{H} \\ \text{O} \\ \text{O} \\ \text{—C—C=C—} \\ \text{H H H} \end{array} + \begin{array}{c} \text{—C=C—} \\ \text{H H} \end{array} \longrightarrow$$

hydroperoxide group and double bond of hydroperoxide of methyl oleate   double bond of oleic acid

$$\begin{array}{c} \text{H} \\ \text{O} \\ \text{—C—C=C—} \\ \text{H H H} \end{array} + \begin{array}{c} \quad\text{O} \\ \diagup\diagdown \\ \text{—C———C—} \\ \text{H} \qquad \text{H} \end{array}$$

hydroxy group and double bond of methyl hydroxy oleate   oxido group of oxidostearic acid

The new compounds, however, did not have disagreeable odors or flavors and, therefore, could not be responsible for off-flavors and odors in rancid fats.

The discovery explained why some of the carbon-to-carbon double bonds disappear during rancidification, or autoxidation, of a fat, even though oxygen of the air does not attack the bonds directly.

The second discovery at our laboratory was that the hydroperoxides break into fragments with the formation of aldehydes which do have objectionable flavors and odors. It had long been known that aldehydes are among the products formed in rancid fats, but the ones we isolated turned out to be quite different from those previously imagined. These aldehydes have not only a typical aldehyde group, but also a carbon-to-carbon double bond just like the original fat.

One of the aldehydes isolated from autoxidized, or rancid, cottonseed oil even has two of these carbon-to-carbon double bonds. To date three aldehydes have been isolated from rancid cottonseed oil and one from oxidized soybean oil. They are called 2-undecenal, 2,4-decadienal, and hexanal. Hexanal contains no carbon-to-carbon double bonds. Still other aldehydes are known to be present in rancid fats and work continues to isolate and identify them.

We can now identify some of the important substances formed in rancid fats and oils, and we also know a great deal about how they are formed. It is not enough to know how and why these substances are formed, however. It is much more important to know how to prevent their formation. This brings us to another phase of autoxidation research—the effect of antioxidants in preventing rancidification.

ACCORDING TO the present theory of autoxidation, the first step of the reaction with oxygen involves only a few activated fat molecules, which react to form an equally small number of hydroperoxide molecules with the simultaneous liberation of energy. The liberated energy is transferred to and activates other fat molecules. The process continues to repeat itself. The chain reaction will continue until all the fat is consumed unless something intervenes to break its sequence. A substance that will break the chain of autoxidation is called an antioxidant.

An antioxidant may be considered as being acted on by the oxygen in preference to the fat, or of using up the energy liberated by the first few fat molecules that react with oxygen. Regardless of how the antioxidant functions, it cannot prevent the oxidation indefinitely, probably because it is itself used up in the process of protecting the fat. But during the time that it does protect the fat only small quantities of hydroperoxides are formed. Thus it prolongs the induction period of the fat, that is, the time before which appreciable quantities of hydroperoxides are formed. During that period, little or no off-flavor or odor can be detected. Once the induction period ends, however, hydroperoxides begin to develop rapidly, and the odor and flavor are increasingly noticeable. In other words, the fat is becoming rancid. Therefore, a measure of the induction period will give an idea of the length of time a fat will keep in ordinary storage.

The chemist has devised a practical method of rapidly determining the keeping quality of fats. It consists of bubbling air through the fat while it is held at a relatively high temperature (208° F.) and periodically analyzing it for its content of hydroperoxides. A high-quality fat shows little formation of hydroperoxides for an extended period; and then suddenly it begins to form them at a very rapid rate. When that happens, the fat is said to break, and the time taken to reach that point (that is, the induction period) is a measure of the stability of the fat and is related to the time a fat will keep in ordinary storage.

The stability can also be determined by measuring the number of hours required for a specified content of hydroperoxides to be formed when the fat is heated under the conditions previously mentioned. That time, too, is related to the time the fat will keep in ordinary storage.

THE NEED for continued advancement of our knowledge of autoxidation and its attendant problem is generally recognized, and many phases of the problem are currently under investigation in industrial, university, and Government laboratories. Until recently the development of fundamental information on autoxidation and antioxidant activity has proceeded slowly and has depended on empirical, rather than scientific, knowledge. Today, however, scientific research in this field

is based on a sound understanding of the fundamental reactions of autoxidation and antioxidant activity and it may be expected that the multitude of problems pertaining to fat deterioration will be solved in the not too distant future.

C. E. SWIFT *received his higher education at the University of Maryland. His association with the problems of autoxidation began with a fellowship at the Technological Laboratory of the Bureau of Fisheries, College Park, Md., and was continued first as a collaborator with the Bureau of Agricultural and Industrial Chemistry as the Fellow of the National Cottonseed Products Association stationed in Washington, D. C., from 1939 to 1943 and at the Southern Regional Research Laboratory from 1943 to 1948, and subsequently as a chemist in the oil, fat and protein division, Southern Laboratory. He is now with the Bureau of Animal Industry in Beltsville, Md.*

F. G. DOLLEAR, *a native of Illinois and a graduate of Illinois College and Northwestern University, has been engaged in chemical research on fats and oils since 1937, when he joined the staff of the United States Regional Soybean Industrial Products Laboratory in Urbana, Ill. Since 1939 he has been stationed at the Southern Laboratory.*

Methods used in United States for processing principal oilseeds in 1949

[Capitals indicate principal process]

Oilseed	Hydraulic press	Continuous press	Solvent extraction	Forepress and solvent extraction	Double pressing
Cottonseed	X	x	x	....	....
Soybeans	x	X	x	....	....
Linseed	....	X	x	x	....
Copra	....	x	....	x	X
Corn germ	....	X	....	x	....
Peanuts	X	x	....	....	....
Castor	....	....	x	X	x
Tung	....	X	....	....	....
Rice bran	....	x	X	....	....
Safflower	....	X	....	x	....

New Ideas on Problems of Storage

Madeline G. Lambou,
Marjorie Z. Condon,
Aaron M. Altschul

The durability of seeds in storage is the key to their usefulness to man and animal. Many seeds have potential value for food, feed, and industrial products, but in any climate only those that can be stored without much deterioration have economic value. In temperate climates, cereal grains need only to remain in the field for a short time after harvesting to dry. In more humid areas, they have to be dried and cooled artificially to prevent deterioration during storage.

The seed-crushing industries in the South have long operated under conditions that imposed losses in the quality and quantity of their products in spite of all they might do to control them. In 1943, the industries asked the Department of Agriculture for help in solving their problems. Aaron M. Altschul and Melvin L. Karon proposed a new approach, that of chemically treating the seed to minimize deterioration during storage. The industries supplied seeds and mill facilities for the research and they set to work on the problem.

The suggestion was based on the fact that a seed is a living entity capable of the many types of biological activity that are characteristic of all living things. The chemical reactions involved in this activity are controlled by enzymes, which in a dry, dormant seed are relatively inactive. They are segregated in the cells in such a manner as to allow no intimate contact with other chemical compounds which they affect. When water is added, the constituents of the individual cells become mobile, contact occurs between the enzymes and the compounds with which they react, and the rates of biological activity increase. Under ideal conditions, the diverse activities are coordinated to produce germination in the seed. But if sufficient moisture for germination is not present, or if the enzymes have lost their activity, or the compounds with which they would normally react have been destroyed or rendered inactive in some manner, degradative processes will set in and result in the production of heat and destruction of the constituents of the seed.

In cottonseed, deteriorative processes cause formation of free fatty acids, from the fat stored in the seed, and darkening of the seed and oil. Deterioration in rice shows up in the form of discoloration of the kernels, increased breakage of the kernels during milling, an increase in free fatty acids in the oil in the pericarp and aleurone layers (which constitute the bran removed during milling), reduction in vitamin content, and development of off-odors and off-tastes in the white milled rice.

Comparatively little is known about the enzyme systems involved in the metabolism of oilseeds and consequently about the type of chemicals that might be expected to inhibit them. It is possible for chemicals differing greatly in molecular structure and properties to inhibit deterioration, because each reacts at a different point in the complex chain of reactions that undoubtedly are involved in spoilage of seeds. Therefore, the problem of selecting protective inhibitors is enormous and cannot be solved by resorting to the use of only the chemicals that have

551

heretofore been reported to be biologically active. A wide variety of chemicals must be tested individually until the inhibitor activity of any given chemical can be correlated with its molecular structure.

THE TIME required to test the activity of chemicals under field conditions and the cost of materials would be prohibitive. The investigators needed a rapid method whereby deterioration of seed could be produced in the laboratory in a few days. Such a method, developed by Madeline G. Lambou, makes it possible to make preliminary tests of the inhibitory activity of chemicals in 6 days, using only a few ounces of seed.

The method comprises conditioning the seeds to a high moisture content, storing the seeds under conditions that will promote rapid heating and deterioration, and comparing stored untreated controls with the treated samples, as to the effect on the temperature of the seed and the formation of free fatty acids in the oils during storage.

The process is carried out by using a simple type of calorimeter in the form of a 1-liter vacuum bottle. The moistened seeds are placed in several bottles, and air is drawn through them at a constant rate, during which time the change in temperature is automatically recorded. After storage for 6 days, the samples are removed and analyzed for their content of free fatty acids. Flaxseed was found to be satisfactory for the rapid testing of a large number of chemicals. Therefore most of the preliminary testing was made with flaxseed. The chemicals that possessed inhibitory activity with it were tried on other seeds.

The first chemical found to be effective in the laboratory was ethylene chlorohydrin. When ethylene chlorohydrin in a concentration of 0.38 percent, based on dry weight of the seed, was applied to high-moisture flaxseed, no heating or formation of free fatty acids occurred during a 6-day period.

Other chemicals have since been found to compare favorably with ethylene chlorohydrin in ability to inhibit heating and the formation of free fatty acids.

The chemicals are: Propylene chlorohydrin; ethylene bromohydrin; allyl alcohol; β-chlorallyl alcohol; diethyl oxalate; diethyl malonate; glycol diacetate; propylene glycol dipropionate; propylene glycol diacetate; vinyl propionate; tributyl borate; ethyl chloroacetate; ethyl chloropropionate; methyl chloroacetate; ethyl isovalerate; triethyl phosphite; diethyl phosphite; propionic acid; β-chloropropionic acid; acetic acid; butyric acid; valeric acid; crotonic acid; sodium cyanide; 1,3-dichloropropene-2; 1,3-dichlorobutene-2; 1,3-dichloropropene-1; phenol; salicylaldehyde; p-tertiaryamyl phenol (Pentaphen); sodium pentachlorophenate (Santobrite); 2-chloro-4-phenyl phenol (Dowicide 4); chloro-2-phenyl phenol (Dowicide 30); o-vanillin; 1,3-dimethyl-2, 4-bis-chloromethyl benzene; 1,3-dimethyl-4,6-bischloromethyl benzene; benzotrichloride; Chloramine T; Dichloramine B; sulfanilamide; p-toluene sulfonamide; Hyamine 1622; Hyamine 10X; 2-aminothiazole; chloroacetamide; acrolein; and methyl vinyl ketone.

Some trade names appear in the list; it is to be understood that it is not the policy of the Department of Agriculture to recommend the products of one company over those of any others engaged in the production of the same or similar products.

Even though a chemical might be effective in a 6-day test, its use in industry would depend on its behavior during a storage period lasting several weeks or months. Therefore, while a test method made possible the selection of the most promising chemicals, it had to be supplemented by laboratory tests of longer duration to determine how long the chemicals would retain their effectiveness in preventing heating and deterioration.

These tests were conducted in the same manner as the original ones, except that they were not concluded until the temperature of the treated seeds began to rise above room temperature. For example, with flaxseed of 22 percent moisture content, it was shown that vinyl propionate, when used in a concentration approximately equivalent to that of ethylene chlorohydrin, prevented heating of the seed for 21 days. The untreated control lot of the same seed heated to 110° F. in 4 days. Grain sorghum, treated with ethylene chlorohydrin, did not heat for 10 days. With ethylene bromohydrin, no heating occurred for 14 days.

The most interesting observation was on the effect of mixing two or more chemicals, each of which had been found to possess inhibitory activity. When two "active" chemicals were mixed, the resultant inhibition was greater than that obtained by treatment with either chemical alone, even when each was used in a higher concentration. For example, heating of flaxseed was inhibited for 62 days by a mixture of propylene glycol dipropionate and 1,3-dimethyl-4,6-bischloromethyl benzene. If twice the concentration of one of them (propylene glycol dipropionate) was used alone, inhibition was maintained for 18 days, while double the concentration of the other one (1,3-dimethyl-4,6-bischloromethyl benzene) was effective for only 15 days. Treatment with the mixture of the two chemicals had an analogous effect on the rate of formation of free fatty acids.

THE OBJECT OF STORAGE is to provide conditions that keep to a minimum the activity within the seed. Obviously, that is best accomplished by drying of the seed in the field before harvesting. If that cannot be done, the seed may be dried in the field immediately after harvesting, as, for example, in shocks of grain or stacks of peanut vines on poles. Both effect drying at atmospheric temperature by free circulation of air of low relative humidity through the seed.

The mechanization of harvesting changed the requirements for handling and storing seeds. Harvesting grains with combines has resulted in a substantial increase in the average moisture content of the seed leaving the fields, and has increased the need for artificial drying before storage. For example, widespread application of mechanical methods for harvesting peanuts will depend on the development of practical methods for drying green or uncured seed.

If the climatic conditions or the method of harvest preclude field drying, the seeds may be artificially dried by the circulation of warm air. Such an operation, if carried out carefully, prevents deterioration during storage. If, however, the moisture is removed too rapidly or the seeds are heated to too high a temperature, irreparable damage will be done. In rice, for example, drying at too high a temperature increases the proportion of broken kernels in milling.

The ideal artificial drying procedure is one that approximates most closely the action of the sun and air in the field. It has never been completely attained because it has never been possible to stop the damage that takes place in seeds during such drying. An example of this difficulty was given in an experiment on storing cottonseed. Twenty tons of cottonseed of 17.6 percent moisture content was stored in a bin, and air at atmospheric temperature was drawn through it continuously for 20 days. In that time, the moisture content of the seed was reduced to 11.5 percent. Nevertheless, the content of free fatty acids of the oil present in the seed increased from an original value of 1.2 to 3.5 percent after 35 days of storage and to 6.8 percent after 71 days of storage. The rate of drying was too slow to prevent damage to the seed during the time that the moisture content was being reduced to one considered safe for storage. Even after the moisture content was reduced, damage continued to occur because seed already injured is more susceptible to additional damage.

Although chemical treatment has been shown to prevent or retard heating and the formation of free fatty acids in moist seeds for long periods, a combination of chemical treatment and reduction of the moisture content of the seed gave even better results in an experiment with flaxseed containing 19 percent moisture and 0.5 percent free fatty acids. One lot of the seed was chemically treated, stored for 1 day to allow the chemical to penetrate the seed, and then exposed to a stream of air for 2 hours, during which the moisture content was reduced to 17 percent. This lot of seed, when stored in vacuum bottles for 3 weeks, did not heat at all and showed only a 0.1-percent rise in the free fatty acids content of the oil. Another lot of the original seed was not chemically treated but was dried by aeration at room temperature until its moisture content was reduced from 19 to 14 percent. Although the moisture content was reduced below that of the chemically treated seed, this seed (when stored in vacuum bottles) heated to 96° F. and had a content of free fatty acids of 12 percent after 3 weeks of storage.

BESIDES THE LABORATORY experiments, mill-scale experiments were made in which cottonseed, flaxseed, and rice were stored. Swift & Co., South Texas Cotton Oil Co., Cotton Products Co., Inc., Converted Rice Inc., and several other industrial concerns cooperated in these experiments, which were conducted on large lots of seeds as received in the mill. The seeds were processed after storage under normal operating conditions. The products were evaluated and compared with those of prime seeds.

In one such test, conducted in Louisiana in the 1949–50 season, 20 tons of cottonseed of 18 percent moisture and 3 percent free fatty acids contents were treated with 30 pounds per ton of the mixture of propylene glycol dipropionate and 1,3-dimethyl-4, 6-bischloromethyl benzene and aerated for the first 23 days of storage. This test demonstrated that chemical treatment inhibited spontaneous heating of the seed for the entire storage period of $4\frac{1}{2}$ months and retarded the formation of free fatty acids for the first 52 days of storage. There were smaller increases in refining loss and Lovibond red color in the oil processed from the treated seed as compared to oil produced from untreated seed stored under the same conditions.

In each mill-scale test performed, naturally moist seed was used while all previous laboratory tests had been conducted on artificially moistened seed. When both types of seed were stored under identical conditions in the laboratory, it became apparent that naturally moist and artificially moistened seed developed free fatty acids at approximately the same rate. When each seed was treated with the same chemical, however, the formation of free fatty acids was retarded for a longer interval in the artificially conditioned seed as compared to the naturally moist seed. Therefore, in the laboratory, emphasis is now directed to increasing the interval during which a chemical retards the formation of free fatty acids in naturally moist seed.

ANOTHER ASPECT OF DETERIORATION is loss of viability, or the ability of the seed to germinate. That does not necessarily involve drastic heating or breakdown of the cell constituents. Disorganization in the seed without readily apparent breakdown of the components is sufficient to destroy viability. As a general rule, loss in ability to germinate precedes other types of deterioration in the seed.

Low concentrations of the chemical mixture, propylene glycol dipropionate and 1,3-dimethyl-4, 6-bischloromethyl benzene, have been found to maintain viability in cottonseed of 12 percent moisture content when the seed was stored for 6 months. Replicated field plantings demonstrated a significant increase in the number of survivals in the hills, as compared to untreated checks. Mature plants from treated seed were healthy and normal and showed no deleterious effects of the chemical. Nor were there any significant changes in the yield, length, or strength of the fiber. Seeds produced by the experimental plants were planted in the spring of 1950. Since no differences occurred in the stand and all plants were observed to be normal at maturity, chemical treatment appears to have no effect on the second-generation seed.

WE CAN REPORT the following definite progress from experimentation on a purely empirical basis: Development of a laboratory method for assaying chemicals for activity of the type suitable for our needs; knowledge that at least 50 chemicals have this activity; valuable information on the behavior characteristics of seeds of several types in large seed piles and, therefore, better knowledge of the requirements of a good chemical treatment and the handling necessary to minimize deterioration during storage.

Any improvements that will be made in the future will depend on our ability to find out what is happening to the seed under these conditions and exactly where and when these changes occur. It appears advantageous, therefore, to step up the tempo of fundamental laboratory work, to apply old methods with variations, and to develop new ones in an effort to ascertain what takes place in the seed. Toward that goal, a method for the measurement of oxidation-reduction potentials in seed slurries is being developed by Marjorie Z. Condon.

MEASUREMENT of oxidation-reduction potentials of seed slurries (homogenized seed kernels in water) offers the possibility of furnishing information on the enzymatic activity of the seed. If, at regular intervals of time, the electrical potentials (voltages) of a slurry, first under nitrogen and then in air, are determined, it is possible to obtain oxidation-reduction potential curves. These curves, which are char-

acteristic of the seed under investigation, give an integrated picture of the vigor of oxidizing and reducing systems. The patterns obtained can be altered by heating of the seed and by chemical treatment as well as by germination. It is expected that certain patterns will be identified with seed which can be safely stored while others will indicate that the level of biological activity is too high for prolonged storage. Also, the effects of heat and chemical treatment can be determined rapidly by this method.

The seed and the micro-organisms associated with it contain enzymes which contribute to the deterioration occurring during storage. It is always difficult to distinguish between the damage caused by the enzymes of the seed and that caused by the enzymes of the micro-organisms. Nevertheless, in each case the pattern of activity is usually the same.

The chemicals that were found active as inhibitors of deterioration are now being used to help differentiate between the contributions of the seed enzymes and those of the enzymes of the associated micro-organisms. For instance, cellosolve acetate and vinyl propionate are being used on cottonseed at $100°$ F. and a relative humidity of 92 percent (conditions under which micro-organisms proliferate readily) to unravel this relationship and to determine the mechanism of the formation of free fatty acids.

The response of the seed to cellosolve acetate was of short duration; 40 percent of the seed was originally infected, but less than 2 percent contained any viable internal contaminants within 1 week after treatment and the seed remained in this condition for a short period. Thereafter molds and bacteria grew rapidly. Accompanying the rise in the percentage of seed internally contaminated was a significant increase in the production of free fatty acids.

Vinyl propionate, on the other hand, reduced the number of seeds containing internal micro-organisms to less than 2 percent immediately and maintained that level of contamination for 6 weeks in artificially conditioned seed. For the first 3½ weeks, no rise in the content of free fatty acids was observed. Thereafter, a rise of approximately 0.5 percent a week in the content of free fatty acids was noted. This slow but steady rise in the quantity of free fatty acids, in the absence of any growth or spreading of internal contamination, possibly may be attributed to the enzyme activity of the seed itself.

Vinyl propionate controlled the formation of free fatty acids in naturally moist seed for 3 weeks. In this seed, which was 100-percent contaminated with micro-organisms, less reduction in the microbial population was observed as a result of chemical treatment. Nevertheless, the rapid rise in free fatty acids content and similar rise in internal contamination did not occur until the fifth week of storage.

Cooperative investigations with the Bureau of Plant Industry at Beltsville, Md., on the maintenance of viability in naturally moist cottonseed by low concentrations of the mixture, propylene glycol dipropionate and 1,3-dimethyl-4, 6-bischloromethyl benzene, applied to the seed at various temperatures, indicated that heat might enhance the effectiveness of the chemical. Treatment at temperatures higher than room temperature may have forced the chemical into the seed more rapidly, and, thereby, prolonged its effect. Other cooperative viability investigations with the Delta Branch Experiment Station at Stoneville, Miss., demonstrated that the storage quality of planting seed could be improved by supplementing chemical treatment with a fungicide. Therefore, heat and fungicides, used as complementary agents to chemical treatment, may increase the interval during which the formation of free fatty acids is controlled.

CHEMICAL TREATMENT, supplemented by one or more methods of handling, may become an accepted method for reducing or preventing deterioration of seeds during storage. Whether or not such treatment may be commercially feasible depends on several factors, not the least of which is the cost of the chemicals. It is impossible now to estimate fairly the cost of chemical treatment, because many of the compounds that were found effective have been manufactured in only small quantities. If their production on a large scale should be undertaken, however, the prices would probably be materially lowered. With increasing knowledge of the mechanisms by which biological activity in seeds is inhibited, it is certain that other chemicals and mixtures of chemicals will be found which will be effective in smaller quantities and presumably at lower costs.

Another factor of importance in the commercial application of such a method is the toxicity of the chemicals used. Many of the chemicals that have been examined, including the mixture of propylene glycol dipropionate and 1,3-dimethyl-4,6-bischloromethyl benzene are relatively nonpoisonous. Others which are known to be toxic will cause no injury to the personnel handling them if reasonable safety precautions are observed. Even more important, however, is the toxicity that may be carried into the products of processing. It will be necessary to study thoroughly this phase of the application of chemicals to seeds before recommending a treatment. Feeding experiments, carried out with meals from various lots of chemically treated seeds, have shown thus far that the treatment has no effect on the value of the products as feedstuffs.

Of course, before any chemical treatment can be recommended for use in industry, exhaustive tests must be made on a large scale under industrial conditions. To obtain the most efficient use of the chemicals, a thorough study of the best means of handling seeds from the time of harvesting to the time of processing or planting will be necessary. Only through the cooperation of the scientist, farmer, and mill operator can the most prudent economic use of seeds be insured. It is conceivable that further increases in agricultural production to meet the demands of an increasing world population will depend to a large extent on the development of improved methods for storing seeds harvested in every type of climate by every conceivable mechanical means.

MADELINE G. LAMBOU, *a chemist in the biochemical section of the protein and carbohydrate division of the Southern Regional Research Laboratory, has been engaged in research in agricultural chemistry for the Department of Agriculture since 1942. Mrs. Lambou is a graduate of Tulane University.*

MARJORIE Z. CONDON *is a graduate of Newcomb College, Tulane University. In 1945 Mrs. Condon joined the group, now the protein and carbohydrate division of the Southern Laboratory, to collaborate on the seedstorage project.*

AARON M. ALTSCHUL *is head of the protein and carbohydrate division. He joined the staff of the Southern Laboratory in 1941 to engage in research on proteins and enzymes in agricultural commodities. Dr. Altschul received his advanced training in the University of Chicago.*

THE FIRST known reference to tung oil is in Marco Polo's account of his travels in Asia. Marco's father, Nicolo, and his uncle, Maffeo, were wealthy merchants of Venice. In 1271, accompanied by 17-year-old Marco, they left Venice for Peking—Peiping—where Kublai Khan had established his principal court a few years earlier.

Marco became a favorite of the Khan, who sent him on many missions over Asia. Marco formed the habit of taking notes on the products and customs of the different parts of the empire so he could report in detail to the Khan.

Marco Polo returned to Venice in 1295, and 2 years later he was taken prisoner in a naval battle between Venice and Genoa. In prison at Genoa, he sent for the notes he had made on his travels in Asia, and from them he dictated the accounts of his travels to a fellow prisoner, who was a scribe.

In describing the construction of Chinese ships, he wrote:

"The ships are all double-planked; that is, they have a course of sheathingboards laid over the planking in every part. These are caulked with oakum both inside and without, and are fastened with iron nails. They are not coated with pitch, as the country does not produce that substance, but the bottoms are smeared over with the following preparation. The people take quick-lime and hemp, which latter they cut small, and with these, when pounded together, they mix oil procured from a certain tree, making of the whole a kind of unguent, which retains its viscous properties more firmly and is a better material than pitch."

For hundreds of years, people ridiculed Marco Polo's tales about the places he had visited, but time has proved that his accounts were correct.—*R. L. Holmes and R. S. McKinney, Bureau of Agricultural and Industrial Chemistry.*

Removing the Glands From Cottonseed

Catherine Hall Pominski,
Leah E. Castillon,
Joseph M. Dechary

Cottonseed differs from other oil-seeds in that it contains dark spots, which are scattered throughout the kernel. The spots are actually pigment glands. They contain nearly all the pigments of the seed and have been the cause of many troubles to millers who process cottonseed into oil and meal, the old standby products of the cotton-seed industry. The amounts and kinds of pigments in the glands and the number of unbroken glands that remain in the meal after processing determine how highly colored the oil will be and how great the food value of the meal. The glands are the only parts of cotton-seed that as yet have no commercial value.

Research on the nature and properties of the glands by Charlotte H. Boatner and others at the Southern Regional Research Laboratory led to the development of a novel method of processing cottonseed. The application of the process on a commercial scale will open the door to new products.

The tiny pigment gland, no larger than a pinpoint, is not the insignificant nonentity its appearance would indicate. Seeds of every species of cotton contain pigment glands. The naked eye sees them merely as black spots. Under the microscope they appear brilliantly and variously colored, from yellow through orange and red to purple. Their size and shape are generally related to one another: Small ones are

almost spherical; large ones are more elongated. They are so small that all the glands in a single seed make up only 1 to 3 percent of its total weight.

Many years before the Southern Laboratory existed, two of the early investigators who examined cottonseed described some of the properties of the pigment glands. Heinrich von Bretfeld in 1887 and T. F. Hanausek in 1903 described the presence in cottonseed of a water-sensitive membrane, which surrounded a greenish-black opaque secretion. More than 40 years later, Dr. Boatner and her assistants found that the outer structure of the pigment gland is a more or less rigid wall, rather than a membrane. They also learned that the wall is exceedingly strong, so strong, in fact, that it was not broken when a cottonseed kernel was rolled out into a flake a few thousandths of an inch thick by applying thousands of pounds of pressure to the rolls. The wall, they discovered, actually is made up of 5 to 8 irregularly shaped and curved plates, fitted together to give the appearance of a baseball cover. The plates, held together by one of Nature's cements, formed the tiny gland which contained the cottonseed pigments.

The walls will break the instant the glands are placed in water—a fascinating thing to watch under the microscope. The material inside a gland becomes cloudy the instant water comes in contact with it, indicating that the water has entered the gland and caused a precipitation of the water-insoluble pigments. Immediately thereafter, the contents of the gland are expelled through ruptures in the walls with a force that resembles jet propulsion. The jetlike streams are usually yellow, but occasionally they are red or purple. The streams consist of finely divided particles, which dance up and down and to and fro, exhibiting what botanists call the Brownian movement.

Organic liquids, such as methanol (wood alcohol), ethanol (grain alcohol), isopropanol, acetone, and dioxane, also rupture the glands, but not in the spectacular manner of water. When water is added to the organic liquids, the speed of rupturing is increased in proportion to the amount added. The hydrocarbons, like hexane (light gasoline) and certain chlorinated hydrocarbons, which will extract the oil from the seed tissue, do not affect the glands or their contents.

DR. BOATNER'S GROUP discovered that the walls of the glands are extremely resistant toward the action of certain solvents and also that they are lighter in weight than the rest of the seed. It occurred to one of her assistants that it should be possible to separate the tiny glands. To do so, they prepared what became known in their laboratory as the "cottonseed cocktail." Very thin cottonseed flakes and a mixture of solvents that would not cause breakage of the walls of the glands were violently agitated in a blender of the kind frequently used to mix fruit juices. The density of the solvent mixture was adjusted to a value between the density of the glands and that of the other seed tissue. When the mixture was allowed to settle in the mixer, the little black glands rose as if by magic to the top, and the yellow meal settled to the bottom. The oil of the seed was dissolved in the solvent.

This method of separating the glands by causing them to float was called the gland-flotation process. The other products, meal and oil, which result from application of this method of processing are actually superior in many ways to those produced by older methods. The third product, the pigment glands, is entirely new.

Prepilot-plant and a pilot-plant operation of this invention provided large enough quantities of separated glands and gland-free meal for studies of their

chemical, physical, and physiological properties.

Of the whole pigment gland, 40 to 50 percent by weight is wall, 35 to 50 percent is a yellow pigment called gossypol, and 0.05 to 3 percent is a purple pigment called gossypurpurin. The presence of the two pigments explains the colors, which are caused by variations in the relative amounts of each pigment inside the gland.

Back in 1886, an English chemist named Longmore first isolated the yellow pigment gossypol from cottonseed. Obtaining even a very small quantity of gossypol from cottonseed has always been a time-consuming task. The development of the flotation process made it possible to get large quantities of pigment glands and, from them, equivalently large quantities of gossypol. Three chemists, Leah E. Castillon, Catherine M. Hall, and Dr. Boatner, devised the simple and relatively rapid method, now available to industry, that will separate pure gossypol from cottonseed pigment glands in yields as high as 60 to 70 percent of the total amount present.

ALTHOUGH COTTONSEED MEAL has long been accepted as an excellent feed for cattle, it can be fed in only very limited quantities to other farm animals. For many years the reason for the differences in the amounts of the meal that could be fed animals was thought to be the presence of gossypol. After it was found that all the gossypol and the gossypurpurin of the seed are contained in the pigment glands, the glands were tested to determine their physiological activity in animals. The work was done through the cooperative efforts of scientists at the Southern Laboratory and nutrition experts in the laboratories of several commercial firms and universities.

Dr. Edward Eagle of Swift & Co. added small amounts of pigment glands to diets of rats, mice, guinea pigs, and rabbits. The glands were deadly to all the test animals in relatively small doses, but when he fed gossypol to his experimental animals he found that much larger quantities fed over much longer periods were necessary to kill them.

At the nutrition laboratories of the Ralston-Purina Company, separated pigment glands, added to the basal soybean diet of chickens, caused a definite slowing of growth. The same effect was noted upon feeding cottonseed that had been extracted by an organic solvent such as hexane to remove the oil without materially affecting the glands or their contents.

The pale yellow gland-free meal obtained by the flotation process produced excellent growth in chicks. The experiments make it apparent that the toxic components of raw cottonseed are confined to the pigment glands.

Feeding laying hens cottonseed meal, processed by the older methods, in the past resulted in the development of objectionable color in eggs during cold storage. No discolored whites and very few dark-colored yolks were found in stored eggs laid by hens fed on the new type of cottonseed meal.

The excellent feed value of the gland-free meal is not entirely the result of being essentially free of pigment glands, but also because it is not heated to high temperatures during processing. That fact has stimulated extensive research on the production of better meals. The present methods, screw pressing and hydraulic pressing, are used in the investigations. The effect of changes in the processing conditions on the quality of meals is now being studied. Industrial cottonseed mills, as well as Government and university nutrition experts, are cooperating in the undertaking.

The oil that is extracted from the seed by use of the gland-flotation process is very light in color and can be refined and bleached by the methods used for ordinary crude cottonseed oils.

So far, we have been talking principally about only one of the pigments in cottonseed. Chemists at the Southern Laboratory found several others in the tiny pigment glands. One is gossypurpurin, the purple one which we have mentioned. Gossyfulvin, an orange pigment, and gossycaerulin, a blue pigment, were also discovered and named by the chemists. Indirect evidence points to the presence of 10 and possibly more pigments in oils and meals prepared by different methods. They have not yet been separated in pure form, and the quantities are so exceedingly small they may defy isolation for a long time.

THE UTILIZATION of gland-free cottonseed flour in markets from which old-process meal has been excluded, mainly for feeding chicks and swine, and as a source of high-quality industrial protein, can result in a larger income for the cotton planter and processor.

Separated pigment glands, an entirely new product, can be the source of further revenue. They represent a source of new raw materials, particularly gossypol, which offers many possibilities for further research. If practical uses can be found for the glands or the pigments, the gland-flotation process makes it possible to produce 90,000 to 100,000 tons of glands and 20,000 to 30,000 tons of gossypol annually from our cottonseed.

CATHERINE HALL POMINSKI *is a chemist in the oil and oilseed division of the Southern Regional Research Laboratory in New Orleans. Since 1944, she has been engaged in investigations of the physical, chemical, and physiological properties of the pigments of cottonseed.*

LEAH E. CASTILLON *is a graduate of Newcomb College, Tulane University, and a native of Louisiana. She has been engaged in research on the pigments of cottonseed since 1945, as a chemist in the protein and carbohydrate division of the Southern Laboratory.*

JOSEPH M. DECHARY *is a native Louisianian and has been working on the nutritive value of cottonseed meal since his employment as a chemist by the Southern Laboratory in 1948.*

Separating the Fractions of Cottonseed

E. F. Pollard, H. L. E. Vix,
J. J. Spadaro

A cotton seed that has been ginned is egg-shaped. It measures about one-half inch by one-fourth inch. It has a fuzzy appearance because of the short linters that remain even after ginning. The linters grow out of the hard, dark-brown seed shell, or hull, which contains the meat part of the seed. The meats consist of oil, meal, and glands.

For the first 80 years of the crushing industry in this country, crude cottonseed oil was obtained by hydraulic and screw pressing of cooked cottonseed flakes. The heat, moisture, and pressure required for this mechanical extraction rupture the pigment glands, so that the meal is highly discolored and suitable only for use in feeding certain kinds of livestock.

Since 1945 several American mills have used solvent extraction to obtain cottonseed oil. The meal fraction obtained by the present commercial solvent-extraction process is dark because of the cooking before or after extraction which is necessary to produce a meal suitable for animals.

Two methods have been developed for the fractionation, or separation, of cottonseed-flake components. The first, the flotation process, takes advantage of the difference in densities of the pigment glands, meal, and hulls—the solid parts of cottonseed. Either defatted or undefatted flakes (that is, the flakes before or after the extraction of the oil) can be used in the process.

In the Southern Regional Research Laboratory, cottonseed flakes were disintegrated violently in a slurry containing inert solvents, such as commercial hexane and tetrachloroethylene, mixed in a proportion to give a resulting specific gravity of 1.378. Separation of the detached pigment glands is effected because the specific gravity of the glands (1.36), lower than that of the mixed solvents, causes the glands to float to the top. The meal and hulls have a higher specific gravity (1.41 and 1.46, respectively) than the mixed solvents and go to the bottom. The oil is left in the solvent solution.

The hulls can be further separated from the essentially pigment-free meal by raising the specific gravity of the slurry to 1.45 (to induce flotation of the meal and the settling of the hulls).

After preliminary investigation in the laboratory, chemists and engineers developed this method on a small scale in runs in which up to 225 pounds of flakes were handled in each run. More than 550 pounds of meal practically free of pigment glands and more than 40 pounds of pigment glands were obtained for utilization studies. Meal was produced with as little as 0.5 percent oil; the content of gossypol, the pigment present in the largest quantity within the gland, was 0.06 percent.

We obtained extensive quantitative data on cottonseed meal-solvent slurries during the development of each of the chemical engineering unit operations, namely, material preparation, size reduction of flakes (by pulverization and disintegration), separation (flotation and centrifugation), filtration, desolventization, and distillation.

Small-scale experiments showed that the process had inherent disadvantages for commercial adaptation. Size reduction of the flake was the immediate hindrance in the operation.

Microscopic tests showed that in order to separate the pigment glands completely from the meal, the flake particles had to be disintegrated in a solvent slurry fine enough to pass an 80-mesh screen. Hence, the percentage of meal through a screen of that size was a standard of efficiency in disintegration.

A high-speed, dissolver-type impeller (3¼-inch diameter) gave the best disintegration. More than 90 percent of 80-mesh material was obtained under the best conditions. Flakes that had a moisture content of more than 5 percent reduced the efficiency of disintegration noticeably and increased both the power consumption and the slurry viscosity. Peripheral speeds of up to 6,000 feet a minute gave the best disintegration. The use of whole flakes gave a better disintegration than did the use of flakes prepulverized in a dry state. The presence of hulls slightly increased power consumption and viscosity, but also increased disintegration efficiency. The effect of using different solvents was negligible.

Screening tests of disintegrated slurries revealed that when 90 percent through-80-mesh meal was produced, 70 to 75 percent of the meal was disintegrated sufficiently to pass a 300-mesh screen. More than 90 percent of the pigment glands were of a size between the openings of an 80- and a 300-mesh screen. This high percentage of fine meal caused interference and entrapment in the separation operation, particularly because of the fluffiness of the fraction. Moreover, the apparent density of the fraction tended to overlap the density of the heavier pigment glands.

Results of centrifugal tests for separation showed no improvement in the process because of the small differences in specific gravity of the components to be separated.

Those factors added to the difficulty of quantitatively controlling the procedure.

Another factor that discouraged commercial adaptation of the flotation process was that the heavier solvents (perchloroethylene, trichloroethylene, and carbon tetrachloride) required to obtain the proper specific gravity cost five times more than hexane. The heavier solvents also are toxic.

There were four other disadvantages. The miscella (when using undefatted flakes) was a three-component system, which complicated and increased the cost of the evaporation, stripping, and fractionation operations. The higher temperature required in the stripping operation increased the possibility of darkening the oil, which is sold primarily on the basis of its color. The higher temperature required for desolventizing the meal had a denaturing effect on the protein in the meal— perchloroethylene boils at 121° C., as compared to 66° C. for hexane. Use of the mixed solvents virtually prevents any possible adaptation of the flotation process directly to industrial solvent-extraction processes.

Collectively, the disadvantages led to the discovery and development of the differential-settling fractionation process, which overcame the difficulties. Primarily on the basis of the data obtained on the reduction of flake size and on the settling of the solid components, the successful differential-settling process was conceived.

THE DIFFERENTIAL-SETTLING PROCESS depends principally on the force of frictional resistance between the solvent and the solid components in the slurry. The method was suggested by the slow settling characteristic of the fluffy, fine meal particles noted during the flotation experiments.

Several characteristics of the solid components bring about the play of frictional resistance. The hulls are dense, solid particles with relatively smooth surfaces and have a specific gravity of 1.45. Compared to the pigment glands, which are compact particles with a granular-appearing surface and have a specific gravity of 1.36, the fine meal particles (2 to 40 microns) are a fluffy, feathery mass of no definite shape, with relatively large surface area per unit weight, and have a specific gravity of 1.42.

A preliminary experiment in which flakes were disintegrated in commercial hexane (specific gravity, 0.68) showed that the hulls and coarse meal settled rapidly. The whole pigment glands settled a little more slowly than the hulls and coarse meal. The fine meal particles, although they have a higher specific gravity than the glands, settled more slowly than any of the other fractions.

The time required for complete settling of hulls and practically complete settling of pigment glands can be established for various conditions.

Laboratory experiments further showed that in order to detach 90 to 95 percent of the meal tissue in a slurry containing a ratio of 1 gram of flakes (solid basis) to 1.5 to 1.8 milliliters of solvent (commercial hexane), a disintegration which reduces 70 percent of the meal tissue to 2 to 40 microns is necessary.

More than 90 percent of the fine meal particles will be in suspension at the end of the settling time, but the amount of pigment-gland fragments remaining in suspension is negligible. Meal particles of more than 40 microns settle at rates intermediate to those of pigment glands and hulls. This coarser meal fraction can be redisintegrated and resettled to increase the yield of fine meal.

With undefatted flakes, the oil content of the slurry may go up to at least 30 percent by weight without noticeably affecting the yield of fine meal by the increase of viscosity.

An excellent solvent for fractionation is one in the low specific-gravity range of 0.67 to 0.98—typically, commercial hexane.

The first results obtained with differential settling were so promising that a full-scale pilot plant was designed, constructed, and installed in the Southern Laboratory, where it occupies 550 square feet of floor area. The equipment for the principal unit operations was specially designed and constructed or purchased ready-made, after consultations and trials with manufacturers. The principal pieces of equipment are a 10-horsepower, high-speed, dissolver-type disintegrator; a 300-gallon specially designed tank; an 18- by 28-inch continuous horizontal centrifuge; two pressure-type rotating leaf filters for filtering various meal fractions, including effluent from centrifugal operation; and one 3-stage evaporator for concentration of oil miscella and recovery of solvent.

The pilot-plant procedure has eight consecutive operations:

1. Preparation of the flakes.

2. Disintegration of flakes in hexane with concentrations of up to 50 percent solids by weight.

3. Dilution of disintegrated slurry to 12 to 15 percent solids.

4. Differential settling to separate the fine meal from the pigment glands and coarse meal—tank differential settling in which the slurry is settled for a predetermined time of at least 10 minutes prior to decanting, or centrifugal differential settling, employing relative centrifugal forces of about 60 times gravity, in which fine meal (8 to 10 percent solids) is discharged with effluent at one end of the centrifuge and the coarse meal and pigment glands (60 to 80 percent solids) are discharged at the other end.

5. Recovery of fine meal from slurry from either tank or centrifugal settling operations—by centrifugation at about 1,500 times gravity, which gives a fine-meal-cake discharge of 60 to 80 percent solids and a solvent-effluent discharge at about 0.6 percent solids, or by filtration of the fine-meal slurry in pressure filters to obtain a fine-meal cake of about 70 percent solids and a clear filtrate of solvent and oil (miscella).

6. Clarification by filtration of the effluent obtained when fine meal is recovered by centrifugation.

7. Removal of solvent from solvent-damp fine- and coarse-meal fractions.

8. Evaporation for recovery of oil and solvent.

This procedure was followed in a series of 15 runs, with the following results: Feed-meal preparation studies showed that either defatted or unde-fatted flakes could be used; low moisture content was necessary for efficient distintegration; high temperatures had a denaturing effect on the protein of the meal. A procedure was developed and maintained for reducing the moisture content to 3.5 percent and for keeping the meal temperature below 145° F.

Utilizing the liquid shear produced by the high-speed, dissolver-type impeller was satisfactory for the size reduction of flakes. Each of seven batch runs used 200 to 350 pounds of flakes. Meal disintegration of up to 80.6 percent by weight through 80-mesh screens and 69.3 percent by weight through 300-mesh screens was obtained. To increase efficiency, two intermittent disintegration runs were conducted. They showed that comparable size reduction could be obtained. With this improved procedure, up to 800 pounds of flakes have been processed in a run. Intermittent disintegration consists of disintegrating for 10 minutes, diluting, and partially differentially settling in the same tank, adding more meal, and repeating the procedure three to five times.

A high hull content of flakes causes breakage of pigment glands and consequent contamination of fine meal. The percentage of meal recovered by tank settling in relation to settling time depends on the hull content of disintegrated solids. If the hull content is reduced to 8.5 percent, only 10 minutes are required to recover 95 percent of the fine meal, with a gland content of only 0.17 percent. When the hull content is increased to 19.9 percent, it takes 75 minutes to recover 76 percent of the fine meal, with a gland content of 0.28 percent. Further reduction of hull content to 2 percent gives a percentage of original pigment glands of less than 0.09 in the top fraction for nearly equal settling times.

The percentage of meal recovered by centrifugal settling depends on the relative gravity at which the centrifuge is operated. At 60 relative centrifugal force, 72 percent of the 300-mesh meal is recovered, compared to 40 percent at 180 relative centrifugal force. This approaches the 92 percent obtained by tank settling and indicates that better results could be obtained with a still lower relative centrifugal force. The low pigment-gland content, 0.08 percent, of the fine meal is also significant.

Continuous centrifugation at 1,500 relative centrifugal force was found to be satisfactory in reducing the solids content of the fine meal-solvent slurries. We were able to reduce the solids content of slurries containing up to 11.4 percent solids down to about 0.6 percent. Meal recoveries were 90 percent.

Filtration utilizing the pressure-type rotating leaf filters gave a clear miscella, or solvent filtrate, with feed slurries of 3.5 to 11.8 percent solids. The feed slurries were the fine-meal fraction from differential settling. However, the effluent from the centrifugal operations at 1,500 relative centrifugal force, which contained about 0.6 percent meal of very fine particle size, could be filtered only when filter aid was used in excessive quantities. The solvent content of the meal cake from the filters varied from 28.7 to 4.1 percent, depending on operating conditions.

The experimental runs showed that for desolventization of solvent-damp meal, the use of present commercial methods with controlled low drying temperatures can be contemplated. In order to produce a cottonseed meal suitable for nutritional and industrial uses, drying temperatures should probably not exceed 140° F.

Oil- and solvent-recovery operations can be conducted with conventional industrial evaporators and strippers for processing the miscella produced when undefatted or partially defatted flakes are used.

Present cost estimates and market surveys indicate that a fractionation process is economically feasible, either with the defatted flakes from a solvent-extraction plant or in conjunction with industrial screw pressing.

In using fractionation in conjunction with a continuous solvent-extraction system, the defatted, solvent-damp flakes from the extractor would be fed directly into the disintegrator of the fractionation system. This would eliminate the necessity of desolventizing the flakes after extraction so that desolventization would be required only at the end of the process. Furthermore, the extracted flakes could be fed to the disintegrator at a higher oil content, because additional extraction of oil would take place in the disintegration and differential-settling steps. That would eliminate the last and most difficult phase of solvent extraction; namely, the reduction of the last 3 to 4 percent of the oil in the flakes to a value below 1 percent. It would also greatly increase the capacity of the extractor, possibly as much as 50 percent. An extractor originally designed for 100 tons of meats per 24 hours would thus be capable of extracting 150 tons per 24 hours. The resulting savings could be applied to the cost of the subsequent fractionation operations. The cost of seed preparation, oil and solvent recovery, and probably storage would be in proportion to the capacity of the plant. The cost of desolventizing the meal would probably be slightly higher in the combined process because of the nature of the meal produced by fractionation.

In the employment of the fractionation process in conjunction with screw pressing, part of the meats from the preparation equipment would be diverted to the fractionation process as clean, practically hull-free whole meats, and the regular fractionation operations could then be followed. The rest of the meats would be screw-pressed in the customary manner.

Viewed from the practical standpoint, then, the fractionation process under present conditions gives a slightly favorable estimated profit spread and provides purified cottonseed products for research. From the long-range viewpoint, the fractionation process makes possible the maximum recovery of oil from cottonseed, gives a new product—pigment glands—and makes the cottonseed meal available as a source of protein for animal feed and for the manufacture of fibers, plastics, and adhesives. If the 4,339,000 tons of cottonseed processed in this country in 1948 had been fractionated, the crop would have yielded 1,345,090 tons of light-colored, practically pigment-free meal and 43,390 tons of pigment glands, in addition to a maximum recovery of the oil.

E. F. POLLARD *was graduated in chemical engineering at the Alabama Polytechnic Institute in Auburn. He received the doctor's degree in inorganic chemistry at Western Reserve University. Dr. Pollard taught at Auburn, Iowa State College, Georgia School of Technology, University of Alabama, and Tulane University before 1942, when he joined the Southern Regional Research Laboratory, where he has supervised a varied program of research on the extraction of rubber from goldenrod, the solvent extraction of cottonseed and other oilseeds, and the fractionation of cottonseed meats.*

H. L. E. VIX, *after receiving his chemical engineering degree from Tulane University in 1934, was connected with the brewing industry for 6 years. He spent the following 2 years as a consulting chemical engineer. In 1942 he joined the Southern Laboratory as a group leader in the chemical engineering research section.*

J. J. SPADARO, *chemical engineer at the Southern Laboratory since 1942, has been engaged in chemical engineering research on solvent extraction of rubber from goldenrod and edible oils from oilseeds, particularly cottonseed. As a member of the chemical engineering research section, he has aided in developing the cottonseed fractionation processes. He is a graduate of Syracuse University.*

Polyamide Resins From Soybeans

John C. Cowan

Norelac is one of several polyamide resins that can be derived from soybean oil. Its name comes from Northern Regional Lacquer, and it belongs to the same chemical family as nylon. Norelac was first prepared by chemists at the Northern Regional Research Laboratory in 1942. Two industrial concerns produced it during the Second World War. One large soybean-processing company has been manufacturing it since 1945. Its continued use and production appear to be assured.

The greatest usefulness of Norelac seems to be in the general field of packaging. Its compatibility with resins, waxes, and plasticizers facilitates the formulation of many useful combinations. Its use for protecting K-ration boxes and for filling pores in magnesium castings is primarily based on its cohesiveness and impermeability to moisture, but another property makes it good for packaging. When two coated strips are placed face-to-face and heated under slight pressure, an excellent moisture-vapor-resistant bond is formed. If the resin-coated back of a label is heated and pressed against a cap, bread wrapper, bottle, or paper box, the label adheres firmly to the container. This heat-sealing method of fabrication is being used more and more in packaging. Norelac is now used in some packages sold in the corner grocery. Another application of Norelac in packaging is its use in lamination, where paper, cellophane, and other packaging materials are combined to make attractive and serviceable packages.

Norelac is a hard, transparent, thermoplastic (heat-softening) resin which is useful in lacquers and adhesives. It can be prepared with melting points ranging from 98° to 116° C. (208° to 240° F.). By using some organic diacids, such as sebacic, the melting-point range can be raised to 188° to 196° C. (370° to 384° F.). Its color varies from light yellow to dark brown. It is compatible with a large number of synthetic and natural resins and with plasticizers and waxes.

As a polyamide, Norelac has unusual characteristics of solubility. It dissolves in the alcohols commonly used by the protective-coating industry, such as isopropyl and butyl alcohols, in amines, in fatty acids, and in certain chlorinated hydrocarbons. It is insoluble in many other solvents commonly used by the trade, such as esters, ethers, glycols, ketones, hydrocarbons, and nitrohydrocarbons. While Norelac is insoluble in most petroleum solvents, its alcoholic solutions will tolerate large volumes of these solvents. Consequently, a wide range of inexpensive solvent combination is available.

Usually films are dry "set to touch" within 2 to 5 minutes. Norelac films possess excellent resistance to water, alkalies, and acids. For example, cold water, 4 percent vinegar, and 20 percent sodium hydroxide did not affect the film on 8 days' standing. Sulfuric acid (75 percent) discolors the film but otherwise leaves it unaffected.

Norelac films adhere well to many surfaces, and they have exhibited good outdoor durability on both wood and metal.

A spirit lacquer prepared with zinc chromate (24.8 percent), micaceous lithopone (15.8 percent), asbestine (4.5 percent), and Norelac (55 percent by weight), was coated on cold-roll steel panels. After more than 3 years of exposure at 45° south, the films were still in good condition. Another formulation, in which we used aluminum bronze as the pigment, was exposed for more than 6 years, and the films were still in excellent condition. In another test, Norelac coatings that contained red iron oxide were in good condition after 4 years of exposure.

Furthermore, it was found that the addition of a small percentage of paraffin wax to Norelac imparts moisture impermeability to the resulting films. A thin film cast on paper from a Norelac solution containing 2 percent paraffin had an exceedingly low rate of water vapor transmission—the value obtained compared very favorably with that of many organic coating materials.

Norelac should find many applications as a protective coating for wood and metal surfaces. It can be used alone or in combination with other resins as a spirit varnish or lacquer. Norelac in solution can be readily pigmented with a ball or pebble mill, or in the "dry" state in a roller mill. Pigmented solutions of Norelac make excellent rapid-drying enamels of outstanding durability. Norelac solutions make superior vehicles for aluminum and bronzing powders.

Because Norelac is thermoplastic and possesses excellent adhesion, it can also be used as a laminating and heat-sealing agent for paper, glassine, cellophane, vinyl films, and metallic foils. A wide variety of laminates, such as glassine-to-glassine, lead foil-to-sulfate paper, and cellophane-to-cellophane, can be prepared with Norelac. The laminates using Norelac as the bonding agent compare favorably with commercial materials.

ONE OF THE most interesting war uses for the resins was in hot-dip stripping compounds. Army and Navy equipment and spare parts were dipped in or sprayed with a hot mixture containing Norelac, which solidified to a continuous film that covered the article completely. The film provided protection during shipping, and it was readily stripped off when the article was needed. The polyamide resins had some advantages over other materials used for this purpose. Liquid film could be applied at lower temperatures, thus minimizing the danger of burns. The alkaline polyamide resins absorbed the acids on the metallic surfaces resulting from perspiration from the hands of factory workers. Indeed, it quickly removed fingerprints from accurately machined parts, and thus prevented rusting under the coating during shipping.

THE CHEMISTRY of these polyamide resins is quite simple. The linoleic and linolenic acids (I) present in soybean oil combine with themselves two and three times to give a mixture of dimeric (II) and trimeric (III) acids, which we call polymeric fatty acids.

The acids will combine readily with a large number of chemicals. Experiments at the Northern Laboratory in 1941 and 1942 showed that the polymeric fatty acids can be reacted with ethylene glycol (nonvolatile antifreeze) to give polyesters. The polyesters can be converted into rubberlike materials by mixing rubber fillers and chemicals. In 1942 and 1943, this rubberlike material was manufactured on a commercial scale, but a conservation order curtailed further production. The product was called Norepol (Northern Regional Polymer).

When the ethylene glycol is replaced by a diamine, such as ethylene diamine (IV) or hexamethylene diamine, the polymeric fatty acids react with the diamine to give a polyamide (V).

$$x \ HO-\overset{O}{\overset{\|}{C}}-R-R-\overset{O}{\overset{\|}{C}}-OH+xNH_2-R-NH_2(IV)\longrightarrow$$

$$HO-\left[\overset{O}{\overset{\|}{C}}-R-R-\overset{O}{\overset{\|}{C}}-\overset{H}{N}-R-\overset{H}{N}\right]xH(V) + (x-1)H_2O$$

In the actual preparation, acids are heated to approximately 150° C., and the aqueous ethylene diamine solution is gradually added until all of it has undergone the initial salt formation. Heating is continued as water from the solution and from the salt transformation to amide is distilled. The temperature of the reaction is gradually raised over a period of 90 minutes to 200° C., and continued for at least 1 hour to produce the resin. Chemically, the resin is known as the ethylene diamine polyamide of polymeric fatty acids; for convenience, we have called it Norelac. Other diamines and dibasic acids may be used to give resins of slightly different properties. The polyamides may be modified by the addition of monofunctional derivatives, such as stearic acid or *n*-monostearylethylene diamine.

The development of a method for suspending polyamide resins in water was announced by industrial researchers in 1950. This development should make it possible to reduce the costs of fabricating paper and other products in which the resins are used. Also, it should extend the utilization of the resins in new products, thus assuring greater industrial use of soybean oil.

The future use of polyamide resins depends somewhat on the price relation of vegetable oils and other resins. Vegetable oils dropped in price in 1949–50; as the supply becomes more abundant, the price of the polyamide resins from these oils should drop and the utilization of the resins increase. A new source of the polymeric fatty acids was announced in 1950, and commercial exploitation of the method should reduce the cost of polyamide resins. The process, developed by a company specializing in fatty acids, can employ any fatty acid stock containing linoleic acid. The linoleic acid is removed from the mixture by polymerization at high temperatures in the presence of water. The polymeric fatty acid will be a by-product in this process, and it will probably be made available at a reduced cost as compared with other possible sources.

JOHN C. COWAN *received a doctor's degree in chemistry from the University of Illinois. He is principal chemist at the Northern Regional Research Laboratory, and is in charge of the oil and protein division. Dr. Cowan has been with the Department since 1940.*

WHEN YOU FINISH PAINTING or working on a greasy machinery repair job and want to get cleaned up for dinner, try this:

Mix 5 volumes of turpentine and 1 volume of liquid nonionic emulsifier by shaking them together in a stoppered bottle. This solution will keep. (Don't be frightened by that emulsifier. There are a number of kinds, but one is readily available at the grocery store, where it is known as a liquid dish-washing soapless soap.) The rest is easy. Pour a little of the solution into your palm and rub it well into the hands to loosen the paint or grease. Wash it off in running water. The paint or grease, turpentine, and emulsifier all wash off easily. You can use the same solution to clean a paint brush right after you finish painting. This time, make the first rinse in a cup or two of water and then follow with running water. Be sure to do it before the paint dries as it will not work on old, dried paint.—*E. E. Fleck, Bureau of Entomology and Plant Quarantine.*

Varnishes and

Paints From

Soybeans

A. J. Lewis

The use of soybean oil in paints and varnishes is largely an American development and a new one. For more than a century the soybean oil we imported was used for food. Even as late as 1909, soybean oil was practically unknown as a paint oil. At that time, however, some chemists advocated the development of varieties of soybeans that would produce superior drying oils, which, they believed, would stabilize the price of linseed oil.

When soybeans started their climb to become the leading oil crop in this country, they found favor first as a hay crop, then as a source of edible oils, and finally as a source of drying oils. The climb was swift. The paint and varnish industry used 8.5 million pounds of soybean oil in 1933 and 150 million pounds in 1949. Other drying-oil industries used another 100 million pounds to make floor coverings, printing inks, and many other items. The use of soybean oil as a drying oil has thus kept pace with the phenomenal rise in production of soybeans.

Even though the 150 million pounds of soybean oil used in paints and varnishes represents only 11 percent of the total oil produced in 1949, it is 4 percent more than the amount used in 1948 and 57 percent more than the total used from 1943 through 1946. The figures indicate that soybean oil now has attained a definite place in the paint and varnish industry, and that its use no longer depends entirely on fluctuations in the price and supply of linseed oil.

SOYBEANS GENERALLY contain only about 20 percent of oil; the linseed oil in flax amounts to 38 percent.

Almost all the oil is processed by one of three methods—solvent extraction, continuous pressing, or hydraulic pressing. The first method is preferred because it produces an oil that is lighter in color and almost free from foreign material and a meal that is practically free from oil and well suited, therefore, for use in water paints, plastics, and glues.

Soybean oil obtained by any of these methods is considered as crude oil, which must subsequently be refined by one of three methods. Mechanical refining consists of emulsifying the oil with hot water or steam and then centrifuging out the foreign material. Acid refining consists of treating the oil with strong sulfuric acid, which chars the foreign material but not the oil, if handled properly. Alkali refining consists of emulsifying the oil at room temperature with a solution containing a slight excess of alkali over that required for neutralizing the free fatty acids of the oil.

The oil obtained by mechanical or acid refining differs from that obtained by alkali refining in that the free fatty acids retained in the oil serve as pigment-wetting agents and make the paint easier to grind. The oil obtained from alkali refining, because of its light color, is preferred for making oil-modified alkyd varnishes, especially those intended for white enamels. However, the oils obtained from any of the refining methods are suitable for protective coatings if they conform to the requirements of Federal Specification JJJ–O–348 for refined soybean oil.

This specification sets standards for specific gravity, iodine number, saponification number, loss on heating at 105° C., unsaponifiable matter percentage of foreign material, and acid number.

Besides those requirements, the oil must be clear and free from sediment and suspended matter when examined by transmitted light at 65° C. (149° F.). Its color must not be darker than that of a solution of 0.38 gram of reagent potassium dichromate in 100 milliliters of sulfuric acid of specific gravity of 1.84, equivalent to the No. 12 tube of the Gardner color scale (1933).

A BODIED OIL is one that has been heated at high temperatures to "body," or thicken, it to a siruplike consistency by the formation of polymers, which result when molecules combine with one another. The soybean oil used for kettle bodying must be free from foreign, or break, material and should have a high iodine number. The iodine number denotes the amount of iodine that is absorbed by the oil molecules and is the measure of the degree of unsaturation, or capacity of the oil to oxidize and to polymerize. Soybean oil that has an iodine number of 130 takes twice as long to body to a certain viscosity as linseed oil with an iodine number of 175 when heated at the same temperature. The time required for bodying soybean oil can be reduced by heating the oil to as high a temperature as possible without creating a fire hazard or by using high vacuum. Also, a number of chemicals, such as β-methylanthraquinone, phenanthrene, and diphenylcarboxyanthracene, have been used successfully to accelerate the bodying of oils without injuring their quality.

Bodied soybean oils have been used to replace all or part of the oil vehicle of interior and exterior paints with some success in drying and in durability. Bodied soybean oil that has a viscosity of approximately 5 poises (similar to a very heavy lubricating oil) has been mixed with tung oil in proportions of 70 parts to 30 parts by weight and heated to 550° F. to make a processed oil with better drying qualities than linseed oil. This processed oil, known as a copolymerized oil, can be cooked with ester gum and other inexpensive resins to make high-grade varnishes. The polymers of high-viscosity bodied soybean oil are insoluble in acetone and can be readily separated from the unpolymerized portion for use in making good soybean oil-ester gum varnishes.

SOYBEAN OIL GAINED POPULARITY in the varnish industry in the Second World War when supplies of tung oil were short. Tung oil had been popular since early in the First World War. Before then, most varnishes were made from linseed oil and natural resins. The coatings from these varnishes dried too slowly to meet the demand for fast production of armaments and war equipment. Soon a new type of varnish, Valspar, appeared. It was made from ester gum (a resin obtained by neutralizing rosin acids with glycerol), tung oil, and mineral spirits. It, and others like it, dried rapidly, were waterproof, and made excellent grinding materials for paints and hard-drying enamels.

Oil-modified alkyd varnishes, generally called alkyds, are made commercially in closed vacuum kettles. The process usually consists of heating and reacting a dibasic acid, such as phthalic anhydride, and a polyhydroxy alcohol, such as glycerol, with the fatty acids of vegetable, animal, or marine oils. The oils serve as plasticizers and are required because the resin produced by the reaction of the acid and alcohol is too brittle for use in surface coatings without modification. A unique characteristic of alkyds is that the plasticizer becomes a part of the resin by chemical combination rather than by physical admixture. The first alkyds, known as glyptals, utilized only the fatty acids of linseed oil, but in the early 1930's small amounts of soybean fatty acids began to be used in blends with linseed fatty acids. The production of alkyd varnishes increased rapidly because they could be produced economically and were outstanding for adhesion, toughness, durability, flexibility, and hardness. Also, they could be produced in large volumes in single closed kettles, required little supervision, and utilized the oils then available.

The use of soybean fatty acids has been favored for alkyds because of their availability and low linolenic acid content. The low acid content enables the manufacturer to produce white and light-tinted enamel coatings that do not yellow appreciably when applied to refrigerators, automobiles, and the like. Although the slow-drying properties of soybean acids limited their use in the alkyd field for a long time, improved methods for the forced drying of coatings by heat (especially infrared lamps) have greatly helped to overcome this limitation. An increasing number of manufacturers now produce alkyds containing 100 percent soybean acids. It is likely that half or more of the soybean oil used in protective coatings is being used in making alkyd varnishes.

Soybean oil-ester gum varnishes of 15- and 20-gallon oil lengths (gallons of oil to 100 pounds of resin), known as short-oil varnishes in the trade, have been made by cooking ester gum and refined soybean oil for $3\frac{1}{2}$ hours at 600° F. But the coatings from these varnishes soften, or "aftertack," badly in hot, humid weather. Nevertheless, the same varnishes, when partly pigmented with small amounts of calcium oxide, produce coatings that dry fast, hard, and flat, and are durable for interior use.

The best soybean oil-ester gum varnishes have been made from either the copolymer of tung and soybean oils, or the polymers extracted from bodied soybean oils, both of which I have described. Other soybean oil-ester gum varnish coatings, which have good drying qualities and resistance to hot and cold water, acids, and alkalies, have been made from some of the special soybean oils, which are described later.

The hardest and most durable varnishes have been those made from an oil-reactive, unmodified phenolic resin and soybean oil. The varnishes were made by heating 20 gallons of refined soybean oil and 100 pounds of phenolic resin (Bakelite resin No. 254) together in a stainless-steel open kettle at 600° F. until bodied sufficiently to give a 5-inch string when a few drops were tested on a cold plate.

The cook was then removed from the heat, allowed to cool to 200° F., and thinned with 24 gallons of mineral spirits followed by 5 gallons of toluene. Cobalt driers of the naphthenate type containing 6 percent cobalt metal were added at room temperature and three-eighths of a gallon of drier gave satisfactory drying qualities to the coatings. The time of bodying at 600° F. to a 5-inch string was approximately an hour; the speed of bodying depended on the use of an oil-reactive resin.

Phenolic varnishes made by this formula and procedure dried rapidly overnight to hard, glossy coatings, which were durable and marproof when tested on floors, launches, bows and arrows, and such. The coatings were highly resistant to hot and cold water, acids, alkalies, gasoline, and alcohol.

Tested comparatively by outdoor weathering, they proved to be more durable than two high-grade commercial varnishes that contain tung oil. Similar varnishes were made with longer oil lengths, but their coatings did not dry so hard and were less resistant than the coatings of the 20-gallon varnish. However, the material costs for varnishes of long oil length are less, and they are easier to apply by brushing. Norelac is another type of varnish that dries by solvent evaporation instead of by oxidation and polymerization.

LITTLE SOYBEAN OIL was used in paints until 1934, when some farmers' cooperative organizations began to distribute exterior paints that contained small percentages of soybean oil and were made by paint manufacturers in accordance with the formulas furnished by the cooperatives. Many of the paints were durable in service, but some became discolored because of dirt collection, a feature that prejudiced many users against soybean-oil paints.

The excessive dirt collection was found to be caused partly by the slowness with which the oil dried and partly by the pigment formulations used in the paints. Soybean-oil paints, especially those containing sobean oil exclusively, when formulated with certain pigments, produce coatings that remain tacky for a long time after application, a condition known as residual track. The coatings may tend to soften and become practically liquid when applied in hot and humid weather. That phenomenon is called aftertack. It is obvious that dirt collected on a coating that has developed aftertack would become so deeply imbedded that it could not be washed away without injuring the coating, while the dirt collected on a coating with residual tack would be removed by the periodic self-cleaning of the coating as it disintegrated into a powder or chalk, which is usually readily washed off by rain. However, both residual and after tack can be eliminated almost completely from the coatings of paints that contain even a 100-percent soybean-oil vehicle by including zinc oxide or calcium oxide in the pigment components.

Zinc oxide, in amounts of 25 to 30 percent by weight in the pigment portion of 100-percent soybean-oil paints, has been found to improve coatings with respect to residual and after tack, as well as chalking, checking, and cracking failures. Many paints have been similarly formulated from various percentages of basic carbonate white lead and zinc oxide and either 100-percent raw linseed-oil or 100-percent refined soybean-oil vehicles. The coatings from these paints have given practically equal results when tested comparatively by outdoor weathering for more than 7 years at Urbana and Peoria.

Similar improvements have been noted, not only when zinc oxide was mixed with a single pigment or with a composite pigment, but also when the paints were made in accordance with either the prewar or the conservation paint formulas.

A BRIEF EXPLANATION of those formulas may be of value. The prewar formulas used nearly all raw oil in the liquid part of paint. The conservation formulas used equal volumes of raw oil, bodied oil, and paint thinner. They were adopted early in the war to conserve the supply of drying oils. Because the paints made from them have proved generally satisfactory in service, I expect that they will be continued with slight modifications. This type of paint presents greater possibilities for the utilization of soybean oil for several reasons—the fast-drying copolymers of soybean oil and tung oil require thinning before they can be utilized in paints, and the slow drying of soybean oil is partly compensated for by the use of bodied soybean oil because smaller percentages of oil are used in the conservation of paints.

Calcium oxide has improved the drying quality and other qualities of 100-percent soybean-oil paint coatings to a greater extent than zinc oxide, according to results obtained when the coatings from outside white paints or red barn paints were tested comparatively. For example, two comparable 100-percent soybean-oil paint coatings varying only in their pigmentation—(1) 75 percent basic carbonate white lead and 25 percent zinc oxide; (2) 90 percent basic carbonate white lead and 10 percent calcium oxide—have dried free from residual tack in 96 and 32 days, respectively, as determined by fine sand falling off completely from the surface of the coating. The coatings from paints containing more than 10 percent of calcium oxide in their pigments generally dry too hard and brittle for satisfactory service; the optimum amount of calcium oxide is approximately 5 percent.

Besides residual tack, comparative outdoor weathering tests of the outside white and red barn paint coatings containing 100-percent soybean-oil vehicles have proved that coatings containing 5 to 10 percent of calcium oxide are superior to similar coatings containing zinc oxide in such respects as aftertack, color and reflection retention, and durability. In these tests, calcium oxide coatings showed much less dirt retention, yellowing, darkening, cracking, and checking than zinc oxide coatings.

Soybean-oil paints have also been improved in their drying qualities by the utilization of special oils that have been treated by chemical or physical methods. Besides the copolymers of soybean and tung oils previously mentioned, a number of others are obtained by reacting soybean oil with the unsaturated organic compounds from the petroleum industry—styrene, butadiene, cyclopentadiene, terpenes, and vinyls.

Another group of special oils is obtained by replacing the glycerol of soybean oil with pentaerythritol, sorbitol, mannitol, and others. Excellent drying oils are produced when soybean oil is heated with maleic anhydride in various percentages to viscosities suitable for use as either paint or varnish oils. These oils are often reacted further with glycerol or pentaerythritol to neutralize the acids present and thus form a harder drying oil of low acidity.

Other methods for improving the drying qualities of soybean oil are based on the separation of the drying components from the nondrying components of the oil. Two of the methods are vacuum distillation and segregation by furfural or liquid propane. Although expensive equipment is required, good drying oils for paints and also improved nondrying oils for edible use are produced.

Excellent traffic paints, which meet all the specifications of a number of States, have been made from soybean oil treated with maleic anhydride. The specifications were set up on the basis of the performance of traffic paints containing principally tung oil, a waterproof oil that dries fast and hard.

Outside white paint coatings that contain the drying components of soybean oil obtained by the furfural-segregation method have been tested for durability by outdoor weathering in Florida and Illinois. In comparison with similar coatings which contained raw linseed oil, they were better in drying, equal in resistance to chalking, and definitely superior in resistance to dirt retention, checking, and cracking. The iodine values of the drying components of soybean oil and of the raw linseed oil were 170 and 181, respectively.

Water paints that are satisfactory in service tests can be produced from soybean oil or from an alkyd varnish modified with soybean oil, by emulsifying either of them in a mixture of soybean protein, water, borax, and water-dispersible pigments, through the use of high-speed stirring methods. The resin-emulsion paints, among them several widely advertised ones, have become popular for interior decorating, not only because of their excellent hiding power in one coat, but also because they dry rapidly with a minimum of odor, possess good adherence, elasticity, and durability, and have fair resistance to washing. The large sales volume of this type of paint has resulted in the consumption of a large amount of soybean oil.

SOYBEAN OIL has now won a definite foothold in the paint and varnish industry.

The shortages and higher prices of the better drying oils have forced the industry to look with more and more favor upon soybean oil. The development of special or treated oils with better drying properties has enabled paint manufacturers to use more or less soybean oil in blends with other oils. The development of the popular oil- and resin-emulsion water paints has made a market for a good deal of soybean oil.

The progress now being made by the

paint and varnish industry in the use of less expensive oils, such as petroleum and tall, may prove a serious factor of competition to the continued use of soybean oil and of its improved drying treatments must be kept competitive with the cost of those oils as well as with that of linseed, tung, dehydrated castor, and other faster-drying oils. The use of small amounts of calcium oxide or lime in pigment formulations appears to be one method for lowering costs and at the same time improving the drying and other qualities of the soybean-oil coatings.

A. J. Lewis *has been a research chemist in the Northern Regional Research Laboratory since 1942. He does research on the use of soybean oil in protective coatings. Previously he was a chemist at the National Bureau of Standards, Franklin Automobile Co., Norfolk Navy Yard and the United States Regional Soybean Industrial Products Laboratory.*

SYNTHETIC RUBBERS vary widely in their physical and chemical properties—so much so that scientists are constantly searching for new types for special uses. One of the new specialty rubbers is acrylic rubber, a material whose resistance to heat is so superior to that of most other rubbers that its higher cost is outweighed by its longer life. It also has excellent resistance to lubricating oils. No other rubber has so good a combination of properties. The availability of such a rubber, in itself, stimulates further development. For example, machine designers are constantly striving to develop higher-powered and more compact motors, pumps, transmissions, and so on. Such equipment usually operates at higher temperatures, so that the lubrication problem becomes increasingly difficult. Over-all performance may hinge on the heat and oil resistance of such items as the rubber in the oil seals, valve packings, diaphragms, or gaskets used.

Lactic acid is one of the potential starting materials for making acrylic rubber. It may be recovered from whey, starch, molasses, and sulfite waste liquors and then converted to one of various acrylates used in making acrylic rubber. Designers and manufacturers now are giving most attention to ethyl acrylate rubber. Both groups, however, hope to find one with even better properties, particularly improved flexibility at −50° F. Two other acrylates, butyl acrylate and octyl acrylate, offer the most promise in the direction of improved resistance to low temperatures.

In the development of specialty rubbers, improvement in one property is often at the partial sacrifice of another. Such is the case in butyl acrylate and octyl acrylate rubbers. Improvement in flexibility at low temperatures is accompanied by a tendency to swell and soften in lubricating oils. Scientists of the Department of Agriculture have been investigating acrylic rubber obtained from lactic acid for several years. Recent developments indicate that butyl acrylate rubber offers a suitable compromise between resistance to swelling by oils and flexibility at low temperature.—*T. J. Dietz, Eastern Regional Research Laboratory.*

The Flavor Problem of Soybean Oil

Herbert J. Dutton,
John C. Cowan

In the years after the Second World War, soybean oil sold for 1 to 9 cents less a pound than competing oils, although in many ways it equals or surpasses other oils. The only apparent explanation for that difference in price is the peculiar flavors that develop in soybean oil on aging. While cottonseed oil grows rancid on standing, soybean oil reverts—that is, it becomes painty or grassy.

Whether a rancid cottonseed oil or a stale corn oil is better or worse than a reverted soybean oil is a matter of consumer preference. It does seem that the American housewife has decided in favor of corn and cottonseed oils. Her decision costs the soybean industry and growers annually 10 million to 90 million dollars, calculated on the differential of 1 to 9 cents a pound. Many people believe that unless research workers succeed in improving the flavor of soybean oil, the wartime expansion in production of soybeans, processing capacity, and edible soybean-oil products may recede before the competition of other well-established edible oils. Industrial, university, and Government institutions are cooperating in efforts to find an answer to the problem.

The problem is not simple. One can taste and smell an off-flavor or bad odor in a concentration of only a few parts per billion. Few chemical or physical tests can rival the sensitivity of the human sense of taste and smell, and we have no such test to measure the off-flavor of soybean oil. Until we can devise an objective physical or chemical test, we have to rely on the variable human senses.

The procedure evolved at the Northern Regional Research Laboratory for conducting taste tests conforms to a definite order. A pair of samples is presented to each of 12 tasters in a blind test; that is, samples are identified only by number. The tasting is done in individual booths in a quiet, air-conditioned room. The samples are held at the same temperature by a heated aluminum block. Each taster records evaluations of odor and flavor on a standardized sheet. Later, flavor scores are averaged and the significance of the results are analyzed by statistical methods. When these precautions are taken, reproducible data can be obtained. The development is a milestone in research progress, because without reliable methods of evaluation we cannot determine when improvements in processing treatments have been made.

SEVERAL THEORIES try to explain the cause of the peculiar flavor instability of soybean oil. Many European refiners believe that traces of lecithin remaining in the oil cause the instability. They use elaborate precautions, involving thorough degumming operations, for removing the lecithin. Exhaustive degumming experiments in our Laboratory and in commercial plants of cooperating refiners, however, have demonstrated no benefits from such operations. Controversial also are the hypotheses that unsaponifiable constituents and isolinoelic acid cause the off-flavors.

One of the oldest theories centers around linolenic acid as the flavor-unstable substance or precursor of the off-odor. The acid is one of the component fatty acids of soybean oil, linseed oil, perilla oil, and other oils that develop painty-grassy flavors. It is absent in cottonseed, peanut, and sesame oils, which are considered flavor-stable or undergo typical rancidity upon storage. The linolenic acid theory has rested, therefore, on this bit of indirect, circumstantial evidence— the coincident occurrence of linolenic acid and flavor reversion.

Direct evidence indicting linolenic acid as the unstable precursor of off-flavors has now been developed in the Northern Laboratory. It was obtained in this way: Highly purified linolenic acid is introduced into the glyceride structure of flavor-stable cottonseed oil according to a recently discovered method. The oil is deodorized with steam until it is bland in flavor. This modified cottonseed oil is stored along with unmodified cottonseed oil and soybean oil until characteristic flavors have developed. The three samples are then presented to the taste panel for identification. Soybean and cottonseed oils are correctly identified, but the modified cottonseed oil containing linolenic acid is identified as soybean oil because its flavors are those of soybean oil. This and other supporting evidence that singles out linolenic acid as a flavor-unstable precursor is of cardinal importance in orienting current research.

Investigators seem now to have agreed on one way in which off-flavors develop. Oxidation is believed to play a part. Even this point has been disputed, however, because of experiments in which off-flavors developed although oxygen was thought to have been removed by exhaustive evacuation or by flushing with an inert gas. The effect of oxygen has frequently been missed because of the low peroxide value at which reversion occurs. Whereas lard rancidity is detected when it reaches a peroxide value of approximately 30, soybean-oil reversion is detected at the low peroxide value

of 2 to 3. After the sensitivity of the peroxide method was increased in our laboratory, a relationship of peroxidation to flavor deterioration became apparent. On samples refined from a single drum of soybean oil, an inverse correlation coefficient of 0.8 was found between flavor score and the logarithm of the peroxide value.

It is pertinent to mention here that conventional antioxidants, which have been used with such marked success in animal and some vegetable fats, are quite ineffective for increasing the storage life of soybean oil. Perhaps this is because of the unusually low peroxide level at which off-flavors develop in soybean oil.

Definite progress is being made in combating the flavor instability of soybean oil. Certain research developments are yet in the laboratory stage, while others have been incorporated in present commercial practice.

For example, the approach suggested by the laboratory experiments on linolenic acid lies both in the laboratory and in commercial practice. This line of attack for improving the flavor characteristics consists in the removal of fat molecules that contain linolenic acid by fractionation processes. However, the completeness with which these fractionations can be made ultimately depends on the pattern of arrangement of fatty acids in the fat molecules of soybean oil. We have employed the most efficient fractionating methods that we know—fractional crystallization, countercurrent extraction, and chromatographic adsorption techniques—and it becomes apparent that the structure of the fat molecules themselves will limit the completeness of removal of linolenic acid. The possibility of fractionating soybean glycerides to remove linolenic acid is not without hope, however. With the combined application of chemical reactions and physical fractionation the restrictions of glyceride structure are removed, in theory at least. Whether practical fractionations can be improved is the subject of current investigation and constitutes one research frontier.

Even with incomplete separation of linolenic acid, the fractionation of soybean oil lowers its reversion tendencies. Countercurrent extraction of soybean oil with furfural has been studied in detail on a pilot-plant scale in this laboratory in an attempt to recover linolenic acid containing glycerides from soybean oil for paint uses. The edible fraction of lowered linolenic acid content has poor oxidative stability, apparently because the extraction removes tocopherol antioxidants along with linolenic acid containing fat molecules. After stabilization with antioxidants and metal deactivators, however, these oils of lowered content of linolenic acid do have less reversion tendencies than the unfractionated oils. The process of countercurrent extraction is now being employed industrially on a tank-car-a-day scale. The high linolenic acid fraction is used in paints, while the low linolenic acid fraction finds its way into shortening. After hydrogenation and blending, the oil also is reported to have a valid position among edible fats because of its good plasticity and color.

Hydrogenation increases the oxidative and flavor stability of soybean oil. We do not know whether it is a result of a reduced level of unsaturation of fatty acids or a result of reduction of linolenic acid content. It should be noted that hydrogenated oils go into different uses than do the salad oils, which have been discussed up to this point. As shortenings, hydrogenated oils are used for high-temperature applications, such as deep frying. Thus the advantage of greater stability gained by hydrogenating oils is reduced by the more exacting nature of the high-temperature applications of the oils.

Increased stability has also resulted from the knowledge that oxidation is a major factor in off-flavor development. This information has led to wider use of inert atmospheres to protect oils from oxidation. There are the so-called

blanketing operations, in which oxygen-free gas, generally a mixture of carbon dioxide and nitrogen, is used to fill the empty space in tank cars of oil during shipment and to cover tanks of hot oil during refining. Bleaching may be carried out under a layer of inert gas or under reduced pressure in certain plants. It has been general practice to break the vacuum over oil in deodorization tanks with air, but inert gas is now used in many plants. Traces of metals, which are picked up during processing and which catalyze or speed up the oxidation of the oil, are becoming a matter of considerable practical concern, as will be discussed more fully later. In general, any method of preventing oxidation improves flavor stability.

There is also developing a general awareness that present processing practice may be overly drastic in one or more steps. It is difficult to conceive of any food product other than oil that may be heated during the tempering of the flake, refined with steam, hot alkali, and bleaching earth, and deodorized by holding in excess of 400° F. with steam passing through continuously for 8 hours—and with all this drastic treatment come out an edible product.

After investigation of the refining procedures in commercial processing plants and checking the results against those obtained in the laboratory, we can put a finger on several steps where loss of stability may occur. For example, in the commercial extraction plants, the final traces of solvent are removed from the oil in tall stripping columns by passing superheated steam countercurrently through the oil. The oil has been found to be damaged in columns of certain plants, where presumably excessive heating or contamination by metals occurred. Degumming and alkali refining remove or destroy naturally occurring stabilizers, such as lecithin and tocopherols. Bleaching earths used in refining to adsorb pigments and to lighten the color of the oil also remove protective antioxidants and thus lower the flavor stability.

Perhaps the most drastic step in the refining procedure is deodorization, which is, in effect, a steam distillation at a high temperature. It removes not only volatile flavor constituents but also the tocopherols and antioxidants. High temperature and steam are conducive to corrosion of the iron of which many deodorizers are constructed. The result is that pro-oxidant metal catalysts are introduced into the oil. In recognition of this hazard of contamination by metals, many processors are replacing iron materials in deodorizer construction with stainless steel and nickel. Also, tank cars for shipment of salad oils are frequently lacquered where the oil comes in contact with metal.

An interesting chapter in the improvement of the flavor stability of soybean oil covers the use of metal deactivators. At the close of the Second World War, Warren H. Goss, then on the staff of the Northern Laboratory, was assigned to investigate the German oilseed industry under the Army's Technical Industrial Intelligence Committee.

Among other things, he learned that citric acid was widely used in deodorization to inactivate traces of lecithin remaining after the double degumming and alkali refining. In subsequent tests at this laboratory, we found that the addition of citric acid was highly effective, not for the reason German processors advanced but because the citric acid complexed metallic pro-oxidants. Hence the description, metal deactivators. Compounds other than citric acid, including sorbitol and mannitol, were found to be active. Free, unesterified polybasic acids, or polyhydric alcohols in general, exhibit these metal-complexing properties. The addition of the compounds to the extent of 0.01 percent at the beginning of deodorization is being widely adopted in this country. Not only does the deactivator afford protection to the oil during deodorization but it also enhances its subsequent flavor stability.

In reviewing the status of soybean oil over the past few decades, it is apparent that marked progress has been made on the flavor problem. In fact, as we observe now the tremendous volume of soybean oil going into edible uses and note the slight differential in price between it and cottonseed oil, we are tempted to believe that we have achieved part of the goal of improving soybean oil until it can compete with other edible oils. However, the industry still considers the flavor stability of the oil to be its first research problem.

HERBERT J. DUTTON *has worked in the Department of Agriculture since 1941. At the Western Regional Research Laboratory he studied the deterioration of lipids of dried eggs and dehydrated vegetables. Dr. Dutton is now on the staff of the Northern Regional Research Laboratory, where he is in charge of the fundamental oil investigations section and is engaged in the isolation and identification of the off-flavor principles and precursors of soybean oil.*

JOHN C. COWAN *received a doctorate in chemistry from the University of Illinois. He is principal chemist at the Northern Laboratory and is in charge of the oil and protein division. Dr. Cowan has been with the Department since 1940.*

Number and distribution of mills in United States processing various oilseeds in 1949

Oilseed	Number of mills	States located in
Cottonseed	372	16
Soybeans	268	29
Peanuts	74	11
Flaxseed	51	15
Copra	16	5
Corn germ	12	7
Tung nuts	12	5
Babassu	5	2
Safflower	3	3

Data compiled from International Green Book, 1949–1950.

Some Industrial Outlets for Seed Flax

Howard M. Teeter

The flax plants from which we get fibers are tall, little-branched, and early maturing. Their seeds are small, and the fibers in the stems are long.

On the other hand, seed-flax plants are short and branched. They are selected for high yield of seed. Processed by conventional methods, they produce short fibers of little value for making cloth.

The seed of the fiber-flax plant yields an oil of good quality. Seed not required for replanting therefore is usually sold in the oilseed market.

Nearly 5 million acres of seed flax is grown each year in the United States. Our acreage of fiber flax has varied from 4 thousand to 18 thousand since 1940. Most of the fiber-flax acreage is in Europe.

How long seed flax will continue to be used almost exclusively for oil is problematical. Considerable research has been done with the object of making satisfactory cloth from the fiber of seed flax.

A continuous process for producing yarn from the straw of ripe seed flax was announced by the University of Minnesota in 1948. The straw is separated into fibers 12 to 18 inches long by chemical and mechanical means instead of by the traditional retting, which depends on fermentation and produces, from seed-flax straw, short fibers of little value. A continuous method of roving, followed by wet spinning, yields a yarn that can be woven into cloth. Linen crash woven from this yarn is said to have the same properties as linen crash made from fiber flax. Commercial success of the process should greatly increase the value of the seed-flax crop.

THE FIRST STEP in utilization of linseed oil is its isolation from flaxseed. Traditionally, this has been accomplished by squeezing the oil from the ground seed (meal) in presses. In early presses, the meal was placed between plates, which were then forced together by driven wedges. Later, screws and finally hydraulic forces came into use for applying pressure to the plates. The most modern method employs screw presses, which operate continuously.

Now, the solvent-extraction process, which has been so successful for soybeans, is not satisfactory for flaxseed. In that process, the seed is rolled into flakes (linseed flakes), which are treated with a petroleum hydrocarbon solvent, such as hexane, to dissolve the oil (linseed oil). But when flaxseed is flaked, and then extracted, the solvent tends to dissolve the connective material that holds the flakes together. Linseed flakes, therefore, tend to distintegrate, become powdery, and cake. The solvent can then run through cracks in the caked material, and the efficiency of the process is lost.

Success has been achieved by utilizing a combination of pressing and solvent extraction. Linseed meal is pressed to an oil content of 10 to 15 percent. The residual oil in the cake is then extracted with solvents. The pressing operation imparts a more rigid structure, which withstands the action of the solvent. The first plant to use this process was built near Minneapolis and put into operation in 1949. It has a capacity of 12,000 bushels a day.

Another possibility, which is being investigated by a commercial processor, is solvent extraction of linseed meal directly in a slow-speed centrifuge. Although the meal still tends to disintegrate under those conditions, the centrifugal action effects separation of the fine particles from the solution of oil obtained.

The continuous screw-press method works thus: Upon receipt at the mill, the flaxseed is cleaned of weed seeds, dirt, particles of metal, and other undesirable materials. It is then crushed or ground to a suitable particle size, after which it is passed through cookers. In the cooker, which is operated continuously, the meal is exposed to heat and live steam. The temperature is gradually raised, as the meal approaches the bottom of the cooker, to 190° to 200° F. The temperature and moisture content of the meal are carefully regulated at this point to assure economical recovery of the oil. The preliminary grinding and cooking operations destroy in part the cellular structure of the seed, so that removal of the oil is easier and more complete.

From the cooker, the meal passes to the continuous screw press, which is essentially a hardened steel block with a tapered bore. By means of an arrangement of screws, meal is forced through the bore, resulting in compression of the meal. The oil released in this operation passes out through fine grooves and perforations in the press. The meal emerging through the outlet of the press contains about 4 percent of oil. After further grinding to a suitable size, the meal is sold as feed for animals.

The freshly expressed oil is warm— 170° to 180° F. In that state it is filtered to remove any fine particles of meal. It is then stored until cool. During cooling, waxes and phosphatides separate and are removed by a second filtration to leave the ordinary double-filtered raw linseed oil of commerce.

For certain uses further refining is required. The refining agent may be acid or alkali. Acid refining is conducted by treating the oil with sulfuric acid in a lead tank. The strong acid chars many of the undesired contaminants in the oil and produces a precipitate, which is removed by filtration. Excess acid is eliminated by washing the refined oil with water. Acid-refined oils are used in grinding pigments, for example, in preparing white lead pastes and in making paints of a high content of lead.

In the alkali-refining process, a sludge of impurities is formed by heating the oil at 60° F. with a small amount of caustic soda solution. After the sludge is removed, the oil is washed, dried, and heated with bleaching clay to remove undesirable color. Alkali-refined oils are important because of their low free acidity. They are used in making varnishes, enamel vehicles (particularly for light-colored enamels), and printing inks.

Linseed oil often is subjected to still further processing. One common operation is polymerization, or heat bodying. Polymerization is accomplished by heating the oil at high temperatures in order to thicken it. By control of time and temperature the body, or viscosity, of the oil can be varied. Polymerized oil is frequently referred to as boiled oil.

Another common treatment of linseed oil is blowing. In that process, air is blown through the heated oil. As a result, the oil is thickened and its acidity is increased. Blown oils generally improve the leveling properties of paint and increase the ability of a paint oil to wet the pigment.

Sometimes linseed oil is heated with excess caustic to form a soap. Acidification of the soap liberates the linseed fatty acids, which are used in the manufacture of resins and various synthetic drying oils.

THE LARGEST SINGLE USE of linseed oil is in paint, varnish, enamel, and similar products. That accounts for about 70 percent of all linseed oil used in the United States.

Any paint is essentially a suspension

of a pigment in a liquid, the vehicle. Its properties depend in a complicated fashion on the kind of materials selected for pigment and vehicle. Most properties can be varied by changes in pigment, in vehicle, or in both—a factor that greatly complicates paint research and tends to prolong the period of testing before new paint formulations are placed on the market.

For many years people believed that the best exterior white paint should consist of white lead and pure linseed oil. Modern research has shown this idea to be wrong. Pigments other than white lead have been found to impart superior weathering properties with freedom from cracking and checking and with controlled chalking, which leave the surface in excellent condition to receive future coats of paint. One excellent pigment in use today is a mixture of titanium dioxide, asbestine, and leaded zinc oxide. Some satisfactory formulations contain no lead in any form.

Linseed oil, basically the best available oil for the vehicle, is seldom used in unmodified form. The modern vehicle consists of a mixture of linseed oil and heat-bodied linseed oil with enough thinner to make the final thickness about the same as that of linseed oil itself. Its use makes a paint that contains a smaller proportion of oil but that has, nevertheless, better leveling, brushing, and flowing properties, better gloss, and better resistance to penetration on new work. That vehicle was originally proposed and used during the Second World War as a replacement oil to conserve stocks of linseed oil.

THE MANUFACTURE of a paint requires two steps.

The first is to grind the pigment into a paste with a small amount of oil. The oil may be the same as the one to be used as vehicle for the paint. It is often advantageous, however, to use a special grinding oil. Such an oil usually contains free fatty acid, which helps the oil wet the dry powdered pigment.

The second step is to dilute, or reduce, the paste with the vehicle to the desired consistency. Driers (soluble compounds of cobalt, lead, or manganese) are also added to promote combination of the vehicle with atmospheric oxygen, to form the dry paint film.

A varnish is a solution of a resinous material in heat-bodied oil, diluted with thinner to the proper viscosity. An enamel is simply a pigmented varnish—a varnish to which pigment has been added to make it opaque and to provide color. Varnishes are prepared by heating oil and resin together at a high temperature until the desired thickening has occurred. Thinners and driers are added when the mixture has cooled. Varnishes are described in terms of their oil length, a quantity indicating the number of gallons of oil employed to 100 pounds of resin. The performance of a long-oil-length varnish (more than 30 gallons of oil) depends mainly on the properties of the oil; a short-oil-length varnish (less than 15 gallons) reflects the qualities of the resin. Films of some short-oil-length varnishes may justifiably be regarded as films of resin plasticized, or made flexible, by the oil present. Most commercial varnishes are of medium (15- to 30-gallon) oil length.

Oil-modified alkyd resins, another variety of coating material, are compounds of glycerin, phthalic anhydride, and fatty acids. They are made with a wide range of properties to serve specific purposes. Some dry to tough films when exposed to air; others do not. Certain forms contain relatively less oil than others and are employed as the resinous components of varnishes and enamels. Still another type contains enough oil to function as the sole vehicle in an enamel. Fatty acids of linseed oil are employed in alkyd resins of the drying type. Alkyd resins are generally used in finishes that must withstand severe abrasion and wear, such as automotive finishes, machinery enamels, and floor and deck enamels.

Linseed oil for many years has been

the preferred oil for use in paints, varnishes, and enamels because it brings to the coating material generally satisfactory performance in drying time, durability, dirt collection, resistance to water and alkalies, and the like. Other oils may perform better in one way or another, but this superior performance is usually offset by some serious weakness. Thus, tung oil dries more rapidly than linseed oil, but its films are too hard and brittle to endure out-of-door exposure. Soybean-oil films are flexible and more durable than those from linseed oil, but they take too long to dry. Certain formulations tend to pick up dirt. Furthermore, blends of oils do not always perform as satisfactorily as might be expected, and therefore are not adequate replacements for versatile linseed oil. An additional factor is that the cost of linseed oil is normally moderate. In general, manufacturers use linseed oil in preference to other oils unless special requirements must be met.

LARGE QUANTITIES of linseed oil are consumed each year in the manufacture of linoleum and oilcloth.

The first step in the manufacture of linoleum is oxidizing and polymerizing linseed oil until a relatively dry, nontacky solid is produced. The solid is mixed with rosin and heated at a fairly high temperature until the desired degree of chemical reaction has occurred. The product, called cement, is mixed with ground cork, or similar material, and pigments and then pressed onto a backing of burlap or other coarse fabric. A final curing at moderately high temperature completes the process. A true linoleum is thus distinguished from the cheaper substitutes, which are made by impregnating felt with bitumen and applying one or more coats of enamel on the surface.

Oilcloth consists of a cloth base on which several coats of enamel have been applied. The enamel must be specially formulated for maximum flexibility. Oilcloth differs from oiled cloth, which is made by saturating fabric with a drying oil, usually linseed or fish oil, and allowing each application to dry thoroughly.

LINSEED OIL is put to a variety of miscellaneous uses.

Printing inks are heavily bodied, or polymerized, linseed oils, called lithographic varnishes in the trade, combined with pigments, thinners, driers, resins, and the like. Where the paper is very absorbent, as is newsprint, the drying oil is replaced by mineral oil. Drying occurs here merely by absorption of the mineral oil by the paper. The exact properties of a printing ink must be carefully adjusted for the type of press, kind of paper, and nature of the printing process involved.

Linseed oil is frequently valuable because of its binding properties when gelled. Core oils, of which linseed oil is an important ingredient, are used to bind sand together to form the core of hollow metal castings. In the process, sand is thoroughly wetted with the core oil, formed to the desired shape, and baked to gel the oil. The properties of a satisfactory core oil must be such as to impart strength to the core without interfering with subsequent breakage for removal from the casting. The tensile strength of a core should be about 200 pounds to the square inch, as measured in an ordinary cement tester.

Linseed oil is also suitable for binding asbestos fiber in brake blocks, shingles, and the like.

Small amounts of linseed oil go into soap. Oils valuable for other purposes ordinarily are not used in soap manufacture. However, linseed-oil soaps, particularly the soft potassium soap, are prized for cleaning automobiles, linoleum, and painted or varnished surfaces.

THE CHARACTERISTIC ODOR AND FLAVOR of linseed oil are unacceptable to most people, although considerable amounts of the oil are consumed as food in eastern Europe, particularly in Russia, Poland, and Hungary. The world-wide shortage of edible oils and fats during and after the Second World War stimulated research, particularly in Canada, on elimination of the objectionable odor and flavor of linseed.

Two lines of research have been followed: Hydrogenation and solvent segregation.

In the hydrogenation process, linseed oil and hydrogen are combined catalytically. Much of the oxidative instability of the oil is lost thereby and odor and flavor are improved. Hydrogenated oils are used in margarine and cooking fats. Moderate amounts of hydrogenated linseed oil may be included with other oils in the manufacture of these products with reasonably satisfactory results.

The purpose of solvent segregation is to separate linseed oil into two fractions, one that is easily oxidized and one that is less readily oxidized. The basis of the separation is the difference in solubility in the solvent of the two types of material. The easily oxidized fraction should be an excellent drying oil for use in paints and varnishes, while the less readily oxidized fraction should be more satisfactory than the original oil for edible purposes. Although excellent drying oils have been produced commercially by this process, edible oils acceptable to the American taste have not yet been made from linseed oil.

Because of the variety and the importance of its industrial uses, linseed oil is essential in our economy. This alone is sufficient justification for the research and effort that have been devoted to fostering domestic production of seed flax. How well the endeavors have succeeded is indicated by the fact that the United States now produces flaxseed in excess of its requirements, whereas previously we were dependent upon imports.

HOWARD M. TEETER *holds a bachelor's degree from Bradley University and master's and doctor's degrees from the University of Illinois. He has been a research chemist on the staff of the Northern Regional Research Laboratory since 1942, and now is in charge of the work with industrial oils. His research fields include organic synthesis, stereochemistry, and the chemistry of unsaturated higher fatty acids.*

CREATION of new industries often can be traced to a few adventurous individuals. One of the group responsible for developing the soybean crop in this country is William J. Morse, who retired from the Department of Agriculture in 1949, after 42 years of service.

His enthusiasm for soybeans as a farm crop for the United States developed during an extended trip to China, Manchuria, Korea, and Japan in 1929 to 1931, when he collected the hundreds of varieties that since have been used as the basis for our extensive soybean program. The increase in the agricultural wealth of our country that resulted from the introduction of the new crop, the subsequent work leading to the improvement in yields and higher oil content, and the development of suitable plant characteristics are a lasting tribute to the work of Morse and his associates. The growing and processing of soybeans is now our largest oilseed industry and involves hundreds of millions of dollars each year in the United States.

Besides an encyclopedic knowledge of soybean culture, Morse brought from the Far East an appreciation of soybeans as food and detailed information on many methods for their preparation.—*Allan K. Smith, Northern Regional Research Laboratory.*

The Domestic Tung-Oil Industry

R. S. McKinney, R. L. Holmes

Tung oil is produced from the seed of the tung tree (*Aleurites fordii* and *A. montana*), a member of the Euphorbia family. The tung fruit is about 2 inches in diameter and normally has 4 or 5 seeds. The entire fruit is covered by a hull about a quarter of an inch thick. Each seed is coated by a hard shell; in it is the kernel, which constitutes about a third of the weight of the fruit and contains about 65 percent oil.

The Chinese have produced and used tung oil for centuries, but Europe and America did not know until the beginning of the twentieth century how to make use of its unique properties to produce water- and chemical-resistant coatings.

You would think that our young domestic tung-oil industry could find a solution to its problems in China, but explorers of the Department of Agriculture reported that the primitive methods used to produce much of the tung oil of China have changed but little since the sixteenth century, when Portuguese traders exchanged European goods for China wood oil (tung oil) at Canton. In China, the tung fruit, picked by hand, is piled into heaps to ferment. The seeds, husked by hand, after being roasted, are ground to a meal in stone mortars. The ground, steamed meal is shaped into cakes, which are wrapped in straw and placed in a hollowed-out log; the oil is pressed out by driving wedges between an end of the log and a wooden block placed against the cakes. Because of the crude methods, the oil has a dark color and a considerable amount of free acids, which may affect its use for some purposes. Obviously, such a process would not be economical in the United States.

The development of the domestic tung-oil industry resulted from the efforts of scientists in the Department of Agriculture and the agricultural experiment stations and individuals having commercial interests in tung production. Early studies showed that tung trees could be successfully grown within about 100 miles of the Gulf of Mexico. Needed are high rainfall, a mild climate, and soil that is a fertile friable loam and has good water and air drainage.

The first commercial planting of tung trees was made in 1925. The domestic commercial production of tung oil started in 1932, when two tank cars (120,000 pounds) of oil were shipped from the first tung mill near Gainesville, Fla. An estimated 192,000 acres of tung trees grow in the Coastal Plains of Florida, Louisiana, and Mississippi; Alabama, Georgia, and Texas have smaller acreages. About 25 million pounds of oil was produced in 1949 at 12 mills in several States.

So many plantings of tung trees had been made in the United States by 1938 and so much interest was shown in this new development that the Congress appropriated funds for investigations on the crop. Field laboratories were set up to carry out the investigations.

TUNG FRUIT is ordinarily processed in the United States by passing the partly dried fruit through decorticators and separators to remove the hulls and a portion of the shells from the seed and kernels. The oil is expressed from the separated, ground, and preheated kernels and seeds. That is done in a continuous press, which has an interrupted screw that moves the material forward within a cylinder of steel bars set close together against a restricted opening. The residue is discharged through the constricted opening at the far end of the cylinder in the form of a cake. The oil flows out between the bars of the cylinder. It is filtered and pumped into storage tanks.

DRYING TUNG FRUIT and seeds so that they can be milled or stored has been a major problem of the industry. The tung fruit that falls from the trees contains about 65 percent moisture and cannot be stored safely until it has dried to about 25 percent. The earliest practice in the domestic industry was to allow the fruit to lie on the ground until it had dried enough to be stored, without danger of heating or sprouting, in especially constructed barns. Under favorable weather conditions, several weeks are required for the newly fallen fruit in an orchard to dry to the proper moisture level; in wet seasons the tung fruit may not dry sufficiently on the ground to permit storage. For efficient oil extraction, the seed should contain 6 to 9 percent moisture. Fruit stored at 25 percent moisture requires several weeks or more to dry enough to permit pressing. A method of drying was needed so that the mills could start operating earlier and could accept wet fruit if they had to.

Tests were made on the artificial drying of the whole fruit, but that method does not seem economical in comparison with natural drying because of the excessive heat and time required. Because the hulls contain more than half of the moisture and have no value as a source of oil, their removal before drying or storage is desirable, so as to lower the heat needed in drying and to reduce the space required for storage.

The disc huller used in tung mills removes the hulls and removes or breaks a large proportion of the shells. It also damages some of the kernels. Experience with other oilseeds indicated that an increase in the free fatty acids through breakdown of the oil might be expected unless the broken seeds were expressed immediately. This was found to be the case. The moist broken seed developed free fatty acids rapidly and heated spontaneously unless forced ventilation was used for drying. However, tests in a pilot-plant tray drier at 165° F. showed that the hulled seed after drying to 10 percent moisture could be stored for several months with little or no increase in the content of free fatty acids of the oil and that the hulled dried seed could be processed efficiently soon after drying or after storage for several months.

Many oil-extraction tests carried out on both laboratory-scale and commercial screw presses indicated that the oil is expressed most efficiently when the ground meal entering the barrel of the press contains 3 to 5 percent moisture. The tempering bin attached to the press at the first tung-oil mill built in the United States was found to remove about 4 percent moisture from the meal, while the stack cookers placed over the press at later mills could reduce the moisture in the meal as much as 8 percent. The meal cooker and drier attached to the newest type of press removed about 5 percent moisture from the meal. Because of the limited capacity of the meal driers, other methods of drying were sought.

Several tung-oil mills have built bin driers similar to those used for drying cottonseed, in which hot air is drawn through the seed for about 24 hours. The driers were found to be somewhat unsatisfactory, because drying is not uniform and the possibility exists of development of free fatty acids in the seeds and kernels during the prolonged drying period. Several producers have installed vertical seed driers, in which warm air is drawn through a layer of seed 12 or 24 inches deep. It has been found that better yields of oil are obtained by keeping the temperature of the drying air in the vertical driers below 160° F. and drying the seed to a content of about 9 percent of moisture. Very satisfactory results have been obtained with the vertical driers, and their use has increased the capacity of the mill and the efficiency of oil expression.

WHEN THE FIRST commercial planting of tung was made in the United States, tung oil had not been recovered in any country by modern equipment. Early tests of a number of mechanical devices for hulling and separating tung seeds showed that that could be accomplished by first passing the tung fruit through a disc huller to remove the hulls and part of the shell from the kernels and discharging the hulled fruit over shaker screens to separate the hulls and broken shells from kernels and seeds. Other experiments indicated that the continuous press was better than the hydraulic press for expressing the oil.

A study of the hulling of tung fruit showed high losses of oil from kernel fragments in the separated hulls when the disc huller was operated on very dry fruit, and low losses on fruit containing 15 to 20 percent moisture; fruit containing much more than 30 percent moisture could not be hulled. A portable drum-type huller developed in the Department of Agriculture permits the hulling of fruit that contains 30 to 45 percent moisture without breaking many shells.

If the intact seed is dried and stored, it is hardly feasible to remove more of the shell just before pressing, and it would be necessary to allow all the shell to remain in the meal. Most mills remove about half the shell, but opinions differ as to the amount of shell that should be left with the kernels to provide friction and drainage during pressing.

Tests were made on a laboratory press and a commercial screw press to determine the effect of varying the proportion of shell on the yield of oil. Meal containing all the shell (about 40 pecent of the weight of meal) processed as efficiently as that containing half the shell. Kernels completely freed of shells yielded a press cake very high in oil content. Apparently a certain amount of shell is necessary to develop sufficient friction for efficient operation.

It was also found to be impossible to obtain efficient recovery of oil with seeds carried over from one season to the next. The difficulty appeared to result principally from the fact that the meal from old kernels does not become plastic when subjected to heat and pressure. When the old seeds are mixed with new seeds, no difficulty is experienced in expressing the oil from the meal.

During the filtration of crude tung oil, filter cake is produced which may contain as much as 50 percent oil and may constitute 20 percent or more by weight of the expressed crude oil. To recover as much oil as possible, the material is either added to fresh tung meal entering the press or is allowed to accumulate and then mixed with press cake and hulls and pressed without addition of fresh meal. Neither process has been satisfactory, as the oil in the filter cake oxidizes readily at high temperatures and the cake ignites spontaneously if not handled carefully. Besides, this fine material tends to pass through the cylinder bars of the press and increases the amount of foots of the crude oil.

Tests made on a commercial press and a laboratory press showed that the oil content of the press cake increased when filter cake was added to the meal and re-pressed. It was also impossible to obtain a press cake of low oil content when the filter cake was mixed with press cake and hulls and processed separately. A better method of handling filter cake is needed; solvent extraction seems to be the answer.

During the Second World War, the supply of tung oil from China was cut off, and the stocks in the United States were allocated for military purposes. Imported oil stored for 4 years increased in acid value from 4.0 to 8.0 and its rate of polymerization increased as shown by a decrease in the time of the Worstall test from 7 to 5½ minutes. In several instances, domestic oil stored in small tanks exposed to the weather formed a polymerized surface layer several inches thick. The layer was useless for the preparation of paints or varnishes. Such layers did not form in large tanks or in a tank under a roof. In a large tank, only a slight increase in the acid value of the oil occurred in about 2 years, the color of the stored domestic oil was good, and there was no evidence of gel formation. In tests at the Tung Oil Laboratory in Bogalusa, La., in 1946–49, domestic tung oil sealed in gallon cans was stored under different conditions and tested at intervals of 3 months. No measurable deterioration was detected, even after storage for 3 years, in cans painted black and standing in the sun.

THE SCARCITY OF TUNG OIL and its high price during the war led to an investigation of the possibility of increasing yields by solvent extraction.

It has been impractical to reduce the oil content of the cake below 3 or 4 percent by mechanical means. At times it has contained as much as 10 percent. In general, yields of oil are not high when the mechanical process is used, and losses of 2 to 3 percent of oil on the basis of the total weight of fruit are common. An advantage would accrue if the oil in the residual meal could be reduced below 1 percent by solvent extraction and if that could be accomplished economically.

Early investigators found that solvent-extracted tung oil solidified as a result of the isomerization of the α-eleostearic glyceride to the β-glyceride. The trade does not like the solidified product. The solidified solvent-extracted oil, however, will remain permanently liquid at room temperature after heating at 200° C. for 30 minutes.

Studies on the recovery of oil from tung meal and press cake with petroleum solvents, on both the laboratory and pilot-plant scale, show that oil can be efficiently extracted from press cake in a batch-extraction process. When ground tung kernels were extracted, difficulty was encountered with channeling, but when alternate layers of a porous material (such as tung press cake) were used with the ground kernels in a batch-extraction tower, 98 percent of the oil could be extracted.

IN EXTRACTION with commercial hexane in a small pilot-plant model of the Kennedy continuous, countercurrent extractor, recoveries of 99 percent or better were obtained on ground tung kernels, ground seeds, commercial press cake, and an experimental press cake that contained 20 percent oil. Preparing a firm flake from kernels as high in oil as tung kernels is difficult. In pilot-plant experiments, the best preparation of tung kernels and seeds for extraction was obtained with the use of roller mills. The oils obtained in the first series of pilot-plant experiments had a very high acidity, which developed in the meal before it was processed and the oils solidified. In later experiments, the seeds were ground and processed immediately; under those conditions, oils were obtained of low acid value. They remained liquid at ice-box temperatures. Tung seeds containing about 7 percent moisture were found best for flaking and for solvent extraction.

The solvent-extracted tung oils obtained in this second series of experiments appeared to have satisfactory quality. The oils were formulated into varnishes, which were tested for durability. The oils extracted from tung meal produced as good varnishes as pressed oil, but the oils from press cake gave a somewhat inferior varnish.

At the Tung Oil Laboratory, we had difficulty with the solvent extraction of the filter cake because of its compactness. We overcame the difficulty by mixing it with press cake; 98 percent of the oil could be extracted by a petroleum solvent. For several seasons, a tung mill has successfully extracted the oil from tung filter cake produced at that mill and at nearby mills.

We investigated variations in the physical and chemical properties of solvent-extracted tung oils that followed the use of several commercial grades of hexane, heptane, and trichloroethylene. Extractions were made in the laboratory by the hot percolation method. Oils extracted with one of the hexanes, with one of the heptanes, and with trichloroethylene remained liquid at temperatures as low as 40° F., but the oils extracted by the other petroleum solvents solidified, at least in part, at that temperature. Spectrophotometric examinations of the solvent-extracted tung oils showed that the oils that solidified at room temperature were relatively high in β-eleostearic acid, whereas the oils that remained liquid in the cold contained none or only a small amount of the acid.

BUYING AND SELLING tung fruit has been a problem in the industry because of the widely varying moisture and oil contents of the fruit, which affect its value.

Investigations showed that the oil content of the individual tung fruit varied from 0 to 28 percent, indicating the necessity of taking a large sample, at least 100 fruits, to get a sufficiently representative sample that would yield accurate results for oil content. The sample must be chosen so that there is a high probability that it will contain the different kinds of fruit in the same proportion in which they occur in the entire shipment. Procedures for the sampling of tung fruit at the mill have been devised; they could help the processor get an accurate evaluation of the fruit.

As tung-oil mills seldom have the services of a trained chemist, we tried to devise methods for testing tung fruit which could be used by the personnel at the mill. Several rapid methods for measuring moisture have been tested and adapted to use on tung fruit. In one, the terminals from a small direct-current ohmmeter, which reads electrical resistance from 1 ohm to 10 million ohms, are tightly inserted into holes bored longitudinally 1 inch apart and 0.5 inch deep into the tung fruit. Using the maximum of internal resistance in the ohmmeter, one can read the electrical resistance of the fruit to the passage of the small direct current. The moisture content of the fruit is estimated from an electrical resistance-moisture curve.

In another method, a large volume of air at 260° F. is blown for 15 minutes through a vessel containing the ground sample of tung fruit. We found that, to prevent loss of moisture in grinding the sample, a Wiley mill equipped with a $\frac{1}{4}$-inch screen should be used and that a correction of 1.2 percent must be added to the percentage of moisture obtained on the tung fruit ground in the Wiley mill, because of the oxidation during drying.

In a third method, the ground sample of tung fruit is placed in the test chamber, the radio-frequency impedance—resistance—of the material is measured, and the moisture content of the sample is read from a moisture-impedance table.

Correlations between the percentage of oil in tung fruit, percentage of oil in kernel, and percentage of kernel in fruit showed that the greatest part of the variation in oil content of the fruit is caused by variation in the kernel content and that the percentage of oil in the dry kernel is relatively constant.

The observation suggested that a reasonably accurate method of estimating oil content of tung fruit would be to determine the percentage of dry kernel in a sample and to assume an average oil content for the dry kernel. The method has been used for purchasing tung fruit in some instances. The oil content of dry tung kernels averages about 65 percent, but it may vary considerably from that figure.

As a safeguard on large-scale transactions, the oil contents of the dry kernels should be determined on a number of samples for the particular location and year, and their average used in estimating the oil in the fruit by this method.

The first analytical method developed by the Department of Agriculture for tung fruit, known as the component method, involved the separation of the sample into all its components—hulls, shells, and kernels—and determining the percentage of oil in the kernels. The percentage of oil in the fruit was calculated from the percentage of kernels and the percentage of oil in the kernels. Members of a committee of the American Oil Chemists' Society, who investigated the analysis of tung fruit by this method for 3 years, found a marked variation in the percentage of oil and moisture. On the basis of an earlier sampling study, the variations could be attributed almost entirely to sampling errors. It appeared that accuracy could be obtained only by using samples larger than the 8-fruit and 25-fruit samples used, but this introduced the problem of manual labor for preparing the samples.

To meet that problem, we developed a new procedure. We ground a 200- to 250-fruit sample in a Wiley mill equipped with a ¼-inch screen, mixed the ground material, and subdivided it into two parts, one part to be used in the moisture determination and the other in the oil determination. We determined the moisture content of the tung fruit by drying 5 grams of the sample at 101° C. to constant weight in a forced-draft oven. We determined the oil content by regrinding part of the sample to a fine meal in a Bauer laboratory-size mill, extracting a 5-gram portion for 4 hours in a Butt-type extraction apparatus with petroleum naphtha, and calculating the oil content to the original moisture basis.

TUNG OIL is the principal drying oil of China, where it has been widely utilized in the crude, heat-bodied, and processed state to waterproof wood, paper, cloth, and other materials. When tung oil was first imported into the United States, in 1869, the paint and varnish makers hesitated to use it because they found that the raw oil dried with a matted, wrinkled, and frosted finish. Also, it rapidly underwent heat bodying; it set to a gel during the bodying operation or production of varnishes unless the operator took great care. It was found, however, that tung oil could be gasproofed by heating it above 500° F. That was usually carried out during the cooking of the varnish, as it had been discovered that the presence of resin, ester gum, synthetic resins, and linseed oil during the heating process would tend to prevent gelation of tung oil. A process was also developed for producing a bodied tung oil in which the tung oil is rapidly heated to about 650° F. and then rapidly cooled to prevent gel formation.

The widespread use of tung oil in varnishes started in 1907, when it was found possible to use heat-treated tung oil and resin esters to make varnishes that surpassed the old-style varnishes made with linseed oil and imported fossil resins.

About 20 years later, the nitrocellulose lacquers threatened to supersede varnishes, but the varnish makers found it possible to produce quick-drying coatings of varnish by using tung oil and the new synthetic resins. Since then, more than 80 percent of the tung oil used in the United States has been utilized by the coating industry. Tung oil also has been used by the oilcloth and electrical industries and has been an important ingredient in automobile brake linings, in gaskets used on steam pipes, pumps, and engines, and in compounds used in the manufacture of wallboard. It has been widely used for waterproofing various kinds of fabrics.

Special care must be employed in bodying tung oil and preparing tung-oil varnishes. Gasproofness in a tung-oil varnish is evidence that it has been properly cooked so that it will dry to a smooth film, even in the presence of gas fumes. Temperatures of about 550° F. are required to gasproof tung oil fully, but at that temperature it will set to a gel in a few minutes. However, a mixture of 60 percent soybean oil and 40 percent tung oil can be heat-bodied at that temperature; the result is a bodied oil with drying properties like those of bodied linseed oil.

Tung-oil varnishes dry rapidly, leave a hard film, and are durable and resistant to water and alkali. Commercial varnishes, to be acceptable to the trade, should have other properties, too, such as clearness, proper viscosity (1.00 to 1.25 poise), and gasproofness. Studies with unmodified phenolic, modified phenolic, ester gum, and the pentaerythritol ester varnishes made with tung oil have shown that the addition of linseed or soybean oil to the formula is often advisable to obtain gasproof varnishes that are clear, nonskinning, and of satisfactory viscosity.

Tung hulls, which constitute about 50 percent of the fruit, contain about 2.5 percent potash and small amounts of nitrogen and phosphorus compounds. They are useful as a mulch in the groves and as a conditioner in mixed fertilizer. The hulls that contain 12.3 percent moisture have a calorific value of 7,160 B. t. u. They have been used as a fuel at tung mills, and the ash from them has been sold for its potash content. Hulls from ripe fruit contain 2 to 10 percent of a tanninlike material, but the prepared tannin solution was found to have no tanning effect on hides.

Tung press-cake meal, one of the principal byproducts of tung-oil expression, contains about 27 percent of crude protein, but it has been found unsuitable for livestock feed. Commercial tung press cake is toxic and unpalatable to rats and young chicks, but it may be possible to detoxify the meal by heating it in an autoclave at 230° C. for 2 hours, followed by extraction of the heated meal for 8 to 10 hours with ethyl alcohol. We have reports that a toxic substance has been isolated from the water extract of tung leaves, kernels, and press cake, and that a second poisonous substance has been separated by the alcohol treatment.

Attractive objects can be molded from tung meal and press cake by the use of high pressures and temperatures, but the plastics absorb excessive amounts of moisture when they are put in water. Better plastics were prepared from the crude protein extracted from tung kernels with a dilute solution of caustic soda. Good results were also obtained with 25 percent of a phenolic resin powder in formulas containing tung press-cake meal and wood flour by molding the mixture for 5 minutes at high pressures and 175° C.

TUNG OIL IS composed of about 80 percent of eleostearic acid, $C_{18}H_{30}O_2$, with smaller proportions of common acids combined as glycerides. Eleostearic acid has the structure $CH_3(CH_2)_3CH=CHCH=CHCH=CH(CH_2)_7COOH$. Each molecule of eleostearic acids contains three double bonds in conjugated positions, with a single bond connecting the carbon atoms between each double bond. It is this configuration that gives tung oil its unusual characteristics, that is, its ability to polymerize to a solid when heated to 282° C. for a few minutes. This phenomenon is the basis of the Browne heat test to determine the quality of tung oil.

At each double bond there can be a *cis*- or *trans*-configuration, making possible eight geometric isomers of eleostearic acid. The tung fruit elaborates only the α-isomer (*cis-cis-trans-*), but upon exposure to ultraviolet light, the α-isomer slowly changes over into the β-isomer (*trans-cis-cis-*). These isomeric eleostearic acids may be illustrated thus:

$$HC(CH_2)_7COOH$$
$$HC-CH$$
$$HC-CH$$
$$CH_3(CH_2)_3CH$$

α-Eleostearic acid (*cis-cis-trans-*)

$$HC(CH_2)_7COOH$$
$$HC-CH$$
$$HC-CH$$
$$CH_3(CH_2)_3CH$$

β-Eleostearic acid (*trans-cis-cis-*)

This change of the α-isomer to the β-isomer is accelerated by the presence of sulfur compounds and has been noted particularly in solvent-extracted tung oils, although the expressed oil rarely undergoes similar solidification, a fact that indicates the presence of large amounts of the β-isomer.

IN STUDIES ON the composition of tung oil, it was learned that the lead salt methods could not be used for separating the saturated and unsaturated acids, because the lead salts of eleostearic acid are only sparingly soluble in alcohol and ether. However, eleostearic acid reacts with maleic anhydride to form an insoluble compound. By measuring the amount of maleic anhydride that will react with a sample of tung oil, the amount of eleostearic acid in the oil can be determined, and adulteration with other vegetable oils can be readily detected.

The α- and β-isomers of eleostearic acid are so similar in their reactions that at first it was impossible to determine their relative proportions in tung oils. We discovered, however, that the α-isomer of eleostearic acid has a slightly different absorption spectrum from that of the β-isomer, whereupon a procedure for determining the proportions of the two isomers by spectrophotometric analysis was developed. This spectral-absorption method showed that the maximum absorption of α- and β-eleostearic acids occurs at 2715 and 2695 angstrom units, respectively. Two Boeger-Beer law equations, which were derived, yield values for α- and β-eleostearic acids. In the application of this method, absorption measurements of the sample of tung oil are made at the two maxima, extinction coefficients are calculated, and their values inserted in the two equations, which are then solved for the percentage of α- and β-acid in the sample at hand.

A tung oil containing 3.7 percent of β-eleostearic acid remained perfectly clear at refrigerator temperature, while an oil containing 17.7 percent of the

β-isomer was liquid at room temperature but deposited crystals at 40° F. Tung oil containing 37.1 percent of the β-isomer was almost completely solid at room temperature.

BECAUSE OF the presence of the conjugated double bonds, tung oil has the highest refractive index of any commercial vegetable oil. In order to insure delivery of high-quality, unadultered tung oil, a value for the refractive index is included in its specification. It has also been found that the refractive dispersion of tung oil measured with monochromatic light of wave length 5890 and 4358 angstrom units is much higher than that of any other common vegetable oil and therefore provides a useful index for determining the purity of tung oil and in detecting and estimating adulteration with other vegetable oils.

R. S. MCKINNEY, *a chemist in the Bureau of Agricultural and Industrial Chemistry, has been in charge of investigations on tung oil and its by-products since 1938. He has been with the Department since 1923, engaging first in studies on the composition of cattle feeds and on the spontaneous combustion of organic agricultural materials. Later Dr. McKinney did research on the composition and properties of vegetable oils and oilseeds, particularly cottonseed, soybeans, and soybean phosphatides.*

R. L. HOLMES *is chemist with the United States Tung Oil Laboratory, Bogalusa, La. He is a native of Mississippi and attended Louisiana State University, where he received a bachelor's degree in sugar engineering and a master's degree in chemistry. From 1929 to 1935, he was chemist for sugar companies in Louisiana, California, Cuba, and Puerto Rico. From 1935 to 1942 he was chemist at the Bureau of Plant Industry at Houma, La.; from 1942 to 1945 he was chemist with the special guayule research project at Salinas, Calif., until he was transferred to Bogalusa.*

Some of the Minor Oil Crops

Ernest B. Kester

In ordinary times we could get along very well·with an adequate supply of the oils and fats from soybeans, peanuts, cottonseed, corn, and milk, which we produce or import in huge amounts. But in times of emergency, when outside supplies are cut off, we must supplement our domestic production with every available pound from every available source. That, plus the fact that some oils have properties that adapt them to specific uses, is why we are interested in minor oil crops.

Furthermore, many of the minor crops can be exploited as small-business ventures and may yield a fair return to a few investors who care to go into the vegetable-oil industry with a moderate outlay for equipment.

The minor vegetable oils fall into four general classes:

1. Oils from oil-bearing agricultural wastes, such as fruit pits, tomato pomace, wine pomace, and olive marc, and the seeds of citrus fruits, apples, pears, pumpkin, squash, and pimento.

2. Oils from seeds and grains that mostly are raised as crops, including rice, safflower, sunflower, okra, castor, mustard, rape, and tobacco.

3. Oils of tree nuts—almond, walnut, pecan, and filbert.

4. Fruit-flesh oils—olive and avocado.

A few of the oils listed are second in importance only to our major bulk oils, but that is true only because of sizable importations. As recoverable oils from domestic crops, they are still in the class of minor oils.

It must be borne in mind that the existence of a potential supply of any given oil does not mean that a profit can be realized by recovering it, even at high market prices. Numerous economic factors have to be considered.

By oils and fats, we usually mean the nonvolatile oils that occur naturally as chemical combinations of glycerin and fatty acids. We shall not consider here the volatile or essential oils that are valued for their fragrance or flavor, such as peppermint, wintergreen, and citronella. Also excluded are certain vegetable waxes, which in many respects resemble oils and fats but do not have the glyceride structure.

Vegetable oils differ from one another mainly in the kind and amount of combined fatty acids, and the classes, kinds, and amounts of impurities present. Therefore, the properties of the various vegetable oils usually differ only in degree, except in a highly individual oil that contains a large percentage of some unique constituent. For example, castor oil contains a high percentage of combined ricinoleic acid, and tung oil a large amount of eleostearic acid, neither of which is ordinarily found in vegetable oils to any great degree.

Oils are characterized also by their iodine value. That term the oil technologists use to describe the drying power, or lack of it, in an oil. High-iodine oils (linseed, walnut, tung) are usable in paints and other surface coatings. Those with low iodine values (cottonseed, rice-bran, olive) do not form hard films when they are exposed to air.

THE PIT OILS of the apricot, peach, prune, and plum strikingly resemble

592

one another in composition and, indeed, are not readily differentiated. Cherry-pit oil has a somewhat higher iodine value. These oils are like sweet-almond oil, for which they are sometimes substituted. If the pits are processed promptly after removal from the fruit, little or no "oil of bitter almonds" will be liberated into the fixed oil by chemical reaction. The pit oils command a premium price over the commoner vegetable oils and are usually handled by brokers in essential oils.

Our annual crop of apricots averages more than 240,000 tons, of which more than 80 percent is dried, canned, or otherwise processed. Many growers dry their fruit and sell the pits at attractive prices. Several plants in California shell apricot pits to recover kernels, for which there is a strong domestic market, particularly for making macaroon paste. The dry-pit equivalent for apricots processed each year in the United States is about 12,000 tons, which would yield about 3,000 tons of kernels. In the cracking process, many kernels are broken; they are used to recover oil. Our production of apricot-pit oil is about 100 tons a year. It is used largely for making cosmetics and pharmaceuticals.

Most of the peach crop in the East and Midwest is marketed as fresh fruit. Because California produces about 90 percent of the peaches processed in the entire country, only there could you consider peach pits as a source of oil and other byproducts. The pits from the peaches processed in California could yield about 1,400 tons of oil a year. At present, peach pits can be obtained from canneries and drying yards for little or nothing except cost of haulage. A comparatively small proportion of the available pits is converted into char for poultry feeds and fuel briquets. Very little peach-kernel oil is extracted, because most of the pits available for byproducts are from canners' clingstone peaches, which when wet yield less than 1 percent of oil, and because many modern canneries use a saw that cuts the entire peach, including pit, in two, crushing the kernel into fragments that are hard to recover. Where freestone pits are available, oil recovery is more practical. The kernels, from the whole pits obtained from drying yards, can be separated in the equipment used for apricot pits. Eleven tons of dry freestone pits yield about a ton of kernels, from which about 0.4 ton of oil can be pressed. Screw presses can be used, but the one plant that operated on peach pits in California employed hydraulic presses used in hot-pressing olive oil.

Processed cherries, both sweet and sour, are marketed pit-free as canned, frozen, and brined products. The oil represented by the total of pitted cherries amounts to about 1,100 tons a year, but no plant at present is recovering it. One company in Wisconsin produced a few tons of cherry-kernel oil a few years ago, and another used cherry pits as a source of the "oil of bitter almonds." The operations for recovering cherry-kernel oil are similar to those used for peach- and apricot-pit oils.

No fruit pits other than peach, apricot, and cherry are likely sources of oil. Only small amounts of prune pits are available for processing because most of the prune crop is marketed without removal of the pits. Volumes of plum and date pits from processing plants are comparatively small. In pressing olives for oil, the whole fruit, including pit, is crushed. In plants where pitted olives are canned, the pits are a waste product, but the oil content of 3.5 to 7 percent is probably too low for profitable recovery. Inclusion in animal feeds has been suggested, but such a material, unless well ground, would undoubtedly contain hard, sharp particles, which might injure the digestive tract.

The oil of citrus seeds resembles cottonseed oil in general properties. The approximate amounts obtainable from food-processing operations are: Grapefruit-seed oil, 2,600 tons; Valencia orange-seed oil, 1,200 tons; and lemon-seed oil, 500 tons.

Florida, Texas, Arizona, and California produce grapefruit in commercial quantities, but only Florida processes seeded varieties in tonnages large enough that the seeds might be considered a practical source of vegetable oil. One plant in Florida manufactures the oil in considerable amounts.

California, Arizona, and Florida produce Valencia oranges, the only major seed-bearing variety grown in this country. The seed content varies greatly. Orange seeds contain about 40 percent of oil, which can be readily expressed or extracted. The oil is easily refined to a pleasing, light-colored, bland product, useful for foods and other purposes.

Lemons, unlike oranges, are not a seasonal crop. Fruit in all stages of ripeness can be found on a tree. It is an interesting fact that a cold snap or freeze will be followed, after an interval of months, by a crop of lemons that have an unusually high seed content. The processing of lemons commercially is confined to southern California.

More than 90 percent of our grapes are grown in California, where the 500,000 acres in vineyards are more than double the acreage devoted to oranges. Here we find principally the Vinifera or Old World type of grape. The Great Lakes region is a center for the production of the Lubrusca or slipskin type, of which the Concord is representative.

Grape seeds are available in the wastes from the raisin and the wine industries, particularly the latter. In former years, raisins were made almost exclusively from seed-bearing grapes (principally of the Muscat variety); large quantities of seeds, rejected from drying plants, were used in making oil, brandy, tartrates, and stock feed. As the Thompson seedless grape has developed, the tonnage of Muscats converted to raisins has dwindled, and in 1948 less than 10,000 tons of that variety was dried. In terms of vegetable oil, it equals about 45 tons. One plant is producing raisin-seed oil by expression methods. This oil is used in oiling packaged raisins to make them free flowing.

The flourishing wine industry in California has made available large quantities of the grape pomace, from which seed can be readily separated by either dry or wet methods. At least three mills in California are now producing grape-seed oil by extraction from the seeds of wine pomace. On the basis of an annual crush of a million tons of grapes, the quantities of recoverable oil would be about 3,200 tons if all the pomace were processed. Only a fraction of the wine pomace is worked for oil and byproducts.

Grape-seed oil is excellent for culinary purposes. As it is semidrying, it can be used together with other oils in paint formulations.

SEVENTY PERCENT of domestic apples used in processing are raised in the Western States and North Atlantic States. The seed from the part of the annual apple harvest that is canned, dried, and frozen would yield about 385 tons of oil. Economical recovery, however, would be limited to the larger districts, in which case the maximum amount of oil would be reduced to 270 tons. Only large packing centers would be justified in separating seed from waste and would in most instances dispose of the seed to oil mills.

California and Washington, centers of production of pears for canning and drying, account for 90 percent of the national total. The output of processed pears in California is roughly double that of Washington. Not more than about 150 tons of oil could be realized from pear seeds as a total for both areas. Apple- and pear-seed oils are quite similar. Both can be refined to a pale, bland product entirely suitable for culinary purposes.

The principal cranberry-producing States are Massachusetts, New Jersey, and Wisconsin. Washington and Oregon account for 3 to 4 percent of the national total. About a third of the cranberries raised are made into seed-free manufactured products, principally sauce. The oil yield possible from the seed rejected in processing would not exceed 50 tons. More valuable than the seed oil is the ursolic acid in the skins. This chemical, in the form of its sodium salt, is a powerful agent for production of water-in-oil emulsions. Neither cranberry-seed oil or ursolic acid is now in commercial production.

About 2,400 tons of oil a year could be produced from the tomato waste discharged from processing plants. Part of the waste is discharged into sewer systems and causes pollution when it is carried into streams. Ordinances against such practice are becoming increasingly severe, and tomato processors are seeking means whereby the pomace can be converted into products that will at least offset the cost of handling. Many plants merely dry and sell whole tomato pomace for feed. Drying, however, is costly because of the high moisture content. In one plant, seeds are separated from skins and sold for oil recovery. Freshly expressed oil is reddish, but it can be easily bleached.

Tomato canneries are located in many parts of the country. This lack of centralization and the fact that the potential supply of tomato-seed oil is not large mean that oil recovery in connection with any one plant would probably be uneconomical unless other oil-bearing materials were also available for processing.

The total annual pack of squash and pumpkin would yield enough seeds to make about 500 tons of oil. Centers of processing for the two vegetables are Indiana, Illinois, California, and, to a lesser extent, Ohio, Washington, Oregon, and New Jersey. None of this oil is being recovered, but in Europe it is expressed and put to edible uses. A nutlike delicacy is made by roasting and salting kernels of pumpkin seed.

Pimento-seed oil has been extracted from cannery wastes occasionally in California plants. The oil content of pimento seeds is 19 to 20 percent. It is deep red when first extracted, but it can be bleached readily.

Oils are obtained from seeds and grains of okra, asparagus, mustard, rape, safflower, sunflower, castor, rice, and tobacco.

Raising okra seed for oil is now approaching a reality, after extensive experimentation, in several Southern States, notably Louisiana and Texas. Farm-machinery companies are developing special combines for harvesting the seed. It is somewhat hard to separate hulls and kernels of okra seed, because the seed is small. Solvent-extracted or expressed oil from crushed whole seed has a greenish cast, but the color can be bleached. The oil is said to have good stability after refining and hydrogenation.

Asparagus seed would become available in quantity for oil recovery in the San Joaquin and Sacramento delta area of California if a practical method for harvesting it were developed. California produces about one-half of our asparagus. The seed contains about 13 percent of oil, which is in the drying class, although its iodine value, 137, is not high for this type of oil.

Oil obtainable from mustard seed grown in the United States amounts to about 6,500 tons. Montana accounts for about 78 percent of all the mustard grown, the remainder coming from California, Washington, Oregon, and North Dakota. Three types of mustard are grown—oriental, brown, and yellow. Besides yielding a fixed glyceride oil, the brown and yellow varieties are useful in making condiments. Mustard-seed oil can be used as a supplement or substitute for rapeseed oil, because it has a high content of combined erucic acid.

The United States has imported considerable rapeseed oil in times past, principally for making special lubricants, but the amounts received fell from a peak of 15,000 tons in 1942 to 2,000 tons in 1948. It contains about 50 percent of combined erucic acid. Some rape is grown in northern Idaho and eastern Washington, but it is a minor crop.

Safflower has been mentioned by different investigators as a new oilseed crop for the northern and western parts of the Great Plains. It has been grown near Deming, N. Mex., in eastern Washington, and in northern Idaho, and is now rapidly growing in favor as an oilseed crop in Colorado, California, Nebraska, and Wyoming. Safflower oil has drying properties. Extensive tests on its use in coating compositions show that, when blended with linseed oil, it improves the resistance of the coating to weathering.

Until 1948, practically all the sunflower-seed oil we used was imported. The small amounts of sunflower seed raised previously in the United States had been used principally in feeds. The success of sunflower crops in Canada, however, in postwar years led to plantings in North Dakota for oil production. The development increased the domestic crop from about 1,200 tons in 1947 to about 10,000 tons in 1948, and, although it fell to about 5,000 tons in 1949, sunflowers sometimes may be an important oilseed crop here. The oil is excellent for use in salad oils and shortening.

Castor is a versatile plant. Its leaves yield ricin, a potent insecticide; its stalks, bast fiber and α-cellulose. The oil has a high density and a low congealing point. It is used widely as a constituent of hydraulic-brake fluids, as a low-temperature lubricant, and as a liquid cushion in artillery recoil mechanisms. It has had a place in medicine a long time. Early in the Second World War, the Department of Agriculture fostered the planting of castor on several thousand acres in Texas. In Florida, successful test plantings by a commercial concern yielded 600 to 900 pounds of beans to the acre. The problem of raising castor beans domestically in competition with foreign supplies has not been completely solved, principally because of harvesting difficulties with mechanical equipment. In most strains of castor, the capsules holding the beans either drop or shatter when ripe, and for that reason mechanical methods have not superseded hand picking, except where frost has

killed the plants before harvesting or where artificial defoliation is practiced. With the end of the war, the commercial raising of castor beans dropped, but in 1948 and 1949 small acreages were planted in Missouri, Oklahoma, Texas, New Mexico, and California. New areas were in production in 1950. One castor-oil company has planned to make large plantings in the Central Valley of California. At one time in the United States, raising of castor beans flourished and supported the operation of numerous oil mills, but the industry had almost died out by 1920.

Rice bran as a source of vegetable oil has certain attractive features: It has a low content of moisture; it is available in large tonnages at central locations; it can be solvent-extracted without pretreatment. A disadvantage is the difficulty of filtering the oil because of a waxy sludge that separates from it, and the presence of fine particles of solid matter. The term "rice bran" signifies not the seed coat alone but rather a fraction of the rice grain removed in milling, which includes also germ and broken grains. The fraction contains on an average about 15 percent of oil, but that value may be higher or lower depending on the way the rice is milled.

Rice oil could be produced in amounts of 15,000 to 20,000 tons a year from the combined milling operations of the South and West. It is now solvent-extracted in several plants in the United States, including one in Texas and four in California. One other company pressed bran in screw equipment but recovered only about one-half to two-thirds of the oil. The deoiled bran is more stable than untreated bran in that it can be stored for longer periods without rancidifying. It is an excellent poultry and stock feed and can be used as a source of B vitamins.

The bran is preferably treated immediately after its removal from the grain, because the oil is then more readily refined and less is lost to the soap stock in the process. If stored even for a few days before extraction, rice bran deteriorates to a point at which the oil is quite high in fatty acids. The oil itself, once it is removed from the bran, does not exhibit that tendency. It is similar in general composition to cottonseed and peanut oils.

One of the largest of the minor vegetable oils in potential volume is obtainable from tobacco seed. It has been estimated that at least 13,000 tons could be produced annually from the seed that develops on the sucker growths of tobacco of the flue-cured type, after the seed heads are topped. Tobacco-seed oil is in the class of drying oils. Iodine values as high as 151 have been reported, although the oil from our domestic tobacco seed usually falls within the range of 140 to 146.

THE TREE-NUT OILS include almond, walnut, pecan, and filbert oils.

We ordinarily think of the tree nuts as luxury foods too high in price and too small in actual volume for use as a source of vegetable oils. This situation has indeed been true for the most part. Exceptions were the almond and walnut crops of 1949, which were so large that a surplus of several thousand tons of walnut and almond meats was diverted to crushing operations. The following discussion applies to a more normal situation.

Commercial production of almonds in the United States is confined to California. Almonds rank third in acreage among the deciduous-tree fruits and nuts of California. Prunes and walnuts are ahead of them. Approximately two-thirds of our almond crop is shelled. Nearly 10 percent of the meats are moldy, shriveled, or otherwise inedible, and contain 40 percent of oil, which means that about 260 tons of almond oil could be realized from that source. Only one or two small companies now press almond oil; they use mostly edible meats. The oil is low enough in fatty acids to be refined to a high-grade salable product by the use of bleaching agents alone. It is consumed almost entirely in the cosmetic and pharmaceutical industries, where it competes with imported almond oil.

The amount of walnut oil produced in this country is 300 to 600 tons annually. Raw material for oil pressing is divided between inedible meats rejected during shelling and meat fragments recovered from shells. One plant in Los Angeles makes most of our walnut oil. It gets its raw material principally from the shelling plant of a large cooperative. Screw-press equipment is used. The shell is reduced to flours of various screen sizes, which are sold as soft grit for blast cleaning of metals, as plastic filler, as an ingredient of nonskid paints, and as a carrier for agricultural insecticides.

Walnut oil is similar to linseed oil. Before the Second World War it was sold entirely to the coating industry. Since then it has been consumed also as a food oil. The outlet for walnut press cake, which contains a considerable amount of shell, is mainly the fertilizer industry, although some was used as stock feed a few years ago.

Pecans are grown in several Southern States, principally Georgia, Oklahoma, and Texas. About 300 tons of pecan oil is produced annually. The source is the discarded meats from shelling plants, which are shipped to a central point for processing. The oil is obtained by hydraulic pressing. It has been found fairly high in free fatty acids. Some difficulties were experienced at first in refining it, but these have been overcome. The press cake is treated to recover tannin, of which it contains about 14 percent, and the residue is sold for stock feed. Pecan oil is suitable as a salad or cooking oil.

The filbert crop, grown principally in Oregon, is small. Oil-recovery operations from any part of it would not be practicable unless surpluses develop or the industry is faced with the disposal of large quantities of damaged or unsalable meats. Filbert growers foresee the likelihood of a surplus, as production is increasing. Like olive oil, filbert oil has a high content of combined oleic acid.

The fruit-flesh oils come only from avocados and olives.

The culture of avocados in the United States is confined to Florida and California, with 83 percent of the total production in California. Commercial plantings are almost entirely in the southern part of the State, particularly in the coastal belt from San Diego to Santa Barbara, where the climate is favorable for this crop. Most of the crop is sold at prices that make oil recovery from very much of it out of the question. The cull portion of the crop is usually small, but adverse conditions, such as the heavy freezes of 1937 and 1948, sometimes make it larger.

The amount of avocados pressed for oil each year is variable, but has not exceeded 100 tons, which would yield 10 to 15 tons of oil. The oil, similar to olive oil in its high content of combined oleic acid, is sold almost exclusively to the cosmetic industry. It commands a high price.

Olive oil occupies a unique position among vegetable oils in that it is valued for its distinctive odor and flavor, as well as for its low solidifying point and adaptability to many cosmetic and pharmaceutical formulations. California accounts for almost all of our production of olives and in prewar years furnished 5 to 10 percent of our national requirements of olive oil. The remainder was imported. War demands imposed a severe strain on the California olive crop and prices rose to unprecedented heights. With the return of imports in the postwar years, production of oil declined until in 1950 it was at about prewar levels. The amount pressed fluctuates widely from year to year, but it is usually within the range of 2,000 to 3,000 tons in normal times. During the war, production of edible grades amounted to more than 5,000 tons.

In considering olive oil, one must distinguish between the cold-pressed (virgin) grade and the hot-pressed or extracted grades. The latter are the inedible grades of commerce and are utilized principally in making soap and other products that merely require high percentages of oleic acid in the raw materials. The inedible grades, which are obtained after the cold-pressing, constitute one-third of the total oil present in the olives. The oil content of ripe California olives averages 18 to 25 percent. Between 50 and 60 gallons of oil of all grades are usually obtained from each ton of olives processed.

Other minor sources of vegetable oil, which deserve passing mention only, include the seeds of watermelon, cantaloup, figs, limes, nectarines, papayas, pomegranates, and several different berries. Economic extraction of the materials will probably not be practicable in the foreseeable future, because either the processing plants are widely separated or the total tonnage of the oil represented by the cannery wastes is relatively small.

The market value of any minor oil is usually based on that of the common bulk oil it most closely resembles, but the law of supply and demand also may affect it. Thus, apricot-pit oil, which closely resembles sweet-almond oil and is recovered only in limited quantities, is sold at a premium. Sometimes an oil will have a "name value" in certain industries, in addition to desirable physical properties. Avocado oil is a case in point. Should an oil be found to have a high content of a valuable constituent, such as vitamin A or D, or perhaps show great resistance to rancidification, its market value may rise appreciably. Otherwise, processors must recognize that minor oils have no unusual merit and must compete on an even basis with the better-known oils of commerce.

ERNEST B. KESTER *has been engaged in research on fats and oils at the Western Regional Research Laboratory since 1939, and is now in charge of the rice-utilization section. He holds advanced degrees from the University of Minnesota and Northwestern University.*

PROTEINS ARE BASIC

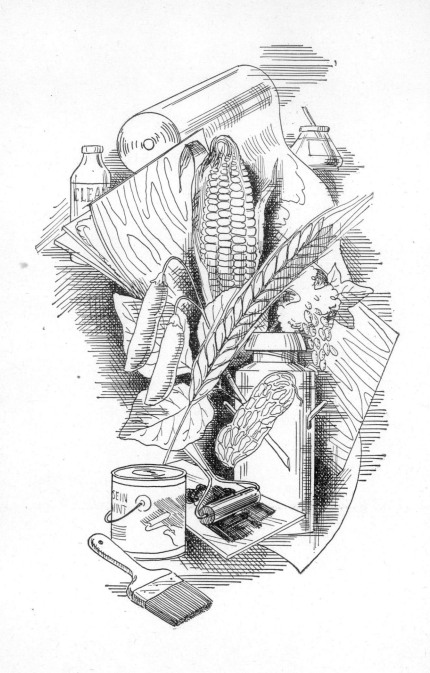

Over-all Look at Industrial Proteins

Allan K. Smith

The proteins for industry come from both animal and vegetable sources. When they are derived from the animal-processing industries, we call them byproducts. When they come from vegetable sources, we call them primary products.

The most important industrial uses of proteins are in making adhesives or glues. From them also are made buttons, sizing for both paper and textiles, fibers, medicines, pharmaceuticals, and many other items.

The type of proteins that can be used industrially is limited. We think of proteins first as food and feed. But recently the potential supply of vegetable and animal proteins in the United States has greatly increased, largely because of the greater efficiency of crop production through mechanized farming and the introduction of the soybean. I have no reason to believe that we have reached maximum production. The need for extra food during the Second Word War caused a temporary shortage of proteins in this country, but at the same time it greatly stimulated agricultural production.

The use of vegetable proteins by industry has a great economic advantage over the use of animal proteins, because an animal uses 6 to 10 pounds of vegetable protein to produce 1 pound of animal protein. That economic relationship limits the use of animal proteins to byproducts of meat packing, fishing, and dairy industries.

Not all proteins are fit for food—for example, fish residues and bones and hides from the packing and tanning houses, which are a source of isolated protein. On the other hand, casein, which is derived from milk, is used preferably in dairy products such as fluid milk and cheese, and only temporary surpluses go into the making of casein. Edible gelatin brings a higher price than gelatin that is to be made into glue. Furthermore, the waste and leftovers of an industry are naturally in limited supply and cannot be given primary consideration as a source material of expanding usefulness.

The cheapest and most abundant supply of primary proteins is found in our vegetable crops—cottonseed, flax, soybeans, peanuts, wheat, and corn. The proteinaceous materials derived from the processing of oilseeds for their oil and cereal grains for starch provide a large and cheap source of crude materials for producing isolated vegetable proteins for industry.

Wool, silk, hair, and hides are important proteins, but I shall not discuss them here because they are used largely in their original form.

In considering the proteins as industrial raw materials, therefore, one has to look at them in the light of the abundance of the materials from which they are prepared, their cost in comparison with the costs of competitive materials, their present uses, and the possibility of developing new products from them. The wartime disturbance of economic conditions and the changing world situation prevent an accurate evaluation of some of those factors, but we can indicate the general trends.

The industrial proteins of animal origin include the packing-house byproducts usually known by the names of animal glue, photographic gelatin, edible gelatin, blood albumin, fish glues, egg albumin, and casein.

The industrial vegetable-type proteins derived from farm crops appeared on the market after the First World War. The first industrial use of soybean meal as a glue was in a plywood mill in the State of Washington in 1922; isolated soybean protein appeared in 1933; and the corn protein, zein, in 1938.

PROTEINS SUPPLY only some of the adhesive materials. Starch and dextrin adhesives are cheaper and are used in larger volume than glues from protein. The synthetic resins appeared on the market in plywood glue about 1936 and are now used in large amounts, notably for waterproof plywood. Natural gums and rubber adhesives are special types. Resistance to water is an important requirement for many adhesive applications. Starch and dextrins have little or no resistance to the dissolving action of water. Properly formulated protein adhesives are highly water-resistant. Many of the synthetics are classified as waterproof.

We need thousands of different formulas for glue because glues have so many different uses. The preparation of the formulas is largely an art. It is based more on an operator's experience than on chemical or scientific knowledge of what makes a glue stick. Glues literally hold the world together: Your wallpaper would fall from the wall and your chair and many parts of your house would come apart if the glue in them were to change to sand.

The gelatin-type glues were used by the early Egyptians. The first glue plant in the United States was established about 1808. We have since become the largest producers of animal glue. Our annual production is about 150 million pounds. Of the glue produced by the meat-packing industry, about 60 percent comes from hides and 40 percent from bones.

ANIMAL GLUES are made principally from hides, connecting tissue, cartilage, bones, and trimmings of cattle and calves, which are byproducts of meat-packing plants. Fish glues are made from fish skins, heads, and trimmings from canneries and fisheries.

Horns and hoofs, contrary to popular belief, contain no collagen or gelatin. Gelatin, or glue, is derived from collagen, a type of protein found in the raw materials I just mentioned. In the process of making and isolating gelatin, the hides are given a mild hydrolytic treatment with lime. The treatment converts the insoluble collagen into water-soluble gelatin, which is then extracted from the parent substance with warm or hot water. Collagen is regarded as the anhydride of gelatin. The tests normally used to evaluate the quality of a glue are viscosity, gel strength, melting point, and setting point. Several batches of glue may be blended to obtain a uniform product.

The gelatin-type glues are used in water solution and are valued in many uses because they form a stiff gel at low concentration. One of their chief uses is for woodworking (especially for furniture) and for products in which long working life is a great convenience but in which high water resistance is not required—sandpaper, matches, gummed labels, and paper boxes. The rayon textile industry has used more than 10 million pounds of animal glue yearly as a sizing material. A good deal also goes into calcimine, paper sizing, a duplicating process, bookbinding, sizing of straw hats, rubber processing, coopering, print rollers, emery wheels, cork gaskets, and protective colloids.

Our production of animal glue from 1937 to 1939, about 60 million pounds, represented about 96 percent of the domestic consumption. By 1947 production had increased to 159 million pounds; the later production data, although incomplete, indicate no further increases.

The United States Tariff Commission classifies photographic gelatin, pharmaceutical gelatin, and food gelatin as edible gelatin because the first two, if they do not meet their intended specifications, may be sold as food gelatin.

DOMESTIC EDIBLE GELATIN is produced from calfskin, pigskin, and oessin (decalcified cattle bones), and is made in much the same way as the animal glues, except that the factory is kept in a highly sanitary condition. Nearly 60 percent of the food gelatin eaten in the United States is in the form of jelly powders. About 35 percent is used for ice cream, candy, and cookies. The rest goes into meat packing, dairy products, and miscellaneous uses. Just before the Second World War, the United States production of food gelatin was about 22 million pounds; in 1948 it was more than 47 million pounds.

Photographic gelatin is a specialized product used for making photographic films, plates, and paper. It is our most expensive packing-house protein, and, although its price has varied, it may be placed roughly at above a dollar a pound. The production of photographic gelatin was about 8 million pounds in 1947.

Pharmaceutical gelatin must comply with standards specified in the United States Pharmacopeia. It is used chiefly for coating pills and making capsules used in dispensing medicines. The production of such gelatin has been about 3 million pounds a year.

Altogether, then, our yearly production of edible-type gelatin has been about 58 million pounds.

A rather important application for protein wastes, such as the horns and hoofs of cattle and fine hairs and bristles sifted from the longer fractions which go into felts and other materials, is in the manufacture of plaster retarder. To make the retarder, the residucs are partly hydrolyzed with lime and soda ash at high temperatures. The proportion used in the final plaster is 0.1 percent or less, but it serves to retard the setting time of the plaster for 30 minutes or longer. The quantity used by the building trades varies from year to year, but it may amount to several million pounds.

Fish glues are used in photoengraving, in the manufacture of gummed paper, and in woodworking, but to a far greater extent as a household glue. The production of fish glue declined during the war from 3.6 million pounds in 1941 to 1.4 million pounds in 1945, but it increased to 2.3 million pounds in 1946.

Isinglass is made mechanically from fish sounds (bladders) and it is used chiefly in clarifying beer and wines. It has been produced now and then in this country, but the maximum output has not exceeded 85,000 pounds a year.

Egg albumin and blood albumin are unique among the animal-glue products in that they change from water solubility in their original state to water insolubility when they are heated. Egg albumin has an important industrial application for sealing the cork into crown seals. Other examples of its uses are for finishing leather, liquoring fat (along with the yolk), and attaching gold and silver letters to leather. Much of our egg albumin was imported from China before the Second World War. The domestic supply came mostly from broken and rejected eggs. The war restricted the importation of egg albumin; even in normal times the supplies for industrial uses are short, and processing is difficult. Prices, therefore, are high. In 1949, dried industrial egg albumin sold for $1.50 a pound or more; the edible product may cost twice that much. Consequently, the use of egg albumin has been drastically limited, and efforts have been made to develop replacements.

Blood serum from packing houses may be dried and sold as blood albumin. Its properties depend largely on methods of handling during its recov-

ery, especially the drying. Its special
property, which should be preserved in
processing, is coagulation with heat. It
has been used to set dyes, size textiles,
and make water-resistant plywood.
The production and use of blood albumin in industry have varied widely and
have never been very great.

Research was started in the Western
Regional Research Laboratory looking
toward the development of protein byproducts of the poultry industry—particularly chicken feathers and whites
from eggs in the powdered-egg industry. One interesting result was the
development of textile fibers. Harold
Lundgren and others have made egg-
white fibers with tensile strength
values, when dry, up to 70,000 pounds
to the square inch and chicken keratin
fibers with strengths as high as 80,000
pounds. Such strength values are significant; they point up the possibilities
of protein fibers.

CASEIN, a dairy byproduct, is second
in importance to the so-called packing-
house glues. It is a protein of skim
milk, precipitated by acid or rennet.
Skim milk is also the source of the important food product known as nonfat
dry milk solids. The dry milk solids
constitute the entire solids content of
skim milk; the precipitated casein
amounts to a third of the total solids.

In a competitive market, the dry
milk solids are the more valuable product and have first call on the supply
of skim milk. Casein therefore is at a
disadvantage, and consequently fluctuates in production and price.

To offset the fluctuations in domestic
production, imports of casein have
been heavy. The principal foreign
source has been Argentina. The import duty was 5.5 cents a pound until
1941, when it was reduced to 2.75
cents. The total of casein imported and
produced domestically increased from
30 million pounds in 1929 to 89 million pounds in 1941. Since 1941 the
imports have increased, and domestic
production has declined; the total
available casein has dropped to 50 mil-

lion pounds or even less in some years.

The most important use for casein
is for coating paper, which normally
takes 60 percent or so of the total supply.

The use second in importance is in
making plastic buttons, buckles, and
ornaments from rennet casein. Plywood
adhesives, tire cords, water paints, and
leather finishes are others. It also is in
demand as a spreader and adhesive in
insecticides, for special foods, and for
medicinal purposes.

Textile fibers known as Aralac were
produced from casein in a plant established in 1938, with a reported capacity
of a million pounds a month. The factory discontinued the production of
casein fibers in 1948, but it is possible
that research at the Eastern Regional
Research Laboratory will improve the
characteristics of the casein fiber and
bring it back on the market.

The work at the Eastern Laboratory
on textile fibers led to the development
of a coarse fiber that can be substituted
for hog bristles and horsehair. The
project was stimulated by war shortages of hog bristles formerly imported
from China. The casein bristle has less
resistance to water than the animal
bristle, but it is outstanding in stiffness
and is used as a stuffing material in
place of horsehair in upholstery and
mattresses, for stiffening coat lapels in
men's suits, and in oil filters. The new
industry, starting in 1949, had a production of a million pounds in 1950
and is expected to grow rapidly.

Casein is the only protein now used
to make bristles, but if supplies should
prove inadequate the vegetable proteins will be available to meet the
requirements.

THE VEGETABLE PROTEINS are comparatively new. They have great importance because we can expect little
further increase in the amounts of animal protein available for industrial use.

The supply of vegetable proteins
is based partly on the fact that soybeans can fit readily into good land-use
practices and cropping plans. Un-

denatured solvent-extracted soybean meal that contains about 45 percent protein (50 percent if dehulled) is the raw material for making isolated or refined soybean protein. The isolated, or extracted, protein yields are about 30 percent on the basis of the meal. The meal sold at 25 to 30 dollars a ton before the war, somewhat more during the war, and $50 to $100 a ton since.

The first plant for isolating the protein, built in 1933, had a capacity of a ton a day. Three plants now produce isolated soybean protein. Their total capacity was estimated in 1950 at more than 15,000 tons. Other processors are preparing to establish plants.

At first, the isolated soybean protein was sold principally to the paper industry for sizing and coating paper. Later, large amounts have gone into water paint, a washing compound, special types of paper sizing, and paper adhesives, such as those for laminating paper into a solid fiberboard from which returnable beer cases and laminated shotgun shell casings are made.

During the war, much of the production was allocated to the Navy as a foam stabilizer for use in a fire-extinguisher preparation. Since the war, because of its marvelous fire-fighting properties, the preparation has become commonplace along railroad sidings as a protection against spill fires when tank cars of gasoline, benzol, or naphtha are unloaded. The foam is supplied through a fixed system of nozzles, and a sizable area is covered with a blanket of foam.

ZEIN, the alcohol-soluble protein of corn, is extracted from corn gluten. The potential yield of zein is 3 pounds to a bushel of processed corn, although no more than 1 pound may be obtained in normal production. The wet-milling industry processes more than 120 million bushels a year.

During the war, zein was combined with rosin as a replacement for shellac. Other important uses are in ink, overprint varnish, other coatings (which are greaseproof and scuff-resistant),

and a cork binder and other special adhesives. Phonograph records have been made with zein.

Research on zein fiber started at the Northern Regional Research Laboratory in 1943 and led to commercial production of the fiber in 1948 by the Virginia-Carolina Chemical Corp. in a plant at Taftville, Conn. The zein fibers first produced were used to replace 10 to 15 percent of rabbits' fur in making felt hats. By 1949, they were accepted for making various fabrics by the textile industry. Zein fiber has a fine, soft feel and other properties that differ widely from the natural and synthetic fibers on the market. I expect that much of it will be used in blends with rayon, cotton, and wool to produce new types of fabrics.

Peanut-protein fiber has been in pilot-plant production in England, the commercial product being known as Ardil. Casein fibers, peanut-protein fibers, and soybean-protein fibers have like properties. In some respects they resemble wool. Their most serious fault is irreversible stretching when wet. The ultimate success of the spun fiber from soybean and peanut proteins will depend largely on new research developments to improve its strength when wet.

The use of proteins as protective colloids in oil-emulsion paints deserves special mention. That application enjoys a good market for interior decorative wall coatings of pleasing pastel colors.

Soybean protein and zein are the only isolated vegetable proteins currently produced in substantial tonnage, but several other proteinaceous materials are available for the production of protein, and an intensive research program is under way to isolate the materials and study their properties. The more important members of this group are peanuts, cottonseed, flaxseed, and wheat.

Other seeds that are being studied as potential sources of protein include sunflower, caster, safflower, mustard, and fanweed. Their acceptance will depend as much on their soil and climatic requirements and ease of cultivation and harvesting as it will on their yields.

The oil-free meal derived from oilseeds or cereal grains contains 40 to 70 percent protein and is a raw material for the manufacture of isolated protein. It is also used directly in many industrial applications.

In 1922, the I. F. Laucks Co. introduced soybean-meal glue to the Douglas-fir plywood industry, where it has had an important role in plywood development. The tonnage used between the two wars was greater than that of any other plywood adhesive, and total consumption in the hard and soft plywood industries has ranged up to 45 million pounds annually. The wallpaper industry uses substantial amounts of soybean meal as an adhesive. The meal has also been used with satisfactory results in combination with casein for the brush coating of paper and in the formulation of water paints.

Soybean meal, corn gluten, and probably the other proteinaceous materials can extend phenolic resin for fabricating waterproof plywood glue. When it is used for that purpose, the meal must be low in water-soluble constituents. The cost of such products is low, ranging from 3 to 5 cents a pound, and their use effects a substantial saving in the cost of a waterproof glue.

Ray Burnett, E. D. Parker, and E. J. Roberts, working with peanut and soybean proteins at the Southern Regional Research Laboratory, demonstrated that those materials can be used to make tacky and remoistening adhesives. The paper industry is developing new types of packaging and other designs of paper fabrication, and an additional supply of tacky adhesives should therefore find a ready market.

A. C. Beckel, Paul A. Belter, and I, at the Northern Laboratory, developed a water-soluble proteinaceous material (55 percent protein) from soybeans. It may find wide usefulness as an adhesive and in certain food applications. For convenience, the product was named Gelsoy because a water solution at 10 percent concentration forms an irreversible gel when it is heated. The first application of the product probably will be to seal cork liners in crown seals. It might also be used in remoistening and heat-sealing adhesive operations. Because it whips like egg white, it has promise in a number of food applications.

THE ISOLATED PROTEINS differ in physical and chemical properties. That difference and a difference in source of supply and price structure have kept them largely in separate fields of application and have minimized competition among them. Most competitive are casein and soybean protein. Soybean protein came into substantial production during a period when the total supply of casein was greatly increased.

Packing-house and fish glues, which have been the only truly water-soluble industrial proteins, are noted for their excellent gelling characteristics at low protein concentration. It is possible that Gelsoy, when it is finally developed, will enter some of the same fields as the gelatin-type glue. The casein and soybean proteins are readily dispersed in a mild alkaline solution, but zein is the only industrial protein that is soluble in organic solvents.

The chemistry of proteins has been slower to unfold than the chemistry of other natural products, but major advances have been made in it. The combination of new advances in protein chemistry with the continued development of fibers, adhesives, and other products, and the natural growth of industries that depend upon proteins indicate a substantial increase in the future use of industrial proteins.

ALLAN K. SMITH *received his doctor's degree in chemistry from Columbia University. He is senior chemist in the Northern Regional Research Laboratory and is in charge of a section that studies protein properties, isolation, and food use. Dr. Smith has been with the Department since 1937.*

The Industrial Uses of Corn Protein

C. Bradford Croston,
Cyril D. Evans

The bulk of our corn crop is used directly as feed for farm animals. About 120 million bushels is processed each year by the wet-milling industries, however, to provide starch and oil for human food and for many industrial applications. Corn gluten, a byproduct of the starch refineries, contains about 50 percent protein.

Like other high-protein products, corn gluten is used without further change, mainly in feed concentrates and in small amounts as extenders for commercial resins and glues. It is sometimes destarched by acid or enzyme hydrolysis to yield a product that is almost entirely protein and is used in paints. Sometimes it is broken down by complete hydrolysis to yield monosodium glutamate, a seasoning for food.

The gluten is also processed to yield zein, a pure protein that has many commercial uses. Zein belongs to a class of proteins called prolamines, which have several unique properties. In fact, the special properties of zein make it widely acceptable for a number of industrial uses for which other proteins are inferior or unsuited.

Zein has been produced commercially since 1938. It is one of the few alcohol-soluble proteins; alcohol is used to extract it in pure form from the corn gluten. Originally, the gluten occurs mixed with starch in the endosperm of the corn kernel, the starchy part outside the germ. Most of the gluten is concentrated in a layer next to the hull of the kernel.

In commercial processing, isopropyl alcohol (about 15 percent water) is used to extract the zein from the gluten meal. The extract is subjected to a complicated process to obtain the isolated protein. It must be clarified by filtration to remove undissolved particles and then mixed with an oil solvent (hexane) to remove oil and coloring matter. The result is two phases, or layers. One contains the oil. The other contains the concentrated zein. After these are separated by centrifugation, the zein phase is squirted into large volumes of cooled water to precipitate the zein as a fibrous solid. The zein, when filtered from the water, must be dried by a carefully controlled process, because wet zein when heated forms a gummy dough that cannot be worked successfully. The final product is a light-yellow, durable powder.

Zein was a relatively expensive protein during the first years of its production because the method of making it was complicated. Its price, however, remained steady during the war years while the price of other commercial proteins increased until there was no difference in cost.

Up to 1950, only one company produced zein, and its capacity was below the actual demand. It is to be expected that the number of producers and their capacities will increase as demand dictates. Based on the amount of corn wet milled by the starch refineries, the potential supply of zein is 100,000 to 150,000 tons annually.

Corn contains proteins other than zein, and methods have been developed for their isolation. The Northern Regional Research Laboratory developed a process whereby corn gluten is first wetted with only a small amount of alcohol instead of the large amount commonly used for extraction. The proteins are then extracted with a relatively inexpensive alkaline solution. The pretreatment with alcohol is necessary to make the zein soluble. The process not only extracts the other proteins of corn along with the zein, but also greatly increases the efficiency of zein recovery. Because of greatly increased yields, the process would undoubtedly result in a less expensive protein for potential industrial uses.

THE PROPERTIES OF ZEIN and most other proteins are solubility in dilute alkali, tackiness (which enables them to adhere to other materials), ability to form films and fibers, susceptibility to coagulation by heat and other forces, and susceptibility to hydrolysis by chemicals and enzymes of organisms.

But zein, which belongs to the prolamine class of proteins, has some characteristics that distinguish it from most other proteins. It is deficient in some of the most reactive side groups, such as amino and carboxyl groups. Those groups have a great attraction for water, and zein therefore has relatively good resistance to water. Zein, on the other hand, contains an abundance of less reactive groups, such as amide and hydroxyphenyl groups. For that reason it is soluble in dilute alkali and, as the distinguishing feature of the prolamine class, it is soluble in low-boiling organic solvents, such as alcohols, ketones, and acids. That solubility factor makes zein useful in varnishes because, when a solution is spread on a surface, the solvent quickly evaporates to leave a coating, or film, of zein. Zein is also soluble in higher-boiling organic solvents, such as glycol ethers, and forms solutions that are used in the formulation of hot melts, cork binders, and printing inks. The constitution of its molecule is such that zein also has good oil resistance and imparts valuable greaseproofness to materials when applied as a coating.

Another noteworthy property of zein, which is unusual for proteins, is its thermoplasticity—the property of softening when heated. Thermoplastic materials are readily formed into inexpensive articles in molds by an application of heat and pressure. Moist zein readily flows under molding conditions to form articles that hold their shape under normal conditions. In combination with rosin and similar materials, it forms hot melts, which can be used as another method for applying coatings. Such formulations are also useful because of their heat-sealing properties.

Zein is resistant to hydrolysis and to putrefaction by micro-organisms. Many proteins, when dissolved in dilute alkali, start to deteriorate and to give off ammonia; zein, however, is relatively stable in alkaline solutions. Also, zein can be stored for a long time in a wet or dissolved state without acquiring the disagreeable odor of putrefaction so evident with other proteins. The resistance to spoilage is convenient in manufacturing plants where wastes are bound to accumulate.

The zein molecule seems to have a relatively long, effective chain length, which enhances the film- and fiber-forming properties of this protein. Though relatively inert, zein is reactive to chemicals, such as formaldehyde, which tie molecules together and thus harden and improve the water-resistance of coatings and shaped articles. It has remarkable adhesive properties, which are necessary in many of its applications.

The most troublesome property of zein has probably been the gelation of its solutions. Varnish in bottles, for example, would solidify, or coating solutions would turn to a gel in the paper coater. This gelling property is inherent in proteins and is closely related to the film- and fiber-forming properties. Solutions of zein can be stabilized against gelation by a special formaldehyde treatment. Also, the zein now sold commercially is a modified protein that forms relatively stable solutions.

ZEIN ITSELF has become an important industrial protein because the combinations of certain of its properties favor its use for specific purposes. For example, its solubility in alcohol makes it a good ingredient of varnishes; furthermore, the coating it forms adheres to the surface, is durable, resists water and chemical agents, is flexible to a certain degree, and has satisfactory color.

Patents cover the use of zein for many products—from a hair-wave set to chewing gum. It can be molded into hard, resistant plastics or converted into sheets of rubbery material. It forms a tough film or coating on other materials. It makes an excellent textile fiber. It can be used as an adhesive to bind other substances together or in compounding printing inks. It has been used in making beer and improving flour.

The most important industrial users take advantage of the properties already discussed and use the commercially supplied product without much further modification. For novelty uses, such as replacements for rubber, celluloid, or linoleum, the properties are often modified by chemical reactions and physical treatments. Zein is seldom used alone—it is generally mixed with such materials as resins and plasticizers, which contribute their own desirable properties to the mixture. Many formulations are available to fit the various needs.

During the Second World War, when imports of shellac were greatly curtailed, zein was used extensively as a replacement in varnishes and phonograph records.

As a varnish, zein was used in an alcohol solution along with other ingredients, generally including rosin. The recommended ratio of zein to rosin ranged from 1:1 to 1:3 parts by weight. The higher proportions cost more, but they make more durable finishes. Various formulations are useful as wood primers, which have excellent sanding qualities, or as gloss finishes. They can be used on a variety of surfaces—wood, paper, asphalt compositions, leather, cloth, glass. Outstanding properties are a high gloss, fast rate of drying, suitable hardness, flexibility, brushability, resistance to water and grease, and good dielectric characteristics. Pigments can be added to the spirit varnishes to make decorative as well as protective coatings.

Zein replaced shellac in phonograph records because it supplied the needed thermoplastic material for the molding process; it was found that zein could be used with very little change in the process. It is said that the zein records wear better and have superior tone qualities.

In the paper industries, zein has value for sizing, impregnating, coating, laminating, and gluing paper. One of the uses is as a glossy protective coating, which is applied as zein varnish and known as overprint or label varnish. It gives a glossy finish and resists scuffing, water, alcohol, and grease.

Zein is also used as size for paper and cardboard. The treatment is usually called tub sizing because the paper is immersed in a water dispersion of the zein formulation before rolling and drying. Good water resistance is given the paper. The addition of materials like oleic acid imparts excellent water resistance to the paper. Zein-sized papers also have the useful property of resistance to penetration by the oils, greases, and waxes. They can be used as wrapping papers and cardboard containers for greasy foods.

Another way to make paper proof against grease is to coat it with an alcoholic solution of zein.

Proteins are generally used as binders in clay coating papers. Zein is a good binder because of its excellent adhesive character and its good water resistance. The coating slurry (which contains clay, zein, and dispersing agents for the zein, such as alkali or rosin soaps) is applied with ordinary equipment. Advantages are that mixtures high in solids can be used and less heat is needed to effect drying.

Zein is used to bind cork particles together to form composition cork. Granulated cork is first mixed with zein in a glycol solvent and with a curing agent, such as paraformaldehyde. The mixture is then molded by slight pressure into blocks, rods, or sheets, which are cured at high temperatures. The finished products have many different uses—as gasket materials, bottle-cap liners, polishing wheels, shoe fillers, textile spinning cots, and novelty and specialty items. A particular advantage of zein as a binder is its resistance to molds in hot, damp weather.

Other adhesive applications include the binding of paper, glass, wood veneer, and materials like nitrocellulose, to which ordinary glues will not adhere. Zein can be used successfully in making impregnated and laminated paper gasket material. It is used in printing inks where it must adhere to the paper and be quick-setting to allow for rapid printing.

An excellent textile fiber is being made from zein. (See p. 469.)

Other uses are numerous. As a sealer for asphaltic compositions, zein protects the surface coating from penetration by the asphalt. It is one of the foaming agents used in fire extinguishers. Some foundries use it as binding material in sand molds. It is used as a binder to stiffen hard felts and as one of the ingredients of oilcloth and linoleum. It serves as backing for photographic films and makes a useful sizing for fibers in the weaving industry.

Thus, corn protein has many applications besides its major use as feed. After zein became commercially available, its industrial utilization expanded rapidly as improved processes and new industries developed. Successful use depends on a sound understanding of its unique properties and how to use those properties to advantage. The great potential availability encourages continued and increased utilization in a wide range of commercial applications for which zein is suited.

C. BRADFORD CROSTON *has been a chemist in the oil and protein division of the Northern Regional Research Laboratory since 1943.*

CYRIL D. EVANS *joined the Department of Agriculture in 1941, when the protein section of the Northern Laboratory was established. His major work has been on the industrial utilization of plant proteins— as fibers, films, plastics, coatings, adhesives, and plasticizers.*

Strength of four glues applied to various woods

	Shear strength (pounds per square inch) when applied to—					
	Birch		Tupelo		Red gum	
Glue mix	Dry	Wet	Dry	Wet	Dry	Wet
Peanut-meal glue [1] .... {	364	157	327	91	382	150
	367	147	374	138	373	110
Commercial soybean meal prepared for use as plywood glue............................... {	393	151	401	0	328	33
	396	142	268	112	352	105
	396	73	274	143	370	138
Casein-glue mix ready for use upon addition of water..................................... {	495	195	408	138	497	151
	523	214	357	185	403	171
Casein-glue mix containing blood and soybean meal..................................... {	489	259	340	166	356	184
	409	167	251	138	341	112

[1] All commercial mixes.

From Burnett, R. S., and Parker, E. D., Transactions of the American Society of Mechanical Engineers, vol. 68, pp. 751–756. 1946.

Peanut Protein for Industrial Uses

Jett C. Arthur, Jr.

The peanut is a pea, not a nut. It belongs to the bean family. It matures its fruit, or pod, underground. Small yellow flowers form at the joints where the leaves are attached to the stems; after pollination the flower fades and a shoot is formed. The shoot elongates and enters the ground, where a pod develops.

By the time it reaches maturity, the cellulosic pod, or shell, contains 1 to 3 nuts or kernels. The shell is 20 to 30 percent of the weight of the mature peanut. The kernels contain 43 to 50 percent oil, 25 to 30 percent protein, 5 to 12 percent carbohydrates, about 3 percent crude fiber, and 2.5 percent ash.

Peanuts grow best where a loose surface of the soil can be maintained. Our principal peanut-producing regions are the Virginia-North Carolina area (Virginia, North Carolina, and Tennessee), the southeastern area (South Carolina, Georgia, Florida, Alabama, and Mississippi), and the southwestern area (Arkansas, Louisiana, Oklahoma, and Texas).

Peanuts have become one of the South's leading cash crops. In 1863, we produced about 10,000 tons of peanuts. During the 1920's, production averaged 395,000 tons annually, with a farm value of about 39 million dollars. During the 1930's, and again during the war years, production increased sharply; beginning with the 1942 crop, the average annual production has been more than 1 million tons, with a farm value of almost 200 million dollars. The 1947 crop was marketed as follows: 200,000 tons were kept on the farm for eating and seeding; 500,-000 tons entered trade as peanut butter, candy, and salted peanuts; and 426,000 tons were crushed for oil or exported. Of the peanuts in the edible trade, 50 to 60 percent were used in peanut butter, 25 to 30 percent in salted nuts, about 10 percent in candy, and about 1.5 percent in bakery products.

Peanuts are nutritious. One pound of peanut butter contains more calories, protein, minerals, and vitamins than a pound of beefsteak.

Peanuts also are crushed to produce oil, which is used for food in the form of margarine, shortening, and cooking oils. After the oil has been separated from the rest of the peanut kernel, the residue is used for feeding livestock.

Since 1940, about 15 to 30 percent of the peanut crop has been crushed for oil and meal, more than half of it from peanuts grown in the southeastern area. Large amounts were exported under the European aid program in 1948. Except for two brief periods, the value of peanut oil and meal since 1935 has not been high enough to permit crushers to pay as much as the Government support price for peanuts; except for small quantities discarded at shelling plants as unfit for food, all the peanuts sold for crushing were subsidized by the Government.

Production for nonfood uses can be made economically feasible by reducing the cost of production, by increasing the value of peanut oil and meal, or by combining the two factors in some way.

State and Federal research is being directed toward the development of improved production, harvesting, and handling methods for peanuts and the development of higher-quality, higher-yielding varieties. At the Southern Regional Research Laboratory research has been directed toward increasing the value of the oil and meal from peanuts. One of the main aims has been to develop industrial uses for peanut meal and protein, such as glues, adhesives, paper sizes, and textile fibers.

Two GENERAL methods are used to separate the oil from the kernels—mechanical pressing and solvent extraction. The only large volume of commercial peanut meal produced in the United States in 1947 was made by mechanically pressing the oil from the kernels. To increase the efficiency of the oil extraction, the peanut flakes are first cooked to temperatures from 175° to 250° F. The cooked flakes thereafter are subjected to high pressure to remove the oil. The high temperature and pressures employed in the expression processes adversely affect the quality of the protein, especially its solubility in water and in salt solutions. The solubility in water of the protein in peanut meal made by expression methods ranges from 15 to 50 percent, depending on the conditions of cooking and pressing. In a weak solution of caustic soda, however, 75 to 95 percent of the protein in the meal can be dissolved.

When the oil has been removed from the flaked peanut kernels by means of low-boiling hydrocarbons (particularly petroleum hydrocarbons, such as hexane), the solubility of the protein in the oil-free meal is about 80 percent in water and more than 95 percent in dilute caustic soda solutions.

In sum, the conditions of processing the peanut kernels for oil and meal markedly affect the solubility of the protein of the residual meal or cake in different solvents. Short periods of processing, low temperatures in preparing the flaked kernels, and low temperatures and humidity in removing the solvent from the extracted meal generally are essential to the production of peanut meals that have a high percentage of soluble proteins.

THE STEPS followed in separating protein from solvent-extracted peanut meal are: (1) Preparation of a water-meal mixture and addition of protein-dissolving chemicals; (2) clarification of the mixture by screening, filtering, and (sometimes) centrifuging; (3) precipitation of the protein as a cheese-like curd from the water-protein solution by the addition of coagulating chemicals; (4) separation of the protein curd from the solution; and (5) drying of the protein curd.

Let us examine a typical process for producing peanut protein. Solvent-extracted peanut meal is mixed with water in a ratio of 10 pounds of water to 1 pound of meal. A solution of caustic soda (30 percent) is added until the water-meal mixture is slightly alkaline, and most of the peanut meal protein has been dissolved. A half pound or so of caustic soda is required to dissolve the protein in 100 pounds of peanut meal. The solution containing the dissolved protein is separated from the insoluble portion of the meal by screening and centrifuging.

The dissolved peanut protein is recovered from the clarified solution by adding gaseous sulfur dioxide until the solution is sufficiently acid to precipitate the greatest possible amount of peanut protein as a dense cheeselike curd. The protein curd is separated from the solution and dried in a forced-air draft at 120° F.

About two-thirds of the total weight of protein in the meal (or about 40 pounds of protein from each 100 pounds of meal) can be recovered in this way. A part of the protein is not dissolved during the process, however, and the insoluble material remaining after extraction of the protein still contains about 20 to 25 percent protein. This residue has a relatively high nutritive value for livestock and is satisfactory for feeding in mixture with other high-protein concentrates.

. Upon addition of salts, the water solutions remaining after separation of the protein may be utilized for the propagation of yeast. It is possible thereby to produce food and feed yeasts and to dispose of the waste solutions without polluting streams.

THE FLOW PROPERTIES, or viscosity, of peanut-protein solutions are important when the protein is used for making adhesives or synthetic fibers. The degree of concentration of the protein, the temperature, the type of chemicals in the solution, and the age of the solutions are among the factors that determine the viscosity.

Caustic soda solutions that contain more than 26 percent of protein are unstable with respect to their viscosity; solutions having protein concentrations greater than 28 percent usually gel or develop a very high viscosity. Protein extracted from hydraulic-pressed peanut meal, when dissolved in a lye solution, has a higher initial viscosity; that is, the solutions are thicker than protein extracted from solvent-extraction meal.

Factory-scale tests show that plywood glues made from peanut meal are the equal of other protein glues used for that purpose.

To be suitable for making plywood glues, peanut meal must meet four specifications. Its content of protein (nitrogen content × 6.25) must be at least 50 percent. At least 70 percent of the protein in the meal must be soluble in 1 molar sodium chloride. A minimum of 80 percent of the meal must be ground fine enough to pass a 200-mesh screen. The residual oil content must be 6 percent or less.

Here is a formula for preparing plant-scale batches of peanut-meal glue: (1) Stir 200 pounds of water and 100 pounds of peanut-meal flour to a smooth paste; (2) add 55 pounds of water, 15 pounds of lime mixed with 35 pounds of water, 4 pounds of caustic soda dissolved in 11.5 pounds of water, and 3 pounds of tetrasulfide, and stir for 2 minutes; (3) mix in 15

pounds of silicate of soda. Thereupon the glue is ready to use. Peanut-meal glue compares favorably with commercial plywood adhesives made from soybean meal, with casein glue, and with casein glue that contains blood and soybean meal.

GLUES easy to dissolve have been prepared from peanut protein made from both solvent-extracted and hydraulic-pressed peanut meals by neutralizing the protein curds with caustic soda before drying them. These glues are suitable for making gummed tape and paper and for making flexible or nonwarping glues. Glues prepared from hydraulic-pressed peanut meal have 65 to 78 percent of the adhesive strength of animal glues. Glues prepared from solvent-extracted meal have 12 to 82 percent of the adhesive strength of glues made from animal proteins.

Paper coatings have been made with peanut protein as the adhesive; their adhesive strength is slightly greater than that of soybean-protein coatings but less than that of casein coatings. The peanut-protein coatings have a wax pick number (adhesive strength number) of more than 4; they are satisfactory for many printing operations. Color measurements (reflectance) indicate that casein and soybean-protein coatings have the same degree of whiteness; peanut-protein coatings are slightly darker.

Fire-extinguishing liquid can be made from peanut meal by this method: Mix 100 pounds of peanut meal with 50 gallons of water containing 15 pounds of hydrated lime. Heat the mixture to 203° F. for 2 hours (to hydrolyze the proteins); filter; neutralize with an acid; and concentrate to 33 to 40 percent solids by evaporation. The foam produced by the peanut-protein solution is dense and comparatively permanent.

A product suitable for sizing paper for lithographing can be made by mixing oil-free peanut meal with alkaline solutions of sodium hydroxide, ammonium hydroxide, or borax. The protein in the meal is extracted, after which the protein solution is clarified and concentrated by evaporating part of the water. The solution may be used directly in the manufacture of paper, or it may be dried to form a powder which dissolves easily in water.

A material that sizes textiles permanently also is made from peanut protein. Cotton muslin sized with it in the laboratory had strength and flexing properties similar to those of samples sized commercially with animal glues. Peanut protein can therefore be used as a sizing material for window-shade cloth and like products. Muslin sized with it can be dried at high temperatures without hardening, blistering, or granulating—an advantage that animal glues do not have.

A molding powder that is water-resistant and is suitable for plastic products has been prepared by mixing synthetic resins (such as the condensation products of phenols and formaldehyde) with finely ground oil-free peanut meal.

Peanut meal has been used as a raw material for the preparation of protein hydrolyzates. The preparation of culture media by the action of pepsin has been reported. The hydrolyzates have been used for the propagation of antibiotic agents.

Economically, peanut-protein fiber is perhaps in a better position than its related products to compete with other proteins and their products. In 1937, David Traill in England reported the extrusion of peanut protein-urea solutions into an acid coagulating bath to form a new fiber, Ardil.

W. T. Astbury, R. H. K. Thomson, A. McLean, and others have continued its development. Two British firms planned commercial production of the fiber in 1950.

A new method for the production of fiber from peanut protein resulted from research started in 1942 at the Southern Laboratory by Arthur L. Merrifield and A. F. Pomes and continued by Hugh G. Many and me. Our process is this: An alkaline solution of peanut protein is matured, then extruded into an acid-salt coagulating bath, taken up on rolls and treated with salt and formaldehyde solutions, and finally collected as a cake on a bobbin. The fiber is further treated with salt solutions and sulfonated oils to improve its hand.

The resulting fiber was named Sarelon. It is cream color in its natural state and has a soft hand and a warmth similar to that of wool. Sarelon has an affinity for dyes normally used on natural protein fibers; it may be dyed with vat and direct cotton dyes. It absorbs dye faster than wool does. Solid shades can be had in mixtures of wool and Sarelon by using a level-dyeing acid dye at the boil.

Sarelon has mechanical properties equal or superior to those of other synthetic protein fibers. Peanut-protein fibers with tensile strengths of 0.95 to 1:05 grams per denier (dry) and 0.5 to 0.6 gram per denier (wet) have been produced. Such values are about 80 percent of the values obtained for wool. The fiber has elongation-at-break characteristics similar to those of wool, with an elastic recovery of 95 percent at 2 percent stretch. It has a high degree of dimensional stability and does not shrink appreciably in hot water. Woven fabrics composed of blends of Sarelon and rayon or Sarelon and wool have been found to be satisfactory for use in suitings, coat linings, and blanket materials.

JETT C. ARTHUR, JR., has been employed as a chemist at the Southern Regional Research Laboratory since 1941. He is engaged in investigations on the production and utilization of cottonseed and peanut meals and proteins. A native of Texas, he holds degrees from S. F. Austin State College and the University of Texas. During the Second World War, he was an officer in a Naval Amphibious Group which participated in invasion and support operations at Lingayen Gulf, Philippine Islands, and Okinawa.

Uses of Soybean Protein in Industry

Allan K. Smith

Soybeans are easily processed for oil and meal. They are formed into flakes more easily than other oilseeds—an unusual property that has given them a strong advantage in solvent-extraction operations. Furthermore, its high nutritional value and great abundance have placed the protein first among the protein concentrates used for animal feeds. Likewise, soybean oil is used in greater tonnage than any other vegetable oil in production of hydrogenated shortening, and its semidrying and other properties adapt it to many industrial uses.

Ahead of the industrial uses of soybean protein, of course, must come its use as feed. The tonnage of soybean protein used industrially is small compared to that used for stock feed; it is estimated that little more than 5 percent of the processed soybean meal finds it way into industrial products. Likewise, the consumption of soybeans for human food in the United States is comparatively small, roughly comparable to the industrial consumption. During the war and the postwar period, soybean flour was shipped to our Allies in rather substantial quantities. While the industrial and food uses of soybean protein are increasing, soybean production has increased at an even faster pace. At the beginning of the Second World War, production doubled, from 100 million to 200 million bushels in a year, and the 1950 crop was estimated at 270 million bushels. Some people are forecasting still larger production for the future.

Industrial utilization of soybean protein covers a broad variety of products. The term "industrial protein" applied to soybeans designates products ranging from crude oil meal (44 percent protein), used in stock feed and in some industrial products, to isolated and refined soybean protein (100 percent protein) and the products derived from the protein.

Each grade finds utilization in keeping with its properties and cost. New uses appear regularly. Soybeans, because of their relatively low cost of production, are an exceptional farm crop for scientific and technical development. The price of a product is always a factor in its success; hence the low cost of the oil and protein gives soybeans an advantage over similar products from other oilseed crops for industrial markets.

Proteins have assumed industrial importance only in comparatively recent years. The slow development may be attributed to their great importance for foods (restricting the available supply for industrial application) and the exceedingly difficult chemistry of the protein molecule. Of all natural products, the proteins present the most complicated puzzle with which science has to deal.

The fundamental problem of protein supply in the United States, however, has changed from one of scarcity to one of plenty, mainly because of the introduction of the soybean. In evaluating what lies ahead for soy protein, we shall consider the utilization of the soybean meal and the isolated protein. Under isolated protein we shall discuss the problem of whey disposal and its influence on locating protein refining plants, and the competition, characteristics, and applications of the proteins.

Dehulled soybean oil-free meal contains about 50 percent protein. It is a raw material for making isolated protein and has several other important industrial applications. It makes an excellent glue that has good water resistance.

The use of soybean-meal glue in fabricating plywood from both hard and soft woods in peak years has reached 45 million pounds. Another well-established and substantial use of the glue is for wallpaper coating. During the war, soybean meal was used in conjunction with casein or isolated soybean protein for brush-coating paper. The results were so satisfactory that this use appears to have been adopted permanently by the paper industry.

Because of the low cost of soybean meal and its good adhesive strength and water resistance, other substantial uses can be expected. The development of tacky adhesives from soybean meal would greatly extend its usefulness in fiberboard construction and in packaging. The paper industry offers many opportunities, especially in the fabrication of high-quality paper boxes, which equal or surpass similar boxes of wood construction. The fulfillment of such applications would require substantial quantities of soybean meal.

THE PROTEIN ISOLATED or extracted by chemical means from undenatured (no heat treatment), solvent-extracted soybean flakes is a highly specialized product with the general name of soybean protein.

Attention to details is necessary to produce a standard product. The process consists of dissolving the protein in the undenatured hexane-extracted flakes with dilute sodium hydroxide and removing the insoluble part of the meal by screening and centrifuging. The protein is precipitated from the solution by adding acid to a pH value of 4.6 to 4.0; the precipitated curd is filtered and dried. Some processors bleach the protein and give it a mild hydrolytic treatment to develop de-

sirable properties. Although the protein is easily prepared in a purified state in the laboratory, the operation of a large-scale plant has many engineering problems.

There also occurs in this process a serious problem of waste disposal.

In the production of isolated protein, two other fractions are obtained. One is a solid residue with a relatively high percentage of unextracted protein. It may be used in feed mixtures or for extending phenolic resin glues and plastics.

The other comes out in a dilute water solution; about one-third of the original meal appears in it. For convenience it is called whey. It contains proteins and sugars which, if recovered, could be used as feed, but evaporation is the only method now available for such recovery, and that is not economically feasible.

Disposal of the whey as sewage is restricted in many localities where authorities are trying to prevent pollution of lakes and rivers. The large rivers, such as the Mississippi, Missouri, and Ohio, however, may be open indefinitely to sewage disposal. Apparently then the waste-disposal problem restricts the location of the factory. A sewage-treatment plant is presently the only other acceptable method for whey disposal. Future research may find a more economical and practical procedure, such as using it as a nutrient for growing yeast.

A NEW PRODUCT from soybeans now coming on the market has been named Gelsoy. It is a result of a series of investigations at the Northern Regional Research Laboratory by A. C. Beckel, Paul A. Belter, Mrs. Letta DeVoss, and me on the use of alcohol (ethanol) as an oil solvent. We found that extracting soybeans with alcohol improved the color and taste of the meal and the protein isolated from it and that the alcohol either removed an antigelling factor or converted the protein into a more readily gelable form.

The process as finally developed includes three steps: First, the washing of the undenatured hexane-extracted flakes with alcohol (ethanol or isopropanol) and recovery of the alcohol for reuse; second, countercurrent batch extraction of the alcohol-washed flakes with water to obtain the highest possible yield and concentration of soluble protein; and, third, spray drying of the solution from the second step. The spray-dried material is Gelsoy.

Gelsoy is about 55 percent protein and 45 percent soluble carbohydrates, ash, and nonprotein nitrogen. When a water solution of about 10 percent total solids of the spray-dried product is heated to 212° F., it forms an irreversible gel—one that does not reverse to a liquid by change in temperature; hence the name Gelsoy.

A water solution of Gelsoy can be whipped into a meringue like egg white. It might also be used in frozen desserts, soup stock, and other foods. It has special glue properties and differs from other soybean glues in that it can be set with heat to improve its water resistance in much the same way that egg white is coagulated with heat. Preliminary trials indicated that Gelsoy may be used as a remoistening and heat-sealing glue. The Allied Mills Co., Inc., of Peoria began producing Gelsoy in 1950.

No SINGLE PROTEIN possesses all of the desirable properties needed for its many and varied industrial applications. The different properties of the proteins, combined with their different prices, have kept them mostly in separate fields of application and have minimized competition. The chemist's job is to develop ways to modify protein so that its uses can be diversified. For example, a dark protein is in disfavor, regardless of its other properties or its intended application. For such uses as paper coating, textile fiber, paper sizing, and water paints a very light color is essential. Soybean protein meets this requirement as well as many others.

Water solubility is often desirable, but only the packing-house proteins, the fish glues, and egg and blood albumin have it. Zein (extracted from corn gluten with alcohol) is distinctive for its solubility in organic solvents (such as alcohol and acetone), while soy protein and milk casein require alkalies for their dispersion. Formation of strong gels, good adhesive strength, water resistance, the property of forming tacky dispersions, and the ability of molecular orientation are all desirable characteristics.

IN APPRAISING FUTURE TRENDS in the utilization of soybean protein, we have to consider the possibility of extending present uses and developing new products.

Several of the uses for soybean protein are in paper manufacture and conversion. The most important is for making coated paper, a product much used for color advertising and high-grade printing. In the coating of paper, a mixture of fine white clay is suspended in an alkaline protein solution and brushed over the paper with brushes of badger hair. The protein acts as an adhesive to bind the clay to the paper. After drying, the paper is calendered by passing it several times between highly polished steam-heated rolls to produce the smooth and glossy surface necessary for fine printing.

Another specialized application of the protein in the paper trade is in making a beater sizing by dissolving the protein in a completely saponified rosin solution (rosin treated with alkali), adding boric acid, and adding this combination to the slurry of wood pulp while it is in the beater. This sizing is effective in some types of paper where ordinary rosin sizing fails. It was the first industrial use of isolated soybean protein.

Surface sizing, also known as tub sizing, may be done with soybean protein. For it, a dilute solution of the protein is used for a very thin surface coating of paper to improve its writing properties.

At the Northern Laboratory we developed a soybean-protein formula for laminating paper tubes used in making casings for shotgun shells. Manufacturers of nearly half the shotgun shells produced in this country now use our formula.

Another unique application for soybean protein is its mixture with alkaline salts to form a well-known washing compound. The protein is brought into solution by the alkalinity of the salts. As it dries on the wall, the solution leaves a thin protective coating.

The isolated protein is used also in water paints. It binds the pigments and colors to give a decorative coating of pastel shades for inside use. It shares this use with casein and certain resins.

Paper coatings normally made with milk casein have provided the largest single use for protein for many years. The urgent demands of the food industries for dry milk solids, however, have caused serious shortages of casein. These are gradually being relieved by adoption of soybean protein.

An ever-increasing amount of protein is being used in the United States. An expansion of the present uses of protein may eventually mean that more soybeans will be used—for tire-cord sizing, textile sizing, bookbinding, sandpaper adhesive, in abrasive wheels, match-head binders, cork binder for gaskets, remoistening adhesives for labels, tacky glues, paper laminations.

From the standpoint of domestic production, the commercially important proteins are packing-house glues, soybean protein, milk casein (exclusive of imported casein), zein, and dried egg white, in that order. Although soybean protein takes second place in production capacity, the soybean meal from which it is derived ranks first as a source of isolated protein for commercial use. That is because it is necessary to use solvent-extracted flakes as the basic raw material in the process of isolating the protein. The high temperatures developed in hydraulic or screw-press operations bring about caramelization of the sugars and denaturation of the protein to give a product that is dark in color and of difficult solubility.

The natural advantage of the soybean over other oilseeds lies in its characteristic property of forming flakes when passed between smooth rolls, which makes it easily adaptable to solvent extraction. This apparently small advantage is important in protein isolation and will continue so until engineers develop new and satisfactory methods for solvent extraction of the other oilseeds.

ALLAN K. SMITH *is a chemist at the Northern Laboratory.*

Principal oilseeds of the United States: Production, imports, and tonnage crushed

Oilseed	Production		Imports		Crushed	
	1937–47 average	1949	1937–47 average	1949	1937–47 average	1949
	1,000 tons	1,000 tons	1,000 tons	1,000 tons	1,000 tons	1,000 tons
Soybeans........................	4,172	6,669	(1)	(1)	3,253	5,853
Cottonseed......................	4,923	6,613	(1)	(1)	3,856	5,710
Flaxseed........................	879	1,223	301	4	979	1,047
Copra..........................	(2)	(2)	255	428	227	383
Corn germ......................	(2)	(2)	(1)	(1)	274	317
Peanuts (Farmers' stock)..........	895	938	6	(1)	129	217

1 Less than 500 tons.
2 Information not available.

Getting Protein From Cotton Seeds

Jett C. Arthur, Jr.,
Melvin L. Karon

From cotton we get more than 4 million tons of cottonseed a year, worth about 250 million dollars on the farm in 1950. From cottonseed we get shortening, margarine, cooking oils, and feeds that are high in protein.

Cottonseed meal and cake, of which we produce approximately 2 million tons annually by extracting the oil from the cottonseed, are an industrial source of raw materials for making adhesives and protein fibers. Further industrial utilization of the proteins would add much to the value of the cottonseed and strengthen the agricultural economy of the South.

Plywood glue from cottonseed meal is prepared by mixing 100 pounds of meal, 3 pounds of borax, 2 pounds of caustic soda, 1.5 pounds of potassium permanganate, 15 pounds of lime, and 8 pounds of copper sulfate with water. Combinations of cottonseed meal with casein, soybean meal, or synthetic resins also can be used to make a plywood glue that is water-resistant and non-abrasive.

Plastic compounds containing equal parts of phenolic resin, cottonseed hulls, and cottonseed meal have good flow properties and can be cured in a relatively short time at temperatures of 320° to 360° F. The water absorption of the plastic after molding is less than 0.8 percent in the first 24 hours, and the strength of cottonseed-meal plastic is about equal to the strength of phenolic plastics. Small radio cabinets have been made from plastics that contain phenolic resins and cottonseed products.

Fire-extinguishing liquids are prepared from cottonseed meal by mixing the meal with lime solution and heating the mixture at temperatures of 200° to 210° F. for 2 hours. The suspension is clarified by filtering to remove the insoluble part of the meal. The protein-lime solution is neutralized by the addition of mineral acid and concentrated by evaporation to 30 to 45 percent of solids. When this protein solution is stirred, a dense and stable foam is produced.

COTTONSEED PROTEIN is made by removing the oil from the seed and then extracting the protein from the cottonseed meal. The first step is to produce an oil-free cottonseed meal that contains proteins soluble in dilute salt or sodium hydroxide solutions.

The two general methods of removing the oil from cottonseed are mechanical pressing and solvent extraction. The solubility in different solvents of cottonseed protein in the meal is determined primarily by the temperature and the duration of heating or cooking to which the cottonseed kernels (meats) have been subjected before, during, or after extraction of the oil. Knowledge of the physical composition of cottonseed proteins is essential to the establishment and control of conditions that must be followed during removal of the oil from the kernels to produce an oil-free meal containing highly soluble and relatively unchanged protein.

If the oil is to be removed by mechanical pressing, it is customary to cook the kernels at temperatures of 175° to 250° F. for several hours before pressing. The cooking makes it easier to separate the oil from the other constituents of the seed. But cooking reduces the solubility of the protein of the residual meal, and, because the cooking practices vary in different oil mills, only about 15 to 50 percent of the total protein dissolves in sodium hydroxide solutions.

If the oil is separated from cottonseed kernels by extraction with organic solvents at room temperature and the oil-free meal is air-dried at the same temperature, about 95 percent of the protein dissolves in relatively concentrated sodium hydroxide solutions. If low-boiling solvents (petroleum naphthas and alcohols) are used to extract the oil at temperatures near the boiling point of the solvent and the oil-free meal is dried at temperatures of 120° to 150° F., however, only about 85 percent of the total protein is soluble in the same sodium hydroxide solutions.

To produce an oil-free cottonseed meal for the protein extraction, therefore, the oil has to be removed from very thinly rolled cottonseed kernels by means of organic solvents at low temperatures, whereupon it is possible to dissolve the protein in salt or sodium hydroxide solutions.

Six steps are necessary to extract the protein from cottonseed meal: (1) Preparation of a water-meal mixture (slurry) in a weight ratio of 10 pounds of water to 1 pound of meal; (2) addition of sodium hydroxide, salts, or other substances to dissolve the protein; (3) separation of the solution containing the protein from the insoluble part of the meal; (4) addition of coagulating chemicals, such as sulfur

dioxide or sulfuric acid, to precipitate and coagulate the protein; (5) separation of the precipitated protein curd from the solution; and (6) drying of the curd. About 50 to 60 percent of the protein contained in solvent-extracted cottonseed meal can be separated from the meal in the form of dried protein.

PROTEIN FIBER is made from the protein contained in cottonseed meal. Cottonseed protein is mixed with water. Sodium hydroxide is added to yield a thick, molasseslike solution. The solution is forced through a die, which contains many small holes, into a solution of sulfuric acid and sodium sulfate. The protein is coagulated, and a threadlike plastic fiber is formed. The fiber is withdrawn from the acid-salt solution, stretched, and reacted with other chemicals. When it is dry, the fiber is yellow or orange and has the soft feel of wool. The process resembles the one the silkworm uses to make silk.

Cottonseed-protein fiber has potential value as a supplement to our domestic wool supplies and for use in furniture, mattress, and air-filter materials, in which its yellow-orange color is not objectionable.

JETT C. ARTHUR, JR., *has been employed as a chemist at the Southern Regional Research Laboratory since 1941.*

MELVIN L. KARON *has been engaged in research on the enzymes and proteins of cottonseed and peanuts since 1942 as a chemist at the Southern Laboratory. He holds degrees from the University of Minnesota.*

HISTORIANS BELIEVE cotton originated in India, perhaps about 3000 B. C. The ancient Brahmans, highest in the caste sysem, were required by one of their oldest laws to use sacrificial threads made of cotton. By the time the first European travelers reached India, the wealthier Hindus were wearing turbans of such finely woven muslin and calico that poets called them "webs of woven wind."

Wheat Proteins, Known and Unknown

Dale K. Mecham,
George H. Brother

A search for new uses for wheat and for means of extending its present uses goes on steadily. Always to be borne in mind is that wheat is usually a more expensive source of protein, starch, or other constituents than crops with which it must compete. When wheat is used for food, its extra cost is justified by its unique value in making bread and other baked goods. Bread is made from wheat flour because the proteins in wheat enable leavened wheat-flour doughs to retain gas bubbles in a manner that provides the desired porous structure of breadstuffs. Flours made from other seed crops lack this characteristic.

The properties, and therefore the possible uses, of wheat proteins depend on the methods of their separation from the other components of wheat and, more basically, on their chemical and physical behavior. Accordingly, we shall discuss the separation and identification of the proteins before we consider their possibilities for utilization. Also to be stressed is that about six times as much starch as protein can be recovered from wheat. Protein can be produced for industrial purposes, therefore, only when suitable markets are also available for the starch.

The total protein content of wheats ranges from 6 to 22 percent, depending on soil, weather conditions, and variety. The commercial classification of wheats as hard or soft in kernel texture reflects somewhat the protein content. A protein content of 12 to 12.5 percent (on a moisture-free basis) can be considered as intermediate. Most soft wheats contain less protein. Most hard wheats contain more.

Several different proteins are present in wheat kernels, but the principal and most characteristic ones are those that make up wheat gluten. The gluten proteins may be separated as a coherent, somewhat rubbery, but extensible mass by gently kneading a flour-water dough in a stream of water; starch and water-soluble constituents are washed away and the crude gluten remains.

Because they are largely responsible for the usefulness of wheat as a bread-making cereal, the gluten proteins have always been of interest in connection with the use of wheat in foods. As far as the industrial nonfood utilization of wheat proteins is concerned, they are of primary interest also because they make up the major portion of the total wheat proteins and can be separated by relatively simple mechanical procedures.

THE SEPARATION of the gluten proteins from wheat ordinarily begins in the flour-milling process. The bran and germ, which contain no gluten proteins, are separated mechanically from the endosperm, which contains the proteins. Then the particles of endosperm are ground to flour of the fineness desired. About 70 percent of the wheat proteins are recovered in flour of various grades. Of the flour proteins, approximately 80 percent are gluten proteins. (The figures vary somewhat with wheats of differing hardness, weight, and total protein content.)

In commercial practice, the gluten proteins are usually separated from other flour components by mechanical washing processes of different types. In the oldest method, a flour-water dough is made and then kneaded in an excess of water. As starch is removed from the dough, the starch-water mixture is replaced with fresh water until all the readily removable starch is washed out and the gluten remains as the characteristic wet mass. Starch is recovered by methods similar to those used for the industrial production of other vegetable starches.

Recently modifications and variations in the basic process have come into use. In one, a very soft dough, formed by adding more than the usual proportion of water, is subjected to a tumbling action in the wash water. In another, developed by Department scientists, a soft dough or batter is mixed with additional water to form a suspension in which the gluten proteins form small particles, large enough to be screened away from the starch but small enough to permit rapid and complete separation of starch from the gluten. These modifications provide more rapid and more nearly continuous processes.

Other methods of separating the proteins have been developed. One—a wet-milling process similar to that used in the production of cornstarch—is applied to the entire wheat kernel. The proteins so recovered are greatly changed in properties and have been used only as animal feed.

In another process, wheat flour is treated with dilute alkali solutions, in which the proteins dissolve, the undissolved starch is removed, and the proteins are recovered by neutralizing the alkaline protein solution. The protein obtained is suitable for the production of monosodium glutamate, although its physical properties have been altered by exposure to alkali.

The wet crude gluten obtained by the mechanical washing processes contains water to the extent of about two-thirds of its weight. Its drying is an important engineering and economic problem. If heat is used, the physical properties are altered so that the gluten no longer forms the typical rubbery mass with water, and the product is known as devitalized gluten. If heating of the gluten is avoided, it will again form a rubbery mass with water; the product is gum gluten.

The processes by which gluten can be dried without heating are costly. Vacuum drying can be used. When the vacuum is applied, however, the gluten mass puffs up to many times its original size so that the capacity of drying equipment is reduced. Or, the gluten can be extruded in a thin sheet or in ribbons or subdivided by other means and dried in an air current; here again the capacity of the necessary equipment is low. The difficulties in the drying process are indicated by the relative market prices of devitalized and gum glutens, which were approximately 16 and 30 cents a pound, respectively, in 1950.

The dried crude gluten produced by the usual washing processes contains 75 to 80 percent protein. The nonprotein material consists mainly of 5 to 15 percent carbohydrates (chiefly residual starch) and 5 to 15 percent fats of different types. More vigorous and prolonged washing will remove much of the starch; gluten containing 85 to 90 percent protein can be obtained in that way. Glutens separated from a wide variety of wheats fall within these ranges of gross composition; when they are wet they form the typical gluten mass.

BECAUSE GLUTEN gives bread its structural framework, it might be expected that the higher the gluten content of a flour, the greater would be its bread-making value. All glutens do not have this ability to the same degree, however. In fact, the variations are so great that, of two flours containing equal amounts of gluten, one could make excellent bread by a variety of procedures, while the other might not produce satisfactory bread by any process. Equally significant differences in behavior can be found in flours in the lower range of protein content used for making cake and cookies.

Those variations present the milling and baking industries with a continuing problem because the quality of their products must be kept uniform. A baker selects flours of different characteristics for use in different products and he tries to obtain the flours best suited to his baking processes. Some bread flours require long mixing and fermenting to produce good bread. Others are easily overmixed or overfermented, but they will yield good bread if they are handled properly. In some shops precise temperature control may be difficult, or adherence to a rigid dough-handling schedule may be impossible; a flour with tolerance to such factors then is required. On the other hand, in a highly mechanized bakery a rigid production schedule may be necessary. Then successive lots of flour must be uniform in characteristics. The miller must buy wheats of widely varied properties and blend and mill them to produce flours of different types but of reasonably uniform qualities within a type in order to satisfy the bakers who buy his flour.

THESE PROBLEMS have stimulated studies of the properties of gluten by both chemical and physical methods in the hope that the fundamental causes of the variations and the essential characteristics of good-quality gluten for different uses would be found. Such knowledge would be of practical value to the milling and baking industries. The suitability of lots of wheat for specific uses could be predicted more accurately and easily, and the proper processing conditions in the bakery for lots of flour specified.

Actually, such information could have a broader usefulness. It could insure that, whatever its variety, wheat would be processed into the type of product for which it was best suited. Some varieties are grown because they yield well or are disease-resistant but are of inferior quality for milling and baking. New methods of using such wheats might be developed if the basic reasons for their lower quality were

known. Finally, physical and chemical properties essential for specific uses could be determined and set up as standards for new wheat varieties developed by plant breeders.

Although much useful information has been accumulated, the basic problem is unsolved; the fundamental differences in the proteins of flours of varied characteristics are still unknown.

INVESTIGATIONS in this field may be said to begin with the work of T. B. Osborne and his associates at the Connecticut Agricultural Experiment Station. A report of their studies was published in 1907.

Osborne concluded that the protein of gluten has two distinct components, gliadin and glutenin, which are present in nearly equal amounts. He also noted the presence of residual starch and fatty materials in gluten, and he studied the nongluten proteins of wheat flour and of the wheat kernel.

The portion of gluten that was soluble in 60 to 70 percent ethyl alcohol Osborne called gliadin. The remaining portion, glutenin, could not be dissolved in water or water-alcohol mixtures, but was soluble in dilute acids and alkalies. Besides the differences in solubility, differences in chemical composition between gliadin and glutenin were noted. The physical properties of wet gliadin and glutenin prepared by Osborne's methods are markedly different from those of wet gluten. Gliadin forms a soft and sticky mass of gluelike consistency; glutenin swells in water to form tough, inextensible particles which do not cohere well.

Until about 1925, Osborne's conclusions on the components of gluten were not seriously questioned, although attempts to predict and interpret the behavior of flours of varied baking characteristics on the basis of the properties of gliadin and glutenin were not satisfactory. For example, it had been proposed (apparently from a consideration of the physical properties of typical preparations) that the ratio of glutenin to gliadin might determine the characteristics of any specific gluten. When attempts were made to determine this ratio for various glutens, it was found that slight variations in experimental procedures produced large changes in the distribution of protein between the gliadin and glutenin fractions. Such results were not in accord with those expected, if only two distinct and individual proteins were present. Furthermore, it was demonstrated that glutenin prepared by Osborne's method had undergone irreversible changes as a result of its exposure to alkali.

At about the same time the development of sensitive instruments and techniques for determining the number of different proteins in a particular material was begun. Protein molecules vary in size and shape and in the number and distribution of the electrical charges they carry.

In the Svedberg ultracentrifuge, a protein solution can be whirled at speeds as high as 1,000 revolutions per second. Under the sedimenting force so developed (up to several hundred thousand times that of gravity) protein tends to be thrown out of solution and the rate at which that occurs can be observed and measured. The rate is related to the size, shape, and density of the protein molecules, and so it can be determined whether all those present are alike in these respects.

In the Tiselius electrophoresis apparatus, the rate at which protein molecules move when an electric current is passed through the solution is measured. Since that rate depends primarily on the number of electrical charges carried by the molecule in relation to its size and shape, a means of determining whether all the molecules present are alike in these respects is provided.

Application of these newer techniques has shown that neither gliadin nor glutenin preparations contain a single protein. In the case of the gluten proteins, however, these methods have not demonstrated definitely the number of components that are present. Some investigators believe that a

great many components, differing progressively from gliadinlike to gluteninlike, are present. Others have suggested that relatively few components may be present, but that under the conditions used for the various investigations the simple components interact with one another, forming complexes of various characteristics.

A major difficulty in the study of the fundamental properties of gluten by any of the usual procedures of protein chemistry is met in its solubility behavior. In those solvents from which the original proteins have been recovered with all their properties unaltered, there has always been evidence that aggregates of molecules of various particle sizes are present. Because the proteins then are not present in solution as single molecules, little possibility of the identification and separation of individual molecular components from such "dispersions" exists.

Probably the solvents most often used have been 50 to 70 percent aqueous ethyl alcohol, for the extraction of gliadin fractions; dilute acetic acid, in which gluten can be disintegrated to a uniform but milky dispersion; and 8 to 10 percent sodium salicylate solutions, in which gluten gives dispersions similar in appearance to those obtained in acetic acid. The gluten can be precipitated from the acetic acid dispersions by either neutralization or the addition of neutral salts, and is recovered apparently unaltered in properties. From sodium salicylate dispersions, the gluten can be recovered by dilution or by the addition of large amounts of salts, also apparently unchanged.

When attempts to separate individual proteins have been made by selectively removing only a portion of the protein by various procedures from a gluten dispersion, the more easily precipitated (less easily soluble) portions are generally the more gluteninlike, and the more soluble generally the more gliadinlike. It has been convenient and useful therefore to retain Osborne's terms, until such time as homogeneous protein preparations may be separated, but these terms are now understood to imply only some general types of protein that occur in gluten, which may overlap to some extent.

Differences other than that of solubility between the two have consistently been found. Gliadin fractions contain molecules or molecular aggregates of smaller size and of less variation in size and are less easily altered by heat than are glutenin fractions. The glutenin fractions retain most of the fatty material found in gluten.

The behavior of the fats and gluten proteins of flour with respect to each other is not well understood and may play a part in modifying the characteristics of gluten. From an average flour, about 1 percent of fat can be extracted with ethyl ether. If a dough is made from the flour and the dough is dried, the amount of fat extractable by ethyl ether is reduced markedly, in some cases to less than 0.1 percent. The gluten proteins are largely responsible for this "binding" of fat, as indicated by the appreciable fat content of gluten as ordinarily prepared.

The shortening effect of added fats on the baking behavior of doughs is well known. The natural flour fats, however, seem to be bound more readily by the gluten proteins than are the fats and oils used in baking. Whether the fat-binding action of glutens can be related to the effects of fats on baking behavior therefore is not clear at present.

PROTEINS ARE CHARACTERIZED chemically by the fact that they are built up of about 20 kinds of relatively simple components, all belonging to the class of compounds known as amino acids, combined in varied proportions and arrangements. The amount of each amino acid in a protein can now be determined fairly satisfactorily. It would seem likely that glutens from flours of differing properties would differ in their amino acid composition. No evidence of such variation has been found, however, in comprehensive analyses of glutens from flours of extremes in

baking characteristics, milled from wheats grown in many parts of the United States and representing several varieties. The analyses have failed to differentiate, for example, between glutens from such different types of wheats as those used for cake flour, for bread flour, and for macaroni.

As for the amino acids in gluten in relation to other proteins, the high glutamic acid content is the outstanding feature; approximately 35 percent of the protein is made up of this amino acid. Gliadin fractions contain even more (up to 46 percent), glutenin fractions correspondingly less. One of the nutritionally essential amino acids, lysine, is contained in gliadin in only small amounts, about 0.5 percent. The amide nitrogen content of gluten is relatively high, contributing 20 to 22 percent of the total nitrogen; gliadin contains about twice as much as glutenin.

A most interesting characteristic of the flour proteins, which can be demonstrated strikingly by baking tests, is their sensitivity to very small amounts of oxidizing and reducing agents. Some flours when freshly milled produce doughs (and glutens) that are relatively soft, extensible, and lacking in elasticity. The addition of certain oxidizing agents (among them potassium bromate, potassium iodate, and chlorine dioxide) in very small amounts (around 0.002 percent of the flour weight in the case of potassium bromate) will alter the physical properties of the doughs and produce a loaf of bread of much larger volume and of improved texture. The effect of such reducing agents as sodium bisulphite and cysteine is the reverse of that of oxidizing agents, as would be expected. The reducing agents cause a softening of the dough and if they are added in excess they will cause extreme fluidity and stickiness.

A completely convincing explanation of the effects of these small amounts of oxidizing and reducing agents has not been given. Some workers believe that inactivation of proteolytic enzymes in flour accounts for them. Others consider it more likely that the added reagents act directly on the gluten. The solution of the problem of the mechanism by which these effects are produced appears likely to have many practical applications.

Almost all of the studies on the characteristics of wheat gluten have been undertaken in the hope of solving problems encountered in the use of wheat in baked foods.

The other uses of wheat proteins now are largely restricted to the production of animal feeds and monosodium glutamate, and the proteins are byproducts of the manufacture of starch, sirup, or alcohol. Because little processing is involved in utilization as an animal feed, we do not discuss it here. We should point out, however, that the relative feeding value of gluten, as distinguished from that of the total wheat proteins, is not high; therefore it must be supplemented with other proteins when it is used as a feed.

Monosodium glutamate (often referred to as MSG) was introduced as a flavor-enhancing agent in Japan about 1914. In investigating the soya sauces produced in the Orient, K. Ikeda found that this glutamate contributed much to their flavoring properties. The advantages of a saltlike, flavor-enhancing material of definite chemical composition (as compared to soya sauces, which have variable properties) were soon recognized, and production of monosodium glutamate was begun. The annual production in Japan has been estimated to have reached 9 million pounds by 1933.

Wheat gluten became the standard raw material at a relatively early time because of its high glutamic acid content, although the Japanese began to use fat-free soybean meal about 1935. Japanese producers' attempts to introduce monosodium glutamate into the United States interested certain industrial concerns in this country, and in 1934 the commercial production of monosodium glutamate began here, with wheat gluten as the raw material.

Since 1936 Steffens waste, a byproduct of beet-sugar manufacture, also has been used as a raw material. In 1948 manufacture from corn and soybean protein was reported. Production in the United States was estimated at 6 million pounds in 1948. Much of this output has been used by manufacturers of canned and dehydrated soups, and in canned meats. In 1949, however, a great deal of monosodium glutamate was packaged for home use.

In production from wheat gluten or similar sources, the protein is heated in hydrochloric acid until broken down and the glutamic acid is separated from the other substances, purified, and neutralized to the monosodium glutamate salt. The most serious problems met in processing are the separation without large losses of the liberated glutamic acid, and the corrosion of equipment resulting from the use of strong hydrochloric acid solutions. Gum gluten is not required for the production of monosodium glutamate, because the protein is completely broken down in the processing.

In the field of nonfood industrial uses, plastics, fibers, films, and adhesives have been prepared from wheat gluten in laboratories. These products are not commercially acceptable, however, because of their brittleness and low water resistance. Satisfactory treatments for meeting the shortcomings have not yet been found. Furthermore, gluten must compete with cheaper and more available proteins, such as those of casein, soybean, and cottonseed, in those fields.

Such results suggest that industrial utilization may have to be confined to products that can be made only from gluten and not from other proteins. Although no such products have been prepared on a commercial scale, laboratory work has suggested some possibilities.

An example is a gel-forming material, gluten sulfate, which is made by treating gum gluten with concentrated sulfuric acid at low temperatures. The product can absorb 100 to 300 times its weight of water rapidly and form a stiff gel. The gel is tasteless, odorless, and nontoxic. Suggested uses for it include the thickening and stabilizing of cosmetics and prepared food products. The cost of manufacturing gluten sulfate is too high to permit commercial production for the suggested uses, principally because of the expense of recovering the product from a large excess of sulfuric acid.

More recently it has been found that another derivative, gluten phosphate, can be produced by a process similar to that used in imparting flame resistance to cotton fabrics, and that gluten phosphate forms a gel much like that formed by gluten sulfate. A large excess of phosphoric acid is not required; hence the cost of production should be appreciably lower. These gel-forming derivatives have not been obtained with proteins other than those in wheat gluten.

A tough, rubberlike material can be formed by mixing gum gluten with glycerin and heating. Several other proteins give similar products. The one obtained with gluten is distinctive in that it retains its rubbery characteristics indefinitely, while those from other proteins become brittle. The material disintegrates in water. The only suggested use now is as gasket material in systems where it would be exposed only to oils. No other promising nonfood industrial uses for gluten have yet been found.

The nongluten proteins of wheat (which are less well characterized than the gluten proteins) include the flour, bran, and germ proteins that are soluble in water and dilute salt solutions. The usefulness of the bran and germ portions of the wheat as feeds, the difficulty of recovering the soluble flour proteins, and the presence of all these proteins in smaller amounts make them less promising as industrial material than the gluten proteins.

DALE K. MECHAM *is acting in charge of the wheat section in the Western Regional Research Laboratory. He has been in that section since 1941; before that he worked on wheat proteins for 4 years at General Mills, Inc.*

GEORGE H. BROTHER, *head of the protein division, Western Regional Research Laboratory, joined the Bureau of Agricultural and Industrial Chemistry in 1937. He was in charge of the meal section at the United States Soybean Industrial Products Laboratory before his transfer to Albany, Calif. He spent 20 years in industrial research before he entered Government service.*

Average analysis of whole cereal grains (moisture-free basis)

Grain	Starch Percent	Protein[1] Percent	Oil Percent	Ash Percent	Germ Percent	Bran Percent
Barley, dehulled	67.20	12.66	1.79	1.93	......	......
Corn, yellow dent	70.56	10.22	4.32	1.57	11.1	6.5
Oats	51.60	15.45	5.41	2.98	......	29.5
Rice, brown	77.20	8.90	2.00	1.90	......	......
Rye	60.20	14.04	1.51	2.11	......	......
Sorghum, miscellaneous and kafir	69.46	13.00	3.61	1.93	10.5	6.3
Wheat, white	66.90	9.90	1.96	1.84	2.0	13.2

[1] Calculated as 6.25 x percentage of nitrogen for corn, sorghum, barley, oats, and rye; and as 5.7 x percentage of nitrogen for wheat.

Unique Place of the Milk Proteins

William G. Gordon

Casein is the main protein in milk. It constitutes about 3 percent of average cow's milk. Other proteins are present in smaller amounts. Often they are considered not as individual substances, but altogether as whey proteins or heat-coagulable proteins of whey.

Because of the properties peculiar to the casein molecule that make it useful for many purposes and because of the ease with which this protein can be prepared from skim milk in relatively pure form, casein has occupied a unique position in industry. We use approximately 60 million pounds of it for industrial purposes each year—approximately 55 percent in paper making, 15 percent for adhesives, 10 percent for paints, 5 percent for plastics, and 15 percent for other purposes.

The casein in skim milk is in the form of its calcium salt in colloidal solution. On the addition of acid, the calcium is displaced and the casein precipitates as a curd. Alternatively, rennet may be added to skim milk to precipitate casein. Both methods are used in the manufacture of casein for industrial purposes. In the United States, the acid-precipitation method is used almost exclusively, because it gives a product suitable for most uses. Rennet casein, because of special properties, is preferred for the manufacture of plastics. It is largely imported, particularly from Argentina.

The first step in making acid-precipitated casein is acidification. Hydrochloric acid or sulfuric acid is added to the skim milk or the milk is allowed to sour, in which case lactic acid, produced by fermentation of lactose, is the effective precipitant. The precipitated curd is then drained, washed, pressed to remove water, milled, dried, and ground.

Rennet casein is precipitated from skim milk by the action of the enzyme rennin, instead of by acidification. Thereafter, the method of manufacture is the same as the acid-precipitation method.

THE BINDING strength and adhesive powers of casein solutions give this protein wide use in the preparation of coated papers. Such papers (also called glazed, enameled, or art papers) are used for lithographic work and for printing books, magazines, and advertisements. Coated papers are made by applying to the paper in a thin, even layer a mixture of mineral substances (clays, blanc fixe, chalks) suspended in a solution of casein. The coating covers the individual fibers on the surface of the paper and fills any hollows between them, so that the paper will have smooth, semiabsorbent surfaces after calendering or polishing. The casein binds the finely divided mineral matter to the paper so that it will not be picked off during printing; the mineral substances form a surface which is receptive to ink. Casein also is used, though to a lesser extent, in the manufacture of washable wallpapers, box papers, water-resistant papers, and playing cards.

Solutions of casein in alkalies (with enough of the protein to give a suitable viscosity) can be used as glue. Such a glue compares favorably in strength with animal glue, but it is not water-resistant. Resistance to water can be imparted to casein glue, however, by modifying the simple formula of casein in alkali; these improved casein glues are widely useful in industry. Prepared casein glues are sold in the form of dry mixtures, which need only the addition of water before use. They are commonly composed of casein, lime, and a number of alkaline salts. Various chemicals have been used to improve the resistance to water, and many colloidal materials with adhesive properties can be mixed with casein to modify the properties of the resulting glues. It has thus been possible to adapt casein glues to a variety of specialized applications. These glues are used in the woodworking industry, in gluing paper, and in many other fields.

The use of casein as a vehicle, or binder, for paint dates from ancient times. Modern casein paints consist essentially of aqueous alkaline solutions of casein plus suitable pigments.

Marketed either as a dry powder or as a soft paste, casein paint mixtures require only the addition of water before application. Newer paints of this type—that is, paints to be thinned with water—are emulsion paints in which the liquid portion is an oil-in-water emulsion and casein is the emulsifying agent that prevents separation of the liquid phases. Each of these paints—dry powder casein paint, paste casein paint, and oil-containing casein paint—has certain advantages, and all are used extensively. In both cost and utility, casein paints stand between calcimines and flat wall paints.

GROUND CASEIN can be converted into fibrous forms by extruding an alkaline solution of the protein into an acid coagulating bath, or by extruding a heated mixture of casein and water into air. The term "casein fiber" is reserved for the fine filaments obtained by the first method. The coarser product of the second method is called casein bristle.

To make casein bristles, a heated mixture of casein and water is extruded through a suitable die and the filaments, as they emerge into the air, are stretched and hardened under tension with quinone or formaldehyde, after which they are washed and dried. At first, the process was a batch process, but it has since been developed into a continuous process. The finished casein bristles are cylindrical. If they are hardened with quinone they are black. The stiffness of the bristle varies with the diameter. Bristles with a diameter of 0.024 inch are extremely stiff, but those with a diameter of 0.008 inch are soft and pliable. Brushes of different types have been made with the material, which seems particularly suitable for paint brushes. Such paint brushes, although made of untapered bristle, have good paint-carrying capacity, leave smooth films, and wear well. The bristles are resistant to oil and fat solvents, but soften when allowed to stand in water.

THE CASEIN PLASTICS industry uses a great deal of casein, but in the United States it is a smaller industry than in Europe before the war.

To make casein plastics, a finely ground, high-grade rennet casein is mixed well with 20 to 30 percent of water. Dyes, pigments, and other chemicals may also be added during the mixing operation. The mixture, still in the form of a powder, is converted by extruding machines into soft plastic, usually in the form of long rods. Sheet material may be prepared from the soft plastic by pressure, heat, and the use of sheet frames of the desired size. The rods or sheets are then soaked in formaldehyde until thoroughly hardened, or they may first be cut into small objects or blanks and then hardened. In either instance, the hardening process is laborious and slow. The hardened product is washed and dried.

Because of the relatively high water absorption of casein and the dimensional instability of casein plastics, the plastics are not used for large objects. They are of particular value for making buttons, buckles, beads, and costume jewelry. The beautiful colors and lustrous finish that can be given casein plastics are largely responsible for the continuing usefulness of casein in this field.

Research on the improvement of casein plastics continues in the Department of Agriculture. A primary objective has been to convert casein by chemical modification into derivatives that could be molded by compression directly into finished articles with improved resistance to water. Some success has been achieved. Derivatives of various types were prepared; some of them can be molded directly into small finished articles, and the time-consuming commercial process thus avoided. The water absorption of the plastics has been reduced. The successful processes of modification, however, have not been cheap, and their commercial development is perhaps unlikely.

Casein is put to many uses in which its adhesive or emulsifying qualities are valuable. These include: In pigment finishes and seasonings in the leather industry; in finishing and sizing operations in the textile industry; as a spreader, sticker, and emulsifier in insecticides; as an emulsifying agent in emulsion polymerization of synthetic rubber; as an adhesive for rayon cord in rubber tires; and as a binder in printing inks. It is used also as a raw material for the production of protein hydrolyzates of high biological value.

THE PROTEINS (only 0.6 percent) in whey represent another possible source of industrial protein. At present they are not separated from whey in large quantities. Limited amounts are prepared as heat-coagulated protein, which is incorporated into feeds or converted to amino acid mixtures of excellent nutritive quality.

Heat-coagulated whey protein, however, cannot be considered a typical industrial protein, for the process of coagulation by heat destroys most of the useful properties of the original protein. Because some 50 million pounds of protein occur in whey, which is either wasted or used in stock feeds, attempts have been made to develop methods whereby this potentially useful protein could be prepared in essentially unaltered form.

One approach to the problem has been to search for a precipitant that would effect separation of unaltered protein from the water, lactose, and minor constituents of whey. For example, when I was conducting research for a commercial laboratory, I suggested the use of hexametaphosphoric acid in this connection. Hexametaphosphoric acid, a complex form of phosphoric acid, combines with whey protein to yield an insoluble compound from which water-soluble whey protein can be regenerated.

In a different approach to the problem, A. Leviton, of the Bureau of Dairy Industry, has used dried whey for the preparation of soluble whey protein. According to his method, the lactose in dried whey is extracted with alcohol, which leaves residual whey protein in water-soluble form. None of the proposed methods has found commercial application; probably more efficient utilization of whey protein will depend on the discovery of some cheaper method for separating the material in a commercially useful form.

Skim milk, produced from the separation of butter and cream to the extent of about 50 billion pounds a year, is a cheap and abundant raw material for casein manufacture. Such developments as casein bristle will provide new markets for the protein and will aid in the more effective utilization of skim milk.

WILLIAM G. GORDON *is a chemist in the Eastern Regional Research Laboratory. He holds degrees from Cornell University and Yale University. Dr. Gordon conducted post-doctoral research in amino acid and protein chemistry at Yale and Pennsylvania State College and was instructor in biochemistry at Stanford University for 4 years. He entered the Department of Agriculture in 1941.*

MEAT, POULTRY, EGGS

Quality in Processed Poultry

Alvin A. Klose, Helen L. Hanson, Edmund H. McNally

The economic disadvantages of transporting and marketing live poultry, the value of equalizing seasonal production by storage, and the trend toward making foods available on a ready-to-cook basis have all contributed to the expansion of production of frozen and canned poultry. Cold-storage stocks of poultry increased from 100 million pounds in 1931 to 300 million pounds in 1950. Much of the frozen chicken marketed now comes from the rapidly expanding commercial broiler industry. While the yearly farm production of chicken has remained very near 2,500 million pounds since 1930, commercial broiler production has increased from 96 million pounds in 1934 to 1,482 million pounds in 1949. Commercial broiler production, processing to obtain a packaged, eviscerated, cut-up product, and marketing in retail frozen-food display cases often are coordinated now into a continuous year-around operation. Greater economy, uniformity, and control of quality are some of its advantages.

In contrast to the stable level of production of farm chickens, turkey production increased from 228 million pounds in 1930 to 754 million pounds in 1949. That increase and the corresponding rise in consumption from 1.8 to 4.5 pounds per capita can be attributed mostly to more economical production through breeding, feeding, and disease control. Frozen storage has been an important factor in the growth of the turkey industry. The seasonal character of turkey production requires frozen storage to relieve the surplus in winter and provide adequate stocks throughout the year. Cold-storage stocks at the beginning of 1930 were 10 million pounds, compared to 127 million pounds in 1950.

Limitations in knowledge and facilities during the early years of the frozen-poultry industry resulted in inadequate storage stability. The term "cold storage" itself was linked sometimes with poor quality. Improper handling of eviscerated fowl for frozen storage sometimes produced bacterial contamination, and thus evisceration became questionable as a practice in the preparation of frozen poultry. Investigations since 1935 have altered some of the earlier views and have provided information on the requirements for many of the steps involved in producing satisfactory frozen poultry. The deteriorative changes in stored frozen poultry have become better understood, and their relation to processing and the storage procedures has been studied. More intensive investigations are needed on certain of the changes, such as oxidative rancidity in the poultry fat and structural changes in the meat protein, in order to develop economical methods for their prevention.

The frozen-poultry industry is in a period of active growth and change. The producer wants to increase per capita consumption by making poultry a year-around, everyday dish. Consumers have the constant desire for good-quality poultry, readily available in handy packages, competitively priced with other meats, and ready to cook with little preparation. Eviscerated, oven-ready birds, cut-up poultry, turkey steaks, precooked frozen poultry, and canned poultry are some answers to those desires.

PROCESSING AND STORAGE hazards are obviously related to the composition of the product. The edible part of the chicken carcass contains 65 percent water, 20 percent protein, 14 percent fat, and 1 percent ash. Evaporation of water from this tissue in frozen storage is serious whenever temperature differences develop between meat and surroundings and no moisture-vapor barrier is present. The first evidence of dehydration is around the feather follicles, where the appearance of small, lighter-colored rings is termed "pock marking." Where large areas of skin are involved, the general term "freezer burn" is applied. Loss of water equal to 1 to 3 percent of total weight is enough to produce a serious freezer burn. Evaporation from the surface of the skin may not be great enough to cause freezer burn and yet may result in small increases in the opacity of the outer layers of skin and a corresponding loss of the natural color of the freshly slaughtered fowl. A lack of juiciness sometimes noticed in frozen poultry has not been adequately characterized, but it may be related more closely to changes in the physical structure of the muscle protein than to dehydration.

One of the commonly recognized objectionable developments in stored poultry is rancidity, which is generally associated with changes brought about by oxidation of the fat. The rate at which fats exposed to air oxidize is related to the temperature, the effective concentration of oxygen present, and the composition of the fat or fatty tissue. Body fat from hens on normal diets contains about 26 percent palmitic acid, 7 percent stearic acid, 7 percent hexadecenoic acid, 38 percent oleic acid, and 21 percent linoleic acid. Of those acids, the last three are unsaturated—they tend to combine with elements, such as the oxygen of the atmosphere. The degree of unsaturation of poultry fat, an indication of its susceptibility to rancidity, is intermediate in the realm of natural fats, being less than that of highly unsaturated, unstable vegetable oils, such as linseed or soybean oil, but more than that of coconut oil and some animal fats. Turkey fat seems to be more susceptible to rancidity than chicken fat. Rancidity may develop in commercially stored frozen turkeys after 6 or 8 months of storage. It can be detected in the odor of the skin fat and exposed visceral fat of the uncooked bird, in the aroma during cooking, and in the fat and meat of the cooked carcass. In the first stages of oxidation, the concentration of peroxides in the fat, determined by chemical analysis, is a good index of the degree of rancidity.

"Visceral taint" is the term used to describe disagreeable odor and flavor in poultry meat due to the diffusion of obnoxious substances from the intestinal tract and other viscera into the meat. It is especially noticeable in dressed, uneviscerated birds that are held at chill temperatures (34° F. or higher) for several days.

Discoloration of bone and adjacent tissue of young chickens held in frozen storage has no effect on odor or flavor. It is due to diffusion of hemoglobin and its oxidation products out of the marrow of the relatively soft bones.

Problems of bacterial contamination in frozen poultry are closely linked with sanitation in dressing and evisceration and with storage conditions. The surface bacterial contamination of eviscerated poultry is largely of intestinal origin. Cutting up poultry before packaging may also introduce a large bacterial load. Gross bacterial growth on dressed birds held at relatively high temperatures results in the development of a green color, attributed to the oxidation of blood pigments.

The development of good meat-type chickens has been subordinated at times to breeding for high egg production. Several satisfactory breeds for broiler and fryer production have been developed, among them the New Hampshire, Barred and White Plymouth Rock, Cornish, and crosses among those breeds. An idea of the ideal meat-type bird can be obtained from the score cards in the Chicken-of-Tomorrow contest, sponsored by a chain of grocery stores. Equal weight was given to economy of production and quality of meat. The qualities scored for the 12-week-old chickens were: Egg production rate of parent flock; percentage of hatchability; percentage of livability; pounds of feed required to produce a pound of chicken at 12 weeks; average live weight at 12 weeks; completeness and uniformity of feathering; uniformity of size, type, and color; well-proportioned body; broad, long, full-meated breast; well-covered, straight keel bone; plump, full-meated thigh joint; full-meated, moderately short drumstick; wide, long, flat, well-fleshed back; few pin feathers; bright, soft, smooth-textured skin; little or no dark meat showing through the skin; entire carcass well covered with fat.

Requirements for a good commercial turkey are like those listed for chickens. Emphasis is on economical and rapid growth, high proportion of edible meat to carcass weight, and early feathering. The Broad-Breasted Bronze is probably the most popular breed. A separate small breed, the Beltsville Small White, has been developed at Beltsville by the Department of Agriculture in order to provide a bird for the small family. Rate of gain per pound of feed is less for the smaller breeds, but that disadvantage is offset by consumer preference for the lighter-weight turkeys. Also, the Beltsville Small White matures more quickly (24 weeks) than the Bronze (28 weeks).

The composition and stability of fat in the carcass of a bird depend on the amount and type of fat in the diet. Feeding fats containing relatively large amounts of linoleic acid, linolenic acid, or other unstable fatty acids results in the production of carcass fat with a much higher content of unstable fatty acids and hence a lower stability. Restricting the diet to no fats or to stable fats provides a slight increase in the content of the more stable fatty acids. Finishing rations therefore should not contain fish oils or other highly unsaturated oils.

V. S. Asmundson and others at the University of California demonstrated that 2 to 5 percent of fish oils (which are relatively unsaturated and hence unstable) in turkey rations fed for 6 weeks before slaughter produced off-flavor and off-odor in the cooked carcass. Good-grade fish meal at a level of 25 percent had no effect.

The finishing, or fattening, of poultry before slaughter adds fat to the carcass and quality to the flesh. W. A. Maw, at Macdonald College, compared the performance of corn, wheat, oats, and barley in the finishing of mature-bodied cockerels. Corn was somewhat the best in terms of percentage of fat in the flesh and flavor and texture of the cooked meat. The feed efficiency (pounds of gain per pound of feed) is greater the younger the bird and the shorter the finishing period. In order to get maximum finish and top-quality price, however, finishing must be carried on for 2 or 3 weeks on approximately mature-bodied birds.

The use of synthetic female sex hormone has been tried commercially. The wisdom of the practice has been questioned. Pellets of diethylstilbesterol are implanted by a syringe under the skin of the neck of the bird 4 to 6 weeks before slaughter. Advantages claimed for this procedure include earlier maturing feathers, better over-all finish and palatability, and less fighting among the male birds.

PREFREEZING PREPARATION, including methods of killing, bleeding, removing feathers, and eviscerating, may all affect the keeping quality of poultry in frozen storage. Modern methods of slaughtering are aimed at killing the birds in such a way that wings are not broken, skin and meat are kept intact, and maximum bleeding is promoted.

The dry-picking method of removing feathers, usually involving piercing of the brain to relax the feather muscles, requires speed and careful timing so that feathers are removed before the muscles contract. A more common method of relaxing feather muscles is the use of a "semiscald," a dip in vigorously agitated water at 126° to 130° F. for about 30 seconds. After such a treatment, the feather muscles are practically permanently relaxed, the feathers are easily removed, and the heat treatment does not damage the skin. Higher temperature or longer scalding times may seriously affect the appearance and keeping qualities of the poultry. Many processors have found that wax dipping, used in conjunction with dry picking or semiscald picking, results in a superior product.

Much of the recent research on maintaining quality in poultry has dealt with the effects of evisceration practices. Off-flavors and off-odors gradually develop in poultry held uneviscerated at temperatures above freezing. The undesirable changes are noticed first in the regions that are in intimate contact with the viscera, and with longer holding they extend to other parts of the bird. Visceral taint is less in birds that are chilled promptly, because a lower temperature lessens the bacterial action and putrefactive changes. In some circumstances, as in certain commercial operations, it is not convenient or practical to eviscerate birds immediately. The supply of local unfrozen poultry is often not enough to maintain a constant eviscerating process; and frozen, dressed birds that can be thawed and eviscerated help to give sufficient volume. The presence of visceral taint in poultry is not exclusively a problem of the frozen-poultry industry. Because of the relatively common practice of freezing uneviscerated

birds, however, the prevention of off-flavor development has of necessity interested the producers of frozen poultry.

In view of the eventual development of visceral taint in uneviscerated birds, it became important to learn how long and under what conditions birds could be held uneviscerated without detrimental effect on the flavor of the meat. Research on the problem showed that if birds are chilled rapidly, the length of time they can be held uneviscerated before freezing is related to the holding temperature. The lower the holding temperature, the longer they can be held without development of off-flavors. Experiments with broilers and fryers at the Iowa Agricultural Experiment Station showed that off-flavors develop within 18 to 40 hours in birds chilled promptly and held at approximately 35° F. Longer holding periods increase the degree of off-flavor. Where it is impossible to eviscerate poultry promptly and where a method of fast freezing is available, the desirable flavor of the birds can be preserved more successfully by freezing than by holding them at chill-room temperatures until they can be eviscerated. The birds can then be rapidly thawed and eviscerated later. Rapid thawing and prompt evisceration are, of course, necessary, since deterioration in flavor continues if the thawed birds are held uneviscerated. The shorter the time birds are held uneviscerated at temperatures above freezing, the less will be the visceral off-flavor. All visceral taint can be prevented by prompt (warm) evisceration of poultry immediately after killing and picking. Warm evisceration is strongly recommended and present trends in commercial operations are in that direction.

The possible disadvantages, as well as the advantages, of warm evisceration have been investigated. Increased bacterial contamination and rancidity have received most attention. It is true that bacterial contamination can be increased if evisceration is not properly done. In modern processing plants, however, adequate sanitary controls can be provided so that this danger should be eliminated.

Evisceration before storage increases the surface exposed in the visceral cavity. This in turn may lead to development of rancidity in the visceral fat under poor conditions of frozen storage. The experiments to date on turkeys and chickens have shown that rancidity is not a major problem under usual conditions of handling. Holding eviscerated turkeys for as long as 30 hours at 35° F. before freezing did not increase the degree of rancidity that could be detected by flavor tests at the Western Regional Research Laboratory after storage at −10° F. for 18 months. Research at the Iowa Agricultural Experiment Station showed that broilers that were eviscerated and chilled promptly were as excellent in flavor after holding 18 hours at 35° F. before freezing as they were when frozen within 2 hours. In experiments with eviscerated and chilled fowls, off-flavors did not develop until after 2 days of holding at refrigerator temperature. Workers at the Kansas Agricultural Experiment Station discovered that the aroma of eviscerated chickens held in frozen storage could be improved by cutting them in pieces and packing compactly in cellophane rather than wrapping them in cellophane without cutting. The better aroma of the cut-up birds was thought to be related to the smaller amount of surface exposed.

Successful frozen storage of poultry depends on the degree to which the original high quality of a freshly killed bird can be preserved.

The loss of juiciness, deterioration in aroma and flavor, and changes in appearance (such as darkening in color and dehydration) are the principal changes during adverse conditions of frozen storage. The extent of such changes and the means of preventing or minimizing them depend on packaging efficiency, storage temperature, and storage time. G. F. Stewart and others found that the actual rate of

freezing had little effect on the final quality of the stored bird. No differences were found in the palatability of broilers that were frozen at temperatures from −5° to −90° F., with freezing times ranging from 5 hours to 10 minutes.

Investigations have been made of eviscerated chicken wrapped in moisture- and vapor-resistant cellophane. C. H. Koonz and his coworkers found that to retain high quality in eviscerated cellophane-wrapped poultry for a year it should be held at −10° F. or lower. Under those conditions, the chicken is still palatable, although it loses about 1 percent moisture, and slight darkening and desiccation are noticeable. If the storage period is limited to 9 months, the storage temperature used with the cellophane wrap can be as high as 0° F. A storage temperature of 10° F. is not satisfactory for periods of more than 6 months, and temperatures above 10° F. can be used only for relatively short periods without darkening in color, desiccation, microbiological growth, loss of juiciness, and deterioration in aroma and flavor.

C. W. DuBois and his coworkers found that poultry wrapped only in wax paper loses 10.7 percent moisture when held at 10° F. for 6 months, and 4.7 percent moisture when held at 0° F. for 12 months. Losses in rubber latex and moisture- and vapor-proof cellophane were slight at temperatures of 10° F. to −25° F. for storage as long as a year.

Experiments performed at Iowa State College showed that differences in appearance of poultry packaged in tin containers and in waxed cartons were pronounced at high storage temperatures, but were less as the storage temperature was lowered to 0° F. or below. In order to prevent undue moisture loss and the accompanying loss in quality, it is advisable to package poultry in some type of moisture-vapor resistant material.

Despite all precautions in the matter of efficient packaging material and low storage temperature, some changes in quality are unavoidable if the storage time is prolonged. The changes often are slight and can be detected only by experts making direct comparisons with freshly killed birds. For example, differences in juiciness and flavor between frozen and freshly killed poultry can be detected when frozen poultry has been wrapped in moisture-resistant material and stored for as short a period as 2 months at $-10°$ F. The dryness of the cooked meat noted in frozen birds is apparently a storage problem rather than a freezing problem, because it does not appear immediately after freezing. It is progressive as the storage time increases and is more pronounced at higher ($+10°$ F.) than at lower storage temperatures ($-10°$ F.). The loss of juiciness is noted in cases of little or no actual moisture loss, when birds have been properly packaged and do not show weight loss in storage. It is not influenced by thawing and refreezing or by different rates of freezing. It is a change that is noticeable with extended storage, but is probably not so objectionable as to detract from enjoyment of the product.

A more serious change takes place with extended storage of frozen giblets, particularly livers. The deterioration in flavor of frozen liver is so rapid that changes can be detected in less than a month in liver held at $-10°$ F. With such a limited storage life, it would seem more practical to use the liver as a fresh product or process it by other means.

AMONG THE RECENT DEVELOPMENTS in poultry processing are cut-up poultry and turkey steaks, precooked frozen poultry, canning, and smoking.

Efforts to increase the consumption of poultry meat depend largely on means of making poultry available in attractive, ready-to-cook, small packages that are enough for one meal for an average family. The increase in frozen-food display cases in retail stores has helped the development of packaged cut-up poultry. The need to make poultry an everyday dish as well as a holiday item is especially pressing for turkeys, which may range from 15 to 30 pounds, live weight. Turkeys have been marketed to a limited extent in the form of halves, quarters, and parts. Packages of 4 to 6 pounds may contain a leg or thigh, a large piece of breast meat, and either a wing or an extra piece of white meat.

F. Z. Beanblossom, poultry marketing specialist at Texas Agricultural and Mechanical College, has developed a way to prepare turkey steaks that weigh 4 to 6 ounces. The raw breast and thigh meat are cut from the bones, and appropriate weights of meat are formed into steaks by means of a cube-steak machine. A 33.5-pound live tom turkey (29.9 pounds dressed, 26 pounds eviscerated) furnishes 8.3 pounds of white meat and 5.6 pounds of dark meat. The wings and giblets may be sold as such; the neck, skin, and carcass have value for soup stock. Another proposed method of providing turkey in individual steak portions involves cutting the frozen eviscerated carcass into transverse slices with a meat saw.

Cutting poultry into parts presents new problems in packaging and storage; the large increase in cut surface encourages dehydration and rancidification. The Department of Agriculture in 1948 investigated the storage characteristics of the two forms of turkey steaks. Deboned steaks, prepared by the Beanblossom method, and transversely cut steaks, with bones intact, were stored in cellophane, polyethylene film, aluminum foil, and parchment at temperatures of $-30°$, $-10°$, $0°$, and $+10°$ F. The steaks prepared from thigh meat were considerably less stable than those made from breast meat. Even under the best commercial conditions of packaging and frozen storage, turkey steaks should not be stored longer than 3 months. It is better to store the whole eviscerated carcass and cut it into steaks just before retail marketing. Incorporation of rendered turkey fat or fatty tissue into the deboned steaks resulted in more rapid deterioration.

A large part of commercial broiler production is now sold as fresh or frozen, cut-up chicken.

M. A. Jull and his coworkers at the University of Maryland studied the distribution of weight in the parts of 12-week (2.7 pounds live weight) New Hampshire cockerels and reported the following percentages of the dressed weight: Breast, 17.5; first wing joints, 4.6; and legs, 25.8. The weights of edible meat, as percentages of chilled, dressed weight were: Breast, 14.6; first wing joints, 3.3; and legs, 20.4. Values for the weight of parts, expressed as the percentage of dressed weight, of 22-week-old Rhode Island cockerels were reported by H. M. Harshaw of the Department of Agriculture as follows: Drawn weight, 79.8; breast, 18.4; drum sticks, 12.8; thighs, 14.7; neck, 4.4; wings, 8.1; back, 15.5; and organs, 5.8.

A relatively new development is cooked frozen products, such as chicken à la king. The completely prepared product needs only to be heated to serving temperature before it is ready to eat. The convenience of such items can be readily appreciated; if the quality is good, the demand for them will undoubtedly continue to increase. At their best, these items retain the characteristics of the freshly cooked products as distinguished from canned products that may have a changed flavor or texture because of their more intensive heat treatment.

The production of cooked frozen food is such a recent development that very little research has been done on the best methods of cooking, packaging, freezing, or storage. The studies on cooked frozen meat to date have shown that the meat retains its flavor better when packaged as a solid pack rather than a loose pack. That is, meat surrounded by a sauce or gravy retains its fresh flavor longer than pieces packed loosely and exposed to the air in the package. A chicken à la king or a chicken loaf would, therefore, be ex-

pected to retain its flavor better than loosely packed slices of cooked chicken. It is also known that any conditions accelerating the development of rancidity, such as high storage temperatures or long storage periods, would hurt the quality of cooked frozen meat in much the same way as they affect raw frozen meat. The rate at which changes take place in cooked poultry products has not been investigated to any extent.

The microbiological aspects of frozen cooked poultry meat have received attention because of the possible health hazard if they are improperly prepared or inadequately handled. The product is not usually given any treatment that would render it sterile after it is cooked. Freezing and frozen storage only reduce the number of viable organisms, and the product is usually warmed only to serving temperature. In order to keep microbiological contamination and growth to a minimum, it is essential that the cooked meat be prepared under sanitary conditions and that the time elapsing between cooking and freezing be as short as possible. Further precautions must be observed after removal of frozen food from the freezer. In order to prevent growth of organisms that may have survived frozen storage, the thawing period should not be prolonged. Heating of frozen foods directly from the frozen state will cut this period to a minimum.

CANNING AND SMOKING are other methods of preserving poultry. Canning aids the poultry industry in several ways. Besides making precooked poultry products available under all conditions, it also makes use of overage birds. A number of birds of poor appearance but of good eating quality are also removed from the household market.

Poultry products are commercially canned in a variety of forms—whole, boned, and deviled chicken and turkey; chicken à la king; chicken curry; chicken and noodles; and chicken soups, including broth, consomme, and

Processing times (in minutes) for home-canned poultry [1]

| Container | Hot pack | | Raw Pack | | |
	With bones	Without bones	With bones	Without bones	Gizzards and hearts
Pint jars........................	65	75	65	75	75
No. 2 cans......................	55	65	55	65	65
Quart jars......................	75	90	75	90	90
No. 2½ and No. 3 cans............	75	90	75	90	90

[1] Processing at 10 pounds pressure (240°F.).

jellied, creamed, noodle, and gumbo soups. Chicken meat and broth have a flavoring ability that is well liked by a great many consumers of canned foods. The mild flavor, tenderness, and digestibility of poultry meat and broth have long made it a food recommended for invalids and infants.

Poultry for canning is inspected for soundness, wholesomeness, and fitness for human food by the inspection service of the Department of Agriculture. Examination of the poultry for canning by licensed inspectors within the plants is similar to that for all eviscerated poultry. It eliminates all emaciated and diseased birds. The inspectors are responsible also for the general plant sanitation and for seeing that all substances and ingredients used in the manufacture or preparation of the various edible canned poultry products are clean, sound, wholesome, and fit for human food. No definite standards have been set up for the various poultry products, so that the canner prepares and seasons the products as he sees fit.

The commercial canning of most poultry products is done by first precooking the poultry in an open kettle or under pressure. The meaty pieces are taken from the broth and the larger pieces of skin and bones removed. The skin is ground and returned to the broth. The excess fat can be skimmed from the broth, leaving enough to flavor it and to give richness to the product without too much fat. The boned meat is cut to a suitable size, placed in cans or jars, sealed, and processed in retorts.

A comparison of the open-kettle method (60 to 90 minutes) and pressure cooking (15–20 minutes) showed that the meat contained 10 percent less moisture when it was pressure cooked, and the broth had better flavor, with two to three times more solids. Pressure precooking also preserved the better quality of grade A chickens; with the open-kettle method, grade C chicken was inferior to grades B and A, but no differences were observed between the A and B classes. It also has been learned that mature hens and dark meat lost more moisture than chickens and white meat when precooked under pressure. The losses or gains in moisture are important when it comes to putting a definite weight or percentage of meat in the can.

Chickens and turkeys may also be precooked by roasting and placed in the cans whole, halved, or cut up with or without boning. That is a highly specialized process and calls for special methods and sometimes cans of special shapes.

The time and temperature for the commercial processing of the various poultry canned products are given in texts on canning. The home canning of poultry often proves to be a convenient method of preserving a surplus. The Bureau of Human Nutrition and Home Economics has explained the methods in Bulletin AWI–110, *The Home Canning of Meat*. A timetable for processing precooked packs with or without bones is given above.

The curing and smoking of chickens and turkeys has been a common method of processing in some areas for many years. The product ranks as a delicacy. Here is a recommended way of smoking turkey: The birds are killed and plucked after slack scalding (126° F. for 30 seconds) to prevent injury to the skin. Then they are eviscerated and the heads, feet, and necks removed, so that the pickle brine can pass completely through the body cavity. The curing mixture consists of 6 pounds of salt, 3 pounds of brown sugar, and 2 ounces of saltpeter dissolved in 4½ gallons of water. The drawn turkeys are packed in a suitable container and covered with the curing solution. The turkey should be kept cool (38° F.) while it is in the curing solution. The cure should go on for 18 to 25 days, depending on the weight of the bird. The cured turkeys are washed in warm water, hung until dry, and then smoked for several hours. A smokehouse temperature of 135° to 140° F. for 16 hours gives an uncooked product of desirable color. A smoke-house temperature of 220° to 240° F. gives a cooked product which may be eaten cold as an appetizer.

ALVIN A. KLOSE *is in charge of the poultry section at the Western Regional Research Laboratory. He received his training in chemistry at the University of California, and from 1935 to 1941 was engaged in poultry research at that institution. Since 1941, he has worked at the Western Laboratory on biochemical research.*

HELEN L. HANSON *is in charge of the utilization and appraisal section of the poultry products division in the Western Laboratory. Dr. Hanson has degrees from the University of California at Los Angeles and Iowa State College.*

EDMUND H. McNALLY, *now with the Bureau of Animal Industry at Beltsville, Md., has been engaged in various phases of poultry research in the Department of Agriculture since 1928.*

AT THE WESTERN REGIONAL RESEARCH LABORATORY samples of fruits and vegetables frozen in tin cans 11 to 19 years earlier were opened recently. During the period they had remained in freezing storage at zero or below. Strawberry and raspberry purees with added sirup had retained their fresh-fruit color, aroma, and flavor exceptionally well. Dry-packed youngberries frozen in 1933 had acquired an off-flavor. Nectarine halves in sugar sirup retained their natural color. The defrosted halves had fresh flavor when eaten raw but a slightly oxidized flavor after they were cooked. Broccoli frozen in 1938 retained an excellent deep-green color and was considered edible. Brussels sprouts frozen the same year had acquired a yellow color in the lighter portions and an off-flavor. Apparently the airtight containers and the low, nonfluctuating storage temperature were responsible for the successful long-term preservation of quality. Air in some of the packs probably accounted for their deterioration.—*D. G. Sorber, Western Regional Research Laboratory.*

Improving

Frozen and

Dried Egg

Hans Lineweaver,
Robert E. Feeney

Dried egg takes about one-sixth the storage space and weighs about one-fifth as much as packaged shell eggs. Dried egg is easier and cheaper to handle. The storage life of frozen egg at 0° F. or below is several years; that of refrigerated dried egg also is several years; the storage life of specially prepared dried egg recently has been increased to many months. Shell eggs deteriorate seriously in a few days at room temperature and in a few months under refrigeration.

But despite the longer storage life, only a small fraction of eggs are now frozen or dried; in 1947 it was about one-seventh of all eggs sold by the farmer. One reason is that fried, boiled, and poached eggs cannot be prepared from frozen or dried egg. Another reason, which is especially true of dried egg, is that the quality of the product has not been so good as it should be. But research is showing how quality can be improved without an excessive increase in cost. When the improvements are realized, the marketing of frozen and dried egg can be expected to expand.

We have in the history of frozen and dried egg a good example of how supply and demand and international conditions affect the handling and processing of a food product. The commercial freezing of eggs began about 1890, but it did not begin rapid growth until the First World War. The drying of eggs had developed significantly some 15 years earlier, and patents were sought for it as early as the Civil War. During the First World War, however, we began to import dried egg from China. Our own dried-egg industry remained relatively unimportant until 1927, when war conditions arose in China. A marked increase in production occurred in 1932, following an increase in tariff and a decline in domestic prices of eggs. Finally, as a result of the stimulus of the Second World War, our production of frozen and dried egg (principally dried egg) went up further in 1941 and reached an all-time high of 29.7 percent of all eggs sold in the United States in 1944.

To appreciate the problems in the processing of eggs we must consider their properties and constituents. More than 20 distinct constituents of an egg have been identified. It is not surprising that so complex a substance has unique properties and can be used in foods in many ways. For example, eggs coagulate on cooking to yield appetizing foods when fried, scrambled, boiled, poached, and shirred. They have a leavening action in some foods, such as angel-food cake and sponge cake; a combining action in noodles and doughnuts; a thickening action in custards; and an emulsifying action in mayonnaise. They prevent or reduce the formation of large crystals in ice cream and candy. The use of tanners' egg yolk in the leather industry is primarily for its emulsifying properties. The coagulating and adhesive properties of egg white make it useful also in several nonfood industries.

When we examine egg white, we find that it is essentially a solution of eight proteins, and its value as a food and in cooking is mainly the reflection of the properties of the proteins. Most of these proteins are well characterized chemically, but we know little about the part that each one has in the cooking and general utilitarian properties of egg white.

Mucin, a protein that occurs to a greater extent in thick than in thin egg white, seems to be responsible for the gel character of the thick white. Some people maintain that it is important in the whipping of egg white, but others disagree.

Ovalbumin, which coagulates more readily than other egg-white proteins (except possibly mucin), is the main protein involved in the heat-coagulation and thickening properties of egg white. Obviously, care must be taken to preserve this protein during processing and storage. To what extent it is necessary to preserve the other proteins of egg white we do not know.

Glucose, though a minor constituent of egg white, is important because it causes dried egg white to deteriorate during storage. Thus, dried egg white that contains glucose darkens and becomes insoluble in a short time, but dried egg white prepared from egg that has been treated (fermented) to remove the glucose keeps very well. This improvement is now used in the production of all dried egg white.

As for the yolk, its chief chemical constituents are inadequately understood. The carotenoids are well characterized, but they contribute only to the color of the yolk, not to its functional properties. A fraction of the yolk—the livetin fraction (about 5 percent of the solids)—is a crude mixture of several proteins, including enzymes.

Neither of the two lipoproteins (proteins combined with fat) has been prepared in pure form. We know, however, that both have unusual properties. For example, solutions or emulsions of one of the lipoproteins become more viscous on freezing and thawing. The substance may therefore be involved in the gelling that occurs on freezing and thawing egg yolk.

Another constituent of the yolk, leci-thin, is well known as an emulsifier, and both the free lecithin and the lecithin that is chemically bound to the lipoproteins undoubtedly have something to do with the emulsification properties of the yolk. The fatty materials of the yolk are thought to be involved in the lowering of the cake-baking values that accompanies spray drying of whole egg. Not enough research has been done to identify the constituent or constituents that undergo change.

The seriousness of the deterioration of dried whole egg led to extensive research during the Second World War by the British, Canadian, and United States Governments, as well as by many college, university, and commercial laboratories. It was demonstrated that the phospholipid fraction of the fatty constituents of the egg started to spoil when dried whole egg or dried yolk was stored at warm temperatures. A continuation of those studies since the war at the Western Regional Research Laboratory has disclosed that the glucose in the egg reacts chemically with the phospholipid during storage of the dried egg material. The chemistry of the reaction involves the reducing group (aldehyde) of the glucose and a nitrogen-containing group (amino) of the phospholipid. In the deterioration of dried egg white, the glucose reacts only with egg-white protein, because phospholipid does not occur in egg white. The glucose-phospholipid reaction seems to be the primary deteriorative reaction that occurs during storage of dried whole egg. A greatly improved product can therefore be obtained by preventing the deteriorative effect of the glucose. That is best done by removing or destroying the glucose in the egg. One way to do that is to ferment it out with baker's yeast before drying the egg. Other forms of deterioration, such as oxidative deteriorations, are being studied by chemists.

The main commercial frozen-egg products are whole egg, egg white, plain egg yolk processed with salt, sugar, or other additives, and mixtures of whole egg and yolk. Satisfactory procedures for the commercial freezing of shell eggs have not been worked out. Because the principles of producing the several types of frozen-egg products are much the same, we shall not discuss the procedure for each product separately.

Good eggs are necessary for a good frozen-egg product. Frozen products with a high bacterial count result from the use of contaminated shell eggs. Dirty eggs usually are washed and the shells dried just before breaking. The eggs have to be candled before they are broken. If they have not been under refrigeration they must be cooled.

The clean, sound eggs are broken, separated into yolk and white if desired, mixed, strained, and placed in suitable containers. One to ten percent by weight of stabilizers (like salt, sugar, or glycerin) may be added to yolk to reduce the changes that otherwise occur on freezing and thawing. The egg white may be packed without mixing to break up the thick white or it may be mixed and thereby thinned. The chalaza is either cut up finely or filtered off along with bits of shell. Newer methods of thinning—devised to avoid the older pressure-milling, or homogenizing, procedures—employ suction through fine screens or the cutting action of rapidly revolving blades to achieve thinning. The new ways are particularly effective with egg white, which is damaged by the shearing forces of conventional homogenizers.

Commercial freezing is commonly done in 30-pound cans. Even with moderately rapid freezing, the egg in the middle of the can may freeze so slowly that the solids move toward the center, and a core is formed. Such cores usually contain large numbers of micro-organisms. A 30-pound can of whole egg will freeze solid in 48 to 72 hours at 0° F. in still air. Freezing times at −20° to −40° F. are one-half to two-thirds those at 0° F. in still air. Freezing times at −20° F. are reduced to about one-half by air blasting the cans in tunnel freezers.

Precooling lowers the freezing time. Slush freezing further cuts the freezing time, but apparently it is not used widely. Temperatures of 0° F. or below should be maintained in storage.

BROKEN-OUT EGGS can be frozen in the home, too. The operation calls for the same care that commercial plants observe to prevent growth of micro-organisms. Fresh, clean, sound, chilled eggs are first broken into small dishes to make sure that they are up to standard in odor and appearance. Then they are put in a clean, larger bowl and slowly beaten, or churned, with a fork or low-speed mixer to a fairly homogeneous batter without incorporation of air. The white can be packed separately with or without churning. Whole egg and yolk, however, must be mixed; they must also be treated with an anticoagulating agent. For this purpose, 2 tablespoons of honey or corn sirup or sugar (or 2 teaspoons of salt) may be added to every cup of yolk; 1 tablespoon of honey or sugar or sirup (or 3/4 to 1 teaspoon of salt) is enough for a cup of whole egg.

The consumer has to thaw frozen egg quickly and properly in order to prevent the growth of microbes. Cans of frozen egg are usually thawed in cool water, either by rotating the cans in the water or by circulating the water around them. Sometimes they are thawed by crushing the contents in an ice-crushing machine and then mixing them quickly in a warmed tank. The older practice of letting the cans thaw by standing in air at room temperature may permit excessive growth of microbes.

THE THREE MAIN dried-egg products are whole egg, yolk, and white.

The spray-drying process, which is more efficient than the tray and belt methods of earlier days, is usually employed for whole egg. It is simple in principle. Liquid egg is sprayed from a nozzle into a stream of heated air. The water in it evaporates, and the liquid egg becomes a powder in a few seconds.

Several types of spray-drying equipment are manufactured, but the conditions and equipment needed to spray-dry eggs are such that small or home-scale operations are not practical.

Processing spray-dried egg generally involves several operations. Liquid egg from the breaking room is thoroughly mixed and strained. It is then usually heated quickly to about 140° F. to improve the drying operation. The warm liquid, under a pressure of 2,000 to 6,000 pounds to the square inch, is sprayed from nozzles into a large drier chamber, through which a stream of air is passing at 250° to 300° F. The air picks up moisture from the egg and leaves the chamber at 140° to 180° F. The rate of liquid flow and the temperature of the inlet air are adjusted to maintain the desired air-outlet temperature. The egg powder settles in the bottom of the main chamber, from which it is continuously withdrawn, or it is in the exhaust air stream, from which it is strained out. Generally, the powder has a moisture content of 4 to 5 percent. If the powder must contain less than 3 percent moisture, another drying step has to be added. Dry air at 140° to 220° F. is brought in contact with the powder until the desired moisture level is reached. The powder is then cooled. As a rule, it is packed in cans. Sometimes, before the cans are sealed, the air in them is replaced by a mixture of carbon dioxide and nitrogen. If the powder is to be used soon after preparation or if it is to be stored at low temperatures, it may not be necessary to reduce the moisture content below 5 percent or to gas-pack in cans.

The initial quality of most of the dried whole egg produced during the Second World War was good. The bad reputation given to dried egg during the war was justified because the product deteriorated seriously between the time it was prepared and the time it was offered for consumption.

By 1943 or 1944 the storage stability, and to some extent the initial quality, of dried whole egg was greatly improved. The improvement came about largely through more thorough drying and the exclusion of air from the packaged dried egg. At the beginning of the war, dried egg was permitted to contain as much as 8 percent moisture. Nearly everybody considered the figure higher than it should be, but it seemed a necessary compromise in order to obtain the required large volumes. The most stable dried egg produced during the war contained less than 3 percent moisture and was packed with the exclusion of air. It could be stored satisfactorily for more than 6 months at ordinary temperatures (70° to 80° F.) and for perhaps 1 or 2 months at 100° F. The improvement of dried egg was accomplished by the cooperative effort of 20 research and control agencies. An important part of this effort was the establishment of a program for the supervision and education of the inexperienced personnel necessarily used in this suddenly expanded industry. During the Second World War, all dried egg for the military or for lend-lease was produced under Government supervision.

Toward the end of the war, the research workers had developed a procedure that further improved the keeping properties of dried egg to be stored in air. That involved acidifying the liquid egg before drying. Enough hydrochloric acid is added to lower the acid reaction from pH 7.5 to pH 5.5. To avoid an acid taste in the reconstituted egg, sodium bicarbonate equivalent to the acid is added to the dried egg. The bicarbonate has no effect on the egg while it is dry, but on reconstitution it neutralizes the acid and the scrambled egg prepared from the product is essentially the same as that prepared from unacidified freshly dried egg. The military began the purchase of acidified dried whole egg in the fall of 1950.

In 1950 the Western Regional Research Laboratory reported that a palatable and fairly stable dried whole egg can be prepared by still another process. The development stemmed partly from the systematic evaluation (which we mentioned earlier) of the research results obtained on dried egg during the war. The process is like the one long used to produce dried egg white. It involves removal of the naturally occurring glucose from the egg by fermentation. Baker's yeast, or some other suitable micro-organism, is added before drying, and the mixture is allowed to stand at room temperature, or slightly above, until the glucose is used up by the yeast. In experimental runs, enough yeast has been used to complete the glucose removal in 2 to 4 hours. In preliminary tests, yeast-fermented spray-dried egg was prepared with little or no yeast flavor. The product, dried to low moisture content (2 to 2.5 percent) and stored in cans under nitrogen gas, was acceptable after 6 months of storage at 100° F.

The dried egg is suitable for scrambled eggs, custards, certain types of cakes, and some other products. It is not entirely satisfactory for making sponge cakes or other foodstuffs that depend on the egg for leavening. The leavening property of whole egg (and yolk also) is lowered during the spray drying. The decrease can be prevented if 10 percent table sugar (sucrose) is added to the liquid egg before it is dried. The sugared egg can be used for most baking purposes but, of course, it cannot be used to prepare such products as scrambled eggs. We do not know why the sugar protects the egg during spray drying. Possibly other means of providing protection to the egg during drying will become evident if we find out why sugar protects it. Further improvements in quality and storage stability are desirable and may be expected to follow a more thorough understanding of the deteriorations that occur during processing and storage.

Dried whole egg prepared by any of these procedures can be safeguarded by pasteurization. Pasteurization of liquid egg products is more difficult than pasteurization of milk, however,

because the heat treatment necessary for pasteurization is very close to treatment that causes undesirable chemical or physical changes in the egg constituents. Nevertheless, some commercial operators have successfully incorporated pasteurization in their process for producing dried whole egg.

DRIED EGG YOLK is prepared by spray-drying processes similar to those used to prepare dried whole egg. It is somewhat more stable during storage than dried whole egg, but the stability is influenced by the same factors that influence the stability of dried whole egg. Dried yolk now has a definite place in the food industry. Increased outlets for dried yolk might be found through research on the preparation of dried yolk with improved properties. For example, spray-dried yolk, as in the case of plain-dried whole egg, does not perform well in cakes in which the yolk serves as the leavening agent.

Dried egg white is prepared to only a limited extent by spray drying. For many years egg white has been dried by spreading the thinned white on trays over which warm air was circulated. Thinning of the thick white before drying was accomplished by allowing the liquid white to ferment. It was not until the early 1930's, long after the fermentation process was developed, that an advantage of fermentation other than thinning was recognized—that is, removal of the glucose, which is essential for good keeping qualities of the dried product. This natural or spontaneous fermentation process used in the past in processing egg white often causes undesirable flavors to develop and therefore is being displaced by better controlled methods that employ pure cultures as inocula. Micro-organisms that produce a minimum of off-flavor and off-odor are used.

The pans or trays on which the fermented white is spread are coated with wax or mineral oil. The trays are placed on shelves or racks in a cabinet, and warm dry air is circulated over them. As now carried out in the United

States, drying usually requires 6 to 24 hours, depending on the temperature and air control in the cabinet. The product is flakelike in form and is usually referred to in the trade as crystalline albumen. Powdered albumen is made by grinding and screening the flakes. In a variation of the pan-drying process, the fermented egg white is given a partial whip and then dried on screens in a stream of air. We mentioned that egg material is more difficult to pasteurize than milk because liquid egg is so easily damaged by heat. Liquid egg white is even more easily damaged than liquid whole egg, and it seems that commercial pasteurization of liquid egg white will be difficult. A new approach to the egg-white pasteurization problem was made by J. C. Ayres and H. M. Slosberg, who reported in 1949 that egg white could be freed of undesirable bacteria by holding the dried product at 135° F. for 4 days.

The spray-drying process for egg white is similar to that for drying whole egg and egg yolk, but the conditions differ because of differences in the character of the materials being dried. For example, it appears necessary to use lower pressures (less than 1,000 pounds per square inch) during spraying in order to prevent damage to the egg white by shear stress forces. Also, lower temperatures must be used, because egg white is so easily damaged by heat. The product is a powder, but its properties differ from those of the powdered egg white obtained by the pan-drying method. Additional research on the properties of egg white and on its behavior during spray drying is needed in order to perfect the application of this efficient method to the drying of egg white.

HANS LINEWEAVER *is head of the poultry products division of the Western Regional Research Laboratory. He has been with the Department of Agriculture since 1929. Dr. Lineweaver holds degrees in chemistry from George Washington University and the Johns Hopkins University. He was with the fertilizer investigations division from 1929 to 1936 and with the food research division from 1936 to 1939, and has been with the Western Laboratory since 1939.*

ROBERT E. FEENEY *is in charge of the egg section of the poultry products division of the Western Laboratory. He was graduated in chemistry from Northwestern University and in biochemistry from the University of Wisconsin. Before joining the Department of Agriculture, Dr. Feeney held a research appointment in bacterial chemistry at Harvard University Medical School and served as a Food and Nutrition Officer in the Army.*

THE PRACTICE of obtaining public service patents for scientific discoveries made by Department of Agriculture employees has been intensified somewhat in recent years. A close relationship between the Patent Office and the Department of Agriculture, however, is almost traditional—the Department of Agriculture had its beginnings in the Patent Office. The first Federal funds expended for agricultural purposes were Patent Office funds. For many years the forerunner of the Department of Agriculture was the Agricultural Division of the Patent Office, and the first Yearbooks of Agriculture were the annual reports of the activities of that Division.—*W. L. Cheesman, Northern Regional Research Laboratory.*

Uses of Frozen

and Dried

Egg

Edmund H. McNally

Frozen egg and dried egg are used mainly by processors of other food products. The baking industry, by far the largest user of them, takes as much as 7 percent of the country's total egg supply in some years. Large quantities also go into mayonnaise, noodles, ice cream, and candy.

Frozen egg and dried egg have certain advantages over shell eggs and liquid egg for manufacturing use, especially in large-scale production. Shell eggs are bulky, fragile, and perishable except under good storage conditions. When frozen or dried, they provide the manufacturer with a more uniform product, which is compact and may be held with much less deterioration. Care in defrosting and in reconstituting is necessary to bring about the best qualities in the processed egg.

The properties of egg white and egg yolk that make them of value in household cookery are largely retained in the frozen and dried products. Frozen whole egg and egg white have all the qualities of shell eggs for leavening, thickening, and emulsification when used in bakery products. They also give flavor and color to cakes and other baked goods.

The baker uses frozen whole egg in making doughnuts, sweet doughs, jelly bases, cookies, pastries, and cakes. The frozen product sometimes gives a greater volume in pound cakes than the natural one, probably because of the variation in quality of shell eggs. Frozen egg is also used as a thickening agent in pie fillings and custards.

Because of its leavening ability and color, frozen egg white is used to give a smooth, light texture to some kinds of cake. Thin egg white when frozen compares well with fresh shell eggs in making angel-food cakes. Cakes made from frozen thick white are not quite so desirable in quality.

Bakers use frozen and dried egg white for meringues and cream icings. Many hold that fermented dried egg white gives foam of better volume and quality than the unfermented. Several tests for evaluating the whipping quality of dried egg white have been devised.

Frozen and dried egg yolk is used in doughnuts, gold cakes, and other bakery products to give color and to aid emulsification of shortening materials. Bakers use frozen egg yolk containing 10 percent sugar because it has a better consistency and is freer from flecks than yolk frozen without the addition of sugar. They sometimes use frozen yolk containing 5 percent glycerin to help in retaining the moisture and thus keep their products fresh.

Noodles are prepared from dough made from semolina, or hard-wheat flour, containing egg yolk or whole egg and rolled and cut into strips, which are dried. Other flours may be used, but finished noodles must have, by standard, less than 13 percent moisture and more than 5½ percent egg solids. About 11 pounds of egg yolk, containing 45 percent solids, is necessary for each 100 pounds of flour of a 14 percent moisture content to give noodles the legally required amount of egg solids.

Noodles are now made by a continuous process, not by batches. Frozen egg yolk or frozen whole egg is the principal source of eggs; dried egg and shell eggs are used to some extent. Because no artificial coloring agent is permitted to give the noodles a rich tint, eggs with dark yolks are preferred.

The nutritional value of noodles can be improved by adding vitamins, as is done with white flour. The enrichment levels established by the Food and Drug Administration in 1945 require that each pound of noodles contain between 4 and 5 milligrams of thiamine (vitamin B_1), 1.7 to 2.2 milligrams of riboflavin (vitamin G), 27 to 37 milligrams of niacin, and 13 to $16\frac{1}{2}$ milligrams of iron.

In the continuous process, the powdered vitamins and iron are delivered by a mechanical feeder as a ribbon into the flour mixer. In the batch process, wafers of the enrichment material are added to part of the water used in making the dough.

Mayonnaise is a semisolid emulsion of edible vegetable oil, the egg yolk or whole egg, vinegar or lemon juice, sugar, and seasoning. The finished product contains not less than 50 percent of edible vegetable oil. Eggs are prepared in various ways for mayonnaise. Most commonly used is the salted form of frozen egg yolk. Next in order are the frozen sugared, fresh refrigerated, specially treated, and dried egg yolk. From 8 to 12 percent of egg is generally used. The mayonnaise manufacturer is especially interested in obtaining egg yolk of uniform quality and dark color.

Mayonnaise, an emulsion stabilized by the egg material, is one of the most fragile of the commercially prepared food products now made. Because of its unstable nature, special care must be given to the various products used in its manufacture and to many details of preparation and distribution.

MANUFACTURERS of ice cream use frozen whole egg, frozen yolk, and frozen sugared yolk. Their choice depends largely on cost. Egg yolk, used up to 1 percent of the mix, increases the whipping properties of the mix and shortens the freezing time of the batch. The smoothness of the ice cream is improved and its color is enhanced by reducing the size of the ice crystals. French ice cream and frozen custards always contain egg yolk. Many States have regulations that $2\frac{1}{2}$ dozen fresh yolks or $\frac{3}{4}$ pound of dried yolk or $1\frac{1}{2}$ pounds of frozen yolk be used in each 90-pound batch of frozen custard. Egg albumen is also used in sherbets to give a smooth texture and a richer flavor. Dried egg is used in ice-cream mixes for household use.

Dried egg white is used a great deal in the manufacture of such confections as cream centers, candy bars, nougat, fondant, and divinity fudge. The egg albumen reduces the size of the sugar crystals and prevents their growth after the candy is made. The egg white acts as an interfering substance, or protective colloid, to prevent crystallization. Eggs are used in marshmallows to give smoothness and whiteness. In divinity fudge, an exact measurement of egg white must be used—small amounts make a grainy, crumbly candy; large amounts cause the candy to dry out and become powdery upon standing, even though it was soft and fluffy to start with.

Prepared flour and baking mixes, the use of which is increasing, offer the chief field of expansion for dried-egg products. Dried yolk is used in ready-mixed doughnut, waffle, muffin, and cake flours to give color and richness. Ice-cream powders and mixes use dried white, or albumen, which also is used in some baking powders as an inhibitor or diluent. Dried yolk is used in beverage powders, which provide a quickly prepared, rich drink.

EDMUND H. MCNALLY *has been engaged in various phases of poultry research in the Bureau of Animal Industry since 1928. He is now working at the Agricultural Research Center, Beltsville, Md. Dr. McNally has degrees in biological science from George Washington University and in poultry husbandry from Maryland University.*

The Problem of Bacteria in Eggs

Mathilde Solowey

The egg is a unique and important food—important because it contains proteins, fats, minerals, and vitamins, and unique because the contents are sealed within a natural package, a membrane-lined shell. How to keep this food as good as when the hen made it has been the subject of many studies, some of which have to do with bacteriology, because bacteria are among the main factors of egg quality.

As long as the shells remain unbroken, the microbial problems are limited to individual eggs. Once the contents are removed from the shells and mixed, however, liquid egg in bulk becomes a highly perishable product.

The microbial content of shell eggs depends on factors like initial quality, conditions of storage, and the porosity of the shell.

Clean fresh eggs usually are free from bacteria, although a small proportion can be contaminated with bacteria of many types. The finding of bacteria, of itself, however, is not necessarily a cause for alarm. One has to determine first whether bacteria are present in large numbers and, if present in small numbers, whether conditions are such as to permit their multiplication. Multiplication can be prevented, or retarded at least, by storing eggs at low temperatures. An egg kept at 34° F. is relatively safe from decomposition, because bacteria do not grow rapidly below 55° F.

Although the internal part of sound, fresh shell eggs is generally sterile, bacteria are always found on the shell, their numbers and kinds varying with environmental conditions. Eggs to which soil or fecal material adheres—the "dirties"—do not keep well. They are contaminated with a variable flora and may act as an inoculum for the shells of sound eggs with which they may come in contact. Because the shell is porous, bacteria on the surface can penetrate it and contaminate the internal portion if temperature and humidity are suitable. "Leakers" (eggs whose shells have minute cracks that permit the contents to seep out) are also a source of contamination, because bacteria multiply rapidly in the seepage, and such heavily contaminated material readily infects sound eggs.

The bacterial problems of individual shell eggs are therefore important if these eggs come in contact with others, and especially if they are to be used in preparing liquid egg in bulk, whether it is to be frozen or dried.

Before 1941, less than one-half million pounds of egg powder was produced annually in the United States. Most of it went into bakery products and prepared mixes. The war increased the demand; in 1941, the production of egg powder reached 31 million pounds; in 1942, 226 million pounds; and by 1944, 311 million pounds. The production has gone down since 1944 but has remained higher than during the prewar years. Production had leveled off to about 125 million pounds in 1950.

Manifestly, more information was needed on microbial quality than in earlier years, when egg powder was used principally as an ingredient of foods that were heated high enough to kill most contaminating vegetative types of organisms. Such information was not available in 1941, because bacteriological research in the egg-dehydration industry had not kept pace with technical developments.

Agencies in and out of the Government in 1941 began cooperative studies on the various microbiological problems. Investigations were made in numerous plants to study processing methods, determine the operational procedures and structural defects responsible for high microbial counts, and devise specific quality-control measures, particularly with respect to the microbial quality of the fresh and storage shell eggs and the frozen liquid egg used for drying. The microbial problems of egg powder were emphasized, but many of the findings apply also to liquid egg, frozen liquid egg, and the shell egg, because all come from the same source.

Extensive surveys were undertaken to get information on the quality of spray-dried, whole-egg powder. The factors affecting microbial quality also were determined. Storage studies brought out the importance of moisture content in the maintenance of quality and indicated the desirability of producing powder containing 5 percent or less moisture. The studies also indicated the need for adequate care in subsequent storage and handling to prevent absorption of moisture. They showed the desirability of holding powder at temperatures of 45° F. and lower, and pointed up the more rapid deterioration of powders with low sanitary quality.

Samples of egg powder were examined for plate and direct microscopic counts and for the presence of *Escherichia coli* and molds, as indicating the initial quality of the shell eggs used for processing and the degree of sanitation in the processing plant. The presence of enteric bacteria, particularly of the genus *Salmonella*, in the powders also was investigated in order to assess their relationship to outbreaks of food poisoning known to be caused by that group of bacteria.

The bacteriological investigations revealed that seasonal variations in quality were associated with shell-egg production trends and the kind of liquid egg dried. During months of high shell-egg production, when more of the liquid egg used for drying was from fresh eggs, the bacterial counts were relatively low. Conversely, as the proportions of frozen liquid egg and liquid egg from storage shell eggs used for drying were increased, the bacterial counts increased. The incidence of *E. coli* and molds fluctuated similarly.

More than 5,000 samples of egg powder were examined, and *Salmonella* organisms were isolated from 35 percent of them. Fifty-two *Salmonella* types were identified among the many strains isolated; they could not be distinguished from types that were known to have been isolated from human or animal infections.

Studies in egg-dehydration plants indicated that soiled eggs are more likely to be contaminated with *Salmonella* organisms than clean eggs. The point was further supported by preliminary shell-egg studies, in which more *Salmonella* organisms were isolated from the lower grades than from the higher grades of shell eggs. The organisms survived for long periods in samples of powder held under refrigeration.

The finding of *Salmonella* organisms in egg powder posed a serious question with respect to safety in the handling of reconstituted liquid egg prepared from such contaminated powders. Another question: Would the usual cooking procedures for eggs—for example, scrambling—suffice to destroy the *Salmonella* organisms present? Investigations indicated that the organisms multiply rapidly in reconstituted liquid egg held at temperatures of 75° to 113° F. Because of this rapid growth, therefore, the holding period for reconstituted liquid egg should not exceed 4 hours. Otherwise, if only a few organisms were present before adding water to the powder, their number might become so great that subsequent heat treatment would not destroy all that developed in the reconstituted liquid egg. Test scrambles prepared from artificially or naturally contaminated reconstituted powders frequently yielded viable *Salmonella* organisms. The recovery depended on one or more of several variables, including the original concentration of the contaminating organisms, the length of the holding period after reconstitution and before scrambling, the holding temperature, the duration of heating and temperature for scrambling, and the type of scramble.

In general, the longer the contaminated reconstituted egg was held before cooking, the more frequently were *Salmonella* organisms found in the scramble. That was due no doubt to progressive multiplication of *Salmonella* organisms in the reconstituted egg. All in all, the findings emphasized the desirability of using egg powder immediately after reconstitution.

STUDIES were made of processing procedures necessary to produce egg powder of low moisture content as a means of destroying microbes and improving the keeping quality of the product.

Preheating the liquid egg at pasteurization temperatures and multistage drying were two new steps introduced to aid in lowering the moisture content of the powder to 2 percent or less. It seemed logical to expect that the longer exposures of the egg substance to high temperatures would lower the content of viable organisms. Marked improvement in microbial quality demonstrated the effectiveness of these procedures. Significantly, only 5 percent of some 500 samples of low-moisture egg powder contained *Salmonella* organisms.

The findings highlight a problem of public health significance. The shell egg is an individual package. Once eaten, the evidence is gone; moreover, any infection by dangerous microbes in the egg is limited to one person, except perhaps when a single egg is used for a salad dressing.

Bulk liquid egg, frozen egg, and egg powder present another problem entirely. Distribution of such contaminated material may be more widespread and therefore can affect a larger proportion of the population.

Satisfactory methods for determining more precisely the numbers of *Salmonella* organisms in those products are lacking. One can reasonably suppose that the numbers are usually small. The significance of their presence is therefore based on the treatment given to the final product which might permit any organisms present to multiply sufficiently to provide an infective dose.

INVESTIGATIONS that were started in 1949 are expected to improve microbiological methods for determining the numbers of *Salmonella* organisms, as well as other pathogens (disease-producers) in egg powder and related egg products. An evaluation study also was undertaken to learn the pathogenicity for humans of the *Salmonella* organisms isolated from egg powder. Such information accumulates slowly, but it is needed before we can assess the significance of the entire problem.

ATTENTION has been centered on microbial problems of eggs and their relationship to the maintenance and improvement of quality in egg products, as well as to possible infection. It is well to bear in mind, however, that eggs are also a basic ingredient of many prepared foods. In order to evaluate in its proper relationship the role of the egg as a possible source of infection, similar studies should be made on other foodstuffs, often used in combination with eggs, in order that the balance of evidence will be more evenly distributed.

MATHILDE SOLOWEY *was acting head of the former microbiology research division in the Bureau of Agricultural and Industrial Chemistry. She has a doctor's degree from Columbia University.*

Transcendental Gastronomic Art

Frank G. Ashbrook

There is no accounting for tastes, so it is said. There is less accounting for the average man's timidity, lack of imagination—call it what you will—when it comes to gastronomical adventuring. Day after day, year after year, he will tread the tiresome trail of meat, gravy, and potatoes, little dreaming of the appetizing side trails, never knowing the challenge of wild foods offered by bounteous Nature.

"I am amazed," observed Jay N. (Ding) Darling, "how many people will not eat, or at least have not eaten, mouth-watering pot-roasted muskrat or smoking-hot broiled sand shark. The same men will instead stuff themselves daily with lumpy, soggy mashed potatoes."

Those who still believe that the basis of a perfect meal is meat, potatoes, and gravy should read a menu of the 1890's, when game was a food for epicures. Imagine sitting down to an elaborate and sophisticated dinner where the courses of soup and fish were followed by "releves," six or more in number, among them turkey à la Toulouse, saddle of venison with currant jelly, and stewed terrapin à la Maryland. And after that came a number of cold ornamented dishes; then the entrees and hors d'oeuvres.

The second main course offered canvasback ducks, pheasants, partridges, and grouse, with 10 vegetables. And finally came 15 desserts and cof-fee. Such was the culinary tradition of the inns, taverns, and hotels of our larger cities during the late nineteenth century.

No one advocates a return to the gay nineties, when game laws were lax. If man hunts for recreation and his own personal needs, the game supply will not decrease, and killing for the market will not be a factor in the reduction of game. From our present point of view, market hunting is a crime against conservation, and the protective laws now in force by the States and the Federal Government conserve and perpetuate our game.

Naturally, the pioneers of our country had a high regard for game because they had to depend upon wild animals for their meat supply. Our ancestors knew how to prepare game; they either cooked the fresh meat for immediate consumption or cured it by pickling, smoking, or drying to preserve it for later use.

Those who live on the land have the greatest opportunity to obtain meat from forest, field, and stream. They, above all others, should use as food all wild game taken in season. Wild game is entitled to high rank in our present culinary set-up. It is well for all of us to learn that the wild birds and animals that live in our fields, streams, and forests can provide good, wholesome food, which is easily prepared, cooked, and digested.

According to data from State game departments and other sources, all game yielded 127,000 tons of dressed meat in 1942. This is a lot of meat—particularly when one remembers that that amount of top-quality protein is raising itself each year on American lands.

What species of wildlife can be used for food? The wild raccoon, beaver, muskrat, skunk, armadillo, deer, antelope, moose, reindeer, buffalo, bear, boar, wild turkey, quail, pheasant, grouse, partridge, prairie chicken, sparrow, crow, and woodcock are all abundant and, as many hunters can testify, are good to eat.

People eating game for the first time usually compare it with beef, pork, or other domestic meats, but it should be remembered that game has a distinctive flavor, which, for the most part, is not comparable with the meat of any other group of animals.

As Anthelme Brillat-Savarin, the eminent French gastronomist, pointed out, the good qualities of game meat are not "so intrinsic as to be in a great measure independent of the skill of the cook."

"If we throw into a pot of water salt and a piece of beef," he said, "we will obtain some boiled meat. But if instead of beef we put wild boar or venison in the pot, we will have but poor fare; in this respect, butcher's meat has the advantage. Under the direction of a skillful cook, however, game undergoes a great number of scientific modifications and transformations, furnishing the majority of highly flavored dishes on which a transcendental gastronomic art is based.

"Game also owes much of its quality to the nature of the soil it is fed on. The taste of red partridge of Périgord is not the same as that of a red partridge of Cologne, and although a hare killed in the neighborhood of Paris is but a poor dish, a leveret from the sunburnt slopes of Valromey or Upper Dauphine is perhaps the finest flavored of all quadrupeds."

The flesh of game, when young, is generally tender, contains less fat than poultry, is of a fine though strong flavor, and is easy of digestion. Game meat is usually of dark color, ruffed grouse and quail being exceptions, and is usually cooked rare.

Climatic conditions, food, and cover all bear a definite relation to the quality and taste of game meat. Many small game species survive and thrive in densely populated farm areas.

Farms on which the crop rotation includes wheat, corn, buckwheat, lespedeza, soybeans, and similar seed-producers are especially attractive to upland game birds and rabbits. In addition, rabbits are fond of almost any green vegetation, especially that grown in vegetable gardens.

Age affects the flavor and texture of the meat from wild animals. It is impossible to state the age at which an animal will be best for meat, but everyone knows that meat from old animals is tougher than that from young ones. The flesh of very young animals, however, frequently lacks flavor and is watery. An old animal, if fat and healthy, is better than a young one in poor condition.

Venison has the same chemical composition as beef but is not nearly so fat as meat from well-fed cattle. A lean venison roast before cooking contains, on the average, 75 percent water, 20 percent protein, and 2 percent fat; a lean beef rump, 65 to 70 percent water, 20 to 23 percent protein, and 5 to 14 percent fat; and a lean leg of mutton, 67 percent water, 19 percent protein, and 13 percent fat. Venison, like beef and other common meats, is thoroughly digestible, whatever the method of cooking.

In nutrition tests conducted in 1944 at the technological laboratory of the United States Fish and Wildlife Service at College Park, Md., proximate analyses and vitamin assays were made on cooked samples of domestic rabbits, raccoons, opossums, muskrats, and beavers. (The results are shown in the accompanying tables.)

On the average, game birds furnish a little more protein than the so-called red meats, but the two classes, red and white meats, are equally healthful. It is probable that the method of cooking, as well as differences in composition or texture, has an effect on the ease with which both white and red meat are digested.

Game nowadays is hunted primarily for sport, with the emphasis on recreation rather than on a need for food;

Proximate analyses of cooked samples of game animals

Meat tested	Mois-ture %	Pro-tein %	Fat %	Min-eral matter %
Beaver:				
Boiled............	56.2	29.2	13.7	0.9
Roasted..........	64.2	30.0	5.1	1.2
	67.1	29.7	3.8	1.5
Muskrat, roasted......	66.4	26.7	5.3	1.4
	70.2	25.2	3.3	1.2
Opossum, roasted....	58.3	30.2	10.2	2.3
	57.2	24.9	13.8	1.4
Rabbit, roasted.......	60.8	32.4	6.2	1.3
	60.2	33.6	5.4	1.5
Raccoon, roasted.....	54.3	29.2	14.5	1.5

Vitamin assays on cooked samples of game animals

Meat tested	Thiamine	Riboflavin
	Micrograms per 100 grams of cooked meat	
Beaver:		
Baked.............	76	380
Boiled............	60	270
Cottontail rabbit, fried.	160	230
Muskrat, roasted.....	160	210
Opossum:		
Broiled...........	150	2,580
Roasted..........	100	375
Rabbit:		
Baked...........	105	105
Roasted..........	104	116
Stewed...........	50	77
Rabbit kidney, broiled.	400	2,300
Rabbit liver, roasted ...	200	2,300–2,500
Raccoon, roasted......	575–600	525
Raccoon liver, broiled..	200	1,840

therefore, little time has been devoted to the preparation and cooking of wild meat.

To PRESERVE game meat, the animal must be bled, dressed, and cooled properly. How completely the carcass should be dressed, cut up, and packaged for transportation depends to some extent on the distance it is to be hauled, the time involved in hauling, and the temperature.

If a deer is taken immediately to camp or hauled quickly to a butcher

shop or home, a much better job of skinning and butchering can be done because the carcass can be hung up correctly and more tools are available to do the work. As soon as possible after the animal is killed, however, it should be "field dressed," that is, the viscera, lungs, heart, and liver removed. Bacteria in the abdominal cavity soon cause spoilage; therefore, the contents of the abdomen and chest should be emptied quickly. This applies also to other big game animals.

Small game animals are much easier to eviscerate and skin while they are still warm than after the carcass becomes cold. They can be skinned in the field, in camp, or at home. Scent and other glands found in some small game should be removed at once; if they are left in, the meat becomes tainted. Those glands are under the forelegs and along the spine in the small of the back near the rump. They are generally pear-shaped, waxy or reddish kernels. The glands should not be cut or brought in contact with the meat.

Upland game birds and waterfowl should be drawn as soon as possible— that is, the internal organs should be removed. Viscera decompose more rapidly than other parts of the carcass, and, if left in, are likely to infect the rest of the bird.

If a hunter stays in the field for several days, he may ship game home at the end of each day, as provided by State and Federal regulations. Express companies give this special service and are familiar with the care of game in transit and its delivery in good condition. In camp and at home it is possible to freeze the meat out-of-doors, if the weather is cold enough. The better plan, however, is to place it in refrigeration.

Renting local refrigerated lockers for storage of perishable food products, such as meat, poultry, fish, and game, is a regular business in many sections of the country. There are thousands of freezer-storage locker plants in the United States that rent compartments for family use. Many people have installed quick-freezing systems at home and in this way have stored game indefinitely, then thawed it, and prepared the meat in its original freshness.

When a hunter eats his kill in camp, game is considered to be fresh meat. Being governed by his appetite, the hungry hunter is not going to wait until venison or birds are hung long enough to season. Culinary methods in camp must be simple.

ALL GAME must be hung in a cool place for a time in order that it may become more tender and palatable. As the meat begins to age, its flavor improves; the process enhances its culinary value. To season venison, the entire carcass should be hung for 10 days at least; 2 weeks is better. Generally speaking, the length of time depends largely on individual taste. Whatever the opinion or prejudice on seasoning game, one thing is certain— the meat of freshly killed game is totally different from that of seasoned, or "high," game. When fresh, meat lacks taste; when it is reasonably seasoned, it is tender and full of flavor. It is all a matter of taste, so store your game to give the meat you like best.

I hope that I have succeeded in encouraging you to lift your recreation by interesting yourself in the care, the preparation, and, above all, the cooking of the game you shoot. No matter how much hunting and fishing the outdoorsman does, he generally keeps in the back of his mind a picture of the •campfire, steaming coffee, and broiled venison or fried fish. Nothing stimulates the lagging appetite so much as a day in the woods and along streams, followed by a sizzling meal of venison, wild fowl, or fish with potatoes and coffee.

WILD RABBITS undoubtedly constitute the largest, cheapest, and most generally available source of game in the United States. Hunters each year take more of them than of any other species of game, large or small. From the earliest settlement of America to the present day they have been an important item in our food supply.

In my opinion, rabbit is best when cooked in the simple ways. Fried rabbit—an excellent game dish when properly prepared—is very popular.

FRIED RABBIT: Skin and clean the rabbit thoroughly. Disjoint the legs and cut the back into small pieces. Sprinkle each piece with salt, pepper, paprika, and flour. Make the flour stick by patting it with the hands. Melt bacon or some other fat in an iron skillet. When melted, fat should be about one-quarter or one-half inch deep in the pan. When the fat is hot, put in pieces of rabbit. Turn them frequently and fry slowly until each piece is golden brown. Add one-quarter to one-half cup of milk. Cover skillet, place it in the oven set for 325° or over a slow heat, and cook for 15 to 20 minutes, or until tender. If desired, thicken gravy and add sour cream, and season. Heat again and serve immediately. If milk and sour cream are not available, water and flour will do for gravy.

BROILED RABBIT: If the rabbits are young, try broiling them. That can be done over the campfire or outdoor grill or in the home oven.

Cut the rabbit into serving pieces. Rub each piece all over with fat; salt and pepper it. Place on a broiling rack, and broil for 25 to 40 minutes, basting the meat every 5 or 10 minutes with the drippings or other melted fat.

Young squirrels are excellent cooked that way. If the squirrels are not so young, parboil them in salt water until tender, and then prepare the meat for broiling.

BROILED AND ROAST QUAIL: The bobwhite—known in the North as quail and in the South as partridge—is loved by every country dweller, and is better known to more hunters in the United States than any other game bird. It is no less appreciated on the table than in the field. Here is a simple and satisfactory way to prepare quail.

Pluck, clean, and split the quail down its back, brush with olive oil, cooking oil, or bacon fat, and sprinkle with salt and pepper. Place on a broiling rack and broil for about 10 minutes, basting frequently with drippings or other fat or oil. Serve on hot buttered toast and sprinkle with chopped parsley and a little onion. Sautéed mushrooms, with a dash of sherry, go well with this dish.

Here is another simple but good recipe for quail:

Pluck and draw the birds, rub a little butter all over them. Tie a strip of bacon over the breast, or fasten it there with toothpicks, and set them in a 300° to 350° oven for 15 to 20 minutes.

Some time ago, Talbott Denmead told me that Bob Rennert, the late manager of the Hotel Rennert in Baltimore, prepared quail in this manner: After plucking and eviscerating, the birds were not split, but left whole. Pork sausage, mixed with an equal amount of bread crumbs and cracker crumbs, was used for stuffing. After the birds were stuffed, salted, peppered, and floured, they were rubbed with olive oil, then roasted just like squabs, doves, or chicken, in a reasonably hot oven until brown and tender. Talbott and I and many others know this makes an excellent dish, for we have had it in our homes many times.

ROAST PHEASANT: The ingredients are one or more pheasants, cut up, frying fat, sour cream, wild rice, a can of mushrooms, spiced currants, and seasoned flour.

After washing, dry the pheasants carefully and roll in the seasoned flour. Brown in skillet and drain on paper. Arrange in roaster, putting a teaspoon of sour cream on each piece of pheasant. Cover and cook 1 hour at 375°. Baste with sour cream once during cooking. Make pan gravy by adding more cream and thinning with the liquid from the can of mushrooms. Add mushrooms, and serve with very hot wild rice. Use the spiced currants for garnish.

GRILLED SQUIRREL: The dressed carcass should remain whole, but opened from tail to neck. Place it on a meat block or board and flatten it with the broad side of a meat cleaver. Salt and pepper both sides; then rub the carcass with fat or olive oil, or place strips of bacon or salt pork on the side facing the grill or broiler. When well browned, turn the meat and lard the other side; when it is well browned all over, the meat should be sufficiently cooked and tender.

WOODCHUCK POT ROAST: Get an animal that is about one-half to three-quarters grown. Disjoint the carcass and soak it an hour in cold water that contains one-half cup of vinegar and 1 teaspoon of baking soda. Salt and pepper the pieces, roll them in flour, and put them in hot fat in which you have previously browned a small clove of garlic. When the meat is browned on both sides, place the cover on a heavy skillet or Dutch oven, and simmer the meat until it is tender. Add a little water, as needed. Just before serving, season with Worcestershire sauce and chunks of butter.

ROAST OPOSSUM: After skinning, dress the opossum much as you would a suckling pig, removing the entrails and, if desired, the head and tail. After it has been dressed, wash thoroughly inside and out with hot water. Cover with cold water, to which has been added a cup of salt, and allow to stand overnight. In the morning, drain off the salted water and rinse well with clear, boiling water. Stuff with opossum stuffing; sew the opening, or fasten it with skewers. Place in a roaster, add 2 tablespoons of water, and roast in moderate oven (350° F.) until tender and richly browned, about 1½ hours. Baste every 15 minutes with drippings. Remove skewers or stitches, and place opossum on heated platter.

Needed for opossum stuffing are 1 large onion, chopped fine; 1 tablespoon fat; opossum livers, if desired; 2 cups bread crumbs; salt; chopped red pepper; dash Worcestershire sauce; and 1 hard-cooked egg, chopped fine.

Brown onion in fat. Add finely chopped opossum liver and cook until liver is tender. Add crumbs, a little red pepper, Worcestershire sauce, egg, salt, and water to moisten.

DING'S RACCOON PIE: "I'm just a catch-as-catch-can cook," wrote Ding Darling, cartoonist and conservationist, "and, like my old Aunt Hester, never measure anything—just a pour and a spill, a pinch of this and that; but things generally turn out all right." He gives this fine way to prepare raccoon:

Skin the raccoon, remove all scent glands and surplus fat. Cut into pieces as you would a rabbit for stewing. Prepare a marinade from 1 quart of water, 1 pint of vinegar, 1 tablespoon salt, 1 teaspoon black pepper, 1 tablespoon sugar (brown preferred), 1/4 package (2 ounces) pickling spices. Mix water, vinegar, seasoning, and spices.

Place the pieces of meat in this brine and allow them to soak for 8 hours. Longer soaking (12 hours) will not injure the meat. Drain the meat, and place it in the ice box until you wish to remove it for cooking. If time does not allow for soaking in the brine, the meat can be parboiled in water to which salt and soda have been added. If the raccoon is old, parboiling can be repeated two or three times to advantage.

Place the meat in a stewing kettle as you would chicken, and cover with water. As the meat becomes tender, add two small onions diced, three or four potatoes and three carrots cut into small pieces. When the meat and vegetables are tender, remove them from the broth. Take out all bones and sinews from the meat, and cut it into small pieces. Thicken the liquor, or broth, with browned flour, and butter and season to taste. Place the meat and vegetables in a baking dish, and pour the hot gravy over them.

Cover the top with a heavy layer of baking powder biscuit dough (a little extra shortening in biscuit dough is usually helpful). Make vents in the dough with a fork or knife to permit steam to escape. Bake in a hot oven until the dough is nicely browned and thoroughly baked.

If preferred, the dough can be cut with a biscuit cutter and placed on the top of the dish, far enough apart to permit steam to escape from below.

ANOTHER excellent suggestion from Ding is that anyone who likes hasenpfeffer will find that raccoon can be prepared after a favorite hasenpfeffer recipe. Lime juice (or claret) makes an excellent substitute for the vinegar.

Marinating raccoon meat in fresh lime juice and salt for a few hours is a fine preliminary treatment to pot roast of raccoon, with potatoes, onions, and carrots.

"I have been surprised at the number of people who will rave about a raccoon pie until they find out what they are eating," Ding says. "Last winter I roasted a whole beaver and cut it up before setting it on the table, so that no one could tell what it was. It was delicious, and met unanimous approval—even after they knew what it was. The beaver's tail is particularly fine eating. Generally speaking, however, beaver meat is no better than young raccoon. Pot roasting is good for both."

MARYLAND POTTED OR BAKED MUSK-RAT: Soak two muskrats overnight, drain and cut into pieces. Pour boiling water over meat, stir thoroughly, and drain.

Place in a thick skillet or iron pot, add a little water, and a pod of red pepper or one-half teaspoon of red cayenne. Season to taste with salt and pepper, a little sage, and 4 tablespoons of bacon or sausage drippings.

If desired, a generous piece of washed salt pork may be used instead. Sprinkle flour over top, cover, and bake in a moderately hot oven until tender. Baste it several times until well browned.

Enough potatoes for the meal may be cooked with the meat, or the muskrat can be served with diced and buttered white or sweetpotatoes, peas, or carrots.

ARMADILLO SAUSAGE: Armadillo is popular prepared as sausage in parts of Texas, especially in the Big Thicket region. Most people prepare it according to their recipes for pork sausage. The ingredients are: 1 gallon ground armadillo meat; 1 teaspoon ground coriander seed; 1 teaspoon white pepper; 1 teaspoon salt; 1 teaspoon onion juice; 3 tablespoons brown sugar; 1 teaspoon saltpeter; ½ teaspoon nutmeg; ¼ clove garlic.

Pour one-fourth cup of hot water over mashed garlic clove. Let stand until cool. Dissolve the saltpeter in this mixture and sprinkle it over the meat. Mix the spices thoroughly through the meat and regrind.

BOILED MOOSE HEAD: Bob Bloom of Fairbanks, Alaska, has his own special way of preparing moose head. As reported by Frank Dufresne, Bob first skins out the head, being very careful to save the ears and nose. Next, he boils the head to remove all flesh and gristle from the bones.

Then he throws away the skull and the hide, and saves the meat and gristle. He simmers this mixture in a heavy iron pot until it is thoroughly cooked and tender. He adds a few bay leaves, a little ground cloves and allspice (as one does in making headcheese from a hog). He adds salt and pepper just before removing the kettle from the fire. He pours this mixture into molds to cool and jell. Then he locks the door to keep out the neighbors.

FRANK G. ASHBROOK *is in charge of wild fur animal investigations in the Fish and Wildlife Service, Department of the Interior. After graduation from Pennsylvania State College, he was an investigator in the Bureau of Animal Industry. He joined the Bureau of Biological Survey in 1921 as biologist in charge of fur resources. This Bureau was transferred to the Department of the Interior in 1939. He is coauthor, with Edna N. Sater, of* Cooking Wild Game, *from which came some of the recipes in this article.*

SOUTHEASTERN farmers in the past few years have planted Kentucky 31 fescue (Suiter's grass) on thousands of acres, principally for grazing. They are using it widely in their soil- and water-conservation projects.

Recently I learned about another of its values. Like many other plants used primarily for erosion control and for feed for domestic animals, this perennial grass makes farm land more suitable for wildlife. In January 1950, while visiting on Sapelo Island, Simon Krock and I saw a flock of about 30 wild turkeys feeding on a recently established fescue-clover pasture. The pasture had not been grazed by livestock. Although the turkeys had grazed the fescue heavily, I saw no sign that they had touched the white clover. People on the island told us that the flock had been using the fescue pasture for more than a month, staying on it most of the day. In the next field oats were planted for grazing. The turkeys had been feeding there but only for very short periods. Obviously they preferred the fescue. Kit Shaffer, a technician of the Virginia Game Commission, reported that wild turkeys used new plantings of Kentucky 31 fescue on Cumberland State Forest lands during the winter of 1950.—*John B. Hungerford, Soil Conservation Service, Waycross, Ga.*

How To Keep Meat From Spoiling

*O. G. Hankins, R. L. Hiner,
W. L. Sulzbacher, A. M. Gaddis*

Fresh meat is highly perishable, even at the customary refrigerator temperature of about 45° F. In the coolers of packing plants and elsewhere where temperatures are only a little above the freezing point, the rate of change is less pronounced; nevertheless spoilage goes on. Everyone should know how to preserve meat from that damage.

Preservation of meat begins with the choice of animals for slaughter.

Cattle, hogs, and sheep slaughtered for meat vary widely in type, age, weight, development of muscle or lean meat, fatness, and other characteristics. Meat packers can sell most of the healthy animals offered by livestock producers because the public demands a wide variety of types and grades of products. The exceptions are essentially the cattle and sheep that would be improved by additional weight and finish; they go to feeders who fatten them in preparation for sale for slaughter. Thus, broadly speaking, there is no critical selection of livestock for slaughter in commercial channels. Rather, the meat industry adapts the animals offered by producers to meet consumer demands.

But the farmer who selects an animal for slaughter for home use often has the chance to choose one that best meets the family requirements. He first considers good growth and development and the absence of signs that the animal is unhealthy.

Next come size and weight, which indicate the sizes and weights of the different cuts and the total amount of meat that will be produced. For example, a 200-pound hog of intermediate type yields hams, bacons, and loin cuts that weigh about 15 to 16, 9 to 10, and 10 to 11 pounds, respectively. The corresponding cuts from a 250-pound hog weigh approximately 19, 12 to 13, and 12 pounds.

Highly important in selecting animals for slaughter is their degree of fatness. Thin, underfinished animals do not make good eating. Moderately well fattened cattle, hogs, and sheep yield the most generally acceptable products. Some consumers prefer highly finished meat, usually because they believe a relatively large percentage of intramuscular fat adds to the eating quality of the lean meat. The meat of highly finished animals is "wasty," however, and in hogs might mean too much lard. A 250–pound hog yields about 60 percent (10 to 15 pounds) more lard than a 200-pound hog—an example of how weight and finish affect the production of lard.

There is no need here to go into details of slaughtering, but some principles bear repetition.

Preslaughter feeding and management call for first consideration. Animals should receive their last feed not less than 24 hours before slaughter, but they should have all the clean, fresh water they want.

The animals should not be frightened or excited. Striking with a stick or whip will cause bruises and bloody spots on the dressed carcass that must be trimmed out.

The actual killing of meat animals should be done quietly and quickly. Bleeding must start promptly and proceed freely and rapidly.

Time and temperature are important factors in the preservation of meat. There should be no delay in carrying out all subsequent steps, such as scalding and scraping hogs, removing hides and skins of cattle and sheep, eviscerating, and splitting cattle and hog carcasses.

Cleanliness at all stages of the operation is imperative.

Fresh meat is an excellent medium for the growth and multiplication of micro-organisms. Therefore dressed carcasses have to be chilled promptly. It is best to cool them to an internal temperature of 35° F. or lower within 24 hours or less. When the temperature exceeds that level or the time of chilling is prolonged, there is danger of spoilage, especially in hogs from which some cuts are to be cured and smoked.

Farmers generally slaughter their meat animals when weather conditions are favorable for rapid cooling of the carcasses. Some packers start the chilling at a temperature well below the freezing point of meat (about 29° F.) in order to hasten the operation.

The dressed carcasses generally lose weight, averaging about 2 to 2½ percent, during the chilling period. Such losses are due to evaporation of moisture and therefore are affected by the relative humidity of the atmosphere in the chill room. Extremely high relative humidity tends to keep down carcass weight losses during the chilling period, but, on the other hand, creates a more favorable environment for an increase in micro-organisms. Because low relative humidity causes excessive chilling shrink, the best level is 85 to 90 percent.

Meats vary in their ability to withstand chill-room storage, or in the rate at which they change during such storage. Pork usually deteriorates the most rapidly. Moreover, in contrast with certain other meats, especially beef, pork apparently is not improved in any way by an extended period of aging or ripening. At a temperature of 35° to 38° F., 3 to 5 days of storage between slaughter of a hog and consumption of the fresh pork is regarded by many as an optimum period. Beef from well-fattened cattle, however, may be kept to advantage for 2 weeks or more, and highly finished beef can be ripened for about 6 weeks.

Bacteria and molds normally grow on the surfaces of aging fresh meat. Consequently, a good deal of surface meat generally must be trimmed off before the aged meat is used. The changes that occur beneath the surfaces of fresh meat during the aging process are due to enzymatic action. Tenderness is increased and a ripened flavor is gradually acquired. But if the aging is carried too far spoilage results.

The three main ways to preserve meat are freezing, curing, and canning. Dehydration can also be a useful method under some conditions.

FREEZING is the only known means by which fresh meat can be preserved in a condition like its normal state. Modern low-cost refrigeration has made freezing and freezer-storage facilities so generally available that seasonal fluctuations and periodic surpluses, once true of meat production, have been leveled off considerably.

Because meat contains different kinds of material—protein, carbohydrate, fat, pigments, flavoring ingredients—it may undergo several types of decomposition. The breakdown of meat is due to the action of micro-organisms and enzymes on its constituents. Temperature largely determines which type of decomposition will predominate. The offensive decay that may take place at room temperature in a few hours is due primarily to the action of bacteria, although other types of breakdown occur at the same time. At 35° to 38° F., the temperature range at which meat is usually ripened, bacterial growth is sluggish, and enzyme action is responsible for the principal changes.

Meat starts to freeze at about 29° F. As the temperature drops to 15° or lower, the growth of micro-organisms ceases, and hydrolytic enzyme action on protein and fat becomes slight. At about 15° oxidation of the fat, which is caused largely by the accelerating effect of enzyme action, begins to become the chief, if not the sole, kind of decomposition. That type of breakdown progresses slowly at first, but as decomposition products accumulate it gains velocity. Because of its greater exposure to air, the surface always oxidizes more rapidly than the inside fat. Modern freezer storage is usually at 0° F. or lower. Because of differences in chemical constitution and activity of enzymes, animal fats vary considerably in their tendency to oxidize. Pork fat oxidizes much faster than beef or lamb fat.

FREEZING IMPROVES meat in some ways. It has a tenderizing action. It destroys any trichinae organisms that may be present in pork. Although freezing at 0° F. for 24 hours is reported to kill trichinae, the Department recommends different holding periods, depending on the temperature and the thickness of the cut or pack.

For instance, the recommendation for pork 6 to 27 inches thick stored at 5° F. is 20 to 30 days; at −10°, 10 to 20 days; at −20°, 6 to 12 days.

Sometimes the freezing produces marked changes in the texture of the meat. When the meat is thawed, a considerable amount of fluid drains off, with a loss of juiciness, flavor, and nutritive elements. The changes in texture can be largely controlled by rapid freezing at low temperatures. When meat is frozen slowly, much of the moisture separates from the cells and forms large intercellular ice crystals, which tend to distort the tissue structure. That causes irreversible changes in the tissue system. Rapid freezing produces minute crystals, which are rather evenly distributed through the tissue. When such a product is thawed, the moisture is reabsorbed as the crystals melt. The different methods of quick freezing fall basically into three types: Direct immersion in low-temperature brine; indirect contact with the refrigerant; and air blast.

If meat is frozen and stored without protective wrapping at 15° F., it will remain wholesome and edible for some time, although the quality goes down rather rapidly. The changes are due principally to desiccation and oxidation. Desiccation, a drying-out process, often is referred to as freezer burn. Oxidation is a chemical union of susceptible constituents of the meat with the oxygen of the air. The red pigments of the meat react with oxygen to form brown pigments, and the fat combines with oxygen to form compounds that gradually break down to produce rancid flavors. The meat changes in color, develops undesirable flavors, and becomes dry and hard. In a sense, it may be well preserved, but no longer does it resemble fresh meat in flavor, texture, and appearance. The rate of the changes may be slowed by lowering the temperature.

At temperatures low enough to check microbiological and hydrolytic enzyme action, the problem of maintaining fresh-meat quality rests largely upon a complete protection from oxygen of the outside atmosphere.

Desiccation can be checked satisfactorily by using wrappers or containers impermeable to moisture, and maintaining suitable conditions in the freezer. Most wrappers and containers give some protection against oxidation. The fat of meat is responsible for a great deal of the flavor, and change in it because of oxidation is probably the important single factor responsible for loss of quality in freezer storage.

Oxidation, which also affects the color of the lean, is hard to control. It can be checked completely only by protecting the meat entirely from the oxygen of the atmosphere. That can be done by packing in a vacuum or in an inert atmosphere of carbon dioxide or nitrogen in tin-plate cans or other airtight containers. Because of the general unsuitability of the available containers, such methods are now considered somewhat impractical, although they have been found to be extremely effective. The application of antioxidants—chemical substances that inhibit oxidation—has been tested experimentally and has shown promise. However, their use has been approved only for preventation of oxidation in stored lard.

The ideal wrapper is proof against water vapor and gases; it has good tensile strength and pliability at all temperatures; it is odorless and nontoxic; and it can be peeled from the frozen meat. It can be sealed with heat; it is easy to mark for identification; and it is proof against moisture and stains.

Few of the wrappers available approach the ideal in all properties, especially in permeability to gases. A wrapper made of rubber latex shows promise. Perhaps better wrappers will be developed from derivatives of polyethylene and vinyl polymers. Dip coatings of thermoplastic materials (such as microcrystalline waxes) are possibly the answer to the need for a practical and effective protector for frozen meats. The procedure merely involves dipping frozen meat in a molten thermoplastic mixture. The coating that results is said to approach the efficiency of an hermetically sealed metal or glass container. Tin cans are best in many ways for frozen meats. They take up space, however, and there is danger that they may be handled as heat-processed canned goods.

Cured meats, especially pork, are sometimes stored in the freezer. Because of an accelerating action of the salt, the fat oxidizes much faster than does the fresh product. The deterioration can be checked by adequate protection from the oxygen of the atmosphere.

Frozen meat that is thawed slowly has less drip than quickly thawed meat. Thawed meat should be used immediately because it is more susceptible to deterioration than fresh, unfrozen meat.

The nutritive value of meat is preserved better by freezing than by any other method. The biological value of proteins is unimpaired, but oxidation of the fat lowers its value because of the destruction of the essential fatty acids. Oxidation also destroys some of the A, D, E, and K vitamins of fat. Some nutritive and mineral content is lost from meats in the drip formed during thawing, but if the meat is frozen quickly the loss is low.

Because freezing does little to improve meat but only tends to maintain its original condition, care is essential in choosing meat to be stored. Lean cuts generally store better than fat cuts. Ripened meat tends to lose quality more rapidly than unripened. Beef and lamb should be held in the cooler only a few days. Pork should be stored immediately after the removal of the animal heat.

The commercial freezing of meats began in the United States about 50 years ago, before the use of mechanical refrigeration became so common. The frozen-food industry has grown rapidly in the past 20 years. In the early days of the industry, little consideration was given to the quality of meat being frozen, or to the temperature, manner of storing, and handling. But careful attention to selection, handling, preparation, freezing, storage, transportation, and marketing has resulted in a product much like the fresh meat; "frosted" meats are widely accepted as equal in quality to the fresh product.

CURING has long been used to preserve meat and, with some modifications, is still in use. The essential ingredient then, as now, was salt. E. W. Callow, of the Low Temperature Research Station, Cambridge, England, reports that salt draws moisture from the muscle cells and at the same time enters the cells by osmosis. In that way it is distributed finally throughout the tissue. The salt checks the action of certain harmful bacteria and inhibits several types of enzymes. If too small an amount of salt is added to the meat, the putrefactive bacteria that can grow in the presence of some salt will not be checked. Spoilage follows. The total amount of salt applied may not be the deciding factor, because complete distribution throughout the piece of meat is essential.

C. N. McBryde, of the Department of Agriculture, found that the salt contents of sour and sound hams did not differ in amount. His findings were confirmed by A. K. Besley and Floyd Carroll, of the Department and the Maryland Agricultural Experiment Station, respectively, in a comparison of whole hams or slices. But when they analyzed individual muscles, they discovered that some contained salt in such small quantities as to have little or no bacteriostatic effect in the area where spoilage generally occurs.

In another series of tests, L. B. Jensen and his coworkers of the research laboratories of Swift and Company found that the salt content of 44 sour bone marrows compared favorably with that of 48 sweet bone marrows.

Sugar, which commonly is used in curing mixtures, is added to lessen the harshness that is found in meat cured by salt alone. It also provides a suitable medium for the growth of the bacteria that are necessary to break down the sugar into organic acids. One of the acids, lactic acid, particularly is said to give a pleasant flavor to meat.

Sugar also helps fix the color. R. B. Oestung and G. W. Beach, of the American Meat Institute, reported that meat cured without sugar faded somewhat and was intermediate in quality and permanence, but meat cured with dextrose held its color. Dextrose is believed to protect the pigment, nitrosohemoglobin, by reacting with oxygen.

Sugars commonly used in meat curing are sucrose (cane and beet sugar) and dextrose (corn sugar). Sucrose is broken down by enzymes and acids to dextrose and levulose, which are then oxidized to lactic acid. If the regular (long-time) cures are used, sucrose is effective; in the quick cures, which are now used extensively, the faster-acting dextrose is better.

Saltpeter (nitrate of potassium or sodium), an important part of the curing mixture, has two functions—color fixation and checking the growth of certain bacteria. Meat owes its red color to hemoglobin, an unstable pigment, which oxidizes to brown methemoglobin and combines with nitric oxide to form red nitrosohemoglobin. Nitric oxide is formed through the reduction of nitrate to nitrite. The reduction is brought about by certain bacteria, which occur normally on fresh meat as it goes into cure or are present in curing vats. The success of the reaction, however, depends on the temperature of cure, curing formula, and acidity of the curing solution.

The reduction of nitrate to nitrite is a relatively long reaction. With our present quick cure, it often results in poor color. That has been overcome by the use of potassium or sodium nitrite. A combination of nitrite and nitrate in a ratio of 1 to 10 makes a superior product. Nitrates also exert a bacteriostatic influence by providing aerobic conditions within the meat, thus inhibiting the growth of anaerobic putrefactive bacteria.

Honey is often added to curing mixtures to give lean meat a distinctive flavor. It can be used with sugar or may replace the sugar. It is used in the same proportion as sugar. Various condiments, mainly spices, can be added to the curing mixture to give more flavor. They do not interfere with the regular curing ingredients and may be added to suit individual tastes.

The success of curing depends on rapid distribution of the curing ingredients before the putrefactive bacteria begin to grow. That may be done by the dry-salt or sweet-pickle method, with or without supplementary stitch pumping or artery pumping.

In the dry-salt curing of meats the curing mixture is rubbed directly on the meat. The method is generally more satisfactory than others when the curing temperature cannot be kept at 38° F. Meat so cured is allowed to remain in cure approximately 2 days for each pound.

In brine curing the meat is covered with a curing solution and kept there until the salt has penetrated to its center. The same amounts and kinds of ingredients are used as in dry salting. A stronger curing solution is used for thicker cuts, such as hams and shoulders, than for bacon. The method takes about twice as long as the dry-salt process.

In stitch pumping, often used in combination with dry-salt or brine-immersion curing, brine is forced into the center of the cut, especially near the bones and joints. Generally, the amount of brine injected should not exceed 10 percent of the weight of the cut. After pumping, the meat is covered with either brine or a dry curing mixture.

During the past 15 years, artery- or quick-cured hams have gradually dominated the commercial market. The process is so named because the curing solution is forced into the large artery, which distributes it through the cut by means of the arterial and capillary system. About 10 percent of the weight of a ham is added in the form of curing solution. Pumping is followed by dry-salt or brine curing for 7 to 14 days.

Smoked meats cured by any of these methods show little difference after an aging period of 6 to 8 weeks. Dry-salt meat loses some weight in curing, but the other three methods result in some gain. After being smoked, dry-salt hams show a still greater weight loss, but after storage for 6 to 8 weeks all are approximately the same.

The proportions of curing ingredients depend somewhat on the desires of the consumer. A good proportion is 8 pounds of fine dairy salt, 2 pounds of brown sugar, and 2 ounces of saltpeter (or 1 ounce of saltpeter and ¼ ounce of potassium nitrite) for each 100 pounds of meat. That amount of curing ingredients is adequate for about twice as much bacon. If one wishes to use the brine method, the same proportions of ingredients are weighed out. For curing hams and shoulders, enough water (approximately 4½ gallons) is added to bring the solution to a density of 75° on a salinometer. For bacon and other thin cuts, the solution strength should be approximately 65°. That requires about 5½ gallons of water. For pumping pickle, a salinometer reading of 90° to 95° is satisfactory. Approximately 3½ gallons of water is needed to dissolve the foregoing ingredients.

To repeat: Meat must be kept cold during cure, because some time is required for it to absorb enough salt to prevent bacterial action. On the other hand, if too low a temperature is maintained, curing is retarded, and more time is needed for the process. The recommended curing temperature is 38° F.

After the meat has been cured, it is removed from cure, washed, and hung up to dry, or it is soaked and then dried. Meat that has remained in cure too long should be soaked for an hour in warm water to dissolve some of the surface salt. After it is washed, it should be allowed to dry overnight.

Cured meat is generally smoked before it is put in storage. Smoking lowers the moisture content, imparts an attractive golden-brown color and mild, smoky aroma, and (through minute amounts of phenols and resins deposited) furnishes some protection against bacteria and oxidation. Excessive shrinkage or moisture losses are avoided by maintaining smokehouse temperatures of 130° to 135° F. Soft woods should never be used in smoking meat; their smoke contains tar derivatives which blacken the meat.

Smokehouse temperatures vary according to the type of cured and smoked product that is being produced. Meat for storage at air temperatures should be smoked in a temperature of 135° F. until the inside of the meat has reached 110°. Then the smokehouse temperature is lowered to 110° and maintained until the desired color is attained. If the cured, smoked meat is to be eaten without further cooking, the smokehouse temperature should be raised to 165° and held there until the internal temperature of the meat has reached 140°, a temperature that insures the destruction of trichinae.

Storing cured smoked meats, especially hams, for long periods gives a product that has unique characteristics and is highly regarded by many. For storage, the smoked ham is wrapped in paper, placed in a muslin bag, and suspended by its butt end in a room that is dark, well-ventilated, cool, and tightly screened against skipper flies and other insects. The meat may remain in storage 12 to 18 months before it is used. During that time, significant changes take place, including a redistribution of the salt.

Curing is not confined to hams, bacon, and pork shoulders, but may be used for preserving pork loins, spareribs, lamb legs, lamb shoulders, and beef. The beef is referred to as corned beef or dried beef. Corned beef is made from brisket, plate, rump, and chuck, preferably of the fat, well-finished type. Dried beef is made from the rounds after they are divided into inside and outside portions.

CANNING of meat dates from the very beginning of canning itself. Nicholas Appert, the first successful canner, was awarded a prize in 1809 by the French Minister of the Interior for devising a method of preserving foods by heating in sealed containers. Appert's techniques were successful from a practical standpoint, but the scientific basis of his work was not understood until Louis Pasteur, in 1860, showed that decomposition is due primarily to the activities of bacteria and that successful canning depends on sterilization rather than on the exclusion of air from the container.

Today, we also recognize the importance of enzyme inactivation by heat in preventing the deteriorative changes. That food sterilized in cans will keep for long periods is now well-established, although chemical changes may make it inedible in time. Corned

beef in cans brought back from an Arctic depot after 86 years was still edible, and roast veal packed for the explorer Sir William Parry in 1824 was in good condition when it was taken from the can in 1937. From that veal, three strains of sporeforming bacilli were isolated which had evidently remained viable for more than a century.

Canning has become an important part of our food industry. In 1948, more than 1,121 million pounds of meat and meat products were canned in federally inspected establishments, and about 77 million pounds of canned meat products were imported from other countries. Besides those products, more than 277 million pounds of canned dog food was produced in federally certified establishments in the same period, and about 170 million pounds of dog food was canned in noncertified plants.

THE MAIN STEPS in preserving meat by canning are precooking, filling, exhausting, processing, and cooling. Most meat products are given a definite cooking treatment that expels air from the mass of food, improves the physical consistency, makes filling easier, and reduces the bacterial load on later processing. The precooked food is packed in cans or jars by machinery or hand. A vacuum is produced in the can by sealing it while hot, or, more generally, by sealing it in an evacuated chamber. Evacuation of air relieves stress on the container during processing, helps to prevent discoloration and chemical deterioration of the product, and prevents "flippers" (slightly bulged ends) at high altitudes. The consumer has learned to expect concave ends on evacuated cans and immediately suspects as spoiled any that have bulged ends. As soon after filling as possible, the cans are processed by heat—usually in a closed retort under steam pressure or in hot water. The cans are cooled rapidly at the end of the processing period. Rapid cooling to temperatures below 105° F. is important in preventing spoilage by thermophilic bacteria that may not have been killed during processing and would grow at high temperatures during slow cooling.

Processing, the most important of these stages, destroys or inactivates the bacteria, which otherwise would quickly spoil the product. When processing results in a product containing no viable bacteria (that is, one that is sterile in the usual bacteriological sense), it is said to have absolute sterility. Canned products from which viable organisms can be recovered, but in which they do not develop to cause spoilage, are said to have commercial sterility. Most canned meat products are commercially sterile.

In determining the length of time and the temperature for the processing of cans, consideration must be given to the thermal resistance of the micro-organisms likely to be present and the rate at which heat will penetrate the food in the can. That is done by determining, in the laboratory, the thermal death times of the test organisms (the time required to kill the organisms at various temperatures). For the purpose, bacteriologists have chosen a number of organisms that can be conveniently handled, spoil foods, and have greater resistance to death by heating (thermal resistance) than does *Clostridium botulinum*. *C. botulinum* is a sporeforming bacillus that grows in the absence of air and produces a toxin which, if eaten, causes botulism.

The thermal death times of the test organisms are compared with heat-penetration data obtained by heating small cans of the food under consideration in which thermocouples (electrical temperature-measuring devices) have been inserted. From the results the proper processing time and temperature for cans of any size of a particular product can be assigned. Most meat products, however, are quite dense; they contain little water compared to the average fruit or vegetable pack; and heat penetration is slow. If cans, particularly of the larger sizes, were heated long enough to kill all bacteria in the center of the pack, the resulting product would be greatly overcooked and of poor quality. Fortunately, canned meat products which have only commercial sterility were cured first and contain enough sodium chloride, nitrates, and nitrites to inhibit the growth of many bacteria, especially such anaerobes as *C. botulinum*. The cans of meat that have not gone through a sterilizing process are marked, so as to warn handlers to keep them refrigerated—a highly important precaution.

A peculiarity of canned meats is that the fat seems to protect certain bacteria from thermal destruction. Thus, cocci, which are not sporeformers and are not particularly heat-resistant in water suspensions, are found generally in commercially sterile canned meats. Thermophilic sporeformers are found, of course, but they are not a source of trouble to the canner unless the cans are not promptly cooled following processing.

Aerobic sporeformers, such as *Bacillus subtilis*, cause swelling of canned spiced ham and luncheon meats because of their peculiar ability to produce gas from a substrate composed of cured meat, sugar, and nitrates. Here again, such cans must be stored under refrigeration if they are to be kept without spoiling.

Anaerobic sporeforming bacteria have also been isolated from canned meat, but L. B. Jensen, of Swift and Company, states that in more than 20 years of control work on canned meats no strain of *C. botulinum* has been isolated. It is a fact also that there have been no cases of botulism in this country in recent years that have been caused by commercially canned food. As we have indicated, that is because of the combined activity of curing ingredients and heat processing.

MEAT WAS dehydrated during the Second World War to save refrigeration facilities and tin-plate cans. Dehydrated meat, a concentrated protein material, is nutritious, palatable, and easily stored for months at ordinary atmospheric temperatures.

The Department of Agriculture studied various methods of drying meat during the war years. The aim was to determine the best methods of dehydration with equipment available to large meat processors, the best packaging materials, the quality and nutritive value of dehydrated meats, bacterial and microbial content, storage temperatures and periods, and preparation of the meat for use.

Six types of driers or methods of dehydration were used—vacuum rotary drier, plate vacuum drier, cabinet drier, air rotary drier, air flotation drier, and a method involving freezing followed by drying in a cabinet drier.

The general procedure was to bone and trim the raw meat of excess fat; grind it and precook between heated double drums, in steam-jacketed kettles or in pressure cookers; regrind it and dry in any of the dehydrators; compress to a density of about 1, which results in a weight per cubic foot equaling that of water; and, finally, hermetically seal it in tin cans, with or without air or inert gas.

The vacuum rotary drier produced meat dried to below 10 percent moisture in from 4 to 6 hours, with a minimum of contact with oxygen. The final product was good.

The plate vacuum drier at low drying temperature required too long a drying period to be practical.

The cabinet drier, in which hot air moved through the trays of meat, produced a fairly good product in 6 to 8 hours.

The air rotary drier, heated either by steam tubes or finned radiator heaters, produced a fair dried meat of limited storage life.

The air flotation drier produced a fair grade of meat, but, like the air rotary drier, subjected the meat to excessive oxidation.

The freezing-cabinet-drier method produced an excellent dried raw meat, but, because no enzyme inactivation had occurred, it was necessary for the moisture content to be reduced to below 0.5 percent. With moisture content much above 0.5 percent, the storage life was short at temperatures over 80° F. In this method, fresh meat was boned, trimmed of excess fat, cut into 2-inch cubes, and frozen at 0°. Frozen meat was ground through a ¼-inch plate onto screen trays. The result was a porous frozen meat. Air at 120° was forced through the meat in a cabinet-type drier, and after about 5 hours the moisture had been reduced to 3 to 4 percent. When reconstituted and heated, meat so produced looked and tasted like fresh meat.

Raw pork that contained 65.3 percent water, 18.8 percent protein, 15 percent fat, and 0.9 percent ash, upon dehydration to 10 percent moisture, would contain 48.7 percent protein, 39 percent fat, and 2.3 percent ash.

From the microbiological standpoint, meat was wholesome after dehydration to below 10 percent moisture. Even under favorable temperature conditions, *C. botulinum* did not produce toxin in properly dehydrated meat. If the relative humidity of the storage room was reasonably low, no mold growth occurred unless the moisture content of the meat was 15 percent or higher.

Determinations were made of the breakdown of fat, protein, and vitamins, during both processing and later storage. Oxidative rancidity of hermetically sealed compressed dehydrated meat was of minor consequence, even over extended storage periods, at 100° F. The addition of 0.07 percent gum guaiac, however, extended fat stability 12 times its normal life. After storage at 110° for a month, the meat was rusty red and had a nutty flavor, which changed to a burnt flavor during further extended storage periods. At temperatures between 70° and 80°, after storage periods of 12 to 18 months, the meat remained in satisfactory condition, if packed to a density of 1 in hermetically sealed containers.

The biological value of fat and of protein remained practically unchanged during processing and storage. Niacin and riboflavin losses ranged from 15 to 30 percent during processing; a little more was lost during storage. Thiamine losses during processing were about 50 percent, with a further loss up to 64 percent after storage at 70° F. for 36 weeks and total loss after storage at 100° for 36 weeks.

During the war, one of our largest packers produced millions of pounds of dehydrated meat by the air rotary drier. Another produced great quantities of dried meat by large dry melters or, in effect, vacuum rotary driers. Still another packer produced an excellent dried corned-beef hash, using a moving conveyor through a heated tunnel, which in principle was the same as the cabinet drier. All commercially dried meats were hermetically sealed in tin cans at a density of approximately 1, and they remained in acceptable condition after many months of storage.

Several producers of high-vacuum drying equipment produced pilot-plant-size samples of raw dehydrated beef and pork. The products were excellent and, with moisture content below 1 percent, stored satisfactorily for many months at 70° F. or lower. The major drawback to large-scale production was the high cost of producing this type of meat.

Meat dehydration on a commercial scale proved successful because the product saved shipping space, was a concentrated source of protein of high biological value, had fair to good palatability, and could be easily stored for long periods at fairly high temperatures.

We believe that future research on meat dehydration will be concerned with production of raw dried meat of low moisture content, in which the quality of protein will be maintained at a maximum.

To repeat: The basic principles of preserving meat have been known for a good many years. Micro-organisms and enzymes, chiefly responsible for the spoilage of meat, are inactivated by the effects of low temperature, salt and nitrate, heat, and dehydration.

Methods of processing and quality and stability have been improved by the use of supplementary treatments, which control other factors, such as oxidation and moisture content, but no fundamental changes have been made in the ways micro-organisms and enzymes are held in check.

Future research may point the way to better and more effective methods of preservation. Many chemical agents can inhibit enzymes and micro-organisms, but none is known which satisfies the requirements for a safe, mild, and efficient meat preservative. Knowledge now being accumulated about antibiotics may have useful applications.

Substances that have antienzymatic properties have been isolated from natural materials.

The bactericidal effect of certain wave lengths of ultraviolet light is well known. Moreover, it has been found that high-voltage X-rays and radio waves of certain frequencies inhibit some enzymes and micro-organisms.

High-voltage electron streams, or cathode rays, apparently are effective, and such treatment is said to be capable of preserving raw meat at ordinary temperatures for 6 to 12 months.

Atomic fission could lead to the discovery of useful preservation tools.

Sonic and ultrasonic vibrations are believed to have bactericidal action.

These developments give promise of new methods for preserving meat.

O. G. HANKINS *is in charge of meat research for the animal husbandry division of the Bureau of Animal Industry. His training was obtained at the University of Illinois and George Washington University. He has served in his present position since 1932. Previous professional experience was had at the Louisiana Polytechnic Institute, University of Kentucky, and in the Bureau of Animal Industry.*

R. L. HINER *is an animal husband-man in the same division. He has been engaged in research on meats since joining the Department in 1929. He is a graduate of Iowa State College and George Washington University.*

W. L. SULZBACHER *is a bacteriologist in meat research, also in the Bureau of Animal Industry. He holds degrees from the University of Pittsburgh, where he served on the faculty from 1936 to* 1938. *Later he worked in a consulting laboratory as a food bacteriologist and in the Navy Department, from which he transferred to his present position in 1945.*

A. M. GADDIS *is a biochemist in meat research in the animal husbandry division of the Bureau of Animal Industry. He is a graduate of Duke University and has been employed in the Department of Agriculture since 1936.*

SOME WASTES are normally so dilute that it is not feasible to attempt to recover byproducts from them. One of the most troublesome is milk waste from dairies, which is becoming a serious stream-pollution problem in many sections. The waste comes chiefly from the washing of milk cans, bottles, and dairy equipment. Most dairies expect to lose as waste about 1 percent of the milk they handle.

Milk itself is about 90 percent water, and in the highly dilute milk waste the content of dry milk solids is only about 0.1 percent. Despite its highly dilute nature, however, milk waste has about 10 times the B. O. D. (biochemical oxygen demand) of ordinary sewage. In other words, its ability to pollute streams is 10 times that of ordinary sewage and, generally speaking, it is 10 times as difficult to dispose of.

Micro-organisms thrive on milk. For that reason, milk wastes are toxic in streams. Milk-fed microbes multiply rapidly and consume the dissolved oxygen in the streams. The fish and other marine life die and the stream becomes putrid.

Our research has led to the development of a mixed culture of micro-organisms that can convert the soluble sugar and protein of milk waste by aerobic fermentation to insoluble yeast cells. The yeast—which may have some use as fertilizer—can then be readily separated from the effluent by centrifuging. The method materially reduces the oxygen demand of milk wastes and makes them relatively easy to dispose of as sewage. The yeast organisms remove the lactose and soluble protein rapidly and almost completely from the solution to produce cell tissue. About half the organic matter is oxidized to carbon dioxide and water to gain energy for this synthesis, and all but 2 or 3 percent of the remaining solids is converted into yeast.

The process has worked well in laboratory-scale operations. Tests were started in 1950 on a large commercial scale in a Connecticut plant.—G. E. Hilbert, *Bureau of Agricultural and Industrial Chemistry.*

Meat Fats of Better Quality

Waldo C. Ault,
Roy W. Riemenschneider,
Steward G. Morris

The edible meat fats, lard and tallow, are almost completely digestible. They are high-energy foods and contain substances necessary for good nutrition. They also are of great economic importance. Our lard production alone amounts to 2½ billion pounds a year—approximately equal to the combined production of soybean and cottonseed oils.

It seems strange, therefore, that they have received so little attention. Probably that is because they are by-products of the meat-packing industry, or because we regard the rapid expansion in the production of soybean oil as more exciting. Be that as it may, the factors that affect the quality and acceptance of these fats deserve careful consideration.

The properties open to improvement are keeping quality, or stability, physical characteristics—such as plastic range, consistency, and the creaming power—odor, flavor, color, and smoke point (temperature at which a fat or oil begins to smoke).

Stability is the main one. Without better keeping quality, the application of other techniques would have little value, because the best shortening is unfit for use if it has a strong odor or flavor—if it is rancid. The chief causes are atmospheric oxidation, absorption of odors, and the action of enzymes and micro-organisms. Rancidity that is caused by atmospheric oxidation and gives a characteristic pungent odor is responsible for most of the economic losses of fats and fatty foods.

Oxidative rancidity in lard is particularly serious. Moreover, most processing that is undertaken to improve other properties (such as odor and color) tends to reduce the stability of fats. It has been difficult, therefore, to apply the various processing techniques to lard.

Before satisfactory progress could be made in understanding oxidative rancidity and in producing fats of satisfactory stability, methods for predicting stability and evaluating antioxidants were necessary. Reasonably effective methods for accomplishing those ends are available, but because of the many factors involved none of them gives perfectly clear-cut results.

The methods most widely used are the active-oxygen method, frequently referred to as the Swift stability test; oxygen-absorption measurements; incubation tests; and baking tests.

The active-oxygen method involves bubbling purified air or oxygen through the melted fat under standardized conditions, usually at 210° F. The time in hours required to develop rancid odor or a peroxide content indicative of rancidity is noted. To an experienced technologist, this time is of value as a basis for comparison in predicting the life of a fat or in estimating the worth of an antioxidant that may have been added to the fat under test.

By use of suitable equipment, the time a sample of fat requires to reach a level of oxygen uptake preestablished as the rancid point may be determined under standardized and comparable conditions. In this instance also, the time is of value in predicting the storage life of a fat or in estimating the merit of an antioxidant. Workers at the Eastern Regional Research Laboratory reported that results obtained by the method usually lead to the same conclusions as those of the active-oxygen method, but because of manipulation difficulties it is not so generally used.

Keeping quality may also be determined by merely incubating samples of fat in open beakers or jars in an oven at a temperature usually of 145° F., although occasionally higher temperatures are used. A comparison of the time required for rancidity to develop in each sample is a measure of their stability. The rancid point may be detected by sense of smell or by chemical determination of peroxide content.

When an effective antioxidant is added to a fat, the keeping time of the fat before development of rancidity may be increased fivefold to tenfold. The test methods we have described provide an approximate measure of the increase in stability of the fat.

However, only a few of the antioxidants that are capable of protecting the bulk fat will continue to stabilize the fat after it has been used in baked products. In other words, most antioxidants do not have "carry over" into baked goods. Consequently, standardized baking tests have become necessary in evaluating antioxidants for edible fats. In such baking tests, the fat (with or without added antioxidant) is baked in a pastry or cracker recipe and the stability of the products is noted. The methods for determining the stability of fats can also be used in studies aimed at minimizing destruction of the natural antioxidants in fats during processing.

The meat fats have a much lower content of the more effective natural antioxidants than do most vegetable fats. The naturally occurring antioxidants include lecithin, or cephalinlike substances, and tocopherols. Many investigators believe that tocopherols, the effective antioxidant of most vegetable oils, are also present in traces in lard if they are not destroyed by processing. Rather extensive experiments at the University of Minnesota offer little hope for increasing the oxidative stability of the meat fats by feeding an antioxidant substance to an animal before slaughter. The investigators reported that of a wide variety fed, tocopherol was the only antioxidant deposited in the adipose tissue to a significant extent.

In attempting to produce a meat fat of good stability, it is therefore important to conduct the processing operations in such a manner as to minimize destruction of any antioxidant substances present. That means the avoidance of unnecessary exposure of the fat to light, air, or high temperatures. The fat must not be held at high temperatures while exposed to air for long periods. It is also important to keep metal contamination as low as possible. Some metals, in the form of their salts or oxides, are known to have a pro-oxidant effect; that is, they reduce the stability of fats markedly. That is particularly true of iron and copper. In fact, copper is such a powerful pro-oxidant that its addition to the extent of a few tenths of one part per million makes lard rancid in about 20 minutes at temperatures of boiling water.

Copper or copper-bearing alloys, therefore, should not come into contact with the fat during the handling and rendering processes. It is hardly possible to eliminate all iron from the equipment, but elimination of rust, especially following shut-down periods, helps. Increased stability can be obtained by equipping the processing and rendering departments with aluminum, stainless-steel, and glass- or plastic-lined tanks, pipes, and pumps.

A process for removing contaminating metals from fats has been described. The fat is treated with tannic acid and subsequently filtered. The filtration apparently removes the metals and the excess tannic acid.

If metal contamination is not too great, the metal may be deactivated by adding a compound that unites with the metallic ion. Such bound metal has no pro-oxidant properties. Citric acid, esters of phosphoric acid, ascorbic acid, and esters of ascorbic acid and isoascorbic acids are examples of edible compounds that are metal deactivators in fats.

The use of such precautions during processing will result in the production of meat fats with increased stability. The low content of natural antioxidant substances, however, probably precludes the preparation of meat fats that have stabilities such as are usually found in the hydrogenated vegetable-oil shortenings unless some substance that will delay oxidative degradation is added. Besides the natural antioxidants, synthetic compounds that will do this are known. Such substances generally contain or consist of compounds having quinol, phenol, amino, or sulfide groupings.

The mechanism by which antioxidants perform their function is still not clear, but an effective antioxidant is always capable of being oxidized in the medium and under the conditions found in the oxidizing substrate. Usually the antioxidant will be nearly gone before peroxides develop in appreciable amounts and before rancidity can be observed.

A large number of compounds bring about a marked enhancement of the stability when they are added to fats that contain phenolic antioxidants. They are ineffective, however, in substrates devoid of natural or added phenolic antioxidants. The compounds are generally referred to as antioxidant synergists, or simply synergists. The substances most frequently considered acceptable synergists for edible purposes are those already enumerated as effective metal deactivators, such as citric acid and ascorbic acid. On that basis, it would seem that synergistic action could be explained as merely metal deactivation. In many instances, that is undoubtedly true. This single mechanism cannot explain the complete role of synergists, however, for some compounds are known to exert synergistic effect with antioxidants, even when no metals are in the fat.

Synergistic compounds are relatively less expensive than most of the antioxidants. Therefore, their use usually results in important economies. Consequently, most of the lard on the market today that has improved stability contains synergistic antioxidant mixtures.

An ideal antioxidant for use in foods should have the following qualifications:

Effective stabilizing action under conditions of use.

No harmful physiological effect, even in quantities considerably greater than those likely to be used and even when ingested over long periods of time.

At least sufficient solubility in fats to facilitate its use; greater solubility is usually advantageous.

Freedom from objectionable odor, color, or flavor even after storage.

Stability to whatever processing is necessary after it is incorporated in the fat.

Protective action which carries over into baked goods.

Economy in use and availability in amounts needed.

Despite this list of requirements, several substances have been declared acceptable as antioxidants for use in lard in federally inspected plants subject to provisions governing the concentration and statements on the label. The substances include gum guaiac, tocopherol concentrates that contain at least 30 percent tocopherol, nordihydroguaiaretic acid (NDGA), propyl gallate, butylated hydroxyanisole, thiodipropionic acid and lauryl thiodipropionate, corn oil, lecithin, citric acid, and phosphoric acid. The last three are generally considered to have their greatest value when used as synergists. If not already, certainly in the near future, satisfactory antioxidants will be available at low cost. In fact, the cost of some already approved permits significant improvements in stability at a cost of 10 cents or less for 100 pounds of lard.

An inexpensive and simple process for improving the keeping quality of home-rendered lard has been developed at the Eastern Regional Research Laboratory. The process, which is nothing more than the addition of about 5 percent of a hydrogenated vegetable shortening, owes its success to the high content of tocopherols in most vegetable oils. The period during which the lard will remain free from rancidity is nearly doubled. Hydrogenated vegetable shortening can be bought in any grocery.

The addition of antioxidants to lard must not be considered as a cure for all the ills of the industry.

THE USE OF BETTER PACKAGING offers great possibilities for improving the keeping quality and increasing acceptance by those who use this important commodity. A large percentage of the lard sold on the retail market now is packaged in cardboard cartons, chiefly in the 1-pound size. The package permits ready passage of air to the contents. The paper used in the past to make the cartons and their liners often had absorbent properties and took up the liquid part of the lard, somewhat like a wick. Such wicking action separated the liquid part of the fat, which was most susceptible to rancidity, in a way that enormously increased its exposure to the deleterious action of air. More recently, lining papers have been developed which are much better in that respect. They are not very convenient, however, and many users do not like such packages. A completely satisfactory package certainly should be easy to open and close. Packages more acceptable to consumers can be made most readily from rigid, nonabsorbent materials, such as metal or glass. Such packages can be evacuated or flushed with inert gas and sealed and protect the contents better.

Suitable antioxidants for protection of the fat during processing as well as during subsequent storage make possible the application of technological processes for improving it in other ways. The processes can be used to modify the texture, creaming properties, and consistency and to eliminate odor, color, and free acidity.

A fat, such as lard or shortening, at a casual glance, looks like a soft, but more or less homogeneous, solid. But at ordinary temperatures it really consists of a suspension of solid fat particles in a liquid matrix. This physical condition is brought about by the presence of a large number of different glycerides, which have widely varying softening points, so that at any given temperature a part is solid but another part is liquid. The plasticity or workability of a fat depends somewhat on its relative proportions of liquid and solid.

Other factors, not so obvious, that influence the plasticity of a shortening include the size of the solid particles and their tendency to form aggregates—in that respect, the meat fats are quite unlike hydrogenated vegetable shortenings. Lard particularly has the peculiar property of solidifying in such a way that large crystals frequently are formed to give a grainy appearance. The housewife dislikes this; besides, it indicates a rather narrow temperature range of workability, which the commercial baker dislikes.

The lard producer chills the rendered fat as rapidly as possible by mechanical means so that the crystals will be small. Fine crystals extend the plastic range of the product, give it a smooth appearance, and make a product of the maximum degree of firmness. Lard and hydrogenated lard that have large crystals are affected by variations in temperature. Consequently, their plasticity in storage and commercial handling is unpredictable.

Chemical methods for modifying lard to eliminate or minimize graininess have been proposed. The methods are designed to alter the glyceride structure by modifying the characteristic manner in which the fatty acids are combined with glycerol to form the fat. This is accomplished by heating the fat in the presence of a small excess of glycerol or in the presence of a catalyst, such as sodium ethylate. Such glyceride modification or rearrangement tends to bring the consistency and melting point of fat to more definite and reproducible values. Such methods for modifying lard require suitable equipment and considerable scientific control.

Simpler methods are available, fortunately, for increasing the firmness of lard, but they may not offer all the advantages of the techniques we described. Lard stearine or hydrogenated lard is often added for the purpose. Lard stearine, the more solid portion of lard, is obtained as a byproduct during the manufacture of edible lard oil. Hydrogenated lard is made by the catalytic hydrogenation of lard and subsequent deodorization. Some experience is necessary to get the best results, because both of the agents frequently vary in their hardening powers, and the consistency of the lard changes from time to time.

A degree of firmness also can be got by a uniform blend of the fat of internal organs and the outer parts of the carcass, the cutting fat, which is less firm than the former.

Closely associated with the physical properties of a fat is its creaming power—meaning its ability to retain a large percentage of air incorporated in a dough or batter in which it is being used. The creaming power seems to be associated with the power of the fat to take up and form stable emulsions with water. Generally speaking, lard does not cream well. It lacks high emulsifying powers. Both properties may be substantially improved by limited hydrogenation of the lard or by the addition of a small percentage of hydrogenated lard. It is also possible to improve the creaming properties of fats by adding emulsifying agents, of which the monoglycerides are the outstanding example. Monoglycerides may be made from lard by reacting it with an excess of glycerol.

Several processes are available for reducing or eliminating undesirable color, odor, and free acidity. To prevent development of excessive color

and odor, the fat tissues must not come into contact with dirty and inedible parts of the carcass. Care must be taken to exclude blood, muscle tissue, detached skin, and large blood vessels from the rendering kettle. Prompt chilling of the tissue also will minimize the formation of free fatty acid, which results from enzymatic and hydrolytic action. Only prompt chilling and rendering of a fat will give products having the desirable low content of free fatty acid. Too much fatty acid causes a high smoke point.

Often the color of a lard can be improved by treating the fat with an adsorptive agent like carbon or bleaching clays. Such a refining treatment is combined with the rendering operation in the so-called drip-rendering process. In it, the fat is charged into a rendering tank with a false bottom, through which the lard drains away as soon as it separates from the tissues. In this way, the time of contact between hot fat and tissue is minimized. The melted fat is then mixed with carbon in the lower part of the tank.

Several new methods for rendering fatty tissues are undergoing evaluation and development. Special emphasis is being given to quick rendering and simultaneous removal of fat and water from the raw tissues without the long heating at high temperatures used in the older methods. Fine grinding of the fat tissues, use of proteolytic enzymes, dilute caustic solutions, centrifugation, and solvent extraction have been claimed by various investigators to facilitate the rendering. In general, lard made by these quick-rendering methods has somewhat greater stability, better color, and is more bland than lard made by the older procedures.

It is hardly to be expected that treatment with adsorbents or modifications of the rendering process will produce lard as free from odor and flavor as that obtained by vigorous steam deodorization under vacuum, which is the only commercial process now feasible for producing the bland products that the modern housewife apparently wants. Equipment is available for de-odorizing lard in either a batch or continuous manner. In general, the treatment consists in subjecting the hot fat to the action of steam under a high vacuum. The exact time varies from a few minutes to a few hours, depending on the type and efficiency of the equipment. Because the fatty acids are somewhat volatile under the conditions used in deodorization, a significant reduction in free fatty acids may be effected during the operation. This raises the smoke point to the highest possible level, a desirable quality in a fat used for frying.

Because lard has reasonably satisfactory properties, producers have tended to consider it a finished product. Lard, though, has been losing ground in the competitive race with hydrogenated vegetable shortenings, which once were substitutes but are now generally considered to be setting the pace. Recently lard has begun to receive more technological and scientific attention; the results are the marketing of improved products and satis-factory methods for use by the farmer in improving home-rendered lard.

WALDO C. AULT *was educated at Ohio State University. After 7 years of experience in industrial research, he joined the staff of the Northern Regional Research Laboratory and, later, the Eastern Regional Research Laboratory, where he now is head of the oil and fat division.*

ROY W. RIEMENSCHNEIDER *was trained at Illinois College, University of Illinois, and University of Maryland. He joined the Department of Agriculture in 1930. Since 1941 he has been in charge of the composition and quality section of the oil and fat division at the Eastern Laboratory.*

STEWARD G. MORRIS *entered the Department of Agriculture in 1936 and has been with the Eastern Laboratory since 1940. He has been engaged in synthesizing new antioxidants and in testing antioxidants and metal-deactivating compounds in lard. He has a doctor's degree from Columbia University.*

WHOLE EGG is about 73 percent water. The solid material is principally protein and fat. The solids, which are responsible for the unique properties of eggs, are approximately 50 percent protein, 40 percent fat, and 10 percent other substances, including dextrose, salts, and carotenoids.

Egg white contributes about 32 percent of the whole-egg solids and about 60 percent of the egg protein. Its solids are mainly proteins, eight of which have been identified and six of which have been isolated and characterized. The proteins and their approximate percentages of egg-white solids are: Ovalbumin, 50–60; ovomucoid, 10–12; conalbumin, 10–12; ovomucin, 2.5; lysozyme, 2.5; and avidin, 0.1.

Egg yolk contributes about 68 percent of the whole-egg solids and nearly all of the fat. Its solids consist of more than 50 percent uncombined fat and about 37 percent proteins. Part of these proteins are combined with fats (lipoproteins).

A dozen medium eggs (about 1.4 pounds) are approximately equivalent in protein value to 1 pound of beef and in fat value to 0.2 pound of butter or margarine. On an equal-weight basis, eggs are equivalent to beef as a source of thiamine (vitamin B_1) and iron, and are twice as good a source of riboflavin (vitamin B_2). They are about one-third as good a source of vitamin A as butter. Beef contains no vitamin A; eggs contain no vitamin C. In nutritional value, the egg is second only to milk.—*Hans Lineweaver and Robert E. Feeney, Western Regional Research Laboratory.*

MILK: FOOD FOR ALL

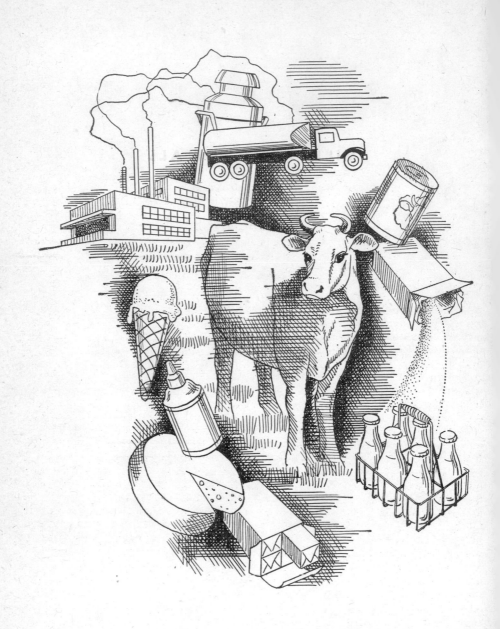

Use of Milk in Manufactured Foods

B. H. Webb

Of the 120 billion pounds of milk produced annually in recent years, about 22.5 billion pounds, or 19 percent, went into manufactured products, as concentrated and dried whole and skim milk, buttermilk, and whey. Approximately 20 percent of the manufactured milk concentrates were used in processed foods, which are considered in this chapter.

High-quality foods can be produced only from high-quality ingredients. Milk and many of its products are extremely perishable and require careful handling and refrigerated storage. Sweet-cream buttermilk is just as satisfactory as skim milk for food manufacture. But buttermilk now churned in great quantities from neutralized sour cream is not suitable for human food. Whey, byproduct of cheese manufacture and quick to spoil, still contains half the solids of milk. It should be processed as soon as it is drained from the cheese curd. Buttermilk and whey, now largely animal food because of their low quality and limited uses in human food, serve as a reserve supply of milk solids, which, if improved in quality, could be made available to the food manufacturer.

The concentration of milk solids in manufactured foods varies from a trace to about 25 percent of the weight of the product. Good-quality bread contains the solids of milk and skim milk to the extent of 2 to 6 percent of the weight of the flour. Milk bread is made with fluid milk, or its equivalent in concentrated or dried milk, and should contain about 6 percent whole-milk solids, based on flour weight. Richer bread can be made with 12 percent of milk solids.

Cakes, cookies, and prepared mixes contain 5 to 15 percent of the flour weight as milk solids. Three and one-half percent nonfat milk solids may be used in sausage; margarine contains less than 1 percent. Top-quality fudge and caramel contain 10 to 25 percent of whole-milk solids, equally divided between the fat and nonfat. Inferior grades of these candies contain no milk fat and as little as 5 percent milk-solids-not-fat. The minimum requirement for milk chocolate is 12 percent whole-milk solids. Canned foods, such as cream-style soup, with 3 to 5 percent, and children's puddings and custards, with 6 to 12 percent milk solids, customarily utilize all the constituents of milk. Whey solids can be substituted for equal quantities of skim-milk solids in most foods, but such a substitution may result in a product of inferior quality. Small quantities of whey and whey protein have also been used to a limited extent to aid in incorporating air and in stabilizing the fat emulsion of salad dressings.

Utilization of milk in manufactured foods improves nutritive value, flavor, color, and body and texture, or physical structure. The contribution of milk to better human nutrition is well known. Milk contains most of the essential

Milk and milk products—production and utilization in manufactured foods

Product	Production		Utilization by [1]—			
			Baking industry		Confectionery industry	
	Product	Fluid equivalent	Product	Fluid equivalent	Product	Fluid equivalent
	Million pounds	Million pounds	Million pounds	Million pounds	Million pounds	Million pounds
Concentrated milks:						
Plain condensed whole...........	175	367	13.40	28.14	5.567	11.681
Plain condensed skim............	402	1,206	110.00	330.00	12.438	37.314
Sweetened condensed whole......	247	544	21.80	46.96	40.699	89.538
Sweetened condensed skim.......	543	1,629	183.00	549.00	38.110	114.330
Evaporated whole..............	3,208	6,737	6.00	12.60	....	....
Dried milks:						
Whole........................	165	1,319	5.50	44.00	13.211	105.688
Skim.........................	678	7,701	214.00	2,182.80	11.908	121.462
Buttermilk	45	500	1.51	16.60	....	....
Whey.........................	156	2,521	....	....	....	....
Fluid milks:						
Whole........................	119,300	119,300	11.00	11.00	3.972	3.972
Skim.........................	48,438	48,438	16.00	16.00	....	....
Buttermilk...................	1,862	1,862	....	....	....	....
Whey.........................	12,293	12,293	....	....	....	....
Form not classified.............	....	....	....	....	15.613	....

[1] Exclusive of cream and butter.

Data based on estimates of production, Bureau of Agricultural Economics; estimates of baking utilization furnished by a milk industry executive; and estimates of confectionery utilization furnished by United States Department of Commerce. Figures are for 1947, an average postwar year.

dietary factors in about the proportions needed in food. But the phrase "high nutritive value" has little sales appeal. Large-scale utilization of milk in food must depend upon the constructive contributions it can make to flavor, color, and structural improvement in the finished product.

The consumer selects many milk-containing foods for their flavor. The appraisal of flavor varies with the individual, and the food manufacturer must please as many customers as possible.

Fat is the most powerful flavor-producing constituent of milk, and its presence in a food imparts richness and promotes high consumer acceptance. The fat and solids-not-fat of milk have not been evaluated with respect to their flavor-producing ability, but their relative market values probably reflect their flavoring potency.

More liberal use of milk fat is hampered by its price, usually several times that of the solids-not-fat fraction. Fortunately, the relatively low cost of skim milk makes its extensive utilization in manufactured foods feasible. In decreasing order, cream, whole milk, buttermilk, skim milk, and whey products improve the flavor of foods to which they are added.

Good flavor is closely associated with the quality that comes with a Grade A milk supply. The fine flavor and aroma of fresh milk are lost with age, and are then replaced by the off-odors and off-flavors that arise from oxidation and growth of bacteria.

The kind of processing given a milk product determines the flavor it will retain and transfer to manufactured foods. The highest milk-flavor transfer is given by Grade A fluid milk and cream. However, the low concentration of milk constituents in the fluid products and their perishable nature limit their utilization in food manufacture. In the decreasing order of milk-flavor transfer are plain and sweetened condensed milk, evaporated milk, and dried milk.

The color of a food to which milk has been added is intensified by heat. A brown color develops when milk protein and milk sugar are heated together during food processing. The reaction rate rises with increases in the time and temperature of heating. The golden-brown color of bread crust and of toast made from bread containing milk is more attractive than the paler color of water bread. Milk ingredients are partly responsible for the brown color of caramel and of fudge. But excessive browning becomes a defect when milk-containing foods are held long in storage. This may produce brown sweetened condensed milk, discolored dried-milk, or darkened evaporated milk.

FOODS OF GOOD PHYSICAL STRUCTURE are demanded and accepted by the consumer as a matter of course. Years of laboratory and pilot-plant experience were required to produce the fine body, texture, and viscosity that spell high quality in finished foods. The ingredients of milk markedly affect the structure of the foods to which they are added. Milk fat contributes to softness, mellowness, or pliability of body. Milk protein is highly hydrated—that is, it absorbs and holds water, thus helping to bind the food ingredients together. Milk sugar (lactose) in low concentrations forms a continuous sirupy phase, as does sucrose. But when the concentration of lactose exceeds the amount that will dissolve in the aqueous phase of the food (17 percent at room temperature), it crystallizes, imparting a short grainy or sandy texture to the product. The effect of the milk salts on the physical structure of a food is obscure. They may influence structure through their effect on the condition of the milk protein. This is particularly

true of the calcium and phosphorus of milk, for casein apparently exists in milk as a calcium caseinate-calcium phosphate complex. Factors that control the water-binding capacity of this complex are not known.

The manufactured foods are carefully processed to prevent loss of milk flavor and to produce a pleasing physical structure. In the usual sponge method of making bread, 60 percent of the flour is mixed with the water, yeast, and yeast food, to form the sponge; this is held for fermentation 4 to 5 hours. The remaining 40 percent of flour, together with shortening, salt, sugar, milk, and other constituents, are then added, and the completely mixed dough is fermented 30 to 45 minutes longer. Next, the dough is molded, proofed (allowed to stand) approximately 60 minutes, and finally baked 25 minutes at 450° to 470° F. When milk is used in the dough, there is more tolerance in the fermentation time, and the dough will hold more water. Milk improves crust tenderness, color, flavor, texture of the crumb, and the loaf volume. It also promotes retention of moisture, thus prolonging the shelf life of the bread.

Cake batter may be prepared by a variety of methods of blending sugar, shortening, eggs, flour, and milk. Dried milk should always be reconstituted with water, but fluid forms of milk may be used directly in cake production. The cake batter is weighed out and baked 20 to 27 minutes at 350° to 375° F. Milk improves flavor, volume, and firmness of structure in cakes and cookies. Soft, tender, even crumbly cakes result when the milk in the batter is replaced by whey.

Prepared mixes for muffins, biscuits, cake, gingerbread, and various kinds of puddings contain dried-milk products. Pudding mixes usually contain dried skim milk. Prepared mixes were made possible by improvements in the keeping quality of shortening. Some of the shortening for dried mix is prepared by coating each fat particle with an envelope of milk or whey solids.

The spray-dried, coated shortening globule is free flowing and well suited for the new dried mixes.

Candy ingredients are mixed and boiled, caramel to about 246° F. and fudge to 250° F. The milk products are usually added toward the end of the boiling process to preserve flavor and lessen the tendency of the milk protein to form a hard, granular coagulum. Sugar fondant is added to the fudge mixture to aid in graining it. Lactose, highly concentrated in whey, crystallizes in whey fudge to aid in giving the candy the proper grainy texture. Milk protein and milk fat impart a smooth, chewy body to caramels.

Canned soups and children's custards and puddings are compounded and precooked, then canned and sterilized at about 242° F. for 15 to 45 minutes. The lowest heat treatment that will insure sterility is used to minimize the development of a cooked flavor. Protein coagulation in the sterilizer cannot be prevented because destabilizing materials, such as salt, sugar, starch, vegetable pulp, and natural fruit and vegetable acids, must be present. A stabilizer, usually 2 percent corn or wheat starch, furnishes numerous starch granules that act as nuclei around which the milk protein can coagulate. A smooth, gellike structure is thus obtained. In the absence of the water-absorbing starch stabilizer, lumpy casein curd and fluid whey would form during heating.

Highly acid sterilized mixtures, like tomato soup, can be more easily prepared from whey than from milk. Whey contains less protein than milk and whey protein coagulates in a finely dispersed form scarcely distinguishable in physical condition from the tomato pulp.

Nonfat dried-milk solids are added to sausage to absorb moisture and improve body and nutritive value. Margarine is manufactured by making an emulsion from skim milk and vegetable fat and subsequently churning out or crystallizing the fat.

The utilization of milk in manufactured foods is increasing. Improved processing methods make possible specialized milk products designed to stimulate the manufacture of new and improved foods. The trend is away from home food preparation and toward furnishing the homemaker with premixed and even ready-to-serve dishes.

B. H. WEBB *is a principal dairy manufacturing technologist in the division of Dairy Products Research Laboratories of the Bureau of Dairy Industry. He has been engaged in research and development work on the concentrated milks and on the utilization of milk products in human foods since 1926.*

LACTIC ACID derives its name from the fact that it is the primary acid constituent of sour milk. (The Latin word for milk, *lac, lactis,* gives us the root *lac,* for terms like *lactation, lactic, lac-*.) Known chemically as α-hydroxypropionic acid, it is a member of the class of naturally occurring hydroxy acids, which includes citric, tartaric, and malic acids. It occurs in the blood and muscle tissue of animals, yeast fermentation, sauerkraut, pickles, beer, buttermilk, and cheese.

Lactic acid is used commercially as a food acidulant and for nonfood purposes, such as deliming and plumping hides in the leather-tanning industry. More than 8 million pounds of lactic acid was produced in this country in 1945; its commercial value approximated 2 million dollars.—*Charles F. Woodward, Eastern Regional Research Laboratory.*

Cheese, Butter,

Ice Cream,

Sherbet

George P. Sanders,
Donald H. Williams

Of an annual production of about 120 billion pounds of milk on farms in the United States, about 54 billion pounds, or slightly more than 45 percent, is utilized in the production of four kinds of dairy-product foods—cheese, butter (including farm-made butter), ice cream, and sherbet.

THE PRINCIPAL TYPES of cheese manufactured, with approximate production in million pounds in 1949, are: American cheese (including Cheddar) from whole milk, 935; Swiss, 81; cream cheese, 54; Italian varieties, 55; brick and Munster, 30; blue mold, 8; Limburger, 7; Neufchatel, 4; and other types, 24. The total cheese production, exclusive of cottage cheese, in 1949 was about 1,200 million pounds. About 9.5 percent of the total milk supply is used in manufacturing these types of cheese.

In addition, approximately 280 million pounds of cottage cheese curd is produced annually, in the manufacture of which approximately 1,770 million pounds of skim milk, equal to nearly 1.5 percent of the total milk supply, is utilized. A large proportion of the curd is used in manufacturing annually some 287 million pounds of creamed cottage cheese. It is estimated that 15.5 million pounds of butterfat, in the form of 78 million pounds of cream testing about 20 percent fat, is utilized in manufacturing this quantity of cottage cheese, including the fat in creamed cottage cheese and the small percentage in cottage cheese curd.

Milk for the manufacture of cheese is placed promptly in milk cans and cooled, usually in a tank in cold, running water or by running it over a cooler. It is delivered early in the morning, while still sweet, to the cheese factory. There it is graded and weighed, inferior lots are rejected, samples are taken for butterfat content and frequently for quality tests, and then it is pumped or flows to a receiving tank.

For most kinds of cheese, including Cheddar, the milk should be pasteurized—heated to 161° F., or slightly higher for at least 15 seconds, or to at least 143° for not less than 30 minutes, and then cooled. Pasteurization improves the average grade of cheese and makes it more uniform in quality and composition, as research by this Department has demonstrated, and also kills any harmful or undesirable micro-organisms that might be present.

Standards of identity for various kinds of cheese, applying to cheese in interstate commerce, have been issued by the Federal Food and Drug Administration. Among other requirements, the standards specify that the milk and cream used in making cottage, pot, baker's, and cream cheeses—the so-called soft, unripened types—is to be pasteurized. For most of the various ripened cheeses, the standards specify that if the milk is not pasteurized the cheese is to be cured for a stated length of time. For example, Cheddar cheese made from raw milk is cured for not less than 60 days at a temperature not less than 35° F. Many of the States have similar regulations. The pasteurization requirements were adopted as a safeguard to prevent the possible transmission of disease-producing micro-organisms to humans. Some kinds of cheese, such as Swiss, are not yet being made generally from pasteurized milk; hence for these a definite curing period is required, which in most cases is little or not longer than the curing period customarily used.

A so-called phosphatase test, which is used to detect underpasteurization or the presence of raw milk in pasteurized milk, cheese, and other dairy products, has been developed in the division of Dairy Products Research Laboratories of the Department (Sanders-Sager test). The test has been adopted as an official method for use in enforcement of the pasteurization requirements.

The milk for Swiss cheese is always clarified—that is, it is run through a high-speed centrifugal clarifier, which removes dust and other particles and greatly improves the eye formation.

The milk then is pumped through a pipe to the cheese vat or kettle. Most vats are rectangular, and Cheddar vats may each hold as much as 10,000 pounds of milk. Swiss cheese is made in round copper kettles holding as much as 3,000 pounds. The vat or kettle is made with a steam jacket for heating the milk. Milk for some kinds of cheese may be standardized; that is, a small proportion of the fat is removed as cream to adjust the composition of the cheese uniformly. For Swiss cheese, about 10 percent of the fat is removed. In some States, such removal of fat from milk used in making Cheddar cheese is prohibited by law. The cream removed in standardizing is either sold as market cream or churned into butter.

The temperature of the milk in the vat or kettle is adjusted to a point in the range of 86° to 91° F., and a bacterial culture, known as a starter, is added. The starter for most kinds of cheese is a mixed culture containing several types of harmless bacteria, which produce lactic acid from the lactose and also aid in the ripening or curing process. For Swiss cheese, two or sometimes three separate cultures are added. The milk may be allowed to ripen, and then it is set with rennet, which coagulates it to form the cheese curd.

After the curd has formed, it is cut into pieces, stirred, and warmed gradually. When the curd is sufficiently firm, the whey is removed. The volume of whey is usually 86 to 90 percent of the volume of milk. Whey obtained from Cheddar cheese contains 0.3 to 0.35 percent of fat; that obtained from Swiss cheese, as much as 0.7 percent. The whey is separated, and the whey cream thus obtained is used in making butter. The utilization of the fat-free whey, which contains nearly one-half as much solids as the original milk, is described in the preceding chapter.

After draining, the curd may be salted. It is placed in hoops or forms, which usually are lined with cloth, and is put under pressure, usually overnight. Some types, such as cottage and cream cheese, are not pressed but merely allowed to drain in cloths, and hence contain a relatively large amount of moisture. Some hard cheeses, such as Swiss, are not salted during the draining and firming stage, but are immersed later in salt brine.

The cheese is cured on shelves, and kept clean, in special curing rooms. The temperature is usually between 45° and 60° F., and the relative humidity is regulated. After curing, the cheese may be stored at a lower temperature, as low as 35° F. At least 3 months is required generally for curing, and some types, such as the very hard Italian cheeses, require more than a year.

No two of the principal varieties of cheese are made by the same method. The details of setting, cutting the curd, stirring, heating, draining, pressing, salting, and curing, as well as the adjustment of the composition of the milk and the use of bacterial starters, vary for different types of cheese. The variations in the process are regulated strictly by the manufacturers in accordance with the art that has been found most favorable for producing the characteristics and quality peculiar to each kind of cheese.

Small quantities of cheese are made on farms from cows' milk. On some farms cheese is made from goats' milk, chiefly for use in the home. However, by far the greater proportion is made in factories. Five thousand pounds of milk a day, or approximately 500 pounds of cheese, is considered a minimum quantity for profitable production for sale.

The kinds of cheese that are still being made in limited quantities on farms for home use are mostly hard, ripened cheese of the Cheddar or American type, and soft, unripened cheese of the cottage type. Directions for making these cheeses, as well as other kinds, can be obtained by writing to the Bureau of Dairy Industry.

CREAM FROM 33.9 billion pounds of milk was used in 1949 in the manufacture of 1,695 million pounds of butter in the United States, including 1,412 million pounds made in creameries and 283 million pounds on farms.

Milk to be used in the manufacture of creamery butter may be separated into cream and skim milk on the farm and the cream delivered to the creamery, or the whole milk may be delivered to the creamery and separated there. The latter practice is becoming more common. The cream is tested to determine the butterfat content. Cream for churning contains usually between 30 and 35 percent of fat. The cream is pasteurized, cooled, and aged to solidify the butterfat, and then churned under carefully controlled temperature conditions. When the particles of butter have gathered to the proper size, the buttermilk is drawn from the churn. The butter is washed with water, salted, and worked in the churn to insure thorough distribution of salt and moisture, as well as the desired body and texture. Then the butter is removed and printed or packaged in cartons. Federal standards require that butter contain at least 80 percent fat.

Thus two byproducts are obtained in the manufacture of butter. Skim milk is produced when the cream is separated; buttermilk is produced in the churning process. Skim milk produced on the farm is fed to poultry, calves, and hogs, and that produced in creameries is utilized in concentrated forms. The lower grade of buttermilk, which is obtained from neutralized sour cream, is used for animal feed. Buttermilk of good quality, produced in churning sweet cream, may be either condensed or dried, and is utilized in preparing food.

Cream gathered from many producers is frequently high in acidity. The pasteurization of sour cream for butter making first requires partial reduction of the acidity. Neutralization is accomplished by the addition of alkaline compounds, containing either lime or soda, to the cream before pasteurization, which makes it possible to pasteurize the cream without coagulation in the pasteurizer. The practice of neutralization is discouraged. It is a procedure for using low-grade sour cream in making butter, and such butter often is inferior. It is better to use only high-quality cream.

The process- or renovated-butter industry, which at one time produced as much as 50 million pounds annually, depends largely on low-grade farm butter as a source of raw material. With the decline in production of farm-made butter, the process-butter industry has declined until now only 1 million to 2 million pounds is produced annually. In 1950, only three factories were bonded to manufacture process butter. The enactment of Public Law 427 in 1946, and the regulations promulgated pursuant thereto early in 1947, placed the manufacture of process butter under rigid inspection by the Department of Agriculture. Since that time, such butter is being made only under the continuous inspection of the Department.

Process butter is made by melting the farm butter received as raw material, clarifying the butter oil, reemulsifying the oil with whole or skim milk, and churning this mixture of "reconstituted cream" in the conventional manner.

The invention of continuous butter-making equipment is the outstanding recent technical development in butter making. Fundamentally, the continuous method of making butter involves breaking the natural fat emulsion in cream to yield a butterfat concentrate, which is then standardized with salt and water and crystallized by chilling.

Among several designs of equipment developed for continuous butter making, two, patented by American firms, are being used to a limited extent commercially. The two processes are being investigated experimentally with a view toward further improvement.

In one process, cream is converted to butter by first homogenizing a highly concentrated or "plastic" cream, which contains 75 to 80 percent of butterfat. The treatment breaks the emulsion, and the free fat, or butter oil, separates readily from the serum. The serum is removed, salt and water are mixed with the oil to give it the composition of butter, and the mixture is chilled rapidly. During the final or chilling stage, the solidified product is worked to produce the desired body and texture, and extruded for subsequent packaging.

In the other process, the cream is heated and at the same time agitated violently to break the emulsion. The butter oil set free by agitation and heat is separated, pasteurized, and standardized to the correct composition with salt and water. The mixture is crystallized by cooling and worked to the consistency of butter, as in the first process.

Variable composition and imperfect body and texture are principal defects in butter made by some of the continuous methods. Apparently it is difficult to develop, by mechanical means, a process that will produce the perfection of body that has been attained in the older art of churning. An important objection also is the possibility of the use of large quantities of undergrade, poor-quality cream that would not be utilized in making butter by the conventional churning method. However, a continuous, mechanical method of making butter would meet the need for more efficient production and improved sanitation in the handling of butter during manufacture.

The butter industry has a stabilizing effect on the dairy industry as a whole. Because it utilizes surplus milk in times of greatest production, it acts as a balance wheel. When the supply of fluid milk is low, milk is diverted from the butter industry into channels where it is needed more.

The skim milk and buttermilk produced as byproducts by creameries are returned to farms for use as feed for livestock; or, if of suitable quality and quantity, they can be processed for human consumption. Both skim milk and buttermilk are used in the manufacture of ice cream. Butter itself, when unsalted, is also used to furnish part of the butterfat for ice cream.

Although modern creameries have largely supplanted the farm manufacture of butter, there is no difficulty, after some experience, in making butter of good quality in the home. The cream is separated from the milk, preferably with a cream separator, but anyone having only a few cows can use gravity-separated cream. The milk or cream should be pasteurized, not only for the sake of keeping quality, but also because pasteurization is a safeguard against the possibility, however remote, that the milk contains microorganisms that might cause sickness. Churns of various sizes for use in the home are available on the market. Directions for making and storing butter in the home can be obtained from the Bureau of Dairy Industry.

ABOUT 6.3 BILLION POUNDS of milk was used in the manufacture of 557 million gallons of ice cream in the United States in 1949. About 157 million pounds of milk was used in the manufacture of 39 million gallons of milk sherbet and ice milk. About 80 million pounds of milk was used in the manufacture of 7.1 million gallons of frosted malted milk, frozen custard, and other frozen dairy products.

Ice cream usually contains from 8 to 16 percent of butterfat, from 9 to 11 percent of milk-solids-not-fat (lactose, protein, and salts), from 14 to 16 percent of sugar, from 0.15 to 0.5 percent of stabilizer, and sometimes from 0.2 to 0.5 percent of egg yolk. The total solids range from 36 to 41 percent.

The components of milk sherbet are essentially the same as those of ice cream, but they are present in much different proportions. Individual manufacturers have their own formulas, and therefore sherbets vary considerably in composition. A typical sherbet, however, may contain from 25 to 35 percent of sugar, from 2 to 5 percent of milk solids, from 0.3 to 0.7 percent of stabilizer, and flavoring material. Sherbet may contain butterfat as well as milk - solids - not - fat—constituents that add to the nutritive value and increase the refreshing properties. Water ices differ from sherbets in that the ices contain no solids derived from milk.

The first step in the manufacture of ice cream is the preparation of the mix. It is customary to combine with the dairy ingredients such nondairy products as stabilizer, sugar, and water, in the correct proportions to provide the desired percentages of butterfat, milk-solids-not-fat, sugar stabilizer, and water. Usually part of the water of the mix is provided in the dairy products themselves. The mix is pasteurized immediately after it is made up, usually in an insulated, vat-type pasteurizer, in which the entire batch is heated to a pasteurizing temperature and held for 30 minutes. The heating conditions customarily are prescribed by local regulatory authorities. Following pasteurization, the mix is homogenized, cooled, and pumped to a storage tank. Subsequently, flavoring materials are added and the mix is frozen in an ice-cream freezer as it is needed. The semifrozen ice cream that flows from the freezer is placed in containers for sub-zero hardening and storage.

Stabilizing materials, usually colloidal in nature, are added to the mix during its preparation in order to produce a smooth body and texture. They retard the formation of large ice crystals. Some stabilizers in common use are gelatin, sodium alginate, Irish moss, locust bean and karaya gums, psyllium seed husks, citrus and apple pectin, and cellulose gum.

Besides its function in partly freezing the mix, the freezer also whips air into it, and thus increases the volume of the ice cream. The increase is known as overrun, and may frequently be as much as 100 percent. Thus, a gallon of mix weighing 9.2 pounds will yield 2 gallons of ice cream weighing 4.6 pounds a gallon when the overrun is 100 percent.

Because ice-cream mix contains a somewhat greater percentage of milk-solids-not-fat and a much greater percentage of fat than does milk, it is necessary to use concentrated dairy products in preparing the mix. The usual components are cream, which contains the fat in concentrated form, and condensed or dried skim milk, which contains the solids-not-fat in concentrated form. Other dairy products used in making ice cream include frozen cream, plastic cream, unsalted butter, condensed whole milk, sweetened condensed whole milk, dried whole milk, sweetened condensed skim milk, and concentrated buttermilk.

CHEESE WHEY has been used experimentally, in research in this Department, to furnish a small proportion of the milk solids in ice cream and to replace conventional milk solids in sherbet. The whey was prepared both as plain condensed whey and as sweetened condensed whey. It was found that concentrated whey in either of these forms can be used to furnish all of the milk solids in sherbet. It cannot be used to furnish more than a small proportion of the solids in ice cream, however, because its solids consist mainly of lactose and the presence of excessive lactose in ice cream may cause the development of the defect known as sandiness.

The use of sweet-cream buttermilk to furnish the milk-solids-not-fat in ice cream is another development in the utilization of surplus dairy byproducts. Experimental work carried out by this Department has shown that sweet-cream buttermilk of good quality, in concentrated form, can be used in ice-cream mix to supply part or all of the milk-solids-not-fat required in the formula. The buttermilk solids improve the quality of the ice cream by imparting a pronounced creaminess not ordinarily obtained with conventional milk-solids-not-fat. In addition, it was found that the buttermilk solids improve the whipping ability of the mix, making it easier to incorporate the desired amount of air during freezing. Although the supply of suitable buttermilk is limited to the areas of the country that produce sweet-cream butter, buttermilk can be concentrated with cane sugar for preservation and economical shipment to other areas where there is a demand for it in the production of ice cream.

Too great a concentration of lactose in ice cream frequently produces the defect of sandiness, which is caused by the crystallization of lactose from the supersaturated solution in which it normally exists in hardened ice cream. This factor is not important in sherbet, as sherbet contains enough water to hold all the lactose in solution.

In an effort to increase the utilization of dairy products in food and at the same time to increase the milk-solids-not-fat content of ice cream, the Dairy Products Research Laboratories of the Department developed a modified, concentrated form of skim milk from which part of the lactose was removed by a special process. About 65 percent of the lactose of skim milk is removed, lowering the lactose content from about 5 percent to less than 2 percent. In the process, 5.9 pounds of cane sugar is added to 100 pounds of skim milk, and the mixture is concentrated (evaporated) under vacuum

until it contains 70 percent total solids. The concentrate is cooled and kept at 50° F. for 20 hours, during which time most of the lactose crystallizes out of solution. Afterward the crystallized lactose is removed by means of a centrifuge or by a filter press.

The resulting ice-cream mix was prepared with 11 to 13 percent of milk-solids-not-fat instead of the usual 9 to 11 percent. The mix, in which the concentration of lactose was reduced by use of this "low-lac" milk, had improved body and texture and withstood adverse handling conditions without developing sandiness. Such processing makes it possible to incorporate increased amounts of food solids in ice cream—improving the product without increasing the lactose content.

A few large-scale manufacturers of ice cream use the high-temperature short-time method of pasteurization instead of the lower-temperature vat method, which takes more time and requires more floor space. In the newer method, the mix is heated at a temperature higher than that ordinarily used in the holding or vat method, and it is held at the higher temperature for only a few seconds.

Research workers are studying the problems of heat-treating the ice-cream mix as well as its various components, particularly the milk-solids-not-fat. Engineers of the Department of Agriculture recently designed and obtained a public-service patent on a high-temperature heating device or pasteurizer that can be used to attain heating exposures over a wide temperature range and that can be used for heat-treating the milk-solids-not-fat part of the mix.

Recent experiments in the Bureau of Dairy Industry indicate the possibility of improving the body and texture of ice cream by use of this special heat-treating equipment. Earlier investigations indicated that extremely rapid, short-time heating of fresh milk to a temperature higher than boiling causes changes in the milk that may be used to advantage in some dairy-manufacturing processes. There is a possibility that, in condensed skim milk that has been exposed to a high temperature under carefully controlled conditions, the milk proteins have a tendency to hold more water in a "bound" condition without meanwhile becoming denatured or heat-coagulated. If further research proves this to be true, the principle may have useful application in the manufacture of ice cream, because the mix may be stabilized in part by the increased water-binding property of the milk proteins. With an increase in bound water, there would be less free water present. Since apparently only free water forms ice, there should be fewer ice crystals in the frozen ice cream, and its body should be smoother.

There are indications also that special heat treatment of the constituents may have other favorable effects on the properties of the mix. For example, heat treatments used in forewarming raw skim milk have been found to alter the viscosity of the sweetened condensed skim milk made from it, which is used commonly in ice cream.

For use with the high-temperature heater, Department engineers have designed and developed also a simple, magnetic flow-diversion valve—an electrical device that automatically controls the heating exposure precisely.

Limited quantities of concentrated (condensed) ice-cream mix are being made commercially and sold for use in the home. A common brand is a semisolid paste, which is sold in small cans or screw-top jars and requires only the addition of water and flavoring material before whipping and freezing in the household refrigerator. Concentrated ice-cream mix, like sweetened condensed milk, is preserved with sugar. The mixes sold commercially are prepared like the usual mixes we have described.

Dried ice-cream mix, in the form of powder, a new product, is sold in one form in 5-ounce paper cartons. The mix is prepared in the usual way from unconcentrated dairy products, and it is pasteurized, homogenized to increase the smoothness of body, condensed by evaporation of water in a vacuum pan to approximately the concentration of a normal mix, and then spray-dried. It requires only the addition of water, or water and flavor, according to directions on the package, and then alternate whipping and freezing in the home refrigerator.

The continuous freezer is a relatively recent technical development in ice-cream equipment. The mix is partly frozen as it passes continuously through the machine and is collected in cans or cartons and transferred to a low-temperature room—a so-called hardening room. New developments in packaging have made it possible to fill packages entirely automatically, on a production-line basis, as the semifrozen ice cream flows from the continuous freezer. Continuous freezing and mechanical packaging save time and labor, eliminate much of the handling required with the batch freezer, and minimize contamination.

Ice cream is one of the most popular of the dairy-product foods that can be made easily on the farm where milk and cream are produced and where ice is available. An ice-cream freezer is the only mechanical equipment required. Formulas for preparing the mix are available by writing to the Bureau of Dairy Industry.

GEORGE P. SANDERS *is a chemist in the division of Dairy Products Research Laboratories in the Bureau of Dairy Industry. He received his bachelor's and master's degrees at the University of Minnesota and his doctor's degree at American University. He joined the Department's research staff in 1926. He has made a large number of contributions and published numerous scientific papers on the chemistry of milk and cheese.*

DONALD H. WILLIAMS *is a dairy manufacturing technologist in the division of Dairy Products Research Laboratories in the Bureau of Dairy Industry. He was graduated from the University of Maryland in 1938.*

Concentrated and Dried Milk

B. H. Webb

The concentrated and dried milks are manufactured to conserve fluid milk for use where fresh milk is scarce and during seasons of low production. Specialized knowledge and equipment enable processors to manufacture the different concentrated milks by removing part of the water from the milk. The products are the source of concentrated milk solids needed for the preparation of many foods, both in the home and in the food factory.

The names assigned by custom to the concentrated milks have confused the layman and provoked the etymologist. Plain condensed whole and skim milks contain no sugar and are perishable products. Sweetened condensed whole and skim milks are preserved by the addition of sugar. Evaporated milk is not sweetened; it is sterilized in cans. Dried milks may be either dried whole or dried skim milk, except that Congress in 1944 amended the Food, Drug, and Cosmetic Act by providing a statutory definition for dried skim milk under the names "nonfat dry milk solids" and "defatted milk solids."

Nearly half of the 120 billion pounds of milk produced annually in the United States is consumed as market milk and cream. From the remainder (except the milk used on the farm), such dairy products as butter, cheese, ice cream, concentrated milk, and dried milk are manufactured. Fifteen billion pounds of skim milk, part of that left from the separation of milk for cream and butter, also goes into manufactured milk products. The fluid milk equivalent utilized in the production of the concentrated and dried milks is about 20 billion pounds. Approximately 6½ billion pounds of milk is made into evaporated milk each year, and 280 million pounds is canned as sweetened condensed milk, both largely for household use. The ice-cream industry uses about 3 billion pounds of skim-milk concentrates to build up the nonfat milk solids of ice cream. The manufacture of foods other than dairy products requires preparation of milk concentrates from 4 billion pounds of milk. About one-third of the production of concentrated and dried milks is used in beverage milks, cottage and other special cheeses, malted milk, and animal feeds.

SWEETENED CONDENSED MILK is manufactured by a few simple but vital operations. Harmful bacteria and enzymes are destroyed by forewarming. In that treatment, the milk is heated to about 185° F., which helps also to control thickening of the finished milk during storage. The hot milk is drawn into the vacuum pan—in which milk boils at temperatures as low as 100° F. and water is rapidly removed without coloring the milk or giving it a cooked flavor—together with 18 pounds of sugar for each 100 pounds of milk. A sirupy milk, which tastes delicious, is drawn from the vacuum pan and cooled with continuous agitation. Tiny crystals of lactose (milk sugar) grow spontaneously when the condensed milk is stirred at about 85°. Improper cooling causes the growth of large, coarse crystals that make the milk taste sandy. Sweetened condensed milk is packed in cans or barrels. When held at 70° for 6 or 8 months, the product darkens and thickens. The change can be greatly retarded by storing it below 60°. Sweetened condensed milk retains its acceptable condition for at least a year if held at a low temperature. It is not damaged at temperatures well below 0° F. because of its high sugar content.

Perishable concentrates, produced and packaged in bulk for food processors, are called plain condensed milk. They contain no sugar and must be held under refrigeration. The manufacturing process consists simply in heating, condensing, and cooling the milk.

EVAPORATED MILK, unlike sweetened condensed milk, contains no added sugar. Spoilage is prevented by sterilization with heat. Steps in the manufacture of evaporated milk are: Forewarming, evaporation, homogenization, standardization, canning, and sterilization.

The time and temperature of forewarming affect the stability of the milk toward heat and the viscosity, or body, developed in it during sterilization. Forewarming is generally done at a temperature of 190° to 212° F., depending on the condition of the milk.

Dairy scientists recently investigated the effect of forewarming milk to temperatures up to 300° on its heat stability and viscosity. They found that milk forewarmed at 250° for 3 to 4 minutes attained a much greater heat stability than when temperatures below boiling were used. The discovery enables manufacturers to raise the solids content of evaporated milk without encountering coagulation difficulties during sterilization. Evaporated milks have been made with a solids content up to 38 percent.

Storage tests on milks containing various percentages of solids, however, have shown that the best milk is produced when the solids are held within the limits of 26 percent to 32 percent. The present evaporated milk with a solids content of 26 percent would be improved in terms of nutritive value and the persistence of good viscosity and body characteristics during storage if the solids content were raised to 28 percent.

Small crystalline particles, about the size of the head of a pin, sometimes appear in stored evaporated milk. They are complex milk salts that have crystallized and settled to the bottom of the can. The conditions governing their separation are little understood; hence their formation cannot always be prevented. Salt crystals in evaporated milk are not harmful, but sometimes they are an annoyance, especially when they obstruct the holes in nipples of babies' bottles.

Bureau of Dairy Industry chemists have studied evaporated-milk salt crystals. The crystals are composed largely of calcium citrate, with traces of phosphates. Crystals generally do not begin to appear in the milk until it has been in storage 6 months or more. They grow more rapidly when the evaporated milk is held at room temperature than when it is stored at 60° or below. The formation of crystals can be accelerated by adding calcium chloride and sodium citrate or by lightly seeding the milk with calcium citrate.

Early in the Second World War the Government had to store much evaporated milk. Some of it, after being held for 2 or 3 years, showed citrate crystals, a thinning in body, and some separation of fat and protein. Dairy scientists knew that evaporated milk was a remarkably stable product; they determined nevertheless to find a way to increase that stability. They found that the magnitude of the storage change depended partly on the temperature. Below 60° F. changes were slight, but above 90° the product deteriorated noticeably in a few months. It was found advisable to hold evaporated milk at a temperature not to exceed 75° and to turn the cases every 6 weeks to retard fat separation.

Fat separation in evaporated milk depends not only on the efficiency of homogenization, on viscosity, and on conditions of storage, but also on the

Approximate composition, degree of concentration, and density of milk and concentrated milks

Product	Water	Milk solids not fat	Fat	Protein	Milk sugar	Ash	Sucrose	Degree of concentration	Density at 60° F.
	Per cent	Per cent	Per cent	Per cent	Per cent	Per cent	Per cent	Ratio	Specific gravity
Milk......................	87.0	9.1	3.9	3.5	4.9	0.7	....	....	1.032
Skim milk.................	90.5	9.4	.1	3.5	5.1	.8	....	....	1.035
Evaporated milk...........	73.7	18.4	7.9	7.0	9.9	1.5	....	2.02:1	1.066
Plain condensed whole milk...	64.0	25.2	10.8	9.7	13.6	1.9	....	2.77:1	1.095
Plain condensed skim milk ...	70.0	29.7	.3	11.1	16.1	2.5	....	3.15:1	1.125
Sweetened condensed whole milk.....................	28.0	20.0	8.5	7.7	10.7	1.6	43.5	2.20:1	1.266
Sweetened condensed skim milk.....................	28.0	29.7	.3	11.1	16.1	2.5	42.0	3.15:1	1.366
Dried whole milk	3.5	69.8	26.7	25.8	38.0	6.0	....	7.50:1	.550
Dried skim milk	3.5	95.5	1.0	35.6	52.0	7.9	....	10.20:1	.600

physical state of the protein that is associated with the fat in the cream layer. Easily dispersed fat layers are less objectionable than layers that are held tightly together by adsorbed, partly denatured protein. Causes for the gradual changes in the milk protein during storage of evaporated milk are still being investigated.

A new canned flavored milk that is high in energy value and suitable for drinking directly from the container was developed by scientists in Government and industry in response to requests by the Army Quartermaster Corps. The milk was wanted for use on invasion beachheads, where the landing forces frequently needed quickly available nourishment. The milk, a sterile product in sealed containers, has excellent storage life. It contains approximately 20 percent total solids; ordinary fluid milk contains about 13 percent. The extra solids consist of sugars, flavoring materials, and added milk solids from concentrated milk. The many flavors tested in developing the formulas included fruits, honey, maple, chocolate, and caramel. Chocolate and caramel gave a product of satisfactory flavor and small batches of both were made commercially for the Quartermaster Corps. These flavored milks have not been extensively manufactured for civilian use, although canned chocolate milk is available in some markets.

DRIED MILK was one of the chief contributions of the dairy industry to winning the Second World War. Before the war the production was largely dried skim milk and dried buttermilk, both byproducts. During the war a great demand for dried whole milk prompted a sevenfold increase in its manufacture. The dried milks are now made by three principal methods, usually designated as spray, atmospheric-drum, and vacuum-drum processes.

In the spray process, partly concentrated milk is sprayed by pressure or centrifugal means into a chamber through which a current of heated air is directed. The shape of the drying chamber may be conical or rectangular, and its size is proportioned to the spray and the amount and direction of the flow of air used. The fine droplets of milk dry almost instantaneously to fine particles of powder, which are removed from the air by gravity and the cyclonic motion of the air, and, in some cases, with the aid of an air-filtering device. Dried milks made by this method are finely divided, very soluble, and hygroscopic.

Although unconcentrated milk can be dried by this method, partly concentrated milk is preferred for economy and the effect on certain properties of the dried product. The milk usually is concentrated in a vacuum pan or a continuous evaporator. The concentration, which varies with the type of spray and the drier used, may be as great as 44 percent solids. Dried milks made from concentrated milks have particles of larger sizes than those made from unconcentrated milks and can be reconstituted more readily. The dried-milk products also retain less gas when subjected to vacuum in packaging.

Dried skim milks are usually made from skim milks that have been preheated to at least 185° F. for varying periods, because it has been found that the dried product made from milk treated in this way has better baking qualities than products made from milks that have received only a pasteurization treatment.

In manufacturing dried whole milk, the milk must be heated sufficiently to destroy the fat-splitting enzymes, lipases. The temperature and the time of heating needed to destroy the lipases have not been established definitely. However, temperatures of 175° to 180° F. for 30 minutes have been used successfully in the manufacture of dried whole milk. The temperature of the air to be used in drying varies with the make of the drier. It may be from 240° to 320°, depending on the efficiency of the spray, the rate of feed, the degree of concentration of the milk used, and other factors. In the manufacture of this product, it is also important to keep the milk from coming in contact with exposed copper or iron. Extremely small quantities of copper, especially, will accelerate markedly the deterioration of the fat.

In the atmospheric-drum process, steam-heated revolving single or double drums are coated with a film of partly concentrated milk, which dries and is scraped off by close-fitting knives after a partial revolution has been completed. The product is then ground to a powder and packed in barrels or sacks.

Because of the high drum temperature necessary for drying the film, there is a slight discoloration of the product and a partial coagulation of the proteins that makes them insoluble. Driers of this type are used mainly in drying skim milk and buttermilk. The dried milk thus made does not absorb water as readily as powder dried by the spray process.

The vacuum-drum process is essentially a roller process. The rolls, or drums, are enclosed in a chamber that is kept under partial vacuum during the drying operation, thus making it possible to dry milks at temperatures below their boiling points. The products obtained by this process resemble those made by the spray process in solubility, color, flavor, and hygroscopicity.

Great quantities of dried milk were used to feed the Allied armies. Scientists and technicians were called upon to solve the problems of packaging and keeping quality which arose when the milk was subjected to the rigors of wartime storage and shipping.

The spray-dried and vacuum-drum-dried milks have a great avidity for moisture and must be packaged so that they are guarded against absorption of moisture from the atmosphere. Dried skim milk is usually packed in slack barrels of 200-pound capacity with moistureproof double liners, or in moistureproof bags of 100-pound capacity. For Army export the 25- and 50-pound hermetically sealed round or square base-metal cans were the most satisfactory. Metal drums and moistureproof fiber drums have also been used for export.

Dried whole milk deteriorates relatively rapidly when packaged in contact with air. To retard or prevent spoilage through oxidation of the fat, the product is packed in tin containers of from 1- to 50-pound capacity and the air is removed as completely as possible by evacuation and replaced by an inert gas, usually nitrogen.

Many flavors may develop during the production and storage of dried milks. For the most part, they can be controlled through the use of advanced methods of manufacture and packaging. Aside from the off-flavors that may be inherent in milk, the principal types of off-flavor likely to be found in dried milks are "cooked" flavors, which are developed during manufacture, and staleness, rancidity, and tallowiness, which may develop during storage.

Some basic rules for the manufacture of spray-dried whole milk of good keeping quality have been developed by research workers:

Milk of low bacterial count should be dried as soon after it is drawn from the cow as practicable.

The milk must not come in contact with copper and iron; stainless-steel equipment is best.

The raw milk must receive a heat treatment of 175° for 30 minutes, or its equivalent in time and temperature of heating, for lipase destruction.

The moisture content of the powder should be below 2.5 percent.

Dried whole milk should be gas-packed in tin cans so that the oxygen content of the atmosphere of the container does not exceed 2 percent.

The temperature of storage should be less than 75° F.

If these conditions are fulfilled, and reasonable care is exercised in the manufacturing operations, the dried milk will remain in good condition for 6 months to 1 year.

Dried skim milk should contain less than 3.5 percent moisture. Powders of more than 5 percent moisture held at high storage temperatures deteriorate very rapidly in color, flavor, and solubility.

FURTHER UTILIZATION OF MILK in the concentrated and dried form will come as improvements are made in these products through advanced methods of processing. Chemists, bacteriologists, dairy technologists, and engineers are constantly engaged on the problems of heating, concentrating, and drying milk.

The development of an improved process for sterilizing fluid concentrated milks affords a great opportunity for increasing their utilization. The production of sterile packaged milks of normal flavor and color and with good chemical and physical stability may some day be possible. Means for accomplishing this include sterilization by dielectric heating, cathode rays, ultrasonics, and antibiotics, or by improved high-temperature, short-time heating. How effective any one of these methods may become in providing the consumer with an acceptable concentrated beverage milk is unpredictable. Most scientists still believe that heat is the surest and safest sterilizing agent. Evaporated milk has already been quickly heat-sterilized by two experimental methods that give products of generally acceptable, though slightly cooked, flavor. By one method, cans of milk are sterilized under severe agitation in less than 4 minutes at 260° F. By the other method, the milk is sterilized at 280° by rapid passage through a special tubular heater, and then aseptically packaged. Both methods produce thin evaporated milk, which lacks long storage stability. The fat and protein separation of such milks during storage must be overcome before these products can be offered to the public with complete assurance that the contents will keep until the can is opened.

Utilization of dried milks will be broadened as scientists gradually learn how to extend the time that a fresh flavor can be retained. There is need, too, for improvement in the physical properties of the powder particle. If dried milk could be made so that it would disperse and dissolve in water as readily as sugar, its popularity with consumers would increase.

B. H. WEBB *is a principal dairy manufacturing technologist in the Bureau of Dairy Industry. He received the 1943 Borden Award in Dairy Manufacturing from the American Dairy Science Association and the Superior Service Award from the Department of Agriculture in 1948.*

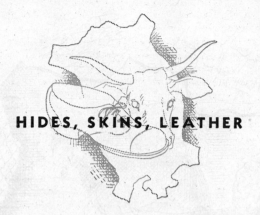

HIDES, SKINS, LEATHER

Advice on Hides and Skins

Ira D. Clarke,
Clifton D. Lowe

For ages man has used the hides and skins of animals to cover his feet and body, to provide shelter, and to make thongs, slings, vessels for liquids, floats, and many other things. Perhaps at first he simply dried the skins before using them, but very early he learned to tan them to make them more durable and useful.

Today the livestock slaughterer derives his largest single byproduct income from hides and skins. Nearly 7 percent of the live weight of a meat animal is in its hide. The tanner must carry a large inventory of this comparatively high-priced, perishable commodity to produce leather.

Before we discuss quality and uses, we should note that in English, as in most of the European languages, a hair-splitting distinction is made between hides and skins, based only on size and thickness. Hides are large and relatively thick. Skins are small and thin. Cattle, horses, and buffaloes, for example, have hides. Calves, sheep, goats, and rabbits have skins.

THE COMMERCIAL VALUE of a hide or skin is based on its size, shape, thickness, smoothness, texture, and its physical condition. The basic value of a hide is determined by the characteristics of the live animal, but its actual value may be lowered by improper care of the animal during its lifetime and of the hide during and after slaughter.

The basic quality of a hide or skin is influenced by the species, breed, sex, age, size, weight, shape, and general health of the animal that produced it.

Species determines the size, weight, and shape of the animal and therefore of the hide or skin. Tanners always name the species when they buy hides or skins. Many tan only skins from one species.

Breed, although important, is seldom particularized by the tanner when he buys hides because of the difficulty in meeting such a requirement. Practically all the skins used by the tanner are byproducts from animals slaughtered for food purposes and, regardless of his preference, he tans all skins that will make leather.

Two studies have been made in which hides from cattle of different breeds were compared. W. H. Black, A. T. Semple, and J. L. Lush, of the Department of Agriculture, reported that part-Brahman animals had heavier, larger hides than Hereford or Shorthorn steers. They believed differences in thickness of skin due to breed are not important, although they were unable to make accurate measurements of thickness.

Dr. J. H. R. Bisschop, A. Gardner, J. Sebba, and S. G. Shuttleworth, who worked at the Leather Industries Research Institute in South Africa, in 1943 examined hides from Africander, Sussex, Red Poll, and Friesland cattle. The Africander hides were largest and heaviest and made sole leather that wore longest on a laboratory testing machine. The Friesland hides were uneven and the poorest of the four groups.

Sheepskins probably vary more with breed than skins of any other animal. Merino sheep, which have the finest wool, have loose-fibered, ribby skins of little value. Cape or Mocha skins, on the other hand, which have worthless hair, make excellent leather.

Shuttleworth in South Africa reported that Merino skins yield ribby leather with a loose, coarse grain; Corriedale skins, thin leather with a smooth grain; and Persian skins, full leather with a tight, fine grain. In cooperation with agricultural experiment stations, he is studying the skins of crosses of the Merino, Persian, and such English breeds as Suffolk and Southdown. He hopes that a breed can be developed that will yield good skins, as well as good wool and meat.

Sex also influences the size and shape of the skin. Skins of female animals generally are lighter in weight and thinner and have a finer grain surface than those of male animals. G. D. McLaughlin and E. R. Theis in 1924 reported more ash in hides from bulls than in hides from cows, and more ash, elastin, and fat, but less water, in hides from steers than in those from cows. But they examined only one hide of each sex and did not specify breed or other characteristics of the animals. F. Stather and II. Herfeld, at the Research Institute and Technical School for the Leather Industry in Germany, examined 10 skins from black-speckled lowland cattle in 1939 and found no differences due to sex in ash, fat content, nature of the fat, moisture content, or weight changes during the preliminary tanning operations. It would seem that sex has little effect, if any, on the chemical composition of skin.

Skins of young animals are smaller, have a finer texture and grain pattern, and contain more moisture than skins of older animals. Skins of very old animals usually are uneven in substance and do not tan well. Stather and Herfeld found more fat, extractable by

ether, in the hides of old cattle than in those of young animals, although the fat was of the same nature in each. They also found that calfskins took up salt more slowly than hides from oxen or cows, probably because of their closer texture.

Latitude, elevation above sea level, climate, and the forage conditions of the place where an animal lives also affect quality. The tanner knows the general type of hide produced in a given area and buys accordingly. But the effects of other factors, such as breed, feeding, care, and management of the animal during life and of the hide during and after slaughter, are interwoven with the effect of environment and are in the tanner's mind when he considers origin of hides as an indication of quality.

Another point that the tanner must note is the season of the year when the hides were taken *off the animals. Sheepskins may have cockle in the spring when the wool is growing rapidly. In the summer, when the sweat glands are active, sheepskins are loose and spongy. Cattle hides are thin in the spring and thickest in autumn.

Tanners prefer cattle hides taken off in the fall when they are plump, have short hair, and carry less dirt and other foreign matter than hides taken off in spring. Fattening the animal, which usually occurs in winter, lowers the quality of its hide, especially under modern methods of intensive feeding. A diet rich in fat and carbohydrate may result in deposition of fat within the skin structure, especially over the rump. This fat deposit may be so heavy that leather made from the skin is not satisfactory for some purposes unless degreased. The type of feed also is important; skins from calves fed on milk up to the time of slaughter make much better leather than those from calves that have been weaned and fed solid food.

Poor nutrition results in a smaller skin with a finer grain. Ira D. Clarke, L. S. Stuart, and R. W. Frey in 1937 examined skins from a number of twin lambs. One of each pair had been fed just enough to maintain body weight without loss or gain; its twin had been fed enough of the same diet to nearly double its weight during the 112 days of the feeding period. The raw skins and leather from the maintenance-fed lambs weighed about 42 percent as much as the skins and leather from the full-fed lambs. Except for size and thickness, there was no difference between the two lots in leather-making quality. Each lot tanned satisfactorily and to the same degree. Although the leather from the maintenance-fed lambs was, on the average, only three-fifths as strong as that from the full-fed lambs, the strengths were the same when calculated to unit thickness.

Bisschop and coworkers in 1943 found an increase in weight and area of hide due to feeding bonemeal. The hide of a Sussex beef animal fed bonemeal had an area of 50 square feet and weighed 77.2 pounds, whereas a hide from a control animal not fed bonemeal had an area of 43.1 square feet and weighed 63 pounds.

NUMEROUS TYPES of disease, injuries, dietary deficiencies, and parasites damage hides.

At least a third of all cattle hides produced in the United States contain five or more grub holes and therefore are sold at a discount. The proportion of damaged hides has been reduced in recent years by the widespread use of effective insecticides, but the loss in value of hides and leather from grub damage in 1947 was estimated by the Tanners' Council of America as amounting to 20 million dollars.

Mange mites, ticks, lice, screwworms, and other pests also reduce hide quality.

Branding is another source of loss in hides and leather. At present prices, damage to hides from branding results in a financial loss of at least 6 million dollars a year. The loss can be reduced materially by using smaller brands, branding only the less valuable parts of the hide, such as the jaw, neck, shoulder, or thigh of the animal, using open-design brands and wide-faced irons to avoid blotching, and branding only animals that cannot be satisfactorily identified by other means.

Shearing marks on sheepskins and cuts and scratches caused by barbed wire, horns, or protruding nails in barns, trucks, or railway cars mar the surface of skins so they cannot be used for articles requiring an attractive finish.

NEARLY A MILLION CATTLE and three quarters of a million calves are slaughtered for food annually by farmers, and many die from natural causes. A substantial loss, therefore, may result from poor skinning and improper care of the flayed skins on farms. Care is necessary throughout the skinning process, first to make the opening cuts in the proper places so the hide will have the correct pattern and then to prevent cuts and scores in the hide. Scores, although they do not pass entirely through the skin, are almost as bad as cuts, because they weaken the leather so it is useless for many purposes.

After removal from the animal, the skin is almost as perishable as meat. Prompt sale is important, but if it is impossible, each hide should be salted as soon as it loses its animal heat. The flesh side of the hide, spread with the hair side down, should be completely covered with salt—about a pound to a pound of hide. The salted hide should be covered—paper can be used—so it will not dry out; otherwise the salt will not penetrate to the middle of the hide and spoilage may occur later. After a couple of weeks, the hide may be folded to a square bundle and stored in a cool place until it can be marketed. Salted hides or skins should be stored under refrigeration, preferably at about 55° F. and 70 to 75 percent relative humidity if they are to be kept longer than 4 or 5 months. The storage room should not be too dry (because drying lowers the value of hides) but, more important, it must not be too wet.

If the humidity is too high the salt in the hide will "draw" moisture and leach out, and the hide will decompose. For the same reason, hides must not be placed, even temporarily, where they will be exposed to rain or drippings or water in any other form.

Hides or skins salted in this manner and kept moist are known as green-salted hides or skins. Hides may also be cured by soaking in a saturated salt solution for 1 or 2 days and then drained. These are known as brined hides and are equal or even superior to green-salted hides. Hides may be salted for a short time and then dried (dry-salted hides), or they may be dried without any salting (dry or flint-dried hides). Dry hides are often produced in arid areas or where salt is difficult to procure but they are inferior to green-salted hides.

A TANNER BUYS HIDES with the object of producing leather of a definite kind and weight, suitable for a particular purpose. If he makes leather for baseballs, gloves, or garments, he may buy lightweight cowhides. For leather for men's shoe soles, he must use heavy steer hides. For shoe uppers he may buy calfskins, goatskins, or reptile skins, depending on his equipment and market. Naturally then, he wants hides that have been sorted and graded, rather than a miscellaneous collection of all kinds and sizes, some of which he could not use. To meet the tanner's needs, hide dealers sort hides into "selections."

No official grades for hides and skins have been established by the Government. Preliminary work between 1928 and 1930 in setting up and defining hide and skin grade standards was never completed because the market dropped to a very low level and industry was not disposed to use grade standards under such conditions. All the factors we have just mentioned as determining or affecting hide quality were considered in defining the grades. The proposed standards for cattle hides were made up of the following

factors: Kind of hide (packer, country, and the like); pattern (perfect or imperfect); selection (branded or free of brands); class (cow, steer); subclass (spready, plump); weight; grade; and subgrade. Grade, indicated by 1, 2, 3, and so on, and subgrade, indicated by A, B, C, et cetera, were based on color of flesh; tightness of grain; thoroughness of salting; number of cuts, scores, salt stains, and grub holes; and extent of damage from scratches, rubbed spots, sores, ticks, lice, and such.

The trade classification is based on about the same factors. The country, province, or town of origin is specified. This is especially important for calfskins, goatskins, and sheepskins; it reveals much regarding quality; often it is the sole specification, except those regarding size and defects. The method of cure also may be specified.

The most elaborate trade classification is for domestic cattle hides, all of which are green-salted. The classes are: *Packer hides:* Heavy native steer hides; heavy Texas steer hides; light Texas steer hides; extreme light Texas steer hides; butt-branded steer hides; Colorado steer hides; branded cowhides; heavy native cowhides; light native cowhides; native bullhides; branded bullhides. *Country hides:* Heavy steer hides; heavy cowhides; buffs; extremes; bullhides; branded hides; kips; calfskins.

Packer hides are taken off in the larger packing plants; they are of high quality and are sorted into classes. Country hides are taken off by farmers and small-town butchers. They are not so well taken off as packer hides and, of course, cannot be sorted into uniform carload lots, except by a dealer who buys them in large numbers.

In the foregoing classes "native" means only that the hides are not branded. Heavy steer hides weigh 58 pounds or more; light steer hides, 48 to 58 pounds; and extreme light steer hides, 30 to 48 pounds. Texas steer hides are small-patterned, plump hides branded in any portion and from any section of the country, although originally only hides from the Southwest were so designated. Colorado steer hides are large, rangy, side-branded hides from any State. Heavy cowhides weigh 53 pounds or more; light cowhides, 30 to 53 pounds. Buffs are country hides weighing between 45 and 50 pounds. Kips are all skins weighing between 15 and 30 pounds. Calfskins weigh 15 pounds or less.

A hide in good condition is classed as No. 1. If the grain surface is damaged or the hide is cut or scored anywhere except in the belly or neck portion, it is classed as No. 2. Grubby hides, those having five or more open grub holes, are sold at a discount.

To ANIMALS, the obvious use of the skin is for protection. It helps prevent the entrance of bacteria or parasites into the body and acts as a buffer against injuries. It also helps regulate body temperature. The hair in winter insulates the animal against cold and so reduces the loss of body heat. To dissipate heat in summer, many animals have sweat glands which cool the animal and also eliminate waste products. The sweat glands are in the skin. Brahman or Zebu cattle have a liberal supply of them. Attached to the base of each hair is the erector-pili muscle, which contracts when the body surface is chilled suddenly, causing the hair to stand on end, forming goose-flesh, and compressing an oil gland just above the muscle. Oil from the gland is forced into the hair follicle and to the surface of the skin, where it retards evaporation and so assists in retaining body heat. Before tanning, the glands, hair, and epidermis are removed completely, because their presence would prevent the production of well-tanned, supple leather.

Leather is used by man for innumerable purposes. The Armed Forces use leather for airplane seats, belts, belting, boots, garments, gas masks, gloves, gun cases, harness, helmet liners, holsters, mattresses on submarines, recoil mechanisms, rifle slings,

rigging on shipboard, shoes, straps, textile rollers, washers, and upholstery on many ships and vehicles. Civilian uses are even more numerous. Shoes, the most important use, require leather from about 80 million hides and skins each year. Approximately a million hides are used annually for belting and mechanical leathers; three quarters of a million for bag, case, and strap leathers; half a million for upholstery leather; and one third of a million for harness and saddlery. Gloves and garments take 10 million sheepskins annually; 5 million are shearlings. Although those quantities meet peacetime needs, in wartime the difficulty in importing hides and the greatly increased demands of the Armed Forces make leather a highly critical material.

Specific kinds of cowhide leathers are: Apron, bag, baseball, basketball, briefcase, buckskin, garment, hydraulic, lace, luggage, moccasin, piano, seatcover, slipper, sole, textile, upholstery, valve, waist-belt, wallet, washer, welting, and whip. Cowhide is also embossed to make imitation alligator, ostrich, pigskin, reptile, and other leathers. Steer hides are used for many of the same purposes that call for a heavier leather. By splitting to proper thickness, steer hides or cowhides can be adapted to almost any purpose for which leather is needed.

Bull hides are used for automobile, gear, harness, mechanical, sole, and upholstery leather. Calfskins are used for making leathers for billfolds, bookbindings, garments, gaskets, handbags, laces, linings, meters, parchment, and pianos.

Goatskins are used for bookbinding, glove, handbag, hat, lining, piano, wallet, and shoe-upper leathers. From sheepskins are made leathers for billfolds, bookbinding, gaskets, gloves, handbags, packing, parchment, pianos, pocketbooks, suede, shoe uppers, and valves and washers. Sheepskins also are embossed and finished to imitate many kinds of more expensive leathers.

Sheepskins and lambskins, particularly those from fine-wool types and carrying wool from one-fourth inch to one inch in length, are called shearlings and are widely used for making garments. Demand for such products was high during the early part of the war because of their use in the production of clothing for pilots and other flying personnel of the military and also for troops stationed in the cold northern areas of the world. Certain of the better quality shearlings go to the ladies-wear trade after being processed to resemble fur. This finished product is called mouton.

Pig and hog skins are tanned into billfold, counter, glove, handbag, insole, lining, luggage, saddle, shoe upper, wallet, and welting leathers. Cordovan is the trade name of a dense leather made from horsehide butts. Leather from the front of horsehides is loose and soft and so is used for garments and gloves.

The domestic supply of hides and skins is not adequate to meet our needs. In 1948, according to Report No. FT–110 of the Bureau of Census, we imported 2,479,807 cattle hides, 247,596 kips, 752,509 calfskins, 406,110 buffalo and water buffalo hides, 23,527,277 sheepskins and lambskins, 3,596,189 hair-sheep and cabretta skins, 38,972,-402 goatskins, 737,739 kangaroo skins, 785,676 deer and buck skins, 859,534 pig and hog skins, 2,676,590 reptile skins, and a number of others in smaller amounts. Although we use a rather low percentage of foreign cattle hides and calfskins, a large proportion of the sheepskins and essentially all of the goatskins we use are imported. Conservation and careful use of our hides and skins are therefore essential, especially in times of emergency.

TRIMMINGS OF FIRST QUALITY from beef hides and calfskins and pieces of skin trimmed from pork products are used, under United States Government inspection, for making edible gelatin. Trimmings not of edible quality, fleshings, sinews, and chrome-leather stock are made into glue.

Animal hair has a number of uses.

Horse manes and tails, cattle switches, and hog hair are mixed, twisted into long ropes, and stored several weeks in coils to make curled hair, which is used for air filters, mattresses, and cushions for furniture, boats, and automobiles. Long cattle hair is used in the spinning of carpets; medium-length hair for cushions and padding, and in upholstery; and short hair for felts in insulation and in plaster. Hog hair is used for insulation. During the war, when imports were cut off, some domestic bristles were used for the manufacture of paint and other brushes. Pulled wool, which is wool removed from the sheepskin after slaughter, makes up one-sixth of all domestic wool production. Leather scrap, hair, wool, and other nitrogenous waste materials that cannot be more profitably used find their way into low-grade tankage and thence into fertilizer.

IRA D. CLARKE, *a native of Indiana and a graduate of Butler College, is a chemist at the Eastern Regional Research Laboratory. He has been an employee of the Department of Agriculture since 1917, engaged in investigations on tanning materials, hides, skins, and leather.*

CLIFTON D. LOWE, *a native of Ohio and a graduate of Ohio State University, is employed as extension animal husbandman by the Extension Service and the Bureau of Animal Industry. He was a member of the Inter-Department Committee on Conservation of Hides and Skins of the 1920's and of the Hide Conservation Committee of the Department during the Second World War.*

Processors of leather will be interested in these publications by Dr. Clarke:

Conserving Hides—Salting and Shipping, Bureau of Agricultural and Industrial Chemistry Publication AIC–24. 1943.

Conserving Hides—Skinning, Bureau of Agricultural and Industrial Chemistry Publication AIC–25. 1943.

Leather Made To Fit Your Needs

C. W. Beebe

Leather is made by treating skins and hides so that they will not be acted upon by bacterial enzymes, will not be gelatinized by warm water, and will not become brittle when dried out. This treatment, known as tanning, gives them the desired softness, flexibility, and firmness.

Heavy leather is used where thickness, firmness, and solidity are needed, as in shoe soles, machine belting, and harness. For it, thick heavy hides from cows or other large animals are needed. Light leather is used where flexibility and softness are desired, as in shoe uppers, gloves, upholstery, garments, luggage, or chamois. It is usually made from the skins of small animals or young animals of larger species, such as goats, sheep, calves, or colts. It may also be made by splitting the hides of large animals into layers. Fur skins are a type of light leather in which the production of leather from the skin, while important, is secondary to the preservation and improvement of the fur.

Leather is of two general classes, heavy and light. Each requires its own type of tanning. The tanning of heavy leather used to take years; indeed, in many parts of the world today it still requires a whole year. Even in modern practice the tannage may last 2 to 3 months. Light leather is tanned quite rapidly; often only 2 days are required.

Leather is made in three stages. First, the hides or skins are prepared for tanning—the beamhouse operations, so called because of the use of the beam, a convex sloping slab of wood upon which a hide or skin is placed while the operator removes hair or flesh with a knife. Second is the actual tanning operation. The third step is the finishing operation. Changes at any stage make a difference in the finished leathers. The best tanning process is the one in which the methods used in any step harmonize with those used in other steps to give the desired final effect.

TANNERS usually receive hides and skins dry or cured; that is, enough water has been removed, usually by salting, to prevent spoiling. Usually the hair is still on the hides and must be removed before tannage. As the wool on sheepskins is more valuable than the skins, it is generally removed by the grower or the wool puller, and the skins reach the tanner in a pickled condition—that is, preserved with a solution of sulfuric acid and salt.

The first step in the preparation of hides or skins for tanning is soaking in water to clean off accumulated dirt, to remove excess salt, and to restore some of the water lost in drying.

The second step is to soak them in a lime solution, usually containing sodium sulfide, to loosen the hair and epidermis, which are then removed, commonly by unhairing machines. The adhering connective tissue, or flesh, is then removed, and the hides or skins are scudded. Scudding means scraping by a blunt blade, which removes the remnants of the glands, hair roots, lime soaps, and dirt. Some of the lime is then removed by washing with water or with acids or deliming agents to remove more of it.

The tanner changes these operations to get the kind of leather he wants.

If he makes hard, firm sole leather,

he tries to prevent loss of hide substance and to get a firm, plumped hide. He soaks and limes for only a short time; he uses lime liquors which are sharp (alkaline) and not too mellow and which contain enough sodium sulfide for rapid unhairing. He delimes by merely washing some of the lime from the hides with water.

The tanner of soft, flexible, light leather soaks and limes for a long time. He gets a mild action by the use of a mellow lime liquor made by using the same liquor for several packs of skins. He can also get a mild action by using arsenic sulfide instead of sodium sulfide.

A tanner must be on the alert to change his methods according to the kind of hides or skins he gets. These come to him from many sources and may be hard as flint or soft and flexible. No matter in what condition he gets them, he must know what to do so that they will be as nearly alike as possible on leaving the beamhouse to be tanned.

After the beamhouse treatment, skins for soft, flexible leather need to be thoroughly delimed and made flat and flabby. The tanner does that by bating. Bates formerly consisted of suspensions of dog or bird dung; now they are commercial preparations, usually a mixture of pancreatic enzymes and ammonium chloride. The tanner may change the concentration, time, and temperature to suit his needs. Some skins after bating are pickled—treated with a solution of sulfuric acid and salt. The acid brings the skin to the necessary condition for tannage. The salt prevents the excessive swelling that would otherwise be caused by the acid. The effects of the pickling may be changed by concentration, temperature, and time of the process.

The hides or skins are now ready for tannage. If you look at an ordinary shoe you can see the difference between the two types of leather. The upper is a typical light leather and the sole is a typical heavy leather—or at least the tanner hopes so. Most sole leather is tanned with vegetable tanning extract made from barks, woods, leaves, or pods of natural vegetable origin. Most upper leathers are chrome-tanned— that is, tanned with chromium salts of mineral origin.

Heavy leather is usually tanned in solutions of vegetable tannins by a countercurrent system. The limed, unhaired, and partly delimed hides come into contact first with a weak, nonastringent (mellow) liquor, which has already been used for the tannage of more thoroughly tanned hides. After a day, the liquor is replaced by one of slightly higher tannin content and greater astringency. The process is repeated for several weeks, each liquor being stronger and more astringent than the preceding one. The liquor from the final tannage goes on less tanned leather and so on until finally, when it has become weak and mellow, it is used for the first tannage. Thus the leather and the liquor proceed in opposite directions through the tanyard. This countercurrent system is necessary because if hides were put into strong liquors they would be case-hardened— tanned hard on the outside and left raw inside.

The system allows an almost infinite variation to produce different types of leather—the tanner can make his leather more firm or more flexible or lighter or darker by his choice of tanning materials. He can shorten the time of process or lower the cost by the proper blend of different materials.

Tanners formerly made their liquors directly from the bark. Now most of them use a strong liquid extract, or a solid or powdered extract, made by a manufacturer of tanning materials.

In the early days, tanning methods were based on the use of oak bark and later hemlock bark. But when oak and hemlock became scarce, tanners had to change their methods to fit new materials. The most widely used tanning extract is quebracho, from southern South America. A blend of quebracho extract with chestnut extract, our most widely used domestic material, forms the basis of most American tannages.

Quebracho extract, used in the usual sulfited form, penetrates rapidly into the hide to give a leather that has good color and feel but tends to be flat and poorly filled. Chestnut extract gives a firm, well-filled leather, but it penetrates slowly if it is used alone and tends to make the leather too firm and brittle. The tanner blends the materials to modify the firmness or flexibility of the leather as he desires.

Tanning blends usually also contain other kinds of tanning extracts, which aid in acid formation, increase penetration, improve the color and general appearance, or lower cost. Myrobalans extract, made from the unripe nuts of the myrobalans tree of India, for example, is used to produce acid. Wattle extract, from the bark of the mimosa tree, now grown in South Africa, may be used to replace some of the chestnut or quebracho extract when high prices make that desirable. Sumac, most of which is now imported from Sicily but which grows wild in this country, is used to improve the color and feel of the leather. In all, several hundred different materials— woods, barks, pods, leaves, and roots— contain enough tannin to justify their use in tanning. But not very many of them are available to tanners in extract form, although enough have always been available to give wide selection.

Sometimes used in tanning blends is the so-called sulfite-cellulose extract, which is a solubilized lignin byproduct of the sulfite paper industry. Its tanning value is doubtful, but it lowers costs and probably has some value in modifying the character of the blend. There are also available a number of syntans. These are usually made from phenols and aldehydes in the same way as bakelite or other synthetic resins, except that they have been made soluble in water by treatment with sulfuric acid or other reagents. They are not true synthetic tannins, but in some cases give results similar to those of natural tannins, for which they may be substituted if their somewhat higher cost will permit.

With that wide variety from which to choose, the tanner has been able to change his blend of tanning materials almost at will to produce the desired effect. However, the trees which provided these materials are getting scarce, and although steps are being taken to develop new tanning materials, either natural or synthetic, it is certain that in the future the tanner will not have the wide choice he has had in the past. Instead of changing his tanning blend to modify the leather, he must now treat the available tanning extracts before use, or modify the tanning process, so that one tanning material may give effects formerly produced by a different type of extract.

To modify the properties of the finished leather, the tanner may also change the tannin content of the liquors at various stages of tanning. These liquors, with an average tannin content of 0.5 percent in the weakest and 9 percent in the strongest, may be made either stronger or weaker. Another factor is the purity of the liquors—the ratio of tannin to total soluble matter. A low purity makes soft and spongy leather; a high purity is required for firm leathers. The acidity, measured either as total acid or as pH (active acidity), also modifies the character of the leather. The hides carry lime over into the tanyard and it must be neutralized and the hides brought to the slightly acid condition necessary for tanning. Generally, enough acid is formed by the fermentation of the sugars present in tanning materials, but sometimes it is necessary to add a weak organic acid, such as lactic or acetic acid. An acid condition of the liquors is required to plump the hides to the swollen condition that gives firmness and fullness to the finished leather. Too much acid, however, may cause an overswelling of the hide and produce tender leather; it may even cause casehardening. The best acid conditions are probably between pH 3.5 in the stronger liquors and pH 4.5, or perhaps slightly higher, in the weaker liquors.

Mineral salts or inorganic material

are also in tanning liquors. If they are salts of the weak acids, they lower the acidity of the liquor and reduce its plumping power. Almost all other types of mineral matter, while not affecting the acidity, reduce the plumping power. In either case, flat, poorly filled leather is made. The mineral matter comes into the tan liquors from the lime brought in by the hides, from the mineral constituents of the tanning material, or from the water used. The countercurrent system already described gives the tanner an opportunity to regulate the amount of mineral matter accumulating in the liquor. A faster flow of the liquors through the tanyard reduces this amount, but it also retards the mellowing of the liquor and cuts down the amount of acids formed by fermentation. One factor must be balanced against the other to determine the proper procedure.

The tanner may also modify the tanning processes. At first the hides are suspended in weak liquor in vats in the so-called rocker section and given a slight rocking motion. The hides stay in the rocker section until the tannin has penetrated them. The customary way of finishing the tanning has been to place the hides flat in vats, laying one over the other, sometimes separated by a thin layer of bark. They remained in these lay-away vats, in which the liquors were strengthened one or more times, for several weeks or months, until they were thoroughly tanned. Tanners have found that by increasing the time in the rockers, using stronger liquors, the time in the layaways may be shortened, or these vats eliminated. This greatly shortens the time of tanning. Another way to shorten it is to tan in revolving drums with strong liquors toward the end of the tannage. Some tanners believe that shortening the time by these methods is accomplished at the expense of some of the firmness and fullness desired in the final leather.

The tanner can modify the character of the leather in the finishing operations. Leathers must be lubricated with oil or grease. For sole leather a mixture of animal or fish oil, such as cod, with mineral oil and sulfonated oil is commonly used. For harness leather a mixture of greases, such as tallow, and oils, is used. To give the leather greater grease-holding capacity it is not tanned so heavily as sole leather is. The leather may be rolled to make it hard and firm, staked to make it flat and flexible, and brushed to polish it. Sole leather may be bleached to give it a lighter color. Loading materials, such as epsom salts, glucose, and sulfite-cellulose extracts, may be added to make it retain its thickness and firmness in the finishing operation. Finally, the leather must be dried—an important step that takes careful watching. The tanner may modify any of these procedures to get the kind of leather he wishes.

The tanning of light leather is a short process as compared to heavy-leather tannage. It starts in the beamhouse, already described.

For some kinds of light leather the tanner uses vegetable tanning materials, syntans, or mixtures of them. The skins may be tanned somewhat as in the early stages of heavy-leather tannage or they may be tanned by tumbling in a drum with a solution of the tanning extract. Sometimes finely ground sumac leaves and water are added to the pickled skins in a tanning drum and the skins are tanned by the tannin leached from the leaves while tumbling.

Some tanners, especially tanners of glove leather, use an alum tannage. They tumble the skins in a drum containing a solution of aluminum sulfate, made alkaline with sodium carbonate and containing salt to prevent swelling. Toward the end of the process the liquor is neutralized with enough borax or sodium bicarbonate to precipitate the alum thoroughly in the skins. A mixture of egg yolk, oil, and flour is rubbed well into the leather, which is then allowed to dry and age for several weeks before being washed and finished. Alum tannage is also used for furs. In that case, the alkaline aluminum sulfate is generally made into a paste with flour and oil and rubbed into the flesh side of the skin.

Some tough, white leathers are tanned with formaldehyde. Formaldehyde, however, is used more as a pretannage than as a single tanning agent. It either imparts new characteristics to the finished leather or it aids in tannage with the other material. The skins are tanned with dilute solution of alkaline formaldehyde, which combines with the skin substance to form a type of leather. The alkalinity must be carefully regulated. The liquors will not tan unless sufficiently alkaline, but if they are too alkaline the leather will be brittle.

Chamois leather is oil-tanned. Although originally made from the skin of the chamois goat, it is now usually made from the inner layer of sheepskins. By alternately impregnating the skin with cod oil or some other suitable oil and drying, the oil combines with the skin to give chamois leather.

The chrome-tanning process is used for most light leathers, especially shoe uppers. Chromic oxide formed from sodium dichromate combines with the skin to form this type of leather. The skins may be impregnated with an acid sodium dichromate solution by tumbling in a revolving drum, and then with chromic oxide formed directly in the leather by tumbling in a sodium thiosulfate solution in a similar drum. In most cases, however, the sodium dichromate is reduced to chromic acid before being used and a tanning liquor is made from the acid. Bated skins from the beamhouse are pickled in acid and salt and drummed until tanned. They are then neutralized with a mild alkali, washed, and finished.

Several other methods for tanning light leather are used to a limited extent. There are so many ways of tanning light leather that it is probable that no two tanneries operate in exactly the same way. Every tanner has his own beamhouse procedures and his own methods of preparing tanning liquors and adjusting the strength, acidity, and ratio of liquor to leather. He determines the time of tanning, the temperature, the mechanical methods, the degree and manner of neutralization, and the amount and type of neutral salts to give him the effect on the leather that he wants.

The finishing operations, particularly staking, have a greater effect on light leathers than on heavy leathers. Most leathers, left to dry by themselves, become hard and brittle because of adhesion of the fibers, but if they are flexed repeatedly at the proper stage of drying the fibers become separated and do not adhere when dry. When the Indians tanned deerskins for buckskin leathers, the squaws did the job by chewing on the leathers. Staking formerly was conducted by hand over a rounded blade fixed vertically. Sometimes the operator used his bare knee instead of the blade; the process is still largely used for glove leather but for other leathers has been replaced by machines.

Tanners may combine different kinds of tannage to make the kind of leather they want. For example, heavy leathers may be chrome-tanned and finished with a vegetable tannage. The time of tannage is thus shortened and the leather retains the properties of a vegetable tannage and acquires new properties, such as resistance to moist heat. Some light leathers are pretanned with formaldehyde before retannage with chrome, alum, or oil to give greater flexibility and resistance.

R. W. Frey and C. W. Beebe found that a combination chrome- and vegetable-tanned bookbinding leather has the resistance to acid deterioration of chrome leather combined with the workability and good appearance of vegetable-tanned leathers and that the vegetable-tanned leathers retanned with alum showed the same effect.

C. W. Beebe, J. S. Rogers, and W. F. Happich discovered that retanning vegetable-tanned insole leather with alum solution, suitably stabilized, imparts resistance to moist heat and to deterioration by molds. In preliminary tests they found that the serviceability of such vegetable-tanned leather may be greatly increased by alum retannage.

Tanners now have the benefit of research results in changing their tanning processes to give them the leathers they wish. G. D. McLaughlin and E. R. Theis, in *The Chemistry of Leather Manufacture,* give the results of investigations which showed that sodium sulfhydrate, instead of sodium sulfide, or methylamine may be used as an unhairing agent in the beamhouse. New sources of tanning materials are being developed, but it is probable that the choice of such materials may be restricted. Therefore, it is of interest to investigate methods of modifying existing tanning materials. Sulfiting quebracho to increase its solubility and ease of penetration into the leather is now an accepted practice.

P. Chambard reported that during the war French tanners modified chestnut extract by increasing the solubility and pH to give it some of the properties of quebracho extract, which was almost unobtainable. In the development of canaigre extract, T. C. Cordon, C. W. Beebe, and J. S. Rogers have devised methods for fermentation of the sugars present to increase the purity of the extract. Tanners generally want high-purity extracts for the production of firm leathers.

Some of the new syntans (developed by H. G. Turley and J. H. Highberger, A. H. Bump and F. O'Flaherty, A. H. Winheim and E. E. Doherty) appear promising. Sulfonyl chloride has been proposed by M. F. White, W. T. Roddy, and O'Flaherty as a substitute for cod oil in making chamois leather. E. R. Theis and T. Kleppinger have found that stabilizing or "masking" salts have been found capable of improving chrome leather. Stabilizing salts of the same type have aided in the alum retannage of heavy vegetable-tanned leathers by increasing the penetration of the aluminum salts.

C. W. BEEBE *is a graduate of the University of California. After 11 years as chemist with a firm of tanners, he joined the Department of Agriculture in 1929. He is now head of the tanning materials and processes section in the Bureau of Agricultural and Industrial Chemistry.*

TOBACCO STEMS and leaf wastes from factories that process tobacco are highly regarded as fertilizer for many crops. They are evaluated commercially on the basis of the nitrogen content as organic nitrogen and the potash on the basis of carbonate of potash. One ton of air-dried stems is usually considered equal to 3 to 4 tons of fresh stable manure. The nitrogen content ranges from 2 to 4 percent and the potash from 3 to 8 percent, depending on the type of tobacco. Tobacco stems are recommended for use on roses and nearly all ornamentals, lawns and hay crops, citrus and small fruits, most truck crops, and the home garden. They have been used to grow spawn for mushroom culture. They should not be used, however, for tobacco or other solanaceous crops unless they are sterilized, because they may carry some of the virus diseases common to those crops. They can be used in nearly every place where barnyard manure is recommended.—*Ernest G. Beinhart, Eastern Regional Research Laboratory.*

Native Sources of Tanning Materials

Jerome S. Rogers

Most of the vegetable tannins used to tan our many kinds of leather we get from other countries. If we want to be independent of foreign supplies and have domestic tannins adequate to meet the critical needs of a national emergency, we will have to increase our production of new tannins, develop tannins from plants that can be grown as farm crops, and salvage more tannin from waste barks.

Tannins occur naturally in most plant materials, but relatively few plants that are rich in tannin are also adapted for cultivation just for tannin crops. Two native materials, canaigre and sumac, seem to be well suited for crop cultivation and are now being studied by the Department of Agriculture.

Canaigre, *Rumex hymenosepalus* Torr, belongs to the dock family. It is native to southwestern United States and northern Mexico. Its tuberous roots, which look somewhat like sweet-potatoes, are rich in tannin and have been used in tanning leather for centuries by the Mexicans and Indians. It is propagated by roots, root crowns, or seed. Canaigre planted in the fall grows during the winter and blooms in early spring. The top dies back in May or June. The roots remain dormant until fall, when they sprout again. Harvesting is usually done in July, August, or September. Under favorable conditions annual yields of about 10 tons of fresh roots to the acre can be expected.

Sandy, well-drained soils and dry climates in Texas, New Mexico, and Arizona are well adapted for growing canaigre. To assure good yields, irrigation is desirable. By selection of planting stock, strains of high yield and tannin content can be developed. Experimental plots have been successfully harvested with standard potato-digging equipment. Washing, shredding, and rapid air-drying 1 or 2 weeks after harvest insure roots that can be stored and shipped without spoilage. Harvested roots exposed too long in the air become hard and difficult to shred. Damaged roots mold readily.

Freshly dug canaigre roots contain 65 to 75 percent moisture. The tannin content of the moisture-free roots usually ranges from 20 to 40 percent. Some samples of wild roots have been found to contain more than 43 percent tannin. The roots also contain 8 to 20 percent sugar and 25 to 40 percent starch.

Two native strains have been observed. They differed in color, in tannin content, and in behavior in experimental studies of leaching.

The problems encountered in extracting tannin and making extracts of high commercial quality from canaigre roots differ greatly from those met in preparing tanning extracts from bark or wood. The starch in canaigre makes it impracticable and inefficient to extract coarse shreds countercurrently with hot water, in accord with the usual commercial practice as applied to barks. The swelling and gelatinization of the starch by hot water prevent effective extraction of the tannin. To overcome that difficulty, several laboratory-scale procedures were investigated. One gave promising results. The properly prepared canaigre was extracted in accordance with the countercurrent principle, by which water at 104° to 113° F. went on the spent material in the tail leach, moved forward through several lots, and came off as a concentrated head liquor from the finely divided fresh material in the head leach. Between each forward step the liquor and partly spent material were subjected to vigorous mixing at 104° to 113° F., followed by mechanical separation of liquid and solids. This procedure gave leaching efficiencies of 75 to 85 percent. For example, from 100 parts of canaigre roots containing 35.5 parts of tannin, 29.4 parts of tannin were recovered in the extracted liquor.

The sugars present in canaigre roots are soluble and are extracted with the tannin by water. When the extracted liquors containing tannin and sugars and other nontannin substances are concentrated, the tanning extracts produced are low in purity because of the sugars present. We raised the purity of the extracts by removing the sugars by fermentation, using specially isolated bacteria. Several strains of *Aerobacter aerogenes*, obtained from canaigre roots and the soil in which canaigre grows, made effective growth and destroyed the sugars in canaigre liquors without material loss of tannin. The principal products of this fermentation are 2,3-butanediol, acetoin, and ethyl alcohol.

Comparison of analyses of powdered canaigre extracts made from unfermented and fermented canaigre liquors shows that by fermentation of liquors the quality of tanning extract can be greatly improved. For example, in one case the sugar content of an extract was lowered from 22.9 to 0.7 percent and the nontannin from 44.0 to 28.7 percent, while the tannin content was raised from 49.7 to 62.1 percent and the purity from 53 to 68.4.

By the fermentation procedure, we got canaigre extracts that compare acceptably with some of the best commercial tanning extracts, such as powdered chestnut (with a tannin content of 61.3 percent and a purity of 66.3) and

ordinary solid quebracho extract (with a tannin content of 68.5 percent and a purity of 87.5).

In laboratory-scale extractions that used aqueous-organic solvent mixtures, those containing acetone or isopropyl alcohol gave best tannin recovery. Both were more efficient than water and had the further advantage that when the solvents were used in proper concentrations starch did not interfere in the extraction. Because of the costs of the solvent, fire hazards, and recovery problems, however, further study and an analysis of costs are needed to establish the economic feasibility of their use.

In laboratory tests, canaigre extracts have been successfully used both alone and blended with other tannins for the tanning of good-quality leathers of the sole-leather type.

Several processes for the preparation of tanning extracts from canaigre are being studied on a pilot-plant scale. For each process, that entails the correlation of drying, grinding, leaching, and clarification operations so as to obtain an integrated process. Also to be determined are the engineering and economic factors that govern the choice of commercial equipment. Both batch and continuous leaching are being studied. The most promising results have been obtained by fine grinding of the dried roots. Tannin yields are enhanced by the addition of less than 20 percent of an organic solvent to the leaching water, but its economic desirability has not been fully evaluated.

SUMAC, a shrub that grows wild in this country, has long been known as a source of tanning and dyeing material. Its tannin is not well adapted for general use in tanning heavy leather. Its present use—to make lightweight leathers—might well be expanded, however, so as to help meet the demand for additional domestic tannins.

Sumac tannin, obtained from the leaves, is used as ground leaf or as a liquid extract. Tanners of lightweight leathers like it because it produces soft, durable, light-colored leathers of desirable feel.

Frequently a product of low quality is obtained because woody stalks low in tannin are collected with the leaves, deep piling during drying causes spoilage, or exposure of the leaves to dew or rain causes loss of tannin. The correction of such unsatisfactory practices will aid in obtaining a commercially acceptable product, and tanners will have less justification for their preference for the imported Sicilian sumac, *Rhus coriaria*.

Workers in the Department have found that sumac leaves of acceptable tannin content and commercial quality can be produced from domestic species if correct procedures are used in harvesting and drying.

The possible economical development of sumac for tannin, therefore, deserves consideration. The development involves the cultivation of high-quality sumac strains as farm crops and the mechanical harvesting and handling of the product by improved methods. Investigations are now in progress.

The three domestic sumacs that seem most promising for cultivation as tannin crops are the dwarf sumac (*Rhus copallina*), white sumac (*Rhus glabra*), and staghorn sumac (*Rhus typhina*). All have compound leaves, which average 32.5, 27.3, and 25.6 percent, respectively, of tannin on a moisture-free basis. They will grow on dry and sometimes rocky soil. Dwarf sumac has winged growths along the midribs between the leaflets and black specks on new-growth stalks. White sumac has smooth stalks and a bluish-white bloom, like the bloom on plums, which covers the stalks and the underside of the leaflets. Staghorn sumac has a hairy growth along the stalks and leaf midribs.

Sumac can be grown satisfactorily from seed or root stock, but roots must be handled promptly or they will die. No seed is yet available that can be guaranteed to produce high-tannin plants. Propagation by means of root

stock is slow in getting large acreages under cultivation, but it has the advantage that high-quality strains can be maintained by its use. Rich soil produces luxuriant growth, but then the leaves are low in tannin and the yield of tannin to the acre is not greatly increased.

A survey of sumac that grew wild over 12,000 square miles in southern Virginia indicated that about 43,000 long tons of dry sumac leaf could be collected there annually.

Ira D. Clarke, A. F. Sievers, and Henry Hopp, and I have studied eight species of sumac native to the eastern and southern parts of the United States to determine tannin content and abundance. The results of our investigations are given in the Department Technical Bulletin No. 986, *Tannin Content and Other Characteristics of Native Sumac in Relation to Its Value as a Commercial Source of Tannin*. (1949.)

We found that leaves, leaflets, and flowers of sumac were high in tannin and that all other parts of the plant were low in tannin and would lower the quality of the leaf product if mixed with it. In a statistical study of the effects of genetic and environmental factors on composition, we learned that leaves of male plants of *Rhus copallina* contained an average of 3.3 percent more tannin than those of female plants; that leaves of *Rhus copallina* and *Rhus glabra* that grew in partial shade averaged 2.8 percent less tannin than leaves of similar plants growing in full sunlight; and that date of collection influenced tannin content, there being an average decrease in tannin of 0.047 percent a day during the summer.

Yields of leaves calculated from small plots of plants 1, 2, and 3 years old indicate that $\frac{1}{2}$ to 3 tons of dry leaves can be had from an acre under varying conditions. More data are needed on methods of harvesting applied successively for several seasons to plots of an acre or more.

Sumac leaves dried rapidly at ordinary temperatures with good ventilation do not change in composition. They produce good, light-colored leather. Slow drying at ordinary temperatures, caused by poor aeration or high humidity, means a loss of nontannin material, principally sugar, but does not change the amount of tannin. Such partly decomposed leaves produce dark leather. Drying at 212° F. results in a slight loss of tannin and sugar, but the product produces good, light-colored leather.

In a commercial tanning test on more-than 330 dozen sheepskin skivers, all three domestic species produced satisfactory leather that was approximately equal to that produced by Sicilian sumac.

F. P. Luvisi and Ira D. Clarke, at the Eastern Regional Research Laboratory, learned that a temperature of 212° F. was most efficient for extraction for the determination of tannin. They also found that heat up to 212° F. had only a slight effect on dry leaves, but that leaves were altered by steeping in water, apparently by a change of tannin into nontannin. Both temperature and time of steeping were factors.

Ivan L. Boyd, in comprehensive research on sumac at Iowa State College in cooperation with the Soil Conservation Service, found that four native species—*Rhus glabra, R. copallina, R. typhina,* and *R. aromatica*—had possibilities for cultivation as sources of tannin and, because of their spreading, shallow root systems, were valuable in preventing soil erosion. Of these, *R. glabra* was the most promising for southeastern Iowa. Propagation of the species by root cuttings gave a survival rate of 10 to 82 percent. Seed from the four species treated with concentrated sulfuric acid gave an average germination of 13 percent. Better germination was obtained with seed selected from clones yielding a high percentage of viable seed. Seedlings from *R. glabra* and *R. typhina* reach harvesting size in about 3 years. The tannin content of leaves increases each year in seedlings but seldom exceeds that of the adult clone. It is increased by de-blossoming the plant and is lowered by growth in shade. Three-year-old seedling plants of the four species gave yields at the following rates per acre: *R. aromatica,* 416 pounds; *R. glabra,* 592 pounds; *R. copallina,* 975 pounds; and *R. typhina,* 2,250 pounds.

E. L. Barger and J. M. Aikman, of Iowa State College, developed a power-driven harvester that was suitable for harvesting sumac from both wild and cultivated stands. Under favorable conditions about 3 tons of green leaf could be harvested a day, an amount equal to what 10 men could harvest by hand in a day. Tests were also conducted on drying and mechanical separation of leaves from woody stalks.

In the development of sumac as a domestic tannin crop, machine methods for harvesting, drying, and separation of leaves from stems reduce labor costs and aid in meeting competition from sumac from foreign countries where labor costs are low.

THE RECOVERY OF TANNIN from available supplies of unused and waste barks could aid materially in meeting the present shortage in domestic tannins. Among the barks that might be used are Florida scrub oak (*Quercus laevis*), with 10 percent tannin; eastern hemlock (*Tsuga canadensis*), 12 percent; western hemlock (*Tsuga heterophylla*), 15 percent; Douglas-fir, (*Pseudotsuga taxifolia*), 10 percent; Florida mangrove (*Rhizophora mangle*), 31.5 percent; and a mixture of oaks from the Tennessee Valley, which would probably average about 8 percent tannin. Although of acceptable tannin content, some of the barks offer no promise as economical sources of tannin.

Bark of western hemlock, one of the largest undeveloped sources, represents a potential annual supply of about 35,000 tons of 100-percent tannin. It is not too promising, however, because the practice of floating logs downstream causes a loss of about one-half of the bark tannin and salt contamination of the bark on logs floated in salt water.

Florida mangrove bark is inaccessible and costly to collect. It probably would not yield more than 1,000 tons of 100-percent tannin annually for 5 years.

The barks of the Florida scrub oaks might be recovered by hogging the logs and branches and mechanically separating the bark from the wood by air flotation, as described by H. N. Calderwood and W. D. May, at the Florida Engineering and Industrial Experiment Station. The bark would be used as a source of tannin and the wood for paper pulp. The bark might furnish as much as 5,000 tons of 100-percent tannin annually for 20 years.

L. F. Bailey and W. H. Cummings, of the Tennessee Valley Authority at Norris, Tenn., found that mixed oak slabs could be extracted to yield about 3,000 tons of 100-percent tannin a year.

The Lake States region has supplies of hemlock bark which, if salvaged, should yield around 17,000 tons of 100-percent tannin annually. The high cost of peeling and collection raises a question, however, as to the economical feasibility of utilizing this bark to make tanning extract.

Douglas-fir bark, now being investigated at the Oregon Forest Products Laboratory, appears to have promise. The investigators found tannin contents of 7.6 to 18.3 percent, and estimated that the average tannin content would be about 10 percent. They found that the bark also contained an average of 7 percent of waxes and 5 percent of dihydroquercetin. They estimate a potential annual tannin recovery equal to more than 150,000 tons of 100-percent tannin. If such a quantity of fir bark tannin could be produced economically, it would aid greatly in solving this country's tanning material shortage. However, the tanning properties of fir bark tannin require further study to determine its suitability for making various types of leather.

The vegetable tannins most commonly used in making leather are water-soluble materials obtained from barks, woods, leaves, and fruits—for example, the barks of oak, hemlock, wattle, and mangrove, the woods of quebracho and chestnut, the leaves of sumac and gambier, and the fruits of valonia oak, myrobalan, tara, and divi divi. Of these, the one most extensively used in our leather industry is the tannin from quebracho wood, which we import from Argentina and Paraguay as solid extract. Second is the tannin from chestnut wood, which is produced domestically but may be exhausted soon because blight has killed nearly all commercially important stands of chestnut.

Fifty years ago most of the leather produced in the United States was tanned with tannins from oak and hemlock bark. Today only a limited amount is produced from them. Small amounts of tanning extracts are made from domestic supplies of sumac leaves and pecan shells. All other vegetable tannins are imported.

Accurate data on our use of tannin are not available, but some idea of the amounts can be obtained from import figures and estimates of domestic production. From 1940 to 1949, the United States consumed annually an average of about 125,000 tons of 100-percent tannin; more than 70 percent of it was imported. Quebracho tannin, from South America, constituted nearly 70 percent of the foreign tannin group and more than 50 percent of the total consumption. Chestnut wood tannin accounted for about 95 percent of the domestically produced tannin and about 25 percent of the total consumption. Tannin from wattle bark, imported principally from Africa, held third place. Mangrove bark tannin, from Africa and South America, was fourth.

Drillers of oil wells have discovered that quebracho tanning extract, treated with caustic alkali, helps in regulating the viscosity and consistency of drilling muds. Several thousand tons of extract are used annually for the purpose. To relieve that added demand, substitute extracts or other materials suitable for the purpose are being sought.

The essentiality of vegetable tannins in the manufacture of leather is illustrated in figures for leather production in the United States in 1949 (in millions):

Hides or skins:	Vegetable- tanned	Mineral- eral- tanned	Total tanned
Cattle_____	8. 2	15. 2	23. 4
Sheep and lamb_	8. 5	20. 3	28. 8
Calf and kip___	1. 0	9. 1	10. 1
Goat and kid_____		34. 7	34. 7

The mineral-tanned leathers were tanned principally with chrome but included alum and all other mineral tannages and also mineral-tanned leathers that were retanned with vegetable tannins.

Vegetable tanning materials were used for tanning approximately 35 percent of the cattle-hide leather, 30 percent of the sheepskin and lambskin leather, and 10 percent of the calfskin and kip leather.

Cattle hides, when vegetable-tanned in their original thickness, yield heavy, thick, firm leathers, which are especially adapted for use as shoe soles, harness, luggage, and belting. Leathers of those types take more tannin than do the lightweight, soft, flexible leathers used for shoe uppers, gloves, garments, and fancy leather goods.

One tanner uses a blend of vegetable tannins containing 51.2 pounds of 100-percent tannin to produce 100 pounds of air-dry sole leather from steer hides. A tanner of light leather, on the other hand, to produce 100 pounds of calfskin and sheepskin leathers uses, respectively, only 36 and 40 pounds of 100-percent quebracho tannin. Heavy leathers are tanned principally with vegetable tannins. For light leathers, mineral tannages, such as chrome or alum, are commonly used. The properties of leather differ according to the tanning materials. For some uses, mineral-tanned leathers

are preferred; for others,. vegetable-tanned leathers are better. Some synthetic tannins are often used in light-leather tannages. They have also been used in some heavy-leather tanning, but their prices are materially higher than those of vegetable tannins.

Present domestic sources of tannin are chestnut wood, oak and hemlock barks, sumac leaves, and pecan shells.

Most of the domestic tannin, probably more than 95 percent, is obtained from the wood of the American chestnut, *Castanea dentata*. It is quite generally known, as I said before, that the trees that constituted the commercial stands of chestnut in the United States are being killed by blight, caused by a parasitic fungus, which was brought into the country on Japanese chestnut trees planted on Long Island about 1893. By 1904 native chestnuts were dying. Progress has been made in developing blight-resistant chestnut trees by G. F. Gravatt, Jesse O. Diller, and Russell B. Clapper, of the Bureau of Plant Industry, Soils, and Agricultural Engineering.

Ira D. Clarke, E. T. Steiner, and R. W. Frey, of the Bureau of Agricultural and Industrial Chemistry, studied the tannin contents of the blight-resistant Chinese chestnut, *Castanea mollissima*, and found that trunk wood from trees 16 and 25 years old contained 8.0 and 12.0 percent tannin, respectively, compared with 8.4 percent for 14-year-old American chestnut. Although the tannin content of blight-resistant chestnuts compares favorably with that of the native chestnut, because of the long time required to produce commercial stands, there appears to be no prospect for the development of a domestic tannin supply from this source.

IN ANY STUDY of the possibilities for the economical development and utilization of available bark supplies, several factors need to be considered—the quantities available, accessibility, tannin content, possible byproducts, and the costs of bark, extract production, and transportation. Of the barks investigated, the oaks from Florida and the Tennessee Valley, the hemlock from the Lake States area, and the fir from Oregon and Washington appear to have promise. The bark from western hemlock would also be a promising source of tannin if it could be salvaged from logs that have not been floated.

The production of tannin from farm crops has many desirable features. It offers a new crop at a time of farm surpluses. The production of canaigre and sumac will furnish two types of tannin that will be available for blending with other tannins. Sumac will be adapted for light-leather tannage and for many purposes could replace quebracho. Canaigre will be a root crop that can be harvested with available farm machinery. Associated with the canaigre tannin will be starch and sugar, byproducts which may be used for production of fermentation products. Canaigre crops can be largely expanded or curtailed to meet rapidly changing demands.

The ability of this country to provide a major part of the vegetable tanning materials that it needs for the manufacture of leather depends on the successful completion of investigations now under way. We can probably best attain this objective by a combination of two lines of activities—one, the development of economical procedures for the salvage and utilization of available supplies of oak, hemlock, and fir barks; the other, the large-scale cultivation and production of canaigre, sumac, and other tannin-bearing plants as farm crops.

JEROME S. ROGERS *is a native of New York State. His undergraduate training was at Syracuse University and his graduate work at the University of Illinois. From 1909 to 1917 he was with the Leather and Paper Laboratory of the Bureau of Chemistry. From 1918 to 1936 he was chemist in charge of the laboratories of Kistler, Lesh & Co. and International Shoe Co. In 1937 he returned to research on leather and tanning materials in the Department of Agriculture. He is on the staff of the Eastern Regional Research Laboratory.*

MOLDING OF BERRIES arising from mold growth on boxes used to transport berries from field to processing plant has been serious in the Pacific Northwest. In response to a request from the industry for help in solving the problem, the Western Regional Research Laboratory in 1948 set up an emergency research project which produced a practical answer in time for the 1949 berry season.

The method found most effective is to treat the wooden boxes with wax, so as to prevent the absorption of berry juices, which support mold growth, and to make washing of the boxes easier. The treatment consists of dipping the boxes in a molten mixture of 95 percent standard paraffin wax and 5 percent microcrystalline wax under carefully controlled conditions of temperature and time. A simple control test, made by placing a drop of a blue dye solution on the treated box, tells whether the treatment has been done right. The treated boxes remain substantially free from mold growth throughout the season if properly washed after each use. Loss of fruit due to mold damage is greatly diminished or entirely eliminated. Wax-treated boxes will probably cost less than untreated boxes in the long run, because untreated boxes must be replaced each year, while the treated boxes should last two or three seasons.—*W. D. Ramage, Western Regional Research Laboratory.*

Ways To Stop Losses of Tanbark

Marvin E. Fowler

One way to husband our limited resources of vegetable tannin materials is to utilize them as fully as possible. That, in turn, calls for cutting out the wastes now resulting from practices that do not prevent deterioration.

Chestnut wood is the most important source of domestic tannin for making heavy leather. Nearly all this wood now being utilized is from trees that have been killed by an introduced fungus blight. Although dead trees can be used for extracting tannin, they will eventually succumb to windthrow, decay, or other deterioration if left in the forests. Extract plants can no longer supply the tanneries with all the chestnut extract they need. After the tannin has been extracted, many plants utilize the spent wood for pulp in making paper and other pulpwood products.

Bark from the chestnut oak and hemlocks comes next to chestnut wood in importance as domestic sources of tannin. Their average tannin content is about 11 percent for hemlock and 12 percent for chestnut oak. The shortage in chestnut tannin increases the existing need for oak and hemlock tannin. Tanneries that use those barks have been unable to obtain as much bark as they need, even at higher prices. For some years we have had to import large quantities of tannin materials— more than two-thirds of the amount we need to make our leather.

Bark will probably provide most of our domestic tannin when chestnut extract is no longer available. As additional supplies of bark tannin are needed, it is important to handle peeled bark so as to prevent loss from improper curing.

The time when the bark of chestnut oak and hemlock separates easily from the wood differs from year to year, depending on the condition of the tree, rainfall, altitude, exposure, and temperature.

Chestnut oak bark peels when there is abundant soft sappy tissue beneath it and before the bark and wood tissues are bound together by interlocking growth projections. Usually that is from just before the time when the buds swell until the leaves reach mature size. The period normally lasts 6 to 8 weeks, but is sometimes shortened by a long spell of dry weather.

In hemlocks, the growth projections do not form and bind the bark to the wood, and usually the sappy tissue beneath the bark is sufficient to permit peeling from early spring until autumn.

The bark tightens earlier on oaks and hemlocks of low vigor than on fast-growing trees. During the peeling season, the bark peels most easily right after a tree has been cut. It tightens rapidly as the tissues dry. Hemlock cut in the winter, however, usually peels satisfactorily the following May or June. Bark peeling of both chestnut oak and hemlock can begin early in spring at lower elevations and on southern slopes. The operations can finish on higher and northern slopes where the bark is slower to tighten.

The heavy bark at the base is usually peeled before the tree is felled. The trunk is girdled about breast high and is peeled to the ground. Some peelers remove the bark from the stumps after the trees have been cut. It is easier to peel the bark from the underside of the trunks if they are felled across a log or on uneven ground.

After trees are felled into open spaces, encircling cuts are made with an ax every 3 or 4 feet on chestnut oak and every 4 or 5 feet on hemlock. Then, with an ax or the sharp side of a spud, the bark is split lengthwise between the girdling cuts on the top of the felled log.

Chestnut oak bark that has begun to stick can be loosened, and peeling made easier, by pounding it with the butt end of a poleax or with a sledge hammer. The bark is peeled from the tree with a blunt instrument, such as a spud. Bark 8 to 18 inches wide is easiest to handle. Smaller pieces increase labor costs, because the bark is moved by hand in the woods and at the tanneries or extract plants. Such bark may also deteriorate more in storage.

During a good bark-peeling season and with mature trees, a man can fell and peel an average of a ton or more of bark a day, but production varies with weather and woods conditions. Hemlock bark generally peels more easily than chestnut oak bark. It is taken off the tree in larger pieces. A ton of bark is usually obtained from 1,500 to 2,000 board feet of hemlock, depending on the size of the timber and the thickness of its bark. Sometimes a ton of bark can be obtained from 1,000 board feet of large virgin hemlock.

Under normal conditions, if the bark is handled properly, it will cure satisfactorily without developing mold or decay. Long rainy seasons or frequent periods of dense fogs may create conditions favorable for the development of molds on even the best handled bark. The results of experiments conducted cooperatively by tanneries, extract plants, and the Department of Agriculture indicate a relationship between curing methods and quality of bark. Under adverse curing conditions, bark may remain very wet and start severe molding. In controlled experiments with chestnut oak bark in the East and with hemlock bark in the East and in the Lake States, improperly cured bark was found to contain less tannin than properly cured comparable bark. Under the most adverse conditions the badly molded bark contained up to 25 percent less tannin.

Under normal weather conditions, no significant difference exists between bark spread out to dry for several days before being placed in ricks and bark ricked immediately after it is peeled. But wet bark should be spread out until the free surface moisture has evaporated before it is placed in ricks. Bark placed in ricks while the outer, or ross, side is wet may mold and deteriorate.

OPEN, DRY, and well-ventilated places are best for bark ricks. A rick of bark in a damp, poorly ventilated place may mold and cause a loss of tannin. Ricks are usually 3 to 4 feet high and 6 to 8 feet long. They are built off the ground. Bark may be stacked across two logs, so that air can circulate under the rick. The outer, or ross, side of the bark should be turned up. Occasional narrow pieces inserted crosswise at the front and back of the rick will separate the bark and improve ventilation. Raising the front of the rick with a few extra pieces of bark permits drainage of rain water. Large pieces of bark placed shinglewise on top will keep out water.

Bark left scattered in the woods, even if the inner side is turned down, does not cure so satisfactorily as that placed in ricks. In some operations the crew peels bark during the morning and early afternoon and then stacks the bark peeled that day. In other operations the bark is not stacked until the second day. In still others one man stacks it continuously. Thin hemlock bark should be stacked soon because it curls easily while drying.

Bark should be left in ricks in the woods until it is dry enough to break with a clean fracture—usually 2 weeks or longer. After drying, it may be left there for several months, if more convenient to the operator and bark buyer. Bark is usually allowed to age for at least 3 or 4 months after peeling before being used for tannin.

Properly cured bark is clean, has a bright flesh on the inner side, and is free from excess moisture. It breaks clean and not in strings, and it is not molded or mildewed. But improperly cured bark may be dark and covered with molds. Such bark is likely to contain less tannin than if it had been properly cured.

It is customary to arrange with a tannery or with a bark buyer for the sale of an estimated quantity of bark before peeling is begun. The distance the bark must be hauled to market or to a railroad siding for shipment by rail is an important consideration.

Bark is usually purchased by weight. A cord (4 x 4 x 8 feet) of cured bark weighs approximately a ton. Bark buyers generally dock the price for bark improperly cured, compensating at least for the weight of excess moisture. Bark so wet that it may decay or otherwise deteriorate in a bark stack may be entirely unsuitable.

Dirt and black mold on bark are objectionable. Logs from which bark is to be peeled should not be skidded through mud or floated in streams or ponds.

Leaving peeled logs on the ground until the peeling season is over or until the following winter results in very little deep checking and most of the cracks are removed in the slabs when the logs are sawed into construction lumber. Peeled wood also may be used for railroad ties, mine props, posts, and paper pulp.

Your regional or extension forester or county agricultural agent can give you information on markets for bark and peeled trees, and on areas in which tanbark stumpage is available.

MARVIN E. FOWLER *is a pathologist in the Bureau of Plant Industry, Soils, and Agricultural Engineering. He has investigated a number of diseases of shade and forest trees and is currently directing surveys for forest-tree diseases in the United States.*

THE BUREAU OF AGRICULTURAL ECONOMICS of the Department of Agriculture has undertaken studies of consumers' preferences among selected crops and products. The basic aim is to help find ways for improving the consumption of agricultural products by exploring new markets or better utilization of existing markets. Or, as set forth in the report of one study of potatoes (issued in May 1949) : "Producing potatoes is only part of a farmer's job. Potatoes must be sold. Growers and shippers want to know as much as possible about markets for potatoes. They want to produce and sell potatoes in line with what consumers want. People naturally buy more when they get what they want. If farmers and handlers have a knowledge of consumers' likes and dislikes they can try to get just the right potatoes moving to the group wanting them." Funds for the research were provided under the Research and Marketing Act of 1946.

Among the available reports are: *Citrus Preferences among Household Consumers in Louisville and in Nelson County, Kentucky; Potato Preferences Among Household Consumers; Men's Preferences Among Selected Clothing Items; Women's Preferences Among Selected Textile Products; Potato Preferences Among Restaurant and Hotel Buyers; Potatoes in Hotels and Restaurants; People and Potatoes; Consumers' Taste Reactions to Three Experimental Blends of Orange and Grapefruit Juice; Mothers' Preferences Among Selected Items of Children's Clothing; Rice Preferences Among Household Consumers; Consumer Preferences for Apples and Pears; Men's Preferences Among Wool Suits, Coats, and Jackets; Preferences for Citrus Among Household Consumers.—Raymond C. Smith, Bureau of Agricultural Economics.*

TO KEEP US WELL

Hazards and Potential Drugs

Floyd DeEds, Robert H. Wilson,
Anthony M. Ambrose

The science of pharmacology in its broadest sense is concerned with the effects of chemical agents upon living protoplasm.

Pharmacology embraces knowledge of the physical and chemical properties of chemical agents, their absorption by the living organism, their excretion, and their physiological actions.

Chemical agents may modify existing physiological functions, but they never create new functions. Pharmacological data permit conclusions as to the harmfulness or usefulness of chemical agents. They permit us to assess their acute and chronic toxicities, and their potential therapeutic values.

The pharmacologist uses the methods and equipment of the chemist, the biochemist, the physiologist, and, at times, the bacteriologist. The pharmacologist must recognize the gross aspects of changes in tissue structure that may be induced by chemical agents, but the details of such structural changes—the deviations from normal histology—belong in the field of pathology.

The pharmacologist determines the routes by which a compound may enter the body—by absorption from the intact skin and mucous membranes, by absorption from the gastrointestinal tract, or by absorption from the respiratory tract. He determines whether the effects of a compound are limited to local action at the point of contact or result in systemic effects following absorption. After the pharmacologist has demonstrated that a given chemical agent produces a physiological effect, he tries to find out how the effect is produced—what physiological or biochemical mechanisms are involved. If a compound raises or lowers the blood pressure, which of several mechanisms is involved? If it modifies the activity of the nervous system, is it acting on the brain, spinal cord, nerves, or nerve endings? When such questions are answered, when information on counteracting measures and proper dosages becomes available, the pharmacologist knows whether he is dealing with a harmless substance, a poison, or a substance with potential medicinal value.

These few comments on pharmacology establish its intimate relationship to the practice and study of medicine. But what is the justification for pharmacological investigations in the Department of Agriculture?

A part of the work of the Department of Agriculture has to do with the production, processing, and preservation of foods and feeds. For production, insecticides and fungicides are necessary—now more than ever because of modern intensive farming. The need for them arises from the constant struggle between man and pests.

Pest control used to be relatively simple. It involved the use of lead, arsenic, sulfur, nicotine, fluorine compounds, and, somewhat later, rotenone. The symptoms of acute and chronic toxicity that man might experience from exposure to such pesticides were known, as were the proper remedial measures. Moreover, the public health hazards of chronic toxicity traceable to excessive amounts of lead, arsenic, or fluorine in spray residues had been brought under a degree of control by the establishment of tolerance limits, which specified the amounts of the substances permitted in residues on foods.

Two factors operate to spoil that relatively simple method of control. Pests may develop a tolerance to a given pesticide, which means that more and more of the agent must be used or that new agents must be sought. The other factor is the happy hunting ground for pests resulting from modern farming methods, with highly specialized and large-scale production. Apples in orchards covering a square mile present a more serious pest problem than does a single apple tree in the back yard. To overcome the mounting difficulties, new insecticides and fungicides are being developed.

However, the difficulties of the problem of pest control do not end with the development of new pesticides. By 1931 workers in the Department realized that the synthesis of new organic compounds to replace or supplement lead, arsenic, and fluorine compounds might be creating new problems in the form of new public health hazards traceable to spray residues. A pharmacology laboratory was established in the Department in 1931. As will be shown later, the results obtained on chronic-toxicity studies of one potential insecticide, 2-acetaminofluorene, justified the pharmacological investigations.

The first problem assigned to the new laboratory was the determination of the chronic toxicity of inorganic fluorine compounds, which were finding increasing use as substitutes and supplements to lead and arsenic compounds as insecticides. The chronic-toxicity data on sodium fluoride, sodium fluosilicate, barium fluosilicate, and cryolite (sodium aluminum fluor-

ide) were needed to supply a factual basis for the establishment of a tolerance limit in spray residues.

The investigations on the fluorine compounds demonstrated that despite their widely different solubilities all were sufficiently soluble and absorbable to provide enough fluorine to mottle the incisor teeth in albino rats. With that as a standard for judging fluorine toxicity, pharmacologists learned that the susceptibility to fluorine toxicity was increased by raising the metabolic rate. The increase in metabolism was induced either by feeding desiccated thyroid or by injecting the thyrotropic hormone of the pituitary gland. The practical significance of the discovery is in its bearing on the public health hazard of fluorine, whether it be in spray residues or in drinking water. Tolerance limits for the allowable amount of fluorine likely to be ingested by the public should be low enough to protect the hyperthyroid individual and the normal one.

The claim that small amounts of fluorine in drinking water or the application of a fluoride, such as sodium fluoride, to the teeth will reduce the incidence of dental caries is undoubtedly correct. Checking dental caries and, in slightly larger amounts, causing mottled teeth, however, are not the only effects of fluorides. These compounds are enzymatic poisons. For example, the work of the Pharmacology Laboratory demonstrated that the fluoride ion inhibits the enzyme bone phosphatase in young rats and thereby retards calcification of the leg bones.

A number of potential organic insecticides have been investigated for acute and chronic toxicity. We have selected for consideration here two of these compounds—phenothiazine and 2-acetaminofluorene—as being of special interest in illustrating how the real fruit of research may sometimes be found along unanticipated side lines.

ONE OF THE FIRST organic insecticides studied was phenothiazine, the "parent" of thiazine dyes. The only signs of acute toxicity noted in rats and rabbits after oral administration of large doses of phenothiazine were temporary loss of appetite and anemia, from which the animals recovered spontaneously. The amount of phenothiazine in a single dose required to produce such temporary reactions was so large that the chance of anyone getting a toxic dose from a spray residue was quite outside the realm of possibility. The danger of acute poisoning from phenothiazine spray residues was therefore eliminated.

But would it be possible for people eating foods to which small amounts of phenothiazine might adhere to develop toxic symptoms from such material ingested at frequent intervals over long periods of time? To get the answer, scientists placed groups of albino rats on an adequate diet to which various amounts of phenothiazine were added. Only when the added phenothiazine constituted 0.3 percent or more of the diet was any effect noted. At those levels of phenothiazine intake, the rate of growth of the rats was reduced, but no abnormality of any of the tissues developed. In these experiments, as in the acute experiments, the amount of phenothiazine required to produce a toxic reaction was so large that toxicity from the amount likely to be in a spray residue would be negligible.

As a public health hazard, phenothiazine was given a clean bill of health. The low toxicity of phenothiazine and the fate of the compound in the animal body, however, led to other important discoveries. Because of the demonstrated low toxicity, the Bureau of Animal Industry investigated the use of the compound as an anthelmintic. Today the recognized value of phenothiazine lies in its use for removal of intestinal parasites from animals, rather than as an insecticide.

THE SECOND DISCOVERY concerns the use of phenothiazine as an antibacterial agent in the treatment of infections of the urinary tract. During passage through the body, phenothiazine is oxidized partly to phenothiazone and thionol. The two compounds are dyes related chemically to methylene blue and, like it, are oxidation-reduction systems that have bacteriostatic and bactericidal properties against certain micro-organisms.

To isolate the dyes, phenothiazone and thionol, from the urine of animals on diets containing phenothiazine, we collected their urine for several weeks. We noted that the urine did not develop a bacterial growth, a fact that could be attributed only to the thiazine dyes. The isolated dyes were tested for antibacterial action, and the suspected cause of the bacteria-free urine was confirmed.

A group of rabbits were given urinary bladder infections with cultures of *Escherichia coli*. Some of the rabbits were kept as controls; others were given phenothiazine by mouth. The bladder infections disappeared from the animals receiving phenothiazine. In view of the demonstrated low toxicity of phenothiazine, a cooperative study was initiated to determine the efficacy of phenothiazine in the treatment of urinary tract infections in man. In a series of 92 cases, the usefulness of phenothiazine was demonstrated.

A THIRD RESULT of our studies on phenothiazine was the observation on photosensitization—a person's sensitivity to sunlight. When practical field tests with phenothiazine sprays were made in apple orchards, severe skin reactions on some of the field workers were reported. Attending physicians diagnosed these reactions as dermatitis, chemical burn, and sunburn. The Pharmacology Laboratory found the cause of the skin reactions and outlined a procedure for prevention and treatment.

The oxidation products, phenothiazone and thionol, formed in the body after absorption of phenothiazine, are reversible oxidation-reduction systems like methylene blue, another thiazine dye. As in the case of leucomethylene blue, the colorless reduced forms of phenothiazone and thionol can be oxidized to the colored form by exposure to light, even though they are kept under strictly anaerobic conditions. Since it was known that the leuco forms of porphyrine and chlorophyll are photosensitive and can sensitize individuals to sunburn, it seemed possible that the leuco bases of the phenothiazine deriviatives might induce photosensitization in man. The skin sensitivity of three laboratory volunteers to the radiation of a sun lamp was determined. Two of the volunteers took doses of phenothiazine; the third took thionol. Eighteen hours later all three showed an increased response of hyperemia to the control dosage of radiation. We examined the urine of an orchard worker who had an unusual reaction to sunlight, and found phenothiazine oxidation products in it.

Once the cause of the photosensitization was known, it was possible to suggest such preventive measures as masks to prevent inhalation of phenothiazine spray and reduced exposure of skin to sunlight by means of adequate clothing or protective ointments. The corrective measures we suggested were that the sensitized individual keep away from direct sunlight and that he drink a lot of fluids to facilitate the excretion of the phenothiazine oxidation products.

ANOTHER ORGANIC COMPOUND that had shown promise as an insecticide was 2-acetaminofluorene. The Pharmacology Laboratory was asked to investigate the possibility that it might be a hazard to health. We have already discussed the inorganic element fluorine. The organic compound fluorene is entirely different. For convenience, the initials AAF are used here in place of the longer term, acetaminofluorene.

AAF is a light-colored, crystalline material. It is practically insoluble in water. Suspensions of AAF in a gum solution were made as thick as could be handled and given to rats, rabbits, and mice by stomach tube and by hypodermic injection. As much of the material was used as could be put into the animal. There were no signs of acute toxicity.

Even more important than acute toxicity is chronic toxicity. A person might, by mistake, take a single large dose of an insecticide, but he is much more likely to ingest small amounts as a spray residue, day after day. Contrary to what many people believe, lack of toxicity from a single large dose does not prove that a substance will be harmless in small doses over a period of time, nor is it necessarily true that a compound with high acute toxicity will have any chronic toxicity.

The AAF was therefore mixed in varying proportions with the diet and fed to rats for considerable periods. The animals were observed regularly and weighed. Their food intakes were determined. After 100 days, most of them were killed and examined carefully at autopsy. Tissues were saved for microscopic examination. No indication of decreased growth or other signs of toxicity could be seen by the naked eye unless the concentration had exceeded that which would be consumed by humans from spray residues. Careful microscopic study of the tissues showed occasional slight overgrowth (hyperplasia) of the epithelium of some of the organs. However, there was nothing very marked and the material would have been passed as safe for use as an insecticide if the investigation had ended at that point.

Experience has shown that a substance that has a chronic toxicity will ordinarily give an indication of it in 100 days. There are enough exceptions, however, to make it unsafe to stop testing at that time. Some of the rats were allowed to live, and on the 136th day one was found with a lump on the side of the head. A week later, two others had lumps—one in the thigh, the other in the abdomen. All the lumps proved to be cancer. Because cancer had never been observed in this colony of rats, AAF was studied more intensively. The early finding was enough to have AAF removed from the list of proposed insecticides, however, at least until our findings had been verified. They have been verified, in our laboratory and in several others, and AAF will never be considered for insecticidal use.

Some of the observations in our study of AAF thus can be summarized briefly. AAF produces malignant tumors in a variety of organs, but almost always it is the epithelium of the organ that is first involved. There have been many carcinomas, a few leukemias, and only one sarcoma. There is a limit below which no malignant growths occur, but it is low. Rats on diets containing 0.004 percent of AAF have developed carcinoma. One-fourth of this concentration was too low, although slight abnormalities of tissues were found after 2 years. AAF does not have to be given continuously. While a single dose has no effect, the feeding of diets containing 0.125 percent AAF for 25 days will lead to cancer some 100 days to 2 years after the start of the experiment. Changes initiated during the 25 days ultimately develop into malignancy.

For all practical purposes, the AAF has to be given by mouth. We believe that the acetyl group is hydrolyzed off in the intestinal tract and that the resulting aminofluorene is the true carcinogen. We know that the aminofluorene causes cancer. Bielschowsky, in England, has produced cancer by applying it to the skin of rats. Similar application of AAF is not harmful.

It appears that AAF is carcinogenic because of the amino group on the number 2 carbon of fluorene. As mentioned earlier, 2-aminofluorene produces cancer, but chlorine in the same position does not. We tested a number of fluorene derivatives, with substitutions in other parts of the molecule; all of them appeared harmless.

The general importance of the work on AAF should be summarized. The immediate effect of the studies was to prevent the use of a dangerous substance as an insecticide. If our studies had been limited to acute toxicity, or if the chronic investigations had been

for too short a time, and we had given the compound a clean bill of health, AAF might have been officially proposed as an insecticide, and the consuming public would have been eating small amounts of the material at frequent intervals. The amounts might have been great enough to produce cancer. But cancer is already known as a disease of human beings; according to statistics, the number of cases seems to be increasing. Consequently, a further increase would show up in the mortality tables, although its cause would be deeply buried.

The studies also have been important in an entirely different way—a new carcinogenic agent has been furnished to researchers to help in the investigations of cancer. Many chemical substances that produce cancer are known, but AAF is unique in several ways. It is one of the few that is effective when taken by mouth. It produces cancer in a much greater variety of organs than do the usual carcinogens. It is already in use in many laboratories, especially in England and this country, and it may be that it will aid in unraveling the mysteries of a major disease.

WHEN THE FOUR regional research laboratories were established, the emphasis of investigations by the Pharmacology Laboratory shifted from the toxicological problem associated with pesticides to the pharmacological problems arising from investigations on the utilization of agricultural surpluses and wastes. The attempts to find new uses for the surpluses and wastes raised problems on the toxicity and best modes of administering antibiotics, the presence or absence of toxic factors in byproduct feed materials, the toxicity of defatted-depigmented cottonseed meal, the irritant properties of formaldehyde-treated starch, the toxicity of antioxidants, the toxicity of products of fermentation, and the toxicity and mechanism of action of rutin, one of the so-called "vitamin P" substances.

It is well established that certain

improperly processed cottonseed meals are toxic. When the Southern Regional Research Laboratory developed the flotation process for separating the pigment glands and producing a defatted-depigmented cottonseed meal, the Pharmacology Laboratory tested the meal to ascertain the presence or absence of a toxic factor and to determine whether the pigment glands were toxic. For comparative purposes, chronic-toxicity studies were also made on hexane-extracted cottonseed meal. In the studies, we were interested solely in the toxicological aspects of the problem, not in the nutritional value of the meal.

We studied the possibility of chronic toxicity resulting from the daily ingestion of defatted-depigmented cottonseed meal, cottonseed pigment glands, or hexane-extracted cottonseed meal by placing groups of young albino rats on an adequate basic diet to which varying amounts of the materials were added. Rates of growth, general appearance and activity, and histopathological examinations of the various organs at time of autopsy were used as criteria of toxic action.

Defatted-depigmented cottonseed meal was fed to the rats in concentrations as high as 32 percent of the diet without any apparent ill effects on growth rate, and no pathological changes in any of the organs attributable to the experimental regimen were found at autopsy. No toxic effects from the feeding of the cottonseed pigment glands were noted unless the basic diet contained 0.25 percent or more of the pigment glands and then a significant inhibition in growth rate was evident, but no pathological changes of significance were found in the tissues at autopsy.

Rats that were fed a diet containing 7.5 percent hexane-extracted cottonseed meal showed no evidence of toxicity, but when the concentration was raised to 15 percent, a definite and immediate inhibition of growth occurred. Because the rats on this diet ate about one-half as much food as did the control rats on the basic diet alone, and because no evidence of pathological change was found in any of the tissues at time of autopsy, we concluded that the hexane-extracted meal may have contained an appetite inhibitor. The checking of appetite cannot be explained on the basis of gossypol content, because rats placed on diets containing amounts of gossypol in the form of pigment glands equivalent to that present in hexane-extracted meal showed less inhibition of growth.

FLOYD DeEDS, *a native of Ohio and a graduate of Western Reserve University, has a doctor's degree in pharmacology from Stanford University. He was assistant professor of pharmacology at Stanford University School of Medicine from 1925 to 1927 and pharmacologist at the Hygienic Laboratory of the United States Public Health Service from 1927 to 1931. Since 1931 he has been in charge of the Pharmacology Laboratory of the Department of Agriculture.*

ROBERT H. WILSON *was born in Denver and was graduated from the University of Denver. After he received his doctor's degree from the University of Michigan, he taught at Yale University and the Louisiana State University Medical Center. Since 1934 he has been a member of the pharmacology division of the Bureau of Agricultural and Industrial Chemistry.*

ANTHONY M. AMBROSE, *a native of Pennsylvania and a graduate of the Philadelphia College of Pharmacy and Science, received the degree of doctor of philosophy from Fordham University in 1929. He was instructor in biochemistry and later assistant professor at Fordham University from 1927 to 1933. He was associate in pharmacology at the Medical College of Virginia from 1934 to 1935 and assistant professor of pharmacology at the University of Louisville School of Medicine from 1938 to 1942. From 1934 to 1938 and since 1942 he has been a member of the pharmacology division in the Department.*

Antibiotics

That Come

From Plants

P. S. Schaffer, William E. Scott,
Thomas D. Fontaine

An antibiotic is an organic chemical substance that is produced by a plant, an animal, or a micro-organism. It selectively checks the growth of bacteria, viruses, fungi, and other disease-producing organisms, or completely destroys them. The term is new, but the idea that such substances can cure diseases is as old as the hills.

Investigations since 1943 have disclosed that many plants, plant parts, and plant extracts have therapeutic values (a point that primitive man knew) and contain antibiotic agents (a point that primitive man might have suspected). Among them are the lotus, olive, laurel, myrtle, asphodel, and garlic, which were used as medicines in ancient Assyria; dates, figs, onions, lettuce, crocus, and opium, used as remedies by the Egyptians; the juices of celery, parsley, asparagus, peppers, and cabbage, favored as a medicine by Greeks and Romans; and amber, musk, manna, cloves, peppers, rhubarb, nutmeg, camphor, croton oil, and nux vomica, which the Arabians introduced and told their neighbors to take for aches and pains.

Only a few antibiotics so far have been isolated from the higher plants in pure form. The detection, isolation, characterization, and evaluation of antibiotics require the coordinated efforts and experiences of plant physiologists, bacteriologists, chemists, and medical men.

The differences in the types of plants investigated, the available quantities of particular varieties, and the kinds of equipment used for processing mean that the methods of extracting plant antibiotics are almost as numerous as the groups of scientists here and abroad who are investigating them. The organisms against which the extracts are tested are varied and many, too.

As to procedure, the investigators disagree. One group believes that only fresh green plants should be used, because, they say, plants should be harvested quickly and handled immediately before enzymatic processes can destroy the antibiotic substances or produce toxic byproducts. In theory, that method is preferred; it can be conducted successfully on a small scale.

Another group works almost entirely with dried material; the commercial preparation of an antibiotic would almost always require the drying or longer handling of the plant material.

In our laboratory, we use some features of both methods. We first assay the extracts of freshly cut green plants and, having detected antibiotic activity, we then dry another portion in a forced-draft oven, usually at 85° C., for extraction. If the antibiotic material is not destroyed by the drying process, we dry a quantity sufficient for work during the winter, when the fresh plants may not be available. We have found it desirable, if possible, to separate the plants into their various parts—roots, leaves, stems, and flowers—since the antibiotic may be present in one or more but not in all parts of the plant. Plants may be extracted with water, saline solution, dilute acid or alkali, or organic solvents, such as alcohol, acetone, and ether. The use of lower-boiling solvents is preferred in order to avoid excessive heating when concentrating the extracts.

The detection and measurement of antibiotic activity can be accomplished by a number of methods.

In the cylinder-cup and paper-disc methods, a Petri dish containing a solid nutrient agar is inoculated evenly with the micro-organism. In the first, cylinders, made of porcelain, glass, or stainless steel, are then placed on the inoculated agar, and the plant extract is pipetted into the cylinders. In the other method, paper discs are immersed in the plant extract long enough to become saturated with the solution, after which they are placed on the inoculated agar. The agar plate is incubated for a fixed period of time at a temperature that is optimum for the growth of the organism. Any zones of inhibition around the cylinders or discs are measured to obtain a relative indication of the amount of antibiotic agent in the extract.

The serial dilution and streak (or transplant) methods differ from the first two mainly in that graded amounts of the plant extract to be tested are incorporated in the nutrient medium, and the micro-organism is then added.

We use all of these methods in our survey work and in purification of antibiotic agents present in plant extracts. We find it advantageous to use routinely several typical test organisms— the gram-positive bacterium *Staphylococcus aureus,* the gram-negative bacterium *Escherichia coli,* the fungus *Fusarium oxysporum* f. *lycopersici,* and the acid-fast bacterium *Mycobacterium phlei.* Plant extracts may inhibit the growth of one or more or all of the organisms, but usually when a crude plant extract inhibits the growth of all four the presence of more than one antibiotic in the plant is indicated.

The widespread antibiotic activity in plants is attested by the published reports of various investigators. At Oxford University, E. M. Osborn in 1943 tested the antibiotic activity of water extracts from 2,300 species of plants that belong to 166 families; she used *Staphylococcus aureus* and *Bacterium*

(*Escherichia*) *coli* as test organisms, and found that 63 genera contained substances that inhibited the growth of one or both test organisms.

In the botanical and bacteriological laboratories at Indiana University, D. W. Sanders and his associates tested the juices from 120 plant species, collected mostly in Indiana, using *Escherichia coli* and *Bacillus subtilis* as test organisms. Twenty-two of the plants showed varying degrees of bacterial inhibition.

H. J. Carlson and his associates at Western Reserve University extracted and tested more than 200 plants, collected in Oregon, in an attempt to separate substances inhibitory to malaria parasites, bacteria, and viruses. Many of them were found to contain substances that were bacteriostatic or bactericidal to micro-organisms *in vitro,* i. e., in laboratory test. Extracts prepared from five of the plants— buttercup, sagebrush, the mountain pasque, dwarf waterleaf, and juniper— were evaluated by many comprehensive tests *in vivo* (i. e., in experimental animals) and by *in vitro* tests. Salt extracts of all five plants were found to have antibacterial and antimalarial activity *in vitro.* Two of the plants, sagebrush and dwarf waterleaf, contained substances that protected chickens during the blood phase of malaria, and an ether-insoluble, water-soluble fraction of a steam distillate of mountain pasque protected mice heavily infected with pneumococcus organisms (*Diplococcus pneumoniae* type 19). Extracts obtained from a species of sumac, *Rhus hirta,* showed marked bacteriostatic activity against gram-negative bacteria but were less effective in inhibiting the growth of gram-positive bacteria and fungi.

L. E. Hayes studied 231 plant species, collected in Ohio, as possible sources of antibiotics. Extracts from 46 inhibited the growth of one or more species of the test organisms—*Staphylococcus aureus, Escherichia coli, Erwinia carotovora,* and *Phytomonas tumefaciens.*

About 100 plants listed in the Indian Pharmacopoeia for the treatment of diseases that are definitely of bacterial origin have been found by Mariam George and associates of the Indian Institute of Science to contain antibiotics. R. R. Rao and associates reported that garlic extract in low concentration was bacteriostatic *in vitro* against the *Mycobacterium tuberculosis* organism.

At the University of Vermont, Thomas Sproston, Jr., and associates tested 73 plant extracts, directing particular attention toward those that show fungicidal or fungistatic properties. The most active antifungal extracts were obtained from *Impatiens* (wild touch-me-not), *Cucumis melo* L. (muskmelon), and *Tropaeolum majus* L. (nasturtium). The crystalline antifungal agent isolated from *Impatiens* was 2-methoxy-1,4-naphthoquinone.

At Columbia University, B. C. Seegal and M. Holden found that the pressed juice or the steam distillate from the pressed juice of buttercup is a strong antibiotic with a wide range of activity. The extracts were effective *in vitro* against selected gram-positive and gram-negative pathogenic cocci and bacilli, against *Mycobacterium tuberculosis,* and against three yeasts, two of which are potential human pathogens. The toxicity of the active principle, protoanemonin, however, is sufficient to preclude its use as an effective therapeutic agent.

At the New York State Agricultural Experiment Station, C. S. Pederson and Paul Fisher noted that the undesirable gram-negative aerobic bacteria on the surface of cabbage leaves ordinarily disappear shortly after the cabbage is cut. They attributed this change in the number of micro-organisms to the presence of bactericidal substances in the cabbage tissue, which caused marked reduction in the number of gram-negative bacteria in 6 to 24 hours. The extract was less active toward gram-positive bacteria and was inactivated by heat.

We have tested some 300 plant extracts, and of these approximately 50 percent showed inhibition against one or more of the representative gram-positive, gram-negative, and acid-fast bacteria or fungi.

In the preliminary survey of plants for antibiotic activity, we use methanol as a solvent in the preparation of extracts. The methanol extract is evaporated to dryness on a water bath under reduced pressure, and water is added to the residue until 1 milliliter of water extract represents 1 gram of dry plant material. Any water-insoluble material is removed by centrifuging, and the supernatant solution is poured off and tested for antibiotic activity. If any is found, the stability of the antibiotic principle or principles to heat is determined by autoclaving a portion of the aqueous extract for 15 minutes at 15 pounds steam pressure.

THE MANY UNIDENTIFIED antibiotic principles of the higher plants vary greatly, not only in their potency and distribution within the plant but also with the species and variety of plant. For instance, E. H. Lucas and R. W. Lewis at Michigan State College reported that the active principles found in the scarlet berries of *Lonicera tatarica,* one of the honeysuckles, were not present in species and varieties of honeysuckles having dark-red, orange, yellow, or purple fruits. C. S. Pederson and Paul Fisher, in their investigation of the bactericidal action of cabbage juice, found that four of the varieties tested showed very marked bactericidal action, five showed intermediate effect, and four showed still less effect. E. M. Osborn concluded from her survey of 2,300 plants that specificity and activity of plant antibiotics were similar among members of the same family. Our own tests on unpurified plant extracts did not indicate any great difference among species and varieties of plants in the same family. There may be differences in antibiotic activity due to climatic conditions, but, so far as we know, none of the investigators in the field has studied this phase intensively.

The ultimate goal of any scientist working on the production of antibiotic substances from plant materials is the preparation of the active principle in a pure and crystalline form. The structure and biological properties of the crystalline antibiotic can then be determined, and its synthesis in the laboratory may possibly be accomplished.

The method of isolation varies with the nature of the antibiotic. Some of the substances are acidic, some neutral, some basic, and some proteinaceous.

The compounds in the acidic group can be extracted at low pH by organic solvents immiscible with water. The basic compounds can be precipitated by base precipitants. Some antibiotics are purified by extracting the plant material with one solvent and then distributing the crude extract between two immiscible solvents. The plant material may also be extracted with a suitable solvent, after which the extract is concentrated and run through a chromatographic column containing an adsorbent capable of removing the active substance. The antibiotic may then be removed from the adsorbent with a suitable solvent, purified, and crystallized. The pure crystalline compound may be identified by determining its chemical constituents and ascertaining its physical and chemical properties. Determination of the spectrum, color reactions, with various reagents, sulfhydryl inactivation, and other special methods are useful in characterizing an antibiotic.

THE FOREGOING description of the procedure for isolating a pure antibiotic has necessarily been very general, as the methods vary with the compound isolated. A few examples will be cited briefly.

In England, N. G. Heatley and associates isolated a crystalline antibiotic from *Crepis taraxacifolia* by adsorption of the active principle from an aqueous extract on charcoal and further purified it by adsorption on alumina. The suggested chemical formula for the antibiotic, named crepin, is $C_{14}H_{16}O_4$, and it is designated as a beta, gamma unsaturated lactone. The crystals are polymorphic, soluble in alcohol and ether, very slightly soluble in water, heat stable, acid stable, and alkali unstable. Crepin is most active against gram-positive bacteria, but its activity is diminished by serum. It destroys the motility of leucocytes at a concentration of 1:450,000 and is lethal at higher concentrations.

Another antibiotic principle was isolated from *Spiraea aruncus* L. (goat's beard). This crystalline compound is thought to be an alpha, beta unsaturated lactone with a suggested formula $C_{10}H_{14}O_4$. It has very low activity against gram-positive and gram-negative bacteria.

C. J. Cavallito and J. H. Bailey of the Sterling-Winthrop Research Institute have isolated antibiotic agents from the following plants: *Arctium minus* (common burdock), *Asarum canadense* (wild ginger), *Allium sativum* (garlic), and *Centaurea maculosa* (spotted knapweed). A crystalline antibiotic from *Arctium minus* was obtained by fractionation of a water extract and subsequent crystallization from ethyl acetate. The suggested formula for this compound is $C_{15}H_{20}O_5$, and it probably is an unsaturated lactone. The crystals are colorless prisms soluble in alcohols, chloroform, ethyl acetate, dioxane, and acetone; slightly soluble in water; insoluble in petroleum ether; optically active; melting at 115° to 117° C. and resolidifying to lose antibiotic activity. The antibiotic is irreversibly inactivated by cysteine. It is active only against gram-positive bacteria. The LD_{50}—that is, the amount that will kill 50 percent of the animals—for mice is 90 milligrams per kilogram intravenously. The substance is not lethal but is toxic at 500 mg./kg. when administered orally.

Two antibiotic principles were isolated from *Asarum canadense* (wild ginger). They are designated as compounds *A* and *B*, with the suggested formulas $C_{12}H_{20}O_8N_2S$ and $C_{16}H_{11}O_7N$, respectively. Both compounds are almost insoluble in water, benzene, and petroleum ether, but are soluble in alcohol, acetone, chloroform, ethyl acetate, and dioxane. Both are active only against gram-positive bacteria. Preliminary toxicity tests indicate A to be lethal in about 3 days after intraperitoneal injection of 5 mg./kg. in sesame oil.

Allium sativum (garlic) yielded a sulfur-containing antibiotic, which was equally active toward gram-positive and gram-negative bacteria. The compound was isolated as a colorless liquid, stable to acid but unstable to heat and alkali, soluble in petroleum ether, and irreversibly inactivated by cysteine. The exact formula for this compound is not known, but two are suggested:

$$CH_2\!\!=\!\!CH-CH_2-S-S-CH_2-CH\!\!=\!\!CH_2$$
$$\overset{\|}{O}$$
or
$$CH_2\!\!=\!\!CH-CH_2-S-O-S-CH_2-CH\!\!=\!\!CH_2$$

In toxicity tests with mice, the LD_{50} was 60 mg./kg. intravenously and 120 mg./kg. subcutaneously.

The dried leaves of the spotted knapweed, *Centaurea maculosa*, yielded about 1.5 percent of an antibiotic which is active against gram-positive and gram-negative bacteria. The suggested formula for this unsaturated lactone is $C_{20}H_{26}O_7$. Its activity is rapidly destroyed by cysteine and thioglycolate.

Two compounds, lupulon and humulon, isolated from the resins of mature hops, were recently found to have antibiotic activity toward gram-positive and acid-fast bacteria (*Mycobacterium tuberculosis*) in research on hops utilization at the Western Regional Research Laboratory.

We have investigated the antibiotic principles in the tomato plant. The total substance (or substances) in crude tomato plant extracts that exhibited antibiotic activity was named tomatin. Tomatin inhibits both gram-positive and gram-negative bacteria, but most noteworthy is its ability to inhibit certain fungi that are pathogenic to plants or animals. Included among these are three plant-wilt organisms—*Fusarium oxysporum* f. *lycopersici* (tomato wilt), *Fusarium oxysporum* f. *pisi* (pea wilt), and *Fusarium oxysporum* f. *conglutinans* (cabbage yellows)—and six fungi that are pathogenic to human beings—*Blastomyces dermatitidis, Coccidioides immitis, Histoplasma capsulatum, Epidermophyton floccosum, Trichophyton mentagrophytes,* and *Candida albicans.*

Fractionation of the tomatin extract has resulted in the separation of an individual crystalline antibiotic, tomatine, which has antifungal activity but little or no antibacterial activity. Rutin, a flavone glycoside, also has been isolated from the extract. Rutin does not have antibiotic activity, but its degradation product, quercetin, does have antibacterial properties. Therefore, we assume that at least part of the antibacterial activity exhibited by tomatin is due to the presence of a small amount of quercetin.

Tomatine was isolated from a crude tomatin concentrate by repeated precipitation from an alkaline solution, dissolving the alkaline precipitate in hot 70-percent ethanol, and cooling, thereby precipitating an amorphous substance, which was dried and then dissolved in hot 80-percent dioxane. Crystalline tomatine was obtained on cooling the dioxane solution.

Tomatine has been characterized as a glycosidal alkaloid. It is soluble in ethanol, methanol, dioxane, and proplene glycol; it is almost insoluble in water, in ether, and in petroleum ether. It appears to be stable in strong alkali, but is readily hydrolyzed in boiling hydrochloric acid solution to yield an insoluble crystalline product, tomatidine hydrochloride, and a clear supernatant solution rich in reducing sugars. Tomatine melts at 263° to 267° C. with decomposition.

Tomatidine hydrochloride is easily converted to tomatidine, which is now considered to be a steroid secondary amine. In cooperation with the National Institutes of Health, tomatidine has been chemically degraded to a sterol,

Δ16 – *allo* – pregnen – 3 (β) – ol – 20 – one. This compound may prove to be valuable starting material in the synthesis of biologically active sterols.

Crystalline tomatine and its aglycone, tomatidine, are more effective against the pathogenic fungi associated with human diseases than against the fungus, *Fusarium oxysporum* f. *lycopersici,* that causes the tomato wilt. They are almost completely without effect on the gram-negative bacterium *Escherichia coli* and are very slightly effective against the gram-positive bacterium *Staphylococcus aureus.* The oral toxicity of these compounds has been determined. Essentially no toxic effects have been observed when albino rats were fed diets containing up to 0.04 percent of these two compounds for 200 days; likewise, subacute and acute oral toxicity results were favorable. However, they are very toxic if administered by intravenous injection.

We have found that sweetpotato vines, which are sometimes used as silage, contain highly active antifungal and antibacterial substances. It is perhaps significant that the edible tuber also contains these substances. From an active water-soluble resinous fraction, a buff-colored crystalline-appearing solid and a clear red-brown liquid, with a distinctively characteristic odor, have been obtained. The solid material exhibits selective activity toward the gram-negative bacterium (*E. coli*), and the liquid toward gram-positive bacteria (especially *Mycobacteria*) and toward fungi.

The banana skin has been referred to as "nature's bacteria-proof wrapper." In our investigations we found that the green banana skin and pulp contain antifungal substances, but ripe banana skin and pulp (naturally and ethylene-ripened) contain both antifungal and antibacterial substances. Our results indicate that antibiotics in the banana skin and pulp appear during the ripening process. Of particular significance is the fact that an antibacterial factor active toward acid-fast bacteria (*Mycobacteria*) does not appear until the banana is well-ripened. The antifungal substance, which inhibits the growth of disease-causing fungi, has been separated from the antibacterial fractions.

AN ANTIBIOTIC must undergo extensive laboratory and clinical evaluation before it can be put into general use as a therapeutic agent. If tests on experimental animals show that the material is either nontoxic or of very low toxicity and that it is capable of protecting or curing infected animals, the compound may be tried on humans with their knowledge and consent. Care must be taken to prove that the antibiotic will kill or suppress the growth of a variety of pathogenic micro-organisms, that it will be readily absorbed into the body, that it has no damaging action on body cells, and that it is stable and effective in the presence of body fluids, cells, and tissue enzymes. If a compound passes those tests, it may be classified as a satisfactory chemotherapeutic agent. None of the few antibiotics isolated thus far from plants have passed all the tests, although some show promise.

The search for antibiotics in higher plants is relatively new. Thousands of plants have been tested for antibiotic activity by numerous investigators, but the search, of necessity, has been narrow. An investigator does not have the time to consider each plant individually when he is trying to survey a larger part of the plant kingdom. He first makes a preliminary survey of a number of plants as efficiently as he can by assaying the extracts against a sufficient number of representative micro-organisms. From such a survey he can select the species and varieties that warrant his further attention. The problem then is to isolate pure substances from the varieties of plants that showed promise in the preliminary survey and to prove the therapeutic possibilities of these pure substances.

P. S. SCHAFFER, *as biochemist in charge of the antibiotic section,* biologically active compounds division, Bureau of Agricultural and Industrial Chemistry, is engaged in research on the detection, isolation, and characterization of antibiotics from agricultural sources. He entered the Department of Agriculture in 1930 and before his present assignment worked on insecticides with the Bureau of Entomology and Plant Quarantine and on milk proteins, fats, and other milk products with the Bureau of Dairy Industry.

WILLIAM E. SCOTT, an associate chemist in the biologically active compounds division, Bureau of Agricultural and Industrial Chemistry, is engaged in research on antibiotics from plants. Before joining the Bureau staff he conducted research on food products in the Production and Marketing Administration, concentrating mainly on vitamins, proteins, and amino acids. He has also conducted investigations on equipment and apparatus designed by industrial concerns for research on cereal products.

THOMAS D. FONTAINE, head of the biological active compounds division, joined the staff of the Bureau of Agricultural and Industrial Chemistry as a chemist in the oil, fat, and protein division of the Southern Regional Research Laboratory in 1941. Before entering the Department of Agriculture, he worked at Mellon Institute on the proteins, amino acids, and enzymes of cottonseed. His fields of research include plant disease, antibiotics from plants, and natural and synthetic plant growth regulators.

INTEREST IN the use of drugs to treat rheumatoid arthritis and related diseases is keen. The most pressing problem in 1950 was to produce cortisone, pregnenolone, artisone, and desoxycorticosterone in quantities large enough for the needs of arthritics. The drugs were first prepared from animal sources, but those sources, it quickly became apparent, yielded too little to meet the demand.

Turning to the plant kingdom, scientists began an intensive search for plants that contain suitable antiarthritic precursors. They have found that the sapogenins, a little-known group of compounds, are excellent precursors for antiarthritic drugs. In plants, the sapogenins are combined with sugars. The combination, known as saponins, is highly poisonous. An acid treatment removes the sugars from the saponins, after which the nonpoisonous sapogenins can be recovered. Some excellent sources of sapogenins have been found in the yucca, agave, and yam, which are native to Mexico and our Southwestern States.

Department of Agriculture botanists are collecting and identifying plants belonging to species that contain sapogenin. Department chemists are investigating the plants to determine whether they contain suitable antiarthritic precursors. When the best plant sources are known, agronomists will determine the best growing conditions, geneticists will find strains with higher sapogenin content, and chemists will develop methods for large-scale isolation of the sapogenins and their conversion to antiarthritics.—*Monroe E. Wall, Eastern Regional Research Laboratory.*

The Drugs of

Microbial

Origin

Kenneth B. Raper,
Robert G. Benedict

Tremendous progress has been made in the past decade in the development of new disease-preventing agents. Foremost among such agents are penicillin and streptomycin, both of microbial origin. Other antibiotic substances of similar origin, such as chloromycetin, aureomycin, and terramycin, are becoming especially valuable.

Still others, including bacitracin, subtilin, polymyxin, and circulin, offer promise for special applications. Although the new disease-preventing drugs are saving untold lives, there are yet many afflictions which take their toll and remain unchallenged.

The quest for useful drugs among the byproducts of micro-organisms was tremendously advanced by the findings of Professor Alexander Fleming, a bacteriologist working at St. Mary's Hospital, London, in 1928. Investigating staphylococci, which cause boils, carbuncles, and septicemia in man, he observed that a contaminating blue-green *Penicillium* inhibited the growth of these disease-producing germs. As a result of his discovery of the antibiotic penicillin, attention was drawn to the possibility of employing the product of one microbe to control or prevent the growth of another. It took the destruction of war, however, and its quickened search for new therapeutic agents, to bring penicillin into its rightful prominence as one of the greatest medical and scientific discoveries of all time.

Howard Florey, E. Chain, N. G. Heatley, and other men at Oxford University in 1939 took up the study of penicillin, and found it to be nontoxic and to have remarkable curative properties when tested on laboratory animals and man. Confirming Professor Fleming's results, they reported that penicillin inhibited the growth of many gram-positive disease-producing bacteria, such as staphylococci, streptococci, and pneumococci. They found also that it was relatively ineffective in combating gram-negative forms, such as the bacteria that cause typhoid fever and dysentery. They developed methods for producing penicillin in limited amounts and introduced a method for measuring its potency. They demonstrated unmistakably the remarkable potentialities of the new drug, but were unable to proceed with its production because of war conditions. They came to the United States in 1941 to enlist the aid of Government and industry. In the succeeding years, penicillin became the preeminent drug that has saved countless lives.

Encouraged by the phenomenal promise of penicillin, yet knowing its limitations, investigators soon began searching for other therapeutic agents of microbiological origin. They have discovered some outstanding drugs, each with its special field of application. Other agents have been reported and are being evaluated in animal experimentation and clinical trials. For some serious diseases of an infectious nature no satisfactory drugs are yet available, but the search for them among the antibiotic substances produced by micro-organisms continues with bright promise.

THE PRODUCTION OF PENICILLIN in quantity required the solution of many difficult problems. A more productive

734

medium than that employed in England had to be devised. Improved methods of production had to be developed. More productive mold strains had to be discovered. Techniques for assaying penicillin had to be refined. Methods for recovering and purifying the drug had to be worked out.

Using corn steep liquor—a byproduct of the corn wet-milling industry—and lactose, or milk sugar, as the two principal ingredients, A. J. Moyer and R. D. Coghill, of the Northern Regional Research Laboratory, developed a production medium that increased yields of penicillin manyfold. Although this medium was developed specifically for penicillin production using surface cultures, the same basic solution was found suitable for submerged cultures when the concentration of the principal nutrients was reduced approximately one-half. Today, and after much experimentation in many different laboratories, this basic medium is still employed with only minor modifications.

A method for producing penicillin in submerged, or tank, culture was introduced, and mold strains especially suitable for this type of production were discovered and made available to industry. From an economic standpoint, this method was particularly attractive and soon supplanted all other methods of manufacture. It reduced labor costs and increased productive capacity enormously. At the same time it obviated the need for large and expensive incubators and the special machinery required to handle the tremendous number of bottles or other containers formerly used in producing penicillin by surface-culture techniques.

Cultures that can produce substantially greater yields of penicillin were developed by Kenneth B. Raper and Dorothy I. Fennell. All early studies in England and the United States were made in surface cultures with the strain of *Penicillium notatum* originally isolated by Professor Fleming. Other strains were found to be more suitable for submerged production. Ex-

tensive search for more productive molds led to the discovery of a strain of the closely related species, *P. chrysogenum*, from which successively better substrains were developed through the selection of natural variants and the production of mutants by exposure of spores to X-ray and ultraviolet radiations. The latter steps were carried out at the Carnegie Institution of Washington in Cold Spring Harbor, N. Y., and at the Universities of Minnesota and Wisconsin. The cumulative result of all the studies was the development of a culture capable of yielding 900 to 1,000 units per milliliter of penicillin, in contrast to 75 to 100 units per milliliter obtainable from the unimproved parent. This culture is still universally employed for the manufacture of penicillin in this country and abroad, and additional selections and mutations have undoubtedly been developed in the research laboratories of the penicillin industry to increase productivity further.

Methods of assaying penicillin were much improved by W. H. Schmidt, R. G. Benedict, and others at the Northern Laboratory, by standardizing the composition and thickness of the nutritive agar layer and by controlling the density and uniformity of the test bacterial growth. Discs of filter paper saturated with penicillin-containing samples have been substituted for porcelain, glass, or metal cups, and various devices have been developed for rapid and more accurate measurement of the resulting inhibition zones. Despite the refinements, the method still generally employed rests squarely on the principles which underlie the technique developed by Heatley and his associates. Serial dilution and turbidimetric methods of assay have been perfected and find special applications in industrial practice. Some progress has been made toward developing an assay based upon chemical reactions and analyses.

Of the four types of penicillin known to be produced by *Penicillium notatum* and *P. chrysogenum* under natural conditions, and commonly referred to as F, G, K, and X, only penicillin G is now manufactured. Penicillin F is comparatively unstable and therefore difficult to recover. Penicillin K, while showing high activity against staphylococci in the laboratory, is not a suitable drug because adequate blood levels cannot be maintained in the animal body. Penicillin X was at first thought to offer possibilities as a drug entity, because it was shown to be more effective than penicillin G against streptococci, pneumococci, and gonococci. Differences in effectiveness between penicillins X and G, however, were soon found to be quantitative rather than qualitative and did not warrant the manufacture of penicillin X with its much higher production costs.

Penicillin may be manufactured as a calcium, barium, or magnesium salt, but it usually comes from the factory as the potassium or sodium salt of penicillin G and is a highly purified, colorless, crystalline product. It is dispensed in or compounded into a variety of dosage forms to meet the physician's needs. The foremost recent development has been the appearance of procaine penicillin formulations, either in aqueous solution or in oil. If given daily, these procaine preparations provide suitable blood levels, eliminating the necessity of painful and monotonous 3-hour injections. Various inhalator devices, which permit penicillin dust of high potency to be drawn into the respiratory tract, have also appeared and promise to provide effective means of combating bacterial infections commonly associated with colds, influenza, and other respiratory disorders. Few outstanding new uses for penicillin have emerged since 1945, but during the intervening period its use as a preventive agent has become increasingly commonplace. Very recently, penicillin, when incorporated in good rations, has been found to stimulate the growth of chickens and turkeys. The anticipated and widely dreaded development of penicillin-resistant strains of disease-producing microbes has not materialized.

The production of penicillin has increased steadily year by year since the industry was established—from less than 21 billion units in 1943 to more than 200 trillion units in 1950. Marked improvements have been made in the quality of the manufactured product. Prices have gone down steadily. The wholesale value of the penicillin produced in 1950 was estimated at more than 125 million dollars. Manufacturing facilities outside the United States constantly are being increased, but a large part of our domestic production is still sold abroad.

Many molds besides *Penicillium notatum* and *P. chrysogenum* have been shown to produce powerful antibiotic substances. Up to this time, however, penicillin is the only antibiotic derived from the higher fungi that has attained the status of an officially recognized and useful drug.

FROM THE ACTINOMYCETES, a group of micro-organisms somewhat intermediate between the filamentous fungi and the bacteria, four important drugs of microbial origin are now obtained—streptomycin, chloromycetin, aureomycin, and terramycin.

Streptomycin, discovered in 1943 by Selman A. Waksman and his coworkers at Rutgers University, was the first antibiotic obtained from an actinomycete whose effective curative level in animals infected with disease-producing bacteria was considerably below that of its toxic level. It has been evaluated in far-reaching clinical trials and is now manufactured on a large scale here and abroad. It is particularly useful in the treatment of certain types of tuberculosis and other diseases not affected by penicillin.

Streptomycin is highly active against various gram-positive, gram-negative, and acid-fast bacteria, including the tubercle bacillus.

Streptomycin is effective in the treatment of tularemia, *Hemophilus influenzae* infections, urinary tract infections, bacteremia, and meningitis caused by gram-negative bacteria. The results in typhoid fever, undulant fever, and *Salmonella* infections have been somewhat disappointing and inconclusive. However, much better results are now obtained with aureomycin, chloromycetin, or terramycin, with less danger of the development of resistant organisms. A new and important use for streptomycin is emerging through its use in combination with one or more other antibiotic agents.

For commercial production, a culture of *Streptomyces griseus* producing high yields of streptomycin is required. It is grown in a medium of meat or vegetable protein, minerals, and a carbohydrate such as dextrose (corn sugar). The operation is carried out aseptically in large fermentors under controlled conditions of temperature, aeration, and agitation. The organisms break down the nutritive components of the medium and usually produce maximum amounts of streptomycin by the third day. The culture liquor is clarified and passed through a large column containing a special ion-exchange resin. The resin takes up the streptomycin which is later removed from the column with a dilute mineral acid, and a crude preparation obtained from the neutralized eluate (washings) by evaporation and precipitation with acetone.

Streptomycin is used in the treatment of some forms of tuberculosis in humans. The former method of overwhelming the infecting tubercle bacilli with large doses of the antibiotic (3 to 6 grams daily) for periods up to 4 months resulted in toxic reactions in the patients, including loss of a sense of balance, neurological disturbances, fever, and skin eruptions. The dosage now recommended is 0.5 gram each 12 hours for 42 days. Miliary or meningeal tuberculosis cases receive 0.75 gram twice a day for 90 to 120 days. *p*-Aminosalicylic acid, also effective against tubercle bacilli, is given by mouth in conjunction with streptomycin.

Failure of streptomycin to eliminate infections is often due to the development in the patient of certain resistant forms of the disease-producing bacteria. Such resistant organisms may tolerate as high as 10,000 times the amount of drug ordinarily required to inhibit the pathogen when treatment was begun.

Credit for elaborating the chemistry of streptomycin goes to research investigators at Merck & Co., E. R. Squibb & Sons, Abbott Laboratories, the University of Illinois, and Ohio State University.

A valuable byproduct of the streptomycin fermentation is vitamin B_{12}, a member of a new group of interesting and essential growth factors. Vitamin B_{12} is effective in treating pernicious anemia and other forms of anemia in humans. It also is a powerful growth factor for certain farm animals. Members of this new group of vitamins are produced also as byproducts of other antibiotic fermentations (for example, aureomycin, chloromycetin, and terramycin) conducted with different species of *Streptomyces*. Vitamin B_{12} supplements added to normal feeds markedly stimulate the growth of chickens, turkeys, and swine. Certain antibiotics (streptomycin, penicillin, bacitracin, polymyxin, aureomycin, and terramycin) when incorporated individually in the feeds produce further gains in weight beyond those encountered with adequate B_{12} supplements.

The commercial production of streptomycin has increased steadily. By January 1950, the monthly production rate was more than 8 million grams (about 8.5 tons) a month, and the wholesale price had dropped to 60 cents a gram.

In 1950, a new form of streptomycin was discovered by Robert G. Benedict, Frank H. Stodola, and coworkers at the Northern Laboratory. The same antibiotic was subsequently reported by W. E. Grundy and coworkers at Abbott Laboratories. The Northern Laboratory workers assigned the name hydroxystreptomycin to the antibiotic since it differs from regular streptomycin in having one more oxygen atom in the molecule. Hydroxystreptomycin is produced by a new actinomycete, *Streptomyces griseocarneus*. At present, the antibiotic is undergoing toxicity and pharmacological tests to determine whether it possesses advantages over streptomycin.

ONE OF THE NEWER ANTIBIOTICS that offers promise as a therapeutic agent is obtained from culture solutions in which the actinomycete *Streptomyces venezuelae* has been grown. This drug, discovered in 1947, has been named chloromycetin (chloramphenicol), because chemical analysis shows that it contains nonionic chlorine, besides carbon, hydrogen, nitrogen, and oxygen. The empirical formula is $C_{11}H_{12}N_2Cl_2O_5$, and chemists at the laboratories of Parke, Davis & Co. have successfully synthesized the antibiotic. Chloromycetin is effective against a number of gram-negative bacteria and has been successfully used in treating rickettsial diseases in man. The rickettsia are minute, bacterialike forms, which had successfully resisted all previous antibiotic therapy. Included among the rickettsial diseases that have shown favorable responses to chloromycetin are Rocky Mountain spotted fever, epidemic typhus, and scrub typhus. Success has been attained in the treatment of typhoid fever with this new drug. Tests on embryonated eggs and mice reveal that one virus is susceptible to it.

Chloromycetin is now produced on a large scale synthetically and by fermentation.

THE THIRD ANTIBIOTIC of increasing clinical significance is obtained from the actinomycete *Streptomyces aureofaciens*. It was discovered by B. M. Duggar and associates in 1948 at the Lederle Laboratories, Pearl River, N. Y., and was named aureomycin because of the yellow color of the culture and the golden color of the crystalline product. It resembles chloromycetin in that it contains nonionic chlorine. The free base has the probable empirical formula $C_{23}H_{27}O_9N_2Cl$.

It resembles chloromycetin in its activity against the rikettsia, undulant fever, and typhoid fever. It is strikingly effective against the virus that causes lymphogranuloma venereum in humans. It has been used successfully for the treatment of complicated ocular infections. It is successfully used for the treatment of atypical pneumonia, probably of viral origin. In addition to its antibacterial, antirickettsial, and antiviral activity, aureomycin is effective against the parasites of amoebic dysentery in test monkeys and may be valuable in treating human cases of this disease.

Aureomycin is available for general clinical use, and it is understood that the antibiotic can be produced in good yield. It is now being produced in quantity by one large pharmaceutical manufacturer.

NEOMYCIN, discovered by Professor Waksman and H. A. Lechevalier in 1948, appears to offer promise for the treatment of urinary infections. It is produced by an actinomycete similar to *Streptomyces fradiae,* and generally resembles streptomycin in its activity— but with certain important exceptions. Strains resistant to streptomycin are highly susceptible to the new drug, and organisms sensitive to neomycin show little tendency to become resistant. Neomycin is a complex of possibly three closely related factors. One of these, neomycin A, has been crystallized, and work is progressing toward the separation of the others. The neomycin mixture is somewhat more toxic than streptomycin, but there remains the possibility of combining the two drugs for treatment of various diseases with beneficial results.

TERRAMYCIN is the most recently discovered antibiotic of medical significance derived from a species of *Streptomyces*. It is produced by *Strep-*

tomyces rimosus and was discovered by A. C. Finlay and coworkers at Chas. Pfizer & Co., Brooklyn, N. Y. The pure hydrochloride of terramycin is yellow in color and the crystalline dihydrate has the probable empirical formula $C_{22}H_{24-26}N_2O_9$. Preliminary reports indicate that it is similar to aureomycin and chloromycetin in its antirickettsial and antibacterial activity. In high concentration, it has shown some antiviral action against influenza A virus in chick embryos.

In May 1947, Robert G. Benedict and A. F. Langlykke, of the Northern Laboratory, reported the production by certain strains of *Bacillus polymyxa* of a water-soluble factor that strongly inhibited the gram-negative bacteria. They did not assign a name to the antibiotic, because it had not been purified sufficiently to compare its chemical and physical properties with those of known antibiotics from other members of the genus *Bacillus*. Independently, P. G. Stansly, R. G. Shepherd, and H. J. White, investigators at the American Cyanamid Co., discovered the same antibiotic and designated it polymyxin. In August 1947, G. C. Ainsworth, A. M. Brown, and G. Brownlee, working at the Wellcome Laboratories in England, independently reported the production of an antibiotic, called aerosporin, from *Bacillus aerosporus*, which is synonymous with *Bacillus polymyxa*.

Stansly and his coworkers showed that high levels of polymyxin could be tolerated by mice and that the antibiotic was effective in counteracting infections in mice, rabbits, and fowls caused by various gram-negative pathogenic bacteria. It was difficult for the bacteria to build up resistance toward polymyxin. From a clinical viewpoint, it thus seemed that the new antibiotic might have an advantage over streptomycin.

A medium consisting of corn steep liquor, dextrose, and calcium carbonate, developed and recommended by Benedict and Langlykke, was cheaper than Stansly's yeast extract-mineral salts-glucose medium. However, the Stansly medium gave higher yields of polymyxin, and the substitution of soy or peanut meals as protein sources in place of yeast extract lowered its cost.

Employing a technique previously used with remarkable success in the search for better penicillin-producing molds, investigators at the Northern Laboratory obtained ultraviolet-induced mutants, which produced polymyxin in greatly increased yields.

By the addition of sterile dextrose solution to the fermentations between the forty-eighth and seventy-second hours, yields were increased still further, and potencies up to 1,000 units per milliliter were often attained. In general, polymyxin yields were highest when the fermentations were conducted at 25° to 28° C., with controlled rates of aeration and agitation.

Just as in the case of the penicillins, where the name is applied to several chemically related compounds, the name "polymyxin" can be properly applied to a family of chemically related antibiotics produced by various strains of *Bacillus polymyxa*. Brownlee and his coworkers showed that there are four polymyxins, A, B, C, and E, chemically different from type D studied by Stansly and by Benedict. Investigators at the American Cyanamid Co. and Lederle Laboratories have shown that polymyxin D has the probable empirical formula $C_{50}H_{94}N_{15}O_{15}\cdot4HCl\cdot H_2O$, with an approximate molecular weight of 1210.

In 1948, F. J. Murray and P. A. Tetrault, of Purdue University, reported the production of an antibiotic, termed circulin, from a strain of *Bacillus circulans*. Upon careful microbiological and chemical examination, D. H. Peterson and L. M. Reinecke, at the Upjohn Company Research Laboratories, proved it to be qualitatively the same as polymyxin A and E. It differs from polymyxin A in that it is unaffected by the enzyme lipase; insofar as is known, it has not been differentiated from polymyxin E.

All the known polymyxins are polypeptide antibiotics, very soluble in water and methyl alcohol, only slightly soluble in ethyl or butyl alcohol, and insoluble in other organic solvents.

The polypeptide antibiotics, including the polymyxins and bacitracin, tend to damage the kidneys in man and experimental animals. Brownlee and his coworkers maintained that polymyxin B is relatively free from nephrotoxic action, but further trials with this antibiotic have failed to substantiate the validity of their original claims.

P. H. Long and associates at The Johns Hopkins Hospital used polymyxin D to treat 21 human cases, which had not responded to previous treatments with streptomycin. The clinical course and laboratory examinations of the patients indicated that polymyxin D was beneficial despite evidence of kidney toxicity, which limited the use of the antibiotic. Promising as were the results obtained by the investigators, unless some means is found to reduce the renal toxicity of antibiotics belonging to the polymyxin family, their use in human medicine will be seriously curtailed. It now appears possible, however, that they may prove applicable for the treatment of infections in lower animals, particularly fowls. Like some of the antibiotics from species of *Streptomyces*, crude polymyxin D, adsorbed on carbon, and fed to normal chickens, was also found to stimulate markedly their growth.

Bacillus subtilis is a common spore-bearing bacterium present in most of our soils. Many strains of the organism produce antibiotics; thus far 11 different substances of this kind have been reported. Of these factors, the best known and most interesting from the viewpoint of possible clinical use is bacitracin.

Bacitracin was discovered by H. Anker, B. A. Johnson, and F. L. Meleney at Columbia University in 1945. The antibiotic is highly active against gram-positive bacteria and has shown promise in the treatment of surgically infected wounds and in eradicating early syphilitic infections in rabbits. In conjunction with penicillin G, it may find use in the treatment of the approximately 10 percent of syphilitic patients who do not respond to penicillin alone. Because its toxicity limits its internal use, it has been approved by the Federal Food and Drug Administration for sale to the public for topical application only. Bacitracin is now produced in fairly large amounts.

It is finding application in the treatment of superficial lesions, for the relief of respiratory congestion, and, in combination with streptomycin and polymyxin B, for sterilizing the gut prior to intestinal surgery. It is valuable also as an antibiotic feed supplement comparable to penicillin, polymyxin, and the three antibiotics from species of *Streptomyces* previously cited.

SUBTILIN, an antibiotic produced by a different strain of *Bacillus subtilis*, was discovered in 1944 by E. F. Jansen and Doris J. Hirschmann at the Western Regional Research Laboratory. Subsequent studies by J. C. Lewis, K. P. Dimick, and others of the same laboratory showed it to be very active against gram-positive bacteria and to inhibit strongly various acid-fast species. A. J. Salle and his coworkers at the University of California found that subtilin protected experimental animals against heavy doses of pneumococci and anthrax organisms. A definite suppressive effect on the course of experimental tuberculosis in guinea pigs was also noted. Its clinical use with humans has been limited because of its low solubility in water and body fluids. More recently this factor has been substantially improved by chemical treatment to increase solubility without materially lowering its antagonistic action.

Investigators at the Western Laboratory found that subtilin might be helpful in processing canned vegetables and meats. The addition of a few parts per million of subtilin before canning may offer promise of reducing the time and temperature of processing.

Much has been accomplished. Curative agents have been developed to control some of man's most serious diseases. Other diseases remain unchallenged, however. A potent and less toxic substance than streptomycin and neomycin is needed for the treatment of tuberculosis. A few factors have been found that will act on some of the larger viruses, but none that will arrest or cure infections by many of the smaller viruses, including those of poliomyelitis, influenza, and equine encephalomyelitis. Also needed are agents that will effect more rapid cures of the deep and superficial fungal infections of man.

More than 150 antibiotic substances produced by micro-organisms, higher fungi, and green plants have been reported. Less than one-tenth of them, however, offer promise for the control of human and animal diseases. Some are inactive in the animal body; many are highly toxic. But the search continues, and periodically, from among the many new antibiotics discovered, one is found to combat or forestall some infection against which previously there has been no satisfactory weapon. The list of curative agents is thus constantly enlarged, and in this expanding array of new drugs, those of microbial origin occupy an increasingly prominent position. The vision of a cure for every type of infection gradually assumes reality.

KENNETH B. RAPER *is principal microbiologist in charge of the culture collection section in the Northern Regional Research Laboratory. He has been associated with the Department of Agriculture most of the past 20 years. Dr. Raper holds degrees from the University of North Carolina, George Washington University, and Harvard University. At the Northern Laboratory, Dr. Raper and his co-workers have built a large collection of cultures of fungi, yeasts, and bacteria, many of which are essential in industrial fermentation processes. During the period in which the penicillin fermentation was being studied, he was instrumental in developing the mold culture from which were derived the high-yielding substrains now used in industry.*

ROBERT G. BENEDICT *is a bacteriologist in the survey and development section, Northern Regional Research Laboratory. He joined the Department of Agriculture in 1942. Dr. Benedict holds degrees from Michigan State College, Virginia Polytechnic Institute, and the University of Wisconsin. He began research work in antibiotics in 1944, and has studied penicillin, polymyxin, and other antibiotics.*

JUST AS some disease-producing germs lose their pathogenicity upon continued cultivation in the laboratory, so some industrially important micro-organisms lose their capacity to produce specific chemicals. The best example of this phenomenon of degeneration is the failure, reported by C. Wehmer, of *Aspergillus fumaricus,* which originally produced fumaric acid in 70 percent yield, to yield any after 10 years in stock culture, although it did yield citric and gluconic acids. So valuable to industry are the strains that produce high yields of penicillin, streptomycin, butyl alcohol, gluconic acid, and so on, that every effort is made to preserve their biosynthetic characteristics. That is best accomplished by storing the dried spores in a high vacuum, so that growth is stopped and change is reduced to a minimum.—*Frank H. Stodola, Northern Regional Research Laboratory.*

Rutin, a New Drug From Buckwheat

James F. Couch

The story of rutin begins in 1842, when it was first prepared by a pharmacist-chemist of Nuremberg, Germany, named August Weiss, who obtained it from garden rue, *Ruta graveolens*. As time went on, chemists found rutin in a number of plants.

Rutin is a yellow, crystalline powder with the formula $C_{27}H_{30}O_{16} \cdot 3H_2O$. It is only slightly soluble in water, more soluble in alcohol, acetone, and alkaline solutions, and insoluble in chloroform, ether, and the hydrocarbons. Rutin is a glycoside, which is hydrolyzed to form one molecule each of quercetin, glucose, and rhamnose when it is boiled with 2 percent sulfuric acid. Quercetin is a well-known chemical substance belonging to the class of flavonols, a class whose representatives are widely distributed in the plant kingdom. Rutin is reasonably stable in boiling water and may be recrystallized from that medium for purification. It has been the subject of many chemical studies and its chemical nature is thoroughly understood. Extensive studies by pharmacologists at the Western Regional Research Laboratory and by others have shown that rutin is nontoxic.

For a century after its discovery, rutin remained without any known use, although plants containing it were sometimes used as dyestuffs. This use disappeared with the advent of the synthetic coal-tar colors.

In 1942 chemists at the Eastern Regional Research Laboratory were studying the constituents of tobacco in a search for compounds that might be useful in some way other than smoking. In the course of the investigations, rutin was isolated from flue-cured tobacco; a Japanese chemist had found rutin in tobacco 10 years previously and the discovery had been confirmed by two German chemists in 1936. The finding of rutin in tobacco raised the question: What use can be made of the glycoside? Its only known utility, that of a dyestuff, did not appear promising, and no other use was apparent.

As a result of a complicated train of reasoning, coupled with previous experience, it occurred to me that rutin might possess a "vitamin P" action—in fact, it might be the long-sought vitamin itself. "Vitamin P" had been postulated in 1936 by a Hungarian biochemist, Albert Szent-Györgyi, to account for certain medical effects produced by citrus extracts that could not be explained by reference to ascorbic acid or vitamin C. Szent-Györgyi and his coworkers attempted unsuccessfully to isolate from citrus fruits and red peppers the substance that had this antihemorrhagic action. They did, however, obtain a mass of chemical information on it; the data pointed to the flavonols.

To test whether rutin had the same action, it was necessary to cooperate with some scientist who was already working in the field and who could conduct the tests properly. Dr. John Q. Griffith, Jr., and Dr. M. A. Lindauer, then of the Medical School of the University of Pennsylvania, had been studying the problem for several years and were using a citrus preparation known as crude hesperidin, which contained the unidentified "vitamin P." Arrangements were made for them to test the activity of rutin. Within a year Dr. Griffith was satisfied that rutin did, indeed, possess the antihemorrhagic activity characteristic of "vitamin P" preparations. The result was announced in 1943 before the Medical Society of the State of Pennsylvania and published in May 1944 in the Proceedings of the Society for Experimental Biology and Medicine. Drs. Griffith and Lindauer continued their study of rutin with special reference to its use for increased capillary fragility in hypertensive patients. A great deal of interest was aroused by the work, and other physicians began experimenting with rutin in their practices. They found that rutin is effective in a variety of hemorrhagic conditions.

As THE DEMAND for the glycoside in medical circles grew, it became apparent that tobacco was too expensive a source of rutin to permit its extensive use. A search began for a cheaper source. A thorough survey was made of plants reported to contain rutin and others likely to contain it. Eventually the green buckwheat plant was discovered to be nearly ideal as a source. It contained several times as much rutin as did tobacco, and it was cheap; the material cost of rutin could be cut to about 1 percent by changing from tobacco to buckwheat. Buckwheat is now the chief American source of rutin for commercial purposes, although much is now being made from a Chinese drug, Wai Fa, the flower buds of the Chinese scholartree.

Rutin may be obtained from dried or green buckwheat in several ways. If dried plant is to be used, the fresh buckwheat must be dehydrated under special conditions; otherwise there may be a large loss of the glycoside. Processes for conducting this drying were studied in the laboratory and pilot plant and also in actual commercial operations. There was finally developed a process for dehydrating fresh buckwheat and producing a leaf meal rich in rutin and stable under ordinary storage conditions.

The extraction of rutin from the leaf meal or the fresh plant was exhaustively studied in the Eastern Laboratory, and the findings were made available to industry. After many trials, a process was developed in which hot dilute isopropyl alcohol, a cheap and efficient solvent for rutin, is employed. By distilling the alcohol from the extract and straining off the fats, which settle out, a watery solution is obtained from which crude rutin crystallizes on standing and cooling.

Refining the crude rutin to a compound pure enough for medicinal use presented many difficulties. We had to remove impurities, some of which stuck tenaciously to the glycoside; recrystallizations caused appreciable losses of material and had to be reduced in number; contact with iron or copper vessels discolored the rutin; and the operations had to be conducted in stainless-steel tanks, stills, and filter presses, although for some operations we could use wooden tanks. Industry has adopted the successful solutions of the many problems involved in the preparation of pure rutin from the crude product.

Some 15 chemical firms now prepare rutin of medicinal grade. Their estimated annual output is 15,000 to 20,000 pounds. Many pharmaceutical laboratories are marketing dosage forms of rutin, principally tablets, for sale in drug stores.

THE FIRST APPLICATION of rutin medicinally was in the treatment of increased capillary fragility, a condition in which the smallest blood vessels become abnormally fragile and rupture, so that small hemorrhages occur. The correction of the capillary fault is known as the "vitamin P" action. The cause of the fragility is not definitely known. Some think that the vessel walls become weakened and no longer can withstand pressure exerted upon them by the blood. Sometimes the capillary walls do not rupture but become abnormally permeable, so that they allow substances to pass from the blood into the tissue spaces in larger quantities or of different kinds than normally filter through the capillary wall. The condition is referred to as increased capillary permeability. Where either of these faults is present, danger increases of retinal hemorrhage or apoplexy, particularly in people with high blood pressure.

Medical studies have shown that rutin, taken by mouth, will correct these capillary faults in a large proportion of cases. Accompanying this return of the capillary condition to normal is a decrease in the tendencies to apoplexy and retinal hemorrhage, so that patients show only the same tendency to these accidents as is shown by patients who have not had a capillary fault.

Diabetics frequently have complications of this sort, with more or less loss of vision and often blindness. Eye doctors who have studied the use of rutin in such conditions feel that, while there has not been a positive cure, the use of rutin has resulted in arresting the progress of the loss of sight and sometimes an improvement in vision, especially in young patients.

Other applications to eye diseases have been studied. Physicians report that the use of rutin in conjunction with certain miotics is of value in glaucoma. Some ophthalmologists have found it effective when combined with dicumarol in treating retinitis associated with clotting in the central vein of the retina.

Similar results have been obtained in certain types of purpura, a disease characterized by bleeding under the skin. Success in these directions led to the use of rutin to protect animals from injury by X-ray irradiation. In such cases one of the early effects of the injury is a breakdown of the capillary wall. Investigation of the subject showed that rutin does have a protective action against this type of injury.

A laboratory method for studying the possible "vitamin P" activity of various substances based on this protective action has recently been developed. The fact of protection against irradiation led to the thought that rutin may be of some use as a defense against injury by radiations from atomic bombs, particularly in borderline cases.

Rutin has been of great benefit in a disease known as hereditary hemorrhagic telangiectasia, in which numerous small hemorrhages occur, with bleeding from the gums and nose, into the stomach and intestines, and engorgement of small skin blood vessels. The loss of blood leads to anemia; sometimes the number of the red blood corpuscles goes down to 2 million. Up to the present, no satisfactory treatment has been found for this disease, which usually persists throughout life. Several cases in which rutin has been used with benefit have been reported. The hemorrhages have been controlled and the patient's health restored sufficiently to permit his return to work.

An interesting application of rutin in strengthening the capillaries was reported by Drs. Frederick Fuhrman and Jefferson M. Crismon, of Stanford University. They were studying the effects of frostbite on animals, with the aim of developing a method for protecting persons exposed to low temperatures from injury due to cold. Because in such cases one of the early effects of freezing is damage to the capillaries, the use of rutin as a prophylactic was suggested. Experiments showed that rutin is of value in protecting against cold injury. The progress of the gangrene was stopped, although usually gangrene progresses until the victim loses the entire foot or other part that has been frostbitten. When rutin was used as a protective, little tissue was lost and rapid recovery was the rule.

Rutin has also proved of value in ameliorating the severity of the symptoms in cases of hemophilia, the hereditary disease in which, through failure of the blood to clot normally, the patient bleeds excessively after injury. Often severe pain is associated with extensive hemorrhages under the skin or into the muscles. After taking rutin, there seems to be less tendency to bleed, and the pain is lessened. The patients are able to return to school and continue their studies, which were often seriously interrupted before the rutin was administered.

We have in rutin a pure substance which by its action on the capillaries is valuable in treating diseases characterized by tendencies toward hemorrhage. Such diseases include rupturing of the skin capillaries with formation of black-and-blue areas, bleeding into the retina of the eye, hemorrhage into the brain, bleeding from the kidney, and similar conditions. Many physicians regard the development of rutin as a notable advance in medical science.

JAMES F. COUCH, a native of Massachusetts and a graduate of Harvard University, received a doctor's degree from American University in 1926. In the Bureau of Animal Industry, 1917 to 1940, he did research on the chemistry of poisonous plants, locoweeds, larkspur, lupines, milksickness, and cyanide poisoning. Since 1940 he has been a chemist in charge of the tobacco section at the Eastern Regional Research Laboratory. In 1947 the Secretary of Agriculture awarded him a gold medal for distinguished service in recognition of his studies, which led to the discovery of the medical applications of rutin. The Philadelphia College of Pharmacy and Science in June 1948 conferred upon him the honorary degree of doctor of science.

EVERYTHING about the orange can be used to good purpose. When it is served fresh, the peel and the rag usually are wasted, but not so when it is fully processed. The peel is used in marmalade, for candied peel, for feed for cattle, and as a source of "vitamin P." Sections are canned. The juice is a base for beverages, frozen and powdered concentrates, wine, and a distilled oil used in perfume and soap. The pulp left after the whole juice has been extracted is used as a feed for cattle.

If fully processed, however, here are some of the things that can be made from it, as well as from other citrus fruits: Methane gas, which is used for fuel in one citrus pilot plant; citric acid, used for a wide variety of purposes; ascorbic acid, or vitamin C; a cold-press oil and a terpeneless oil, both used for flavoring; molasses for feed or for production of a bland sirup, yeast, and pectin; press cake for feed; dry pulp for feed or for production of "vitamin P" and pectin; naringin, a rather bitter glycoside used by the British in marmalade and beverages and also in medicine. Six classes of pectin come from citrus pulp: Slow and rapid set, used by jelly makers; medical, sometimes used as a substitute for human plasma in transfusions; confectioner, used in candies, especially gum drops, that will retain shape and consistency; pectin-albedo, used in treatment of colitis; and low methoxyl, also used in medicine. The seeds are the source of a cake for livestock feed, an oil for making salad dressing, and hulls for use in feed or fertilizer.

As Fred Lawrence, citriculturist of the Florida Agricultural Extension Service, points out, "It would be fine if demand for all these products were strong enough to make extensive production of them profitable to the grower and processor."—*Clyde Beale, Agricultural Extension Service, University of Florida.*

Mechanism of Rutin Action

Floyd DeEds

The value of the work of James F. Couch and his associates extends beyond the isolation of rutin and the demonstration of its therapeutic usefulness. It has aroused renewed interest in the controversial subject of "vitamin P," a group of biologically significant polyphenols, whose nature has not yet been established. Rutin is only one of a number of substances possessing "vitamin P" properties in varying degrees. But in rutin we had for the first time a chemically pure entity that could be tested clinically; we had in rutin a "vitamin P" substance whose structure was known, and a substance that could be weighed on an analytical balance so that physiological effects in experimental animals could be correlated with dosage.

The term "vitamin P" is widely used in scientific literature, although in 1950 the existence of such an entity as "vitamin P" had not been established. There was evidence, however, to indicate that no state of nutritional deficiency attributable to "vitamin P" exists, as is the case with the well-established vitamins. That does not mean that rutin and related compounds do not have valuable and useful physiological and nutritional effects.

The conditions for which rutin is useful therapeutically require dosing over long periods. Doses of 60 to 300 milligrams daily may be given to patients for a long time. It was there-fore necessary to obtain data on the chronic toxicity of rutin so as to be certain that continued long-time administration would not produce undesirable side effects.

We placed groups of albino rats on an adequate basic diet to which various concentrations of rutin as high as 1 percent were added. The animals were kept under observation for 400 days, about one-half of their life span. As compared with control rats on the same diet without added rutin, the animals showed no decrease in growth or fertility or any signs of toxic effects. A histopathological examination of all tissues at autopsy revealed no abnormalities in any organ. Because the amount of rutin fed in relation to body weight of the animals was far in excess of the amounts used therapeutically, the use of rutin can be considered safe.

The next major problem in the pharmacology of rutin is concerned with the mechanism of its action and with development of a biological method for detecting "vitamin P" activity.

Obviously, the nature of the clinical conditions in which treatment with "vitamin P" preparations has given beneficial results would direct the experimental approach to an understanding of the mechanism of rutin action. A brief summary of the nature of these clinical conditions and their causes is therefore in order.

Since the original announcement by Albert Szent-Györgyi of the probable existence of a "vitamin P" factor, almost every known form of abnormality of capillaries has been treated with one or another substance for which "vitamin P" properties have been claimed. In many instances favorable results have been reported.

At a symposium on "vitamin P" sponsored by the American Chemical Society, J. M. Crismon, of the Stanford University School of Medicine, classified the capillary abnormalities into three groups: Those that are characterized by a "bleeding tendency," either spontaneous bleeding or bleeding in response to some minor injury; abnormalities that generally manifest themselves as a true increase in capillary permeability (specifically, the leakage of plasma protein from the capillaries); and a group of conditions in which the capillaries of the skin and mucous membrane are dilated and engorged with blood and produce localized or diffuse areas of redness in the involved regions.

Dr. Crismon pointed out that a remarkable feature of such capillary disability is the very diverse nature of the identifiable causes. In each class there are dietary deficiencies; hereditary abnormalities; hypertension; allergy; chemical, bacterial, and virus toxins; and injury by radiation, heat, or cold.

The pharmacological data necessary to explain the mechanism of rutin action are best obtained on experimental animals where conditions can be controlled. Such experimental work meets two important questions at the outset.

Are the clinical conditions in which "vitamin P" substances have been found beneficial due primarily to the lack of a dietary constituent—or are they disease states susceptible to specific drug therapy? Stated another way, is rutin a vitamin in the same sense that ascorbic acid, dihydroxynaphthaquinone derivatives, and riboflavin are vitamins—or is rutin a compound possessing chemical and physiological properties that make it useful as a drug in certain disease states? Agreement on the answer is lacking.

Is it possible to reproduce in experimental animals the counterpart of the clinical conditions in man reported to be benefited by rutin and related compounds? No clear-cut answer has been given to this second question, either.

The beneficial effects of rutin have been studied in experimental animals subjected to scurvy and to various forms of irritation, such as that produced by local application of chloroform, histamine, negative pressure, frostbite, and local and total body X-ray radiation. Unless it is assumed that the basic effects produced by these experimental procedures duplicate the abnormalities in the clinical conditions, it is difficult to understand how the experimental work can explain the action of rutin in the disease states.

Clinical literature and much of that dealing with experimental work use the terms "permeability" and "fragility" of the capillaries interchangeably and loosely. Unfortunately, the idea has become fixed rather firmly that the disease states benefited by "vitamin P" preparations have a common characteristic in that the capillaries are too permeable or fragile. It is true that the petechial hemorrhages seen in the clinical conditions and those produced during a determination of petechial index are the sort of thing that would occur if the capillary permeability or fragility were abnormal. But that is not proof that such abnormality exists. Care should be taken not to interpret the petechial hemorrhages occurring spontaneously in clinical conditions and those formed during a petechial-index determination as evidence of a primary change in the physical properties of capillary walls. It must be borne in mind that the capillary rupture responsible for the hemorrhagic areas may well be an end result determined by preceding changes. Failure to consider the nature of these preceding changes and emphasis upon physical changes in the capillary walls tend to exclude consideration of other mechanisms of action for the "vitamin P" substances.

It therefore seemed logical in our studies of the mechanism of rutin action to investigate properties that might influence the capillaries. The following observations are not only interesting in their own right, but they contribute to an understanding of the action of rutin on capillaries.

The molecular structure of rutin suggested the existence of antioxidant properties. It has been demonstrated directly *in vitro*, that is, in the test tube, that rutin retards the rate of oxidation of epinephrine (adrenalin) and ascorbic acid (vitamin C). The same protective action has been shown indirectly in animals, that is, *in vivo*. The *in vitro* antioxidant action was shown by measurement of the effect of rutin on the rate of oxygen uptake by epinephrine and ascorbic acid by the Warburg technique.

A step closer to conditions of biological importance was the demonstration of antioxidant action of rutin on epinephrine by the excised-organ technique. The technique depends on the fact that epinephrine temporarily stops the rhythmic contractions and relaxes the smooth muscle of surviving excised intestinal strips. It was shown that in the presence of rutin the effect of epinephrine was markedly prolonged. If this protective action of rutin against oxidation of epinephrine occurs in the living animal, slight increases in the amount of this important hormone in the blood stream might result. The effect of this increment of epinephrine on the pattern of local blood flow in the tissues could have important physiological consequences.

Attempts to demonstrate directly that minute increases in the epinephrine content of the blood stream occur after administration of rutin to an animal have failed. However, four phenomena, which can be explained best by increases in the blood epinephrine level, have been demonstrated.

These phenomena, which occur in the presence of rutin in the circulation, are: A decrease in the mortality of guinea pigs receiving injections of a dose of histamine that normally kills 50 percent of the animals; an increase in the acute toxicity of thiourea; an increase in the mortality of rats exposed to an atmosphere of pure oxygen; an increase in the dye-escape time in rabbits subjected to local chloroform irritation; and a significant degree of protection against experimental frostbite.

The phenomena, with the exception of histamine death, involve an action of epinephrine on the pattern of local blood flow in the capillary network. In the case of histamine, death is due to a constriction of the bronchial musculature, which interferes with respiration. Epinephrine relaxes the bronchi and therefore any increase in the blood level of this hormone due to the antioxidant action of rutin would tend to counteract the toxic action of histamine. The possibility that an increase in the blood level of epinephrine may have an important function in phenomena involving the capillary network is well illustrated in our studies on the dye-escape time in areas of irritation.

When an irritant is applied locally to the intact skin, the first visible effect is rubefaction, or reddening. The reaction is due to an increase in the number of true capillaries that are open and contain flowing blood and possibly to a dilation of the vessels supplying the true capillaries. If the irritation is mild, the reaction may go no further, and the capillary network will return to its normal state. If it is more severe, an actual increase in the permeability of the vessels occurs, with a resultant edema due to the escape of the noncellular elements of the blood. In the trypan-blue experiments to be described, we are concerned with short-time intervals involving principally the first phase of the response to irritation, that is, the enrichment of the blood supply in the irritated area.

When trypan blue is injected intravenously, by way of an ear vein, into an albino rabbit, the abdominal area, from which the hair has been removed, gradually turns blue, light blue at first, darkening with time. Rabbits vary in the time required to show this blue coloring, but in general one to several hours pass before a distinct coloration is noticeable. This bluing is due to the slow leakage of the trypan blue from the capillaries, and in normal animals the bluing time is a function of the number of skin capillaries that are open and contain flowing blood rather than a function of the permeability of the capillaries. If the bluing were a function of the capillary permeability, an animal that turns blue rapidly should have a skin showing evidence of edema, but edema is not apparent in a normal animal.

If, in a normal rabbit injected with trypan blue, a local and standardized degree of irritation is produced by application of chloroform before generalized bluing occurs, it is possible to measure the time required to produce a bluing of the irritated area. This local bluing is due to the more rapid escape of trypan blue because of the increased number of capillaries opening and containing flowing blood in the first phase of response to irritation. When a number of such measurements of the dye-escape time have been made and they are in reasonably close agreement, the normal dye-escape time for a given animal has been established. The rabbit is then given an intravenous injection of rutin dissolved in propylene glycol, the dose of rutin being 100 milligrams for each kilogram of body weight. After administration of the rutin, the dye-escape time is measured periodically in new chloroform-irritated areas. In practically every animal studied in this manner, it has been shown clearly that the dye-escape time is definitely longer after than before the rutin injection. The onset of this prolongation usually occurs in about 10 minutes and lasts for periods which vary from animal to animal.

The speed of blood circulation is such that this evidence of a protective action by rutin should appear much sooner if the effect is due to a direct action of rutin on the capillary walls. A more satisfactory explanation is suggested by a consideration of the anatomy of the capillary network. The simplest description consistent with the facts is that a sphincter of smooth muscle fibers exists at the arterial end of a capillary. The opening and closing of this precapillary sphincter determine whether blood does or does not flow in the capillary. Such sphincters tend to remain in a state of tonic activity or contracture because of the influences of the sympathetic nervous system and the blood level of epinephrine. Periodically these constrictor effects on the smooth muscle of the sphincters are abolished by the action of the locally accumulating products of metabolism. This rhythmic fluctuation between a constrictor and a dilator phase is known as vasomotion.

The constrictor phase of vasomotion is characterized by a state of relative ischemia, or reduced blood flow, during periods of low activity. The dilator phase of vasomotion represents a state of relative hyperemia, or increased local blood flow, during periods of activity or during response to irritation. The constrictor phase of vasomotion can be induced by concentrations of epinephrine in the blood which are too small to affect the level of systemic blood pressure.

The level of epinephrine in the circulation is a balance between the rate of secretion of this hormone by the adrenal gland and the rate of excretion or destruction by the tissues of the body. If the antioxidant action of rutin toward epinephrine, demonstrable in the test tube, exists in the body, then the slower rate of epinephrine oxidation in the body could result in a slight increase in the amount present in the circulating blood. The result could be the closing of a greater number of precapillary sphincters. In a rabbit exhibiting this response to rutin, mediated through the increased epinephrine content of the blood, there would be a less marked response to local irritation, and, with fewer capillaries opening up, the dye-escape time would be prolonged.

Our investigation, then, suggests that the dye-escape time may be used for the biological evaluation of the "vitamin P" potency of compounds which may be given intravenously. It shows how a significant change can take place in the pattern of local blood flow in the capillary network without a primary change in the physical properties of the capillary wall. Lastly, it offers an explanation of a contributory factor in the hemorrhagic manifestations of scurvy.

Ascorbic acid has an antioxidant action toward epinephrine. Therefore, a deficiency of ascorbic acid in scurvy may result in a decrease in the blood level of epinephrine, and a consequent increased susceptibility to bruising.

The ability of rutin to retard the rate of ascorbic acid oxidation *in vitro*, as already mentioned, appears to be important in the living animal. One of the first claims for beneficial action made for a "vitamin P" substance was the ability to prolong the life of scorbutic guinea pigs. Later investigators were unable to substantiate this claim, but the rationalization of the conflicting reports appears to depend on the presence of small amounts of ascorbic acid in the experimental diets employed. In other experiments in the Pharmacology Laboratory, the addition of rutin to a scorbutogenic diet did not prolong the lives of scorbutic guinea pigs, but the addition of rutin with subminimal amounts of ascorbic acid did prolong the lives of guinea pigs as compared with animals receiving the same amounts of ascorbic acid alone.

FLOYD DeEDS, *a native of Ohio and a graduate of Western Reserve University, received a doctor's degree in pharmacology from Stanford University in 1924. Since 1931 he has been in charge of the Pharmacology Laboratory of the Department of Agriculture.*

THE FRENCH CHEMIST Friedel, in 1897, analyzed the contents of a number of earthen vases found in Egyptian tombs believed to predate the First Dynasty. One of the vases contained a pale-brown, porous, granular substance, which was found to consist of palmitic acid mixed with less than 51 percent of tripalmitin. Apparently the original material was palm oil which had undergone oxidation and partial saponification. Another vase contained a firmer, more granular, paler mass, consisting of stearic acid with about 30 percent tristearin. It probably was beef or mutton tallow. A third vase contained material that looked like that in the first one and proved to be palmitic acid and 41 percent tripalmitin. These materials were probably intended as provisions for the dead. Other smaller vases contained unidentifiable fatty material mixed with galena, doubtless used as a cosmetic.

Fats and oils were used in the arts, technology, and medicine from the dawn of Greek and Hebrew knowledge (ninth and eighth centuries before Christ). Homer refers to the use of oil in weaving. Soap, both as a medicinal and as a cleansing agent, was known to Pliny (A. D. 23 to 79). Candles made from beeswax and tallow were used by the Romans and probably before their time.

Waxes, as well as resins, were used as protection against moisture, especially in shipbuilding and in wall painting. An early form of painting known as *encaustic,* actual specimens of which remain in the portraits on late Egyptian mummy cases, employed a mixture of pigments in natural waxes. Another early form of painting, known as *tempera,* employed an emulsion of wax or oil, water, pigments, and an emulsifying agent, such as a vegetable gum or egg yoke.— *K. S. Markley, Southern Regional Research Laboratory.*

The Growing
of Buckwheat
for Rutin

J. W. Taylor, J. W. White

Buckwheat, a native of central and western China, belongs to the botanical family Polygonaceae, which includes such weeds as dock and smartweed. It is a shallow-rooted, fast-growing, succulent plant, which comes into flowering 3 to 5 weeks after planting. It produces a single stem, but an extensive branching occurs with favorable growing conditions and thin stands. The branches and flowers rise from the leaf axils. It is not seriously affected by plant diseases or insects.

Buckwheat has been grown in the United States largely as feed for livestock or for grinding into flour for food and as a cover crop for soil improvement. About two-thirds of the buckwheat crop harvested is produced in Pennsylvania and New York, where it is often grown on the poorer, sour soils, because it can produce a crop where the cereals fail. Many of these soils have an acidity reaction as low as pH 4.6. Buckwheat is not grown for grain in the South or where hot, dry winds blow, because the flowers are easily blasted by high temperatures.

For rutin, buckwheat is needed that has a maximum of leaf tissues with a minimum of stem. (Most of the rutin is in the leaves and flowers; there is a little in the stems but none in the seeds.) That type of growth is best obtained on fertile soils, with due attention to proper date and rate of seeding and the variety best adapted for producing rutin. The stage of harvesting also is important.

Experiments by the Pennsylvania Agricultural Experiment Station and the Department of Agriculture have shown that on the better soils phosphorus was the only fertilizer needed for growing buckwheat for rutin. On the less fertile soils, nitrogen was also needed to give larger plants and higher yields of rutin. An application of 24 pounds of nitrogen and 48 pounds of phosphorus to the acre is recommended. Too much nitrogen leads to a tall, succulent plant, which lodges easily and has an excess of stem as compared to leaf tissue. In none of the experiments did fertilization increase the percentage of rutin in the plant.

Buckwheat is ordinarily seeded for grain production in late June or early July. Good yields of rutin were obtained in Pennsylvania by seeding Japanese and Tartary buckwheats on May 13, as the growth of the plant was slow and the proportion of rutin high. Seeding on June 13 and August 1 gave larger plants, especially with the Tartary variety, and more rutin per acre, although the percentage of rutin in the plant was lower.

The proper seeding rate of buckwheat for rutin is approximately the same as for seed production. Three to four pecks of seed to the acre, depending on the variety and viability, gives best results. A 7-inch or 8-inch grain drill is commonly used for seeding, with a seeding depth of 1 to 1½ inches.

Three species of buckwheat are grown commercially in this country—*esculentum,* or common buckwheat, which includes the Japanese and Silverhull varieties; *emarginatum,* a type resembling Japanese but with a winged seed; and *tataricum,* or Tartary buckwheat, grown primarily for poultry or stock food and sometimes referred to as mountain or bitter buckwheat or duck wheat.

Using colchicine, W. J. Sando, at the Plant Industry Station, Beltsville, Md., has produced a new species—a tetraploid, which has double the ordinary number of chromosomes—from the Tartary.

This tetraploid has produced leafy plants and consequent high yields of rutin in preliminary tests. The seed was not available in commercial quantities in 1951.

Many strains or varieties of Japanese and Silverhull are grown in this country, but pure seed can seldom be obtained because they cross-pollinate freely and are often inseparable. They are the fastest growing of all buckwheats, often reaching the flowering age in 3 or 4 weeks. The Emarginatum grown in this country was selected in New York. It is tall and late and has winged seeds but otherwise resembles the Japanese. When it is seeded early enough, it often produces high yields of both straw and grain. The common and Emarginatum varieties are self-sterile; cross-pollination largely is effected by bees and other insects.

The Tartary species is self-pollinated. The types grown in this country and Canada are similar. All grow slowly in the early stages and are inclined to set seed over a long period of time. The Tartary stands both heat and cold better than do the other buckwheats. Tartary is better adapted for rutin production than any of the Japanese or Silverhull varieties tested. It seldom matures rapidly, but it has a continuous growth habit that gives new leaves and a higher percentage of the plant in leaf. In some studies it has run 45 to 80 percent richer in rutin than the Japanese. Japanese loses its rutin rapidly once seed setting begins, but Tartary is slower to flower and slower in setting a full crop of seed. Tartary retains its rutin content longer and is also better for drying; experiments have shown that higher temperatures and more rapid drying can be used than is advisable with Japanese.

Buckwheat should be harvested for rutin production before many seeds have set. The best time varies with the season and variety, but at least 4 to 6 weeks should be allowed to obtain a crop. Artificial drying is necessary to make buckwheat meal for rutin, because a serious loss of rutin occurs in field drying. The drying must be done rapidly. Some types of alfalfa driers have been used satisfactorily in producing whole buckwheat meal.

J. W. TAYLOR *is an agronomist in the division of cereal crops and diseases, Bureau of Plant Industry, Soils, and Agricultural Engineering. He has engaged in the breeding of disease-resistant grains since 1920.*

J. W. WHITE *is professor emeritus of soil technology at the Pennsylvania Agricultural Experiment Station, State College, Pa. He has devoted many years to research in the growth and culture of the different species of buckwheat.*

WHEN I WAS WORKING in Korea in 1945 to 1948, I once asked the village master, a rice farmer, at what time of the year he plowed and prepared his land for rice. He said they all prepared it in the spring, just before rice-planting time. I informed him that the National Agricultural Experiment Station at Suwon, Korea, had carried out many experiments and had found that rice yields were increased if the land were plowed in the fall and left to freeze and thaw during the winter. He and all of the men in that village, he replied, knew about the experiments and the increased rice yields, but in his village it was a custom to plow the land in the spring. Thus I was reminded again of how deeply ingrained are local customs.—*Ford M. Milam, Head, Department of Agronomy, Centro Nacional de Agronomia, Santa Tecla, El Salvador.*

Eggs in the Fight Against Disease

Oren E. Herl

Eggs help in our fight against disease in two ways.

They are a nutritive food for producing and maintaining strong bodies. They contain protein, fats, minerals, and vitamins. They combine well with other foods. They are particularly valuable for ill or convalescent humans.

The other use is newer. Fertile incubated eggs are now used for culturing and propagating many viruses, some rickettsiae, and a few bacteria. The bacteria are usually grown on artificially prepared media. Rickettsiae grow best in the yolk sac. Numerous viruses grow in the fluid and tissues of the embryonated egg. Because of their numbers and extensive growth, this article deals primarily with viruses.

In the bacteriologist's scale, the rickettsiae lie somewhere between the bacteria and the viruses and are responsible for such diseases as typhus fever and Rocky Mountain spotted fever. Bacteria and rickettsiae can be seen with the aid of the ordinary microscope, but the viruses are so small they can be seen only with the aid of the electron microscope.

Embryonated eggs (containing live embryos) now provide a means for research in diseases and the production of vaccines and serums that have high potency and are employed in both human and veterinary medicine.

The use of the fertilized egg in studying pathological conditions and its possible use in growing viruses were reported as early as 1911 by Peyton Rous and James B. Murphy, biological scientists of the Rockefeller Institute, New York City, in their work on tumor implantation in the developing embryo. They inoculated embryonated eggs with finely divided tumor (sarcoma) material into the embryo and its surrounding membranes with a hypodermic needle through a window in the shell. Then they sealed the eggs with strips of moist shell membrane and returned them to the incubator. When the men opened the eggs a week later, they found definite flattened tumor nodules on the inner surfaces of the punctured chorioallantoic membranes to which blood vessels had converged and coursed over. They also found nodules along the track of the needle.

Recognition of the potentialities of the method for combating disease came in 1931 and was almost entirely due to Ernest W. Goodpasture, dean of the School of Medicine, Vanderbilt University, and his collaborators. They first studied fowl-pox virus and obtained well-marked lesions, characteristic of the disease, in embryonated eggs.

In 1933 F. M. Burnet, director of the Walter and Eliza Hall Institute in Melbourne, Australia, described a modification of Goodpasture's technique on inoculation whereby an artificial air cell was created on the side of the egg over the chorioallantoic membrane to provide a relatively large area on which the inoculation was made.

Since that time many modifications have been developed, until today nearly every tissue of the embryonated egg has been utilized in one way or another in growing rickettsiae and viruses. Herold R. Cox, virologist at the Lederle Laboratories in Pearl

River, N. Y., in 1938 fully developed the method of propagating rickettsiae in the yolk sac. As a result of these developments and further research, much has been added to our knowledge of these disease-producing organisms about which comparatively little was known in 1935.

As early as 1930 it was recognized that viruses grow and multiply primarily in living cellular tissue. Research workers soon tried special artificial media to which they added fresh tissue cells from the species of animal known to be susceptible to the virus to be propagated. The results were moderately successful, but only limited quantities of virus have been thus produced. The embryonated egg containing much suitable cellular tissue, however, offered wide possibilities.

Frequently, by some variation in the method or technique of inoculation, a virus is propagated that has not before been successfully grown. In dealing with disease in man and animals, certain viruses grow in one type of tissue of the host and others develop in another type. For example, rabies virus develops in nerve tissue, while fowl-laryngotracheitis virus has an affinity for respiratory epithelial cells. Scientists and doctors took advantage of the resistance of certain tissues to specific viruses. They selected for inoculation special sites that stimulate immunity. For example, fowl-pox and Newcastle disease vaccines (live viruses) applied by the stick method through the web of the wing produce a local reaction and subsequent immunity.

Apparently the secret to the growth and propagation of so many viruses in embryonated eggs is that the cells of the developing embryo are so young, immature, and relatively undifferentiated that the viruses can and do utilize the tender cells as a media for growth. Many of them multiply on embryos incubated 3 to 15 days but will not grow—or only perceptibly—if inoculations are made after 15 days. Scientists have not fully proved, but evidence exists, that the younger the embryo, the more likely the growth of a virus in its tissues.

A wide range of experimental study in this expanding field of virus diseases is provided by varying the method of handling and inoculating the embryonated egg, as follows:

Varying the route of inoculation: Chorioallantoic membrane; amniotic cavity; yolk sac; allantoic cavity; intravenous; and extra embryonic body cavity.

Varying the time of inoculation after incubation of egg is begun (3 to 15 days).

Using duck, turkey, or guinea fowl eggs instead of chicken eggs.

INVESTIGATIONS AND RESEARCH on those variables are being continued and, of course, new methods and procedures will be developed as time goes on; viruses not presently grown on embryos will be added to the list of 35 or more now successfully propagated. Poliomyelitis and foot-and-mouth viruses are examples of those that have not been successfully grown in eggs.

Eggs for biological work must come from healthy flocks, free of virus and bacterial infections. Such eggs, of course, must be fertile and preferably from one breed of fowls for uniform results. Eggs with white shells mostly are used because they are more satisfactory for candling, which is essential to determine nonfertile eggs, air cells, and the position of embryos and whether they are alive or dead.

Fertile eggs supply all the requirements for growth; the shells serve as sterile containers and offer excellent protection against contamination from outside sources.

The chances of cross-infection always exist with free-living laboratory animals, but egg embryos remain in their sealed-in shells until they are opened and the materials are ready for examination or harvest. Some viruses produce only a mild inflammation at the point of inoculation. Others produce more extensive lesions. Still others produce a septicemia and death to the embryos in a few hours to as long as 8 days. Such variations in the character of lesions, together with the death of the embryos, materially assist in diagnostic work.

Research and vaccine production have built up a sizable egg-producing industry, which must cooperate closely with the biological laboratory. Some institutions find it advantageous to have their own flocks and facilities for producing and incubating eggs as needed. The egg producer must have incubation and candling facilities so that he can deliver eggs certified as to live embryos and as to the age of each. This also includes delivery in incubator trucks. At laboratories where diagnostic work is regularly conducted, fresh fertile eggs are placed in the incubator daily so as to have embryonated eggs of various ages available for inoculating specimen material forwarded for diagnosis.

SEVERAL BIOLOGICAL PRODUCTS are produced from chick embryos. Only the parts or tissues which, after inoculation and incubation, contain the infectious material are utilized. The rest is discarded.

Vaccines developed on a commercial basis for use in man are those for yellow fever, murine typhus, epidemic typhus, influenza types A and B, Rocky Mountain spotted fever, Japanese encephalomyelitis, and equine encephalomyelitis (horse sleeping sickness).

Vaccines produced on a commercial basis for animals are for fowl-pox, pigeon-pox, fowl-laryngotracheitis, Newcastle disease, wart, and eastern and western equine encephalomyelitis.

Rabies vaccine produced from the chick embryo is of recent development; it was being distributed on an experimental basis in 1950.

Many other vaccines have been produced by use of chick embryos in the laboratory experimentally and may in time replace those now produced by more expensive methods. For example, the cost of preventing encephalomyelitis (sleeping sickness) of the horse

was greatly reduced by the discovery that virus could be developed in inexpensive embryo chicks instead of in the brain tissue of horses.

Several virus diseases are common to both man and animals, rabies and equine encephalomyelitis among them. A vaccine prepared to immunize one will usually protect the other.

Some vaccines are crude tissue suspensions. Others are highly refined by such methods as centrifuging or filtering to remove the coarse inert and unwanted material. The virus of influenza vaccine is nearly free of all egg protein; typhus vaccine is moderately purified; yellow-fever vaccine is an aqueous suspension of the finely ground chick embryo without head and feet.

A solution containing a foreign or heterologous protein, which differs biologically from the species receiving the injection, may occasionally cause reaction or shock. An unrefined vaccine from chick embryos, for instance, probably would not produce any reaction when injected into chickens, but might when injected into other creatures. Certain refinements in production and adjustment in dosage lessen these responses. By the use of embryos younger than 12 to 15 days, the protein complication is mostly avoided, as the unabsorbed albumen is discarded and not employed in vaccine production.

TWO TYPES OF VACCINES are produced from chick embryo material—inactivated-virus vaccine (killed virus) and live-virus vaccine. To prepare the former, an antigenic strain of the virus is selected. The strain may or may not be virulent. It is essential, however, that it grow well and produce a large quantity of virus. Sometimes it is necessary to adapt the strain to egg growth by passing it through embryonated eggs a number of times. Conversely, some strains, after being propagated for a number of generations on eggs, must again be passed through the species of animals from which they were isolated to make them suitable for further vaccine production.

After a suitable strain is selected, incubated eggs containing embryos of proper age are presented for inoculation. The technique used depends on the virus and the tissues to be inoculated.

If the chorioallantoic membrane is the one of choice, the shell is disinfected and a small opening made in it over the air cell and another in the side of the egg by a small drill or vibrator. Suction is applied through small rubber tubing to the hole in the shell over the natural air cell. An artificial air cell is thus produced beneath the hole in the shell on the side of the egg whereby the chorioallantoic membrane is pulled away from the shell and shell membrane to provide an area upon which a small quantity of virus material may be inoculated by the use of a suitable hypodermic syringe and needle. All operations must be done under strictly aseptic conditions. Embryos contaminated with bacteria are unfit for vaccine. Since penicillin does not materially affect viruses or disturb the embryos, it is frequently used to assure the sterility of the virus inoculating material. After inoculation, the openings are sealed with tape or wax and returned to the incubator for a suitable time to permit multiplication and growth of the virus; after that, the material is harvested under sterile conditions.

Depending upon the virus disease for which a vaccine is being prepared, the harvested material may consist of infected areas of the chorioallantoic membrane, or the entire membrane including the embryonic fluids. Some viruses infect the entire embryo and membranes, thus making practically all of the material suitable for use, with the possible exception of the shell and albumen.

The material is then further processed into a homogeneous mass, and the virus is inactivated by the use of formalin or some other inactivating agent. Following inactivation, it is further processed, refined, and, finally, placed in sterile containers and labeled. Other steps in the production process are special handling, centrifuging, refrigerating, refining, and testing the sterility, safety, and potency of the vaccine. The inactivated type of vaccine will not infect the individual inoculated but its antigenic properties will stimulate immunity. Such immunity is usually of shorter duration than that produced by the use of a live-virus vaccine.

The live-virus vaccine is produced in much the same way as the inactivated, except that a strain of low virulence or one that has been modified or fixed by special handling is selected. No inactivating agent is used. If improperly administered, some of these vaccines are capable of reproducing the disease. They should be used only under professional direction or by someone trained in their use. This type of vaccine is designed to produce a subclinical, or mild, form of the disease, which is characterized in various ways, frequently only by a local reaction. The site of vaccination and the method of application are important. Immunity resulting from this type of vaccine is usually more lasting than that provided by the killed-virus vaccine. Examples of this type of vaccine are smallpox vaccine, fowl-pox vaccine, and fowl-laryngotracheitis vaccine.

IT IS DIFFICULT to estimate the total number of fertile eggs required to meet the yearly demand for human biological products in the United States. It would reach many millions, especially in event of a threatened outbreak of influenza.

The records of the Department reveal that in 1949 the production of embryo-propagated veterinary vaccines totaled 67,107,930 cubic centimeters of liquid vaccine and 54,714,-924 milligrams of dried vaccine. These vaccines would treat approximately 335 million animals, including fowls. Their production required an estimated 500,-000 dozen eggs.

The use of the embryonated egg materials provides the means for the production of greater quantities of

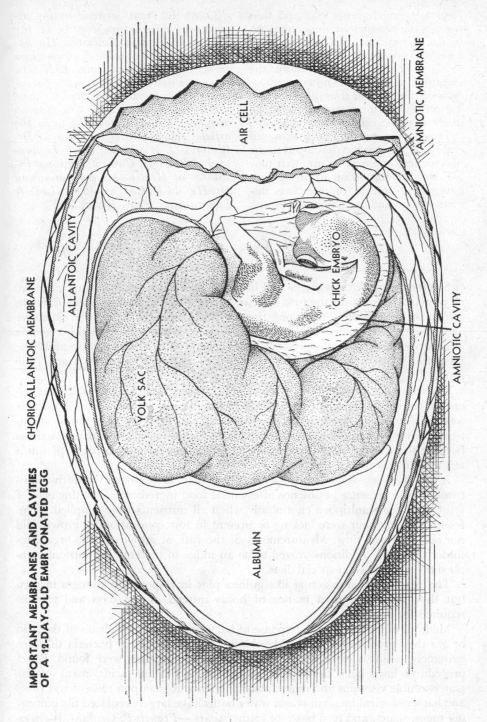

IMPORTANT MEMBRANES AND CAVITIES OF A 12-DAY-OLD EMBRYONATED EGG

CHORIOALLANTOIC MEMBRANE

ALLANTOIC CAVITY

AMNIOTIC MEMBRANE

AIR CELL

CHICK EMBRYO

AMNIOTIC CAVITY

YOLK SAC

ALBUMIN

virus at a much lower cost and thus permits the production of more potent, more concentrated, and more effective vaccines and serums than have yet been available. Their use makes possible the identity of many viruses and early diagnosis of disease and thus aids in warding off threatening outbreaks, which might become epidemic or epizootic.

Present knowledge in the use of embryonated eggs has developed to the place where one may be sure that they will be most important in the investigation and control of infectious diseases of man and animals in the future.

OREN E. HERL *is head of the division of virus-serum control in the Bureau of Animal Industry. He has been engaged in regulatory virus-serum work in that Bureau since 1917. Dr. Herl is a native of Ohio and a graduate of Ohio State University.*

For information regarding human biological products referred to in the article, the author is indebted to Dr. William G. Workman, chief, Laboratory of Biologics Control, National Institutes of Health, his associates, and Dr. Herold R. Cox, virologist, Lederle Laboratories, Pearl River, N. Y.

SCIENTISTS try ceaselessly to find how much of each vitamin, trace element, or protein is present in the food we eat. Frequently the task has been difficult, sometimes impossible. For a long time, vitamin research called for expensive and time-consuming tests with animals. Vitamin C was determined by feeding guinea pigs and noting the presence or absence of scurvy. The growth and bone formation of small white rats were used as measures of vitamins A and D in foods.

The existence of many other vitamins was recognized as probable, but scientists could not separate or identify them because of the lack of suitable analytical methods. A trace constituent in food, for example, could not be identified because we had no precise analytical test for it—no reliable method existed because the substance had never been isolated in sufficient purity to permit a test to be developed.

A few years ago scientists discovered that yeasts are extremely sensitive indicators of the presence or absence of essential food ingredients. The tiny cells of yeast grew and multiplied enormously when all nutrients were supplied. If an essential component were lacking or present in low concentration, growth did not occur or was slow. Measurements of the rate of growth of the organisms under standard conditions proved to be an index of amounts of nutrients supplied the yeasts in their special diets.

The yeast cells were acting like guinea pigs in response to changes in diet, but they responded in a matter of hours instead of the days and months required for animals.

Methods of measuring the response of bacteria or yeasts by means of the acid or gas they produced were also developed. Special strains of bacteria that are extremely sensitive to small amounts of dietary substances were found. Exact procedures have been developed for determining amino acids, many of the water-soluble vitamins and others trace nutrients. Rows upon rows of test tubes and bacteriological incubators and water baths have largely replaced the guinea-pig cages, scales, and feed boxes of former years.—*Francis P. Griffiths, Western Regional Research Laboratory.*

Production of Riboflavin by Fermentation

Fred W. Tanner, Jr.,
Virgil F. Pfeifer

The term "vitamin" has reached everyday usage, yet it cannot be defined readily. Vitamins are organic compounds and are requisite to the normal growth of man and animals. They are not generally produced within the animal body; they must be derived from the food consumed. Vitamins do not become a part of body cells, but are essential for the metabolic processes conducted by the cells.

One of the important vitamins is riboflavin, sometimes referred to as lactoflavin, vitamin B_2, or vitamin G. It belongs to the group that is soluble in water. Riboflavin deficiencies, like deficiencies of other vitamins, are marked by poor rates of growth and inefficient utilization of food by animals. Severe or complete deficiencies can lead to death.

Riboflavin is rather widely distributed in food and feedstuffs, but in amounts generally inadequate for high animal efficiency. High-potency sources of the vitamin have been needed for enriching such foods and feeds. Today riboflavin is produced in quantity by chemical and fermentation processes. Small but nutritionally substantial amounts are incorporated in most bread flours and breakfast foods, in some pharmaceuticals, and in nearly all poultry and hog feeds.

The vitamin activity of riboflavin is well recognized today, but some 50 years passed before its vital importance in animal nutrition was proved. Nearly 70 years ago, A. W. Blythe, an English chemist who was studying the composition of milk, directed attention to a water-soluble yellowish pigment, which he termed "lactochrome." Other chemists succeeded in concentrating the pigment and in 1925 recorded some of its more obvious characteristics, but they considered it solely as one of the minor constituents of milk. That was at the beginning of the era when biochemists intensified their studies of the relationship between food composition and the growth and well-being of animals. The reports of Christian Eijkman (1897) and others had demonstrated already that a disease, beriberi, common in the Dutch East Indies, was of nutritional origin. Casmir Funk, an American, also interested in nutritional diseases, a few years later (1911) coined the term "vitamine" for the trace chemicals in foods that are responsible for promoting normal well-being in animals.

Workers soon found that two classes of vitamins existed, one class being essentially fat-soluble, which they first termed "vitamin A", and another they called "water-soluble B." The multiple nature of each class became obvious as research progressed. By 1929 two of the water-soluble group, vitamin B_1 (thiamine) and vitamin B_2 or G (riboflavin), were distinguished on the basis of greater heat stability of vitamin B_2.

The identification of any new chemical of therapeutic importance involves five major steps. Its existence is recognized by appropriate biological tests. Concentrates and later the pure compound are prepared by isolation from natural materials. The chemical structure of the compound derived from natural substances is determined. The compound is reproduced by chemical synthesis. The natural and man-made

Riboflavin requirements established by the National Research Council, 1946

Livestock	*Riboflavin requirement* *Milligrams per pound of feed*
Chicks:	
Starting (0–8 weeks)............	1.6
Growing (8–18 weeks)...........	.9
Hens:	
Laying........................	.9
Breeding......................	1.3

Swine (growing-fattening pigs):	*Milligrams a day*
50 pounds.....................	2.1
100 pounds....................	3.8
150 pounds....................	5.0
200 pounds....................	5.7
250 pounds....................	5.7

Humans	*Milligrams per pound of food*	
	Male	Female
Children:		
Under 1 year..............	0.6	0.6
1–3 years.................	.9	.9
4–6 years.................	1.2	1.2
7–9 years.................	1.5	1.5
10–12 years...............	1.8	1.8
13–15 years...............	2.4	2.0
16–20 years...............	3.0	1.8
Adults:		
Sedentary.................	2.2	1.8
Moderately active.........	2.7	2.2
Very active...............	3.3	2.7
Pregnancy, latter half......	......	2.5
Lactation.................	......	3.0

compounds are tested biologically to prove their identity.

The identification of riboflavin as a vitamin stemmed from several scientific fields. In 1932 Otto Warburg and Walter Christian, in Germany, isolated a new oxidation enzyme from yeast. Water solutions of the enzyme were yellow, but they exhibited a characteristic greenish fluorescence when viewed in ultraviolet light. By brilliant work, the investigators succeeded in separating their enzyme into two parts, a protein and a yellow pigment.

Animal nutritionists, notably Lela Booher, then at Columbia University, had suspected that the yellow pigment in whey might be responsible for the prevention of the characteristic vitamin B_2 deficiencies in rats. Phillipp Ellinger and Walter Koschara suggested it might be related to the yellow pigment described by Warburg and Christian. In 1935 two groups of European chemists, directed respectively by Richard Kuhn in Germany and Paul Karrer in Switzerland, succeeded in synthesizing the yellow pigment in the laboratory. Animal-feeding tests proved that the laboratory product was the same as that obtained from yeast.

RIBOFLAVIN is the common name for 6,7-dimethyl-9-(d-1′-ribityl)-isoalloxazine. The molecule has the following structure:

Pure riboflavin has needle-shaped, practically odorless, orange-yellow crystals, which begin to darken at about 240° C. (464° F.) and completely decompose at about 280° C. (536° F.). Water solutions show a characteristic yellowish-green fluorescence.

Riboflavin is slightly soluble in water (12 milligrams in 100 milliliters at 27.5° C.; 19 milligrams at 40° C.) and in several organic solvents. It is very soluble in alkali. Solutions are relatively stable to acid, but riboflavin is readily destroyed by alkali and light. In neutral water solutions, the compound exhibits a characteristic light absorption spectrum, with maxima at 445, 365, 265, and 220 millimicrons.

Riboflavin occurs in nature in free and "bound" forms. In urine it is entirely free, in milk principally free, but in plant and animal tissues it is largely combined with proteins, which are called flavoproteins. These are yellow enzymes in which riboflavin mononucleotide (riboflavin phosphate) or riboflavin dinucleotide (riboflavin phosphate and adenosin phosphate) is combined with specific proteins. Several such oxidizing enzymes are known, each with specific functions in tissue metabolism.

The water-soluble B-complex vitamins appear to serve as biologically active portions of enzymes. Enzymes are responsible for releasing energy from food; they also effect the chemical reactions associated with the synthesis of new body tissue and the repair of damaged tissue. Life itself is the result of a very complex series of enzyme reactions, for each of which nature has provided appropriate regulatory means. A vast amount of research has thrown light on this complex picture, yet much remains to be done before man can fully understand the wonders of life and the processes that sustain it.

DISEASES OF ANIMALS AND PLANTS can be classified into two general groups—those caused by the invasion of disease-producing micro-organisms and viruses, and those caused by inadequate or unbalanced nutrition, which impairs the functioning of tissue cells. The vitamins are especially effective in treating diseases of the second group.

In animals, riboflavin deficiencies are shown in many ways. The degree of deficiency may vary considerably and, of course, the appearance of the specific symptoms will vary accordingly. Retarded growth is common to all classes of animals. "Curled-toe paralysis" is a symptom in chicks, and poor hatchability is a result of such deficiency. Dermatitis and eye cataracts are frequent among rats. Dogs, in acute deficiency, exhibit a characteristic collapse; they may die within 6 to 8 weeks. Chronic deficiencies lead to nervous abnormalities.

In man, abnormal conditions in the eyes generally appear before other symptoms. As the deficiency progresses, symptoms include inflammation of the lips and tongue, fissures at the corners of the mouth, dermatitis, and other less specific conditions.

VITAMIN REQUIREMENTS depend on the age of the animal and the physiological functions it performs. Nonruminant animals, such as man, swine, and poultry, require preformed B-complex vitamins in their food. Ruminants, such as sheep and cattle, do not. There is some evidence that B-complex vitamins should be supplied to young calves until the rumen functions. The micro-organisms in the rumen then produced sufficient B-vitamins for the animal.

Committees of the National Research Council have recommended minimum amounts of dietary riboflavin for humans, poultry, and swine.

From all these data, we learned that chemical structure of riboflavin and the advent of suitable analytical methods, foods and feeds were analyzed for their content of the vitamin. Simultaneously, animal nutritionists engaged in studies that established quantitatively the requirements by various animals.

From all these data, we learned that the usual animal rations, particularly those composed largely of cereal grains, contained inadequate amounts of riboflavin for the best rate of growth. Milk products, such as whey or skim milk, supplied the additional riboflavin needed, but milk products are expensive. To meet the need for additional sources of the vitamin, organic chemists began producing riboflavin by chemical means. The synthetic vitamin appeared on the market in 1938. Since then, it has been produced in large quantities at progressively lower cost.

Used to fortify feeds, however, riboflavin concentrates are just as efficient as the pure compound. The fermentation industry, which produces chemicals such as alcohol, butanol, and acetone from grain and molasses, has long been confronted with the problem of the disposal of its fermentation residues. The residues were found to be good sources of riboflavin and other vitamins. They contain the vitamins originally in the grain, in addition to those produced by the fermenting micro-organisms. By proper drying methods, the vitamins were concentrated into useful products. Progressive members of the industry immediately undertook to recover the residues. The byproducts from grain fermentations are now marketed as distillers' light grains, distillers' solubles, and distillers' dark grains, the latter being essentially a mixture of the first two products.

The need for acetone during the First World War led to the development of butanol-acetone fermentation, which continues as an important chemical process. Research workers frequently had noted that a yellow pigment became pronounced in the course of grain fermentations, even before riboflavin was known. Some workers suspected that the pigment was being extracted from corn by the solvents made by the fermenting organism, Clostridium acetobutylicum. However, by 1940, research confirmed that the pigment was riboflavin synthesized by this bacterium as it produced the neutral solvents, butanol and acetone.

Methods of improving riboflavin yields without impairing solvent yields were soon devised. The byproduct residues of this fermentation became an important source of riboflavin concentrates for feed fortification. The fermentation is now applied also to whey and other milk byproducts to obtain rich concentrates for poultry and livestock.

In 1935, Alexander Guilliermond, a French mycologist, observed that a yeastlike organism, Eremothecium ashbyii, originally isolated as a pathogen for cotton plants in the Belgian Congo, produced a yellow pigment in laboratory cultivation. In fact, microscopic examination revealed crystals of the pigment within the threadlike cells. Later research, particularly in the United States, proved that the organism could produce the vitamin in such amounts that riboflavin was the sole useful fermentation product.

Other yeasts, belonging to the Candida genus, produce significant amounts of riboflavin, but they are not applicable to commercial exploitation because of their extremely low tolerance for iron.

Guilliermond and his colleagues, when studying Eremothecium ashbyii, reported that a related species, Ashbya gossypii, produced only traces of riboflavin. In 1943 L. J. Wickerham, zymologist at the Northern Regional Research Laboratory, obtained a culture of Ashbya gossypii from W. J. Robbins, director of the New York Botanical Garden. After extended growth, the culture acquired a greenish-yellow cast. Suspicions that this pigment was riboflavin were confirmed. Using microbiological isolation procedures, Dr. Wickerham obtained a strain of the micro-organism capable of producing the vitamin rapidly and abundantly under laboratory conditions. To promote industrial interest in this new fermentation process, an inexpensive substrate and conditions applicable to commercial practice have been developed.

IN THE FERMENTATION production of riboflavin by Ashbya gossypii, the culture medium, comprising glucose (corn sugar), corn steep liquor (byproduct of corn wet milling), and animal stick liquor (a packing-house byproduct of wet rendering), is prepared in a mixing tank. The medium is pumped at a controlled rate through a steam jet heater, where by injection of high-pressure steam the solution is almost instantaneously heated to 275° F. (135° C.). The hot solution circulates through insulated pipes to retain the high temperature for 5 minutes, then through additional pipes or coils surrounded by cold water to reduce the temperature to 82° to 86° F. (28° to 30° C.). Through steam-sterilized pipe lines, the cooled solution is pumped to a sterile fermentation vessel. This is a closed tank equipped with a jacket or coils by which the tank contents may be maintained at a uniform temperature of 82° F. (28° C.). In the bottom of the tank are fine-porosity stones or perforated coils through which sterile air is supplied. A mechanical agitator assists in providing adequate air distribution.

After the sterile culture medium is transferred to the tank, a small volume of a day-old culture of *Ashbya gossypii* is added, and sterile air is introduced through the air distribution system at a rate of one-fourth to one-half volume per volume of medium per minute. By the fourth day, the maximum yield of riboflavin has been obtained, and the culture medium has acquired a beautiful, intense yellow color.

Two types of products can be produced. A potent riboflavin concentrate, ideally suited to enriching poultry and livestock feeds, can be had by evaporating the water from the fermented medium to prepare a sirup of about 30 percent solids. The sirup is converted to a dry powder by such conventional equipment as a drum or spray drier. The drum drier has a pair of cylindrical rolls, mounted horizontally, which are steam heated. The sirup is continuously fed to the valley between the rolls, and as the rolls rotate in opposite directions a thin film of sirup adheres to each. The water rapidly evaporates before a revolution is completed, and the dry material, scraped off by knives, is conveyed to bagging equipment. In the spray-drier method, the sirup is sprayed into a chamber through which heated air is passed; the air absorbs the water; and the dry riboflavin concentrate is mechanically removed to packaging equipment. Concentrates containing 25,000 micrograms of riboflavin per gram (11,350 milligrams per pound, or 2.5 percent riboflavin) are thereby produced.

Pure crystalline riboflavin may be recovered from the fermented solution. Synthetic riboflavin was marketed in 1938. The price was $7,945 a pound. Within a year the price was reduced to $3,642, and by 1944 it had dropped to $90 a pound. Despite substantially increased costs of manufacture during the war and afterward, improvements in the processes and the economies of mass production have cut the costs further. Riboflavin was priced at about $56 a pound in 1950. In 1943 more than 75,000 pounds of crystalline riboflavin was produced from all sources. Production figures are not available for the additional amounts in the form of high-potency concentrates that have been made by fermentation procedures.

FRED W. TANNER, JR., *is a native of Illinois and a graduate of the University of Illinois and Cornell University. From 1943 to 1948 he was engaged at the Department of Agriculture's Northern Regional Research Laboratory in investigating the use of agricultural commodities as raw materials for useful chemicals produced by fermentation. Dr. Tanner is now employed by Chas. Pfizer & Co., in Brooklyn.*

VIRGIL F. PFEIFER *is a native of Missouri and a graduate of Washington University in St. Louis. He has been engaged in chemical engineering investigations relating to the processing of agricultural commodities in the Department of Agriculture since 1939, first at the United States Regional Soybean Industrial Products Laboratory in Urbana and later at the Northern Regional Research Laboratory.*

Illustrated on the next page are some steps in producing an insecticide. At the top are pyrethrum flowers, mentioned on page 767, which yield pyrethrins. The middle picture is a drawing of a model showing the structure of a molecule of the substance. Below is a device used to test the efficiency of an insecticide on insects.

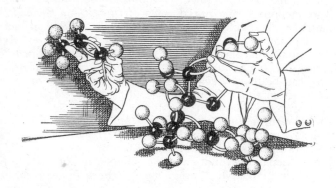

Plants That

Help Kill

Insects

Ruth L. Busbey

In June 1943, DDT was revealed to the American public. Floods of publicity told of its amazing powers as an insect killer. Announcements of other synthetic insecticides have followed in rapid succession. It is not surprising that many who read those accounts assumed that insecticides of natural origin, derived from plants, are outmoded and of little importance nowadays. The assumption is far from true.

As each new synthetic insecticide is studied and the ramifications of its toxicity to man and animals explored, the problems of removing its residues from foods encountered, and its possible injurious effects on plants examined, we appreciate the value of insecticides, like pyrethrum and rotenone, which are nontoxic to warm-blooded animals in the small quantities needed for insect control, are safe for plants, and leave no harmful residues.

Within the plant kingdom are many species, known or yet untried, whose insecticidal properties are worth a careful search by chemists and entomologists. Today nicotine, pyrethrum, derris, and cube are by far the best known and most commonly used insecticides of plant origin, but a few others are utilized for specific purposes or in a few localities. Others still in experimental stages have been found to contain substances highly toxic to insects. The indications are that many plant insecticides await discovery.

Nicotine is the chief insecticidal principle in tobacco. It belongs to the class of compounds known as alkaloids, which are basic, nitrogen-containing plant products having a marked physiological action. Other related alkaloids, notably nornicotine, also may be present in tobacco.

Nicotine derives its name from *Nicotiana,* the genus of plants to which tobacco belongs. The genus was named for Jean Nicot, who introduced tobacco into France in 1560. Chemically, nicotine is 1-methyl-2-(3-pyridyl)pyrrolidine. Most preparations that contain it have a strong tobaccolike smell. Its boiling point is 477° F., yet it evaporates rather rapidly at ordinary room or outdoor summer temperatures. It is peculiar in that between 140° and 248° F. it is soluble in water in all proportions, but above and below those temperatures its solubility is limited. It is highly toxic to warm-blooded animals and to most insects, but because of its volatility it disappears rapidly from products that have been sprayed or dusted with it. Its freezing point has not been determined, but it is a liquid even at −110° F.

Nicotine has been isolated from at least 18 species of *Nicotiana* and from a few species in other plant genera. In this country it is produced commercially from *Nicotiana tabacum,* the ordinary tobacco used for smoking and chewing. From the woody stems and leaf midribs, which are not suitable for smoking or chewing, we extract the nicotine. A coarser species of tobacco, *Nicotiana rustica,* of higher alkaloid content, is cultivated in Soviet Russia, Germany, Kenya, and Hungary as a source of nicotine.

THE ALKALOID is obtained by treating the plant material with an alkali solution and distilling by passing steam through the mixture. The nicotine is volatilized and carried off by the steam and afterwards condensed by cooling. All parts of the plant contain the alkaloid, but it is chiefly in the leaves. The proportion of nicotine present varies from almost none in high-grade smoking tobacco to as much as 12 percent in leaves of *N. rustica*.

Most of the nicotine used as an insecticide in the United States is sold in the form of the sulfate, in a water solution containing 40 percent of the alkaloid. Free nicotine also is available, but it is not so widely used in spraying because it evaporates too quickly and because it is much more toxic to man than the sulfate. The spray is greatly diluted for use, as concentrations of 0.05 to 0.1 percent of nicotine are enough to control most aphids and other soft-bodied insects.

Many attempts have been made to fix the alkaloid and lengthen its period of effectiveness. One of the most effective forms is nicotine bentonite, which was developed by a Department of Agriculture chemist, C. R. Smith, in 1934. It is made by adding nicotine to a suspension of bentonite (a kind of clay) in water, then drying and grinding the mixture. The nicotine combines with acidic constituents of the bentonite and the product, when properly made, is effective for several weeks after it is sprayed. It has been used especially to control the codling moth on apple trees.

Finely ground tobacco, or nicotine sulfate diluted with a carrier, such as clay, pyrophyllite, fuller's earth, or talc, often is used as a dust on vegetable crops. If a quick-acting dust is desired, alkaline diluents such as hydrated lime are useful.

For the fumigation of greenhouses, nicotine is ordinarily used as the free alkaloid in concentrated form to be volatilized by heating, or as a mixture with a combustible organic material and an oxidizing agent, like potassium nitrate, to be applied by burning.

Further details about nicotine are given in the chapter that follows.

Anabasine, a compound isomeric with nicotine (that is, containing the same proportions of carbon, hydrogen, and nitrogen), is like it in chemical, physical, and insecticidal properties. Russian chemists in 1929 isolated from the Asiatic shrub *Anabasis aphylla* an alkaloid that they identified as 2-(3-pyridyl) piperidine and called anabasine because of its source. The year before, C. R. Smith, who was synthesizing a number of compounds related to nicotine in order to study their toxicity to insects, found one that appeared to be equal to nicotine. The compound, which he named neonicotine, was identical with anabasine. It was unique in being first prepared synthetically and later found to occur as a natural plant constituent. In 1935 Mr. Smith found anabasine in *Nicotiana glauca*, the wild tree tobacco native to our Southwestern States and Mexico.

The Russians have produced anabasine sulfate commercially as an insecticide from *Anabasis aphylla*, which is a salt-loving perennial plant of the family Chenopodiaceae, growing in the semiarid steppes of Transcaucasia, Russian Turkestan, and neighboring parts of Central Asia. A Russian commercial product that was marketed in the United States for a few years before 1934 contained about 40 percent of anabasine and associated alkaloids. Anabasine has been used extensively in the Soviet Union in the form of insecticidal dusts.

The production of anabasine has not been developed commercially in the United States. Small-scale tests by entomologists of the Department of Agriculture have shown that it is of the same order of toxicity as nicotine to a number of species of aphids and other insects. H. H. Smith, a geneticist in the Department of Agriculture, and C. R. Smith in 1942 studied the alkaloid content of several species and interspecific hybrids of *Nicotiana*. They found that anabasine was the predominant alkaloid in *N. debneyi*, *N. glauca*, and the hybrid *N. tabacum* x *N. glauca*. Russian workers have reported as much as 8 percent of anabasine in hybrids of *N. glauca* and *N. rustica*. Department chemists in 1948 began to investigate *N. glauca* as a source of anabasine for insecticidal use and to study methods that might be feasible for extracting the alkaloid on a commercial basis. Wild plants, collected in Texas, which contained 1 percent or less of the alkaloid were used in the studies. L. Feinstein and P. J. Hannan developed methods of extraction that are satisfactory on a laboratory scale. A plant-breeding program to develop strains or hybrids of *N. glauca* of higher alkaloid content is necessary before development as a cultivated crop can be undertaken profitably.

EARLY IN THE NINETEENTH CENTURY an insecticide powder was introduced into Europe by an Armenian trader, who learned its secret while traveling in the Caucasus. The preparation consisted of powdered dried pyrethrum flowers, which had been obtained from certain species of *Chrysanthemum* and probably had been used as an insecticide in Persia for a long time. The trader's son began to make it on a commercial scale in 1828. Pyrethrum powder was introduced into the United States about 1860.

Although the pyrethrins, the insecticidal constituents of pyrethrum, occur to some extent in several species of the genus *Chrysanthemum,* only *C. cinerariaefolium* is used for the commercial production of insecticides.

The use of pyrethrum powder grew rapidly. Originally, it was employed mainly to control household insects, because, in the dosages needed to kill insects, it was nontoxic to man and domestic animals. About 1916 kerosene extracts of pyrethrum flowers appeared on the market and were widely used as sprays against flies and mosquitoes. Nowadays we have highly refined, odorless grades of kerosene for household sprays. Another and more efficient way of preparing sprays consists of extracting the pyrethrins from the flowers with a solvent like ethylene

dichloride, and then removing the solvent by evaporation to leave a semisolid residue, which can be diluted with kerosene or other solvent.

Many chemists, beginning with an Italian named Ragazzini in 1854, tried without success to isolate the active principles of pyrethrum flowers. In 1924 two Swiss chemists, H. Staudinger and L. Ruzicka, obtained two insecticidally active esters, which they called pyrethrin I and pyrethrin II.

A group of Department chemists, headed by F. B. LaForge, finally established the exact chemical structure of the pyrethrins in 1947. They discovered that two other very similar insecticidal esters also are present in pyrethrum, and they named them cinerin I and cinerin II.

METHODS of making highly purified, standardized concentrates from pyrethrum have been so successful that extracts containing 20 percent of pyrethrins now are commercially available. The extracts are especially useful in insecticidal aerosols, which contain the pyrethrum concentrate and a liquefied-gas propellent, like Freon–12 (dichlorodifluoromethane). Usually the aerosols also contain one of a number of synthetic or natural compounds that greatly enhance the effectiveness of the pyrethrins when mixed with them. (Most of the aerosols now sold also have DDT and an auxiliary solvent as ingredients.)

Pyrethrum in the amount needed as an insecticide has little toxicity to warm-blooded animals and is not injurious to plants to which it is applied. It rapidly paralyzes insects, such as houseflies, and therefore is often used in combination with other slower acting insecticides that have a longer residual effect. Because the pyrethrins deteriorate rather quickly on exposure to light and air, various materials have been employed as antioxidants to prevent the decomposition, among them hydroquinone and certain substituted cresols. Better antioxidants for pyrethrum are needed, and Department entomologists and chemists are working on the problem.

The pyrethrum plant, a herbaceous perennial, has flowers that look like our common daisy. The pyrethrin content is concentrated in the flower heads and increases up to the time the flowers are fully open. Before the First World War, most of the pyrethrum was produced in Dalmatia, on what is now the Yugoslav coast. Shipping difficulties there resulted in an expansion of production in Japan until, in the middle 1920's, Japan had a virtual monopoly of the trade, although the quality of the Japanese flowers was low. In 1928 experimental pyrethrum culture was undertaken successfully in Kenya, a British colony in East Africa. The quality of the flowers raised there was superior to the Japanese, and by 1940 the United States imported five times more pyrethrum from Kenya than from Japan. The war ended our imports from Japan. Limited amounts of pyrethrum have been imported from the Belgian Congo, Tanganyika, and Brazil. In 1945 we imported more than 18 million pounds of pyrethrum flowers.

Pyrethrum could be grown in the northern United States or in irrigated areas in the West. The hand labor required in harvesting and drying the flowers has been a deterrent to its culture here. A mechanical harvester developed by the Bureau of Plant Industry, Soils, and Agricultural Engineering would reduce the cost of harvesting. The cultivation of pyrethrum has been attempted in Pennsylvania, Colorado, and California, but in 1950 there were no plantings in this country.

SINCE EARLY TIMES, natives in many tropical countries, especially the East Indies, Africa, South America, and India, have used various plants to catch fish. As a rule, the plants were crushed in water and the mixture was poured into a stream; the fish were stupefied and rose to the surface, where they were collected. Some of the plants so used were species of *Derris, Lonchocarpus, Tephrosia, Mundulea,* and *Millettia,*

all members of the family Leguminosae and subsequently found to contain a compound called rotenone. Besides serving as fish poisons, some of the plants were used locally to control insect parasites on humans and animals.

The Chinese are believed to have used "tuba" root, obtained from *Derris,* as an insecticide long ago. In 1848 an Englishman named Thomas Oxley published a report on growing nutmeg in British Malaya, in which he told about washing with a decoction of tuba root the leaves of nutmeg trees attacked by insects. In 1909 the botanist A. T. Bryant found African Zulus killing head lice with an extract of *Tephrosia* leaves. In 1910 cube (*Lonchocarpus*) was used to destroy ticks on llamas in Peru. In 1911 a British patent was issued for the use of tuba root as an insecticide, but these plant products were not commonly employed until about 1930.

Since that time consumption has increased greatly. In 1939 we imported more than 4 million pounds of derris and cube roots. During the war, imports of derris were cut off, and many derris plantings in the East Indies were destroyed or neglected. Our rotenone imports now consist mostly of cube root from South America.

A Japanese chemist, Kazuo Nagai, isolated a crystalline insecticidal compound from *Derris chinensis* in 1902. He named it rotenone from the native name of the plant, roh-ten. About 30 years passed before the complete chemical structure of rotenone was learned. Then it was determined almost simultaneously by three groups of chemists in the United States, Japan, and Germany. The American chemists, who published their results in 1933, were F. B. LaForge, H. L. Haller, and L. E. Smith, of the Department of Agriculture. They soon devised analytical methods for rotenone, so that it was possible to assure the farmer that he could buy standardized rotenone dusts to treat his crops.

Several other related compounds, some of them insecticidal, occur along with rotenone and are called rotenoids. In order to get a good idea of the total insecticidal value of rotenone-containing roots, usually both the rotenone content and the total amount of material that can be extracted by a solvent like ether or chloroform are determined. The rotenone content may vary from almost none to as much as 15 percent in rare cases. Market prices are quoted on the basis of 5 percent rotenone content.

The original way of using derris as an insecticide, employed by Chinese market gardeners in the Malay Peninsula, was to beat the fresh root into a pulp in water and spray the liquid on the plants to be protected. Now derris and cube are used mostly in the form of dusts made by grinding the dried roots fine and mixing them with an inert material (like talc, clay, or pyrophyllite) to give a final rotenone content of about 1 percent. Dusts also are made by impregnating materials like walnut-shell flour or exhausted pyrethrum marc with an extract of the derris or cube in a volatile solvent, such as chloroform, that can be removed easily by evaporation. Liquid extracts of the roots sometimes are made with a water-miscible solvent like acetone, to be diluted with water to make a fine suspension for spraying. For fly sprays, extracts are made with a solvent like ethylene dichloride and then diluted with kerosene.

In 1947, the late L. W. Brannon, a Department entomologist working with the Virginia Truck Experiment Station on methods to control the Mexican bean beetle, discovered that rotenone, like pyrethrum, could be increased greatly in effectiveness by mixing it with certain synthetic compounds, especially one called piperonyl cyclonene. This opened a promising field of investigation to chemists and entomologists.

A North American plant, *Tephrosia virginiana,* common as a weed in the Eastern and Southern States under the name of devil's-shoestrings, contains rotenone in its roots. Workers in the Department have shown that the rotenone content of this species varies widely and is an inherited characteristic. Since about 1931, breeding experiments have been carried on by Texas Agricultural and Mechanical College and by the Bureau of Plant Industry, Soils, and Agricultural Engineering to develop strains of higher rotenone content for ultimate commercial use. Strains containing 5 percent rotenone have been obtained. Unfortunately, they are not very vigorous. Under the direction of L. M. Pultz, a horticulturist, experiments are in progress on crossing them with strains of greater vigor. Roots of devil's-shoestrings are difficult to grind, and mills of different kinds will have to be tried.

MANY OTHER PLANT SPECIES have been tested against insects. A former Department entomologist, N. E. McIndoo, found reports in the literature on nearly 1,200 species of possible insecticidal value. D. E. H. Frear, professor of agricultural chemistry at Pennsylvania State College, has published a list of about 1,450 plant species with which insect tests have been made. Several of them appear promising.

For hundreds of years it has been known that the seeds of several species of lilies of the genus *Schoenocaulon,* commonly known as sabadilla, which grow in Mexico and the United States, will kill insects. In 1938 a group of workers at the University of Wisconsin, headed by T. C. Allen, began to study the insecticidal properties of sabadilla. The active substances in the seeds are several alkaloids, usually referred to jointly as veratrine. The Wisconsin investigators learned that heating the seeds or treating them with alkali greatly increases the toxicity to insects. Sabadilla seed can be used as a dust mixed with a diluent such as lime or pyrophyllite or as kerosene extract. It loses its toxicity quickly when exposed to air and light. It is irritating to the mucous membranes and causes sneezing if the particles are inhaled.

In the course of an extensive testing program on botanical materials, carried on cooperatively by the New Jersey Agricultural Experiment Station and Merck & Co., *Ryania speciosa,* a tropical shrub native to Trinidad, was found to have high, specific toxicity to the European corn borer. A group of Merck chemists in 1948 reported that the insecticidal principles in *Ryania speciosa* can be extracted with water or many organic solvents. They had isolated an alkaloid, which they called ryanodine. Although the active material occurs in greatest concentration in the *Ryania* roots, the stem wood is the source of the commercial insecticide, because this part of the plant is available in larger quantities and also because leaving the roots intact permits further production of the stem wood. The finely ground plant material is used as a dust or suspended in water as a spray.

Workers at the Puerto Rico Agricultural Experiment Station at Mayaguez began a study of the insecticidal possibilities of the West Indian tree named *Mammea americana,* or mamey. They have found that the seeds contain an insecticidal substance, believed to be an ester. The ground seeds or kerosene extracts of them are toxic to houseflies, mosquitoes, cockroaches, ants, and a number of chewing insects, like codling moth larvae and southern armyworms.

In 1945, three Department chemists, Fred Acree, Jr., Martin Jacobson, and H. L. Haller, isolated an insecticidal compound, an amide, from the roots of a Mexican plant, which they thought was *Erigeron affinis.* (An amide is a compound derived from an organic acid and ammonia.) Later the plant was identified as *Heliopsis longipes,* a member of the family Compositae. Roots of the plant have been used in Mexico as an insecticide. Mr. Jacobson is now investigating three other species of *Heliopsis,* which are native to the United States, *H. scabra, H. gracilis,* and *H. parvifolia.* He has found that all three species, particularly their roots, are toxic to houseflies. Early in 1950 he isolated from the roots of *H. scabra,* which are especially toxic to houseflies, an amide closely related to the one found earlier in *H. longipes,* and named it scabrin.

In 1948 Jacobson found a very similar insecticidal amide in the bark of another American plant of a completely different kind, the southern prickly-ash tree *Zanthoxylum clavaherculis.*

In 1941 a group of Department men—Walter T. Swingle, a plant physiologist, E. H. Siegler, and M. C. Swingle, entomologists, and H. L. Haller, a chemist — reported the promising insecticidal properties of the roots of *Tripterygium wilfordii,* a perennial vine native to China, which has been used in that country for insect control for many years. This plant, called thunder god vine by the Chinese, is related to the American bittersweet. The Bureau of Plant Industry, Soils, and Agricultural Engineering has made experimental plantings of thunder god vine, first at the Bureau's plant introduction garden at Glenn Dale, Md., and later at Knoxville.

Haller and Acree began in 1939 to investigate the insecticidal constituents of the root. They had obtained the active material in a rather pure state and had shown it to be an ester alkaloid, when their work was interrupted by other activities connected with the war. In 1949 the study of the material was resumed by another chemist in the Department, Morton Beroza. After he had found that the alkaloidal fraction isolated by Haller and Acree contains at least two different compounds, he began the work of separating and identifying them.

Many plant products are not in themselves toxic to insects, yet have properties that make them useful in the preparation of insecticides. For example, I have already mentioned that certain substances greatly enhance the effectiveness of the pyrethrins against insects. Sesame oil contains a compound called sesamin that does so.

The ability of sesame oil to increase the insect toxicity of pyrethrum, called by biologists a synergistic effect, was discovered by Craig Eagleson, a Department entomologist, in 1941. Our chemists separated the oil into different fractions for testing and soon found that it was the sesamin that was effective. Combinations of sesamin and pyrethrins are now much used, especially in aerosol bombs. Usually a sesamin concentrate is used that is obtained as a byproduct in the purification of sesame oil for food.

Another compound that is much like sesamin in chemical structure and has a synergistic action with the pyrethrins is asarinin. It occurs in the bark of the southern prickly-ash tree, which, as you already know, also contains an insecticidal substance. Other plant constituents have been found that are synergists for pyrethrum and are chemically related to sesamin and asarinin. A common one is piperine, in black pepper.

Essential oils from some plants are attractive to insects. A well-known example is citronella grass, *Cymbopogon nardus,* from which we get geraniol and eugenol, used as baits in traps for Japanese beetles. Some plants contain substances that repel insects. Nearly everyone is familiar with the use of oil of citronella, also obtained from *C. nardus,* to repel mosquitoes, and with the storage of woolen goods in chests of cedar wood to protect them from clothes moths.

Vegetable oils have some value as insecticides, but are not often used for that purpose in the United States because they are more expensive than the equally effective petroleum oils. They are sometimes included in horticultural sprays, however, because they are good stickers or adhesives. Soybean oil is used in this way in nicotine bentonite sprays. Rosin also has been used as an adhesive in sprays.

Waste materials from such plant products as nutshells and bark, when finely ground, may be useful as diluents for insecticide dusts. Walnut-shell flour serves as a diluent in some commercial insecticides. E. L. Gooden, a physicist in the Bureau of Entomology and Plant Quarantine laboratories at Beltsville, is examining samples of many such materials to see whether their physical properties are suitable for this purpose. Some of the waste products he has examined are: Almond, coconut, filbert, pecan, black walnut, and English walnut shells; peach and apricot pit shells; redwood, fir, and southern pine barks; sumac leaves; rice hulls; corncob fractions, corn stover; flax shives; hemp hurds; and wheat straw. The most promising of these so far appear to be the nutshells, fir and pine bark, and the hard component of corncob. Wettable DDT powders containing them as diluents are being tested in the field by entomologists. The botanical diluents are not so fine in particle size as the mineral diluents ordinarily used, but the size is more uniform. Testing has not yet gone far enough to fix definitely their value.

The utilization of plants in insecticides has three aspects that should interest the American farmer.

First, plant products can control many of the insect pests that attack his crops, without leaving persistent poisonous residues at harvest time. Such residues may interfere with marketing of produce or with feeding of forage to livestock.

Second, several of the insecticidal plants that have been discussed could be grown in the United States and offer possibilities as new crops for future cultivation.

Third, the use of byproducts as insecticide diluents would offer a market for materials now discarded as waste.

RUTH L. BUSBEY *is a chemist in the Bureau of Entomology and Plant Quarantine. After graduating from the University of Maryland she joined the Department in 1930 to carry on chemical studies on synthetic organic insecticides at College Park, Md. Later she was engaged in investigations on fumigants.*

Estimate of the major uses of nicotine in the United States in terms of 40-percent nicotine sulfate equivalent

Host	Insect	40-percent nicotine sulfate
		Pounds
Animals (other than poultry)...............	Lice, ticks, internal parasites.............	25,000
Apples.....................................	Aphids......................................	100,000
	Codling moth............................	100,000
Broccoli....................................	Aphids......................................	75,000
Cabbage and cauliflower....................	.....do.....................................	85,000
	.....do.....................................	20,000
Cantaloups.............................	Cucumber beetle.......................	10,000
	Squash borer..........................	5,000
Celery.....................................	Thrips......................................	35,000
Cherries...................................	Aphids	10,000
	Thrips......................................	25,000
Citrus.....................................	Aphids......................................	70,000
Cotton.....................................	.....do.....................................	50,000
	.....do.....................................	5,000
Cucumber..................................	Cucumber beetle.......................	7,000
	Squash borer..........................	3,000
Currants...................................	Aphids......................................	5,000
Eggplants..................................	.....do.....................................	5,000
Gooseberries...............................	.....do.....................................	5,000
Grapes.....................................	Berry moths............................	25,000
	Leafhopper..............................	50,000
Greenhouse flowers and commercial plants...	Aphids, thrips, white flies, mealy bugs....	150,000
Greenhouse vegetables.....................	.....do.....................................	50,000
Home gardens..............................	.....do.....................................	400,000
Hops......................................	Hop aphid.................................	70,000
Mushrooms.................................	Flies, mites................................	5,000
Onions....................................	Thrips......................................	5,000
Peaches....................................	Aphids......................................	40,000
	Twig borer................................	12,000
Pears	Pear psylla..............................	25,000
	Thrips......................................	40,000
Peas.......................................	Aphids......................................	100,000
	.....do.....................................	30,000
Pecans..................................	Nut casebearer.......................	5,000
	Phylloxera..............................	5,000
Peppers....................................	Aphids......................................	5,000
Plums and prunes.........................	.....do.....................................	15,000
	Pear thrips.............................	50,000
Potatoes...................................	Aphids......................................	10,000
Poultry.....................................	Mites, lice, internal parasites............	150,000
Shade trees, ornamentals, and nursery stock..	Aphids and other sucking insects.........	50,000
Spinach....................................	Aphids......................................	30,000
Strawberries...............................	.....do.....................................	5,000
Tomatoes...................................	.....do.....................................	10,000
Turnips....................................	.....do.....................................	20,000
Walnuts....................................	.....do.....................................	80,000
Watermelons...............................	.....do.....................................	20,000
	Cucumber beetle.......................	10,000

Production and Use of Nicotine

Ernest G. Beinhart

Tobacco is produced the world over. Fifty-four countries grow about 7 billion pounds of it annually on 7¾ million acres. It is smoked in cigarettes, cigars, and pipes. It is chewed in its natural leaf state or, ground to a powder to which various materials have been added, as snuff. Or it may be treated with a mixture of sugars, honey, licorice, and other flavors, and oil and formed into plugs, ropes, or pellets for chewing or smoking. A few people snuff it into the nostrils to clear the head. Some call it a filthy weed, but the fact is that tobacco has tremendous economic significance.

Varieties, soil, cultural practices, and curing methods develop characteristic properties of the leaf. Curing methods include natural air-curing, sun-curing, fire-curing (in which smoke is used to add flavor and aroma), and flue-curing (in which heat produces a bright yellow leaf). Perique is an unusual tobacco which is processed entirely by the farmer, who uses an anaerobic fermentation to produce it. In parts of India and Pakistan bulk fermentation of the green leaf is part of the curing process.

The species *Nicotiana tabacum* supplies most of the world's tobacco, and it is the only species grown in the United States for tobacco purposes. The species *Nicotiana rustica*, which was being used by the North American Indians when the first white explorers reached the continent, is now grown extensively in India, Pakistan, and the Soviet Union, and to a lesser extent in Arabia, Persia, Syria, Abyssinia, Poland, and Hungary. The total production of *N. rustica* is estimated to be 750 million pounds from 700,000 acres. It is used for smoking, chewing, snuff, and nicotine extraction.

THE ALKALOID nicotine is an important insecticide. It is used universally to protect plants and animals against pests and parasites. It is especially valuable as a contact insecticide for the control of aphids, scales, and leafhoppers. In some of its fixed forms it is a stomach poison for chewing insects. Its effective control of scab and ticks has made sheep husbandry possible in many parts of the world.

The United States production of this alkaloid is approximately 1,350,000 pounds a year. We usually export about 120,000 pounds, although in 1949 we shipped more than 400,000 pounds abroad. The annual production in other countries (except Soviet Russia, for which we have no figures) is more than 500,000 pounds of alkaloid. Nicotine products are made in England, France, Algeria, Italy, Germany, Hungary, Switzerland, Japan, and Soviet Russia. More recently, small developments have been reported under way in Australia, Brazil, Rhodesia, and South Africa. The government tobacco monopolies of Turkey and Thailand have announced that nicotine-extraction plants will be part of projected tobacco factories.

Most of the nicotine comes from stems or midribs and other wastes and dusts discarded in the manufacture of tobacco products from the leaves of *Nicotiana tabacum*. Because our consumption of tobacco has been increasing steadily, an increasing amount of factory byproducts is going to the nicotine extractor. At the same time the demand for nicotine has kept pace with the available supplies. The net amount of nicotine now available, however, is not in proportion to the increased tonnage of tobacco byproducts. Improved agronomic practices have reduced the nicotine content of our domestic cigarette tobaccos. Furthermore, increased freight charges have tended to limit the area to which byproducts can be profitably shipped for extraction.

At times the prices of low-grade leaf tobaccos of the dark fired and heavy air-cured types permitted their use for nicotine production. That use has not been possible since 1939, when support prices established values for the low grades above their nicotine values. Two subsidized diversion programs in 1943 and 1944, however, used low and medium grades of surplus leaf to obtain enough nicotine for food production for the war effort. For those reasons, the suggestion has been made to grow *Nicotiana rustica,* a species that has a high content of nicotine, solely for the alkaloid.

NICOTINE, $C_{10}H_{14}N_2$, in its pure state is a colorless liquid with a faint characteristic odor. Its vapor pressure at 68° F. is only 0.08 millimeter of mercury. The pure alkaloid volatilizes readily when exposed to the air, although part of it may turn into a dark resinous material.

Nicotine is a basic compound, which forms salts with acids. The simple salts do not readily crystallize, most of them being hygroscopic. Others, however, such as benzoate, oxalate, salicylate, and tartrate, are crystalline solids and are stable under atmospheric conditions. Nearly all of them are readily soluble in water. There are several water-insoluble nicotine compounds, like the combinations with the bentonites, some of the zeolites, tannic acid, peat, and certain resins. The bentonite and tannate compounds have found commercial application.

A rather comprehensive series of more complex metal double salts has been prepared by combining the metal and the nicotine salts of the same acid. Another series of nicotinammino compounds has been prepared by combining the alkaloid with a metal salt of the selected acid. Many of these are insoluble in water, and so far have been of interest chiefly in fundamental insecticide studies. A few that contain copper or cadmium show fungicidal properties. Nicotine readily combines with certain of the dye acids to form water-insoluble compounds, but their practical application is yet to be determined.

Nicotine can be oxidized rather readily with certain oxidizing agents to nicotinic acid and nicotinonitrile, the nitrile of nicotine acid, which have become important as antipellagra vitamins.

TOBACCO AND ITS EXTRACTS were used for the control of insects long before it was known that nicotine was the toxic agent. The first reference to the use of a tobacco extract for spraying plants was in 1690. English and continental gardeners early recognized the value of tobacco from the American colonies. According to present standards it must have been strong tobacco. In a letter dated January 20, 1734, Peter Collison of London suggested to his American correspondent, John Bartram, the Philadelphia botanist, the use of tobacco leaves to protect letters and packages containing seeds and plants being shipped to him. In 1746 he advised Bartram to use a water extract of tobacco for the control of the plum curculio on nectarine trees.

Tobacco dusts and extracts were recommended for the control of plant lice in France in 1763. In 1773 Richard Weston developed a hand bellows for fumigating insects with tobacco smoke. The first American reference was in 1814 by Peter W. Yates of Albany, who used tobacco water against sucking insects. William Cobbett, in England, in 1829 recommended tobacco extract for the control of the woolly aphid. Thomas Fessenden in 1832 included tobacco in a list of insect repellents and insecticides.

By 1884 tobacco was described as one of the three most valuable insecticides in general use, the other two being white hellebore and soap. Tobacco was then used as a dust or water extract, or the leaves and stems were burned as a smudge for fumigating greenhouses. Specially prepared papers impregnated with tobacco extracts were extensively used. Special burners were developed for burning the tobacco or nicotine preparations and to blow the heavy smoke into the greenhouses or about the infested plants. Tobacco washes, prepared by gardeners and horticulturists from specially prepared tobacco leaf and stem materials, were in common use. They preceded the tobacco extracts soon to be manufactured commercially.

Commercial tobacco extracts found extensive use for the control of sheep ticks and scabies. In the early years, the extracts were often prepared from leaf tobacco, tobacco dust, or tobacco stems at the site of the dipping vats. Later, commercial extracts were offered in Europe, Australia, New Zealand, South America, and the United States. The first manufactured products were simple water extracts that contained 1 to 10 percent nicotine. In 1895 a product containing 40 percent free nicotine was offered to the trade, followed in 1898 with one containing 80 percent free alkaloid.

In 1910 a product containing 40 percent nicotine as the sulfate appeared. It marked the beginning of the modern nicotine business, as it made possible transportation in gallon cans instead of casks or large hogsheads, previously required to carry the weaker extracts or the raw leaf and stems to supply the same amounts of active alkaloid. The 40-percent nicotine sulfate offered fewer hazards in handling in sheep dips and for other applications than the pure alkaloid, and it proved more effective because it also contained other distillation products of tobacco with adhesive properties.

Today nicotine still has its widest use in agriculture as a contact insecticide for the control of important groups of sucking insects, such as aphids and scales. For these insects, it is used as a dilute spray, or as a dust, or it is vaporized in smoke or other aerosol form. In those forms, the alkaloid is readily available, and its lethal action is immediate upon contact with an insect. A similar action, but of more extended duration, follows the use of nicotine sulfate alone, as in the control of poultry lice and mites. Here the alkaloid is released more slowly over a period of 24 to 48 hours. In a third form—the so-called fixed nicotine combination—the alkaloid is very slowly given off over a relatively long period, often up to 30 days. The fixed forms include nicotine bentonite, bentonite fused with sulfur combined with nicotine, and nicotine tannate. Materials of this type act as a stomach poison to leaf-chewing insects.

The development of fixed nicotines, like nicotine tannate and nicotine bentonite, marked an advance in insecticide chemistry, and greatly broadened the field of nicotine usage. Before their discoveries, nicotine was used almost entirely for quick action as a contact insecticide in a nascent form. The use of nicotine sulfate on poultry roosts, however, takes advantage of rather slow volatility. In the fixed forms, nicotine is an excellent and effective stomach poison for certain insects of economic importance. Other combinations may have wider applications. Moreover, nicotine is unique among insecticides in that it is relatively safe, because it ultimately disappears, even in the fixed forms, and leaves no residues that might be dangerous to consumers of food products sprayed with it.

A nicotine bentonite preparation also is used widely to control internal poultry parasites. A mixture of nicotine sulfate and copper sulfate gives effective control of some internal parasites of sheep.

The pure alkaloid, offered in concentrations of 50, 80, 95, and 98 percent, is adapted for direct fumigation, especially in greenhouses, but also in fields and orchards. This form has been replaced in part by smoke aerosols, where the nicotine is impregnated on paper, on tobacco dust, or on a similar slow-burning material so as to make a smudge quickly. Special burners have been developed for making the smudges. A combination of nicotine and DDT in a tobacco base makes an effective smudge for freeing an area of mosquitoes.

Another type of smudge, or vaporized nicotine fumigant, is offered in a mixture containing 80 percent nicotine alkaloid and 18 percent oil. The mixture, when dispensed by a heating device, has proved effective in treating large acreages. Nicotine has also been successfully used in the bomb-type aerosols, in which materials of low boiling point furnish the impelling power.

Nicotine-bearing dusts are available in a wide range of alkaloid contents. Some are prepared from the natural leaf tobacco and contain 0.45 to 1.0 percent nicotine. When prepared from air-cured tobaccos, they are alkaline in nature and slowly give up their nicotine on exposure to the air. When they are prepared from flue-cured tobacco, which is acid in nature, the nicotine is less readily given off. The acid-type material is adapted for use in controlling some internal parasites of poultry and sheep.

Concentrated tobacco dusts that carry 10 or 20 percent nicotine are available. They are used as a dust base and are diluted to the desired nicotine content with tobacco dust of very low nicotine content, with pyrophyllite, or with certain talcs or clays. When they are reduced to 4 percent or less of nicotine they are easily dustable and effective.

Nicotine is compatible with most of the other insecticides and standard fungicides used today. Because of its versatility, a large part of its commercial and home-garden usage (when several insects and plant pathogens are to be controlled in one application) is in combination sprays and dusts.

Statistics on the use of nicotine in any one year or on any one crop are difficult to compile because of the year-to-year variations in infestations of insects it can control. When used as a contact insecticide, nicotine acts quickly, and the commercial grower usually does not apply it until an infestation is present. On the other hand, insecticides for chewing insects are often applied as a regular routine, and usually ahead of an expected insect emergence. Thus, when the more stable forms of fixed nicotine are used (for example, for the codling moth on apple or the European corn borer on sweet corn) their application is on a more or less regular schedule, ahead of the insect's appearance.

Some of the newly developed synthetic organic substances that threaten the position of nicotine as an insecticide for use on certain crops carry hazards in their application and in their residues. Their permanent position is not yet clear, despite their insecticidal efficiency. The demand for nicotine continues to be as strong as ever.

An estimate of the major uses of nicotine in American agriculture for an average year is shown in the table on page 772. The variation in the probable insect infestation may raise or lower the quantities indicated for any one crop from year to year.

TOBACCO SAUCES for flavoring chewing and smoking tobaccos were, strangely enough, the first manufactured tobacco extracts employed in agriculture. They were extensively used in Europe, especially in Germany and Scandinavia. Such tobacco extracts were manufactured in Europe and the United States. Sometimes they were produced from the finest American tobaccos. The extracts were often of special formulation as to type and grades of tobacco and were designed for particular usages. Their nicotine content varied from 1 to 10 percent, depending on formulations and degree of concentration.

One reason for the rapidly growing market that developed for nicotine products was that entomologists and veterinarians who joined agricultural pest-control agencies relied more and more on the products in the fight against increasing infestations. They suggested that the sources of tobacco then available be improved. Tobacco solutions that once were poured away after having served their purpose in tobacco factories were reclaimed and sold for insect control. The effective control of sheep mites and ticks with nicotine dips created a large market for nicotine products. Outbreaks of the parasites during the 1890's brought about Federal regulations in the United States and made sheep dipping mandatory for interstate shipments. Important markets for nicotine had also been developed in other sheep-growing areas. The chemist and chemical engineer were brought into the tobacco business in order to manufacture concentrated products more efficiently.

The expanding demand for nicotine caused the development of methods for recovering the alkaloid from tobacco extracts. The alkaloid was removed in whole or in part from such extracts, which thereby improved in quality, because nicotine was neither desirable nor required in flavoring extracts. Continued progress was made in purifying and concentrating the insecticide product.

Before 1880, tobacco flavoring sauces and home-made tobacco extracts were in general use. In 1881 extracts carrying 2 to 3 percent nicotine were offered. The alkaloid content was increased to 6 and 10 percent by 1885. A 40-percent solution of free alkaloid appeared in 1895; an 80-percent solution, primarily for greenhouse use, was put out in 1898. Nicotine sulfate appeared in 1900, first with 10 percent alkaloid and later with 40 percent. It has since become the standard nicotine solution of the agricultural trade.

Nicotine tannate appeared in 1929 as the first fixed nicotine compound. It was followed in 1933 by nicotine bentonite. The alkaloid of 99.9 percent purity was offered for commercial use in 1940.

Because of a reduced demand in Europe for strong-flavored tobaccos, the once important flavoring-extract business has greatly declined. On the other hand, the demand for nicotine has continued to increase, and extraction units of substantial capacities have developed.

NICOTINE AND OTHER ALKALOIDS can be removed from tobacco by dry distillation, by water or hydrocarbon solvents, and by steam distillation. In the United States most of the extraction is by steam distillation in a continuous or batch process. The alkaloid is recovered by liquid-liquid extraction, or by scrubbing the alkaloid from the vapors with sulfuric acid. Ion-exchange reactions have been suggested for recovering nicotine from solutions.

The stems and other materials are usually cut or ground to pass a ¼-inch screen. A lime slurry is added to free the alkaloids and to impart from 22 to 35 percent of moisture to the material.

Continuous extraction is done in a rotary steam-tube drier. The drier may be 50 to 55 feet long and 6 feet in diameter. It is usually equipped with two rows of heating tubes with steam at a pressure of 100 pounds per square inch, gage, equivalent to 338° F. The revolving movement keeps the material in constant motion as it passes down the slightly inclined drier. In the first part of the drier the tobacco material is maintained on a moist basis by steam. Heat from the tubes of the drier drives off the moisture, carrying with it the alkaloids and ammonia vapors. The rate of flow of the tobacco is so adjusted by the operator that the recovery of the original nicotine content is practically complete within an hour; the moisture of the extracted material as it leaves the drier is about 5 percent. The dried residue, containing important amounts of nitrogen and potash, is used as a fertilizer material.

Instead of a continuous extracting system, a batch method may be used. It employs rotary driers, which hold about 4 tons of tobacco material to which a lime and water slurry has been added. Stripping steam at 300° F. or higher is fed into the driers. The material stays in the driers for 2 to 3½ hours at 300° F. or higher. Under those conditions, about 95 percent of the contained nicotine is extracted. At the completion of the run, a vacuum is drawn on the drier, which removes some of the fine dust and obnoxious vapors that otherwise would saturate the atmosphere in the drier building.

In either system, the vapors pass first through a dust collector. They may then be sent through a sulfuric acid scrubbing tower to recover the nicotine as sulfate, or they may be condensed and the nicotine alkaloid removed by liquid-liquid extraction.

Where an acid-recovery system is used at substantially atmospheric pressure, the vapors are maintained at a temperature above 212° F., so that the steam in the vapors does not condense in the recovery system, thus diluting the acid solution. The acid towers are arranged in series to allow one of them to be cut out when the product has reached maximum concentration.

The concentrated product can seldom be brought to the usually desired alkaloid content of 40 percent in the recovery system. It is cooled and the excess ammonium sulfate is crystallized out, the nicotine sulfate layer being decanted. This layer is then brought up to the desired strength, usually about 40.25 percent nicotine content, by adding sufficient pure alkaloid to react with the free sulfuric acid. Another method of concentrating the nicotine sulfate solution is to draw it off from the towers at around 10 percent concentration, and evaporate this to 40 percent nicotine content in an open kettle or under vacuum.

In a third method, the vapors from the still are condensed and the nicotine is recovered by a liquid-liquid extraction process. Advantage is taken of the solubility of nicotine in some of the hydrocarbons, such as hot kerosene. In practice, the warm condensate from the drier (temperature about 180° F.) is passed through a packed column, in which the kerosene or other solvent passes countercurrently. These columns are high enough to allow complete removal of the nicotine from the condensate. The heated kerosene enters the extracting column at the bottom, and the condensate with the nicotine enters at the top. Such columns are usually packed with porcelain rings or saddles for nearly their entire length in order to expose as much surface as possible to the action of the solvent. The warm kerosene absorbs the alkaloid from the water solution as it meets the solvent. The condensate, now free of nicotine, goes to waste, carrying with it whatever ammonia it might contain. The recovery of the ammonia in this system usually costs more than it is worth.

The kerosene-nicotine solution flows to a series of tanks where it is mixed successively with 25-percent solutions of sulfuric acid. The mixing can be effected with a centrifugal pump system ahead of the tanks. The sulfuric acid reacts with the nicotine and removes it completely from the kerosene. The kerosene is returned to storage to be used again in the system.

When the nicotine sulfate solution in the first tank contains approximately 40 percent alkaloid, it is centrifuged to remove any tarry and resinous material. It is then made up accurately to 40.25 percent alkaloid content. The solution is adjusted with alkali to pH 6 for safety in transport in metal containers.

The direct acid recovery in a tower system is probably the more economical method for recovering and concentrating nicotine vapors to the sulfate. Its advantage is that it is a direct, continuous operation and involves the minimum of product handling. The distilled nicotine vapors are accompanied by evolved ammonia, which encumber the system with ammonium sulfate. The amount of ammonia varies with the kind of tobacco material used.

BECAUSE OF THE CONTINUED strong demand for nicotine, the increased prices of low grades of leaf tobacco, and increased freight rates for moving the raw material, experiments have been under way for several years to find an environment in the United States where high nicotine-producing strains of *Nicotiana rustica* might be profitably grown.

Extract plants in the growing areas might put out the finished product, like 40-percent nicotine sulfate, or a semifinished product of perhaps 10 percent nicotine content which can be shipped to a central plant for purification and concentration. In the absence of available low-grade leaf tobacco, the American production of nicotine now is confined to large plant operations, where the supplies of raw material consumed are thousands of tons annually. Such raw material now is of relatively low nicotine content— from 0.3 to 1 percent. In order to use high-nicotine material like *N. rustica,* which has 6 to 10 percent nicotine content in the leaves and a correspondingly high ammonia content, special methods were developed at the Eastern Regional Research Laboratory. These, however, do not differ in essential detail from those used in processing tobacco-factory byproducts. They are designed for small factory operations which utilize the whole plant (stalks and leaves) and which might process about 2,000 tons of high-quality raw material annually.

Yields of 125 to 325 pounds of nicotine per acre have been obtained with *N. rustica.* Even the lower yield should give the producer a profit. Because of the relatively high income per acre now obtained in most tobacco-growing areas, as compared with that which might be expected from a nicotine crop, it is believed that the growing of *N. rustica* will find interested growers only outside of the established tobacco-growing areas, and in such areas that might use a cash crop of medium value.

ERNEST G. BEINHART *is a senior tobacco technologist in the Eastern Regional Research Laboratory. He has had extensive industrial and Government experience with American tobaccos. His early training was in cigar and tobacco manufacturing and the agricultural and processing phases of all of the American tobacco types, including the production of Nicotiana rustica for nicotine. As a means of stabilizing the tobacco supply situation, he first suggested in 1933 the conversion of surplus tobacco stocks into nicotine.*

WHILE I was traveling in the interior of the province of Kuangtung in the south of China, I felt concern that only the land in the valleys right along the streams was cultivated, while thousands of acres of hill lands were left to grow in grass and weeds. I realized that rice farmers could not profitably grow rice on hill lands, but I remarked to my interpreter that no doubt in the past these sections had been covered with subtropical forests. I asked him if trees would not grow again.

"Yes," he replied, "they will grow well, but there are not enough soldiers."

His answer puzzled me, and I asked what soldiers had to do with planting trees.

"Nothing," he said, "but if we did not put a soldier beside each tree guarding it day and night, the people would cut them down for firewood."—*Hubert Maness, Agricultural Attaché, American Embassy, Montevideo, Uruguay.*

Acids of

Many Uses

From Corn

C. L. Mehltretter

Most of the commercial sugar acids come from dextrose, the sugar derived from corn. They are cheap and mild and, chemically, maids-of-all-work. Their uses range from the simple process of cleaning milk cans and bottles to the complex production of vitamins.

Veterinarians and farmers know best the calcium salt of gluconic acid, which they use for the treatment of milk fever in cows and which doctors sometimes recommend for bee stings.

The housewife is most familiar with cream of tartar, an ingredient of the baking powder she uses for her pies and cakes. Citric acid, the acid that gives the tang to citrus fruits, she also uses for flavoring lemon pies. Its magnesium salt—citrate of magnesia—has often been prescribed as a laxative for her family. No doubt she is also acquainted with ascorbic acid, the sugar acid that is made in chemical factories and is the same as the vitamin C in oranges and lemons.

Chemists have known about the sugar acids for a long time, but new uses for them are being discovered constantly. For instance, doctors recently learned that glucuronic acid, first isolated from the body in 1875, may relieve the pains of rheumatism and sciatica.

The versatile nature of the sugar acids has aroused increasing interest in them as raw materials for the production of such things as plastics, deter-

gents, and medicines. More attention is being given, consequently, to the development of practical methods for obtaining them from dextrose.

Processes for the fermentation of dextrose to citric, gluconic, 2-ketogluconic, 5-ketogluconic, α-ketoglutaric, and itaconic, and similar acids have been developed in the laboratories of the Department of Agriculture. Some, particularly those for citric and gluconic acids, have achieved commercial importance. The large-scale production of itaconic acid appears promising. Lactic acid, a widely used food acid, is being produced in large volumes by the corn-products industries by fermentation of cornstarch hydrolyzates.

The acids I have mentioned have also been made by nonfermentative methods, but of the purely chemical processes only those for obtaining gluconic and itaconic acids merit consideration from a practical standpoint. Some years ago workers at the National Bureau of Standards devised a procedure for the electrolytic oxidation of corn sugar to gluconic acid. It appears to be competitive with the fermentation method. The electrolysis is carried out between carbon electrodes in the presence of bromides and calcium carbonate buffer, and the gluconic acid is neutralized as it is formed to give calcium gluconate.

Itaconic acid was originally produced in pilot-plant quantities from citric acid. The dehydration of citric acid with mineral acids yields aconitic acid, which is readily decarboxylated to itaconic acid. More recently, however, chemists at the Southern Regional Research Laboratory have demonstrated that the calcium magnesium aconitate present in sugarcane molasses can be recovered in commercial amounts without significantly altering the proc-

essing of the molasses for sugar production. A practical method was also
devised for converting the crude
alkaline-earth aconitate to itaconic
acid of high purity. It has been estimated that at least 4 million pounds of
aconitic acid a year are potentially
available as a byproduct of the sugarcane grown and milled in Louisiana
and Florida alone. In 1950 there was a
demand for at least a million pounds
of aconitic acid for conversion to esters
for plasticizers. The remaining 3 million pounds of potential production
would yield about 2 million pounds of
itaconic acid for use in the manufacture of plastics, detergents and such.

The sugar acids—levulinic, tartaric,
ascorbic, isoascorbic, arabonic, saccharic, and glucuronic acids—cannot
be produced at all, or only inefficiently,
by the direct fermentation of dextrose.
When not derived from natural
sources, they are generally made by
chemical conversion of dextrose.

LEVULINIC ACID has been manufactured on a commercial scale by heating
starch hydrolyzates with mineral acids.
The low cost, stability, and chemical
activity of this interesting keto acid
have encouraged its development from
both a practical and a theoretical
standpoint. Some of the compounds
that have been synthesized from
levulinic acid have been found to
possess local anesthetic and analgesic
action. Others have bactericidal and
detergent properties.

SINCE THE BEGINNING of the century, practical methods for the synthesis
of tartaric acid have been sought. The
search has been stimulated by the increased use of the acid and its salts
and by our dependence upon foreign
sources of argols, the crude potassium
bitartrate that crystallizes in wine barrels, from which most commercial tartaric acid is made. In the Second
World War, the shortage of argols
brought the price of tartaric acid up
from about 40 cents to more than 70
cents a pound. To alleviate this situa-

tion, processes were devised to recover
the residual tartrates in domestic grape
pomace and in brandy-still slop. These
significant developments were achieved
by chemists in commercial wineries and
at the Western Regional Research Laboratory. At the Atlas Powder Company, pilot-plant experiments had also
been carried out for the production of
tartaric acid by the nitric acid oxidation of dextrose. Still another method
of synthesis is the catalytic oxidation of
5-ketogluconic acid by oxygen. The
raw material for this process, calcium
5-ketogluconate, can readily be produced by a biological process developed in the Department of Agriculture.

Because of the low cost of tartaric
acid, the synthetic processes are not
now being used. However, the tartrates
in grape wastes are being successfully
recovered on a large scale. It is estimated that 10 million pounds of tartaric acid is potentially recoverable
from grape residues. Because of the
threat of the synthetic processes, the
price of tartaric acid may never again
rise to the exorbitant levels reached in
1941 to 1946.

VARIOUS ASCORBIC ACIDS are known.
They can be prepared from corn sugar
as the starting material. The most important one, vitamin C, has the chemical name l-xyloascorbic acid. It is used
mainly in the treatment of scurvy and
other diseases due to vitamin C deficiency. It is thought that subnormal
amounts of ascorbic acid in the body
lead to ready infection with such diseases as rheumatic fever, tuberculosis,
and diphtheria.

Of secondary importance is the compound d-araboascorbic acid, which is
usually called isoascorbic acid. The ascorbic acids have the same general
formula, except that the hydroxyl
group on the fifth carbon atom of each
has an opposite spatial position. Both
of these substances have similar antioxidant properties, but isoascorbic acid
has only one-twentieth the antiscorbutic activity of vitamin C. Vitamin C
is found in nature in citrus fruits, cab-

bage, paprika, pine needles, and walnuts. It is generally produced commercially by the Reichstein process (or a modification of it), whereby dextrose is catalytically hydrogenated to *d*-sorbitol, which may then be fermented to *l*-sorbose by a method developed by Department of Agriculture scientists. The sorbose is reacted with acetone in the presence of sulfuric acid to form diacetone sorbose. Alkaline solutions of the diacetone sorbose are oxidized with potassium permanganate or sodium hypochlorite to diacetone 2-keto-*l*-gulonic acid, which, when hydrolyzed, yields 2-keto-*l*-gulonic acid. This acid may be esterified with methanol and then transformed to vitamin C by the action of sodium methylate, or it may be converted directly to vitamin C by heating with hydrochloric acid. By an analogous procedure, the methyl ester of 2-keto-*d*-gluconic acid is rearranged to produce isoascorbic acid.

THE CHIEF VALUE of *d*-arabonic acid lies in its use as an intermediate in the chemical synthesis of riboflavin—vitamin B₂. The riboflavin molecule contains a carbohydrate residue, which is derived from *d*-ribose. The 5-carbon sugar, *d*-ribose, is generally obtained from the nucleic acids found in yeast cells or from dextrose and arabinose, via arabonic acid. Arabonic acid is usually produced by the oxidation of corn sugar in alkaline solution with oxygen or air. In 1946, however, a new method of preparation was developed at the Northern Regional Research Laboratory. In it, calcium 2-ketogluconate is electrolytically oxidized to calcium arabonate in 85 percent yield, in a manner similar to that used for the production of gluconic acid. Apparently in this reaction decarboxylation of the 2-ketogluconic acid first occurs. The resulting product is immediately oxidized to arabonic acid, which is neutralized by the excess calcium carbonate present. Pure calcium arabonate pentahydrate crystals are obtained by evaporation of the filtered oxidation liquor.

The arabonic acid obtained from the calcium salt is rearranged to *d*-ribonic acid by heating it in pyridine solution, a process called epimerization. By devious and costly methods, *d*-ribonic acid may be converted to *d*-ribose for use in the riboflavin synthesis. Processes have recently been developed, however, whereby ribose can be prepared directly by the electrolytic reduction of ribonolactone. The ribose is isolated as an aniline-ribose-sodium sulfate complex from which the ribose can readily be obtained in crystalline form. It is believed that this development will reduce the cost of making ribose to such an extent as to revive interest in the production of crystalline riboflavin by chemical means.

SACCHARIC ACID is more correctly named *d*-glucosaccharic acid or *d*-glucaric acid, because it is the dibasic sugar acid derived from *d*-glucose by oxidation of the terminal groups. Although saccharic acid has been prepared by the nitric acid oxidation of corn sugar and starch for more than a century, no practical method for its large-scale production had been devised until 1948. Chemists at the Northern Laboratory have now developed a feasible process for making saccharic acid in yields nearly twice as great as those previously obtained. In this process, corn sugar is gradually added to concentrated nitric acid so as to maintain the temperature of the reaction at about 60° C. After several hours the oxidation mixture is neutralized with potassium hydroxide and then adjusted to the desired acidity with nitric acid to precipitate practically pure potassium acid saccharate in 40 to 45 percent yield.

The white crystalline product is filtered, washed free of contaminating salts with water, and dried. It may be converted to calcium saccharate by reaction with a mixture of calcium chloride and lime. Saccharic acid may be obtained by the addition of sufficient sulfuric acid to remove the calcium ions as insoluble calcium sulfate.

Investigation of the practical applications of the acid and its salts is now in progress.

GLUCURONIC ACID is of great physiological importance. A detoxifying agent in the animal body, it reacts with such poisons as phenols and amines to form innocuous glucuronides, which are eliminated in the urine. It is also a significant constituent of fibrous tissue and of heparin, the blood anticoagulant that is present in many of these body tissues. The specific polysaccharide of type III pneumococcus, which possesses immunological reactivity, has also been shown to contain glucuronic acid in its structure. In 1947 an apparent correlation between glucuronic acid deficiency and rheumatic diseases was discovered and the successful treatment of a number of such cases with salts of glucuronic acid has been reported. The use of glucuronic acid as a detoxicant in sulfa therapy has also been indicated.

Although numerous attempts to prepare this important acid have been made in the past, no practical chemical syntheses were available until 1950, when the Northern Regional Research Laboratory and Corn Products Refining Co. independently announced processes for its production. In the Northern Laboratory process, corn sugar is reacted with acetone and the product catalytically oxidized to acetone glucuronic acid with air. Simple hydrolysis of acetone glucuronic acid produces glucuronic acid which is isolated in good yield as crystalline glucuronolactone. Translation of these new processes to large-scale operation will expedite both therapeutic and industrial research on this sugar acid.

CALCIUM SALTS of gluconic, lactic, arabonic, and levulinic acids are being used in the treatment of calcium deficiencies in the human and animal body. Because in water solution they are practically neutral, they are less irritating to the skin upon injection than the calcium salts of the inorganic acids. They are also more palatable when taken by mouth. With the exception of calcium levulinate, the calcium salts of the sugar acids are not soluble enough in water for their efficient utilization in the treatment of lactating cows for hypocalcemia, or milk fever. It is often necessary to inject as much as 50 to 75 grams of calcium gluconate into the jugular vein of a cow in a single dose. Such a treatment would require as much as 1 to 2 quarts of a saturated calcium gluconate solution.

Various methods have been successful in increasing the solubility of calcium gluconate. The introduction of boric acid results in the formation of soluble calcium borogluconate, which has been found to be an effective source of calcium in veterinary medicine. Also in use are stable supersaturated solutions of calcium gluconate of at least 10 percent concentration, made by the addition of small amounts of stabilizing substances, as calcium saccharate, calcium salts of sulfonic acids, and strontium salts. The solubility of calcium sodium lactate in water has also been enhanced by the addition of calcium gluconate.

Since the discovery in 1906 that antimony compounds are effective therapeutic agents for the treatment of the protozoan diseases, African sleeping sickness and kala-azar, the death rate from those diseases has declined enormously. One of the original substances tried and one that still is in use for the control of the diseases is the potassium antimonyl salt of tartaric acid. Another sugar acid antimonial, sodium antimonyl gluconate, has been reported helpful in the treatment of kala-azar.

Tartaric acid in combination with bismuth, as bismuth sodium tartrate or bismuth potassium tartrate, has been used intramuscularly to obtain the systemic effect of bismuth in the treatment of syphilis. Bismuth potassium saccharate has also been used.

Water solutions of iron, copper, and manganese salts of sugar acids are used to obtain the effects of the respective metal ions. Sodium lactate has been indicated for the prevention and treatment of acidosis, and aqueous solutions of magnesium citrate have been used for many years as a saline laxative. More recently, citric acid and sodium citrate have become important for the preservation of whole blood. It appears also that sodium citrate may have value in the treatment of lead poisoning. Lactic acid has been used effectively as an aerial bactericide. Ascorbic acid has been reported to be useful in the healing of wounds. Recently, calcium gluconate solutions have been found of value in the treatment of bee stings. Phenyl mercuric tartrate, gluconate, saccharate, and lactate have been prepared for bactericidal purposes. The use of such compounds as ephedrine gluconate, procaine gluconate, gluconophenetid, and ergotamine tartrate has been indicated for the treatment of various ailments.

C. L. MEHLTRETTER *holds degrees in chemistry from the Polytechnic Institute of Brooklyn and Iowa State College. Since 1937 he has been engaged in research on sugar acids and related carbohydrates—3 years in industry and the rest at the Northern Regional Research Laboratory. Dr. Mehltretter's work is concerned with the development of industrial products from starch and dextrose.*

VARNISHES were used in Egypt on mummy cases of the New Empire. Many are insoluble, but their method of preparation is not known with certainty. The earliest mention of the use of a drying oil in a process connected with painting is given by Aetius, about the sixth century. He stated that nut oils dry and form a protective varnish. From that time on, the use of drying oils and varnishes seems to be well established and formulas for transparent varnishes composed of linseed oil and natural resins dating from the eighth or ninth century after Christ are known.

Theophilus Presbyter, an obscure craftsman, who lived at the end of the eleventh century, used linseed oil with some kind of resin, probably amber, copal, or sandarac, to prepare oil colors. He worked out many formulas for paints, varnishes, and dyes. However, the discovery of the effect of driers in linseed-oil paints, which is accredited to the brothers Van Eyck, was not made until the first half of the fifteenth century.

The extensibility of oil on the surface of water appears to have been known to Greek sailors, who used oil to subdue waves during a storm. The phenomenon of surface tension of extension of oil on the surface of water was investigated by the great Hindu mathematician Bhaskara, who is presumed to have lived about A. D. 1114 to 1178.—*K. S. Markley, Southern Regional Research Laboratory.*

Your Health and Your Glands

David Klein

Glands are small parts of our bodies that profoundly influence our physical and mental states. They make some of us tall and others short. They give some of us pleasant voices and others voices that should be controlled even in the shower. They put hair on some chests, affect our happiness or discouragements, influence the rhythms of life of both men and women, and much more besides.

Useful—and often vital—medicinal products are made from the glands of animals, an excellent example of the utilization of natural products as starting materials for the manufacture of other useful products.

Present-day glandular therapy is based on the assumption of scientists that conditions arising from a lack of glandular function in mankind could be corrected by the administration of glands or extracts of glands of animals. But first, of course, it was necessary to know the functions and composition of the different glands. That called for a program of sound experimentation and observation. As was to be expected, enthusiasm outran the slower-moving research, and claims of "miracles" were made that did not stand the test of time. Despite the claims and some failures, however, the record as a whole is good.

The process of living is a complex series of chemical reactions, in which the ductless glands, the ones we are considering, play an important part. The ductless glands, or glands of internal secretion, apparently have no ducts or connections with other parts of the body. Yet they govern much of the rest of the body.

How do we know this? How do we demonstrate that a part of the body belongs in this group?

One way is to remove from an animal the part of the body under study and observe any changes that follow. The next step is to administer to that animal the gland that has been removed, or an extract of it, and see if the changes have been reversed. On the basis of past research, it is now generally accepted that the following are ductless glands: Pituitary, thyroid, parathyroid, suprarenal, pancreas, liver, and the sex glands. From time to time, other glands have been included in this class, but on not too convincing evidence.

First, the pituitary. Of all the ductless glands, it is the top, not because of its highest position in the body (just below the brain and back of the nose), but because it controls the workings of so many of the other glands. Its name, of Greek origin, means a thick secretion in the nose, because, centuries ago, it was thought to have something to do with nasal affections. We know that is incorrect; it has more important duties. The pituitary gland is protected by the skull and also by a further bony housing, the sella turcica.

The anterior pituitary lobe (the front portion) apparently controls the activity of other glands. It secretes several principles, or hormones: Thyrotropic hormone, which governs the growth and activity of the thyroid; adrenocorticotropic hormone, which governs the growth and activity of the adrenal cortex; growth hormone, which influences bone development and thus determines how big or small a person will be; gonadotropic hormone, which influences the growth, pubertal changes, and functions of the sex glands; mammotropic hormone, which has to do with mammary development and secretion; and pancreatropic hormone, which regulates growth and function of the pancreas. And the whole story is not yet told. All this is done by different chemical substances, secreted into the blood stream, by a gland that weighs about 1/222 of a pound.

We do not yet know how to use all the anterior pituitary principles in the treatment of human ailments. For example, growth-hormone preparations do not produce an increase in stature in human beings, although giant rats and dogs can be made with the same extracts. Likewise, the gonadotropic hormone, which has a profound effect on sex development and function in the lower species, has been disappointing in its effects on human females.

By contrast, the adrenocorticotropic hormone (commonly abbreviated to ACTH) does many astonishing things. It brings relief to sufferers from rheumatoid arthritis, rheumatic fever, asthma, and gout. It does not cure, however. How it works is still unknown.

The anterior pituitary lobes of various species contain the active principles in different amounts. The pituitary of cattle is a good source of the growth hormone, but not of ACTH. The pituitary of swine is a good starting material for ACTH; that of sheep is next best. Although millions of hogs are handled every year by the meat-packing industry, the supply of hog pituitaries will furnish ACTH for only a small proportion of the arthritics who need it. About 1,700 hogs are required to make 1 pound of raw pituitaries, and ACTH is only a small part of the gland. Some day, when the formula of the hormone is known (and we are far from knowing it today) and if it is not too complex, the chemist may be able to make it synthetically.

The growth hormone is one of the things that govern the size of an individual. Too little of it results in a certain type of pygmy, the kind whose body proportions are normal but whose height is below normal. They are normal persons, with their bodies scaled down. In Africa, there are tribes of such pygmies. It should be possible to make people taller through the use of growth hormone, but thus far the results have not been too good. There are authentic records of individuals more than 8 feet tall. Such unusual height is due to an oversecretion of the pituitary caused by a tumor on it. Thus, the giant and possibly the dwarf of the circus sideshow are examples of abnormal growth-hormone secretions by the pituitary. As will be seen later, lack of thyroid activity may also stunt a person's growth.

The posterior pituitary lobe (rear portion) provides an extract, official in the United States Pharmacopoeia, that is used extensively in childbirth, in surgery, and in the treatment of diabetes insipidus, which is not to be confused with diabetes mellitus, the more common kind. The extract has the property of contracting involuntary muscle, thus shortening childbirth. It also contains a substance capable of raising blood pressure and, presumably, another that regulates the volume of urine.

THE THYROID, in the neck astride the Adam's apple, regulates the rate at which we burn up to furnish the heat and the energy that keep us alive. Iodine is involved in its action. The thyroid is capable of taking the minute amounts of iodine from our food and elaborating from them a chemical substance having about 65 percent iodine in its make-up. This chemical substance, thyroxin, in combined form with protein, circulates through the blood stream. A measure of thyroid activity is the metabolic (burning-up) rate. A low metabolic rate can be raised through the judicious use of thyroid powder, an official preparation in the

United States Pharmacopoeia. No glandular extract that will reduce an above-normal metabolic rate is known. The common symptoms of a low metabolic rate are obesity, a slow pulse, and sluggishness. Thyroid, under strict medical supervision, may be beneficial.

Deficiency of thyroid activity in infancy results in a condition known as cretinism, which is characterized by stunted, disproportionate size and retarded mental development. Many midgets of the circus are cretins. If thyroid therapy is instituted early enough and continued, marked improvement can be effected.

The hormones are powerful substances, to be thought of in terms not of pounds or ounces, but rather of small fractions of an ounce. The total amount of the active principle of the thyroid gland in a human being is probably not more than 1/1500 of an ounce. It is this amount, or perhaps one-half of it, that makes the difference between an idiot and a normal infant. The usual size of a thyroid tablet is one grain, which is 1/437.5 of an ounce. Only a small fraction of this is thyroxin, so that this one grain of U. S. P. thyroid contains about 1/150,000 of an ounce of active material, a truly small amount, but sufficient to produce a marked physiological response.

Iodine is in sea water, but not in fresh waters that are distant from the sea. Large areas of the United States therefore are naturally deficient in iodine. The lack is now supplied by judicious use of iodine in the form of iodized salt, or through the consumption of sea foods. As a result, the incidence of goiters caused by insufficient iodine in the system is decreasing.

The human being is not alone in the need for iodine. Animals also must have it for growth and well being. Once a large proportion of sheep were goiterous. Not so today, because of iodized salt and iodine in the feed. Pigs that receive too little iodine in the diet sometimes lose their hair, a condition that can be corrected by administering iodine.

Associated with the thyroid in human beings is another gland, the parathyroid. Its function is to keep a normal amount of calcium in the blood. Too little calcium causes tetanic convulsions and also retards the coagulation of the blood. Too much calcium causes death by the coagulation of the blood in the circulatory system. Removal of the parathyroid gland lowers the blood calcium, with the characteristic symptoms of too little calcium. Administration of parathyroid extract increases the blood calcium and alleviates the symptoms of too little calcium.

The process of living is a series of amazing chemical reactions. The human body is a far more complicated chemical factory than any that man has made. In a normal individual in good health, these chemical reactions take place in proper sequence and to a controlled degree. The glands of internal secretion have much to do with this orderly procession. Thus, to mention a few, the thyroid regulates the rate at which food is burned; the parathyroid, the amount of calcium in the blood; the suprarenal, among other things, the amount of sodium chloride in the blood; the pancreas, the amount of sugar in the blood.

THE PANCREAS, often referred to in packing-house parlance as the liver sweetbread, is a gland of both internal and external secretion. The remarkable thing is that although the external secretion destroys the internal secretion when the two are in contact, both are present in the pancreas of the normal individual but are kept from coming into contact with each other.

The internal secretion is of great importance in maintaining the blood sugar (glucose) at the proper level. Too much sugar is bad; it indicates a diabetic condition. Too little is just as bad, if not worse, because it is more difficult to control. The story of the discovery of insulin, the pancreatic internal secretion, is too long to be told here. For 34 years or more before its successful extraction from the pancreas, it was known that something in the pancreas was involved in keeping the blood sugar at its proper level. Yet it remained for Frederick G. Banting and Charles F. Best to give to the world the clue to how a pancreatic extract could be used to treat diabetes. That was in 1922. Today, hundreds of thousands of diabetics owe their longer lives to insulin. Who can evaluate in dollars the value of this one chemurgic product? The annual market value of the raw pancreas alone, in 1950, was probably 5 million dollars greater than it would have been if insulin had not been discovered.

Insulin apparently is protein in nature. Because of its complex structure, chemists have not yet succeeded in synthesizing it.

The pancreas does more than furnish insulin. It secretes a liquid that runs into the intestines, where it acts upon the food to digest it. The enzymes of the pancreas are essential for life. The trypsin breaks protein down into small building blocks, the amino acids. The diastase converts starches into sugars. The lipase assists in the digestion of fat. Pancreatic products have been prepared to help overcome deficiencies in pancreatic secretion.

The two main portions of the suprarenal gland are embryologically different. The inner part, the medulla, secretes epinephrine, a powerful substance that raises the blood pressure. Doctors use it to treat asthma, allergies, and bleeding. Mixed with procaine it is used in dentistry.

The outer portion, the cortex, is necessary for life. Removal results in death. Once there was no hope for the unfortunate individuals afflicted with a diseased adrenal cortex. Now, through the administration of potent adrenal cortex extracts, persons suffering from Addison's disease can be kept alive and useful for years. The adrenal cortex secretes a number of substances, the full functions of which are not known. Some are involved in the maintenance of the proper amount of sodium chloride in the blood; others, in the amount of glycogen in the liver and its conversion into sugar.

Investigators throughout the world have devoted a vast amount of study to the chemistry and function of the adrenal cortex. In 1949, the Mayo Clinic in Rochester, Minn., announced that one of the chemical substances found in the adrenal cortex, compound E, now called cortisone, is effective in the treatment of arthritis, rheumatic fever, and other ailments. The amount of cortisone needed per person is in weight very little—300 milligrams the first day and 100 milligrams daily thereafter for a varied length of time. But in terms of the quantity of adrenal glands that would be required it is enormous. It would take about 1,000 pounds of beef adrenals, or the two glands from about 22,500 cattle, to obtain 300 milligrams of cortisone.

Obviously, the adrenal gland is not a practical source of cortisone. There is no natural source of it in the quantities needed by arthritic patients. It is being made synthetically from ox bile, but that is not the final answer to the problem, from the standpoint of either availability or cost, as the supply of bile is insufficient.

Before ox bile was used in the synthesis of cortisone, it served many other purposes. Bile is essential for life. Formed in the liver, it flows down a duct into the intestines, where it aids in the absorption of fat.

Bile is a complex product. The important constituents are compounds of the bile acids, of which there are many. Bile acids in man are like those in cattle and sheep. Those in hogs are quite different chemically and, unfortunately, cannot be as readily used as those of cattle for making cortisone. The bile acids belong to the same chemical family as cholesterol, the steroids of the adrenal cortex and of the sex glands.

The secretion of bile is only one of the many properties that have given such prominence to liver in recent years. Liver is valuable in the treatment of pernicious anemia. It contains vitamin A and many components of the vitamin B complex. From liver has been isolated a crystalline substance, vitamin B_{12}, that is active in the treatment of pernicious anemia when as little as $1/28,000,000$ of an ounce is injected daily.

Vitamin B_{12} is part of the animal-protein factor. The better digestibility and utilization of animal protein versus plant protein has been explained in part by the presence of something in animal protein, but not in vegetable protein. Vitamin B_{12} is involved. The liver is a veritable storehouse of important nutritional factors.

Cholesterol is present throughout the body as a constituent of cells. Its exact function has not been established. It serves as starting material for the synthesis of one of the female sex hormones, progesterone, and of the male hormone, testosterone. It is the starting material also for 7-dehydrocholesterol, which, on activation, becomes vitamin D_3, essential to the poultry and livestock industries. Thus from packing-house material that formerly was tanked now come many useful medicinals and vitamins.

The inside lining of the stomach is used in making pepsin and mucin, the latter important in the treatment of ulcers. The stomach of the normal human being and of certain animals secretes something called the intrinsic factor, which presumably combines with vitamin B_{12}, permitting the vitamin to be absorbed from the intestinal tract. The stomach of a person suffering from pernicious anemia apparently does not secrete the intrinsic factor; as a consequence, even the small amounts of vitamin B_{12} necessary for proper blood formation cannot be absorbed.

The milk-clotting enzyme, rennet, used in making junket and cheese, is prepared from the stomach of the young calf.

THE SEX GLANDS, besides their procreative function, possess internal secretions, which govern the attributes associated with males and females, such as bodily contour, pitch of voice, and distribution of hair on the body and head. The active hormones have been isolated from both testes and ovaries, but their actual commercial production makes use of other starting material. Thus, the male hormone is made synthetically from cholesterol. Substances having physiological activity similar to that of one of the ovarian hormones are now prepared in large quantities from the urine of pregnant mares. Another ovarian hormone, progesterone, is prepared from cholesterol and plant steroids.

THE VARIOUS PARTS of the animal that I have mentioned are often referred to as byproducts. This has an unfavorable connotation as being something of low value, of minor importance. I submit that when a part of an animal has a commercial value well above that of the choicest beefsteak, it deserves respect. Market values change, but in June 1950, raw beef pituitaries cost about $4.50 a pound, and pork pituitaries $25 a pound. Beef parathyroids cost from $5 to $15 a pound, depending on quality. Beef suprarenals brought $1.50 a pound and pork suprarenals about $2.50.

To be sure, the tonnage of the commonly edible portions is greater. Yet, let us consider liver. Time was, within the life of those who will admit the years, when the butcher would throw in a piece of liver free, for the cat, with a purchase of meat. Those were the days when liver was figured on the basis of its tank value, about a half a cent a pound. Today, pork liver has a carload value of about 24 cents a pound; beef liver, one of about 45 cents a pound. Figures are not available, but probably 60 million pounds of liver is used annually for preparing medicinals.

Pancreas sells for between 40 and 50 cents a pound, depending on the species. The higher prices for glands over tank value mean higher prices for the live animals. No accurate values are available, but it is probable that the annual sales value of the products derived from packing-house material of the type used medicinally in one form or another is more than 100 million dollars at the consumer level.

ALL APPLICATIONS of glands to medicinal purposes have not been mentioned. Even if they were, the story would not be finished, because, through further research, additional uses are being found. The possibilities have not been exhausted. Protein administration as amino acids is still an undeveloped area. The packing house, with its huge supplies of high-grade protein, is a logical source of starting material for the acids. Other lines of investigation are being studied. Those that become actualities will mean better health through utilization of the products of the soil, via the meat-packing industry, through applied science.

The raising of food animals is primarily a means of gaining a livelihood, but it carries a twofold satisfaction. It provides essential food; it alleviates sickness.

DAVID KLEIN *is general manager of the Wilson Laboratories, Chicago. He holds degrees from the University of Illinois and the University of Wisconsin. He taught chemistry at both universities and later was associate professor of chemistry at The Johns Hopkins University. Dr. Klein joined the Wilson Laboratories in 1920 as technical director.*

SAWDUST is used as a soil conditioner and as a source of humus in many southern forest-tree nurseries. The soils there are low in organic matter, which ranges from less than 1 percent to 2 percent, depending on the crop rotation employed and the physical structure of the soil. Seedlings grown on soils with a high organic content are more vigorous and have more fibrous roots. Likewise, tilth and moisture relationships are improved, all pointing toward the need for a higher soil-humus content.

Since 1945, decomposed sawdust has been added to soil at rates varying from 35 to 100 cubic yards an acre, together with 600 to 900 pounds of fertilizer. A legume soiling crop then is planted and plowed under, preparatory to a tree seedling crop the following year. Tests show that the soiling crop is heavier and contains more plant food than where sawdust is omitted.

An interval of 1 year between tree seedling crops is considered essential to permit the sawdust to decompose. The soil-fertility drain, particularly of nitrogen, is extremely heavy, and large quantities of raw humus cause mineral deficiencies in the seedling crop. A pine seedling crop requires three to five times as much nutrient volume as a good crop of cotton or corn.

It is expected that sawdust will be applied at least biennially for many years. To raise the soil organic content from 1 percent to 2 percent requires about 40,000 pounds of material per acre. Oxidation is rapid in the South; consequently, large quantities of sawdust will be used as a source of soil humus. Thus, a forest product is used indirectly to create more forests.—*Floyd M. Cossitt, Forest Service, Atlanta, Ga.*

CROPS FROM THE FOREST

Backbone of the Vegetable World

Kyle Ward, Jr.

A fiber is any tough substance that is made up of threadlike tissue. Some fibers can be torn apart easily into small units between the fingers. Others have to be teased apart under the microscope to make the fragments visible. The fibrils so obtained can be separated—by solution, for instance—into individual molecules, the smallest possible units of matter that retain their chemical identity. These molecules themselves prove to be long and flexible (or threadlike) structures.

Fiber molecules belong to the class called linear high polymers, a large group of substances that contains examples of every type of organic and inorganic compound. The organic compounds that compose the natural vegetable fibers, with which this article deals, are all carbohydrates, and mostly are made up of one particular carbohydrate, cellulose, a polymer of glucose.

Cellulose is the most abundant of the naturally occurring organic compounds. It is not limited to vegetable fibers or even to the vegetable kingdom; it constitutes probably a third of all vegetable matter. It can be called the backbone of the entire vegetable world.

None of the various theories of cellulose formation in plants has received complete acceptance in scientific circles, but at least one thing is certain. Cellulose is the main constituent of the cell walls of the higher plants—indeed, it receives its name from that fact—and occurs as well in many of the lower members of the vegetable kingdom.

The higher plants are the chief sources of cellulose. The two most important commercial sources are wood pulp and cotton, especially the shorter cotton fibers, or linters. The grasses and the straws are another source. They are used less than wood pulp and cotton linters, but they form a reserve supply, which could be utilized should the need arise. Other agricultural residues, which remain after our farm crops have been harvested, form a potential source of cellulose.

Cellulose is almost as useful to man as it is to the plant. His ingenuity has developed a variety of uses, which fall into two broad categories: Unchanged cellulose, where it is used as such; and chemical cellulose, which serves as a raw material to be transformed into something else.

Unchanged cellulose is used in three major industries—the building and furniture trades, as a structural raw material; the pulp and paper industry, as sheeted fibers; and the textile industry, as fibers, usually spun and woven.

Wood, one of the earliest structural materials, was until comparatively recently the only cellulosic material used in the building and furniture trades. But within the past century several other materials have entered the field to replace wood, especially in items in which the stresses to be borne are not too great. Some have become established industrial products. Essentially, the substitutes are formed by recombining separated cellulosic fibers, frequently with an adhesive binder, into a dense sheet. Wood fibers themselves are often the basic raw material for fiberboard sheets. Another material used is bagasse, the residue consisting of the pulped sugarcane stalks after the juices have been expressed. Other agricultural residues, such as straws, have been used, but their collection and transportation are not so simple as for wood and bagasse.

In the pulp and paper industry, cellulose is an even more essential material than in the building industry. Almost every piece of paper used for any purpose is cellulose. Wood cellulose again ranks first as a source. There is also a certain amount of rag paper, usually made from waste cotton and linen, as the name implies. For the heavier paperboards, especially, a certain amount of cereal straw or other agricultural residue has been used. Rye straw has a high cellulose content and a long fiber and therefore is preferred. Wheat straw is second. Oat and barley straws are less desirable. Seed-flax straw, an agricultural residue from the linseed-oil industry, is utilized in cigarette and other special papers.

The grasses, too, have been an important source of cellulose for papers. Bamboo, in Asia, and esparto, in Europe, are the chief representatives. From an historical point of view, we should mention papyrus, which is closely related to the grasses and was one of the earliest sources of cellulose for paper.

In the textile industry, cotton, a seed hair, is chief among cellulosic materials used. A few other seed hairs, notably kapok, find commercial utilization, but by no means to the extent that cotton does.

Most of the other textile fibers from the vegetable kingdom are either bast or leaf fibers. The bast fibers include linen, hemp, jute, and ramie. The leaf fibers, used mainly for cordage, include abacá or manila hemp, sisal, and henequen. There are also a few unclassified vegetable fibers, such as coir fiber (from coconut husks) and Spanish moss.

For chemical cellulose, the main outlet is in the manufacture of cellulose derivatives, which have a multitude of industrial uses. Like all carbohydrates, cellulose contains aliphatic hydroxyls, or alcohol groups, which react with acids to form stable esters and with active derivatives of other alcohols to form still more stable ethers. As a high polymer, cellulose contains many of these reactive alcohol groups, making possible the formation of a long series of mixed compounds with a wide range of industrially useful characteristics. The derivatives remain high polymers, for in the chemical reaction it is desirable to decrease the size of the molecule as little as possible.

Cellulose is not an economical source for compounds other than its high-molecular-weight derivatives, but circumstances may sometimes warrant its use for preparing low-molecular-weight substances. If it were necessary, glucose, alcohol, and oxalic acid could all be produced from cellulose. In fact, until comparatively recently, the destructive distillation of wood was the chief means of producing methanol and acetic acid.

Cellulose, as wood or agricultural residue, is probably the oldest fuel, and this is today the only established use involving complete breakdown of the molecule.

One of the largest fields for cellulose derivatives is in the manufacture of textile fibers. Here the derivative either is used as such or is reconverted to cellulose. Such man-made fibers from cellulose include viscose rayon, regenerated from cellulose xanthate; cuprammonium rayon, regenerated from the solution of a copper-ammonia-cellulose complex; cellulose acetate, where the derivative itself is spun; and Fortisan, which is a saponified cellulose acetate. They may be prepared from wood pulp or from cotton linters, but for economic reasons more wood pulp is used than linters.

Cellulose acetate is one of that large group of cellulose derivatives known as esters, being the reaction product of cellulose and acetic acid. As such, it finds far greater utility than just in textiles. It appears in protective coatings of the lacquer type, in films and foils, and in plastics. It reappears in the textile industry as a coating or finish. The properties of cellulose acetate may be modified by hydrolytic degradation during manufacture to reduce the chain length of the molecule, by varying the degree of acetylation, or by preparing mixed esters in which acids other than acetic are also used. These types of modification can be applied to other cellulose derivatives as well.

Another important cellulose ester is cellulose nitrate, an ester of an inorganic acid. The usefulness of the compound is similar generally to that of cellulose acetate. Some important differences exist. Cellulose nitrate is no longer used—in the United States, at least—as the base for a synthetic fiber, as is cellulose acetate, although it is still used in certain textile finishes and coatings. Cellulose nitrate is of paramount importance in the explosives industry, being the main constituent of smokeless powder and the stiffening agent in blasting gelatins. As an adhesive it finds much greater use than cellulose acetate.

When the unprecedented demand for cellulose nitrate for explosives during the Second World War led to a corresponding shortage of suitable sources of cellulose, the Department of Agriculture developed equipment for cutting low-grade lint cotton to lengths which made it suitable for processing on existing nitrating equipment. This, of course, would have provided another source of cellulose nitrate. The war ended before the equipment was used.

Cellulose ethers, used for much the same purposes as the esters, are soluble in a wider variety of solvents and are generally more resistant to alkalies and to hydrolysis than the esters. The most important in industrial use today is probably ethyl cellulose, which is an ether of ethyl alcohol and is usually prepared by the reaction of ethyl chloride on alkali cellulose. It has increasing uses in protective coatings, plastics, films, and adhesives.

Another cellulose ether, benzyl cellulose, is much like ethyl cellulose, but has not been developed commercially in this country to the same extent.

A third cellulose ether, methyl cellulose, is a striking example of the variation of the physical properties of these derivatives with the degree of substitution. We also observe an interesting new phenomenon, water solubility. In methyl cellulose, the change of solubility characteristics with degree of etherification is very striking. The original cellulose is insoluble in practically every solvent. As methyl groups are added the material gradually acquires solubility in cold water. As more methyl is added, this water solubility disappears. The completely methylated cellulose is insoluble in water, but has become soluble in organic solvents. The intermediate, water-soluble stage represents the industrially important material. In fact, the commercial product is soluble in cold water and insoluble in hot water. Solutions therefore, when heated, either thicken and gel or precipitate, depending on the conditions. Methyl cellulose is being used more and more in cosmetics, adhesives, and textile finishes, as a thickening and stabilizing agent for textile printing pastes and sizes, and for various types of emulsified food products.

Two other ethers of cellulose, hydroxyethyl cellulose and carboxymethyl cellulose, are being put to a variety of specialized uses in fields similar to those of methyl cellulose. The two ethers are soluble in dilute alkali and can be precipitated with acids. Hydroxyethyl cellulose is widely used as a textile finishing agent. Carboxymethyl cellulose is an ingredient in some types of detergents.

In fundamental research at the Southern Regional Research Laboratory, we are interested in a more exact knowledge of the cellulose molecule. We need to know not just that cellulose is a polymeric carbohydrate; we need to know also just what type of carbohydrate it is. During the past century, world-wide research has established that the cellulose molecule is composed predominantly of glucose units linked together by oxygen between the first carbon atom of one unit and the fourth of the next.

We have seen that the cellulose molecules are long and threadlike. They are not all of the same length, for the number of repeating units (glucose residues) may vary from a few hundred to many thousand. As an approximation, the molecules run parallel to each other in the vegetable fibers. Usually they are packed closely, side by side, to form continuous regions of such regularity that they give a crystalline X-ray diffraction pattern. From this upper extreme of order we may have every stage down to completely random tangles of molecules. In order to get a clear picture of the internal submicroscopic structure of cotton cellulose we are interested in a good many variables—the average length of the molecule, the length distribution of the molecules, the percentage of well-ordered and crystalline material in the sample, the size and the orientation of the individual crystallites.

The length of the molecule determines many of the physical properties of cellulose without appreciably affecting its chemical properties. Everyone familiar with cotton knows what these physical properties are, for the cotton when dry is more than 95 percent cellulose. The physical properties include high tensile strength, fair elasticity and flexibility, and excellent toughness and durability.

The length of a high-polymer molecule is usually measured by the degree of polymerization or the number of repeating units present. In cellulose the repeating unit is the glucose residue. High polymers differ from compounds of low molecular weight in that all the molecules do not necessarily have the same weight. One molecule of cellulose, for instance, may contain 200 glucose units and another 2,000.

While the molecules differing only in length, or number of glucose units, will have the same chemical reactions, the physical properties of cellulose with an average degree of polymerization of 200 to 300 glucose units will vary greatly from those of a cellulose with 2,000 to 3,000 units. Below about 200 units, the molecules no longer have sufficient orientation affinity for one another to form fibers of useful strength. It is common industrial practice to use degree of polymerization for a measure of utility. The textile industry, the paper industry, and the plastics industry use this or some related value as a control. Generally speaking, desirable strength and durability are found only in cottons with a high degree of polymerization.

The distribution of molecular size is also important. Large gaps still exist in our knowledge on this subject. The desirable distribution of long and short cellulose molecules in a cotton for any one purpose is not known. Certain it is that there are differences in the physical properties of cellulose derivatives that are comparatively homogeneous and those that have a high degree of polymolecularity. It is reasonable to suppose therefore that similar effects will be seen in the unchanged cellulose.

When we come to the degree of order of the cellulose molecules, that is whether regular or random, we have a somewhat better background of information. In general, it can be said that a high degree of order brings about high tensile strength and low flexibility. A low degree of order, on the other hand, brings about high flexibility and low strength.

The arrangement of the crystallites is also important. This can be seen by comparing fibers in which the crystallites are oriented at different angles to the fiber axis. In general, strength increases and flexibility decreases as the axis of orientation approaches the axis of the fiber.

We have fewer experimental data for a basis when we consider the question of the effect of crystallite size. Theoretical considerations lead us to believe that this factor will make considerable difference in the physical properties of the material. Experimental corroboration of this is being sought, but the determination of crystallite size is complicated and may be expected to take a long time to obtain.

Now that we have seen why these structural factors are important in efforts to increase the utilization of cotton, let us look briefly at research on them at the Southern Laboratory.

Chemists here are investigating the molecular structure of cotton cellulose through common types of breakdown reaction—oxidation, hydrolysis, and alcoholysis. In their work on oxidation they are trying to determine which points in the cellulose molecule are attacked first when cotton is oxidized. Whether oxidation occurs from the action of air, which is usually present, or of the oxidizing agents used in finishing cotton goods, a knowledge of the weak spots in the cellulose molecule will enable us, by shielding them chemically, to protect cotton fabrics and thus extend their life. Because cotton is susceptible to the action of acids, similar studies of hydrolysis and alcoholysis are being made.

The degree of polymerization has been given as a measure of the average molecular length of cellulose. The simplest and most commonly used method of determining the degree of polymerization of a high polymer is by the determination of the viscosity of very dilute solutions. For cotton cellulose, a solution of cuprammonium hydroxide is the most commonly used solvent. The accuracy of this determination has been much improved by workers at the Southern Laboratory. They also have modified the cupriethylene diamine method used in the paper industry to make it suitable for cotton cellulose.

The determination of differences in the degree of polymolecularity for various strains of cotton and the correlation of the differences with the physical properties of the cotton fiber have begun at the Laboratory. The distribution of molecular size is determined by application of the ultracentrifuge to cellulose dispersions.

The degree of crystallinity of cotton is being investigated by a specially developed method in which the rate of hydrolysis by acid is the measure. The method has shown that crystallinity differences between varieties of cotton are not great, but that those between cotton and other cellulosic fibers, particularly fibers of regenerated cellulose, such as the rayons, are.

Other work has shown that the degree of crystallinity of cotton can be changed very much by various treatments. As a result, it is expected that the elastic recovery of cotton can be greatly improved by reducing the molecular order, and making the change in order permanent by chemical reaction to prevent recrystallization of the amorphous areas. The effects of crystallite size and of orientation are important and are being studied simultaneously.

The practical applications of the results of our work on cellulose properties are described in other chapters. Other agencies of the Department— the Northern Regional Research Laboratory, the Forest Products Laboratory, and the Bureau of Plant Industry, Soils, and Agricultural Engineering— are conducting research in the field of cellulose chemistry. These groups, too, are furnishing basic information which will make possible the fullest utilization of the cellulose resources of the Nation —whether in the form of cotton, wood, agricultural residues, or other fibers.

KYLE WARD, JR., *is a native of Texas and a graduate of the University of Texas. He has been associated with the Department of Agriculture since 1936 and has been in charge of the cotton fiber research division of the Southern Regional Research Laboratory since its founding.*

Hemicelluloses and Cellulose of Wood

George J. Ritter

Hemicelluloses and cellulose occur in immense quantities in the vegetable kingdom. They make up, in a mixture with some lignin, roughly 72 percent of all vegetable matter, in the form of exceedingly tiny, thin-walled, tubular fibers. These fibers, or cells, are the structural elements of wood in trees.

Only within the past 25 years have chemists learned that the substance long considered to be cellulose is actually composed of two parts, hemicelluloses and cellulose.

Hemicelluloses, when they are separated from the cellulose, appear as a white, porous, powderlike solid. They are composed of the solid element carbon in combination with two gases, oxygen and hydrogen. Because they consist of these three elements, the hemicelluloses fall within a class of materials known as carbohydrates.

Hemicelluloses readily adsorb water; in doing so, they form a sticky adhesive. They are useful in drying fruit juices. They react or unite readily with other materials to form valuable commercial products. Thus their presence with cellulose in wood-pulp fibers makes it possible to form a wide variety of papers that range from hard glassine to soft blotter sheets. They are necessary in pulp fibers because the adhesive they produce in combination with water holds the cellulose fibers together and thereby imparts strength to paper sheets.

When treated with acid, hemicelluloses become sugars that can be used for molasses and the growing of yeast, both of which are excellent livestock feeds. Scientists are investigating the possibility of changing the hemicellulose sugars to valuable chemicals by bacterial means. Among the chemicals thus obtained in promising quantities on a laboratory scale are butyl alcohol, acetone, and acetic, butyric, and lactic acids.

Butyl alcohol (which also can be made in a roundabout way from the cream of cow's milk) is used extensively in the preparation of foods, explosives, glass, leather, perfumes, textiles, and refining oils.

Acetone finds wide industrial application for the absorption of gases, the extraction of water, oils, and fats from chemical materials, and the preparation of dyes, explosives, glues, adhesives, gums, paints, varnishes, pharmaceuticals, and textiles.

Acetic acid is also made synthetically. It is the principal component of vinegar. It has many industrial uses in the making of dyes, foods, essence, glues, adhesives, leather, vegetable fibers, lacquers, varnishes, photographic films, plastics, and rubber.

Butyric acid is a component of rancid butter. Uses for it include rubber vulcanization and the preparation of plastics, foods, glues, leather, drugs, disinfectants, and perfumes.

Lactic acid is commonly produced when milk turns sour. It is employed in the preparation of poultry and stock feeds, to control brewing processes, in the preparation of ceramic compositions, for growing yeast, and to make disinfectants, dyes, paints, varnishes, and plastics.

Together, the hemicelluloses and cellulose constitute 70 to 78 percent of the weight of the wood in the hardwood (broad-leaved) trees and 69 to 70 percent of the wood in softwood (needle-leaved) trees. Of each amount, two-thirds is cellulose and the remainder hemicelluloses.

HEMICELLULOSES consist of several kinds of sugar and sugar acid molecular groups, which are linked to one another by means of oxygen atoms to form slender, chainlike molecules from 10 to 150 sugars long. In a hot acid-water solution, the oxygen linkage between sugars and sugar acids is broken and the sugars and sugar acids are separated. This process of changing hemicelluloses to simpler compounds by the introduction of water is called hydrolysis.

More specifically, hemicelluloses from softwoods are hydrolyzed to two pentose sugars, called xylose and arabinose. These pentose (5-carbon) sugars produce furfural when they are treated with hydrochloric acid. Furfural is also produced from corncobs, peanut shells, and oat hulls. It is used for the purification of petroleum oils and wood rosin from pine trees, and for the manufacture of nylon textiles. Besides the two pentose sugars, hydrolysis of softwood hemicelluloses also produces 43 percent of 6-carbon, or hexose, sugars, known as glucose, mannose, and galactose, and some sugar acids of glucose and galactose.

Glucose from softwood hemicelluloses is the same as the glucose that is known as dextrose in baby foods, and the glucose part of table sugar, maple sugar, maple molasses, cane molasses, and milk sugar. Mannose made from softwood hemicelluloses is identical with the mannose that occurs in large percentages in the meat of ivory nuts. Galactose from softwood hemicelluloses corresponds in chemical structure to the galactose portion of milk sugar.

In contrast, hydrolyzed hemicelluloses from hardwoods yield principally the two pentose sugars, mostly xylose, with a low percentage of arabinose, and 10 percent of glucose, together with small percentages of galactose

and the acids of glucose and galactose.

Since 1935, the University of Arizona, the Institute of Paper Chemistry, and the Forest Products Laboratory, a unit of the United States Forest Service in Madison, Wis., have developed methods for the isolation of hemicelluloses from wood. Hemicelluloses in general are dissolved from the cellulose and lignin in wood by means of water to which has been added a small amount of acid or alkali. They are then recovered from the water by alcohol or acetone, which precipitates them, and they are filtered from the liquid part of the entire mixture.

Hemicelluloses that are hydrolyzed from the wood with a water-acid solution differ from those prepared from the wood by a water-alkali solution. Those prepared with the water-acid solution contain acetic acid, with which they were combined in the untreated wood. Those prepared with the water-alkali solution contain no acetic acid because it is removed by the alkali during hydrolysis of the wood. Thus it is apparent that hemicelluloses have reactive chemical groups that act as hands to join with other materials for which they have an affinity to form hemicellulose derivatives. Some of these reactive groups are known as hydroxyls and carboxyls.

Hydroxyls make hemicelluloses react with nitric or acetic acid to form hemicellulose nitrate or hemicellulose acetate, which are esters and have possibilities for use as water-insoluble lacquers. Carboxyl groups make hemicelluloses react with solutions of barium acetate or calcium acetate to form insoluble barium or calcium hemicellulose salts.

Hemicelluloses in solution can be separated on the basis of their insolubility in organic liquids, such as alcohol or acetone. Alcohol, when added gradually to a water solution of hemicelluloses, first precipitates the most insoluble long-chain materials, which are filtered off. More alcohol is added to precipitate shorter-chain hemicelluloses; after they are removed, the operation is repeated in order to obtain several fractions of the hemicelluloses.

Physical properties of hemicelluloses prepared from wood depend largely on the way they are recovered from the water solution. If the alcohol or acetone is added slowly, the hemicelluloses are obtained as a fine-grained, slimy material. In this condition they are difficult to filter and wash free of the mother liquor. In contrast, if the alcohol or acetone is added rapidly during vigorous stirring of the mixture, the hemicelluloses are recovered as a crumbly, fluffy mass that filters readily and can be easily washed with the alcohol or acetone.

Short-chain hemicelluloses adsorb water more copiously than do the long-chain ones. That can be explained on the basis that their carboxyl content is higher than that of the long-chain materials. The tendency to adsorb water is readily reduced by soaking and washing them consecutively with alcohol and ether and then air-drying them. Hemicelluloses, when exposed to air or sunlight, change from white to brown, an indication that they oxidize readily.

CELLULOSE also has unique properties that make it a versatile commercial product in our everyday life. Like hemicelluloses, it is composed of sugars linked together through oxygen atoms to build up long, slender-chain molecules. It differs in that the molecules are from 150 to 1,000 sugars long, as compared to the 6- to 150-sugar length of the hemicellulose molecules. Furthermore, the cellulose molecules are more alike than those in the hemicelluloses, in that they are composed of glucose with only occasional other sugars, such as mannose and xylose.

The comparatively large size of the molecule of cellulose tends to make it more resistant than the hemicelluloses to the action of solvents or the attack of dilute acidic or alkaline reagents. The bigness of the molecule is a fortunate property; it is an important factor to consider in the development of methods for the separation of cellulose from wood and for its subsequent purification. Thus, cellulose will resist the attack of carefully controlled alkaline and acid wood-pulping liquors that will largely dissolve the lignin and the hemicelluloses. It further resists detrimental effects of subsequent bleaching and purification treatments for the removal of the residual lignin and cellulose. Even after withstanding the pulping and purification treatment for the removal of the other wood components, cellulose still has sufficient molecular size and stability for uses that include paper and natural and artificial textiles.

Although cellulose is composed of large molecules, which impart sluggish reactivity toward other materials, it nevertheless has some useful reactive chemical groups. Each glucose sugar which is tied to its glucose neighbor through an oxygen atom, has three hydroxyl groups, which will react with other materials and thereby form cellulose derivatives. Moreover, the oxygen linkage between adjacent glucose sugars allows for reduction of the length of the cellulose molecules so as to make the material suitable for different commercial products that include viscose rayons, cellophane, and lacquers.

Separation of cellulose from wood by conventional commercial processes may leave as much as 18 percent of hemicelluloses and only a small percentage of lignin in the cellulose. If the lignin is removed by bleaching, the hemicelluloses can be dissolved by means of a 17.5-percent alkali solution, in which the cellulose is insoluble.

Cellulose is the major component of the structural wood elements, comprised of fibers, ray cells, and vessels, of which the fibers play the important role for papers and cellulose products in commerce. The cellulose fibers average 1 millimeter, or $\frac{1}{25}$ inch, in length in hardwoods and 3 millimeters, or $\frac{1}{8}$ inch, in softwoods. They are highly crystalline in character, whereas the minor components, lignin and hemicelluloses, are amorphous. Removal of the lignin and hemicelluloses makes the cellulose fibers soft, porous, and pliable, which properties they impart to paper.

To ISOLATE cellulose quantitatively, one takes advantage of the differing properties of lignin, hemicelluloses, and cellulose. According to laboratory procedure developed at the Forest Products Laboratory, the wood is disintegrated into fine fibers. The lignin is then removed from the wood by treatment with chlorine gas to form a soluble lignin chloride, which is later dissolved with alcohol to which has been added 2 percent of ethanolamine. The white residue is holocellulose, which is composed of the cellulose and the hemicelluloses of the wood.

Next, the hemicelluloses are removed from the holocellulose with the 17.5-percent caustic solution, which leaves the white fibrous cellulose as a solid, equivalent to about 50 percent of the wood. The procedure is mild, and the cellulose is obtained with only slight injury to it. Conventional commercial pulping processes for the removal of lignin and hemicelluloses are less selective and more drastic. As a result, a considerable part of the cellulose is made soluble in 17.5-percent caustic solution with the hemicelluloses. Under such conditions, yields of only 35 percent are obtained, as against 50 percent by the laboratory procedure.

Nearly 12 million tons of pulp are produced annually in the United States. The leading kinds are bleached sulfite paper grades, unbleached sulfate, and ground wood. It is calculated that in producing this amount nearly 5 million tons of cellulose and hemicelluloses are lost.

Naturally, the most inefficient conventional commercial process for the preparation of pulps is that employed for dissolving or rayon-producing pulps, in which losses run as high as 49 percent of the cellulose and hemicelluloses. At the other extreme, the most efficient process for the utilization of wood is the ground-wood operation, which holds the loss of cellulose and hemicelluloses to 2 percent. The next two in line of efficiency for the production of wood fibers are the processes for producing semichemical pulps and the defibered and exploded type of fibers, in which losses range from 12.5 to 17.5 percent, respectively.

Progress is being made in improving the efficiency of cellulose recovery in pulping, and ways are being found to use much of the material now being lost. At the Forest Products Laboratory and elsewhere, more selective methods are being devised for the removal of lignin and hemicelluloses when necessary for a specified product. There are promising new methods for bleaching ground-wood pulp, purifying high-yield semichemical pulps, and developing procedures for the use of high-yield semichemical pulps in different kinds of paper.

Cellulose and hemicelluloses lost in the sulfate- and soda-pulping processes are now burned as fuel for the recovery of the chemicals in the pulping liquors. Possibilities are being investigated for the utilization of the waste cellulose and hemicelluloses as byproducts rather than as fuel for the recovery of the pulping chemicals.

Hexose sugars in the waste sulfite-pulping liquors are being fermented to grain alcohol by a wood-pulping plant in the Pacific Northwest and by one in Canada. Yields of the alcohol are about 47 percent of the hexose sugars consumed. The pentose sugars, xylose and arabinose, are lost in the process. Both the hexose and the pentose, however, are being utilized for growing yeast for stock feed on a commercial basis in one small trial plant in northern Wisconsin. Yields of yeast are approximately 45 percent of the sugar consumed. Production and feeding experiments to determine the feasibility of the project are in progress.

Research is being done to convert the hemicelluloses and the cellulose in wood wastes to sugar by means of acid hydrolysis. The water-sugar solutions are evaporated to a 50-percent concentration of sugar to form molasses. One ton of wood will produce 1 ton of wood-sugar molasses. The molasses is being used in cattle-feeding experiments to determine its suitability as a substitute for a part of the carbohydrate feed, such as corn and other grains, for dairy and beef cattle, hogs, and chickens.

Purified cellulose is used extensively. Its hydroxyl groups make it suitable for the chemical production of cellulose derivatives, which are widely employed industrially. Under controlled conditions, cellulose reacts with nitric acid to form cellulose nitrate, which is used for celluloid and collodion to increase the acid resistance of cloth, for fingernail enamels and lacquers, as raw material for the manufacture of cordite, dynamite, and guncotton and gunpowder, as an ingredient of shatterproof glass, glues, artificial leather, and coatings for leather, and for paper, photographic films, and rayon textiles.

The hydroxyl groups of cellulose also react with acetic acid and acetic anhydride to form cellulose acetate. This cellulose derivative has a number of industrial applications. It is spun into a thread for use in rayon textiles; it is used as a constituent of decorative coatings for ceramic ware, as insulating material in electric condensers and electric wiring, as a cement for shatterproof glass, as an adhesive in gums and resins, and as coatings that increase the luster of artificial pearls and leather.

Cellulose that has been treated with caustic soda and allowed to ripen can be made to react with ethyl sulfate to form a beautiful, white, fibrous compound called ethyl cellulose. The compound lends itself to molding into various shapes for jewelry and clock cases. It softens on heating and can be used in making adhesives, ceramic coatings, an ingredient of artificial leather, shatterproof glass, wrapping films, waterproofing agents, and varnishes.

Cellulose is transformable into another widely used material, methyl cellulose. It is first treated with caustic soda and allowed to ripen; the ripened material, on treatment with methyl sulfate, forms methyl cellulose, which is a fluffy white material similar to ethyl cellulose. Methyl cellulose is an ingredient of shatterproof glass and of coatings for leather, metalware, stoneware, rubber, and wood items.

Fundamental research is giving us added information on ways and means of using hemicelluloses and cellulose, both in mixtures with one another and alone. We are learning to increase the percentage of hemicelluloses in mixtures for making strong papers in greater variety for special uses. We are making it possible to increase the percentage of lignin by slight modifications of the hemicelluloses and cellulose in pulp furnishes for strong wrapping and bag papers. This innovation lowers the cost of production and raises the attendant pulp yield. New research data doubtless will result in better processes for separating the two materials with lower losses of cellulose.

Research can be confidently expected to chart a course for the development of new uses for these two chemically versatile materials. One such development, for example, could originate from current research on the controlled action of bacteria on wood waste to produce chemicals of value in food, shelter, and clothing.

GEORGE J. RITTER *is a chemist at the Forest Products Laboratory. He joined the Laboratory in 1920 and has been in charge of studies of the chemistry of wood and cellulose since 1926. Dr. Ritter is a native of Wisconsin and did his undergraduate and graduate work at the University of Wisconsin. His pioneer work in developing basic microtechniques for chemically dissecting wood and cellulose fibers gained international recognition. He was the first to show photomicrographically the orientation of wood cellulose crystallites from which it is possible to predict the shrinking and swelling properties of the structural wood elements.*

New Sources of Paper Pulps

E. R. Schafer

The fiber in wood is a base material of one of our largest industries— the pulp, paper, and fiberboard industry, whose products are as common to our everyday living as food and clothing. We found out during the war that paper can be substituted for many things, but there is no substitute for paper.

We Americans use more pulp and paper than anybody—about 25 million tons a year, or nearly 350 pounds for each of us. We used almost 10 million tons more paper in 1950 than we did just before the Second World War; it seems that we shall steadily use more and more. Some reasons are that paper is relatively cheap and available; it is being improved in quality and extended in usefulness, thanks to ever-continuing improvements in manufacturing methods, although the supply of high-quality softwoods ordinarily preferred is becoming more and more inadequate.

About a third of the paper has more or less permanent use—in libraries, in office files, and in building construction, for example, or it is exported, soiled, or destroyed in use. Of the 17 million tons remaining after a primary but temporary use, a great deal has a number of secondary, though still impermanent, uses in millions of homes. More than 6½ million tons were collected in 1949 (in 1947 it was 8 million) and used again in making more paper and paperboard. Several million tons of uncollected, usable waste paper are available, but some of it is so widely scattered that collection and reuse are not practicable. Any great increase in the quantity collected would take special effort through drives and more elaborate systems of collection.

As the demand for paper increases and the usual supply of first-class raw fiber material runs out, new sources must be found. Paper makers use a number of other fibrous materials. In North America the most important one is pulpwood. The use of pulpwood in the United States in 1948—more than 21 million cords—was the highest on record. The consumption of agricultural waste material now amounts to more than 800,000 tons a year. Probably more could be used, but the economics and facilities of the paper industry do not favor a large increase in materials of that kind for some time to come. Possibly a great deal more waste paper could be used. Much wood waste also is available and becomes more and more useful as research shows the way. Some examples are the demonstrated possibilities of its use in roofing felt, shipping-container board, structural hardboard, and fiber-cement compositions.

Spruce, balsam, pine, and hemlock have long been the principal pulping woods. They and one or two other less-used softwoods now comprise 85 to 90 percent of the pulpwood used. Supplies of these softwoods in the Northeastern and Lake States and of western hemlock in the Northwest are not sufficient to satisfy the need for pulpwood. In the South, the supply of pine is adequate for present needs, but competition for it in pulp manufacture and other products is strong. The importation of pulpwood from Canada in 1949 was more than 1½ million cords, but steps taken by the provincial governments to protect their forest resources may eventually reduce that supply. The excellent stands of softwood timber in the Rocky Mountains and Alaska, now becoming available, some day may help offset the cut in importations. Douglas-fir is available in large quantities in the Northwest.

The prospects of using a number of hardwoods that grow in the Southern, Eastern, and Lake States have a special interest for farmers there. The use of more hardwoods as pulpwood would help meet the demand for pulp products and would promote proper management of their forest land and its growth potentials. For many years the research program of the Forest Products Laboratory has recognized this need and has developed suitable pulping processes and formulated various papers and paperboards from them.

Industry also is becoming alert to the need. During the Second World War the use of hardwoods expanded. The use of aspen and poplar pulpwood, for example, nearly doubled, and that of other kinds of hardwoods increased about 75 percent. In proportion to the total pulpwood consumption, however, the use of hardwoods has not changed greatly since 1939.

Some of the woods classed as little-used species often are crooked, knotty, and difficult to bark—they are hard to prepare for pulping and sometimes make a dirty pulp. Many of the hardwoods are fairly dense in comparison with the common softwoods used for pulping. Others, notably the aspen and cottonwood, have a high content of cellulose. High density and high cellulose content are favorable characteristics from the standpoint of yield of pulp on a cord basis and on a weight basis, respectively, and counteract somewhat the higher preparation costs. The hardwoods are often shorter-fibered than the softwoods. Papers made from them may not be so strong as those from softwoods, but hardwood pulps mixed with softwood pulps give the papers a desirable texture and surface. Hardwood pulps are therefore used extensively in book and magazine papers.

Nearly all hardwoods can be made into a usable pulp or fiber of some kind, although some are more difficult to process than others. The Forest Products Laboratory has examined more than a hundred American species of hardwoods and softwoods for paper-making. Nearly all possess some measure of quality for paper—but that does not mean all may be economically used, because availability, form, and condition of the material, as well as costs of harvesting and transportation, are weighty factors in their utilization.

Five processes are used commercially in making paper pulp from wood. One is the mechanical, or ground-wood, process, in which the wood is reduced to pulp on a grindstone. Three processes, the sulfite, sulfate, and soda, depend upon the dissolving action of chemical reagents, which remove essentially all the lignin and leave the cellulose fibers in a fairly pure state. That is accomplished by digesting the wood chips with a solution of the chemical under steam pressure. A fifth process, the semichemical, causes the removal of only a part of the lignin by chemical means and completes the pulping action by mechanical refining.

Because they have similar pulping characteristics, aspen, cottonwood, and yellow-poplar are lumped together as poplar. They comprise the largest group of hardwoods used for manufacturing pulp and paper. They can be pulped by the chemical and neutral-sulfite semichemical processes or by the ground-wood process, by which they yield short-fibered pulps that are relatively low in strength. The chemical pulps, when bleached, are used in higher-grade printing papers; when unbleached, in the cheaper printing and wrapping papers. The unbleached semichemical pulps can be used in wrapping paper, container boards, and insulating board. The ground-wood pulps are used in book and other printing papers, tissues, and structural insulation boards.

American beech, sweetgum, and the several varieties of birch, maple, and tupelo are the second largest group of hardwoods used for pulp making. Like the poplars, they can be treated by the chemical and semichemical processes to give pulps somewhat similar in quality to poplar pulps, but their use is limited by their low strength. The ground-wood pulps, although short-fibered and low in strength, have value as filler stocks. Experimental work at the Forest Products Laboratory and industrial and institutional laboratories shows that most of them can be used in the manufacture of newsprint, book, toweling, and specialty papers, structural board, and purified cellulose for rayon manufacture.

Miscellaneous hardwoods used for making paper include principally ash, chestnut (after tannin extraction), elm, oak, willow, and such less-used woods as alder, basswood, buckeye, butternut, catalpa, sugarberry, hickory, locust, and sycamore. All may be pulped by the soda and sulfate processes, most of them quite readily. Most of them can also be pulped by the sulfite and neutral-sulfite semichemical processes. The lighter-colored woods generally are suitable for pulping by the ground-wood process. Their principal use is in book, magazine, and cheap printing papers, and in corrugated board.

The development of more extensive, better, and new uses for these less-used woods requires continued investigations of pulping procedures, studies on the compounding of fiber mixtures, and development of techniques for converting the mixtures into paper, paperboard, and other products. Great interest is now being shown in the semichemical pulping processes and their recent applications. The neutral-sulfite semichemical pulping process is particularly adaptable to hardwoods and gives high yields of pulps that are suitable for a wide variety of uses. In one or two instances, hardwood semichemical pulp has been substituted for spruce pulp.

New processes for bleaching ground-wood pulps offer a partial solution of the problem of using certain darker hardwoods for this kind of pulp. The development of improved methods of chemically treating hardwoods before grinding, resulting in the production of ground-wood pulps with better strength, has considerable promise.

An example of how economic and technical improvements were obtained by the use of a new type of fiber in a relatively standard product is the development of a saturating paper used principally in the manufacture of asphalt roofing and linoleum felt that contains appreciable quantities of coarsely fiberized wood. As I mentioned, the raw material from which this fiber is made consists largely of small wood, forest thinnings including the bark, and sawmill waste. Both hardwoods and softwoods suitable for the purpose are widely available from farm woods and sawmills.

The successful and profitable utilization of these woods will not be attained by improvements in manufacturing methods alone. A great deal depends on the costs of harvesting and handling. Attention must be directed to harvesting methods that will reduce the cost of the wood delivered to the mill. Low-cost logging is often complicated by the variety of sizes and species encountered. Effective pulping and paper-making processes for naturally occurring mixtures would be a big help in reducing logging costs; we have evidence that they can be worked out and used in some localities.

Another line of effort to attain lower costs is to combine properly the production of pulpwood and the production of sawlogs, veneer logs, tie logs, and stave bolts. The owner of farm woodland often has to depend on sorting and segregating his woods-run material so that each class of material goes to the market in best position to use it and so that the cost of logging can be distributed according to sales return. Local wood-using industries will give him information as to their needs. His county agent and the nearest office of the United States Forest Service will give him advice on cutting practices and marketing.

E. R. SCHAFER *has done research in wood-pulping methods and problems*

for 30 years as a member of the staff of the Forest Products Laboratory. He has specialized in ground-wood pulping of the southern yellow pines and various hardwoods and has investigated the use of seed-flax straw for making paper.

THE FIRST STEP in the development of new uses for a farm commodity is an exhaustive study of its composition. The next steps are to isolate the pure materials, determine the chemical and physical properties, and evaluate their prospects for use in industry. All agricultural materials are complex mixtures of groups of closely related compounds from which each must be isolated in pure form before it can be studied.

In the past, the principal methods of accomplishing this were extraction with solvents, crystallization, distillation, and precipitation of known derivatives. Those methods, usually tedious and likely to produce mixtures unless the physical properties are relatively different, remain of utmost importance.

Another method, discovered in 1906 by a Russian botanist named Tswett, however, facilitates the separation of a mixture of materials of closely related compounds into pure fractions. Natural mixtures of plant pigments had defied separation before Tswett's discovery. While working with extracts of plants, he passed a solution of plant pigments through a column of talc in a glass tube. As the solution moved down the column, a series of distinct colored bands was formed, grading from green (chlorophyll) at the top to yellow (carotene) at the bottom. The resulting color distribution was termed a chromatogram, a term derived from the Greek word *chroma,* meaning color. Each band could be cut from the others and the pure component recovered.

It is hard to explain why this apparently simple separation occurs so perfectly. However, it can be compared with what happens when a piece of wool is dyed. A fast dye is held strongly by wool, so that it is exceedingly difficult to remove. A less fast dye is removed easily by washing. There are all levels of fastness between the two extremes.

In the plant pigment chromatogram, the chlorophylls are fast and so are held near the top, their first point of contact with the talc. The carotene is not fast; it is washed away through the column of talc.

Since Tswett's day, the technique has been developed to a point where pigments have been separated into many different components. For example, two chlorophylls have been separated, and the yellow fraction has been resolved into several xanthophylls and numerous kinds of carotenes, designated as carotene isomers. Besides the pigment compounds, many other mixtures of important substances have been separated and identified. Among them are amino acids, fatty acids, carbohydrates, and organic acids. Chromatography was one of the most important tools in developing penicillin, streptomycin, and drugs of the sulfa family. It is now employed in every field of organic chemistry. Even though its name suggests color, it is equally useful for separating and identifying many colorless compounds. The field of agricultural chemical research has been advanced immeasurably by the use of chromatographic methods in resolving natural mixtures that long defied separation or detection by other means.— *W. L. Porter, Eastern Regional Research Laboratory.*

Stabilizing the Dimensions of Wood

Alfred J. Stamm

The chief shortcoming of wood for exacting structural use is its tendency to shrink and swell. Shrinking and swelling cause undesirable changes in dimensions and indirectly are responsible for warping, checking, and such.

Many investigators have tried to stabilize the dimensions of wood. So far about all they have accomplished is to retard the rate of shrinking and swelling. That they have done with surface coatings and water-repellent treatments. Such treatments aid in the shedding of water, but they do not minimize the dimension changes that result from seasonal changes in relative humidity.

Studies at the Forest Products Laboratory showed the futility of trying to attain permanent dimensional stabilization by those means. They indicated, however, that permanent stabilization might be attained by depositing non-volatile materials within the cell-wall structure. The first successful attempts to do so involved depositing water-soluble salts or sugars within the fibers by soaking the wood in water solutions, after which the water was evaporated off. Wood, when effectively treated in this way, is always damp. It may also lose its dimensional stability, because the deposited material may be readily leached from the wood.

Chemists in the Forest Products Laboratory next developed a means of depositing water-insoluble waxes within the cell walls. The method was free from the leaching hazards of the salt-treated wood. Melted waxes will not enter the cell walls because they have no affinity for wood. The scientists, therefore, found it necessary to replace water in water-swollen wood by a mutual solvent for water and wax, and then to replace the solvent with the wax. This double replacement was effective but impractical, for it was difficult to apply to small pieces.

These experiments led to the treatment of wood with water solutions of resin-forming chemicals, followed by evaporating off the water and then heating the wood at higher temperatures to cause the setting of the resin. Several types of resin-forming chemicals have been tried in this way. The most successful is a treatment with water-soluble phenol-formaldehyde resin. Heat sets this material to an infusible type of resin within the fiber. The resin becomes such an intimate part of the wood, when the wood is properly treated, that the product looks just like normal wood.

It is hard to distribute the resin-forming chemicals properly in sizable pieces of wood. So, the process is limited to the treatment of veneer, from which large panels can be fabricated, or to short pieces of solid wood. The treating is done either by merely soaking veneer in the solution of resin-forming chemicals overnight, or by forcing the solution into the wood by applying an external pressure or pulling a vacuum in a treating cylinder. The veneer is then stacked to allow the chemicals to diffuse into the cell walls, after which it is dried in a kiln or on a continuous drier. The temperature is further raised (after the wood is dry) to set up the resin in making the product that has been named "impreg," or the wood is simultaneously compressed and cured in making "compreg." Impreg is about 15 to 18 percent heavier than the wood from which it is made. Compreg may be two to four times as heavy as the original wood.

These resin-treated woods have high dimensional stability, resistance to face checking and decay, and improved electrical properties. Impreg has practically the same strength properties as normal wood, except that it is slightly harder and decidedly less tough. Most of the strength properties of compreg improve in direct proportion to its weight increase, except for hardness, which may be increased as much as twentyfold, and toughness, which is decreased slightly.

Resin-treated wood was made for various specialty uses during the Second World War on a rather large scale. Although production declined just after the war, it is again on the increase for use in many specialties, such as knife handles, textile shuttles and picker sticks, for forming dies, and for decking, for which its superior properties warrant the extra cost.

A NEW treatment was developed by laboratory chemists to overcome the brittleness of resin-treated woods, which made them unfit for certain military uses. The brittleness, or lack of toughness, of resin-treated wood is due to too much stiffening of the fibers by the resin as a result of forming cross ties or bridges between the structural units. The chemists hence tried to find a bulking material that would give a less rigid structure. The replacement of the hygroscopic hydroxyl groups in cellulose and lignin with less hygroscopic, more bulky acetate groups looked promising, as these groups attach at only one point and should not give the rigid cross bridging that causes embrittlement.

The procedure for replacing hydroxyl groups in cellulose with acetate groups in making cellulose-acetate rayon could not be adopted, because strong acids are used to promote or catalyze the reaction. The acids themselves would embrittle the fiber, not by stiffening it, but by breaking the cellulose chains. Nonacid catalysts therefore were sought to promote the acetylation reaction. Pyridine, a vile-smelling organic chemical, was the only one found suitable. In preliminary experiments, wood was soaked in a mixture of acetic anhydride and pyridine, and then the pyridine, the excess acetic anhydride, and the acetic acid formed in the reaction were vaporized off. Later it was found desirable merely to suspend the wood in the vapors of acetic anhydride and pyridine so as to avoid the taking up of excess chemicals by the wood.

That treatment, like all other dimension-stabilizing treatments, requires a thorough distribution of chemicals throughout the wood. Hence it has so far been effectively applied only to veneer. The procedure for treating veneer consists of (1) drying the spaced sheets of veneer in an acid-resistant kiln, (2) introducing the acetic anhydride and pyridine into an acid-resistant tray beneath the load while continuing circulation of the vapors and thus causing their absorption by the wood, (3) draining off the chemicals from the tray, and (4) circulating fresh air through the load and out through a condenser, thus removing the excess chemicals.

The equilibrium swelling of wood is reduced to 20 to 30 percent of normal by the treatment without embrittling the wood. An appreciable resistance to decay, termites, and marine borers is imparted to the wood. The weight of the wood is increased by only 6 to 8 percent. Most species are bleached slightly by the treatment. All strength properties are practically the same as those for the untreated wood. The wood, however, can be compressed to obtain a product, like compreg, with an increase in practically all strength properties.

The treatment has not yet been used commercially. One obstacle is that pyridine has increased greatly in price and become difficult to procure because of the great demand for it in making drugs. If current experiments directed toward the recovery of chemicals are successful, this treatment may be used as much as—or more than—the present resin treatment. It should be pointed out, however, that no treatment sufficiently penetrating, simple, and cheap for application to lumber for general use has yet been developed.

ALFRED J. STAMM *has degrees in chemistry from California Institute of Technology and the University of Wisconsin. In 1925 he became an associate chemist at the Forest Products Laboratory, where he now is chief of the division of derived products.*

BEFORE THE dawn of agriculture, when primitive peoples were food gatherers, acorns probably were relatively more important than wheat is now. Today, though eaten by hogs and wildlife, acorns are an undeveloped food resource for humans. The American Indians, who gathered and stored quantities of acorns for making bread, developed several simple methods of washing out the tannin and bitter taste with water.

As a rule, acorns of the white oak group are preferred for human food, being less bitter than those of the black oak group. The species of white oaks generally are recognized by the leaves and their lobes, which have blunt or rounded teeth and are not bristle-pointed, by the light-gray, scaly bark, and by the acorn shell, which is not hairy inside. Slightly sweetish acorns, produced by a few kinds and by individual trees, can be eaten raw or roasted and should be selected for tree-breeding investigations.

Acorn meal and acorn bread are easily prepared, whether for a variation in the diet or for camping trips and emergencies. Gather acorns as soon after they fall as is convenient. Then crack and remove the shells and grind the kernels in a food chopper. If acorns are to be stored, they should be dried by heat or fumigated to prevent damage by insect larvae or decay.

The bitter tannin is easily removed by spreading the acorn meal about one-half inch thick on a porous cloth or by putting the meal into a jelly bag. Then pour on hot water and let this percolate through. Repeat once or twice until the bitter taste is removed, and squeeze out excess water. Then spread out the wet meal to dry and parch in an oven. Grind the meal again if it has caked badly. Another method of extracting the tannin is to boil the dry kernels for 2 hours before grinding. Next pour off the darkened water and soak the darkened kernels in hot water, changing occasionally until the bitter flavor is lost. Then grind into paste and dry.

Acorn meal is used like corn meal in recipes for bread or muffins. Some prefer to mix with equal parts of corn meal or wheat flour, as bread from acorn meal alone tends to be friable and crumbly. Acorn bread is pale chocolate brown and has a taste suggesting a mixture of corn meal and nuts.

Breakfast cereal can be prepared from acorns also. After grinding and washing, put the doughy mass in a pot, add water, and boil. The mush thus prepared swells to about double its original volume and has a chocolate color. It is eaten with milk and sugar, with a pinch of salt added.

As acorns are high in carbohydrates and fats, nutritious acorn bread is similar to bread and butter combined. Experiments indicate that an edible salad oil similar to olive oil could be obtained from acorns of California live oak and perhaps other black oaks with relatively high fat content.—*Elbert L. Little, Jr., Forest Service.*

Production and Uses of Charcoal

Edward Beglinger

Charcoal has been produced for industrial use since Colonial days, when carbon needed for iron smelting was made in simple earth kilns. Today charcoal is in demand for many industrial applications and is used widely as domestic and recreational fuel. Kilns and the oven-recovery plants that produce other chemical products now make upwards of 300,000 tons of charcoal a year, more than half of which is used for cooking and heating.

Charcoal can be made from any kind of wood. The hard, dense material from the heavier hardwoods and softwoods is usually in greatest demand for most commercial uses. These denser woods are chiefly beech, birch, maple, ash, hickory, cherry, gum, oak, and longleaf and slash pine stumps. Lighter hardwoods, such as soft maple, alder, and willow, give lighter charcoals, which are best suited for the manufacture of black powder, crayons, resins, and pharmaceuticals.

Both kiln and oven methods are used to produce hardwood charcoal in this country. Forest, wood-lot, and mill refuse is generally used. This includes down and cull timber, the larger tops left after logging operations, and such mill scrap as slabs, edgings, and blocks. Special equipment is needed for chips, hogged wood, and sawdust, or a mixture of them. One large plant that uses a special process for treating small-sized wood waste has been in operation since 1924. All the charcoal produced in the plant is of fine size and is made into high-grade fuel briquets.

The same kiln and oven methods are used for softwood as for hardwood charcoal production. Stump sections from old, cut-over pine areas of the South and some timber and mill waste comprise the raw material used by the softwood operators. Of the estimated total of 300,000 tons of charcoal produced annually, about 60,000 tons are obtained from pine stump wood. Of this total, also, about 75,000 tons are produced in kilns. An estimated 550,-000 cords of low-value and unmarketable wood are used to produce the charcoal.

In general, the largest charcoal production has been within the areas of suitable and plentiful wood supply—in the hardwood forests of the northern and northeastern parts of the country and the pine stump lands of the Gulf States. Only scattered kiln operations are carried on in the West; large amounts of wood waste are available there, but petroleum coke, anthracite coal, and other forms of carbon appear more suitable and economical for the industrial uses.

Approximately 25,000 tons of charcoal a year, mostly imported, are used chiefly for metallurgical and chemical purposes.

WHEN WOOD is gradually heated to a temperature of 700° to 750° F. with little or no air present, part of it is changed to vapors and gases. The rest is impure carbon, or charcoal. Oven plants are equipped to recover such byproducts as acetic acid, methanol, and tars from the vapors. Because oven operation is more efficient, higher yields of charcoal are recovered. Average yields are about 37 percent by weight of the dry wood.

An important outgrowth of the kiln method of producing charcoal began in 1850 with the use of hand-loaded iron retorts. By this step byproducts as well as charcoal could be made, and the production of all products increased. The start of a real chemical industry, however, came in 1875 with the use of the larger, car-loaded ovens. All three operations—kiln, oven, and retort—are in use today. The use of retorts is now limited to a few of the pinewood recovery plants in the South.

The method and end result of heating wood to produce charcoal are generally the same in an oven or a retort. Heat is applied to the outside of the large steel ovens until an internal temperature of approximately 750° F. is reached. During this heating period, vapors and gases are given off by the wood and led through oven outlets to condensers, where crude liquids are formed. The liquids are refined for the recovery of other byproducts. Unliquefied volatiles are vented to the outside air or burned as plant fuel. The charcoal is removed by cars from the oven to coolers after a distillation period of 22 to 24 hours. This type of hardwood operation is now producing about 165,-000 tons of the annual charcoal output.

Because of economic conditions, a few hardwood oven plants have been changed over and are producing only charcoal. The vapors, instead of being condensed and used for byproduct recovery, are led with the gases to an outside burner or under the ovens as an additional fuel supply. The reduction of refinery, overhead, and wood costs, which is possible in this method, usually allows further operation and a profit for the plant. Between 9,000 and 10,-000 tons of charcoal a year are now being made in this way.

TWO HARDWOOD recovery operations use heating methods different from those employed in the oven process. Together they produce annually about 25,000 tons of charcoal. One is the Badger-Stafford operation, in which preheated, small-sized wood waste falls continuously downward through an insulated vertical steel retort. As the wood moves it is heated by the reaction heat produced during distillation. Vapors and gases are taken off at the top of the retort, and the charcoal is collected in an airtight receiver at the base. The small-sized charcoal produced does not have a ready market as such, but, on the other hand, it needs only limited grinding for making briquets. All the charcoal, after grinding, is milled with a starch binder and formed into briquets.

THE SECOND OPERATION uses fairly large blocks of wood charged in batches. The wood is placed in a vertical steel retort and distilled by circulating heated wood gases or other suitable gases through the charge for about 20 hours. The vapors are passed to condensers, and the charcoal is dropped to a cooling chamber at the base of the retort. Part of the uncondensed volatiles is burned. The remainder is circulated through the charge. A better grade of charcoal and greater yields of acetic acid can be obtained from this operation.

Charcoal is made from southern pine stump wood at the rate of nearly 60,000 tons a year. Production is limited to the use of raw material that contains at least 20 percent resin. Because the pine tar obtained from the same process is as important a product as the charcoal, the wide use of other softwoods and material having less resin is not practical. The industry employs the old, hand-loaded retorts at some plants, as well as the more modern, car-loaded ovens at others. Heating of the wood charge, collecting and refining of the liquid byproducts, and recovery and cooling of the charcoal are carried on much the same as in the hardwood-distillation industry. The yield of charcoal from pine stump wood is 28 to 30 percent by weight.

MORE CHARCOAL is being made in kilns each year. Wood lots and cut-over forest areas supply a good deal of the hardwood raw material, as do mills from their operations. The large beehive and smaller portable kilns produce practically all the kiln charcoal, although several other types could be used. Small quantities are still being made in sod or pit kilns. In all instances, the principle of charring is the same, but the methods of application may vary widely.

Fully 90 percent of kiln production is conducted in brick beehive kilns. These circular, dome-topped structures have capacities of 45 to 90 cords of wood and are operated in groups of 2 and 3 to as many as 18. The units are hand-loaded; the cordwood material usually is end-stacked, and slab and edging material flat-piled. The charge is fired and allowed to burn until a "coaling," or glowing, zone can be maintained, with only small amounts of air entering the kiln at different places. Part of the charge is lost by complete burning of the wood, and the amounts obtained from a cord of wood are less than by oven methods. On the average, about 800 pounds of charcoal are obtained from a cord of wood. The operation requires 4 to 5 days to load the kiln, 5 to 8 days to burn, 7 days to cool, and 4 to 5 days to unload.

IN ONE large operation, the kilns are equipped with brick fire arches for indirect flame heating of the wood. Natural gas and wood gases are used as fuel. Higher yields are possible by this method, because no flame burns the charge. Approximately 10 percent of the charcoal made in kilns is of fine size and does not have a good market. Such material is suitable for making briquets, however, and in one kiln operation this form of charcoal is turned out successfully. Heretofore it has been profitable to produce briquets only at the larger oven plants.

Many of the smaller, portable-type kilns are operating in scattered locations, chiefly wood lots or nearly cutover forest areas. These kilns, in order to be suitable for use in areas where wood is cheap, must also be inexpensive. Development of the units, therefore, has been along the lines of low construction cost, portability, and ease of operation. The Black Rock Forest kiln developed by H. H. Tryon, director of the Black Rock Forest, Cornwall-on-the-Hudson, N. Y., is of this type. Another of the same general design, known as the Indiana charcoal oven, was developed by Torkel Holsoe, of West Virginia University.

The kilns are circular, of light sheet-steel construction, and consist of a bottom, a middle section, and a shallow lid. Each unit can coal a cord of wood in 18 to 24 hours. Cooling of the charcoal in the kiln takes about the same period of time.

In operation, the coaling part of the charge goes from the point of firing at the center of the kiln to the outside, against the air entering the draft holes. The gases and vapors that are formed as the wood chars leave the kiln through smokestacks. The finish of the burn is indicated by a marked decrease in the volume of the smoke, together with a color change from grayish yellow to bluish white. Yields of 30 to 32 bushels of charcoal per cord of the heavier hardwoods are obtained.

MORE RECENT developments of the small portable and semiportable types of kiln have come from the work of H. W. Hicock and A. R. Olsen at the Connecticut Agricultural Experiment Station. Both rectangular sheet-metal and rectangular cinder-concrete-block units have been developed. A number of the latter are now operated commercially. The use of a somewhat different burning method in these kilns has given better yields. Greater operating efficiency is possible in the concrete-block unit because less heat is lost through the kiln walls. Cooling of the contents of the kiln after burning is hastened by spraying with water. The rectangular metal and concrete-block kilns can be built to hold 1, 2, or 5 cords of wood and can be operated in groups if desired. Yields of 42 bushels of charcoal from a cord of seasoned mixed hardwoods have been reported.

Good-quality charcoals are produced in ovens and kilns alike, and both have the same market applications. Each kind also commands the same market price, although returns from kiln operation have been more favorable than from oven operation. Kilns, being somewhat more portable, can be moved to areas of cheaper wood and have the further advantage of comparatively low plant investment. The large oven plants, with their fixed locations and heavy investments, must depend upon wood sources that are not always suitable. Wood costs, which are a large part of total charcoal production costs, are generally more favorable to kiln operations for those reasons. During the past 10 years, wood costs to the oven operations have gone up from about $5 to $10.50 a cord. Under the most favorable operating conditions, the average costs of producing a ton of charcoal are estimated to be $25 to $28 from the small kiln, $27 to $29 from the large beehive kiln, and $32 to $35 from oven recovery operations.

Charcoal, in the form of lumps, screenings, powder, or briquets, has a variety of uses. The main ones are for domestic and specialized fuel and in the metallurgical, chemical, and allied fields. Direct and indirect end uses within these fields include:

For domestic and specialized fuel: Curing tobacco, meat, and fish; heating and cooking in railroad dining cars; heating foundry, tinning, and plumbing equipment; heating houses, laundries, and incinerators; and heating salamanders in shipyards and citrus groves.

Metallurgical: Production of copper, brass, bronze, iron, steel, nickel, cobalt, aluminum, magnesium, molybdenum, and electromanganese, and manufacture of armor plate, and foundry molds.

Chemical: Manufacture of calcium carbide, sodium cyanide, potassium cyanide, carbon disulfide, magnesium chloride, hydrochloric acid, carbon monoxide, activated carbon, fireworks, electrodes, black powder, catalyst reactor, glass, molding resins, rubber, brake linings, gas cylinder absorbent, paint pigment, nursery mulch, crayons, pharmaceuticals, and poultry and stock feeds.

THE DEMAND for charcoal in 1950 was about equal to production. An increasing demand for briquets is strongly indicated. Large-tonnage outlets for it as a fuel in tobacco curing and in railroad dining cars have been available for some time. Excellent outlets as picnic fuels already exist for both briquets and lump charcoal and may be greatly expanded. Such expansion will probably offset the large-tonnage losses, particularly in metallurgical and chemical uses. In the production of iron and steel, aluminum, and some alloys, coke and other carbon materials have all but replaced charcoal. Market losses for charcoal are also increasing in some chemical uses, notably in the manufacture of carbon disulfide, a use for which semianthracite coal soon may largely replace charcoal.

Higher costs of wood and labor will affect directly the future production of both recovery-plant and kiln charcoal. Consumer price levels have already become sufficiently high for serious competition from other carbon sources. If costs remain as they are now, however, and further progress can be made toward improved and simplified methods of operation, it is likely that profitable production and good markets may be available for some years to come.

EDWARD BEGLINGER *is a chemist at the Forest Products Laboratory. For several years he has been associated with wood-carbonization research, which has covered both fundamental and pilot-scale studies, as well as periodic plant surveys of the hardwood and resinous wood-distillation and charcoal-producing groups. He directs investigations on continuous methods of decomposition of wood and wood waste at high temperatures.*

Details of terpenes commonly present in turpentines

Name	Molecular configuration	Boiling point at 760 mm. pressure °C.	Specific gravity at 20° C.	Refractive index at 20° C.
α-Pinene		156	0.8582	1.4653
β-Pinene		164	.8706	1.4790
Camphene		159	.872	1.472
Δ³-Carene		170	.863	1.470
Dipentene		176	.8415	1.4717
Terpinolene		188	.862	1.489

Chemicals We Get From Turpentine

Leo A. Goldblatt

Turpentine is a volatile oil that consists primarily of a number of terpene hydrocarbons having the general formula $C_{10}H_{16}$. It is obtained by distilling the oleoresin exuded by or contained in the wood of certain species of pine trees. The formula means that the individual molecule of each of the terpenes contains 10 atoms of carbon and 16 atoms of hydrogen. The 26 atoms may be arranged differently in some molecules, thus constituting different terpenes.

The United States produces well over half of the total world supply of spirits of turpentine. Federal laws regulating its designation have been enacted. The Federal Naval Stores Act, passed in 1923, recognizes four kinds of turpentine classified according to methods of production—gum spirits of turpentine, steam-distilled wood turpentine, destructively distilled wood turpentine, and sulfate wood turpentine.

Gum turpentine (gum spirits) is made from the gum, or oleoresin, collected from living trees. Steam-distilled (S. D.) wood turpentine is obtained from the oleoresin within the wood (scrap wood, knots, or stumps, and other wood waste, commonly called lightwood) by steam distillation of the wood or of an extract of the wood with a solvent. Destructively distilled (D. D.) wood turpentine is obtained by fractional distillation of certain oils recovered by condensing the vapors formed during the destructive distillation—heating to a high temperature in the absence of air—of lightwood. Sulfate wood turpentine is recovered as a byproduct during the conversion of wood to paper pulp by the sulfate process.

Several hundred different compounds with the formula $C_{10}H_{16}$ can theoretically exist. Only half a dozen, however, are present in appreciable quantities in most commercially available turpentines—α-pinene, β-pinene, camphene, Δ^3-carene, dipentene, and terpinolene. The molecular configuration and some of the physical characteristics of those terpenes are shown in the chart opposite.

THE FOUR KINDS of turpentine differ in composition, and different samples of the same kind of turpentine may differ materially in composition. The composition of gum turpentine may vary with the species of tree from which the oleoresin was derived, but turpentine obtained from the same species, or even from the same tree at different times, may differ somewhat in composition. Steam-distilled wood turpentines may differ in composition with the wood used by the processor or with the techniques and operating conditions used in their production. Such differences within any specific class of turpentine are generally rather small.

Before petroleum refining became an industry, turpentine was used extensively as an illuminating oil. Its outstanding use now is as a solvent. Just a half century ago, when only about a dozen solvents were available for commercial use, turpentine reigned supreme. But the American chemical industry has developed more than a hundred commercial solvents to challenge the supremacy of turpentine. The suit-

902722°—51——53

ability of a solvent for a specific purpose often is determined by many factors other than solvent power. Development of synthetic solvents has nibbled away at turpentine's markets; replacement of older products with newer synthetics has removed other markets; and the competition from cheaper petroleum and coal-tar solvents has made heavy inroads on still other uses of solvents for which turpentine might be preferable but not so superior as to warrant the difference in price. Further, the petroleum industry has developed products that have even greater solvent power than turpentine.

THE LAYMAN almost always associates turpentine with paint. Master painters generally consider turpentine a better paint thinner than petroleum products, especially for outside white house paints, because, they believe, turpentine makes paint more durable and easier to work under the brush. Although all chemists do not agree on the point, many think that turpentine has an advantage. The solvent and wetting properties of turpentine are generally regarded as superior to those of straight petroleum solvents.

Few exposure tests of the effect of paint thinners on the durability of coatings have been reported. Certain weathering tests on exterior white house paints reduced with different types of volatile thinners, however, have shown that turpentines contribute slightly more to the durability of paint coatings than do mineral spirits. Turpentine has long been used as a solvent and thinner for paints and varnishes. That is still by far its major use, but this use has not kept pace with the greatly increased production of the paint, varnish, and lacquer industry. The bulk of the turpentine so utilized is used by painting contractors, individual painters, and property owners. Changes in the character of protective coatings, which require new solvents, and improved methods of refining petroleum, which make available petro-

leum products more nearly suited for use as thinners, have reduced the use of turpentine by paint manufacturers.

Turpentine is used as a solvent in many industries. As a solvent for waxes, it is used extensively in friction paste shoe polishes, stove polishes, furniture and floor polishes, liquid floor wax, and wax auto polish, in modeling and grafting waxes, and in drawing crayons. It is an ingredient of wood fillers and wood stains. It is used in ceramic work for application of colors and as a lubricant in grinding and drilling glass. A small amount is used for medicinal purposes, both alone—as an antiseptic or an anthelmintic, for example—and in prepared drugs, liniments, and pharmaceuticals. Many insecticides contain turpentine for its solvent and insect-killing properties.

Home owners use a great deal of turpentine. In fact, less than a third of the turpentine used in the United States is reported as "industrial consumption"; most of the rest, listed as "not accounted for," is distributed over-the-counter through retailers who are not covered by the surveys and is used as a paint thinner by painters and property owners.

The importance of the over-the-counter market to the pine gum farmer is apparent when one considers the relative proportion of gum and wood turpentine used industrially. In 1949–50, the production of gum spirits in the United States was 323,010 barrels of 50 gallons each; the production of wood turpentine of all types amounted to 350,280 barrels. That year we used 555,636 barrels, of which 112,442 barrels were reported to be "industrial consumption." However, of this industrial consumption, only 11,991 barrels were gum turpentine and 100,451 barrels were wood turpentine. Thus, nearly 30 percent of the wood turpentine, but only about 4 percent of the gum turpentine, produced in the United States in 1949–50, went into "industrial consumption."

Gum turpentine competes with wood turpentine for the over-the-counter market. Both kinds are meeting increasing competition from the petroleum industry, which has developed new and improved refining techniques and modern merchandising methods. These petroleum products are cheaper than turpentine and price is a potent factor in this market. It is, therefore, to the chemical-utilization field that we must turn for the development of future uses for turpentine. Turpentine must be regarded as a source of chemicals. Markets that have been lost because of the research by the aggressive, technically minded organic-chemical industry can be regained by equally aggressive and imaginative research by the naval stores industry.

THE CHEMISTRY of the terpenes, of which turpentine is the most plentiful source, is fascinating. Literally hundreds of chemical derivatives have been prepared from the terpenes, and thousands of articles have been published in scientific journals on the behavior of this unusual class of chemically reactive compounds. Several Nobel Prize winners have explored this field. One of them, Otto Wallach (1847–1931), was awarded the prize specifically for his work on the chemistry of the terpenes. These researches have been primarily of academic rather than industrial interest. Most of the compounds that were prepared have remained laboratory curiosities; hardly a dozen have attained the production level of a million pounds a year, often considered by the chemical industry as the turning point between successful and unsuccessful development. Yet only a decade ago but one strictly chemical use of turpentine had gained that enviable status—the synthesis of camphor. The field is wide open to research.

The earliest successful efforts to use turpentine as a chemical in an industrial-chemical process was in the manufacture of synthetic camphor. Even this was not without its failures, however. The first commercial attempt to manufacture camphor in the United States, at Niagara Falls in 1900, failed, chiefly

by reason of the low yields obtained, even though turpentine was then available at 35 cents a gallon, a fact that influenced the initiation of the venture. Another attempt was made during the First World War, again a period of low-priced turpentine and high-priced natural camphor. When the war ended turpentine prices went up and the price of natural camphor was pegged by the Japanese Camphor Monopoly Board. So the factory was shut down for good. In the 1930's the E. I. du Pont de Nemours & Co., an important user of camphor, wishing to be independent of the Japanese camphor monopoly, undertook the manufacture of synthetic camphor from turpentine. The process this company initially developed was subjected to continuous research, modification, and improvement. Although accurate figures are not available, it is generally believed that by December 7, 1941, consumption of synthetic camphor exceeded that of natural camphor.

This industrial development was initiated in periods of low-priced turpentine. It declined when prices were high. In 1920, the price of turpentine rose to $2.33 a gallon; it was less than 20 cents a gallon in 1938 and was $1.50 in 1946. Such fluctuations in the price of a raw material are a serious deterrent to the allocation of research funds for the development of new uses. The manufacturer must consider the possibility that, even if the research is technically successful and a promising new product is developed, rising costs for his raw material will necessitate such increased prices for the new product that it cannot successfully compete with products already on the market.

Isoprene is a case in point. Isoprene is chemically related to turpentine. In 1860 it was observed that isoprene, a hydrocarbon with the formula C_5H_8, could be obtained during the destructive distillation of rubber. Many attempts were made to reverse the process and make synthetic rubber out of isoprene. Turpentine, because the terpenes that compose it have the formula

$C_{10}H_{16}$, was obviously a possible source for the desired isoprene, and numerous experiments on making isoprene from turpentine were conducted.

During the Second World War, efficient processes were developed for the production of isoprene from turpentine, and methods were devised for preparing high-quality synthetic rubber from it. Large quantities of isoprene were made from turpentine at moderate cost, but after OPA ceilings were removed the price of turpentine rose to $1.50 a gallon. At that price, isoprene from turpentine could not compete with petroleum, which cost less than a tenth as much. The plant producing isoprene from turpentine was shut down. Several million pounds of isoprene are now being made annually from petroleum, even though its purification is more difficult than would be the purification of isoprene from turpentine. If a reasonably stable price of 30 to 40 cents a gallon for turpentine could have been maintained, the development might have been different.

One way to illustrate the variety of chemical reactions of which the terpenes are capable and to indicate some of their possibilities is by means of a chart, like the one opposite. It shows only a few of the reactions of α-pinene (I) and β-pinene (II), which might be considered of interest for industrial application. β-Pinene can readily be converted to α-pinene, but the reverse reaction (the conversion of α-pinene to β-pinene) is not feasible. Consequently, any product that can be made from α-pinene can also be made from β-pinene (although the reaction mechanism is not necessarily through prior conversion of β-pinene to α-pinene). The converse is not true, however; certain chemical reactions are peculiar to β-pinene.

Both α-pinene and β-pinene can be readily converted (isomerized) to dipentene (III) by a variety of methods. Dipentene itself has many uses—for example, as a solvent or antiskinning agent in paints or as a rubber reclaiming and processing aid. It may be iso-

merized further to terpinolene (IV), and terpinolene in turn to terpinene (V). There are many ways of producing these isomerizations, but it is often difficult to control the extent of isomerization. Terpinolene and terpinene are useful as solvents, but they are also very reactive chemically. They react with such diverse chemicals as maleic anhydride, sulfur and sulfur-containing compounds, phenols, formaldehyde, halogens, and oxygen to produce materials suitable for industrial-chemical application. For example, reaction with maleic anhydride is the basis for the commercial production of acids used in the manufacture of varnish resins, paper coatings, printing inks, and masking tapes, and some of the sulfur-containing compounds have found use as lubricating-oil additives.

Furthermore, dipentene (III) itself reacts with many chemicals to form useful products. For example, with phenol it reacts to produce menthyl phenol, which has found use as a stabilizing agent for ethyl cellulose. It may be polymerized to produce high-melting hydrocarbons, or conversely it may be "cracked" to produce isoprene (VI). Still again, dipentene may be dehydrogenated to produce p-cymene (VII).

p-Cymene has exceptionally strong solvent properties and is capable of a host of chemical reactions. Like any aromatic compound, it may be chlorinated, nitrated, sulfonated, and oxidized. Chlorinated p-cymene has been considered for use as a wood preservative and as an insecticide. Sulfonation provides a route to thymol (VIII), itself useful as a pharmaceutical and from which menthol can be obtained. Nitration leads to nitrocymenes and thence to amines which have been considered for use as dye intermediates and as antiknocking agents for automotive fuels.

Oxidation of p-cymene, most economically with air, leads to a series of interesting compounds. Cumic acid (IX) is similar to benzoic acid, can be

A few reactions of α-pinene (I) and β-pinene (II)
Of Interest for Industrial Application

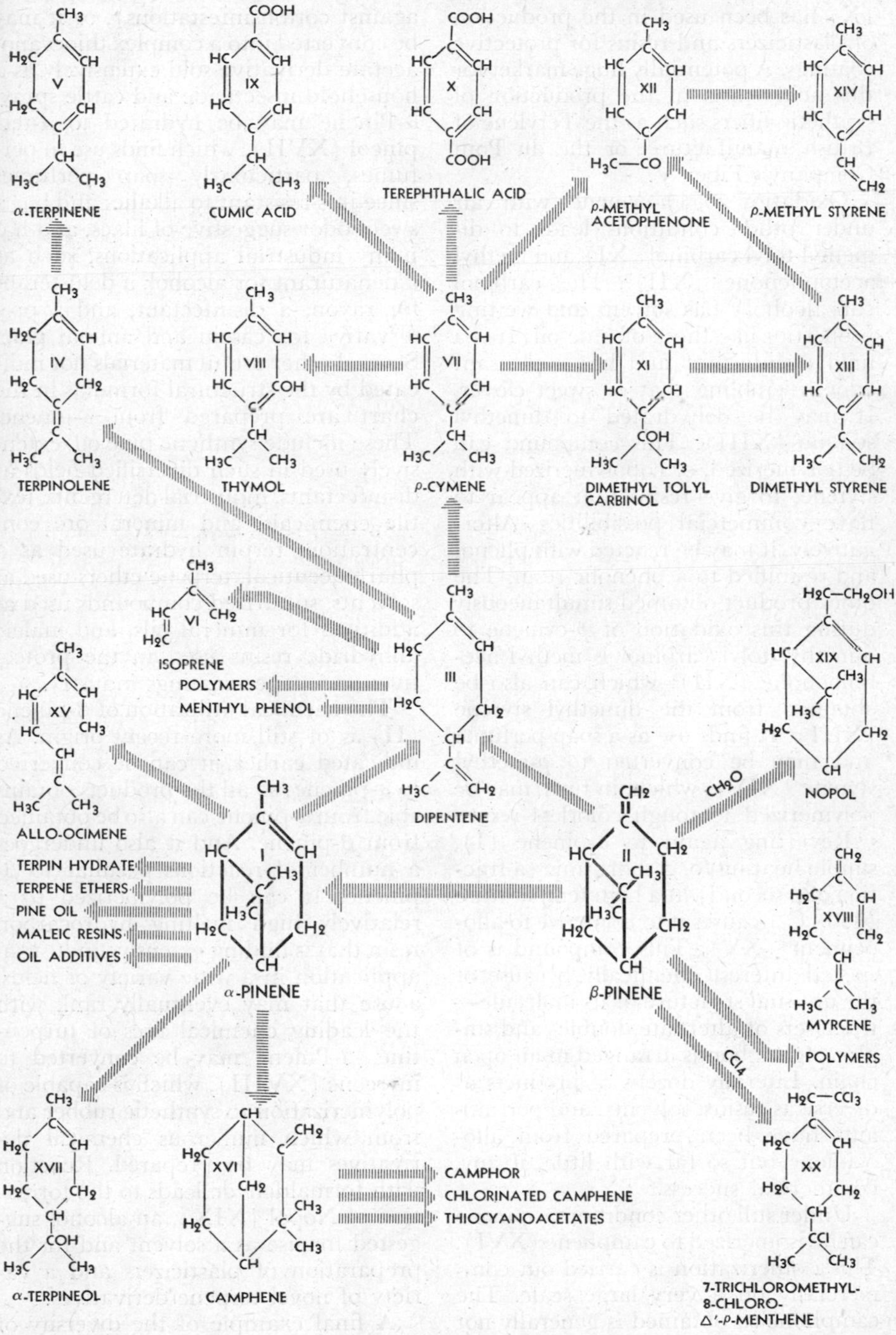

V

α-TERPINENE

IX

CUMIC ACID

X

TEREPHTHALIC ACID

XII

p-METHYL
ACETOPHENONE

XIV

p-METHYL STYRENE

IV

TERPINOLENE

VIII

THYMOL

VII

p-CYMENE

XI

DIMETHYL TOLYL
CARBINOL

XIII

DIMETHYL STYRENE

VI

ISOPRENE
POLYMERS
MENTHYL PHENOL

III

XIX

NOPOL

XV

ALLO-OCIMENE

TERPIN HYDRATE
TERPENE ETHERS
PINE OIL
MALEIC RESINS
OIL ADDITIVES

I

α-PINENE

DIPENTENE

II

β-PINENE

CH₂O

XVIII

MYRCENE

CCl₄

POLYMERS

XVII

α-TERPINEOL

XVI

CAMPHENE

CAMPHOR
CHLORINATED CAMPHENE
THIOCYANOACETATES

XX

7-TRICHLOROMETHYL-
8-CHLORO-
Δ'-p-MENTHENE

substituted for benzoic acid for several uses, and may replace that acid in many applications. Terephthalic acid (X) has been used in the production of plasticizers and resins for protective coatings. A potentially huge market for this acid exists in the production of synthetic fibers such as the Terylene of British manufacture, or the du Pont Company's Fiber V.

Oxidation of p-cymene with air under other conditions leads to dimethyl tolyl carbinol (XI) and methyl acetophenone (XII). The carbinol (an alcohol) has solvent and wetting properties like those of pine oil. It is a mild disinfectant and has a pleasant odor resembling that of sweet clover. It may be dehydrated to dimethyl styrene (XIII). This compound can be polymerized, or copolymerized with styrene, to give resins that appear to have commercial possibilities. Alternatively, it may be reacted with phenol and resinified to a phenolic resin. The other product obtained simultaneously during this oxidation of p-cymene to dimethyl tolyl carbinol is methyl acetophenone (XII), which can also be obtained from the dimethyl styrene (XIII). It finds use as a soap perfume and may be converted to p-methyl styrene (XIV), which, in turn, may be polymerized to tough colorless resins.

Reverting again to α-pinene (I), simple heating for a short time (a fraction of a second) at a high temperature (450° C.) causes it to isomerize to alloocimene (XV). This compound is of special interest chemically because of the unusual structure of its molecule— three sets of alternate double- and single-valence bonds arranged in an open chain. Literally dozens of products as diverse as resins, solvents, and perfumants have been prepared from alloocimene but so far with little, if any, commercial success.

Under still other conditions α-pinene can be isomerized to camphene (XVI). This isomerization is carried out commercially on a very large scale. The camphene so obtained is generally not used as such, but is converted to syn-

thetic camphor or chlorinated to produce chlorinated camphene (a widely used agricultural insecticide, especially against cotton infestations), or it may be converted into a complex thiocyanoacetate derivative sold extensively as a household insecticide and cattle spray. α-Pinene may be hydrated to α-terpineol (XVII), which finds use in perfumes, particularly soap perfumes since it is resistant to alkalies and has a sweet odor suggestive of lilacs, and has many industrial applications, such as a denaturant for alcohol, a delusterant for rayon, a disinfectant, and a preservative for casein and animal glue. Several other useful materials not indicated by the structural formulas in the chart are prepared from α-pinene. These include synthetic pine oil, extensively used in such diversified fields as disinfectants, industrial detergents, textile chemicals, and mineral ore concentration, terpin hydrate used as a pharmaceutical, terpene ethers used as solvents, sulfurized compounds used as additives for mineral oils, and maleic anhydride resins used in the protective- and paper-coatings industry.

The chemical utilization of β-pinene (II) is of still more recent origin. As indicated earlier, it can be converted to α-pinene; so all the products obtainable from α-pinene can also be obtained from β-pinene. And it also undergoes a number of reactions peculiar to β-pinene. It can be polymerized to a relatively high melting hydrocarbon resin that is finding extensive industrial application in a wide variety of fields, a use that may eventually rank with the leading chemical uses of turpentine. β-Pinene may be converted to myrcene (XVIII), which is capable of polymerization to synthetic rubber and from which numerous chemical derivatives may be prepared. Reaction with formaldehyde leads to the formation of Nopol (XIX), an alcohol suggested for use as a solvent and for the preparation of plasticizers and a variety of novel terpene derivatives.

A final example of the diversity of reactions of which these terpenes are capable is the simple reaction with carbon tetrachloride, familiar to all as a household solvent and fire extinguisher, to form the compound (XX) to which has been assigned only the chemical name 7-trichloromethyl-8-chloro-Δ'-p-menthene. This compound, which can be obtained in excellent yield by a very simple process, has insecticidal properties and may be useful as a flameproofing material or as an

oil additive—or to produce still other compounds.

LEO A. GOLDBLATT *is a graduate of Clark University and the University of Pittsburgh. A principal chemist in the Bureau of Agricultural and Industrial Chemistry, he is engaged in research on the composition, properties, components, and derivatives of naval stores.*

THE SOIL Conservation Service Research Branch and the Purdue Agricultural Experiment Station in Lafayette, Ind., made a study of wheat straw grown on experimental watersheds, which are on prairie soils of high native fertility but were at a moderate state of depletion when the experiments were started in 1940. The following analysis of values is based on the study.

Wheat grown under a prevailing system (low rates of fertilization in a 3-year rotation of corn, wheat, and mixed meadow) had the following quantities of the main fertilizer components per ton of straw: Nitrogen (N), 12.4 pounds; phosphate (P_2O_5), 26.0 pounds; potash (K_2O), 19.2 pounds. These were worth, at 1950 straight fertilizer prices, $1.43, $2.16, and $0.99, respectively. Each ton of straw in the prevailing system has contained $4.58 (more or less) worth of nitrogen, phosphorus, and potassium. The straw left on the land has had a fertilizer value between $6 and $9 an acre.

Wheat grown on adjacent areas under an improved system (high rates of fertilization and moisture conservation) with the same rotation contained the following quantities of the main fertilizer components per ton of straw: Nitrogen, 19.4 pounds; phosphate, 34.4 pounds; potash, 38.8 pounds. They were worth, respectively, $2.23, $2.86, and $2.00. Each ton of straw in the improved system has contained $7.09 (more or less) worth of nitrogen, phosphorus, and potassium. The straw left on the land had a fertilizer value between $15 and $18 per acre.

Mineral nutrients in straw other than nitrogen, phosphorus, and potassium may have small fertilizer value. Although difficult to evaluate, there are probably benefits to the soil as a result of returning strawy residues to the land through greater nitrogen fixation by legumes in the meadows following wheat, additions of organic matter, and improvement of soil structure. The damage done to meadow seedlings by wheat straw is often overemphasized and may be minimized by a high fertility level in the soil and caution in combining and spreading the straw.

Before selling, it is wise to consider the value of straw for soil maintenance and the costs of harvesting and marketing. The approximate cost of raking, baling, and hauling to market in central Indiana is about $6 a ton. The sale of straw may add to the immediate cash income of a farming enterprise, but it is an unprofitable action unless the selling price covers all costs and assures a reasonable profit.—*H. A. Jongedyk and R. B. Hickok, Soil Conservation Service.*

The Industrial Utilization of Rosin

Ray V. Lawrence

Two types of rosin are produced in this country, wood and gum rosin. Wood rosin, along with other constituents, is extracted by a petroleum solvent from resinous stumps and deadwood of the pine tree. Gum rosin is the residue in the still after the turpentine has been steam-distilled from the oleoresin made to flow by wounding certain species of the living pine.

Rosin is graded and sold on the basis of color, the paler colors bringing the higher prices. The color grades range from pale yellow, graded X, to dark red (almost black), graded D. The colors between these extremes increase progressively through the grades, WW, WG, N, M, K, I, H, G, F, and E. Because of improved modern methods, about 80 percent of the gum rosin produced is grade M or better. Unrefined wood rosin, as produced directly from the extracting solvent, is ruby red. It is graded FF. The highly colored material obtained in refining wood rosin is no longer classifiable as rosin. It is sold as B resin or under various trade names. (Resin, a general term, refers to a wide variety of natural and synthetic products. Rosin, a specific kind of resin, is obtained only from pine trees.)

The color of gum rosin is due almost entirely to iron contamination and oxidation products. The oleoresin as it exudes from the tree will yield a rosin that is practically colorless. The color of wood rosin is due to the presence of oxidized resin acids and other organic compounds extracted from the wood along with the rosin. The color bodies are most commonly removed from wood rosin by means of selective solvents and by selective adsorption on solid adsorbents, such as fuller's earth.

In the selective-adsorption method, a 10- to 15-percent solution of dark wood rosin in gasoline is pumped up through a bed of fuller's earth. The dark products removed from the rosin solution remain on the fuller's earth. When the fuller's earth becomes saturated, it is washed with alcohol, which removes the colored products. The washed fuller's earth is freed from alcohol and used again. The dark material washed off by the alcohol is known as B resin. Such a method is also suitable for improving the color of gum rosin, but it is much simpler just to keep the color bodies out of gum rosin.

Rosin consists of about 90 percent resin acids and 10 percent neutral matter. Of the resin acids about 90 percent are isomeric with l-abietic acid, whose composition is $C_{20}H_{30}O_2$, (20 parts of carbon, 30 parts of hydrogen, and 2 parts of oxygen). The other 10 percent is dihydroabietic acid, $C_{20}H_{32}O_2$, and dehydroabietic acid, $C_{20}H_{28}O_2$. Although the ultraviolet absorption of the acid portion of pine gum and gum rosin indicates that l-abietic acid may be present to the extent of about 10 percent, this acid has not been isolated from the unisomerized resin acids. About half the total resin acids in rosin can be converted to l-abietic acid by acid or heat isomerization. The neutral portion of rosin has not been thoroughly investigated, but it has been shown to contain methyl chavicole, stilbene derivatives, terpene dimers, aldehydes, and a mixture of hydrophenanthrene hydrocarbons, all of them plasticizers for the resin acids.

The United States produces more than a billion pounds of rosin a year, or about 72 percent of the total world production. In 1949, we exported 306 million pounds of rosin, valued at 20 million dollars. Rosin for export is packaged in drums holding about 500 pounds each. Rosin for domestic consumption is packaged in 500-pound drums and in paper bags holding 100 pounds each. For many large consumers rosin is shipped in the molten state in railroad tank cars.

About three-fourths of the rosin used here goes into varnishes, lacquers, and other protective coatings, and into paper and soap. Each of several other industries—rubber, linoleum, grease, adhesive, and the foundry-supply—accounts for 1 to 3 percent of the total domestic consumption.

A varnish is usually prepared by heating a drying oil and a resin together until the desired amount of polymerization, or combining of the molecules, of the drying oil has taken place. When the mixture has reached the proper consistency it is thinned to a satisfactory viscosity with a volatile solvent. A wide variety of resins may be used, rosin being a common one. To convert rosin into a desirable varnish resin, it is necessary to raise its melting point and lower its acidity. This is usually done by converting the rosin to one of its derivatives—generally as a separate step in the process. Some rosin esters, however, may be prepared during the cooking of the varnish. In that case, the rosin, drying oil, and polyhydric alcohol are heated together until the esterification of the rosin and polymerization of the oil are complete.

The rosin derivatives most commonly used as the resin in varnish are the esters, including the maleic-modified esters; rosin phenol-formaldehyde resins; limed rosins; zinc resinates; and various combinations of these classes of derivatives. Rosin may also be hydrogenated, dehydrogenated, disproportionated, or polymerized to obtain derivatives more suitable for use in varnish than the original rosin.

The rosin esters most commonly used in varnish are the glycerol and the pentaerythritol esters. The glycerol ester, commonly called ester gum, has the better solubility characteristics; the pentaerythritol has the higher melting point. If maleic anydride is reacted with the rosin before esterification, the modified rosin will have a higher melting point and will react more rapidly with the glycerol or pentaerythritol. While rosin will react with 25 percent of its weight of maleic anyhdride, 10 to 15 percent is much more commonly used.

Rosin is combined with a heat-reactive phenol-formaldehyde resin to give a widely used varnish resin having much more desirable properties than either the rosin or the phenol-formaldehyde alone. The properties of these resins vary with the ratio of phenol and formaldehyde to rosin and with the type of phenol derivative used. The resin obtained by this reaction is usually esterified with glycerol to give a varnish resin with a low acid number and high melting point. The development of these resins has made possible the rapid-drying (4-hour) varnishes.

One of the simplest methods of forming a derivative suitable for use in varnish is to combine the rosin with a small amount of lime. The melting point and acid number of this limed rosin can be controlled (within certain limits) by varying the amount of lime used. The rosin may be limed in the presence of drying oil, so that the varnish is prepared in a single step.

Zinc resinate resembles limed rosin in that the rosin has been reacted with a metal oxide or salt to reduce the acidity and raise the melting point. Zinc resinates are more difficult to prepare, but they have several advantages, including greater resistance to water.

Some rosin derivatives have uses in paints and varnishes other than serving as a resin. Certain metal resinates are used as driers, which act as catalysts. For a drying-oil film to harden within a reasonable time, a small amount of drier has to be present. The most commonly used driers are the oil-soluble salts of cobalt, lead, and manganese, generally the resinate, naphthenate, and linoleate salts. The resinates may be prepared by the addition of the metal oxide, hydroxide, or acetate to molten rosin, or by the precipitation of the metal resinate from an aqueous solution of sodium resinate with a water-soluble salt of the desired metal. The products prepared by the first method are known as fused resinates; those prepared by the second, as precipitated resinates. The fused resinates contain less metal but have better solubilities in the varnish solvents. The precipitated resinates, being in a fine state of subdivision, are more difficult to store since they are readily damaged by oxidation.

Unmodified rosin is preferred for other uses. Because of its excellent solubility it may be mixed with poorly soluble resins to make possible their use in formulations in which they would not otherwise be satisfactory.

Another use for rosin in varnish is to retard gelation of certain highly reactive drying oils. For example, one difficulty in preparing varnishes from tung oil is the rapidity with which this oil polymerizes into an insoluble gel. The use of rosin as the resin greatly retards the rate of gelation of tung oil, thus facilitating processing and improving the quality of the varnish. If the tung oil has already gelled, rosin may also serve as a peptizing, or solubilizing, agent.

The use of rosin and a wide variety of its derivatives in printing ink closely parallels their use in ordinary varnish, since a printing ink is essentially a varnish having a high resin and a high pigment content with little or no thinner.

Present-day lacquers consist largely of cellulose derivatives, resins, plasticizers, and solvents. The cellulose derivatives, usually cellulose nitrate or acetate, are the film-forming materials, but they lack adhesion, gloss, and workable viscosity. For instance, the viscosity of a solution containing 20 percent nitrocellulose would be so great that it would be unworkable for application purposes. Viscosity characteristics are improved by use of various natural and synthetic resins, rosin esters, rosin-modified phenolics, and maleic-modified rosin esters. A 20-percent solution of ester gum has a very low viscosity in lacquer solvents and when mixed with a like concentration of nitrocellulose in similar solvents it gives satisfactory viscosity. Because both the nitrocellulose and the resin are usually too brittle to form satisfactory films, a plasticizer is required. The methyl ester of rosin and other low-melting rosin esters are often used for that purpose.

Paper is sized to reduce its penetration by liquids. Numerous sizing agents are used, of which rosin is one of the most important. Rosin size represents the greatest use of a single derivative of rosin—the greater amount consumed by the protective-coating industry is in the form of numerous derivatives whose end uses are difficult to trace. The size is usually added to the pulp in the beater. Here rosin size is precipitated by adding 1 to 2 parts of alum for each part of rosin. The amount of rosin required for sizing varies with the type of pulp and grade of paper manufactured, from as little as 0.2 to 2 percent on regular grades up to 8 percent on special types of paper.

Combinations of rosin with wax, with casein or soy protein, or with glue are also used for sizing. Maleic-modified rosin is said to have much greater sizing power than rosin. One pound of modified-rosin size can do the work of about 4 pounds of ordinary rosin size.

In preparing rosin size, the rosin is usually cooked for a few hours with a sodium carbonate solution. Ordinarily only enough alkali to neutralize from one-third to three-fourths of the rosin is used, so as to yield a product that will remain emulsified when it is diluted. The finished size contains from 40 to 60 percent water. Other methods of preparation are sometimes used. For example, B wood resin, which has a high neutral content, may be completely neutralized with sodium hydroxide, and the neutralized size extracted with a hydrocarbon solvent to remove the portion of the rosin that did not react with the sodium hydroxide.

Rosin is used in a wide variety of soaps. Rosin soaps are much more soluble in water than are the ordinary fatty acid soaps. Soaps with a fairly high rosin content, therefore, are particularly useful in liquid soap. Laundry soaps and soap powders may be prepared from blends of fatty acids, rosin, and other components in minor amounts. Rosin improves the sudsing, the detergency, and the wetting rate of the soap. Rosin soaps also have germicidal activity.

Soaps composed entirely of sodium or potassium rosinate find specialized uses. A stabilized rosin soap, for example, serves as an emulsifying agent in the emulsion polymerization of butadiene and styrene for the manufacture of synthetic rubber. In fact, this type of rosin soap is used as the emulsifying agent in about one-third of all synthetic rubber now being produced. Because of its good solubility in water, this soap is especially effective in the low-temperature polymerization of butadiene and styrene. Rosin used for this soap should contain less than 1 percent abietic-type acids and should be free of inhibitors which retard the rate of polymerization.

Another advantage of using rosin soap in the emulsion-polymerization step in the preparation of synthetic rubber is that the rosin serves a dual purpose. The polymer is coagulated by the addition of salt and acid, the acid decomposes the soap, and practically all of the rosin used remains in the rubber to act as a softener.

Rosin soap is used in the polymerization of synthetic rubber. Rosin is used as a softening agent or plasticizer in both natural and synthetic rubber. A softener is usually included when the compounding ingredients, such as carbon black, sulfur, zinc oxide, and accelerators, are being mixed with the raw rubber on the mixing rolls. In natural rubber the softener is usually chosen for its effect on processing or, in some cases, as an extender. In synthetic rubbers the effect on the properties of the compounded product is more important.

Frequently a small amount of terpene solvent is added to rosin used for this purpose. Both the rosin and the terpenes impart tack (a property in which the early synthetic rubbers were noticeably deficient) to the finished product.

Because of its peptizing or solubilizing action on gelled oils, rosin finds use in the preparation of linoleum and linoleum-type floor coverings. Since color is not of great importance here, the darker grades of rosin are commonly used.

A mixture consisting of about 20 percent rosin and 80 percent drying oils, with a small amount of oil-soluble salts of cobalt, manganese, and lead, is blown for about 15 hours. The mixture is thus converted into a rubbery plastic substance known as cement. The cement is used as a binder for the linoleum sheet. It is mixed with pigments and ground cork or wood flour and then passed between heavy rolls to form sheets on a woven or felted fabric base. These sheets must be seasoned. This is done by hanging them in large ovens at 150° to 200° F. for 1 to 10 weeks, depending on thickness.

Most of the rosin used in lubricating greases is in the form of rosin oil, a derivative prepared by the destructive distillation of rosin. It is a viscous liquid consisting of a mixture of resin acids, decarboxylation products of the various resin acids, and other acid and neutral pyrolysis products. Rosin oil is particularly useful in the preparation of lubricating grease by the "cold set" process. In this process the grease is prepared at a relatively low temperature (usually about 120° F.) by mixing mineral oil and a rosin oil with an emulsion of lime and water. This mixture sets up into a gel quickly.

Both rosin and rosin oil are also used

in the more common type of lubricating grease, which is essentially a gel prepared by dissolving a soap (usually of a heavy metal or alkaline earth) in a lubricating oil and allowing the solution to cool. In this type of grease, however, the fatty acid soaps are more common than those of rosin or rosin oil.

A wide variety of formulations of rosin and its derivatives enter numerous types of adhesives. They are particularly acceptable in the field of pressure-sensitive adhesives. Rosin, rubber, and a plasticizer, such as methyl abietate, in combination, make an excellent adhesive of this kind. The backing may be cellophane, paper, cloth, or metal foil, depending upon the intended use of the adhesive. Some other low-melting rosin derivatives used are abietyl alcohol, monoethylene and diethylene glycol esters of rosin, ester gum, and similar derivatives of hydrogenated, dehydrogenated, and the polymerized rosin.

Rosin is used frequently as a bonding agent to strengthen the sand cores of molds in preparing steel castings.

Most steel castings are made in sand molds which use a special type of sand or sand blended with other refractory materials. The interior surfaces of the castings are generally formed by sand cores, which may be formed by the pattern itself or may be made in a core box from special core-sand mixtures. Cores made in core boxes are baked and inserted in the mold after the pattern has been withdrawn. To give the molding sand the strength it requires to hold its form, various bonding agents are used. The darker grades of rosin are commonly used for this purpose. The highly oxidized portion obtained in refining FF wood rosin is particularly well adapted to this use.

The foregoing uses account for about 90 percent of the total rosin consumption. The innumerable minor uses for rosin and rosin derivatives range from violin bows to preparations for dehairing hogs. Rosin and rosin derivatives are used in leather dressings and shoe polishes, belting adhesives and belt dressings, sealing wax, shoemaker's wax, soldering flux, and disinfectant and insecticide compositions, as a filler for bending pipe and copper tubing, and to harden candles.

Rosin is one of the few agricultural products that is not used primarily for food, clothing, and shelter. It is used almost entirely in manufacturing. With the increasing recognition of the chemical nature of the products manufactured from rosin there is an increased demand for specialized chemical products. In the past, rosin has been used without further modification, but with the increasingly rigid requirements and specific needs, improved rosin and rosin derivatives will be needed. This presents a challenge to naval stores producers—and an opportunity.

RAY V. LAWRENCE *has been engaged in naval stores research since 1938. A graduate of the University of Alabama and the University of Tennessee, he is a member of the naval stores research division of the Bureau of Agricultural and Industrial Chemistry.*

ABOUT HALF of today's commercial production of rosin comes from pine stumps that have been in the ground for half a century. One naval stores processor has recovered rosin from the ground itself—from a "rosin mine" in South Carolina. It is not a natural formation, of course. It is the result of supply and demand a century ago, when gum turpentine was in great demand, but rosin was not. The half ton of rosin produced with every barrel of turpentine that was distilled and collected was allowed to flow into some nearby gully, where it solidified and remained unchanged through the years. Today the market for rosin has increased, while industrial uses for turpentine have decreased.—*E. P. Waite, Southern Regional Research Laboratory.*

WASTE NOT, WANT NOT

Using Residues

To Conserve

Resources

S. I. Aronovsky, L. E. Schniepp,
Elbert C. Lathrop

The industrial market for our agricultural residues today is comparatively small. The reason is plausible: We have been able to obtain our industrial raw materials with greater ease and economy by using what most of us have considered as unlimited natural resources. But when we calculate our assets and attempt to write off the enormous destruction and waste of two great wars, we are brought up sharply.

Many of our natural resources and raw material supplies have been reduced alarmingly. We now are at the point where utilization of low-grade and formerly wasted raw materials is essential. Agricultural residues, overlooked and wasted, are in this category. Some industries have already pointed the way to greatly extended use of such materials.

Some natural resources, like wood, require many years for replenishment. Countless centuries are needed to produce coal and petroleum. But agricultural residues are renewed annually in the production of food, feed, and fiber. The increase in those crops, stimulated by population growth, economic factors, and better farming, has greatly increased production of the residues. Progress also has been made in methods and equipment for harvesting, collect-

ing, and storing them. The laboratories of the Department of Agriculture, the State agricultural experiment stations, and industrial and private research organizations are rapidly developing new processes for residues and new products from them.

AGRICULTURAL RESIDUES are the materials that remain after the desired grain, seed, fruit, or primary fiber has been removed from a plant. They include straws, stalks, stems, hulls, cobs, nutshells and fruit pits, and bagasse. Weeds, reeds, uncultivated grasses, and other vegetation on unused or abused land can be considered residues because the problems of their utilization are the same.

Agricultural residues, because of their variety and because they are part of so many crops, are present in practically every section of this country. They are in greatest concentration, however, where cotton, corn, and wheat grow. We estimate that 230 to 260 million tons of residues on a dry basis are produced each year. Probably half of the tonnage is available for industrial utilization, mainly because it is in heavy producing areas or because its harvesting and collection can be carried on economically. Its use to the farmer ranges from that of low-grade fuel to filler in feeds.

To get an idea of relative amounts, compare the tonnage of residues (say, 250 million tons) with figures for some other natural products. The total growth of timber for 1944 was reported as 13.7 billion cubic feet, equivalent to approximately 218 million tons of dry material. About 592 million tons of coal was produced in 1946. The production of petroleum amounted to 1,733 million barrels, equivalent to 291 million tons. The average annual consumption of food in the United States is approximately 110 million tons—not more than 55 million tons on a dry basis.

Straws from small grains and the byproducts of the corn plant make up most of our agricultural residues. Most important, from the standpoint of tonnage, high concentration in a few relatively small areas, present industrial usage, and possibilities, is wheat straw. About 90 percent of the 95 million tons of wheat straw produced in the United States in 1947 was grown in the North Central States of Ohio, Indiana, Illinois, Michigan, Minnesota; the Great Plains States of North Dakota, South Dakota, Nebraska, Kansas; the Southwest States of Oklahoma and Texas; and the Mountain and Pacific States of Colorado, Montana, Idaho, Washington, and Oregon.

Cornstalks are also produced in large quantities in a relatively limited area, but their use on an industrial scale awaits the solution of several economic and technological problems. Cotton stalks, produced in fairly large amounts in the South, have found no industrial use as yet. The next residue in point of volume, corncobs, is finding increasing usage in industry. Of the other agricultural residues, only seed and grain hulls, nutshells, and sugarcane bagasse have found a place in commerce.

Before discussing the economics and technology of the utilization of agricultural residues, we must stress that if a residue is needed on the farm that is where it should be used. Only when residues are surplus to the needs of the farm should they be sold. Dairy farms or others requiring an abundance of litter should retain the residues that suit their needs. Soils that require the crop residues for fertility should receive them or suitable substitutes.

Using the residues as litter or returning them to the soil would not necessarily be the best practice on all farms.

Each soil has its own characteristics. Each farm has its own problems of management, production, and economics. The treatment suitable for one farm or soil might not do for another. For instance, instead of returning dry straw to the soil, it might be better, from the standpoint of monetary profit to the farmer and of benefit to the soil, to sell it and plow a legume crop back into the land. The farmer must determine which improvements and changes in farm practices will net him the largest return on his investment and labor and, at the same time, improve (or at least not reduce) productivity.

Before the residues can become commodities in an industrial market they must be collected, packaged for transportation, storage, and handling, and, in many instances, preserved against the elements and microbial attack during storage. To be suitable for industrial use, also, the residues generally have to be stored and preserved for long periods, because the seasons for harvesting and collecting them are relatively short and the economical operation of most industrial plants involves running practically continuously throughout the year—all this, of course, at a cost low enough to meet competition from other raw materials.

Some residues can be handled to meet those conditions fairly well. Sugarcane bagasse, a byproduct of the sugar mill, where the juice is extracted from the cane, is concentrated at the mill. The cost of collecting the cane and bringing it to the processing plant is borne by the mill. Heavy-duty stationary balers produce compact bales for economical handling and transportation to the processing plant, where they are piled in large stacks or ricks. Specially developed methods keep to a minimum the losses that otherwise would occur in storing the moist or wet bagasse for periods up to a year.

Corncobs, seed and grain hulls, and nutshells also are concentrated at the hulling or shelling plants, where the main crop materials are removed and processed. Their transportation is somewhat more difficult than that of bagasse, because their relatively low densities make them more bulky.

Corn, cotton, and soybean stalks pose a different problem. They are generally left in the field after the crop has been harvested. No practical, economical methods have been developed for collecting, baling, and preserving them. Until we have such methods, the possibilities of using the stalks and stems for industrial purposes are not very promising. Before the mechanical corn picker came into general use, some cornstalks were harvested for use in the production of insulating board. The stalks were collected when the ground was frozen and after the leaves had blown away. They were then relatively dry. But when mechanical corn pickers came into use, the stalks were broken, so that it was no longer possible to procure them relatively clean or to collect them economically. The board mill that formerly used cornstalks is now using other raw materials.

When the binder-thresher method of harvesting small grain was in general use, the straw was piled in large stacks, from which it was baled with stationary balers. In combine harvesting, however, the straw is left on the ground and can be collected and baled economically only with pick-up balers. During the time the combine was displacing the binder and thresher in the small-grain areas, the manufacture of equipment for picking up the straw lagged far behind. Consequently, an apparent shortage of commercial straw developed, despite the greater production of small grains.

The strawboard industry, which requires 400,000 to 600,000 tons of straw annually and is concentrated in Ohio, Michigan, Indiana, and Illinois (with one mill each in Iowa and Kansas) had to go as far north as North Dakota, as far south as Texas, and as far west as Colorado to get enough baled straw during the Second World War. To relieve the situation—the result of a lack of coordination between strawboard

mills and farmers and of a shortage in pick-up baling equipment—the Northern Regional Research Laboratory arranged meetings at the Laboratory between the strawboard and farm-equipment industries. A cooperative campaign was launched to inform farmers of the situation and a possible remedy. Suppliers of straw were advised about available markets, the quality of the straw required for industrial use, the best methods and techniques for gathering and baling it, and how to handle the mechanical equipment involved. The effort was successful. Most of the mills reported in 1949 that they obtained their straw within a radius of 75 miles; a large part of it came from areas less than 25 miles distant.

The relatively short harvesting season makes it necessary to store a large proportion of the straw for industrial use for most of the year. For instance, a 100-ton-per-day strawboard mill uses about 150 tons of straw a day, or 45,000 tons a year. Assuming a month for harvesting, collecting, and baling the straw, all but one-twelfth, or about 41,000 tons, must be stored on the farm or at the mill. Unless the straw is protected from rain, snow, and microorganisms, some material is sure to be lost. Building a permanent cover for such large stacks is neither practical nor economical. Portable covering—for example, metal plates, tarpaulins, or heavy paper—are not entirely satisfactory, and the upkeep is fairly high. That problem was solved in 1948 through commercial-scale cooperative experiments by the Northern Laboratory, the strawboard industry, and several manufacturers of preservative chemicals. Dusting or spraying borax over the top layer and on the upper surface of the second layer of bales in the rick prevented rotting of the straw almost entirely.

THE STRAWS, stalks, cobs, and so on are unlike in physical appearance. Nearly all, however, are composed of cellulosic fiber. They differ mainly in the length and thickness of fiber and in the way the individual fibers are assembled. The residues are alike in chemical composition. Practically all of them contain cellulose, hemicelluloses, and lignin as the main constituents. The differences from the chemical standpoint are mainly due to variations in the proportions of their chemical constituents.

Their physical forms and structures determine largely their suitabilities for use in industrial products. The straws and stalks, which contain relatively long fibers, are more or less suitable for paper and board. They are also very well adapted for mulching and stock litter and bedding—age-old uses that have developed on the farm because of good absorbency and relative ease of handling with common tools.

The medium short fibered residues (among them woody cotton and soybean stalks, flax shives, hemp hurds, and some of the grain and seed hulls) can also be used in fiberboard manufacture. They are useful mainly as filler fiber, that is, short-fibered material for filling in the meshes formed by the network of long fibers. Thus they aid in producing a more compact, denser board with smoother surfaces.

The fibers of corncobs, nutshells, and the pithy portions of some residues are so exceedingly short that the materials are generally considered unsuitable for most purposes that require matting or felting of the fibers. An exception is the powdered fiber, which can be used as a filler in plastics and glues. The industrial uses of these very short fibered residues depend mostly on their physical structures in the mass—that is, whether they are hard or soft, dense or light, brittle or tough, absorbent or nonabsorbent, and so on.

As the major chemical constituents of the residues are similar in composition and vary only in the proportions in which they are combined in the material, it follows that the choice of residue for chemical processing will depend largely on the concentration of the desired component present. For example, furfural, an industrially important new solvent and synthetic chemical, is produced commercially from corncobs, oat hulls, cottonseed hulls, and rice hulls. These residues contain exceptionally large amounts of pentosans (hemicellulose), from which the furfural is obtained. Similarly, absorbent carbon, or charcoal, is produced preferably from fruit pits and nutshells, which yield products with the desired density.

THE SIMPLEST, and sometimes the most economical, method of disposing of agricultural residues to industry is to sell them directly, in baled or other packaged form, without doing further work on them. They are bulky and generally cost little. Any additional expense for work on them therefore represents a relatively large increase in the cost of the raw material, and might force it out of the competitive market. The cost of farm labor, although somewhat lower than that of industrial labor, would usually be greater per unit of material processed on the farm than for the same unit processed on a large industrial scale with the attendant economies of streamlined, large-scale equipment and operation. For most agricultural residues their sale as raw material direct from the farm appears, therefore, to be the most suitable method for their disposal.

The subject of partial processing on the farm has been discussed for a good many years at meetings and in the press. Some enthusiastic advocates of partial processing have even claimed that chemical semiprocessing is economically feasible on farms or in small rural plants. Careful consideration of the facts involved shows that such processing is neither practical nor economical. Chemical processing generally involves relatively costly chemicals, expensive equipment, and skilled operators. Small-scale, intermittent operation of such processes on farms or in small rural plants would be, therefore, quite impractical and uneconomical. Furthermore, because chemical processing is generally carried on in water or other liquids, any saving in transportation costs by removing extraneous material from the product in partial processing would probably be more than offset by the transportation cost of the additional liquid or by the cost of removing the liquid before shipping the semiprocessed material to the final conversion plant. It is therefore obvious that for such raw materials as agricultural residues, which go into relatively low-priced products, chemical semiprocessing on a small rural scale is entirely out of the question at this time.

Mechanical semiprocessing, on the other hand, is feasible. It is being done successfully in some places. The shelling of corn and peas, the ginning of cotton, and the dehulling of tree nuts are examples of the successful partial processing of the basic crop materials. Corncobs can be crushed or coarsely ground economically on the farm or at the country elevator. Tow can be separated from seed-flax straw in rural decorticating plants. Grinding cobs on a farm of ordinary size, however, is practical only if the grinding equipment, usually a hammer mill, is already available. The cost of a machine for the sole purpose of grinding a small amount of cobs annually would probably make the procedure uneconomical.

Making a finished product from an agricultural residue on a farm or in a small rural plant would probably be impractical. The generally accepted premise that the residues are best suited for the manufacture of low-cost products indicates that only large-scale and highly efficient operations can be successful with these materials. It might be possible, however, to carry on small-scale operations successfully in certain restricted localities where unusual conditions exist. For instance, a process developed at the Northern Laboratory for the production of insulating board entirely from wheat straw might be operated without loss in some of our straw-producing centers to which

transportation charges from the present board mills are prohibitive. Even there, though, the operation would be marginal, economically, unless demand for the products were sufficient to keep the plant going at full capacity.

THE COST of a raw material often determines its suitability for industrial manufacture. Many factors enter into the cost—the price paid for the raw material at its source, baling or other packaging, transportation to the industrial plant, and storage and preservation for processing at a later date. Savings made at any of those stages will be reflected in a higher price for the raw material, or a lower price for the finished product, or both.

Although residues like straw, bagasse, and corncobs are being used in industry, their increased use for the same or different products will depend to a large extent on lowering their cost at the processing plant. That can be done—without reducing the price of the raw material at its source—by better mechanized collection and packaging and by improved storage and preservation methods. Rail-transportation costs can be reduced by more compact and denser packaging of the raw material. Any new plant for processing agricultural residues should be put up as close as possible to the source of the residues, with due consideration, of course, for the other factors necessary for economical plant operation.

MULCHING materials are used to keep the soil porous by preventing compacting by heavy rains, to prevent too rapid moisture evaporation from the soil, and to discourage weeds or other undesirable plant growth. Mulching is practiced in plant nurseries, in gardens, and in orchards. Baled straws and stalks, sold for the purpose, generally do not last more than a season. They are rotted rapidly by the soil micro-organisms under the practically ideal conditions of moisture and temperature prevailing during the growing season.

Larger quantities would be used for mulching if the residues could be made resistant to microbial attack, thus lasting for several seasons. Preliminary experiments at the Northern Laboratory, in cooperation with the Michigan Agricultural Experiment Station, have indicated that wheat straw treated with any of several commercial chemical preservatives has greater resistance to microbial attack. Tests by soaking the treated straw in water indicated that the preservatives will not be leached out readily by heavy rains. The treatment should not be very expensive. Although existing data are insufficient for definite recommendations at this time, the practical possibilities for producing a long-lasting mulch from straw appear to be good.

A FAIRLY LARGE proportion of small-grain straw is used on the farm for litter and bedding. A sizable quantity of baled straw is sold to the railroads, to commercial truckers, to race tracks, and to stock and other farms that do not grow enough for their needs. Railroads and commercial truckers use about 100,000 tons of straw annually for bedding livestock in transit. Race-track requirements probably exceed a half million tons.

Straw is a good litter and bedding material because of its cleanliness, softness, and absorbency. Other residues with similar properties, such as shredded cornstalks, sorghum stalks, and sugarcane bagasse, can also be used for the purpose. Stalks are so used on the farms where they are grown. Baled bagasse, produced in Louisiana and Florida, is too far from the large livestock and dairy centers of this country, and most of the bagasse that is not used for board manufacture, mulch, or poultry litter is burned as fuel in the sugar mills where it is produced. The recent discovery that shredding cornstalks kills the corn borer should mean that more of this baled material will be available for litter and bedding.

Ground corncobs, bagasse, peanut hulls, and flax shives, the woody inner portion of flax straw, are sold for poultry litter. They are ground or cut to a definite size to eliminate the particles that might cause a baby chick or hen to choke. The high absorbency of the corncob makes it an ideal poultry litter.

THE USE of certain residues for cleaning and burnishing metals is increasing. The method was developed early in the Second World War by cooperative efforts of the Northern Laboratory and the Navy. It speeded up the cleaning of the alloy pistons, cylinders, and other relatively soft parts of airplane engines. The residue grits used with ordinary sand-blast equipment removed the carbon, dirt, and grease quickly and completely from the machines without affecting appreciably the dimensional tolerances. The cleaned surface had a satin finish. The soft grits consisted of 60 percent corncob particles (ground to pass a 12-mesh sieve and be retained on a 32-mesh sieve) and 40 percent cracked or whole rice hulls. The method has been extended to engines and other parts of automobiles, soft alloy castings, and various articles of metal alloy. Newer uses are for the cleaning of electric motors and motor generators and for removing the "flash" from small plastic molded articles. It is also effective for removing paint, lacquers, and nonceramic enamels from metal or other fairly hard surfaces.

Nutshells and fruit pits, ground to about the same particle size as the corncobs, are also used for soft-grit cleaning, with and without rice hulls. The nutshells are somewhat harder than the corncob particles and tend to pit the soft metals lightly. Corncobs cut metal least; rice hulls, most.

The Navy used about 500 tons of soft grits during the last year of the Second World War. Several companies were formed to grind nutshells, corncobs, and other residues for various industrial uses. They now produce soft grits to meet the ever-increasing requirements for cleaning.

Another increasing demand for ground residues is for cleaning and polishing metals without the use of an air blast. The metal articles are tumbled with the residues in a drum. Large amounts of residues were used in this way to clean and burnish gunshell casings. The particle size of the ground residue is not critical for this operation, and the softer, finer, and lighter particles may be included. Metal polishing is accomplished in the same way, except that the softer, non-gritty residues are used.

MOST RESIDUES — straws, stalks, cobs, hulls, shells—can be ground to form flours similar to wood flour. Ground to pass an 80-mesh sieve, the residues may be used with various resins to form plastics. The strength properties equal, and sometimes surpass, those of the present commercial articles. Experimental work on plastics at the Northern Laboratory has brought out some interesting facts. Using any one type of resin, we produced stronger plastics with some residue flours than with others. With a different modification of the resin or with another type of resin, however, the effects of the various residues were quite different. The work thus demonstrated that strong plastics can be made from all of the residues by blending a flour with the type of resin best suited for it. We also found that, in using the flours, the amounts of phenolic resin necessary to produce the plastics could be reduced considerably—a fact of great significance in a period of crisis, because phenol, an ingredient of the resin, is a highly critical military material.

Walnut- and pecan-shell flours are already used in commercial plastic molding powders. We expect that the constantly increasing production of plastics will call for more and more flours from residues.

Residue flours serve as filler in resin glues, particularly for plywood. Laboratory tests showed that including the flours saved 25 to 40 percent of the phenolic resin, without reducing the adhesive properties of the glues—they were stronger than the wood itself; when the veneers were pulled apart, the wood split but the glue line remained intact. The flours also increased the water resistance of the glue.

Ground corn meal is used in many soaps, particularly hand soaps, to increase their dirt-removing efficiency. Tests at the Northern Laboratory showed that ground corncobs can replace the corn meal without lowering the cleansing power of the soap to an appreciable extent. Large quantities of ground cobs are being used by hand-soap manufacturers.

Many of the residues are sold for filler in commercial fertilizers.

A number of the residues have been put to industrial uses that are based on their ability to do a particular job. Ground corncobs are used for cleaning furs, because the cobs absorb oil well. They are also used to absorb molasses to produce, with added protein, an excellent stock feed. Rice hulls spread on the red-hot steel plate in rolling mills burn rapidly to a dense ash, which insulates the plate surface and results in more uniform cooling of the metal. Sugarcane-bagasse pith is used as a carrier for nitroglycerin in low-density dynamites. Ground corncobs make excellent sweeping compounds. The corncob pipe is an institution in the United States.

More than 400,000 tons of straw is used in 20 mills in the Middle West each year to produce strawboard for corrugating. Corrugated strawboard is used for protecting glassware, china, and other delicate articles during shipment and for common shipping containers. It is also used in place of wood veneer as the top covering for baskets and other containers for transporting fruits and vegetables. Flat strawboard until recently was the only material used for egg-case fillers and egg separators. Molded separators and egg cartons made from waste paper, however, are rapidly displacing the strawboard articles.

Straw antedates wood by about 50 years as a major raw material for paper, board, and other fiber products in the United States. Since the development of wood-pulping processes in the latter half of the nineteenth century, however, wood pulp has assumed the dominant position in the paper and board field, except for corrugated paper. Wood is even encroaching upon straw in the manufacture of corrugated products; the greatly increased production of fiber shipping containers during and since the Second World War has been based on wood pulp, while strawboard production has remained practically unchanged. All this happened despite the greater potentialities of straw to produce better quality corrugated material because of its larger content of hemicellulose. The reason for the dominance of wood over straw in paper and board production lies simply in the continuous research and development on the technology and economics of collecting and handling wood and of its processing into pulp, paper, and board. The strawboard industry has lagged far behind the wood-pulp and paper industry in this respect.

As we pointed out, however, progress has been made recently in the collection and handling of straw and similar residues. Also, cooperative efforts of the strawboard industry and the Northern Laboratory have already resulted in improvements in the technology of straw-pulp and strawboard production. In a recent project, in which several strawboard mills participated actively by sending collaborators to work in the Laboratory, different chemical methods for pulping straw were developed. The methods, designed for use by the mills with practically no change in their present equipment or the procedures, produced strawboard pulp with decidedly superior strength characteristics. Most of the mills have adapted the better pulping methods to their operations and are producing greatly improved corrugated strawboard.

Late in 1948, the Northern Laboratory perfected a new method—the mechano-chemical process—for pulping straw and other residues. The process, which operates in an open vessel at atmospheric pressure and with the kinds and quantities of chemicals used for pulping under elevated steam pressures, produces good strawboard pulp in 10 to 20 percent of the time required for pressure pulping. Equipment designed to defiber pulp or waste paper, available in most paper and board mills, is used for the process.

The mechano-chemical process is particularly suitable for straw, bagasse, and other residues of the grass family, but it is not well adapted for pulping wood or the woody residues, such as cotton stalks, soybean stalks, hemp hurds, and flax shives. Besides the advantage of drastic reduction in pulping time, the process eliminates the need for pressure vessels, with a consequent lowering of safety hazards and insurance rates. It reduces labor requirements, steam consumption, total equipment costs, and the fixed and other charges per unit of pulp produced. It can be a part of streamlined, push-button operation, a goal toward which the pulp and paper industry is constantly striving. Several commercial-scale, 24- and 48-hour trial runs in two strawboard mills corroborated the results obtained with the laboratory equipment; corrugated paper at least as good as that obtained by the older methods was made. As a matter of fact, mechano-chemical pulping worked better on a large production scale than in the laboratory. The management of one mill approved the change-over to the new process in 1950.

With the increasing demand for fiber containers and with improvements in the quality of strawboard and in its economical production, it may be expected that utilization of straw and similar residues for corrugated board will at least hold its own.

Wheat and rye straws are the preferred raw materials for strawboard. Others (rice, barley, and oat straws;

bagasse; corn, soybean, and cotton stalks; and certain reeds and grasses) were used to eke out when wheat and rye straws were in short industrial supply. They are less satisfactory than wheat and rye straws for various reasons. Rice, barley, and oat straws produce softer papers. Stiffness and resistance to crushing are the two most important requirements for good strawboard. The leafiness of oat and barley straws, which makes them less desirable for strawboard production, makes them more desirable on the farm, particularly for stock feeding. Sugarcane bagasse and cornstalks make good corrugated paper, but the bagasse is too far from existing strawboard mills, and practical, economical methods for handling cornstalks are still lacking. The fibers of soybean and cotton stalks are too short to make strong papers by themselves, and problems in their collection and preservation remain to be solved. One mill farther than the others from the wheat-growing centers uses some flax shives. The more woody residues, such as soybean and cotton stalks, flax shives, and hemp hurds, require more pulping chemicals, with consequently higher production costs.

ABOUT 400,000 tons of seed-flax straw is processed annually to provide the paper for practically all of the cigarettes produced in this country. In 1937, about 10,000 tons was sold to industry for uses other than for paper, and almost all the cigarette paper was imported from Europe. After many experiments with the large variety of domestic fibrous raw materials and with particular attention to collection, an eastern manufacturer found that the tow fiber of seed-flax straw was suited for cigarette paper and fully equal for that purpose to the linen rags used in France. Hemp fiber and ramie (China grass) were also suitable, but they were not available in constant or sufficient supply. Wood and woody fibers do not have the burning characteristics, bland flavor, and other properties required of cigarette paper.

Seed-flax straw is separated into tow (the long bast fiber that forms the outer layers of the straw) and shives (the inner woody portion), by machines especially designed for the purpose. The tow comprises approximately 20 percent of the whole straw. The rough separation, or decortication, is carried out in small rural plants, and the crude tow is sent to a central plant for further cleaning and shipping to paper mills. The shives are used as fuel in the tow mills, and, to some extent, for fiberboard and poultry litter. The large excess of shives is usually burned in the open.

The rapid expansion in the manufacture of domestic cigarette paper, after its start in 1939, satisfied the market in a few years. Manufacturers, looking around for new outlets for their wares, found that excellent airmail, bond, bible, and other high-priced papers can be made from seed-flax tow. The rapidly expanding production of these specialty papers has boosted the collection and processing of straw in the accessible seed-flax areas in Minnesota, the Dakotas, and California. New plantings of seed flax in Texas will make more straw available, and should result in increased production of flax-straw papers.

FINE BLEACHED papers and boards can be made from wheat and rye straws and bagasse. Straw papers and boards are in commercial production in practically all grain-growing countries, except the United States and Canada. The excellent formation, or structure, and surface and printing characteristics of these paper products are due mainly to the inherent properties of the residue fibers, which have higher length to diameter ratios than most wood fibers. In forming a felted web of paper, more fiber-to-fiber contacts are produced per unit area by the relatively short but very thin residue fibers. The result is a more uniform structure of the paper. The longer and thicker wood fibers tend to flocculate in water suspension and form a nonuniform, cloudy paper web. The blending of the two types of fibers, as generally practiced in the residue-pulp-producing countries, gives paper with better all-around properties than can be obtained from either type of fiber alone.

The United States, with probably the largest annual crop of straws and other residues in the world, wastes these materials, except for the relatively small tonnage used for corrugated paper and cigarette paper. Many experiments have been carried out in American paper mills and laboratories on the production of pulp and paper from agricultural residues. The results, however, have been either too meager or too academic to serve as a sound technological and economical basis for commercial operation.

A NEW approach to the problem was developed at the Northern Laboratory. It involves the study of the properties and characteristics of the various agricultural residues and the fundamental differences among them and also between them and other paper-making fibers. Then, by making the most of the particular properties of the residues, it might be possible to establish their rightful place in industry on a utilitarian and economic basis. Following this general plan, a modification of a known process (neutral sulfite) was developed to produce strong, easily bleached pulps from wheat straw in yields 8 to 10 percent higher than had been obtained heretofore. The strength characteristics of the pulp are practically as high, except for tear resistance, as those of bleached softwood sulfite pulp, a major constituent of a large variety of papers. Most of the residue fibers, as well as hardwood fibers, are deficient in tear resistance, which is almost directly proportional to fiber length. The estimated production cost of the straw pulp is about the same as that of competitive chemical wood pulps.

The yields and properties of the pulp have been corroborated by laboratory and large-scale trial runs on wheat and rye straws in the Netherlands, Italy, France, England, and Canada.

A commercial trial on wheat straw was made in a large Canadian pulp and paper mill in 1948. The yield and quality, even under an adverse production schedule, were similar to those obtained in the laboratory. A blend of about 20 percent of the pulp with the regular wood pulps was made into 35 tons of newsprint paper in the regular production schedule on a high-speed paper machine. The paper was then printed on the high-speed presses of a large American daily. Both operations went smoothly. The paper was somewhat smoother and printed a little better than the all-wood pulp newsprint.

This straw pulp could be produced in the present types of alkaline wood-pulp mills with little or no modification of available equipment. For best results, the pulp should be blended with the other paper-making pulps to produce specialty papers and paper products to each of which the pulp would contribute its particular properties to best advantage.

The mechano-chemical process is particularly suitable for making pulps for fine papers. As with corrugating pulps, the time required for producing bleachable pulps from straw is reduced below that required for pulping under pressure. Besides, larger yields of high-quality pulps can be produced by the new process. Many of the economies and improvements discussed in connection with strawboard pulp are possible with the new process.

Commercial production of straw pulps by these two new processes would increase greatly the pulp and paper resources of this country. It also would yield cash returns to farmers for part of the straw now wasted or burned.

The outer fibrous layers and fibrovascular bundles of sugarcane bagasse are also suitable for making fine pulps and papers. A pulp made from them contains a mixture of longer and shorter fibers in the general proportion used for book paper. Whole bagasse, however, contains 20 to 25 percent of the very short fibered pith material. Its presence in the pulp is all right for strawboard, but it should be removed from the bagasse used for the manufacture of fine pulps. The pith increases the over-all cost for cooking, bleaching, and processing the bagasse pulp; relatively large amounts in the paper web weaken the paper.

A practical, economical method for depithing bagasse was worked out in a pilot plant at the Northern Laboratory. The depithed bagasse produced somewhat better pulps, with these two new pulping processes, than was obtained from wheat straw. The separated pith, mixed with blackstrap molasses and a protein concentrate, would make a suitable, economical stock feed. Depithing the bagasse thus results in two raw materials, each having greater industrial value than the original bagasse.

INSULATING AND BUILDING materials were first made from sugarcane bagasse in 1920 in Louisiana. About 500,-000 tons of bagasse is now used for that purpose.

The use of other fibrous residues has declined in competition with wood products, but the use of bagasse for insulating board has increased fairly steadily. One reason probably is that the bagasse is available in large volumes at sugar mills. Another is that the long, tough, springy bagasse fiber bundles produce a rugged, strong, low-density board. It is not possible by known means to produce fiber bundles with similar properties from wood.

Many attempts have been made to produce insulating building board from straws. One mill in the Midwest made straw insulating board for several years before the Second World War. Since then there has been no commercial production of such boards from straw.

The successful use of bagasse for board products and the similarity in the properties between bagasse and wheat-straw fibers led us to fundamental studies for reevaluating straw

for insulating board. We gave chopped wheat straw a mild cook in water and then defibered it in a double-disc attrition mill. The softened, defibered straw was separated into fiber bundles of various lengths by a special wet-screening method. The blending of different amounts of the isolated fiber bundles with the wheat-straw pulp prepared for corrugated strawboard produced an excellent all-straw insulating building board. The experimental product had strength properties superior in many respects to those of wood-fiber boards, and equal to those of bagasse board. The particularly high impact resistance at relatively low densities of the all-straw board indicated its ruggedness, ease in handling, and insulation value.

On the basis of these results and experience in the industry, we developed a detailed plan and equipment lay-out for the commercial production of all-straw insulating building board. The mechano-chemical method of cooking can be used to prepare both types of the required straw fibers. Large-scale operation of this board process seems feasible and economical. The development holds promise for industrial utilization of a considerable tonnage of surplus straw.

Good insulating building board was manufactured from cornstalks in a midwestern mill for about 15 years. It produced up to 50 tons daily. When the use of the mechanical corn picker made the stalks no longer available economically, the mill shifted to waste paper and flax shives as raw materials.

Licorice root has also been used as a raw material for insulating board. For some years hard panel board has been manufactured from sugarcane bagasse in England. A Dutch factory started to make such a board from wheat straw in 1949.

FURFURAL is made most cheaply and easily from such residues as corncobs and hulls of oats, cottonseed, and rice. Furfural is an oily, straw-colored liquid that smells like oil of bitter almonds.

Its uses range from the refining of lubricating oil to the manufacture of nylon. Its history is a typical example of how a one-time curiosity can become the basis for an important chemical industry.

Furfural was first described in 1832, but it was not produced in commercial quantities until 90 years later. Between 1917 and 1924, Department chemists who were investigating possible uses for corncobs found that boiling them with strong acids produced furfural. At that time also a cereal company, seeking uses for its waste oat hulls, hired chemists to study the problem. The chemists found that furfural could be produced in quantity by treating oat hulls with acid and steam under pressure. The furfural was removed from the mixture by steaming and could be easily separated from water and refined. That was the basis of the first commercial process by which furfural was made in 1922. Essentially the same process, with some improvements and better equipment, is in use today.

The uses for furfural were limited in 1922, but its availability stimulated imagination and research. Many of its early uses were later found to be impractical, but many good ones were also found. The demand for furfural has grown steadily. Two large industrial plants, operated by the original producer, now use up nearly 300,000 tons of residues, mainly corncobs, to produce 28,000 to 30,000 tons of furfural a year.

The main uses for furfural are in refining lubricating and Diesel engine oils, vegetable oils, wood rosin, and butadiene, and in manufacturing resins, plastics, and intermediates for numerous chemically derived products. Its unique solvent properties determined its chief uses. In the 1930's, petroleum refiners found that furfural mixed with a lubricating oil could dissolve much of the gum- and tar-forming constituents. This furfural solution separated from the undissolved portion of the oil and could be drawn off. The oil so treated was an improved lubricant for automotive engines. An estimated 60,000 barrels of oil a day was refined by furfural extraction in 1948.

Because of its selective solvent property, furfural is also used to refine wood rosin. The light-colored product thus obtained goes into varnishes. In recent years it has been used in the fractionation of vegetable oils. For example, when soybean oil is mixed with furfural and the oil and furfural layers are separated, the undissolved oil is much better than ordinary soybean oil for making edible fats, such as margarine and shortening. The oil recovered from the furfural solution has good drying properties and is used in paints.

The development of the synthetic-rubber industry brought with it a greatly increased demand for furfural. Several processes were used for making butadiene from petroleum-refinery gases. This butadiene was too impure for direct use in making synthetic rubber, and some of the largest producers found furfural to be an excellent refining agent. In a process known as extractive distillation, furfural separates butadiene from the impurities and makes it suitable for use in the manufacture of synthetic rubber. This use alone made it necessary to build a new plant that produces 12,000 to 15,000 tons of furfural a year.

After many years of research on its chemistry, furfural is now used as a raw material for many chemically derived products. Most important is its conversion into one of the chemical intermediates from which nylon is made. That development, announced in 1947, makes possible the manufacture of nylon hosiery from corncobs.

Furfural also has moved into the field of medicine. Research started in 1940 showed that certain furfural derivatives can kill or retard the growth of many harmful bacteria. One of these germ-killers—Furacin—is made into a water-soluble ointment for treating burns, carbuncles, impetigo, and certain infected surface wounds.

Plastics, similar to Bakelite, and resins for use as bonding agents, surface coatings, and adhesives also are made from furfural. One interesting use of such resins is for cementing abrasives to make grinding wheels. Resins made from furfuryl alcohol, a furfural derivative, harden when they are treated with acids and become acid-resistant. They are used for coating acid-storage tanks, as acid-resistant cements for brick- or tile-lined vessels, and for the manufacture of corrosion-resistant equipment.

Chemical derivatives of furfural are widely useful. Laboratory methods have been developed for converting furfural into intermediates for plasmochin, an antimalarial drug, for thiamine (vitamin B_1), and for lysine, an amino acid essential to good nutrition. Hundreds of other chemical compounds that are potentially useful for plastics, plasticizers, synthetic rubber, solvents, resins, fungicides, and bactericides have been made. The greatly increased research on furfural and its derivatives since 1940 undoubtedly will uncover many more uses.

PECAN SHELLS, particularly the soft inner lining and nut-meat-supporting portion, are a source of tannin. A plant in Texas has used the waste shells to produce tannin extract in tank-car quantities.

Investigations at the Northern Laboratory showed that by control of grinding and screening operations the soft, paperlike portion of pecan shells can be separated readily from the hard, woody outer shell. The separation of the tannin-rich fraction may make extraction of the whole shell unnecessary and improve the economics of the process.

AGRICULTURAL RESIDUES contain, besides cellulose, carbohydrates known as pentosans, in which the residues are much richer than wood. On treatment with acids, pentosans are converted first into a sugar, xylose, which is not fermentable by yeast, but which, on further treatment with acid, is converted into furfural.

Work at the Northern Laboratory showed that under right conditions 85 percent of the pentosans of corncobs can be brought into solution with dilute sulfuric acid, as pentoses. A concentration of 15 percent pentoses can be attained. The residual cellulose can be converted in 65 percent yield to dextrose in a solution of 5 percent concentration. Further work disclosed a method for fermenting the solution of pentoses to butanol, acetone, and alcohol. It is likely that the sugars can be converted to furfural in higher yields than have been possible commercially with solid residues. The dextrose ferments with yeast to alcohol in industrial yields. It is possible to obtain crystalline xylose in 50-percent yields from the pentose solution. It is probable that crystalline dextrose can be obtained in good yields from the dextrose solution. Either the pentoses or dextrose can serve as a medium for the production of fodder yeasts.

The Congress authorized the Department of the Interior in 1944 to undertake an investigation of the production of synthetic liquid fuels from nonpetroleum sources, including products of agriculture and forestry, and to build demonstration plants to evaluate such processes. Preliminary cost estimates of the process for producing sugars from agricultural residues warranted the transfer of funds from the Synthetic Liquid Fuels Investigations of the Department of the Interior to the Department of Agriculture for the construction and operation of a plant at Peoria, Ill., to prove the process. It is an attempt to obtain full utilization of cellulose, hemicellulose, and lignin from residues. The project is directed to a determination of the most practical and economical means for producing the sugar solutions and for converting the pentoses into furfural. Complete manufacturing process and cost data will be obtained, together with engineering design data for a commercial-scale plant.

The Synthetic Liquid Fuels semiworks operation, now under way, is capable of processing 4,400 pounds of agricultural residues in an 8-hour day. As the process is continuous in operation, it is necessary to study each step of the process in turn.

This research is carried on cooperatively with the program of the Northern Laboratory. The sugar solutions produced will be fermented to butanol, acetone, or alcohol in the Laboratory's alcohol pilot plant. The motor fuels produced are under test in its motor fuel testing laboratory. A study of methods for crystallizing xylose and dextrose from their solutions is being undertaken. Uses for lignin, other than as fuel, are being sought.

S. I. ARONOVSKY, *chemical engineer in the Bureau of Agricultural and Industrial Chemistry, is in charge of the pulp and paper section of the agricultural residues division, Northern Regional Research Laboratory.*

L. E. SCHNIEPP, *chemist of the Bureau of Agricultural and Industrial Chemistry, is in charge of the industrial chemicals section of the agricultural residues division, Northern Laboratory.*

ELBERT C. LATHROP, *chemical engineer in the Bureau of Agricultural and Industrial Chemistry, organized and has directed the research of the agricultural residues division at the Northern Laboratory since 1939.*

Annual production of agricultural residues

Residues	Grain or seed per bushel	Dry residue per pound of grain or seed	Dry residue per 1,000 bushels grain or seed	Production of dry residue			
				Average 1935–46	1947	1948	1949
	Pounds	Pounds	Tons	1,000 tons	1,000 tons	1,000 tons	1,000 tons
Wheat straw..................	60	2.3	69.00	61,515	94,336	90,634	79,106
Rye straw...................	56	3.1	86.80	3,373	2,255	2,296	1,623
Oat straw...................	32	1.6	25.60	30,567	30,705	38,229	33,867
Barley straw................	48	1.5	36.00	10,276	10,123	11,372	8,572
Flax straw..................	56	3.0	84.00	2,040	3,405	4,580	3,668
Rice straw..................	45	1.5	33.75	1,949	2,641	2,871	3,009
Total.................				109,720	143,465	149,982	129,845
Corncobs....................	56	0.22	6.16	14,727	13,166	20,954	19,150
Oat hulls...................	32	.30	4.80	5,731	5,757	7,158	6,350
Rice hulls..................	45	.20	4.50	260	352	383	401
Cottonseed hulls.............	32	.21	3.36	1,048	922	1,170	1,275
Peanut shells...............				278	387	415	329
Tree nut shells..............				65	76	92	96
Total.................				22,109	20,660	30,172	27,601
Corn stover.................	56	1.2	33.60	80,331	72,352	114,294	104,456
Soybean stems and pods.......	60	1.2	36.00	4,283	6,529	8,028	8,003
Cotton stems and pods........				15,887	14,979	19,328	20,971
Bagasse fiber, continental U. S..				688	622	784	855
Bagasse fiber, insular U. S.....				2,704	2,707	2,700	2,700
Total.................				103,893	97,189	145,134	136,985
Grand total............				235,722	261,314	325,288	294,431

Making Use of Vegetable Residues

Edward G. Kelley

The job of finding out how to utilize millions of tons of vegetable wastes, which have many of the same food elements as the edible parts, but which mostly serve no good purpose, was turned over to us in 1941.

We began by making a survey at farms and processing plants in the Middle Atlantic States to determine what quantities of wastes are available and when. Starting in early spring in the Philadelphia area, spinach waste is found at fresh-market packing houses and at plants processing canned and frozen products. This waste consists of trimmings, inferior leaves, and field wastes.

Pea vines, the next product available, are most plentiful in June and early July. Beet and carrot tops and broccoli leaf waste are found in the field and at packing houses in summer and fall. Lima bean vines are another big waste in late summer and early fall. Celery tops and trimmings are available in late fall, and again in winter from Florida. Turnip and rutabaga tops and kale can be obtained in fair volume in late fall and early winter. Many other vegetable tissues were available in quantities large enough to warrant further study.

Our survey brought out an all-important fact: Something had to be done with the wastes within a very short time after they were harvested if a desirable end product was to be obtained. There are a number of ways to preserve vegetable tissues and prevent their complete breakdown and spoilage. Perhaps the best known are ensiling, as practiced by farmers the world over for preservation of fresh corn and other fodder; freezing, as used in the vegetable-processing industry; and dehydration. Although ensiling and freezing have not been completely ruled out as practical methods of preservation under certain conditions, dehydration was considered the best bet for preservation of most of the materials under the greatest variety of conditions. Reducing the moisture content of a vegetable tissue to approximately 10 percent will give a stable product, which lends itself readily to further laboratory experimentation and commercial application.

Much work has been done on the composition of the edible portions of vegetables, but little on that of the waste portions. Therefore the logical starting point for our research program was a study of certain of the more valuable ingredients. For the laboratory study we obtained some 80 different dried vegetable tissues by separating them by hand into leaves, petioles, stems, and roots. We then dried them on trays in a stream of heated air.

We analyzed the dried ground tissues for crude protein, crude fiber, ether extractables or crude fat, and the two vitamins, carotene, or provitamin A, and riboflavin, or vitamin B_2. Typical analyses of a number of the products studied, which are presented in the first table, show that leaves are highest in protein, fat, and the vitamins and lowest in crude fiber. Stems are low in protein, fat, and vitamins, and usually higher in fiber.

Because the analyses showed a higher concentration of protein and vitamins in the leaves, it seemed desirable to try

1. Composition of typical dried vegetable tissues

Vegetable tissue fraction	Mois-ture	Proportion of whole top		Chemical analyses (moisture-free basis)				
		Fresh basis	Dry basis	Pro-tein	Crude fiber	Ether extract	Caro-tene	Ribo-flavin
							Parts per million	Parts per million
	Percent	Percent	Percent	Percent	Percent	Percent		
Beet:								
Leaf	90.4	52.6	54.2	27.3	6.0	6.2	568	21.5
Stem	91.0	47.4	45.0	13.6	14.7	1.7	48	7.4
Broccoli:								
Leaf	81.5	36.4	53.7	35.9	7.6	8.5	803	25.6
Petiole and stem	91.0	63.6	46.3	19.0	16.5	3.3	81	8.5
Cabbage, leaf	......	......	......	22.4	8.2	4.7	295	9.9
Carrot:								
Leaf	79.0	51.2	65.1	27.9	10.1	5.6	295	15.7
Stem	88.1	48.8	34.9	11.1	19.3	5.4	41	8.1
Cauliflower:								
Leaf	......	......	......	26.6	9.5	4.1	185	23.2
Petiole	......	......	......	17.1	17.3	......	28	9.2
Celery:								
Leaf	87.0	......	......	27.2	3.5	6.9	352	18.4
Stalk	94.0	......	......	12.6	14.3	3.1	11	5.7
Collard:								
Leaf	......	......	......	27.3	6.8	5.3	251	15.8
Petiole	......	......	......	14.8	9.8	......	28	......
Corn, sweet, leaf	......	......	......	17.1	26.6	5.5	578	5.5
Kale:								
Leaf	77.3	57.5	63.3	29.4	7.6	5.8	340	21.0
Petiole and stem	82.3	42.5	36.7	16.2	10.0	4.2	21	8.0
Lima:								
Bean	61.6	20.8	28.1	23.9	6.0	3.7	3	2.4
Leaf	67.7	15.8	18.0	19.4	10.5	6.4	465	12.4
Pod	77.1	25.8	20.9	10.0	37.8	3.0	14	3.7
Stem	74.3	36.9	33.5	9.2	40.1	2.2	36	3.9
Parsnip:								
Leaf	......	......	......	22.9	8.0	5.0	232	11.9
Stem	......	......	......	6.0	17.2	......	4	4.3
Pea:								
Leaf	65.7	12.3	14.1	21.7	14.4	5.8	346	26.2
Pea	80.1	22.4	19.9	28.8	9.2	1.7	4	7.8
Pod	84.0	35.5	25.2	14.1	18.4	1.2	23	7.8
Stem	67.4	29.9	41.0	11.0	39.2	2.3	47	9.6
Rutabaga:								
Leaf	82.2	36.1	51.4	31.5	6.3	6.5	257	20.9
Stem	90.5	63.6	48.4	18.5	14.9	......	13	8.5
Turnip:								
Leaf	87.3	46.8	61.9	30.9	7.5	4.4	473	20.3
Stem	93.1	53.2	38.2	18.0	10.3	......	54	11.6
Spinach:								
Leaf	90.4	45.1	54.7	32.0	6.8	4.1	314	14.6
Stem	93.5	55.0	45.3	22.5	9.3	......	120	8.5

to work out a method for the best possible separation of the leaves and stems.

This we did by means of a new method, based on the principle of fractional drying. We found that when fresh material was dried in a high-velocity stream of air, at a temperature of approximately 250° F., the thin leaf blades dried more rapidly than the thicker petiole and stem parts of the waste. The dry leaf blade was brittle, and when it was subjected to a breaking and screening action it could easily be separated from the partly wet and tougher stemmy material.

A pilot-plant unit was designed that successfully accomplished the separation of the leafy portions of a number of vegetable wastes. The method was not so successful with pea vines as it was with the wastes having larger leaf surfaces, such as broccoli, kale, and beet and turnip tops. Pea vines could be dried, however, by chopping in a fodder cutter, followed by total drying and hammer milling, with later separation of a leafy fraction by screening. This is the method commonly used in the alfalfa industry for preparing alfalfa leaf and stem meals.

The average yield and composition of leaf meals from various vegetable wastes are shown in the second table.

The yield by the fractional-drying method is much lower than the yield by the total-drying procedure, and the cost of a pound of finished product is higher. The method was designed to produce a leaf meal of highest possible quality, rich in protein and vitamins and low in crude fiber, however, and that has been accomplished. In many cases a greater total yield of a lower-quality product could be obtained by chopping and drying the partly dried stemmy residue. The advisability of using this stemmy fraction would depend upon the economic value of the dried product.

Once the methods for preparing the vegetable leaf meals on a pilot-plant scale had been worked out, we had enough material for studies on their possible value. They appeared to

be promising as a supplement for broiler feeds, because diets high in proteins and vitamins and low in fiber are essential to good growth. At the Delaware Agricultural Experiment Station, we tested a variety of leaf meals under many different conditions to show that they make excellent feed supplements. As can be seen in the third table, preliminary investigations established the fact that at a level of 8 percent most of the meals were better than alfalfa as a green supplement and were not toxic to broiler chicks. The rate of growth, feed consumption, and palatability were satisfactory. Pea vines were less valuable as a supplement than the richer leaf meals, but when they were mixed with lima leaf meal they were entirely satisfactory.

The use of some of the meals of higher carotene content at a level of 8 percent of the diet was wasteful of the carotene, and feeding trials showed that much lower levels of the meals could be used to produce good growth. As little as 1 percent of broccoli leaf meal promotes better growth than 5 percent alfalfa leaf meal, as shown in the fourth table.

In other trials, we found that as much as 30 percent of broccoli leaf meal could be added to a broiler diet with no harmful effects. In one trial the chicks did not gain quite so much weight as those that got less leaf meal, but in a second trial no differences were found except for the color and taste. The meat of chicks that had 30 percent meal was dark, like duck meat, at 12 weeks. Some tasters found no resemblance to a cabbagelike taste or odor; some, but not all, liked the richer taste. The shanks and beaks were a deep orange, much too deep in color to make the birds acceptable for marketing. Anyway, the use of 30 percent leaf meal in a diet would be impractical because of cost. Lower levels, from 1.5 percent up, would give more desirable birds. It is apparent, however, that broccoli leaf meal contains no growth-inhibiting factor.

When we found that the carotene in

2. Average yield and composition of leaf meals from vegetable wastes

Vegetable waste	Mois-ture	Yield [1]	Composition (bone-dry basis)					Yield of wet residue
			Protein	Crude fiber	Ether extract	Carotene	Ribo-flavin	
						Parts per million	Parts per million	
	Percent	Percent	Percent	Percent	Percent			Percent
Beet tops.................	92.0	5.6	29.6	6.2	7.6	460	18.4	5.5
Broccoli....................	88.5	6.6	35.7	6.1	9.5	460	24.7	19.4
Carrot tops................	80.7	9.6	18.0	8.5	5.1	158	10.1	32.0
Lima bean leaves..........	73.8	17.8	21.2	6.9	6.0	297	14.0	8.1
Pea vines.................	81.5	9.7	14.6	18.8	4.1	85	16.8	[2] 10.7
Rhubarb...................	88.6	10.7	27.4	6.8	......	285	7.0	2.4

[1] On basis of fresh material.

[2] Dry residue. Pea vines are totally dried before separation.

3. Results of feeding alfalfa and vegetable leaf meals to chicks

Diet	Analyses of diet				Feeding results				
	Protein	Crude fiber	Ribo-flavin	Carotene as vita-min A	Palata-bility index	Mor-tal-ity	Average weight	Feed ef-ficiency	Pigmen-tation index
	Per-cent	Per-cent	Parts per million	I. U. per pound		Per-cent	Pounds	Pounds	
Basal plus 8 percent of—									
Alfalfa meal.........	20.8	6.5	1,410	4,500	......	11	2.55	4.6	48
Pea vine meal.......	20.0	5.0	1,568	2,200	62	15	2.10	5.1	48
Lima bean vine meal..	19.8	4.4	1,290	9,000	78	7	2.51	4.6	59
Turnip leaf meal.....	20.4	4.5	1,558	21,000	87	11	2.59	4.4	66
Broccoli leaf meal....	21.6	4.3	1,976	26,400	96	9	2.73	4.3	95
Carrot leaf meal......	19.4	5.2	1,430	5,900	93	6	2.65	4.5	53
Control..............	20.2	3.8	1,290	1,100	......	60	1.94	4.7	6

4. Results of feeding low levels of alfalfa and vegetable leaf meals to chicks

Diet	Analysis of diet					Feeding results		
	Protein	Crude fiber	Ether extract	Ribo-flavin	Carotene as vita-min A	Mor-tality	Average weight	Feed effi-ciency
				Parts per million	I. U. per pound			
	Percent	Percent	Percent			Percent	Pounds	Pounds
Basal plus—								
5 percent alfalfa meal..........	21.1	5.65	4.42	1,122	4,244	6.6	2.70	4.31
1 percent broccoli leaf meal.....	20.8	5.47	4.26	919	3,790	7.0	2.84	4.24
1 percent broccoli leaf meal plus crystalline riboflavin........	20.5	5.26	4.45	2,119	4,167	5.2	3.17	3.82
High-quality commercial broiler mash.	24.3	6.57	6.05	1,634	5,911	9.6	3.07	3.84

these leaf meals was an excellent source of vitamin A for poultry, we undertook a test of its activity against vitamin A from fish-liver oil in order to determine its relative economic value. In three feed trials on broiler chicks, standardized amounts of carotene in broccoli leaf meal and in a leaf-meal extract were compared with an equivalent amount of vitamin A ester from fish-liver oil. As shown in the fifth table, growth was better in all groups at 1,500 and 3,000 International Units a pound than at 500 International Units, but even at the lowest level, where a slight difference in efficiency of utilization would be most likely to show, the carotene-fed birds were a little heavier than the chicks fed vitamin A.

In later trials on mature pullets fed exactly equivalent amounts of extracted carotene in oil and vitamin A ester from fish-liver oil, the records of egg laying, fertility, and hatchability showed no significant differences between the groups receiving the two types of vitamin A.

It is apparent that vegetable-leaf carotene, either in the form of the leaf meal or as a concentrate in oil, is just as well utilized, unit for unit, as vitamin A from fish oil by growing chicks and mature poultry.

Although poultry feed offers the best outlet for concentrated feeds like the leaf meals, it is probable that the whole dried waste and dried residues from the preparation of leaf meal might find a use in livestock feeding. A preliminary trial disclosed that whole dried pea vines made a satisfactory feed for sheep. We plan further trials with other livestock.

THE OIL-SOLUBLE FRACTIONS, or lipids, have formed an interesting chapter in the study of the nature of leaf meals. From 3 percent to 10 percent of the meals are soluble in fat solvents, such as petroleum ether and acetone. Fractionation of the ingredients obtained in both analytical and large-scale experiments has led to the separation of many interesting substances.

Besides carotene and tocopherols (vitamin E), the leaf meals are rich in sterols, chlorophyll, and xanthophyll.

The leaf sterols may be valuable precursors for the manufacture of sex hormones and the antiarthritic compounds. Chlorophyll, the green coloring matter of plants, has found use as a therapeutic agent in several commercial products and as a deodorant. Xanthophyll is a deep-orange pigment responsible for the yellow color of chick beaks and shanks when a "green" feed is incorporated in the diet. It is also used as a food color.

We can extract and purify the lipids in a number of ways. The method depends on which constituent is desired in greatest purity. Many organic solvents have been used. Among them are petroleum ethers having boiling points 35° to 59°, 63° to 70°, and 88° to 98° C., respectively, and acetone, chloroform, trichloroethylene, and carbon tetrachloride. In general, acetone has been used to obtain chlorophyll; petroleum ether, whose boiling point is 63° to 70° C., has been used for the rest. Analytical procedures for the determination of carotene, xanthophyll, tocopherols, sterols, and chlorophyll have been worked out.

The object of most of the research on the lipids has been to devise procedures that can be used to obtain the maximum number of constituents, because the value of the leaf meal would be proportional to the number of products that could be prepared from it.

We can get the valuable carotene, xanthophyll, tocopherols, and sterols by extracting with hexane, and precipitating out the phospholipids with cold acetone, followed by evaporation of the hexane filtrate in the presence of a vegetable oil. This vegetable oil can then be fractionated by molecular distillation to give concentrates of carotene, tocopherol, and sterol, as outlined in the sixth table.

The carotene concentrate is a deep-red oil containing 15,000 to 30,000 International Units per gram; it is odor-

5. Relative efficiency of vegetable leaf carotene and fish-liver vitamin A esters in broiler feeding

Diet:	Vitamin A	Average weight at 12 weeks	Feed efficiency at 12 weeks	Mortality
	I. U. per pound	Pounds	Percent	Percent
Basal plus—				
Broccoli and lima bean leaf meal..........	500	2.45	3.72	23.0
	1,500	2.80	3.48	6.5
	3,000	2.92	3.58	6.5
Carotene concentrate.....................	500	2.26	3.80	13.0
	1,500	3.03	3.48	13.0
	3,000	2.81	3.66	10.0
Vitamin A esters......................	500	2.16	3.85	13.0
	1,500	2.72	3.70	3.3
	3,000	2.95	3.47	10.0

6. Results of molecular distillation of vegetable leaf lipids

Fraction	Appearance	Weight	Carotene		Tocopherol		Sterol	
		Grams	Percent	Grams	Percent	Grams	Percent	Grams
Original oil.........	Green oil............	657.0	0.55	3.40	0.57	3.70	1.45	9.50
Distillate at—								
120° C..........	Viscous yellow oil....	3.6	0	0	3.1	.11	6.70	.24
140° C..........	Orange solid.........	9.2	0	0	9.3	.86	26.90	2.48
160° C..........	....do..............	9.7	0	0	12.5	1.22	30.20	2.92
180° C..........	....do..............	11.3	(1)	(1)	8.0	.90	20.00	2.25
200–220° C......	Red oil.............	100.0	1.25	1.25	.42	.42	1.12	1.12
Residue.............	Green oil............	500.0	.18	.90	(1)	(1)	(1)	(1)

[1] Trace.

7. Amino acid content of vegetable leaf meals

[Percentage of amino acid calculated to basis of crude protein (N x 6.25)]

Leaf meal	Protein	Histidine	Arginine	Lysine	Leucine	Isoleucine	Valine	Methionine	Threonine	Phenylalanine	Tryptophane
	Percent	Percent	Percent	Percent	Percent	Percent	Percent	Percent	Pecent	Percent	Percent
Beet.............	24.3	1.3	4.1	5.4	6.4	4.2	5.1	1.7	3.8	5.8	1.2
Broccoli..........	41.0	1.5	4.8	4.5	6.4	3.2	4.5	1.8	3.3	6.0	1.4
Carrot..........	19.6	1.2	4.3	4.5	7.1	4.5	5.5	1.7	4.4	6.5	1.4
Celery..........	23.2	1.5	4.0	2.4	6.8	3.9	4.8	2.2	3.4	4.5	1.3
Corn............	19.4	1.3	3.9	3.2	6.9	3.6	4.8	2.8	3.3	5.4	1.3
Kale............	24.7	1.6	5.1	3.1	6.5	3.4	4.6	.9	3.5	4.4	1.1
Lima bean.......	16.9	1.3	4.2	3.6	6.6	3.6	5.0	1.2	4.0	7.0	1.4
Pea vine........	23.6	1.6	4.6	4.9	7.8	4.4	5.7	1.0	4.4	6.0	1.5
Rhubarb........	26.1	1.9	4.7	5.4	8.4	4.0	5.3	1.0	4.0	6.1	1.6
Spinach.........	25.7	1.3	4.4	4.7	6.8	3.6	5.0	2.3	3.9	4.7	1.1
Turnip..........	23.9	1.4	4.5	3.0	6.8	3.9	4.8	2.2	4.0	5.3	1.3

ess and bland tasting. The tocopherol concentrate contains 10 to 20 percent tocopherol. The sterol concentrate has 20 to 30 percent sterol. Phytol, a medicinal alcohol, can be obtained in pure form from saponified extracts.

The method is suitable for commercial application because industrial-size molecular stills are in present-day use and their efficiency in separating various oil components is even greater than that of the laboratory stills.

Crude chlorophyll can be obtained from the hexane-extracted leaf meal by extraction with acetone. It can be purified by adsorption on bauxite, elution (washing) with methanol, and concentration of the eluate, from which either oil or water-soluble chlorophyll can be made.

Water-soluble sodium copper chlorophyllin, which has come into wide use for the control of body and breath odors, can best be prepared from vegetable leaf meals by extraction of magnesium chlorophyll with acetone or ethyl or isopropyl alcohol, followed by alkaline methanol saponification. Nonsaponifiables can be removed with hexane and the resulting sodium magnesium chlorophyllin can be converted to the acid chlorin-e by acidification to pH 5. Fatty acids can be removed with hexane at this stage and the hydrogen of chlorin-e can be replaced with copper by boiling with copper acetate in acetic acid. The stable, water soluble sodium salt of copper chlorophyllin can then be made by careful treatment of the moist acid copper derivative with sodium hydroxide in aqueous ethanol. The resulting dried product has a purity of 85 to 90 percent.

Proteins are major constituents of the vegetable leaf meals. Their efficient utilization is necessary if the vegetable wastes are to be economically salvaged. A relatively large amount of protein occurs in the leaf meals and a smaller amount in the stem fractions. When the leaf meals are fed as a source of vitamin A and other vitamin factors, the protein forms a small but definite

addition to the protein value of the feed. If markets develop for the lipid constituents of the meals, the plant residue that remains after extraction is a rich source of protein for feed or possible industrial use.

As a feed, the value of the protein depends on its amino acids, because at least 10 of the amino acids are basic elements for building all animal body proteins. Within recent years methods have been developed for the fairly accurate determination of the essential amino acids in crude protein materials such as feeds and vegetable and animal products. The methods are based upon the requirements of certain nonpathogenic bacteria for the various amino acids. By devising synthetic media that contain all but one of the essential amino acids, it is possible to determine quantitatively the amount of any one of 10 acids in an unknown protein solution by comparison with known standards.

The percentages of the 10 essential amino acids found in various leaf meals are listed in the seventh table.

Some degree of purification of the proteins was considered advisable because certain substances which may be present in the crude product are known to interfere with the analyses of the amino acids. Two entirely different methods for separation of nonprotein material were used. Roughly they accomplish the same end, the removal of the large carbohydrate fraction of the vegetable leaf, along with some of the water-soluble sugars and nitrogenous compounds.

Because the solubility of proteins can be greatly altered by drying, we prepared the protein concentrates from fresh or frozen materials. In the first method, the macerated vegetable tissue was fermented with a bacterium known as *Clostridium roseum*. Under the right conditions of temperature and in the absence of oxygen, that organism digests the cell walls of vegetable tissues and leaves the center of the cell relatively intact. This center, known as the protoplast, contains most

8. Average amino acid contents of vegetable leaf meals and vegetable leaf protein concentrates

[Percentage of amino acid calculated to basis of crude protein (N x 6.25)]

	Histidine	Arginine	Lysine	Leucine	Isoleucine	Valine	Methionine	Threonine	Phenylalanine	Tryptophane
	Percent	Percent	Percent	Percent	Percent	Percent	Percent	Percent	Percent	Percent
Leaf meals (7).........	1.5	4.4	4.7	7.1	3.9	5.2	1.5	3.9	6.0	1.4
Leaf protoplasts (5)....	1.9	5.9	5.2	9.1	5.3	6.2	1.6	5.0	7.7	2.0
Formic-acid-extracted protein residues (8)...	1.7	5.4	4.7	8.0	4.6	5.6	1.1	4.1	6.9	.55
Formic-acid-extracted protein hydrolyzates(7)	2.0	5.7	5.5	9.0	5.0	6.3	2.1	4.7	6.8	......
Comparison:										
Purified casein.......	3.1	4.0	7.7	9.9	6.0	7.3	2.8	4.3	6.1	1.2
Purified ovalbumin...	2.2	6.2	6.4	9.1	6.9	7.8	4.4	3.9	8.1	1.2

of the protein and a good deal of lipid material. The solvent extraction of the lipids gives a fairly good concentration of the proteins.

The second method depends on the solubility of proteins in warm formic acid. The vegetable-leaf tissue was frozen to break down the cells, the lipids were extracted with acetone, and the proteins and some carbohydrates were extracted with 90 percent formic acid at 80° C. Most of the carbohydrate could then be precipitated from the final extract with alcohol. The carbohydrate-free protein solution was vacuum-dried, or the amino acids were released by acid hydrolysis for direct determination by the microbiological procedure.

The two products are referred to in the table above as formic-acid-extracted protein residues and formic-acid-extracted protein hydrolyzates.

Instead of presenting the data for each type of leaf, I give the average value in the table for comparison with the average values of the amino acids in the leaf meals. This is justified because of the great similarity of the amino acid contents of the different leaf meals and of the two types of preparations made from the corresponding fresh leaves.

The table shows that the majority of the values found for the amino acids are a little lower in the leaf meals than in the corresponding protoplasts and formic-acid-dried residues and hydrolyzates. In the case of methionine, the value for the leaf meals is from one-half to one-third that in the other preparations. Recovery studies have indicated that methionine is destroyed when carbohydrates in some form are present during acid hydrolysis. The removal of the carbohydrates by fermentation or precipitation allows much greater recovery of the acid. The lower values for the other amino acids in the leaf meals are due probably to the same type of destruction.

If we accept the values found in the protoplasts or formic acid preparations as more nearly correct, it is apparent that those proteins have a nutritionally well-balanced mixture of the 10 essential amino acids and should be entirely suitable as a source of protein.

EDWARD G. KELLEY *is in charge of the vegetable section of the biochemical division in the Eastern Regional Research Laboratory, where, since 1941, he has been associated with all phases of the development of the utilization of vegetable wastes.*

Byproducts as Feed for Livestock

N. R. Ellis, H. R. Bird

Byproducts make up about one-third of the poultry ration and about one-seventh of the ration for growing and fattening swine in the United States. They are also important in feeding beef and dairy cattle. Almost every food industry furnishes some byproducts for animal feed, but the most important sources are the milling of grain, the processing of oilseeds, the fermentation of grains and molasses, the manufacture of dairy products, and the slaughter of meat animals.

The byproduct feeds discussed here have been grouped for convenience according to their origin.

WHEN CEREAL GRAINS are processed for human food, part of the grain is removed and becomes a byproduct, which is used mainly in feeds for animals. Most of the grain byproducts have higher levels of protein, fat, and fiber than do the original grains. Some contain more of certain vitamins. The higher protein, fat, and vitamin contents add to their value. The higher fiber content limits their use in feeds for swine and poultry.

When corn is processed to produce degerminated corn meal or hominy for human food, the byproduct is hominy feed. It contains some of the starchy portion, besides the corn germs and the corn bran, which consists of tip caps and outer layers of the kernels.

From the wet milling of corn to produce starch and glucose, the byproducts are the germ (which is usually separated into oil and meal), the gluten meal (mostly gluten), and the gluten feed (containing both gluten and bran).

The gluten meal and, to a less extent, the gluten feed and the oil meal may be regarded as protein supplements. Gluten meal is comparable to the oilseed meals in protein content. The quality of the protein is generally inferior from the nutritional standpoint to that of the oilseed meals, however. Hominy feed, gluten meal, and gluten feed prepared from yellow corn contain carotenoid pigments, and hence have some vitamin A activity. That is not true of the byproducts from white corn.

Corn-gluten feed, corn-gluten meal, and hominy feed are widely used in livestock feeding, especially for dairy cattle.

Gluten feed also serves as a protein supplement in the fattening of beef cattle and sheep. It is not used extensively in rations of swine, although small amounts may be included with other supplements which contain proteins of high biological value. Gluten meal is fed under much the same conditions as gluten feed and is generally considered somewhat more valuable in keeping with its higher protein content. Hominy feed is generally used as a replacement for part or all of the corn in the rations of livestock. It can also replace grain in poultry rations.

Yellow corn-gluten meal is valued as a constituent of the diet of growing chickens because of its carotenoid pigments and its protein content. The pigments provide vitamin A and give the desirable yellow color to the shanks and skin of chickens.

In the milling of wheat to produce flour, the bran layers that cover the outside of the kernel, the aleurone layer just inside the bran layers, and the germ are removed, together with some of the starch portion, which cannot be readily separated from the other fractions. Wheat bran is the coarsest byproduct, having the highest fiber content. The finer byproducts are standard middlings, flour middlings, wheat red dog (mostly derived from spring wheat), and brown shorts, gray shorts, and white middlings (generally derived from winter wheat). All of them, except red dog and white middlings, are higher in fiber than whole wheat. They also exceed whole wheat in protein, thiamine, riboflavin, niacin, and vitamin E.

The wheat byproducts are among our oldest supplemental feeds. Their place in rations is well established. The byproducts with the higher fiber contents are mostly used for cattle, sheep, and horses; those with lower fiber contents, for swine and poultry. Wheat bran is especially prized as a supplement in the rations of cows and ewes. It has been widely used in feeding horses because of its bulky nature and laxative effects. However, it is considered best to limit the proportion in the feed mixture for horses, or to feed it in large amounts only occasionally. For swine, the various shorts and middlings products, along with wheat red dog, are used most efficiently with tankage, fish meal, and milk byproducts as supplements to corn and other cereal grains. Products like wheat red dog, wheat-flour middlings, and white middlings are useful in the diets of pigs.

All the wheat byproducts mentioned have been widely used in poultry feed, but recently the popularity of low-fiber diets, especially for growing birds, has limited their use. When they are omitted from starting and growing mashes, the addition of synthetic niacin may be necessary.

Oat millfeed, barley feed, and rye feed contain the combined byproduct fractions obtained in the production of oatmeal, pearled barley, and rye flour, respectively. Oat millfeed is high in fiber. The others are similar to the wheat byproducts in composition.

In milling rice for human food, the hulls are first removed, and then the germ and outer layers of the kernel as rice bran. The kernels are polished to remove another fraction known as rice polish, which is much lower in fiber than the bran. Rice bran and rice polish are not so high in protein as are the wheat byproducts, but they are high in fat and become rancid rather readily. They are high in thiamine and niacin, and contain more riboflavin than do whole grains. Buckwheat middlings, obtained in the production of buckwheat flour, are higher in protein than the comparable fractions from wheat.

The principal outlet for oat millfeed is as a feed for cattle, sheep, and horses. As a substitute for part of the grain allowance, it is generally worth somewhat less than half as much as corn and other cereals. In tests with horses doing moderate work, oat millfeed has been used to replace both the hay and the grain portions of the ration.

Barley feed and rye feed are suitable as partial replacements for cereals or other cereal byproducts in rations for cattle, sheep, and swine. In total digestible nutrients, barley feed is at least equal if not superior to barley. The supply of both barley and rye feeds is rather limited, however.

Rice bran is fed to dairy and beef cattle, sheep, and swine. Rice bran and rice polish may be fed to swine only in limited amounts; otherwise, the body fats, or lard, become soft. Large proportions in the diet also tend to produce scours. Rice polish is higher in total digestible nutrients than rice bran, a fact that is worthy of note in feeding cattle and sheep as well as swine. The high content of several of the B vitamins is also noteworthy in the use of the two feeds for swine.

Buckwheat middlings are suitable as both cattle and hog feeds, provided they are used in limited amounts.

None of the byproducts of grains other than corn and wheat has attained more than local importance in poultry feeds, but all except oat mill-feed and rice hulls are used.

AFTER THE FERMENTATION of grain mash to produce alcohol and the removal of the alcohol by distillation, there remains the stillage, which consists of a watery suspension of the unfermentable portions of the grain, together with yeast. The stillage is usually separated by straining into distillers' grains (light grains), which may be fed wet or dry, and solubles.

The concentrated solubles may be added in whole or in part to the grains and dried to form distillers' grains with solubles (dark grains), or they may be dried to form dried distillers' solubles. Because fermentation removes most of the starch but little of the other constituents of the grains, the byproducts are higher in protein, fat, fiber, and several vitamins than are the original grains. Distillers' grains are valued primarily for their protein, although their contents of fat and vitamins add to their value. The solubles have approximately the same protein and fat contents as the grains, but are valued chiefly as a source of riboflavin, pantothenic acid, and niacin.

Three byproducts of the brewing industry are important as feeds—brewers' dried grains, malt sprouts, and brewers' dried yeast.

Brewers' grains are the residue of the barley after digestion and extraction of most of the starch. Malt sprouts are the roots from the sprouting of the barley during the malting process. Brewers' yeast, which is separated from the mixture after fermentation, is valued primarily as a source of riboflavin, niacin, pantothenic acid, and choline. It is also relatively high in protein.

Byproducts are obtained from the bacterial fermentation of grain or molasses to produce acetone and butyl alcohol. They are designated dried-grain (or molasses) fermentation solubles. By definition of the Association of American Feed Control Officials, they

must contain not less than 18 milligrams (about 0.0006 ounce) of riboflavin a pound on the moisture-free basis.

Feeding tests have shown that the distillery byproducts have wide application in the feeding of all classes of livestock. In general, the dried grains and the dried grains with solubles have found their widest use through practical experience in rations for dairy cattle, beef cattle, and sheep.

Although not so high in protein as the oil meals, such as linseed, soybean, and cottonseed, distillers' grains rank well in feeding value. Fed on an equal protein basis, there usually is little choice. Tests by the Nebraska Agricultural Experiment Station, for instance, have shown this to be true in the feeding of soybean meal and distillers' grains to fattening cattle.

Combinations of the two supplements gave indications of some superiority over either one fed alone. The distillery byproducts have had wide use as an ingredient in mixed concentrate feeds for milking cows. Both distillers' solubles and distillers' grains with solubles have been found by the Pennsylvania Agricultural Experiment Station to be excellent ingredients in feed mixtures for calves. In general, the dried grains from corn and wheat have given somewhat better results than the products from rye, presumably because of the higher protein contents.

As a swine feed, distillers' solubles are to be preferred to distillers' grains. Distillers' dried grains with solubles stand between them. The reason is largely explained on the basis of fiber and vitamin content. The proteins, being largely those from the original grains used in the fermentation mashes, are not of so high a quality as those in the animal-protein supplements or in most of the oilseed meals. Distillers' solubles included in the diet at levels of 5 to 10 percent make a significant contribution of vitamin factors to many swine rations, comparable in varying degrees to alfalfa meal, dried whey, and other vitamin-rich supplements.

The product is useful in rations for growing and fattening pigs and for pregnant and lactating sows.

If adequate supplements of other high-quality protein feeds are included, distillers' solubles and distillers' grains with solubles help make up the protein deficit of corn in the ration.

Brewers' grains are predominantly a cattle feed to be used interchangeably with other feeds of similar type as to bulk and crude-fiber and protein contents. Sometimes they are used as a partial replacement for grains in rations for cattle, sheep, and horses.

Dried malt sprouts are used chiefly in mixed feeds for dairy cattle, frequently along with brewers' grains. Brewers' yeast, being primarily a vitamin-rich supplement, is used in swine rations, in dog, fox, and mink foods, and in poultry feeds. The protein content is high and this contribution to diets is often significant. Brewers' yeast also has been used successfully as a cattle feed.

Dried fermentation solubles and dried distillers' solubles are important sources of riboflavin and other water-soluble vitamins for poultry. Dried brewers' yeast is also used for this purpose and, although it does not furnish riboflavin at as low a cost as the solubles, it has some additional value as a source of choline.

Distillers' grains with solubles contribute protein and vitamins to poultry diets, but their high content of fiber limits their use. Dried fermentation solubles and distillers' solubles sometimes produce a laxative effect if fed as 5 percent or more of the diet, especially if the diet contains other ingredients that tend to be laxative. Ordinarily the levels required to supply riboflavin are well below the laxative level.

THE RESIDUES after the removal of most of the oil from soybeans, cottonseed, flaxseed, and peanuts are known as oilseed meals. They are among the most important sources of protein for livestock. The oil is removed either by hydraulic or screw presses or by extraction with organic solvents. All three methods are in general use for processing soybeans, but solvent extraction has not been widely used for the others.

Soybean meal is the only major protein supplement that has been increasing in supply in recent years. The proteins of soybeans and some other legumes differ from most proteins in that they must be heated for maximum value to nonruminants. The heat may destroy antienzymes known to be present or it may improve the availability of the protein or it may do both. In screw-pressing soybeans, heat is unavoidable, but not in solvent extraction. Extracted soybean meal requires a separate heat treatment. Proper processing of either type of meal gives an excellent feed.

Soybean meal has become the leading protein supplement in recent years for nearly all classes of livestock. It is used interchangeably with linseed meal and cottonseed meal in rations for cattle, both dairy and beef, for sheep, and even for horses and mules. For dairy cattle, many feeders prefer expeller- or hydraulic-produced soybean meal to solvent-process meal in concentrate mixtures otherwise low in fat. Tests with fattening beef cattle generally have not shown a significant difference between meals produced by different processes. On the range, pelleted meals have met with favor because of convenience and economy in feeding.

As a protein supplement to corn in feeding swine, soybean meal has met with wide favor. Pigs on pasture grow and fatten efficiently and rapidly on rations of corn and soybean meal, supplemented with ground limestone and salt. In dry lot, inclusion of ground legume hay and an animal-protein concentrate is generally beneficial. Depending on availability, other oilseed meals, such as cottonseed, linseed, and peanut, can be used as replacements for part and sometimes all of the soybean meal.

The proteins of soybean meal have been thought to be much less effective than those of animal byproducts in supplementing the proteins of grains, at least in diets of nonruminants.

We now know that diets composed mainly of grains and soybean meal are deficient in some previously unknown vitamins that are supplied by animal-protein supplements. Vitamin B_{12} is one of these. It is believed to be the one most often deficient in practical diets for poultry. Its presence makes possible the successful rearing of chickens on diets in which all the protein is of plant origin, most of it being supplied by soybean meal and grains. Care must be taken to see that such diets contain adequate contents of riboflavin, calcium, and phosphorus. The quantities of these nutrients in soybean meal are much less than those in the animal-protein supplements. The other oilseed meals are similar to soybean meal in this respect.

Cottonseed meal, like soybean meal, is heated during processing, but for a different reason. Raw cottonseed contains several compounds that are toxic, at least to nonruminants. The one that has received the most study is gossypol. Proper heating reduces toxicity to the extent that such cottonseed meals can serve as the only protein supplement in diets for swine and growing poultry.

Even the highest quality cottonseed meals are not recommended at present for laying hens because the minute, nontoxic levels of gossypol in the ration cause egg yolks to develop a green color in storage.

The proteins of cottonseed meal are generally supposed to be somewhat inferior to those of properly heated soybean meal and animal-protein supplements. This supposed inferiority may be due in part to inadequate vitamin B_{12} in the diets used and to deterioration of cottonseed protein from the heat required for detoxification. A process of solvent extraction now available removes the toxic portions of the seed mechanically, making heating unnecessary. The resulting meal has superior qualities, but it has not yet been produced commercially.

Linseed meal is valued in the diets of cattle, sheep, and swine, not only as a protein supplement but also for its conditioning, appetite-stimulating, and laxative effects. The protein is perhaps somewhat inferior to that in soybean meal as a supplement to corn in swine rations. Accordingly, linseed meal is used most effectively with other oil meal and animal-protein supplements. In fattening beef cattle and lambs, linseed meal is very popular and is widely used as a supplement, either alone or in combination with other protein supplements, for its protein and conditioning values. Much the same is true for fattening dairy cattle.

Linseed meal is toxic to poultry except in very low proportions. The toxicity can be largely eliminated by soaking the meal in water for 24 hours or by adding pyridoxin, one of the B vitamins, to the diet. The reasons for the effect of the vitamin are not known.

Peanut meal, so far as now known, contains no toxic compounds or anti-enzymes and therefore requires no heating or water treatment. It is palatable to all classes of livestock. It is a valuable protein supplement and is high in niacin and pantothenic acid. In the South especially it is widely used as the principal protein supplement to grain feeds, especially in swine feeding. Its wide use for different classes of livestock in areas where it is available is comparable to that of soybean meal in the North.

The protein of peanut meal has been reported as slightly inferior to that of soybean meal for poultry, but the comparison may have been influenced by vitamin B_{12} deficiency.

Oilseed meals produced in small quantities as agricultural byproducts in this country include sunflower-seed meal, sesame meal, safflower meal, rapeseed meal, and hempseed meal. Coconut meal, largely an imported product, is used extensively in feeding dairy cattle and, to a less extent, beef cattle and lambs.

The more important animal byproducts used in feeds are tankage, meat meal, meat and bone meal, blood meal, bonemeal of several types, liver meal, and liver and glandular meal.

Meat scraps, trimmings, offal, and the rejected carcasses are sometimes cooked with steam under pressure in closed tanks to separate most of the fat. The watery portion is removed, concentrated, and returned to the solid portion, which is then dried and designated as tankage. The alternative process is to remove the fat by dry cooking in an open steam-jacketed vessel to produce meat meal. Products that contain more than 4.4 percent of phosphorus are designated tankage with bonemeal or meat and bone meal. The principal animal-protein supplements used in feeds are the materials mentioned, together with fish meal, which is also a byproduct, though not of agriculture.

These animal byproducts contain proteins that are good sources of the amino acids in which grain proteins are deficient. Hence they have long been used to supplement grain rations. They are also good sources of calcium, phosphorus, and niacin, and variable but fairly good sources of riboflavin and vitamin B_{12}. The presence of each of these nutrients adds to the value of the animal byproducts as supplements.

Meat meal, meat and bone meal, and fish meal are widely used in poultry feeds. Tankage, on the other hand, is used primarily as a swine feed. The levels of these products in individual diets have been decreasing in recent years as the level of soybean meal increased. Under the circumstances, for poultry at least, fish meal has come to be regarded as superior to meat meal, because it more effectively supplements a diet composed largely of grains and oilseed meals. For growth and for reproduction the superiority of fish meal is due to its higher content of vitamin B_{12}.

In swine feeding, tankage and meat meal have long been used as the main supplement to corn. These and other animal-protein supplements remain an integral part of the more dependable rations for young, growing pigs and for the breeding herd.

Blood meal is prepared by heating blood until coagulated, pressing out the excess moisture, and drying and grinding the solid residue. It is higher in protein than any of the previously mentioned animal byproducts, but its protein is generally considered to be of poor quality, even though relatively rich in some of the essential amino acids, maybe because some of it is damaged by heat during processing. It is not a good source of niacin, riboflavin, or vitamin B_{12}.

Bonemeal is called raw if it is cooked in water at atmospheric pressure to remove excess fat and meat, steamed if it is cooked with steam under pressure, and special steamed if it is steamed in the process of obtaining gelatin or glue. Bonemeals are valued primarily for their calcium and phosphorus.

Liver meal and liver and glandular meal are described by their names. By definition the former must contain 27 milligrams of riboflavin per pound and the latter 18. Both are valued especially in poultry feeds, not only for their riboflavin but for their vitamin B_{12} and probably other factors now unknown.

THE MILK BYPRODUCTS include skim milk, buttermilk, and whey, each of which is fed in the liquid, condensed, and dried forms.

Skim milk is the low-fat fraction separated from the cream by centrifugal separators. Buttermilk is the byproduct remaining after butter has been produced from cream by churning. It contains slightly more fat than does skim milk. A little more than one-third of the solids of both consist of protein of high quality. Whey is the byproduct remaining after the making of cheese from milk. It is lower in protein than skim milk and buttermilk. All three contain lactose, a sugar which is readily converted by bacteria into lactic acid. All are fed in both sweet and sour forms.

The liquid milk byproducts are fed

principally on the farms where they are produced. The condensed and dried forms are important commercial feedstuffs. Condensed skim milk and buttermilk contain by definition not less than 27 percent of solids and condensed whey contains not less than 62 percent of solids. Both are valued for their protein and for their riboflavin and other water-soluble vitamins. Large amounts of whey are fermented to increase the riboflavin content. The dried product may be sold as dried whey fermentation solubles if it contains not less than 18 milligrams of riboflavin per pound on the moisture-free basis.

All three dried milk byproducts were formerly used in large amounts in poultry feeds, and dried whey is still an important ingredient. The quantities of dried skim milk and dried buttermilk available for animal feeding have decreased greatly in recent years, and their place has largely been taken by soybean meal, to supply the protein, and fermentation byproducts, to supply the vitamins.

Nutritionists generally agree that decreases in availability of milk byproducts on farms for swine feeding have left a void to be met by greater use of other supplements capable of supplying protein of equal quality, along with vitamin factors contained in milk.

AMONG THE MISCELLANEOUS PLANT BYPRODUCTS are molasses, beet pulp, potatoes, and citrus pulp.

Cane molasses and beet molasses are byproducts from the manufacture of sugar from sugarcane and sugar beets. They are the condensed juices remaining after as much sugar as possible has been removed by concentration and crystallization. Both are low in true protein and high in sugar. Both are laxative, beet molasses more so than cane molasses because of its higher mineral content. Both are used commonly in feeds for cattle and rarely in feeds for swine and poultry. They are valued in cattle rations for their nutrients and palatability.

Another byproduct from the manufacture of sugar from sugar beets is beet pulp, the residue after extraction of the sugar-containing juice. On the dry basis, it is low in protein and fat and high in fiber, but its fiber is well digested by ruminants. It is fed either wet or dry, principally to cattle.

The wastes that result from the production and processing of vegetables for canning, freezing, and dehydration include tops of carrots, turnips, and rutabagas; leaves and stems of broccoli, spinach, and kale; and vines of peas and lima beans.

Bean and pea vines, in the form of silage, have been used as feed for cattle. Otherwise the products have not been widely used in animal feeds, although experiments have shown that dehydrated leaf meals of broccoli, turnip, carrot, and kale, and meals from pea vines and lima bean vines can all be used to advantage in diets for poultry. They would be of value primarily for their vitamin A potency, and secondarily for their riboflavin and protein content, and probably for unknown factors. When used in poultry feeds they would replace wholly or in part the alfalfa meal that is commonly used.

Surplus and cull potatoes make satisfactory animal feeds. They are high in starch and low in fat and fiber. Their protein content, on the basis of dry matter, is comparable to that of the whole grains. They should be cooked before being fed to poultry or swine. They may be fed raw to ruminants, sometimes ensiled with hay or dry corn fodder, but also when fresh, preferably after chopping. Dehydrated potatoes may be a partial substitute for grain in livestock feeds, including those for swine and poultry if the drying temperature is high enough for thorough cooking.

Surplus and cull sweetpotatoes also are dehydrated and used to feed animals. They are low in protein, fat, and fiber, but high in starch and in vitamin A potency. Dehydrated sweetpotatoes may be used as a partial substitute for grain in diets for cattle, sheep, swine, and poultry.

Peel, seeds, and pulp are left in large quantities from the canning of citrus juices and other citrus products. This byproduct, known collectively as citrus pulp, is fed to ruminants, sometimes fresh and sometimes ensiled or dried. The juice may be pressed from the pulp and concentrated to make citrus molasses, which is used at low levels in concentrate mixtures for cattle.

Apple pomace is the byproduct from expressing juice from apples. It may be fed to cattle fresh, as silage, or dry.

Tomato pomace consists of the skins, pulp, and crushed seeds that remain after manufacture of tomato juice. It is high in protein, fat, and fiber, and has been fed successfully to swine in the wet form. Dried tomato pomace is a common constituent of dog foods.

Research on animal nutrition includes a continual search for new byproducts to use in feeds and for better ways of combining byproducts with other feedstuffs into rations that give a better balance of nutrients and thereby improve the efficiency of use of feeds by livestock. Changes in manufacturing methods for producing byproduct feeds may affect the content of specific nutrients and thereby necessitate a reevaluation of the feed and its place in the ration. The search for new feeds becomes more important as byproducts are transferred from the list of feedstuffs to the list of human foods. Thus in the past decade dried skim milk has largely disappeared from animal feeds to become a constituent of human foods where it commands a higher price.

Cost is important in determining the value of a byproduct in animal feeding. Assembly costs are nearly always borne by the primary product. Sometimes there is no practicable means of disposing of the byproduct except by processing, and then even the costs of processing are charged to the primary product.

The list of byproduct feeds has increased year by year. The identification and classification of the new feeds is an important item in their marketing and use. For the past 40 years the Association of American Feed Control Officials has been describing and defining feeds. The terminology adopted by the association, which is followed generally by the feed industry and by users of the products, is used here.

The byproduct feeds defined by the association include many not discussed here. Some are derived from nonagricultural sources, such as whale meal, crab meal, and fish solubles. Others are derived from agriculture but are too new to warrant consideration here.

Among them are ramie leaf meal, the poultry byproduct meal, extracted penicillin meal, extracted streptomyces meal, dried milk albumin, and dried torula yeast. Each year new byproducts resulting from research and technological development are defined and described by the association, become available to feed manufacturers and feeders, and make their contribution to an efficient livestock industry. Increased use of byproducts reduces costs of animal production and the competition of livestock with humans for our food supply.

N. R. ELLIS *is assistant chief of the animal husbandry division, and in charge of the section of animal nutrition investigations of the Bureau of Animal Industry. He has been with this Bureau since 1920. His research activities include biochemistry investigations on animal fats and on animal feedstuffs and nutrition studies on farm animals dealing with mineral, vitamin, and protein nutrients.*

H. R. BIRD *received his doctor's degree in biochemistry from the University of Wisconsin in 1938. He was associate professor of poultry nutrition at the University of Maryland from 1938 until 1944, when he was appointed biochemist in charge of poultry nutrition investigations in the Bureau of Animal Industry. Since 1948 he has been in charge of poultry investigations in that Bureau.*

The composition of byproduct feedstuffs

Cereal-grain byproducts

Feedstuffs	Moisture Percent	Crude protein Percent	Ether extract Percent	Crude fiber Percent	Ash Percent	Nitrogen-free extract Percent	Calcium Percent	Phosphorus Percent	Carotene mg/lb.	Thiamine mg/lb.	Riboflavin mg/lb.	Niacin mg/lb.	Pantothenic acid mg/lb.	Choline mg/lb.
Barley feed	7.9	15.0	4.0	13.7	4.9	54.5	0.03	0.41	0.2	.....	.....	.....	.....	.....
Buckwheat middlings	12.4	28.0	6.6	5.3	4.6	43.1	.....	.....	.....	.....	.....	.....	.....	.....
Corn bran	10.0	10.0	6.6	8.8	2.1	62.5	.03	.14	.....	2.0	6.8	.....	.....	.....
Corn-germ meal	7.0	20.8	9.6	7.3	3.8	51.5	.05	.59	.....	8.2	1.6	14.1	5.0	726
Corn-gluten meal (yellow)	8.0	43.0	2.7	3.7	2.2	40.4	.10	.47	10.0	.....	1.1	13.6	6.3	.....
Corn-gluten feed (yellow)	9.5	27.6	3.0	7.5	6.0	46.4	.11	.78	1.1	.5	2.5	39.9	.....	.....
Corn-oil meal	8.7	22.1	6.8	10.8	2.2	49.4	.06	.62	.2	9.1	3.0	20.4	1.2	.....
Hominy feed (yellow)	9.5	11.2	8.3	6.3	2.9	61.8	.03	.44	.....	.....	6.8	8.0	.....	.....
Oat hulls	5.8	4.3	1.9	30.8	6.5	50.7	.09	.12	.....	.5	1.2	.....	.....	.....
Oatmeal	8.9	16.5	4.8	3.6	2.3	63.9	.08	.43	.....	2.2	.5	7.0	5.0	685
Oat millfeed	6.9	6.3	2.2	27.9	6.0	50.7	.20	.22	.....	.....	.....	.....	17.9	.....
Rice bran	8.8	12.8	13.8	12.2	12.2	40.2	.10	1.84	.....	10.4	1.4	163.0	.....	.....
Rice hulls	6.5	2.1	.4	44.8	21.9	24.3	.08	.06	.....	.5	.....	.....	.....	.....
Rice polish	10.0	12.4	13.2	2.8	7.6	54.0	.03	1.52	.....	9.1	9.5	235.0	46.0	572
Rye feed	10.2	15.6	3.2	4.3	4.0	62.7	.....	.....	.....	.....	.....	.....	.....	.....
Rye middlings	9.5	16.7	3.7	5.5	4.4	60.2	.....	.59	.....	1.5	1.0	7.8	10.5	.....
Sorghum-gluten feed	9.1	25.2	3.8	7.1	7.3	47.5	.....	.....	.....	.....	.....	.....	.....	.....
Sorghum-gluten meal	8.6	41.0	4.9	3.3	2.5	39.7	.....	.....	.....	.....	.....	.....	.....	.....
Wheat bran	9.4	16.4	4.4	9.9	6.4	53.5	.10	1.14	1.1	3.6	1.2	126.5	13.2	648
Wheat-flour middlings	10.4	18.8	4.0	4.2	3.3	59.3	.09	.80	.....	6.0	.8	42.4	4.5	.....
Wheat germ	9.5	31.9	9.1	3.3	5.2	41.0	.....	.83	.....	11.4	2.3	27.2	9.9	1765
Wheat red dog	11.1	18.3	3.4	2.3	2.2	62.7	.12	.....	.....	9.7	1.6	25.1	6.2	.....
Wheat shorts, brown	10.8	17.8	4.8	5.8	4.0	56.8	.08	.86	.....	.....	.....	55.1	.....	.....
Wheat shorts, gray	11.0	17.5	4.4	5.4	4.1	57.0	.08	.86	.1	.....	1.3	44.2	.....	.....
Wheat standard middlings	10.4	17.0	4.3	5.4	3.9	59.0	.09	.90	1.4	7.5	1.1	56.1	7.1	.....
Wheat white middlings	10.9	15.6	3.7	2.4	2.2	65.2	.....	.....	.....	.....	.....	39.3	.....	.....

The composition of byproduct feedstuffs—Continued

Distillery, brewery, and yeast byproducts

Feedstuffs	Moisture	Crude protein	Ether extract	Crude fiber	Ash	Nitrogen-free extract	Calcium	Phosphorus	Carotene	Thiamine	Riboflavin	Niacin	Pantothenic acid	Choline
	Percent	Percent	Percent	Percent	Percent	Percent	Percent	Percent	mg-lb.	mg-lb.	mg-lb.	mg-lb.	mg-lb.	mg-lb.
Brewers' dried grains:														
18–23 percent protein	7.9	20.7	7.2	17.6	4.1	42.5	0.16	0.47	.....	.....	0.6	31.5	.....	.....
23–28 percent protein	7.7	25.4	6.3	16.0	4.3	40.3	.16	.47	.....	.....	.....	.....	.....	.....
Distillers' dried grains:														
Corn	6.0	27.6	8.7	12.5	2.4	42.8	.10	.45	0.8	0.7	1.3	17.4	2.7	74
Milo	6.9	40.8	13.1	11.8	1.6	25.8	.....	.....	.....	.3	1.3	25.0	2.6	79
Rye	6.5	20.9	6.4	14.4	2.3	49.5	.....	.....	.....	.7	1.8	8.9	2.6	.....
Wheat	7.0	30.4	6.6	13.4	2.2	40.4	.06	.42	.5	.8	1.8	38.2	3.1	.....
Distillers' dried grains with solubles:														
Corn	7.3	29.1	9.0	9.5	3.8	41.3	.....	.....	.5	.8	3.0	36.5	5.0	206
Milo	4.2	32.8	9.7	12.1	3.7	37.5	.....	.....	.....	.6	2.0	28.0	5.7	141
Rye	.....	.....	.....	.....	.....	.....	.....	.....	.....	.....	3.8	.....	.....	.....
Wheat	7.4	32.9	5.6	9.4	4.8	39.9	.15	.68	1.1	.....	5.6	.....	.....	.....
Distillers' dried solubles:														
Corn	7.2	27.4	7.6	4.3	7.5	46.0	.43	1.30	.3	3.2	6.1	64.5	10.4	339
Milo	6.9	29.4	5.9	3.5	7.7	46.6	.....	.....	.....	2.2	4.9	60.0	11.1	352
Rye	6.5	35.5	.6	2.4	7.8	47.2	.....	.....	.....	1.2	6.3	18.7	14.1	.....
Wheat	7.5	30.1	2.0	8.0	8.0	50.4	.35	1.51	1.0	3.0	5.3	103.5	17.5	.....
Distillers' (potato) dried residue	3.9	25.9	4.1	13.0	7.4	45.7	.....	.....	.....	.....	.....	.....	.....	.....
Fermentation solubles:														
Grain	7.3	35.8	6.2	8.1	6.2	36.4	.....	.....	.....	.....	.....	.....	.....	.....
Molasses	4.5	28.0	1.2	1.8	12.6	51.9	.....	.....	.....	.....	.....	.....	.....	.....
Malt sprouts	7.2	24.6	1.8	13.9	7.5	45.0	.....	.....	.....	.....	5.5	25.4	.....	.....
Yeast, brewers' dried	5.5	47.2	.9	3.0	7.3	36.1	.....	.....	.....	31.2	14.1	216.7	50.0	.....
Yeast, feed, dried	6.0	52.6	4.3	17.2	7.7	12.2	.07	1.55	.....	10.0	30.0	159.0	.....	.....

Oilseed meals

Coconut meal	9.9	20.6	8.4	10.2	6.3	44.6	......	......	0.1	......	......	......	......	......
Cottonseed meal:														
36–39 percent protein	7.5	37.2	5.8	14.4	5.4	29.7	0.30	1.20	.1	6.1	4.1	20.4	6.4	1525
39–43 percent protein	7.4	41.0	6.5	10.8	6.2	28.1	.23	1.18	.1	6.1	4.1	20.4	6.4	1525
43–48 percent protein	7.0	43.9	6.6	10.5	5.8	26.2	.20	1.03	.1	6.1	4.1	20.4	6.4	1525
Linseed meal:														
31–34 percent protein	9.6	33.1	5.8	7.9	5.6	38.1	.39	.90	.1	2.5	1.3	20.3	3.2	......
34–37 percent protein	9.1	35.4	5.7	7.9	5.6	36.4	.38	.86	.1	2.5	1.3	20.3	3.2	......
37–40 percent protein	9.1	38.6	5.7	7.6	5.6	33.4	.36	.32	.1	2.5	1.3	20.3	3.2	......
40–43 percent protein	8.5	41.2	5.7	7.3	5.3	32.0	.34	.77	.1	2.5	1.3	20.3	3.2	......
Peanut meal:														
38–43 percent protein	6.4	41.6	7.2	16.0	4.4	24.4	.10	.50	.1	2.6	1.6	96.6	24.7	1025
43–48 percent protein	6.7	45.1	7.2	14.2	4.6	22.2	.17	.55	.1	2.6	1.6	96.6	24.7	1025
Sesame meal	9.8	37.5	14.0	6.3	10.7	21.7	......	......	......	......	1.5	......	4.5	......
Soybean meal:														
38–43 percent protein (exp.-hyd.)	7.8	42.0	6.0	6.1	5.7	32.4	.24	.63	.1	6.1	1.6	16.0	6.4	1330
43–48 percent protein (exp.-hyd.)	8.2	44.4	5.7	6.0	5.9	29.8	.26	.62	.1	6.1	1.6	16.0	6.4	1330
43–48 percent protein (solvent)	8.7	46.0	1.1	5.7	6.0	32.5	.25	.68	.1	6.1	1.6	16.0	6.4	1330
Sunflower-seed meal	4.6	52.8	4.5	4.1	6.5	27.5	......	......	......	......	......	141.6	19.5	......

Animal and milk byproducts

Blood meal	8.8	83.1	1.1	0.8	5.3	0.9	0.28	0.22	......	......	1.6	17.1	2.4	......
Bonemeal:														
Raw	6.7	25.2	3.3	1.4	62.1	1.3	24.20	11.50	......	......	......	......	......	......
Steamed	3.1	6.2	2.2	1.3	83.6	3.6	30.00	13.90	......	......	......	......	......	......
Special steamed	2.7	11.1	6.5	1.7	75.1	2.9	27.00	13.20	......	......	......	......	......	......
Buttermilk, dried	5.5	34.3	7.0	.3	9.4	43.5	1.32	.93	1.2	......	13.7	7.7	18.6	......
Liver meal	7.3	65.2	14.9	1.9	8.0	2.7	......	......	......	......	22.0	......	47.5	......
Liver and glandular meal	6.5	65.1	16.5	1.5	4.7	5.7	......	......	......	......	20.6	......	......	......

The composition of byproduct feedstuffs—Continued

Animal and milk byproducts—Continued

Feedstuffs	Moisture	Crude protein	Ether extract	Crude fiber	Ash	Nitrogen-free extract	Calcium	Phosphorus	Carotene	Thiamine	Riboflavin	Niacin	Pantothenic acid	Choline
	Percent	Percent	Percent	Percent	Percent	Percent	Percent	Percent	mg-lb.	mg-lb.	mg-lb.	mg-lb.	mg-lb.	mg-lb.
Meat and bone scrap:														
42–48 percent protein	5.8	45.6	14.0	2.4	28.9	3.3	9.63	5.00	......	......	1.5	17.8	1.2	......
48–53 percent protein	5.7	50.3	10.4	2.0	29.3	2.3	9.34	5.07	......	......	1.9	21.4	1.5	......
53–58 percent protein	6.5	55.5	9.1	2.2	25.1	1.6	8.28	4.04	......	......	2.1	21.8	1.8	......
Meat scrap:														
48–53 percent protein	6.4	50.8	10.4	3.2	26.0	3.2	7.80	4.17	......	......	2.3	23.4	1.7	......
53–58 percent protein	6.1	55.3	9.7	2.3	24.4	2.2	7.68	4.00	......	......	2.5	30.6	2.3	602
58–63 percent protein	7.2	60.0	9.6	2.3	19.8	1.1	5.72	3.02	......	......	2.7	29.0	2.1	......
Skim milk, dried	4.7	35.8	1.0	.1	8.8	49.6	1.34	.99	......	1.6	8.4	4.8	13.2	722
Tankage:														
53–58 percent protein	7.3	56.0	9.6	2.2	23.3	1.6	7.49	3.86	......	......	.7	13.6	.8	......
58–63 percent protein	6.3	60.3	9.1	2.0	20.7	1.6	6.37	3.28	......	......	1.2	19.4	1.2	1047
Whey, dried	6.7	12.8	.6	.2	10.1	69.6	.73	.66	......	.8	10.9	8.3	23.9	......
Miscellaneous byproducts														
Apple pomace	78.6	1.3	1.2	3.7	0.6	14.6	0.02	0.01	......	......	......	......	......	......
Beet pulp, dried	9.2	9.3	.8	20.0	3.2	57.5	.66	.06	......	0.2	0.1	1.4	......	......
Citrus pulp	9.5	6.5	3.7	12.8	7.4	60.1	2.08	.11	......	......	......	......	......	......
Molasses, beet	20.5	9.7	......	......	9.1	60.8	.30	.04	......	......	......	22.0	......	......
Molasses, cane	24.0	3.1	......	......	6.8	66.1	.35	.06	......	.4	1.0	21.3	17.9	390
Pea vine meal	8.0	13.5	3.2	22.5	8.1	44.7	......	......	......	......	......	......	......	......
Potato meal	10.8	8.8	.4	2.3	4.4	73.3	......	......	......	......	......	......	......	......
Sweetpotato meal	9.1	3.6	.8	3.1	4.2	79.2	......	......	......	......	......	......	......	......
Tomato pomace	6.3	27.0	13.2	25.8	4.8	22.9	......	......	......	......	......	......	......	......

Some Goods From Wool Grease

John T. Scanlan

Lanolin closely resembles the natural oils of the human skin and hair. It has an amazing capacity for holding water—it will take up twice its own weight. It has excellent emulsifying properties. Because of those qualities, it is useful as a base for medical ointments; in them, it serves as the vehicle that holds a water solution of the medicament in contact with the skin, the ideal condition for absorption by that organ. Its emollience can also be attributed to its affinity for water, because it is loss of moisture that causes skin to become hard and dry, a condition that is not benefited by greasy materials, for they tend to repel water and thus prevent its natural deposition in the tissues.

Lanolin is a purified form of the heavy mixture of fatlike waxes that protect the fleece of sheep against the weather and keep its fibers strong and supple. This mixture is only a part of the complex conglomeration of substances in the fleece. Also present is a large quantity of material called suint, which is generally considered to be the residue of dried sweat, although there is still some doubt that sheep perspire. (One classic experiment showed that there was little if any increase in the moisture content of the fleece of sheep that on a hot day were chased until they would be chased no more by men on horseback. The test confirmed that humans and horses perspire profusely under such circumstances.) Suint is water-soluble and is usually lost when water is the scouring medium, even when the wax is recovered.

Also present are varying quantities of proteinaceous material, such as weathered fiber tips, dead skin, fecal matter, and adventitious impurities, which vary according to the animal's environment—such things as sand, dirt, burs, and other vegetable matter, dip residues, paint, tar, or pitch used in branding, and moisture. A troublesome impurity is sulfur, presumably a dip residue. The term "yolk" is generally used to describe this mixture; the terms "wool grease" and "degras" usually mean the crude wax after it has been removed from the fleece and separated from the suint and heavy solids.

Three principal grades of recovered grease are on the market. The first is crude or common degras, which includes acid degras, solvent-extracted grease, and lower grades of centrifugal grease. The second is a partly refined grade known as neutral degras, neutral wool grease, or technical lanolin, and frequently further subdivided according to its free fatty acid content. Last is a highly refined, bleached, and deodorized product suitable for medicinal or cosmetic use, commonly known as lanolin (hydrous or anhydrous), but sometimes as wool fat or *adeps lanae.* "Wool wax" is the best term for this part of the yolk because it is a mixture of compounds of the class called waxes by the chemist.

The relative quantities of the components of raw (greasy) wool vary widely according to type of fleece, but the over-all average percentage composition (on a moisture-free basis) will approximate: Clean wool fiber, 50 percent; sand, dirt, burs, and other vegetable matter, 15 percent; wool wax, 15 percent; suint, 20 percent. The moisture content of raw wool varies between 6 percent and 26 percent.

All of the processes by which grease is removed from wool are primarily designed to produce a suitable fiber. The grease is a byproduct. Most wool scourers use water and a detergent for the purpose. The detergent is usually a mixture of soap and soda ash. Less frequently the water-soluble suint of the wool is used; occasionally synthetic detergents are employed. When such a method is used, the scouring liquors are discharged into the sewer.

A few scourers recover part of the grease by centrifuging, but more than half of the grease stays in the discharged liquors. Such liquors cause serious stream pollution and for many years the States in which much wool is scoured have had increasing difficulty with the problem. In Bradford, England, where about four-fifths of Britain's wool is scoured, the municipal government had to spend 14 million dollars to construct a sewage-disposal plant to cope with the pollution of the Bradford Beck and the River Aire. At one time the stagnant pool formed by the sluice gates at the juncture of the Bradford Beck and the Leeds-Liverpool Canal was described as "so corrupt that large volumes of flammable gas were given off and although it had usually been considered an impossible feat to set the River Thames on fire, it was found practicable to set the Bradford Canal on fire, as this at times formed part of the amusement of boys in the neighborhood."

Some States have prohibited disposal of wool-scouring wastes in sewers. Others undoubtedly will do so soon. When that occurs, wool processors will be required to remove essentially all of the grease from their sewage effluent. It can be done by the acid-cracking process, used in England for most of the liquors processed and by a few scourers here. The process consists in decomposing the soaps by adding sulfuric acid. That breaks the emulsion and the heavy solids can be removed by hot filtration. The melted grease and

soap fatty acids separate on top of the hot water and can be separated from it by decantation. Another method, recently introduced in the United States, involves treatment of the scouring liquors with calcium hypochlorite. As in the acid-cracking process, the emulsion is broken and the grease separates. The process is said to give a satisfactory effluent, which contains little grease or putrescible substances and does not have an excessive oxygen demand.

Water scouring with soap and soda ash is the cheapest degreasing process if the scouring liquors can be run into the sewer without further treatment—but not if the grease and other material have to be removed. A possible alternative is solvent scouring. A satisfactory fiber can be produced by solvent scouring. For 50 years Arlington Mills, one of the largest wool processors, has been degreasing its wool batchwise with petroleum hydrocarbon solvents.

Solvent scouring has one definite advantage over soap scouring, an advantage that stems from the high value of the wool fiber. The fiber is agitated less during solvent scouring; hence there is less tangling, breakage, and loss of fiber during the subsequent combing and carding operations. Solvent scouring does not yield harsh or brittle fibers. The process can be so controlled that any desired concentration of grease can be left on the fiber or all can be removed and a suitable lubricant applied later. The modification of the affinity of the fibers for dyes resulting from the action of the alkali usually employed in aqueous scouring can be accomplished at will by subsequent treatment with ammonia or other suitable alkali.

Apparatus for continuous scouring with trichloroethylene has passed successfully through the pilot-plant stage, and industrial units are now being put into operation. Solvent-extraction processes recover all the grease. The water-soluble suint, which is removed from the fiber by a clear water rinse, can be recovered if desired or disposed of by sewer. In the latter case further treatment may be necessary to achieve a satisfactory sewage effluent.

Whatever methods are adopted, it is apparent that instead of our present annual production of 9 million pounds of wool grease, which is probably more than present uses normally consume (our prewar annual consumption was about 6 million pounds), perhaps as much as 150 million pounds of crude grease will be available each year. The net result will be some increase in the cost of the degreasing operation and an apparent market for only about 6 percent of the grease produced. It will therefore be necessary to increase the utilization of wool grease or face the consequences of an increased burden of cost carried by the fiber. Because of the variety and unique character of the constituents of wool grease, however, it is entirely conceivable that, with increased knowledge of their chemistry, they will return a substantial profit in their own right.

UNLIKE MOST WAXES, which are hard and somewhat brittle, wool wax is soft and fatlike but tenacious to the touch. It is a mixture of esters of long-chain fatty acids with alcohols of high molecular weight. Both free acids and free alcohols are usually present. There are at least 32 different acids in wool wax. They belong to four or more different classes: Normal fatty acids, about 10 percent; the branched-chain fatty acids, with a methyl group in the penultimate position (iso acids), about 29 percent; dextrorotatory, branched-chain fatty acids, with a methyl group in the antepenultimate position (ante-iso acids), about 37 percent; optically active 2-hydroxy acids, about 4 percent; unaccounted for, about 20 percent. The ante-iso acids contain an odd number of carbon atoms; those of the other classes contain an even number.

The alcohols, which may represent roughly half the weight of the wax, belong to at least three different groups, each of which represents about one-third of the total weight of the alcohol fraction. The steroid group is represented only by cholesterol, which is the best-known constituent of wool wax. Another group, the triterpene alcohols, is represented by two compounds known as lanosterol and agnosterol. The exact structure of these compounds is not known, but they are not steroids. They differ from each other only in the number and location of double bonds. Lanosterol predominates. Apparently agnosterol is not always present. The alcohols of the third group are referred to as the wax alcohols. They include two compounds that are normal constituents of other waxes: Cetyl alcohol, a straight-chain primary alcohol containing 16 carbon atoms; and ceryl alcohol, apparently a mixture of 26-carbon alcohols. Some other alcohols have been reported as present, but their structures have not been definitely established. One is believed to be unsaturated and to contain two alcoholic (hydroxyl) groups. Still other uncharacterized alcohols belonging to this group may be present.

The crude and neutral grades of wool grease are used principally in lubricating greases, the cutting oils, leather-dressing products, carbon paper, paints, and printing inks, and for weatherproofing cordage and super-fatting soaps.

Wool grease is unexcelled as a corrosion-resisting coating for metals. A concentrated solution in petroleum naphtha gives a thin but effective temporary coating, which can be easily removed when desired. For greater permanence, a resin which gives a lacquer-like coating can be added. The effectiveness of this type of coating can be increased by adding rust-inhibiting pigments, such as zinc chromate. Occasionally crude wool grease is used in bituminous emulsions for road building where the application of hot mixtures is not feasible. The Italian Government used most of the surplus grease that accumulated in the United States during the depression of the early 1930's for the construction of military roads in Abyssinia.

For some uses the grease is subjected to drastic modification. Distillation with superheated steam at 450° to 750° F. produces unsaturated hydrocarbons that appear to be dehydration products of some of the alcohols of the esters originally present. Accompanied by large volumes of hydrogen sulfide and other obnoxious gases, they distill over with some of the acids. The condensate can be separated into a liquid and a solid fraction. The liquid fraction, known as wool oleine, was formerly an important wool lubricant, but other wool oils have apparently taken its place in this country. In England it is still used in processing low-grade materials. The solid fraction, called wool stearine, and the still residue, called wool pitch, are used in high-temperature lubricants.

A relatively new development, whose application is at present probably limited to England, is the dry-saponification process, in which the grease is heated with powdered caustic soda without addition of water. The effect of the treatment is the usual conversion of the acids of the grease into sodium soaps, but the alcohol fraction is so modified that it has drying properties, that is, if spread out in a thin layer and exposed to the air it forms a tough film. The modified alcohols can be removed from the mixture by extraction with suitable solvents. Because of their drying properties they are suitable for use in protective coatings. The residual sodium soaps (and also the original saponification mixture) can be used in making lubricating greases or converted to other metallic soaps for lubricants, gland-packing materials, oil thickeners, bitumen-addition products, roofing felts, and concrete waterproofing by incorporation of the finely powdered calcium soap in cement.

SUINT IS A MIXTURE of the potassium salts of lactic, hippuric, succinic, and various fatty acids, urea, a colored substance called lanaurin, and other unidentified nitrogenous substances. Sometimes it is used in scouring, but it is seldom recovered. At various times in the past when potassium was scarce, aqueous suint solutions were evaporated and the residue calcined. In that way the organic material was eliminated and the potassium recovered as the carbonate. This expensive procedure could not compete with recovery of potassium salts from the natural deposits later found in this country.

Work done in the Department more than 25 years ago by F. P. Veitch and Leon C. Benedict showed that the dried and degreased evaporation residue from wool-scouring liquors, corresponding essentially to the suint, contained enough nitrogen and potassium and had physical properties suitable for use in fertilizers. Apparently that application has not yet been developed commercially.

FOR MEDICINAL and cosmetic purposes, wool grease is intensively purified. It is refined to remove any free fatty acids, deodorized, and bleached. The pure grades are designated as lanolin, U. S. P., or lanolin, cosmetic grade, and may be anhydrous or hydrous. As an ointment base, lanolin is superior to fats like lard in several ways. It absorbs more water and is less likely to become rancid. Because of its greater stickiness it adheres more pertinaceously to the skin; because it is difficult to saponify it is less likely to be washed off. Although wool wax penetrates the skin less readily than fats like lard, when aqueous solutions of water-soluble substances are dispersed in lanolin ointment bases they are absorbed more readily than when dispersed in lard, petrolatum, or washable ointment bases. This has been demonstrated by experiments with radioactive sodium chloride, movements of which can be readily traced in the tissues. Lanolin is used in skin-protective creams and also in the waterless ointments, in which solid medicaments are incorporated mechanically.

In cosmetics, lanolin is used with other emulsifiers in various water-in-oil and oil-in-water emulsions, such as cold creams, cleansing creams, vanishing creams, emollient creams, night creams, antiperspirants, shaving soaps, brushless shaving creams, skin lotions, lipsticks, hair oils, and shampoos. It is considered especially desirable in these applications because of its emollient qualities and its similarity to the natural oils of human skin and hair.

Sometimes wool wax is saponified and the alcohol fraction is separated and used in medical ointments and in the cosmetic preparations I mentioned. The alcohol fraction, which probably contains some residual soap and some unsaponified esters, is said to be superior to lanolin as an ointment base. This may very well be true, for the process eliminates inert constituents and impurities, which are dark and odorous, and any residual soap would probably enhance the virtues of the mixture as an emulsifying agent.

The only pure individual constituent of wool wax produced commercially is cholesterol, the raw material for the commercial preparation of vitamin D_3 and some of the sex hormones. Vitamin D_3 is one of a group of vitamins (the "sunshine" vitamins) that are useful in the prevention and treatment of rickets. A disease of infancy or early childhood, rickets is characterized by faulty ossification due to defective deposits of calcium phosphate at the growing ends of the bones. By any one of several chemical processes, cholesterol can be converted to 7-dehydrocholesterol (provitamin D_3), which becomes vitamin D_3 when it is subjected to ultraviolet radiation of a certain kind and intensity. This product is apparently identical with the natural antirachitic vitamin obtained from fish-liver oils.

THE SEX HORMONES comprise the following: Three female-acting estrogens, estrone, estradiol, and estriol; two androgens, or male-acting hormones, testosterone and androsterone; and the gestogen, progesterone.

The estrogens act in conjunction with progesterone to control the uterine cycle. They prepare the female reproductive organs for the reception and the development of the fertilized ovum. The androgens control the development of the male genital tract and the accessory organs and they influence the longevity and mobility of the sperm. Another function of both is the induction and maintenance of the appropriate secondary sex characteristics, such as bodily contour, pitch of the voice, and distribution of hair.

In therapy, the estrogens are used in correcting functional amenorrhea, scanty menstruation, menopausal disturbances, delayed puberty, sexual frigidity, and functional sterility.

Progesterone finds application in the prevention of abortion and treatment of postpartum psychoses.

The androgens are employed in the treatment of impotence, senility, sterility, prostatism, and cryptorchidism. They also are used to alleviate the symptoms of the male climacteric corresponding to the menopause in females. They are effective in some gynecological conditions.

Testosterone is produced commercially by a series of chemical or microbiological reactions upon dehydroepiandrosterone, which is prepared from cholesterol by chromic acid oxidation of the side chain of cholesteryl acetate dibromide. Androsterone can also be derived from cholesterol, but it lost its temporary importance in hormone therapy with the discovery of the more potent testosterone. Progesterone, too, is prepared by a series of chemical reactions from cholesterol by way of the same dehydroepiandrosterone from which testosterone is derived, and some is produced from the pregnenolone isolated as a byproduct in the production of dehydroepiandrosterone from cholesterol. Estradiol, the most potent and most commonly used natural estrogen, can be prepared from cholesterol, but, like other natural hormones, it is extremely expensive. For this reason stilbestrol, the cheaper, nonsteroid synthetic estrogen, is currently more commonly used. If the natural hormones were available at a comparable price they might eventually find wider use than the synthetic substitutes.

All the foregoing uses are important, but the bulk of material so consumed is not large at present and is not likely to keep pace with the inevitable increase in production of wool grease. In the process by which cholesterol is made, byproducts are obtained that represent about 80 percent of the starting material. They consist of the acid fraction in the form of soaps, the triterpene alcohols, and the so-called wax alcohols. There is now little, if any, application for these products.

As PART OF A GENERAL project on the utilization of wool, there was set up in the Eastern Regional Research Laboratory in 1948 a project designed to develop processes for the utilization of the potentially valuable wool wax and suint, now largely wasted. In this project, an attempt will be made to isolate each individual constituent in a pure state and to learn as much as possible about its structure and its physical and chemical properties. Accurate knowledge of this sort will contribute to greater utilization of the original mixture as well as of the constituents themselves. It will reveal possible new uses, especially of the constituents, when the information is made available to workers in other fields.

The following are some of the problems toward which this program is directed. There is need for better methods of purifying the crude materials, methods of eliminating the sulfur, for example. The first step in isolating the constituents is saponification, the process by which the esters are broken down into their component acids and alcohols. No method at present in use is entirely satisfactory and there is much room for improvement in the methods of separating the alcohol fraction from the acids. Even more difficult is the problem of separating cholesterol in pure form and in good yield from the mixture of alcohols. An important step toward the solution of this problem

will be taken when more is known about the other alcoholic constituents with which it is associated.

The structure of the triterpene alcohols has not been elucidated as yet, and their possible application as intermediates for production of hormones, chemotherapeutic agents, or other useful products depends upon more accurate knowledge of their structures.

Most of the wax alcohols remain unidentified, but they are long-chain compounds of the type useful in the preparation of surface-active agents (detergents, emulsifiers, wetting agents, penetrants, froth-flotation agents, demulsifiers), synthetic waxes, and other synthetic products, such as plasticizers.

The branched-chain fatty acids of wool wax are unique among naturally occurring fatty acids. When enough is known about them to permit development of a method of separating them, products may be derived from them which will be suitable for applications different from those of the fatty acids at present available for industrial uses.

JOHN T. SCANLAN, *an Illinoisan, after serving in the American Expeditionary Forces in the First World War, entered the University of Illinois where he received his bachelor's degree in chemistry. In 1923 he was appointed junior chemist in the Bureau of Chemistry. He received his doctorate at George Washington University in 1929. He has been in charge of the chemical modification section of the oil and fat division in the Eastern Regional Research Laboratory since its organization in 1939.*

―――――

The work on wool grease at the Eastern Laboratory has been conducted under authority of the Research and Marketing Act of 1946. Late in 1950, the Wool Advisory Committee, set up under the Act, recommended continued emphasis on developing new industrial uses for wool grease and other wool byproducts and better methods of refining them for specific uses.

Utilization of Poultry Wastes

Harold P. Lundgren,
Hans Lineweaver,
Edmund H. McNally

Inedible wastes of the poultry and egg industry amount to more than a half million tons annually. The wastes are not all at processing plants, but the amounts so centralized grow bigger and bigger because of the strong trend toward the production of ready-to-cook poultry.

Potentially available each year are more than 60,000 tons of feathers, 25,-000 tons of blood, 150,000 tons of offal (heads, feet, and inedible viscera), and 25,000 tons of egg waste (mostly shells from breaking plants).

The wastes contain materials that are similar to the constituents of large meat animals. We have not made use of poultry wastes in the way that we use the wastes from animals, because of the cost of collection from widely distributed slaughterhouses, the small size of the organs of poultry, and the lack of information on the special properties of the wastes.

The waste has been used for fertilizer and also, in small quantities, in the pharmaceutical and industrial fields. Yet its constituents are potential sources of digestive enzymes and hormones (insulin, for example) and of raw material for the manufacture of fibers, adhesives, soap, emulsion stabilizers, paper sizings, foams for fighting oil fires, plaster retarders, plastics, and agents for binding rubber cement to cellulose. Improved characterization of the constituents through research is needed to show how we can take advantage of the waste for some or all of these purposes.

This article deals with the recovery of valuable material from feathers by dissolving them, with the potential usefulness of biologically active proteins of egg white, and, in less detail, with the present status of eggshell, offal, and poultry-manure waste.

ALL PROTEINS are similar in composition. The proteins of feathers, eggs, blood, and viscera and those in milk, soybeans, silk, and wool are built from the amino acids, of which about 30 are known. Every protein molecule contains at least several amino acid groups, which are attached end to end to form the long, stable, threadlike molecule.

The microscopic threads are flexible and can attach themselves to one another as if they had hooks and eyes along their length. The chemist calls the hooks and eyes cross-bonds. In nature the threads are cross-bonded together in various forms, having proportionately differing properties that may be soft and flexible or rigid and tough. They also differ in solubility over an extreme range. When Nature decides that she needs a protein for eggs or blood, she rolls up the threads and cross-bonds them as small globular particles. When Nature needs a material that is tough, to serve as a protective coating, such as feathers, she hooks the threads into extensive networks.

From a study of Nature's architectural plans, the research chemist can design materials to meet specific purposes (within limits, of course). In seeking to make synthetic fibers, plastics, films, and the like, he has learned that he too must start with threadlike molecules. It is only natural that he should look to feathers as a source of raw material, for here is a large supply of ready-made, threadlike molecules; only slight chemical modification seems to be needed to convert the threads into utilizable form, in contrast to the complex operations required to produce many purely synthetic materials.

How are we going to transform the threadlike molecules of feathers into more useful shapes and forms? There are several ways. One is by a partial breakdown of the material. For example, it is possible to mince the feathers and spin the shredded material into yarns or glue them into sheets. Such procedures, which are comparable to the manufacture of paper and fiberboard from wood, have been described by the Bureau of Animal Industry and by the United States Rubber Co. Another approach, one that offers greater range of properties in the prepared materials, is a more complete breakdown of the feathers, so that the building materials (the threadlike molecules) can be redesigned to create new structures. The procedure, now being investigated by the Bureau of Agricultural and Industrial Chemistry, is comparable to the manufacture of such products as rayon and cellophane from wood. Wood, like protein, consists of threadlike molecules, but they have different qualities.

Feathers are reduced to their constituent molecules by a procedure like the one a contractor follows in salvaging lumber from an old house for use in a new one. Special precautions must be observed in the removal of the building materials; otherwise, they may break and become useless. We have found that treating feathers under special conditions and with special chemical agents severs the cross-bond connections between the molecules, causing them to come apart and go into solution. Moreover, we can select agents and conditions that minimize any tendency for the long molecules themselves to break down. For instance, feathers can be dissolved by heating in caustic soda solution, but such treatment is so severe that the molecules are broken down and become useless for many purposes for which protein molecules are desired. They no longer form fibers, films, and plastics.

The selection of chemical agents and cooking conditions for the controlled disintegration of feathers is guided by studies of the nature of the chemical cross-bonds that tie the threadlike molecules together. These chemical cross-bonds are so firm that they are not broken by wetting or simple digestion; hence, feathers are tough for the same reason that vulcanized rubber is tough.

When Goodyear, a century ago, discovered that rubber could be vulcanized by treatment with sulfur, he was unknowingly duplicating the natural cross-bonding process. We now know that rubber, like feathers, consists of long, flexible molecules, and we also know that the molecules in feathers are tied together by sulfur cross-bonds, as well as by two other types of chemical bonds—hydrogen bonds and salt links. Accordingly, agents that specifically attack and sever these three types of bonds must be selected to dissolve feathers.

On that basis, chemists in the Department of Agriculture have developed two procedures for solubilizing feathers. One uses sodium bisulfite and a synthetic detergent, both dissolved in water. The second uses sodium bisulfite dissolved in a mixture of alcohol and water. The procedures are relatively simple; if feathers are treated with the solutions by mild cooking in an open kettle, they disintegrate and dissolve to the extent of about 80 percent. The soluble material comes from the quills as well as from the barbs. If higher temperatures and a pressure kettle are employed, the same proportion of feathers dissolves with the alcohol and water alone without the bisulfite. The solubilized protein is easily recovered from the solutions.

When the alcohol-water solvent is used, the hot filtered solutions are simply cooled. The whole mixture sets, and the solvent can be expressed by pressing and by washing with excess water. The solid protein residue is dried, after which it is ready for use. The alcohol is regenerated by distillation and is used again with the next batch of feathers.

When the detergent method is used, the solubilized protein is recovered by precipitation with salt, followed by washing of the precipitate with a mixture of acetone and water to recover the detergent, leaving behind the pure protein. The acetone and the recovered detergent are used again with the next batch of feathers.

Of the two methods, the alcohol-water process is simpler, but the detergent process seems to give a somewhat better product. In both there is a small but certain tendency for the molecules to be broken down; the alcohol method, particularly with the higher temperatures, is somewhat more severe. The recovered protein prepared by both methods is suitable for conversion into fibers and plastics.

To make synthetic fibers from the recovered protein, it must be redissolved in water or alcohol-water mixtures, each containing a detergent. Solutions containing up to about 20 percent of the dispersed protein are highly viscous—indicative of the unfolded condition of the separated protein molecules.

They become directly spinnable into fibers simply by extruding the sirupy mixture through the tiny opening of a spineret into a solution of acid, which congeals the protein. Stretching and drying tend further to unfold and aline the molecules and to permit them to come close together to hook up again into a new network—one having a more commercially usable form than that of the original feathers.

An important difference exists between the original feathers and the regenerated products, however. The cross-bonds in the regenerated material are not so strong; accordingly, the material is weaker when wet than we would like it to be. The defect can be remedied somewhat by treating the fibers (as is done with rubber) with curing agents designed to increase the number of cross-bonds. But so far we have not achieved the degree of cross-bonding that we desire. However, the products in their present state could be used for certain purposes in which strength is secondary. Fibers that we have prepared could be used, for example, for such specialty purposes as industrial filters (in which desirable resilience is required) or mannequin wigs (for which appearance is the primary factor). These new fibers have the warmth, softness, and dye characteristics of wool. We feel confident, of course, that new and better properties will be realized as we and other research chemists learn more about the basic chemical nature of proteins. In other words, we want more knowledge of the mechanism of cross-bonding the threadlike molecules from which the protein of feathers is built.

The chemist can also make other materials from the recovered soluble protein of feathers. The possibilities have not been fully explored, but we have some evidence that the protein can be used as a binding agent in paper coating. Immense quantities of the more expensive proteins are now used for the purpose, and tests have shown that the feather protein can be adapted for such use. The principal limitation is that a white sizing material would necessitate use of white feathers.

Another possibility is adhesives. Protein adhesives are used in the plywood industry and for pasting labels in the canning industry. Still another possibility is in the plastics industry. Samples of feather protein have been molded into experimental dishes and buttons. The protein also appears to have characteristics at least as promising as other proteins now being used, for example, in cold-water paints, foams for fighting oil fires, plaster retarders, and inks. In other words, feather protein appears to have a wide range of application where proteins that are economically more valuable are now being used.

An alternate approach to the utilization of feathers is provided by results from the Western Regional Research Laboratory. Treating feathers with moist steam under pressure (a calcining treatment) gives a product that has characteristics of practical value as a fertilizer. For example, when cooked for 20 minutes at 250° F. feathers lose all their resiliency and tensile strength; when the product is dried it is friable and easily powdered. Such powdered material does not rot easily, as feathers do. It has found a ready market, well above the cost of production, as a fertilizer component. It contains about 16 percent nitrogen in such a form that it is released only gradually in the soil. In the presence of inorganic fertilizers, such as phosphates, the feather material prevents the undesirable tendency to cake when the materials take up moisture. Powdered feathers, being of pure protein, might possibly be used for animal feed supplements. If the material can be shown to be digestible, there would be a considerable demand for it as food for livestock.

At this stage of the development it is hard for us to say what commercial demands will be made of the keratin (the protein material of which feathers are composed) and particularly of products derived or prepared from it. All that can now be said is that there are methods for obtaining high-molecular-weight protein from feathers, and also for preparing a powdered fertilizer material on a laboratory scale. We foresee the possibility that other keratins may be similarly handled and that the solubilized protein from them will find their way into such commercial products as synthetic fibers, bristles, fertilizers, feed supplements, shellac substitutes, adhesives, paper coating, printing inks, paints—in other words— wherever proteins have already been successfully used. But before these applications can be made, we must learn how to improve the existing methods for dispersing the proteins, adapt the solubilized protein to specific applications, and, finally, modify the products so prepared to give the desired properties.

We have so far dealt with the special properties and potential uses of feather protein. Protein of another kind is found in egg white, egg yolk, and various parts of the whole bird. The proteins of egg white have been characterized in more detail than those from the other sources. Also, some of them are especially interesting because of their biological activity and hence potential medicinal or pharmaceutical value.

Egg white is composed of a number of proteins and other substances. It is about 87 percent water, 11.6 percent protein, 0.2 percent fat, 0.4 percent free sugar as glucose, and 0.8 percent minor constituents. Eight proteins account for about 90 percent of the egg-white solids.

Although the composition of eggs varies somewhat, the proteins approximate the following average percentages on a solids basis: Ovalbumin, 52; *conalbumin,* 11.9; *ovomucoid,* 11.4; G_2 globulin, 4.0; G_3 globulin, 3.7; mucin, 3.2; *lysozyme,* 2.4; and *avidin,* 0.05. All these proteins probably play some part in the development of the chick from the egg, but only the four we have italicized are known to have specific biological activity. That is, they are known to influence specifically some process or reaction that is closely related to life. All of the proteins of eggs, of course, have nutritional value.

The possibility that these biologically active proteins might be useful in medicine makes them of special interest as individually isolated materials. An example of such a protein is the hormone insulin, which is prepared from hog or beef pancreas for use in the treatment of diabetes. Other examples include antitoxins, vaccines, and enzymes. The egg proteins are not used now in medical therapy generally, but lysozyme is being produced commercially and is attracting attention among medical research workers. The four biologically active proteins that we shall now describe are discussed in the order in which their biological activities were recognized.

The trypsin-inhibiting activity was the first biological activity of egg white to be recognized. Yet more than 40 years elapsed before it was demonstrated, in 1947, that ovomucoid is the constituent that causes the inhibition. Ovomucoid is not readily destroyed by heat and a good deal remains in a soft-boiled egg. It does not interfere with the assimilation of food by animals, however, apparently because ovomucoid is destroyed by the pepsin of the stomach before it reaches the region of the intestinal tract where trypsin occurs. Ovomucoid is such a specific inhibitor of trypsin that it can be used to identify the presence of trypsin in a mixture of enzymes that are similar to trypsin. This use of ovomucoid is valuable in research, and it may also be of value in medicine for diagnostic purposes. Ovomucoid is fairly readily prepared from egg white, and is being produced commercially for sale to research workers. It contains 25 percent sugar and has a molecular weight of about 29,000. It does not coagulate on heating.

The ability of egg white and some other fluids to destroy certain bacteria by dissolving them was first described in 1922 by Sir Alexander Fleming of the University of London, who was knighted in 1944 for his discovery of penicillin. He named the active substance, or substances, lysozyme. Purified preparations of lysozyme from egg white were obtained about 1936; crystallization by readily reproducible methods was reported in 1944 and 1946. Lysozyme is by far the easiest of the egg-white proteins to prepare in crystalline form. The action of lysozyme on bacteria may be observed visually. As little as 1 part lysozyme in 100 million parts will cause clearing of an opaque suspension of susceptible bacteria, such as *Micrococcus lysodeikticus*. The lytic, or dissolving, action is preceded by the destruction of complex sugars that are a part of the bacteria.

The limitation of growth by this action is an antibiotic action. The retardation or destruction of microbial life by a substance produced by another living organism is in a broad sense an antibiotic action. The antibiotic activity of pure lysozyme is not well characterized. A great many antibiotic tests have been reported with egg white, but we now know that egg white contains two other substances, avidin and conalbumin, that limit microbial activity. The growth-limiting properties of egg white therefore cannot be attributed exclusively to lysozyme as has frequently been done. The critical evaluation of the over-all usefulness of lysozyme as an agent for retarding microbial activity is needed. An important limitation that now exists for the general use of lysozyme is that its continued injection into the body may cause the development of a serious sensitivity to it. Such a sensitivity would preclude further use of lysozyme as a therapeutic agent.

A lysozymelike substance in the gastrointestinal tract of man may have a part in the formation of certain types of ulcer. The availability of egg lysozyme which does not cause ulcers as normally ingested in the diet, provides a valuable tool in the study of this disease. Because of its bacteriolytic action lysozyme was also found useful in the preparation of vaccines against other diseases. It may prove useful as a food preservative in special cases, even though it does not kill all food-spoilage bacteria.

R. E. Eakin, E. E. Snell, and R. J. Williams, of the University of Texas, in 1940, showed that the injury caused by feeding raw egg white to chicks is due to avidin, a protein that combines with the vitamin biotin. Injury results only when the amount of avidin in the diet exceeds the amount of biotin. Most diets contain ample biotin, so that injury to animals occurs only when special diets including large amounts of raw egg white are fed. The human diet contains so much biotin that there is practically no danger of egg-white injury from eating eggs.

The most interesting indication that

avidin may be useful in medicine comes from its ability to retard the growth of a certain type of induced cancer. It is not a cure for cancer, but it may be useful in the experimental study of the disease.

Avidin can be prepared fairly readily in small amounts, but not in large amounts because it occurs in egg white in very small quantities.

The most recently recognized biological activity in egg white is its ability to prevent or retard the growth of *Shigella dysenteria* and certain other micro-organisms by depriving them of iron. This growth-retarding, or antibiotic, activity was discovered in 1944 by A. L. Schade and L. Caroline, of the Overly Biochemical Research Foundation; in 1946, Gordon Alderton, W. H. Ward, and H. L. Fevold, of the Department of Agriculture, showed that it is due to conalbumin.

Conalbumin resembles a protein in human blood that transports iron through the body. The possibility of using the egg-white protein to supply deficiencies of the iron-transporting protein in human beings cannot be evaluated until further research is done. Conalbumin has the same limitation as lysozyme—the body would become sensitive to egg protein. To avoid sensitization, it may be possible to modify the proteins chemically so that the sensitizing property is reduced while the desired property is retained. That is a difficult assignment and, indeed, one that may never be successfully terminated. However, several instances are known where a protein has been selectively modified with respect to one and not the other of its biological functions.

Conalbumin is fairly easy to prepare. Heat destroys its iron-binding property.

Three of the biologically active proteins—lysozyme, avidin, and conalbumin—are known to retard microbial growth under one condition or another. It seems likely that all of them are involved in the tendency of egg white to resist contamination. At the same time, it seems unlikely that this is their only

purpose in egg white. Obviously, the conalbumin may be involved in the transportation of iron throughout the developing embryo, but we do not know this certainly, nor do we know the part played by any of the other proteins, including ovomucoid, in the development of the chick embryo. These proteins may find uses that have not been mentioned here, or have not even been thought of today.

APPROXIMATELY 10 percent of the total egg is shell. More than 25,000 tons of shells accumulate each year at hatcheries and plants where eggs are broken for freezing and drying. About 94 percent of the eggshell is calcium carbonate. Approximately 4 percent consists of organic matter that contains some calcium or magnesium phosphate. Other elements, such as boron, copper, chromium, and iodine, occur in trace quantities. The opportunities for utilization of a calcium carbonate product like eggshell are rather limited, because it comes in direct competition with limestone products, which are available in large quantities at a number of places.

Because eggshells are animal products, they should be suitable after sterilization as calcium supplements in human foods and in prepared animal foods, such as canned dog food and poultry mashes. Elsie H. Dawson, Marylee Duehring, and Vivian E. Parks, in the Department of Agriculture, have found that ground eggshell can be used as a supplement to increase the calcium content of dried egg.

When shells were ground fine enough to pass through a No. 400 sieve with openings of 0.0015 inch, grittiness was not detected by two out of three tasters in the laboratory. Dried egg containing 0.4 percent of ground shell was tested in baked custards, ice cream, foundation cake, muffins, yeast rolls, popovers, and mayonnaise. Ground shell at this level did not affect the palatability or cooking quality of the products. Ground shell can be sterilized during processing of canned foods or it may be necessary to heat the ground shell separately. For ground shell that is used in poultry mashes, sterilization is especially important because the shell may transmit poultry diseases.

About the only other possibility for the use of eggshell in any quantity at present is for soil liming. The 4 percent of organic matter and the trace elements present in eggshells make them especially suitable for this purpose. The value of liming material is very low, 2 to 5 dollars a ton in many places. This low value means that facilities for handling and crushing the shells must be very efficient.

THE MANY SUBSTANCES in poultry offal make its potential uses numerous. The small size of glands and other organs, however, has discouraged work on methods of utilization that depend on segregation of each organ. Only presently used methods of disposing of or using the offal will be discussed here.

The heads, feet, and inedible viscera from the chickens and turkeys sold in 1949 amounted to over 250,000 tons. Most of that waste was widely distributed and frequently was disposed of by the housewife. With recent trends toward centralized evisceration operations, more than 150,000 tons of offal may become available each year. The yield of offal ranges from 24 percent for broilers and 16 percent for roasters to possibly 12 percent for turkeys.

The simplest disposal method is to use the offal while fresh as hog feed or as fertilizer material. The wastes may also be used as food for cats, dogs, and fur-bearing animals. The composition and biological value of a blend of poultry viscera are such that they can be substituted for horse meat in feed for dogs. The Department of Agriculture Fur Animal Experiment Station at Saratoga Springs, N. Y., has found that evisceration waste can be substituted for horse meat in mink feeding. Poultry processors should keep gizzard linings and leg bands, either celluloid or metal, from the waste to be used for animal feeding, and should freeze the waste as soon as possible. Any residual hormone implants used for finishing poultry should be excluded from the waste.

If poultry-evisceration wastes are available in large enough quantity they can be made into tankage.

Experiments at the Iowa Agricultural Experiment Station show that a satisfactory tankage can be prepared by either a wet or a dry rendering of the wastes. Offal from hens has more fat and is more easily handled than that from young chickens. Gizzard linings should be removed from the offal, as the grit they contain may interfere with the agitators. The free and expelled fat and oil were found to be suitable for soap stock. The tankage when tested in chick-growth experiments was equal to meat scrap as a protein supplement in the ration.

Both large poultry producers and poultry-processing plants may have poultry manure in sufficient quantity to make it an important byproduct. Poultry manure is an excellent fertilizer either with or without litter. It contains large amounts of good-quality nitrogen, phosphorus, and potash. Fresh poultry manure contains bacteria and enzymes which may cause loss of ammonia from the manure during storage. The addition of 200 pounds of superphosphate per ton, well mixed into the manure, aids in the retention of the ammonia. Hydrate of lime may be used at the same rate. Although some ammonia is lost with use of lime, the lime requirements are greater for many soils than the need of phosphorus. Caution is necessary in the application of poultry manure to prevent burning of lawns and meadows during dry, warm weather. The cost of artificial drying is the chief obstacle to the commercial production of a dried poultry manure.

THE BEDDING AND UPHOLSTERY industries are the largest users of feathers in their natural state, which they obtain directly from farms or from poultry-processing plants. The greatest demand is for clean white water-fowl feathers. Not enough geese and ducks are produced in our country, so chicken and turkey feathers are sometimes used.

Feathers to be used on the farm should be plucked while dry. The white ones should be kept together. The large quill feathers of the wings and tail should be removed first and placed in a pile by themselves. The softer body feathers and down should also be kept separate, for such special uses as down cushions and comforters. The feathers can be washed and dried in loose sacks of cheesecloth, using ordinary soap and water, and then run through the wringer. Some advantage in fluffing is gained by spreading the feathers out in a dry room and stirring them well while drying. They may be picked up with a small vacuum cleaner.

THE METHODS of picking followed in poultry-processing plants do not leave the best-quality feathers. The plants use slack-scalding and picking machines. Wax picking means a complete loss of feathers.

To prevent noxious odors or disintegration, the feathers should be dried as soon after plucking as possible. If it is impossible or inconvenient to dry them, the wet feathers may be kept overnight in a solution of 30 gallons of water in which 15 pounds of salt has been dissolved and to which a pint of muriatic acid has been added.

Often the feathers are partly dried in a basket centrifuge and then placed in a cabinet containing steam coils for final drying. Then they are baled or sacked for shipment to the processing plants. There the feathers are first washed with a mild soap solution to remove blood and dirt. An ordinary wringer is sometimes used to squeeze out excess water. Chicken feathers that have a bad odor may be given a preliminary cleaning by immersion in Stoddard's solvent (a high-flash-point gasoline). After washing, the feathers are sometimes bleached with potassium permanganate, hydrogen peroxide, or chlorine solutions. The feathers should be well rinsed after bleaching because the chemicals may damage the texture and may make the feathers brittle.

The feathers are dried in well-ventilated lofts and fluffed by blowing air through them. Sometimes a small amount of mineral oil is sprayed on them to replace part of the natural oil removed in washing.

THE FEATHERS are blown into a tower or tunnel to separate them for size. The smaller feathers and down are blown free of the larger feathers. The bigger quill feathers are left. Steam, blown into the tower, reduces the effect of static electricity. The body feathers can be removed at different levels. The feathers from different levels may be blended to give various mixtures.

Color, cleanliness, source, and size determine the commercial value of feathers. Clean white goose and eider-duck down are most valuable. Some attempts have been made to establish grades and tolerances. A 10-percent tolerance is often permitted (for example, 10 percent of feathers in down) to allow for error in separation.

HAROLD P. LUNDGREN *is in charge of the wool section in the Western Regional Research Laboratory. Before he joined the Laboratory staff in 1941, he was a research associate at the University of Wisconsin and a postdoctorate research fellow at the University of Upsala, Sweden. Dr. Lundgren is a graduate of North Dakota State College and the University of Minnesota.*

HANS LINEWEAVER *is head of the poultry products division of the Western Laboratory. He has been with the Department of Agriculture since 1929. Dr. Lineweaver holds degrees in chemistry from George Washington University and The Johns Hopkins University.*

EDMUND H. MCNALLY *is engaged in poultry research in the Bureau of Animal Industry at Beltsville, Md. He has degrees in biological science from George Washington University and in poultry husbandry from the University of Maryland.*

Wastes That Improve Soil

Myron S. Anderson

Every gardener and every farmer can conserve his supply of organic matter and use it to improve the soil. For the gardener it means a compost pile; the farmer may prefer to spread the material immediately on the land.

Nearly everything that derives from tissues of plants and animals can go into the pile, where it rots into a brown or black, pleasant-smelling, life-containing, and life-giving mixture that improves the fertility and texture of a soil.

The raw materials include those from farm wastes (straw, spoiled hay, stalks) or from the processing of farm products (like corncobs, cotton motes, husks). Garbage from restaurants and home kitchens makes excellent compost.

Productive soils, whether used for field crops or for gardens, often have a suitable content of organic matter, which should be maintained. To do so, the farmer uses crop rotations in which sod-forming crops and barnyard manures have a place. The gardener, however, must solve his problems in other ways; he usually finds it impractical to rotate crops and sod covers. Because the garden must serve the full growing season, little chance is left for effective use of cover crops, and local supplies of manure are often nonexistent or expensive. Composts or prepared manures, therefore, appeal especially to the man who tills a small plot.

Another general aspect is that in certain areas, rich in good-quality mineral matter, organic materials alone can be used satisfactorily. Other soils have enough humus and respond best to chemical fertilizers. But great areas of our soils produce best when both organic manures and chemical fertilizers are applied, not just one or the other.

The addition of organic matter to soil tends to have at least seven benefits:

It makes a heavy soil lighter, more crumbly, and friable—especially important where the soil is high in clay, as in parts of the Southeast and Midwest.

It holds light soil particles together and helps anchor them against erosion. This increases the water-holding capacity of soil in sandy areas, such as are frequently found in New England, on the East and Gulf Coasts, and in sections of California.

It provides some of the large quantities of nitrogen needed by plants.

It releases nutrients already in soil by turning them into soluble compounds that can be absorbed by the roots of plants.

It permits growth and functioning of micro-organisms.

It furnishes some of all the elements essential for plant growth.

It provides micro-elements in more readily available condition.

A compost heap is a place of great biological activity. The numbers of bacteria and fungi present become enormous. Carbohydrate materials, such as cellulose, are drastically lowered in quantity, thereby increasing the nitrogen content of the remaining mass of material. Earthworms and other small creatures abound; they enhance the quality of the organic matter, although they reduce somewhat the total supply. A compost heap to which some soil is added normally has no objectionable odors.

Soils are so varied, and the organic wastes differ so greatly in chemical composition and physical character, that we often have only sketchy knowledge of what may be expected from the use of a particular kind of organic matter under specified conditions.

Composting processes are employed because straw and many other organic wastes have nitrogen contents ranging roughly from 0.5 to 1.0 percent. That means the ratio of carbon to nitrogen ranges from about 80 to 40. The materials normally have relatively large contents of cellulose, lignin, and other carbon compounds. When they are added to the soil, micro-organisms responsible for decomposition consume nutrients, particularly nitrogen. The materials of low nitrogen content draw on the available nitrogen supply of the soil. At the same time, bacterial bodies, which contain a reserve of nitrogen and other nutrients for use some time in the future, are being accumulated in the soil. The bacterial cell is likely to contain about 8 percent nitrogen and at least 1 percent of phosphoric acid. Myriads of these cells mean the formation of a reserve of available plant nutrients in sufficient amount to be of great importance in materials added to the soil.

When a compost heap is started, animal manures and chemical nutrients are sometimes added, but often the slower course of nature's action is unaided. Frequently it is advantageous to add enough of some kind of readily available nitrogen to bring the carbon-nitrogen ratio down to 25 or lower. Decomposition processes will then act under proper temperature and moisture conditions to diminish drastically the carbohydrates present and, perhaps to a much smaller extent, decompose the lignin and other constituents. The carbon-nitrogen ratio tends to stabilize within a range of around 10 to 12, but the compost may be of good quality before that stage is reached.

The following is a formula for making compost from miscellaneous organic matter: Organic waste material (dry basis), 1,000 pounds (1 cubic yard); ammonium nitrate (33 percent nitrogen), 20 pounds; superphosphate (20 percent phosphoric acid), 20 pounds; ground dolomitic limestone, 30 pounds.

The nitrogen is added primarily to hasten rotting. The phosphate improves the quality of the compost. The limestone neutralizes the acids formed, because the acid compounds usually retard the rate of decomposition. The heap of organic materials should be kept moist throughout but should not be subjected to much leaching. Turning, to aerate the heap, is desirable but not essential.

Extensive variations of the formula are possible. When the material has decomposed to a point where an organic nitrogen content of 2 to 2.5 percent is reached, it approximates the freshly dropped manure (dry weight) from domestic animals, and is suitable for general use.

COMPOSTS ARE USED in many ways, essentially as a substitute for rotted barnyard manure. Applications of 3 or 4 tons of compost an acre on a dry-matter basis correspond to farm practice with animal manures. The gardener places some in a hole when he sets out a tomato plant or a rose bush. When small seeds are planted, a light mulch of partly rotted compost may be used until the plants are an inch high; then the excess is raked off and returned to the heap or used otherwise. Surface applications of compost around many kinds of ornamental plants are desirable.

Under some circumstances, farmers and gardeners prefer to make their composts in the soil rather than in a heap. Corn Belt farmers frequently haul manure directly from the barn to the field. Sometimes it is allowed to lie on the ground for a long time. Sometimes its is plowed under soon after spreading. Crop residues, including straw, are frequently handled in a similar way. The same principles apply then as in the heap, particularly the need for soluble nitrogen during the early stages of decomposition.

The gardener may spade under leaves and household garbage, but enough chemical nitrogen should always accompany the organic matter to insure rapid decomposition. When leaves are used, a fertilizer of 10–6–4 grade (that is, the material contains 10 percent nitrogen, 6 percent phosphoric acid, and 4 percent potash, each constituent being present in available form) may frequently be used to advantage instead of the 5–10–5 grade, which often is used on gardens.

The Florida Agricultural Experiment Station prepared composts with water hyacinths, a great nuisance in southern waters. The artificial manures were prepared in different ways with various reagents. In one case, 42 pounds of urea (equivalent to about 19 pounds of nitrogen) was added to 10 tons of green plants. The green but drained hyacinths contained about 75 percent moisture. The original weight of the material in the compost heap was about 5,000 pounds. The added urea would then increase the nitrogen content in the fresh heap by about 0.5 percent on a dry basis.

F. B. Smith and G. D. Thornton, of the Florida Agricultural Experiment Station, got a general picture of changes within the heap during a 4-month period. The percentage of nitrogen (1.3 at the start) was 1.74 by the end of the second month and 2.57 at the end of the fourth; the percentage of soluble sugars plus polysaccharides (31.2) was 25.4 and 22.7 at the same stages. At the end of the first, second, and fourth months molds per gram numbered 5,000, 25,000, and 300,000; the numbers of bacteria were 3,250,000, 2,300,000, and 76,000,000; and the temperature of the heap went from 130° F., to 107°, to 118°.

Other State agricultural experiment stations—among them Missouri, Georgia, New Jersey, New York, Rhode

Island, Ohio, and Michigan—have studied composts and issued reports on their use. The emphasis is frequently on the use of such materials as components of potting soils and for use on gardens and lawns. There is little doubt about their value as substitutes for animal manures.

PAPER MILLS discharge enormous quantities of crude lignin, its derivatives, and ligninlike materials.

The possible use of such products for soil improvement has long been considered. Lignin is acidic and has a capacity for holding bases comparable to that of good-quality humus or soil organic matter.

The disposal of sulfite liquors, often used for extraction of the lignin, poses a problem that offers a challenge to paper manufacturers and agriculturists. The paper manufacturer must dispose of his lignin with a minimum of pollution to the stream that furnishes water for his plant and carries away his waste products. This means that some of the organic material may be decomposed without serving any useful purpose, while some goes down the stream and harms aquatic life. It is hoped that some day byproduct lignin may cease to be a stream-polluting material and become useful to agriculture.

When cocoa beans are used for the preparation of theobromine, later to be converted into caffeine, the greater part of the mass of the beans is left as a residue that contains a small amount of ash and about 2 percent of nitrogen.

Cannery-waste disposition has long plagued processors. The water content is usually high, and large streams are seldom near for rapid disposition. The nitrogen content, dry basis, of a number of the waste materials is relatively high, at least 2 percent. Composts prepared from cannery wastes should find a good local market in places where high-acre-value vegetables and fruits are grown.

Tannery wastes are particularly difficult to dispose of because they decompose slowly when they are added to streams in any quantity. They normally contain lime and are often used locally as a substitute for high-grade manures or organic ammoniates.

Citrus waste is utilized in several ways. When frosts cause fruit to drop, it may be left under the trees as fertilizer. Some citrus peel from canneries is converted into dried cattle feed, but a great deal of the unprocessed waste is transported to nearby pastures to be used partly as feed and partly for soil improvement. A small amount is converted to a compost before being applied to land, especially material for the home garden.

Spent mushroom soil is a product from the caves or houses where mushrooms are grown. Horse manure, including straw used as bedding, is the common source of organic matter. The soil selected is of good native fertility, and the compost has been adjusted to a neutral or slightly alkaline reaction. The spent material contains approximately 25 to 30 percent organic matter and is highly regarded by growers of market-garden crops, particularly melons. Some of this compost is utilized by the producer who may also grow garden crops; some is sold locally; limited amounts are transported in carload lots for use in gardens or on lawns or golf courses.

Sawdust piles dot the landscape in some parts of the United States. Some times they are set on fire because people do not know how to make use of them. The nitrogen content of pulpwood usually ranges from 0.2 to 0.3 percent. The cellulose range is 55 to 60 percent and lignin around 25 percent. It is apparent that readily available nitrogen should accompany such material when it is added to soil. Research results on the influence of sawdust on soil are scarce. Tillers of fine-textured soils, however, have found that incorporation of sawdust with chemical fertilizers has greatly improved the physical properties of the soil. Apple pomace is often found in the vicinity of sawdust piles. The two materials composted together have been reported as producing good

material for local soil improvement. In one of the nationally known gardens where azaleas are extensively grown, much of the soil is a little too near neutrality for the best growth of the plants. The manager reports that sawdust placed in the holes of a transplant is highly beneficial. The presumption is that the mild acidity formed on decomposition is adequate for good growth of the azaleas.

Commercial preparations of compost have appeared on the markets in the United States. Various materials are used in their preparation, mostly of initial nitrogen content in excess of 1.2 percent. Hot-fermentation processes develop temperatures around 160° F. in the specially constructed digestion chambers used. The nitrogen contents of products sold are likely to be below those of most of the so-called organic ammoniates used in the fertilizer industry. These products should have somewhat higher nitrogen contents than dried but otherwise untreated animal manures.

Sewage products in limited quantities reach the soils of the United States. In some of the densely populated parts of the world human wastes play an important part in maintaining soil fertility. The Japanese often use a system whereby human excreta, collected in cities or towns, is transported in watertight containers to the country, where the materials undergo fermentation in tanks before use, primarily as a source of nitrogen. In that way, disease-promoting organisms are drastically reduced in number, but the material would not meet American standards of health protection. In China similar products are collected and sometimes dried in the sun before transportation to the country. In India progress has been made in the direction of partial sterilization of the organic materials through composting, under conditions favorable to hot fermentation. In this way human wastes become less dangerous to health.

In the United States, the population pressure has not developed to a degree even closely approaching that in the Orient. Our national and local problems relative to human wastes are primarily those of disposal by means not too detrimental to quality of water in streams. In preparing sewage for delivery to streams, large quantities of organic matter are decomposed. In a few cases the gases given off, principally methane and hydrogen, are utilized for power. The sewage sludge from numerous city disposal plants is recovered and applied to soil. This class of sludge is likely to have about 50 percent organic matter when considered on a dry basis. The total nitrogen content varies, but is likely to be around 2 percent. This means about 4 percent on an organic-matter basis. Other nutrient constituents are usually smaller in quantity.

The effluents of our city and town sewerage plants often discharge the most valuable portion of plant nutrients into streams because it cannot be applied to the land economically. Sewerage irrigation is utilized in several areas in the West. Results reported have been favorable, but vegetables to be eaten uncooked should not be grown on land thus irrigated. A New Jersey State institution discharges effluent waters from its disposal plant on a large area of sandy farm land. Excellent field crops are grown there with modest applications of commercial fertilizers.

A substantial portion of the nitrogen of sewage can be used for the preparation of high-nitrogen organic fertilizer, but such recovery has not been regarded as economic under most conditions. Lawn keepers in many parts of the United States are familiar with a product of this kind from city plants. The nitrogen content is as high as 6 percent, and the material is sometimes treated so as to be sterilized adequately during preparation to render it safe for use.

A leading journal concerned with sewage and sewage products estimates a daily per capita elimination of about 0.15 pound of matter, on a dry-weight basis, in the United States. On the basis of a population of 150 million, the plant nutrients in the human wastes have been estimated as 1,400 tons of nitrogen, 450 tons of phosphoric acid, and 400 tons of potash daily.

In India, with a population of about 400 million, the quantities of solids eliminated by human beings are estimated at about 0.1 pound a day, and the plant nutrients present are in lower percentage than in the United States. The utilization of these materials for soil improvement has, however, been much greater than in the United States. C. N. Acharya, chief chemist of India, has conducted a strong campaign for utilization of human wastes along with all other waste organic products. His instructions to farmers on the proper means of composting for development of high temperatures, 150° to 160° F. within the decomposing mass, have gone a long way toward reducing health hazards from use of human wastes for soil improvement.

Garbage utilization has been extensive but often expensive. On farms, home garbage is conventionally used as hog or chicken feed. In cities, collection of garbage is costly; sometimes the garbage is used as hog feed and sometimes for soil improvement. More frequently it is discarded as waste.

THE CITY administration of Miami, Fla., after a study of the Beccari hot-fermentation process, had engineers design a plant like one in Cannes, France. The French plant has been in operation nearly continuously since 1927. The garbage of a city of 60,000 population is converted into compost or humus.

The process is identified as "an aerobic oxidation process of fermentation," meaning that the bacteria live in the presence of oxygen and create an end product that is of commercial value as a low-grade nitrogen-carrying humus material. The process requires about 20 days. The material in the storage cell reaches a temperature of 160° to 170° F., which destroys all pathogenic organisms and produces a product sufficiently aseptic for general garden uses. It is also free from weed seeds. The process is odorless. Only water vapor and carbon dioxide are given off.

The Beccari process has undergone many variations for adaptation to different conditions in the United States and in other parts of the world. The success of such a process necessarily depends primarily upon the rate at which nonnitrogenous organic matter is decomposed and the nitrogen content of the residue correspondingly increased. Experimental data along this line are needed.

Peat used alone as a substitute for compost or animal manure usually gives disappointing results. The Ohio Agricultural Experiment Station found, however, that the addition of a little barnyard manure or compost (even as little as one-twentieth of the volume of the mixture) produces good results in growing greenhouse plants. Peat was also found to be valuable as a constituent of composts when other organic materials are present.

Peat, properly used, is of value to growers of many kinds of plants. Ways that it may be used include:

Mixed with small amounts of manure, it may be applied directly, or composts may be made with it.

Worked into about 4 inches of topsoil at the time of establishing a lawn, greater penetration of roots may be expected.

Used as a mulch for shrubbery, better moisture conditions are provided.

Applied in seedbeds of shade-grown tobacco, greater usefulness of added fertilizers is said to be obtained.

Cuttings of certain kinds of trees and shrubs root better in peat than in sand.

Seed germination in peat is frequently better than in soil.

Peat may be used to advantage in many ways in a small garden or greenhouse. It may, however, prove disappointing unless its place in the garden program is adequately understood.

Dried and ground peat is used as a conditioner in commercial fertilizers.

The current annual expenditure for peat in the United States is about 4 million dollars, on a wholesale basis. About 75 percent of the amount is for imported goods of sphagnum moss origin, and 25 percent is for domestic peat or muck, mostly derived from reed and sedge plants. Experimental work has not proceeded to a stage where it is always possible to make an intelligent selection of peat on the basis of botanical origin. The user of peat as a constituent of general potting soil is usually not too particular about its acid reaction, but growers of the acid-loving plants, such as azaleas, want to be sure that the peat is acid enough, perhaps pH 4.5.

Crop residues and farm manures constitute the really large sources of farm-waste materials used for soil improvement. Roots, stubble, and other crop residues in relation to quantities of harvested crops vary widely with kind of crop and often with method of harvesting. A first approximation indicates that probably as much organic matter remains in the field from production of an average crop as is removed in the harvested portion. If all of the material voided by farm animals were returned to the soil, it would mean utilization of about 65 percent of the portion consumed. Unfortunately, only a minor part of the farm manures produced effectively reach the land. One estimate made in the Department of Agriculture indicates that 1,370 million tons of manure are produced annually. Only 208 million tons, or 15 percent, is utilized by application to harvested crops. The nutrient content of the utilized manure is estimated as follows: Nitrogen, 1,300,000 tons; phosphoric acid, 796,000 tons; and potash, 1,102,000 tons.

MYRON S. ANDERSON *was trained at Simpson College and Iowa State College. Since coming to the Department of Agriculture in 1917, he has worked on various chemical problems of soils and fertilizers. Dr. Anderson is a senior chemist in the Bureau of Plant Industry, Soils, and Agricultural Engineering.*

Lignin for Better Crops

Elwin E. Harris

Lignin is the part of the wood that remains after its carbohydrates and extractives have been removed by hydrolysis or by the action of molds and bacteria. In that respect it is like the material from which soil humus is formed. For the formation of soil humus, plant material (such as straw, leaves, and sawdust) must be acted on by soil bacteria, which use the carbohydrates and convert the residue to humus. In their utilization of the carbohydrates, bacteria require nitrogen; unless an abundance of nitrogen is present, plants growing in the soil may suffer from nitrogen deficiency. Lignin does not have so high a nitrogen demand as do plant materials that contain carbohydrates.

Lignin is slowly changed to humic substances when mixed with soil. Even before it is converted to humus, however, it has many of the properties of humus, such as ability to react with minerals in the soil, to control the size of aggregates in clay, and to aid in controlling the alkalinity of soil.

Lignin in solid form remains as an insoluble residue when sugar is made from wood. When wood is treated with dilute acid under pressure, as in the Madison wood-sugar process, the cellulose is converted into soluble sugar and the lignin is left as a dark-brown residue. The residue contains about 50 percent moisture, about 0.5 percent sulfuric acid, and small percentages of unextracted carbohydrate. The residue may be applied directly to the soil without further treatment, if care is taken to avoid contact with growing plants, for the acid in the lignin causes burns. After the residue is rained on, washed, or treated with lime to neutralize the acid, it loses its tendency to cause burns.

Lignin left as a residue from the Scholler process of alcohol production in Germany has been reported to be a suitable soil conditioner. The first experiments in the United States on such use of lignin left as a residue from an acid hydrolysis were started in 1936, when research workers at the Forest Products Laboratory treated clay garden soil with lignin at the rate of 5 tons to the acre. At the same time they compared the treated soil, some of which had had inorganic fertilizer, with untreated soil, some of which also had received the fertilizer. Tomato plants grown in the soil receiving both lignin and fertilizer were more vigorous and bore more fruit. The plot receiving fertilizer and no lignin was next in yield. Plants in the plot receiving lignin and no fertilizer were healthy and bore good fruit, but were smaller than those fertilized. Plants receiving no lignin and no fertilizer suffered during dry weather and gave poor yields. The soil in plots that received lignin was easier to cultivate and did not become hard when it dried after a rain.

Wood-hydrolysis lignin, when used as a mulch between rows of tomatoes, kept the soil moist and was easily worked into the soil.

Stuart Dunn, of the New Hampshire Agricultural Experiment Station, tested the use of lignin from wood saccharification supplied by the Forest Products Laboratory for potato production. Plants were grown in 14-quart pails in Newmarket sandy loam with thin layers of lignin between layers of soil. The lignin was equivalent to 5 tons an acre. The plants were compared with controls in the same loam without lignin and with plants of another group in loam containing lignin and sulfur. Commercial fertilizer was added to all pails. The average yield of the potatoes per pail in each group was: Lignin alone, 451.2 grams; lignin plus sulfur, 411.4 grams; and the control with fertilizer but no lignin or sulfur, 319.2 grams. Analysis of the tubers gave the following starch content: Lignin alone, 19.68 percent; lignin plus sulfur, 11.77 percent; and control, 10.24 percent.

W. B. Bollen, of the Oregon Agricultural Experiment Station, has reported on wood-saccharification lignin used in much the same manner as horticultural peat moss. He found that lignin is preferable to leaves, straw, and sawdust as a mulch and soil conditioner in gardening; and that it forms smooth mulches, incorporates readily with the soil, and eventually contributes to humus formation. In this experiment, lignin was used as a mulch for starting plants from seeds in flats and as a light mulch over seeding. By holding moisture, the lignin enhanced germination. By maintaining a loose, open soil, it permitted sprouts to break through the soil readily. The use of lignin in potting soil or as a bottom layer in flats and pots resulted in vigorous plant development. As a heavy mulch around raspberry and other cane-fruit plants, and around blueberry plants in depths of 4 to 6 inches, it gave smooth, compact mulches that held moisture and provided conditions approximating the natural habitat of the plants.

Lignin supplied by the Forest Products Laboratory was compared in 1949 and 1950 to other materials for subsoil drainage in golf greens at the Missoula Country Club in Montana. A report of the condition of the greens after a year was favorable to lignin.

F. M. Harrington, of the Montana State College and Agricultural Experiment Station in Bozeman, used lignin supplied by the Forest Products Laboratory in both greenhouse and field work. He reported a distinct value to greenhouse operators in its use. Lignin from wood-sugar production and without any treatment lowered the alkalinity of greenhouse soils and, at the same time, was a good soil conditioner. Chrysanthemums grown in soil to which 10 percent of lignin had been added produced longer stems and bore larger blooms than the control. From actual weights of every stem cut, the flowers from this plot showed approximately a 30-percent gain in weight.

Lignin that was applied in 1948 and 1949 to alkaline spots in irrigated fields in Montana improved soil conditions.

Harry L. Hamilton, of the Forest Products Laboratory, and Emil Truog, of the University of Wisconsin Agricultural Experiment Station, in 1948 and 1949, tested the use of lignin in both field and greenhouse. An improvement was noticeable in the greater ease of cultivating and in a more open structure of the soil. Physical properties of the soil were improved by the addition of lignin. The improvement continued through several crops with respect to soil hardness, water-holding capacity, porosity, and rate of water flow through the soil.

Lignin from wood saccharification is not yet commercially available, but if industries find it practical to put up plants to convert wood waste into molasses for feeding livestock, large quantities of lignin may become available, because each ton of dry wood waste yields about 600 pounds of lignin. A plant producing 50 tons of molasses a day would produce 15 tons of dry lignin, or about 4,500 tons a year. At a rate of 5 tons of lignin to the acre, this would treat 900 acres of land a year. If all the sawmill wood waste collected in the United States (60 million tons) a year were converted into sugar and lignin, the lignin, applied at the rate of 5 tons an acre, would be sufficient for the total acreage (about 6,000 square miles) in one of the smaller States.

As the lignin comes from the process, it is a moist residue containing about

50 percent solids and 50 percent water. Where it is to be transported for short distances, it need not be dried.

ELWIN E. HARRIS *is in charge of the work on wood saccharification and*

lignin products at the Forest Products Laboratory, Madison, Wis. He received his bachelor's degree from Hamline University, and has advanced degrees from the University of Minnesota.

THERE IS GOLD in sea water. A generation ago much was heard about various schemes for recovering it in commercial quantity. An eminent German chemist, Fritz Haber, analyzed numerous natural waters from all over the world and found that nearly all of them really did contain measurable traces of the precious metal. The water of San Francisco Bay ranked high in gold content among Haber's samples. It contained 0.01 milligram per cubic meter of water—or 92 pounds of gold per cubic mile of Bay water, worth $47,000 at a gold price of $35 a troy ounce. No factory for extracting it has been built. If there had been, the operators might soon have been diverted from their original purpose by the lure of the other valuable chemicals in that same cubic mile of sea water: 230 tons of iodine, worth 700,000 dollars; 330,000 tons of bromine, worth 140 million dollars; 4 million tons of magnesium, worth 1.5 billion dollars; 75 million tons of chlorine, worth 5.7 billion dollars; and 50 million tons of sodium, worth 18.5 billion dollars.

Those facts are not unrelated to agricultural research. Any farm commodity you can name is a veritable mine of rare and expensive chemical compounds. Anyone armed with a reasonably complete analysis of alfalfa, say, and a chemical price list, can easily show that a ton of alfalfa should be worth at least $2,000—just as a cubic mile of sea water evidently should be worth at least 25 billion dollars.

But what's wrong with such a conclusion? Two things: First, the cost of extraction of a pure substance from a natural source may be so high as to price it out of the market; second, the market may be so thin or so inelastic that even a little extra production will break the price. If someone were so ill-advised as to produce 50 million tons of sodium in a single year he would find himself embarrassed by a thousand-year stockpile, and unable to find takers for most of it at any price.

Nevertheless, sea water is an important commercial source of salt, bromine, and magnesium. The value of the salt produced annually from San Francisco Bay water far exceeds the value of all the gold in the bay.

The story of bromine is instructive. Chemists had found long ago that sea water contains a little of it. Many years later the development of antiknock gasoline multiplied the demand for bromine enormously. The chemists worked out a method for recovering it from sea water more cheaply than it could be produced from other known sources. Engineers developed a practical large-scale process. Businessmen put up the money. And a new industry came into existence.

A similar thing happens constantly in agricultural research. Scientists discover unsuspected values in farm products, a market opportunity is glimpsed by someone who can command enough capital to go after it, and the engineers and technologists bring another new industry into being. It is no fairy story—it's the way our industrial civilization operates.—*W. B. Van Arsdel, Western Regional Research Laboratory.*

Molasses and

Yeast From

Wood

Elwin E. Harris

One way to use the timber resources of our country more efficiently is to convert the refuse from logging and manufacturing operations into food. Research at the Forest Products Laboratory therefore is aimed in part at the conversion of wood to sugar solutions, which have been tested as livestock feed by several agricultural experiment stations. The investigations indicate that wood wastes can add materially to the supply of feed.

For example, the dry and bark-free wood of logging and manufacturing residues contains 50 to 70 percent of carbohydrate material. When treated with dilute acids under steam pressure, the material can be converted to dilute solutions of simple sugars. The solutions, when evaporated and used as livestock feed, can release for direct human consumption some more expensive food that is now fed to livestock while maintaining, or perhaps increasing, the supply of livestock products.

The sugars also can be used to grow a yeast containing protein, fat, and vitamins, which is suitable for human food or livestock feed, or they may be used as a source of solvents and chemicals at present being made from sugars suitable for human consumption.

The carbohydrates of wood are of two types, cellulose and hemicelluloses.

The cellulose portion, comprising about 50 percent of the wood, is more resistant to chemical action and is the part isolated as pulp in paper-making processes. It consists of a large number of glucose molecules that are linked together chemically.

To change cellulose to glucose, high temperatures and pressures are required when dilute acid is used. The change to glucose can be carried out at room temperature if a concentrated acid is used, but the percentage of unrecovered acid makes the cost too high. The hemicelluloses comprising about 20 percent of wood, are a mixture of sugars that are chemically bound. The chemical bonds in hemicelluloses are more easily broken, and they are converted to simple sugars in a short time by heating in the presence of dilute acid at boiling-water temperatures.

The hemicelluloses from the hardwoods—maple and beech, for example—yield a high percentage of xylose, a 5-carbon sugar. Xylose is also obtained by the action of the acid on straw, oat hulls, and corncobs. The hemicelluloses from softwoods, such as pine and fir, yield a mixture of sugars composed of about one-half xylose and one-half 6-carbon sugars, such as glucose, mannose, and galactose.

Ruminants can assimilate both 5-carbon and 6-carbon sugars. It is generally believed that swine, horses, and poultry cannot assimilate 5-carbon sugars; therefore, sugars from hardwoods, high in xylose, are believed not to be so suitable for swine, horses, and poultry as sugars from softwoods. Xylose and other 5-carbon sugars are not fermentable by yeast to ethyl alcohol, but they are suitable for growing food yeast.

Processes for converting wood into sugar have been known for more than a century. H. Braconnot, in 1819, reported the production of sugar from wood. In 1898, E. Simonsen described a process that yielded 6 percent of sugar from wood. Between 1913 and 1923 improvements in the processes were made in both Europe and the United States. The work in Germany was described by Dr. Emil Heuser.

Experimental plants were built in the United States in Highland Park, Ill., and Port Hadlock, Wash. Later, after several difficulties had been overcome, commercial plants were built in Georgetown, S. C., and Fullerton, La. F. W. Kressman, of the Forest Products Laboratory, described the development and pilot-plant work for these plants in Department of Agriculture Bulletin 983 (1922). The process in the plants employed a short hydrolysis treatment—about 45 minutes—with dilute acid at about 170° C. A yield of 20 to 25 percent of sugar was obtained. The sugar was used to produce high-quality industrial alcohol, the yield of which was about 22 gallons of 95-percent alcohol from a ton of dry wood waste. Some of the sugar was concentrated and added to the residue from the wood hydrolysis. The partially hydrolyzed residue, with the added sugar, was fed to cattle. A report by J. G. Archibald on the work in Massachusetts showed that the food value of the product consisted of the soluble sugars and not of the residual cellulose, which was not broken down sufficiently to be digestible.

Because of the low prices for agricultural products and the plentiful supply of blackstrap molasses at give-away prices after the First World War, the commercial alcohol plants were closed and experimentation on the use of wood sugars for feed was discontinued.

Later, in Germany, H. Scholler announced a dilute-acid process, which took about 18 hours and gave 40- to 50-percent yields of sugar from wood. W. R. Ormandy, in England, developed a strong-acid process that took about 24 hours and gave 60-percent yields of sugars. Both processes were primarily for the production of alcohol, although some experimental work was done on the use of the sugars for feed in the form of molasses.

In 1933 and 1934 the German Ministry of Nutrition arranged with the plant at Tornesch for production of yeast from wood sugar for both human and animal consumption. By 1943 wood-sugar and paper- and rayon-pulp plants in Germany were producing about 8 million gallons of alcohol and 20,000 long tons of food yeast a year, and steps were being taken to increase production.

The War Production Board in 1943 financed a project at the Forest Products Laboratory to conduct pilot-plant experiments on the conversion of American species of wood into sugar to be used for the production of industrial alcohol and other products. The experiments, with the aid of improved equipment, resulted in the development of a process that yielded 50 percent of sugar from wood in 3 hours.

THE NEW PROCESS, known as the Madison wood-sugar process, consists of continuously pumping a spray of hot 0.5 to 0.6 percent acid on chips heated in a stationary digester to 302° F. at the start and gradually increasing to 365° F. The cellulose and hemicelluloses are changed to sugar by the action of water in the presence of acid and are extracted by the dilute acid as it flows over the chips. The flow of dilute acid and rate of temperature increase are regulated to give the maximum concentration with the minimum decomposition of sugars. After removal from the digester, the sugar solutions are cooled to 280° F. and neutralized with lime, forming an insoluble precipitate of calcium sulfate that is removed by filtering under pressure. The resulting sugar solution contains 5 to 6 percent of a mixture of simple sugars. The sugars can be used in dilute solution for alcohol or yeast production, or can be evaporated to a sirup for feed.

Wood-sugar solutions may be evaporated economically in new-type evaporators to produce solutions containing 50 percent of simple sugars. About 1 ton of 50-percent sugar solution can be obtained from 1 ton of wood. Proper control of the neutralization keeps down scaling in the evaporator caused by calcium sulfate and aids in maintaining a low ash content. The sirup or molasses thus produced has the odor of slightly caramelized sugar, but the sweet taste is masked by water-soluble bitter substances extracted from the wood. The bitter taste does not seem to make the molasses less palatable to cattle. The sugar content represents about 80 percent of the total solids in solution.

The molasses from the Madison process was tested in 1950 and earlier as a cattle feed without purification. It appeared to be entirely palatable. If the wood molasses can be used without purification, it will cost less.

Estimates of the cost of producing wood molasses by hydrolysis of wood depend on the size of the plant, the cost of wood and labor, and the facilities available from other manufacturing processes that do not make full use of existing equipment and plant. Assuming that a site, steam-power plant, and water supply are available and that wood molasses would be produced at a plant having much of the needed equipment and operating for only short seasons of the year, such as beet-sugar plants or sugar refineries, plant costs could be low. The installation of $100,-000 to $250,000 worth of equipment at such plants would make it possible to produce 25 to 50 tons of wood molasses a day.

The cost of wood may vary from $2 to $7 a ton, depending on the type used. If sawmill waste that now is burned were used, the cost would be little more than that of transportation. If cull wood from forest-management and stand improvement or limbs and branches from cuttings in the woods were used, labor and transportation would make the cost higher. Because wood that would normally go to the waste burner is as satisfactory as high-quality material, it is assumed that only mill-waste wood should be used.

The only chemicals needed for the process are sulfuric acid and lime.

Chemical cost per ton of wood has been about $1.60 for each ton (170 gallons) of molasses produced. On the basis of these estimates and estimates for labor, plant amortization, power, fuel, and overhead, it should be possible to produce wood molasses for less than 10 cents a gallon. It is estimated that four to six men for each shift would be needed to operate the plant.

Lignin, a byproduct of the process, may be used as boiler fuel to supply the heat for the process, or it may be used in other ways, such as a source material for chemicals, charcoal, and a soil-conditioning agent. Other byproducts are methanol, an industrial solvent, and furfural, which is used for nylon production.

Approximately 350 tons of wood-sugar molasses, which had been produced by July 1950, with funds provided by the Research and Marketing Administration, was made available for feeding tests with cattle, sheep, swine, and poultry.

Tests at the University of Wisconsin and Michigan State College showed that wood molasses could supply part of the high-energy feed needed for high milk production. Grass silage put up at Washington State College, Oregon State College, and the University of Wisconsin with wood-sugar molasses as a preservative kept better and was more palatable than ordinary grass silage.

Range cattle in Montana, Oregon, and Mississippi readily ate roughage to which wood-sugar molasses had been added to increase palatability.

Swine at Oregon State College consumed feed in which up to 15 percent of the carbohydrate had been replaced by wood-sugar molasses and made gains comparable to those from feed-grain mixtures.

Lambs at Montana State College readily ate feed mixtures containing up to 15 percent of wood sugar as a replacement for grain and made weight gains comparable to those fed mixed-grain feed.

Cattle at Washington State College,

Oregon State College, and the University of Wisconsin that were fed feed mixtures containing up to 6 pounds of wood-sugar molasses a day made good gains in weight.

Chickens and turkey pullets at Oregon State College and Washington State College given feed mixtures containing up to 20 percent of molasses made gains similar to those made by birds fed corn.

Nutrition experiments at the New Hampshire · Agricultural Experiment Station showed wood molasses to have a gross energy of about 4 calorics per gram of digestible material.

The results of feeding tests by July 1950, covering 4 years of experimental feeding of cattle and calves, as well as swine and poultry, seem to prove the value of wood molasses as livestock feed. If long-term feeding tests give as satisfactory results, and if molasses can be produced at a competitive price, markets may be very large. In 1946, approximately 78 million gallons of blackstrap cane and beet molasses, or less than 1 gallon for each head of cattle in the United States, was used for stock feed in the United States; 366 million gallons was the total molasses available, or less than 5 gallons for each animal. Feeding tests indicate that 3 to 5 pounds of 50 percent molasses may be profitably fed to cattle daily as a supplement to other feed; at that rate, 5 gallons would last only 12 to 20 days. Thus, feeding molasses on the scale that is nutritionally practical would provide markets for all the molasses that can be imported, as well as all that can be produced from wood waste.

About 60 million tons of sawmill wood waste in excess of that used for fuel, plastic filler, and other purposes is now produced annually in the United States at the larger mills where quantities are large enough to justify a plant for chemical utilization. An average of about 150 gallons of wood-sugar molasses can be produced from 1 ton of the usual sawmill wood waste. It would require 80 percent of this wood waste to feed 3 pounds of wood-sugar molasses a day to each head of cattle in the United States.

Another use for the wood sugar is the production of a food yeast, which can be made from both hexose and pentose obtained from the hydrolysis of the wood waste. The yeast is high in protein, fats, and the B vitamins. It may be produced in 40- to 50-percent yields from the wood sugar or in 20- to 25-percent yields based on the dry weight of the bark-free wood. It can be a suitable food or feed.

Yeast is being produced in the Forest Products Laboratory pilot plant by continuously feeding a solution of wood sugar, which has about 5 percent concentration and contains the necessary nutrients, into a propagator in which air is supplied by a rotating sparger that also pumps the solution around through a central draft tube for foam control. The volume of feed an hour is one-third to two-fifths the liquid content of the propagator. The liquid is kept in a foamed condition, approximating three times the volume of the liquid, for most intimate contact of the air with the liquid. Spent liquor and yeast overflow continuously from the propagator. When yeast is produced that way, no antifoam is needed, and the air requirement is only about 200 cubic feet to the pound of dry yeast produced.

Yeast is separated from the spent solution by centrifuging. Then it is washed by adding water at the proper pH value and centrifuged again. The yeast cells are killed by heating and dried on either a spray drier or drum drier. The drum drier, which operates at a slightly higher temperature than the spray drier, appears to give the better-flavored product.

Quantities of this yeast were fed swine and poultry as a source of protein and B vitamins in 1948 to 1950. The yeast aided in maintaining the health of both and high hatchability of the eggs produced by the poultry.

Most yeast used for human food or livestock feed in the United States is a byproduct of the brewing industry. Because the production at any one plant is small for the manpower required, its cost is high. Surveys show that were yeast available at low cost, many times the present production could be used.

The use of yeast as human food in many European countries, amounting to 20,000 tons a year during the war in Germany alone, and the tests with many animals requiring vitamin B in their diets indicate that large quantities

of food yeast from wood waste may be used for humans, for swine, for young calves, and for chickens.

ELWIN E. HARRIS *is a chemist in the Forest Products Laboratory in Madison, Wis. Since 1930 he has specialized in organic chemistry, the chemistry of lignin, wood saccharification, kinetics of wood hydrolysis, wood analysis, fermentation of wood sugars, and yeast production on wood sugars.*

WHAT CAN BE done with two kinds of wastes is exemplified by the development through Department of Agriculture research of methods for utilizing the wastes from pear canneries. The three Pacific Coast States pack about 90 percent of the canned pears consumed in the United States. The wastes from their operations—cores, peels, and trimmings—have amounted to some 140,000 tons a year.

At a large cooperative cannery in Hood River, Oreg., a process was developed for the recovery and refining of an edible juice from carefully handled pear waste. It provides the sirup in which the fruit can be canned. Waste pear juice contains as much sugar as the juice from sugarcane. Packing pears in sirup made from the waste juice, instead of in the ordinary sirup, permits the plant to use about 30 percent less sugar. The saving thus made will apparently be more than enough to pay for recovering the juice from the waste.

The process utilizes a substantial proportion of the fruit waste to replace a relatively high-priced product—refined sugar. It appears to be feasible, however, only at large canning plants, where the waste is plentiful, can be kept clean and uncontaminated, and can be processed as an integral part of the canning operation as fast as it is produced.

Often, however, pear waste contains rotten or otherwise inedible fruit, and the simplest procedure is to throw all this waste together and treat it as garbage. This is particularly true where one waste-utilization plant serves several small canneries and the waste has to be transported from each cannery to it. It is then difficult, if not impossible, to prevent spoilage or contamination of the waste. Here a different kind of waste-utilization procedure is needed. One was developed at a disposal plant in San Jose, Calif., in cooperation with the Canners' League of California. In the alternative process, the whole garbage is taken from the canneries and converted into products suitable for animal feed, industrial fermentation, and other nonfood uses. The method involves pressing the ground waste after it has been limed under carefully controlled conditions. The pressed material is dried to pomace and the juice is concentrated to a sirup. During the 1949 canning season, several tons of dried pear pomace was produced for evaluation as livestock feed and as a soil conditioner, as well as large quantities of sirup concentrate, intended as a raw material for fermentation to industrial alcohol. It appears that the value of these byproducts will enable the San Jose canneries to dispose of their wastes satisfactorily at a cost below what they now pay for the undesirable practice of dumping the wastes on unused land.—*G. E. Hilbert, Bureau of Agricultural and Industrial Chemistry.*

Glossary

Compiled by
H. P. Holman,
Catherine F. George

a-   In chemical names: A symbol for the combining form *alpha-,* used to distinguish one of two or more isomers or modifications; or to indicate the position of substituting atoms or groups in certain compounds. In the names of acids, it commonly indicates that the atom or group substituted is in union with the carbon atom to which the carboxyl group is attached.

ABSORPTION   The holding by capillary action of a liquid in the pores of a solid, as water is held by a sponge or by soil. In chemistry: The holding by chemical attraction of the molecules of a gas or liquid between the molecules of a liquid or solid.

ACETONE (*ass*-eh-tone) A colorless organic liquid that forms fragrant and inflammable vapor at room temperatures. It dissolves natural and synthetic resins, guncotton, and cellulose acetate, and is extensively used as a solvent in lacquers and as nail-polish remover.

ACETYLATION (ah-set-ih-*lay*-shun) The process of introducing an acetyl radical into an organic molecule.   The word is from the Latin for vinegar, which is essentially dilute acetic acid. Acetic acid is the commonest compound containing acetyl radicals. Acetylation is an important industrial process; a major use is its application to cellulose, either from wood or cotton linters, to produce cellulose acetate. Cotton also may be partly acetylated to improve its properties.

ACIDITY   The state of being acid in reaction, which would be evident to the taste as sourness. The degree of acidity of a solution (or soil) may be expressed as pH (hydrogen-ion concentration). The percentage of effective acid in solution can be de-

termined by measuring the amount of alkali solution of known composition required to neutralize exactly a measured quantity of the solution.

ACTINOMETERS (ack-tih-*nom*-eh-ters) Special chemical reactions used to determine the intensity of light in certain wavelength regions. The method is based on the knowledge that every photochemical reaction is sensitive to a particular part of the spectrum in a manner characteristic of the reaction. By observing the extent or rate of reaction, one can determine the photochemical efficiency of different parts of the spectrum. The procedure can be applied also in finding the ratio of light intensities from different sources having the same spectral composition.

ACTINOMYCETES (ack-tih-no-my-*seet*-eez) Filamentlike micro-organisms that are between the bacteria and the smaller fungi, or molds. Some resemble true bacteria; others are moldlike; a third group appears to be intermediate between the two extremes.

ACTIVATED   Rendered active, capable of reaction, or promoting reaction; descriptive of various unrelated chemical and physical conditions. Carbons and bleaching clays used for adsorbing color bodies and other substances from liquids are considered as being activated when they have been treated to increase their surface areas. It is said that a pound of activated carbon can have 1.5 million square feet of surface area.

ACYL (*ass*-ill; *ass*-eel) The organic radical or group that remains intact when an organic acid forms an ester; more specifically, the group left by the removal of the hydroxyl group from an organic acid.

ADJUVANT (*ad*-jew-vant) A material added to an insecticide to aid its action. Adjuvants may act in various ways—as emulsifying agents, wetting agents, spreaders, and stickers.

ADRENALIN (add-*dren*-a-lin) A trademark name for a drug, also known as epinephrine. A hormone produced in the medulla of the adrenal glands. An increase in the amount of adrenalin in the blood raises the blood pressure, increases the level of blood sugar, causes blanching of the skin, and is largely responsible for the characteristic symptoms of fright.

ADSORB   To retain upon its surface through the force of adhesion some of the gas, liquid, or dissolved substance with which a solid body has been in contact. Activated carbon in granular form is used as an adsorbent in gas masks. Fuller's earth adsorbs coloring matter from hot vegetable oils filtered through it.

AEROBIC   (ayer-*oh*-bick)   Living or active only in the presence of oxygen. When bacteria or molds are grown aerobically, air or oxygen is supplied continuously during the operation, and the fermentation is called an aerobic one. See ANAEROBE.

AGAR PLATES   (*aah*-ger)   Round, covered glass dishes, generally 4 inches in diameter, and one-half inch deep, containing a thin layer of agar, a gelatinlike substance extracted from Ceylon moss. The plates are used to study the growth characteristics of micro-organisms.

ALBUMEN   (al-*bew*-men)   The liquid white of egg, consisting largely of proteins, the chief one of which is ovalbumin. Eight distinct proteins have been shown to occur in albumen.

ALBUMIN   Any of a class of proteins found in blood serum, milk, muscle, egg, etc. Formerly regarded as different occurrences of a single substance, called at first albumen because it was supposed to exist nearly pure in a white of egg. See also OVALBUMIN.

ALCOHOLYSIS   (al-ko-*hall*-ihsis)   The process of cleaving a chemical bond with the addition of a molecule of alcohol. It is derived from the word "alcohol" by combination with the suffix "lysis," signifying a splitting. Alcoholysis is analogous to hydrolysis except that the elements of alcohol are added instead of those of water.

ALDEHYDE   (*al*-deh-hide)   Any one of a large class of substances derived from the primary alcohols by oxidation and containing the group -CHO.

ALEURONE LAYER   (ah-*lew*-rone)   A layer of cells containing protein granules lying underneath the bran coats of a seed or grain.

ALIPHATIC   (al-ih-*fat*-ick)   Having or belonging to an open-chain structure. The word is derived from the Greek word for fat. The aliphatic compounds are distinguished from the cyclic compounds, which contain rings of carbon atoms instead of chains. Aliphatic groups or compounds are sometimes called fatty, since the fats and oils are representative, common examples of the type. More generally, however, "fatty"

is reserved for the higher members of the unbranched chains, which are more closely related chemically to the natural fats.

ALKALOID   (*al*-kah-loyd)   Any of a group of nitrogenous organic compounds (especially one of vegetable origin). They have a powerful physiological effect on animals, and constitute the active principles of the common vegetable drugs and poisons. Atropin, codeine, morphine, nicotine, quinine, and strychnine are alkaloids.

ALKOXIDES   (alk-*ox*-ids)   Metallic salts of alcohols or phenols in which the hydrogen atom of the hydroxyl group is replaced by a metal, as in CH_3CH_2ONa, the sodium alkoxide of ethyl alcohol, CH_3CH_2OH.

ALLANTOIS   (al-*lan*-to-is)   A tubular sac that in early fetal life develops from the hind-gut of the embryo. It later arches around so as to envelop the embryo completely. Through its development of blood vessels, it performs the function of interchange between the embryo and egg albumen. In mammals it performs the function of metabolic interchange between embryo and mother. The sac contains a fluid called allantoic fluid.

ALLERGEN   (*al*-er-jen)   A foreign substance, generally a protein, which upon being introduced into the tissues of a sensitive person causes inflammation, swelling, or more serious consequences.

AMINES   (aeh-*meenz*)   A group of compounds derived from ammonia (NH_3) by substituting organic groups for the hydrogen, such as NH_2R or NHR_2 and NR_3, where R represents the organic group.

AMINO ACIDS   A group of nitrogen-containing organic compounds that enter into the composition of proteins. Each amino acid molecule contains one or more amino (NH_2) groups. The presence of certain amino acids in the proteins fed to animals is essential to maintenance and growth.

AMNION   (*am*-nih-on)   The innermost fetal membrane, consisting of a sac which encloses the embryo and forms a sheath for the umbilical cord. This amniotic sac contains a watery fluid in which the embryo is suspended. Adjective: amniotic.

AMYLASE   (*am*-ih-lays)   Any of the enzymes that speed up the hydrolysis of starch and glycogen, or their intermediate products of hydrolysis, as dextrin to maltose. α-Amylase produces maltose only slowly from starch, going through the dextrin stage. β-Amylase produces maltose rapidly and directly from starch.

AMYLOLYTIC   (am-ill-oh-*lit*-ick)   Pertaining to the action of enzymes on starch to produce soluble products, such as dextrins and sugars. An enzyme system might act on several materials, but amylolytic power of enzymes refers specifically to the ability of the agent to convert starch to soluble products.

ANABASINE (ah-*nab*-a-sin) An insecticidal compound in certain plants. The name comes from *Anabasis aphylla,* the first plant in which it was found, which grows in Russia. It also occurs in *Nicotiana glauca,* the tree tobacco that grows wild in the Southwest. Anabasine is an alkaloid much like nicotine in its chemical composition and its insecticidal effects. It is used as an insecticide in Russia, but in the United States a commercial supply has not yet been developed.

ANAEROBE (an-*ay*-er-obe) Adapted from a Latin word meaning literally life without air. Any bacterium that can grow in an oxygen-free atmosphere and that derives the oxygen necessary for its life processes from solid or liquid compounds with which it is in contact. Some anaerobic bacteria cannot live in an atmosphere containing oxygen. Others are dependent on gaseous oxygen for their metabolism. See AEROBIC.

ANHYDRASE (ann-*high*-drase) An enzyme capable of accelerating the removal of water from a substance; e. g., carbonic anhydrase removes water from carbonic acid.

ANIMALIZE A term used to indicate a chemical treatment of vegetable fibers, such as cotton or flax, so that the fibers will resemble animal fibers, such as wool, in their behavior toward wool dyes. Wool and silk, being of animal origin, are composed of proteins and attract certain dyes that affect cotton only slightly. By addition of protein-like material to the cotton, it is animalized and may be dyed by the wool dye.

ANODE The positive pole or electrode of an electrolytic cell, vacuum tube, etc.; opposed to cathode.

ANTHOCYANIN PIGMENTS (ann-tho-*si*-a-nin) Naturally occurring plant colors (soluble glucoside pigments) that produce reddish-purplish-blue coloring in flowers and plants.

ANTIBIOSIS (an-tih-bye-*oh*-sis) In nature, large numbers of micro-organisms are found living together in soil, water, and decomposing plant and animal wastes. Some of them are capable of hindering the growth of other microbial forms by the production of acids or other growth-inhibiting metabolic substances.

ANTIBIOTIC (an-tih-bye-*ah*-tik) A chemical compound, derived from or produced by a living organism, which, in high dilution, can inhibit the life processes of some or many micro-organisms.

ANTIGEN (*ann*-tih-jenn) A substance that, when introduced into the blood or tissues of an animal, will stimulate the formation of antibodies. When the antigen which is introduced is disease-producing, the antibodies formed are regarded as immunizing antibodies.

ASCORBIC ACID (ah-*skor*-bick) Vitamin C. An essential growth factor that occurs in fruits (especially citrus) and vegetables.

ATMOSPHERIC PRESSURE The pressure exerted by the earth's atmosphere upon the surfaces of the earth and of objects on the earth. At sea level atmospheric pressure is usually sufficient to support a column of mercury 760 millimeters (almost 30 inches) high or a column of water 33.9 feet high. In either case the weight of liquid supported (under conditions defined as standard) is 14.6974 pounds for every square inch of cross section. Therefore, in expressing high pressures as so many atmospheres per square inch, each "atmosphere" is equivalent to 14.6974 pounds.

ATOM The smallest particle of an element that enters into the composition of molecules. For example, a molecule of water consists of two atoms of hydrogen and one of oxygen. Adjective: atomic.

ATOMIC PILE An extensive structure consisting of many tons of pure graphite and uranium for the production of plutonium; first achieved at Chicago University on December 2, 1942, followed by production units at Oak Ridge, Tenn., and Richland, Wash. It is an essential unit for the production of atomic bombs.

AUREOMYCIN (aw-ree-oh-*my*-sin) An antibiotically active chemical compound, with the approximate formula for the crystalline free base, $C_{22}H_{26}O_6N_2Cl$. It is produced by fermentation during the growth of the actinomycete *Streptomyces aureofaciens* in a suitable culture medium. The pure substance is golden yellow.

AUTOCLAVE (*auto*-clave) An airtight vessel into which superheated steam can be introduced under pressure, at temperatures above 212° F. It is used for sterilizing.

AUTOLYTIC (auto-*lit*-ick) Self-digestive; the process of self-digestion, occurring in vegetable and animal tissues, particularly after they have ceased to be a normal part of the organism to which they belong; hence, the tenderizing of beef during hanging is an autolytic process.

AUTOXIDATION (au-tock-sih-*day*-shun) The reaction of the oxygen in air with fats, oils, or other substances. It occurs at ordinary temperatures. Its rate increases as it proceeds. Oils and fats develop rancid odors and flavors after autoxidation.

AVIDIN (*av*-id-in) A protein of egg white comprising only 0.5 percent of the total solids; so named because of its unique property of avidly combining with the vitamin biotin and thus causing the biotin to be unavailable to animals when raw egg white is consumed. Sufficient cooking of egg white inactivates the avidin, thereby preventing any such effect.

β- In chemical names: A symbol for the combining form *beta-*, used to distinguish one of two or more isomers or modifications; or to indicate the position of substituting atoms or groups of atoms in the molecules of certain compounds. In acids, it commonly indicates that the atom or group substituted is in union with the carbon atom next to the one to which the carboxyl group is attached.

BACITRACIN (bass-ih-*tray*-sin) A complex antibiotically active chemical compound belonging to the polypeptide class produced during the fermentation of suitable culture media by a special strain of the bacterium *Bacillus subtilis.*

BACTERIA (bak-*teer*-i-uh) A large group of one-celled, microscopic organisms, widely distributed in the air, water, soil, and animal and plant tissues, including foods. The cells occur singly and also in colonies or long chains and filaments. Bacteria cause many infectious diseases in plants and animals; they also exert many beneficial effects in agriculture (fixing of atmospheric nitrogen, decay of dead matter), in food industries (vinegar fermentation), and in chemical industries (acetone, butanol, and organic acid production).

BACTERIOSTATIC (bak-teer-e-o-*stat*-ik) Preventive of growth of bacteria. Certain chemical compounds, notably various dyes, prevent the growth of bacteria.

BAGASSE (ba-*gahs*) The mill residues from the cane-sugar industry, consisting of the crushed stalks from which the juice has been expressed. The word may be applied to similar residues from other plants, such as sorghum, beet, or sisal, but it usually refers to sugarcane bagasse when unmodified.

BAST The phloem or sieve tissue of plants. The word is also applied to the fibers making up this tissue. These are also called bast fibers. Loosely speaking, any commercial fiber arising from the stem of the plant is called a bast fiber. This group includes such important fibers as flax (linen), hemp, jute, and ramie.

BATING (*bate*-ing) One of the steps in the tanning of leather, following dehairing with lime, in which the skins are soaked in a bath containing enzymes and ammonium salts. The purpose is to remove residual lime, hair, skin, glands, and such.

B-COMPLEX VITAMINS The term "vitamin B" was first used to distinguish water-soluble accessory food factors from those that are fat-soluble. It was gradually realized that vitamin B is really a mixture, or complex, of many chemicals which were at first designated as B_1, B_2, etc. When the composition of the chemicals became known, each was given a name; i. e., thiamine (B_1), riboflavin (B_2), pyridoxine, niacin, biotin, choline; folic acid, *p*-aminobenzoic acid, etc. The most recently well characterized member of this complex, B_{12}, although pure, has not had its constitution completely worked out.

BETA RAY (*bay*-ta ray) A stream of electrons emitted from a radioactive substance. It is like the cathode ray but has a much higher velocity.

BETATRON (*bay*-ta-tron) A device for speeding up electrons in a vacuum chamber, resembling a large doughnut, by means of very strong magnetic fields; these electron projectiles, with speeds up to 30 million volts, are used for producing penetrating X-rays for atomic research.

BIOSYNTHESIS (bye-o-*sin*-the-sis) The building of chemical substances, often complex ones, by living organisms, generally from simpler materials.

BIOTIN (*bye*-o-tin) One of the B vitamins (B_4), which prevents pellagra in rats. Biotin deficiency seldom occurs in man because of its wide distribution in foods.

BIREFRINGENCE (bye-rih-*fringe*-ence) The property, common to most crystals and many colloidal aggregates, of exhibiting different optical properties in different directions. Birefringent materials have more than one index of refraction, depending both upon the direction of vibration of the light passing through them and upon the direction of transmission of the light.

BOLOMETER (bo-*lom*-i-ter) An electrical device used to measure radiant energy by changes in resistance of a blackened platinum strip exposed to the radiations.

BOTULINUM (bot-you-*lye*-num) A species of anaerobic bacteria of the genus *Clostridium*, capable of producing a highly poisonous substance in preserved foods, especially in sausages and in canned meats and nonacid canned fruits or vegetables that have not been heated high enough or long enough for complete sterilization. The word is derived from the Latin word *botulus* meaning sausage, since the effects of this organism were first observed in sausages and were referred to as sausage poisoning. The poisonous substance, produced in the absence of air, can be readily destroyed by heating at 212° F. The bacteria themselves are very heat-resistant in the spore form and apparently cause no injury if taken into the body.

BROWNIAN MOVEMENT The rapid vibratory motion of extremely small particles suspended in a liquid, caused by bombardment of the particles by the moving molecules of the liquid. This movement may be observed with a microscope if a strong beam of light is caused to traverse the solution across the line of sight. The particles appear to dance about, back and forth, up and down, in and out, with a restless, haphazard sort of motion.

BUFFER A substance which, when added to a solution, causes resistance to any change in acidity or alkalinity.

BUTANEDIOL (byou-tane-*dye*-ol) Synonymous with butylene glycol and dihydroxybutane. Diol, like glycol, indicates an aliphatic organic compound having two hydroxyl (OH) groups, that is, a dihydroxy alcohol. Butanediol, therefore, is butane (C_4H_{10}) in which two of the hydrogens have been replaced by hydroxyl groups. Each hydroxyl group is attached to a different carbon atom in the chainlike molecule. Four isomers of butanediol are theoretically possible, depending on whether the hydroxyl groups are attached to adjacent carbon atoms at either end of the chain, to adjacent carbon atoms in the center of the chain, to alternate carbon atoms, or to carbon atoms at both ends of the chain. These four isomers are known. All are colorless liquids having different densities and different boiling points. They absorb moisture from the air, mix with water in all proportions, and dissolve in alcohol and ether. Some may replace other glycols or glycerin in antifreeze, humectant, or brake fluids where their particular properties offer an advantage.

BUTANOL (*byou*-ta-nol) or BUTYL ALCOHOL An alcohol derived from butane, a gaseous compound, and is similar to ethyl alcohol. It, together with acetone, is made by a bacterial fermentation of carbohydrates. It is widely used as a solvent for resins, waxes, fats, etc.

CALORIMETER (kal-o-*rim*-i-ter) An instrument for measuring the quantity of heat produced.

CAPILLARITY (kap-i-*lar*-i-ti) The action by which the surface of a liquid, where it is in contact with a solid, is elevated or depressed. Capillarity depends upon the relative attraction of the molecules of the liquid for one another and for those of the solid, and is especially observable in capillary tubes, where it determines the ascent or descent of the liquid above or below the level of the liquid in which the tube is dipped. The size of capillary vessels in fruit and vegetables limits their rate of drying.

CAPILLARY FRAGILITY The ease with which the true capillaries rupture when subjected to stress or injury. In a true rupture of capillaries the formed cellular elements of blood as well as the plasma escape into the surrounding tissues. Such an escape of whole blood occurs in a bruise resulting in a black-and-blue area.

CARBOHYDRATES Organic compounds containing only carbon, hydrogen, and oxygen. Among them are sugars, starches, and cellulose. Carbohydrates are formed in plant material as the result of photosynthesis and are the chief energy-producing constitutents of all vegetable food materials.

CAROTENE or PROVITAMIN A A crystalline carbohydrate material that accompanies chlorophyll in green plants and serves as a source of vitamin A in animal nutrition. Several chemical variants of carotene are known. The ruby-red, crystalline form of carotene, found in carrots and some other vegetable materials, is sometimes used as a coloring pigment in butter and cheese.

CAROTENOIDS (ka-*rot*-i-noids) A group name for lipochromes or carotenelike plant pigments (yellow polyenes), which, through food, are deposited in animal tissues.

CASEIN (*kay*-see-in) A protein compound found only in milk. It is the principal ingredient in cottage cheese.

CATALASE (*kat*-a-lase) An oxidizing enzyme of tissues which splits hydrogen peroxide to oxygen and water.

CATALYST (*kat*-a-list) A substance that induces, or changes the speed of, a chemical reaction, either by influencing the degree of contact between the reacting substances or by temporarily forming an intermediate compound, and appears to be unchanged after the reaction is over. Finely divided nickel is used as a catalyst in the commercial hydrogenation of vegetable oils to obtain fatlike products.

CATHODE (*kath*-ode) The negative pole or electrode of an electrolytic cell, vacuum tube, etc.; opposed to anode.

CAUSTIC SODA The hydroxide of sodium. A white, brittle, deliquescent solid prepared chiefly by the electrolysis of a solution of common salt and by treating sodium carbonate with slaked lime. Solutions of caustic soda and water are strongly alkaline and constitute the most common type of lye found in the household and industry. Large amounts of caustic soda are used in the refining of edible oils and in the manufacture of soaps.

CELL In biology the cell is the basic structure of which all living things are built. This microscopic unit consists of a membrane within which one can usually distinguish a central portion (nucleus) and surrounding cytoplasm, which contains a sticky material (protoplasm). Living organisms may consist of one cell (the amoeba) or of billions (man).

CELLULOSE   A carbohydrate of high molecular weight consisting of a long chain of glucose residues joined together by glucoside linkages. The name, originally French, was given because cellulose is the major component of the plant-cell wall. The chief commercial sources of pure cellulose are cotton and wood pulp, but almost all vegetable tissue contains cellulose. Cellulose is a white fibrous material, insoluble in water and common organic solvents, which is the basis of the vegetable textile fibers and of rayon. Paper and wood are also essentially unchanged cellulose.

CENTRIFUGE   (sen-tri-fuge)   A device which utilizes the property of any body to move outward from the center while rotating to separate material which is suspended in a liquid of different density. Thus cream is separated from milk with a centrifuge, and water is separated from clothes by centrifugelike action in some automatic washing machines.

CHEMOTHERAPEUTIC   (kem-o-ther-a-pew-tik)   Pertaining to the treatment of diseases by the use of specific chemical compounds which have immediate toxic effects on the micro-organisms that cause the disease without seriously harming the patient. Penicillin, streptomycin, quinine, and sulfa drugs are examples.

CHLOROMYCETIN   (klor-o-mye-see-tin)   An antibiotically active chemical compound ($C_{11}H_{12}NO_5Cl_2$) produced by Streptomyces venezuelae during the fermentation of a suitable culture medium. This substance is also produced by chemical synthesis. "Chloro" means containing chlorine.

CHLOROPHYLL   (klor-o-fill)   The green coloring matter of plants, extracted from their green parts as a mixture of about three parts of chlorophyll a to one part of chlorophyll b, accompanied by other pigments, such as carotene and xanthophyll.

CHLOROPHYLLIDES   (klor-o-fill-ides)   Any of the pigments obtained from chlorophyll by removing that portion of the molecule called the phytyl group, which can be accomplished by hydrolysis (reaction with water). Chlorophyllides can be regarded as degradation products of chlorophyll, the green coloring matter of plants. Oilseeds, like cottonseed and soybeans, contain some chlorophyll, especially when the seeds are immature; and crushing or solvent extracting of such seeds yields an oil containing chlorophyll or its derivatives.

CHOLINE   (ko-leen)   A crystalline chemical that is widely distributed in plant and animal life. It is important in nutrition and is sometimes classified as one of the B vitamins. It occurs in lecithin, a compound obtained from plant materials and extensively used in food products as an emulsifying agent.

CHROMATOGRAPHY   (krome-a-tog-ra-fi)   A method for the separation of certain chemical mixtures into their constituent parts. It is based upon differential adsorbtion, or partition between solvents, or both. An early application of the method was for the separation of mixtures of plant substances, the separated pure compounds appearing as colored bands on an adsorption column.

CHROMOSOMES   (kro-mo-somz)   The bodies in cells of plants or animals that transmit hereditary characteristics to succeeding generations.

CHYMOTRYPSINOGEN   (kye-mo-trip-sin-o-gen)   A substance that forms chymotrypsin. It occurs in the body in pancreatic juice, which is secreted into the small intestine. There it is converted by the enzyme trypsin into chymotrypsin. Chymotrypsin is another enzyme which aids in digesting proteins. Unlike trypsin, it clots milk.

CITRIC ACID   (sit-rik)   This acid, having the formula $C_6H_8O_7$, occurs widely in nature, especially in the citrus fruits, oranges, lemons, grapefruit, limes. It is also manufactured from carbohydrates by a mold-fermentation process. Citric acid is widely used, especially in beverages and foods.

COAGULATION   The act or state of becoming jellylike or of uniting into a coherent mass. The change from a liquid to a thickened curdlike state, not by evaporation, but by chemical reaction or heat; as the coagulation of blood, milk, or egg white.

COEFFICIENT   An expression of a relationship between two kinds of observations. Thus the speed of a car in miles per hour is a coefficient. It gives the relationship between miles traveled and hours elapsed. A correlation coefficient is a measure of the closeness with which two kinds of observations are related. A very close relationship exists if this coefficient approaches 1, and no relationship exists if it approaches 0. A close relation would be expected between the distance a car travels and its speed; little relationship would be expected between the distance traveled and the color of the driver's hair.

COLCHICINE (koll-chi-seen)   An alkaloid present in the seeds and corm of meadow saffron, or autumn crocus (Colchicum autumnale L). It may be obtained in the form of pale-yellow amorphous scales or powder from water solution or yellow crystals from chloroform solution. Colchicine is odorless, has a bitter taste, and is poisonous. It has some use in human and veterinary medicine and is also used in plant-breeding experiments. Application of an aqueous solution of colchicine to plant foliage promotes growth and causes the chromosomes of the seeds to double in number. The treatment is used by commercial seed growers to obtain varieties of flowering plants that are larger and have larger blossoms than their parents.

COLIFORM (*koll*-i-form) Resembling or designating a certain group of bacteria, some species of which are normally present in the large intestine and feces of all warm-blooded animals. Other species are present on grains, grasses, and other plant materials. Because organisms of this group occur on feeds and in manure, they are usually present in raw milk. All organisms of the coliform group are ordinarily destroyed during proper commercial pasteurization of milk. The presence of coliform organisms in pasteurized milk is direct evidence of improper pasteurization or recontamination of the milk after pasteurization.

COLLAGEN (*koll*-a-jen) A gelatinlike protein occurring in vertebrates. It is the chief constituent of the fibrils of connective tissue and an important part of hides to be tanned.

COLLODION (kol-*loe*-dee-un) A thick sirupy solution consisting of pyroxylin (nitrated cellulose) dissolved in alcohol and ether, or in acetone, which may be used to make photographic film or as a coating for wounds.

COLLOID (*koll*-oid) Any substance in a state of fine suspension or dispersion with particles ranging between one one-hundred-thousandth and one-ten-millionth of a centimeter in diameter, as colloidal gold, sulfur, soil particles.

CONALBUMIN (kon-al-*byou*-min) A protein of egg white comprising approximately 12 percent of the total solids. It possesses the unique property of firmly binding iron into a pinkish-colored, iron-protein complex. The pinkish discoloration of egg white occurring in the shell or in egg white stored in rusty containers may be caused by the formation of this complex. Iron is so firmly bound by conalbumin that growth of certain micro-organisms may be inhibited by iron starvation. This property of egg white is destroyed by cooking.

COPOLYMERIZED (ko-*poll*-i-mer-ized) Formed by polymerization when two or more polymerizable substances are present, the product being an intimate mixture of more complex substances. An example of such a product is GR–S synthetic rubber, which is formed by the copolymerization of butadiene and styrene.

CRYSTALLITE In general, a small or imperfectly formed crystal. The word is used in the chemistry of high polymers, such as cellulose, to designate those regions of the material which are sufficiently well ordered to give a regular X-ray diffraction pattern and to give other evidences of high molecular order. Crystallites in this sense, however, are submicroscopic and do not exhibit the plane surfaces and angles characteristic of macro crystals.

CUBE (*kew*-bay) A Peruvian name for the roots of *Lonchocarpus* species containing rotenone. Large quantities of cube root are imported into the United States from South America for the manufacture of insecticides.

CYCLOTRONS (*sigh*-klo-trons) Devices for producing high-speed projectiles for disintegrating the nucleus of atoms; protons and deuterons move in spiral paths as they are accelerated twice per revolution, until they attain speeds up to 350 million-electron-volts.

d- A symbol for the combining form *dextro*-, indicating that the compound to whose name it is attached is dextrorotatory.

DEHYDRATION The process of removing water from substances.

DENATURATION Modification of a protein (from milk, blood, egg) by heat, acid, or alkali so that it no longer has all its original properties. Protein denaturation is usually considered to consist in a little-understood but irreversible change.

DENSITY The weight of any substance contained in a given unit of volume.

DEODORIZATION The process of removing, correcting, or repressing undesirable odors. Deodorization is one of the most important operations in the processing of fats; practically all edible fats are subjected to it before being offered to consumers. The odoriferous constituents of fats comprise both compounds naturally present and those formed during other processing operations. All are removed by heating the fat to a high temperature and bubbling steam through it while a partial vacuum is maintained above the surface of the fat.

DERRIS (*dare*-is) A genus of tropical plants containing rotenone. Derris root imported from the East Indies was widely used as a source of rotenone insecticides until war cut off shipments and resulted in the destruction of many of the plantings. Derris species, growing in the East Indies, have long been used by the natives as fish poisons. The species generally used as an insecticide is *Derris elliptica*.

DETERGENT A cleansing agent. Any material that aids in removing undesirable matter from the surface to be cleaned.

DEXTRINS   Products obtained by the partial chemical breakdown of starch by the action of heat, acids, enzymes, or a combination of these agents. A dextrin is not a definite chemical compound but usually contains a mixture of molecular types ranging in size between the simple sugars and the original starch molecules. Dextrins also differ from starch in that they dissolve in water. Two main types of dextrins are made. The more important pyrofaction or torrefaction dextrins are produced by the action of heat or heat and acids on dry starch. These dextrins are used as adhesives in the sizing of paper and textiles, and as sealing agents in the manufacture of paper bags, envelopes, etc. Other dextrins are produced as constituents of sirups. In the conversion of starch by acids or enzymes to sirups, where the primary objective is the production of simple sugars such as dextrose and maltose, a portion of the starch remains incompletely broken down to sugars, so that a fair percentage of dextrins remains in the final sirup. This is an advantage, since the sirup might be bitter if the conversion is complete. The word "dextrin" is derived from the Latin word *dextro* meaning to the right and was selected because water solutions of the dextrins rotate the plane of polarized light to the right.

DEXTROROTATORY   (dex-tro-*ro*-ta-to-ree) Descriptive of certain optically active organic compounds, including some sugars, which, when dissolved in water and tested in a polariscope, turn the plane of polarized light to the right (clockwise). The opposite of levorotatory. A solution of dextrose or of sucrose is dextrorotatory, whereas a solution of levulose or of invert sugar is levorotatory. The magnitude of the rotation when a solution of standard concentration is used is indicated by the angle through which the plane is turned and can readily be measured on the scale of the polariscope. The fact that sucrose (cane sugar) solution shows a definite optical rotation under standardized conditions of concentration and temperature, made possible the design of a special polariscope, called a saccharimeter or polarimeter, for quickly and easily determining the percentage of sucrose in raw sugars from the reading on the scale.

DEXTROSE   See GLUCOSE.

DIALYSIS   (dye-*al*-ih-sis) The separation of small molecules (usually crystalloids) from large molecules (colloids) in solution by taking advantage of their unequal rates of diffusion through natural or artificial membranes; the small molecules diffuse readily, whereas the colloids diffuse very slowly or not at all.

DIASTASES   (*dye*-ah-stays-ez) An older designation for the enzymes responsible for the breakdown of starches to sugars. Since this conversion from starch to sugar, probably the first type of enzyme reaction observed, was recorded in the scientific literature by a Frenchman, the term is synonymous with *enzymes* in the French language.

DIATHERMY   (*dye*-a-ther-mi) The generation of heat in the body tissues due to the resistance offered by the tissues to high-frequency radiation forced into them; the greater the resistance, the greater is the heat produced by a given radiation. The wave-length region, utilized for this purpose covers a range of 3 to 30 meters, which is found in approximately the center of the Hertzian region of electromagnetic vibrations. See WAVE LENGTH.

DIELECTRIC   A nonconducting material, so called because the lines of force of an electric field will pass through it, thereby making it the seat of strain.

DIFFRACTION   A modification which light undergoes in passing by the edges of opaque bodies, or through narrow slits, or in being reflected from ruled surfaces. Diffraction is a phenomenon of wave motion in general and occurs whenever the full wave front is not brought to a focus or made use of.

DIFFUSION   In physics and chemistry: (1) A spontaneous process of equalization of physical states; specifically (a) diffusion of temperature by heat conduction, (b) diffusion of concentration in a solution in which the particles in solution become uniformly distributed, (c) diffusion of gases when one gas is liberated in another. (2) The process of reflection of light by a rough reflecting surface or of transmission of light through a translucent material.

DIGESTION   In physiology, the transformation of food into living matter; e. g., the change of proteins, carbohydrates, and fats, under the influence of enzymes, into substances which are assimilable.

DIMENSIONAL STABILITY   As applied to fabrics, the ability to retain original dimensions and shape; that is, to resist shrinkage or stretching—for example, in laundering, dry cleaning, pressing, and wear.

DISPERSION   A state of extremely fine subdivision. When one speaks of a dispersion of a high polymer, such as cellulose, it is generally understood to be liquid, either a true solution, an emulsion, or a very fine homogeneous suspension.

DISTILLATION   A process in which a substance or mixture of substances is heated in a closed container (often called a retort or still), with the liberation of a vapor or gas, which is conducted from the container and is later converted entirely or in part to a liquid by cooling. In *steam distillation*, steam is used to carry over the vapors of substances not readily miscible with water, like turpentine and other essential oils. In *vacuum distillation,* vaporization is effected at lower temperatures by reducing the pressure within the system.

DIURETIC (dye-yew-*ret*-ik A drug that tends to increase the secretion of urine.

DIVALENT (dye-*vail*-ent) Having the ability to enter chemical combination simultaneously with two other atoms or combining units. Example: In magnesium chloride ($MgCl_2$) the divalent magnesium atom is combined with two monovalent chlorine atoms. A divalent element is capable of losing two electrons to, or acquiring two electrons from, the elements with which it combines. Thus, magnesium loses two electrons, one to each chloride atom. In the compound calcium oxide (CaO), in which both elements, calcium and oxygen, are divalent, the calcium atom loses two electrons to the oxygen, and, conversely, the oxygen acquires two electrons from the calcium. Loss or acquisition of electrons is never complete, the electrons shifting their orbits to vibrate in pairs between the nuclei of the combined atoms.

DRYING OIL Any natural oil of plant or animal origin which in thin layers absorbs oxygen more or less rapidly and polymerizes to form a skin or film. The process of film formation is known as drying. If the film is formed in a few hours, the oil is said to be a *fast-drying oil* (tung, oiticica, dehydrated castor); if film formation requires a day to several days, the oil is referred to simply as a *drying oil* (linseed, perilla); if film formation requires several days to several weeks, the oil is classified as a *semidrying* oil (soybean).

EDEMA (e-*dee*-ma) Swelling due to entrance of watery liquid into the connective tissue.

ELASTIN Fibrous, yellow, connective tissue in skin, ligaments, tendons, blood vessels, and all other supporting and protective tissues.

ELASTOMER A generic term for all substances having the properties of natural, reclaimed, vulcanized, or synthetic rubber.

ELECTROMETER (ee-lek-*trom*-i-ter) An instrument for measuring very small electric currents, or the difference in potential between two points of a conductor or two electric charges in air.

ELECTRON The most elementary charge of negative electricity. Its mass is about 1/1800 of that of the atom hydrogen. Electrons constitute cathode rays and beta rays and are emitted by hot bodies; the filaments of radio and television vacuum tubes are sources of electrons.

ELECTROPHORESIS (ee-lek-tro-fo-*ree*-sis) The movement of electrically charged particles, including proteins, when an electric current is passed through a solution. The rate at which proteins migrate depends primarily on the number of electric charges carried by the molecule in relation to the size and shape of the molecule. Since proteins vary in this respect, electrophoretic measurements can be used to determine the number of different proteins in a solution.

ELUTE (ee-*lute*) To wash off, or remove from; specifically, to remove by extraction a chemical compound from a substance on which it has been adsorbed.

EMPIRICAL (em-*peer*-rih-kal) Pertaining to, or founded upon, experiment or experience. An empirical formula is one that expresses the kinds and numbers of atoms as indicated by a quantitative chemical analysis, but does not show how the atoms are grouped. $Fe_2S_3O_{12}$ is the empirical formula for ferric sulfate, which is commonly represented by the rational formula $Fe_2(SO_4)_3$.

EMULSIFY To make a milklike fluid from two liquids that do not blend (like oil and water) by vigorously agitating a mixture of the two, whereby minute droplets of one liquid become suspended in the other.

ENDOSPERM The main portion of the grain kernel. With exception of the small space occupied by the germ, the endosperm tissue fills the interior of the kernel. It is the nutritive material on which the embryo feeds when germinating. In general, there are two types of endosperm, the corneous (horny) and the floury. The former is quite hard and occupies the outer part of the kernel under the bran coat. The innermost portion of the kernel, made up of floury endosperm, is fairly friable.

ENTEROTOXINS (*en*-ter-o-*tox*-ins) Products of bacterial growth that cause inflammation of the intestinal tract, a form of food poisoning. Certain kinds of staphylococci can produce food poisoning owing to enterotoxins if they gain access to improperly refrigerated milk or soft foods such as custards, gravy, and creamed meats. Enterotoxins are heat-resistant to the extent that they are not destroyed by pasteurization.

ENZYME (*enn*-zyme) A natural chemical product of plant or animal cells that brings about changes in organic materials, like ripening, fermentation, or digestion. The word is derived from Greek words meaning in leaven (yeast): Enzymes retain their activity after being separated from living organisms. They induce or speed up chemical reactions in substances of plant or animal origin. Each enzyme has a specific action and greatest activity at a definite pH value. Their classification is based upon the type of reaction or the material (substrate) acted upon. About 60 kinds are known. They are generally proteins. Enzymes are important in many industrial fields. If not inactivated, certain enzymes cause deterioration of processed foods. In brewing the enzymes of malt are required to convert the starch to fermentable sugars. Enzyme preparations are also used in preparing hides for tanning.

EPIMERIZATION (ep-i-mer-i-*zay*-shun) A term used in carbohydrate chemistry to denote the process of reversing the positions of a hydrogen atom (H) and a hydroxyl group (OH) on a particular carbon atom in the carbohydrate molecule.

EPITHELIUM (ep-i-*theel*-i-um) The tissue, consisting wholly of living cells of varying form and arrangement forming a practically unbroken sheet, or membrane, which covers the free surfaces of the skin, mucous membranes, and various organs, and lines, tubes, or cavities in the body. It encloses and protects the various parts of the body and facilitates the absorption of nutrients and the excretion of waste products.

EPOXY- (ep-*ox*-i) A prefix denoting the presence of oxygen attached to two different atoms of a molecular chain.

ESSENTIAL OILS Odorous organic liquids that exist in plants or plant products or that are developed from plant constituents by the action of enzymes or the effect of heat. They differ from fatty oils in that they are not greasy and do not form soaps. They are volatile and therefore can be recovered by distillation with steam. Familiar examples are oil of sassafras, spirits of turpentine, oil of citronella, oil of bitter almonds, oil of spearmint. Essential oils are inflammable, soluble in alcohol or ether, and only slightly soluble in water.

ESTER A compound formed by the combination of an alcohol and an organic acid with elimination of water. An ester is sometimes referred to as an organic salt, because it corresponds to an inorganic salt in being formed from an acid and a base. In the case of esters, the base is an alcohol (which contains the OH or hydroxyl group), whereas in the case of an inorganic salt, the base is the hydroxide of an alkali or other metal (like $Zn(OH)_2$, zinc hydroxide). So-called banana oil is an ester made from isoamyl alcohol and acetic acid; artificial oil of wintergreen is an ester made from methyl alcohol and salicylic acid; cellulose acetate is an ester of acetic acid and cellulose, which contains hydroxyl (OH) groups and acts like an alcohol; lard oil is an ester of oleic acid and glycerin, a trihydroxy alcohol.

ETHANOLAMINE (*eth*-a-nol-a-*meen*) A nitrogen-containing basic compound occurring naturally in some plant and animal tissues. It is an essential part of cephalin, a constituent of nerve tissue. Ethanolamine has many of the physiological characteristics of choline and is of interest for its possible effect on the character of fat deposited in animals.

ETHERIFICATION (ee-*ther*-i-fi-*kay*-shun) The process of preparing ethers. The word "ether," derived from the Latin, originally meant the clear firmament and is akin to the Greek word meaning to blaze. The common ethers are transparent, colorless, volatile, and inflammable, which properties presumably contributed to the derivation of the word. Chemically, ethers are formed by combining two alcohol molecules with loss of one molecule of water. Etherification is an important industrial process, particularly in the case of cellulose. Cellulose ethers are mixed ethers in which one alcohol is cellulose and the other alcohol may differ. The degree of etherification refers to how large a proportion of the cellulose hydroxyl has been etherified.

ETHYL ALCOHOL An alcohol made by the yeast fermentation of carbohydrates and found in all alcoholic beverages such as beer, wine, and whisky. It has many uses, in medicine as an antiseptic, in automobile radiators as an antifreeze, and in chemical products as a solvent for a wide variety of materials. Also known as grain alcohol or ethanol.

EUGENOL (*yew*-je-nol) An aromatic liquid compound occurring in a number of different essential oils including oils of cloves, pimento, star anise, and citronella.

EXOTHERMIC (ex-o-*ther*-mik) A term indicating the liberation or escape of heat. The word is derived from two Greek words, one meaning outside and the other heat. For example, converting cottonseed oil into shortening by catalytic hydrogenation liberates enough heat to raise the temperature of the oil by 125° F. The burning of wood is another example of exothermic reaction.

FACTICE (*fak*-tis) A rubberlike substance, obtained by the reaction of such oils as linseed, soybean, and cottonseed with sulfur or certain of its compounds; a vulcanized oil. The sulfur converts the oil into a rubbery compound by serving as a connecting link between molecules of oil. Factice is used as a rubber filler and softener and as a rubber substitute. Art gum erasers are a form of factice.

FATTY, or FAT, ACID Any one of a series of saturated acids having the general formula $C_nH_{2n}O_2$, so called because some of the members, as stearic and palmitic acids, occur in natural fats and are fatlike substances.

FELTING The interlocking of wool fibers produced by fiber movement caused by pounding and rubbing of loose wool or wool fabric.

FERMENTATION Any transformation induced by micro-organisms, or by their enzyme products. Organic substances are fermented to a wide variety of products, such as ethyl alcohol, lactic acid, penicillin, and vitamin B_2.

FIBER In a general sense, any threadlike material; specifically, those threadlike tissues having sufficient toughness for use in the textile or similar industries. The textile fibers may be one-celled, like cotton, or multicellular, like wool. They may derive from the vegetable (cotton and flax), animal (silk and wool), or mineral (asbestos) kingdom. There are also man-made fibers produced by chemical processes, such as viscose rayon, nylon, and cellulose acetate.

FIBRIL (*fye*-brill) A small thread or fiber; a fiberlike chain of molecules arranged in one direction.

FIBROVASCULAR (fye-bro-*vas*-kew-ler) Having, or consisting of, both fibers and conducting cells or vessels; as a fibrovascular bundle of a stem or leaf.

FILAMENT A single continuous fiber of indefinite length, such as rayon, nylon, or silk, in contrast to staple fibers, such as cotton or wool, whose lengths are limited to one or several inches. A filament often extends for several thousand yards.

FILM YEAST A type of yeast (microscopic fungus) which grows on the surface of certain nutrient liquids and produces heavy, folded films. Such yeasts are widely distributed in nature and are generally found in fermentation processes on the surface of sugar-containing solutions, pickle brines, or other acid- and sugar-containing liquids. These yeasts are usually able to grow in very high concentrations of salt, acid, and sugar.

FILTRATION The process of separating solid particles from a liquid by bringing the mixture in contact with a sheet or continuous and compact layer of porous material in such a way that the liquid passes through by gravitation. Filtration may also be effected by centrifugal force, by hydraulic or air pressure applied to the liquid, or by sucking the liquid through the filter with a partial vacuum. The purpose of filtration may be either to recover a precipitate or suspended solids, or simply to strain or clarify the liquid. The removal of solid and liquid particles suspended in air or other gas by passing the gas through a porous substance is called air or gas filtration. The partial absorption of light by passing a beam of light through a colored glass or other transparent or translucent medium is called light filtration.

FIXED NICOTINE Fixed nicotine or nicotine bentonite is formed by adding nicotine sulfate to a suspension of bentonite clay in water, resulting in a base-exchange reaction. Bentonite clays, mined in various places in the United States, are variable complex compounds of aluminum silicates, combined with calcium, sodium, magnesium, and other metals. In the fixing reaction, nicotine alkaloid combines with the bentonite to form a stable compound, thereby releasing some of the metals as sulfates.

FLAVANONE (*flay*-van-own) A substance related to the class of plant pigments called flavones (from Latin *flavus* meaning yellow) because of their yellow or yellowish colors. The parent substance, flavone ($C_{15}H_{10}O_2$), from which numerous flavones are derived, is not yellow. It is a colorless crystalline compound found as a dust on the leaves and seed capsules of primroses. It is soluble in alcohol but insoluble in water and melts just below the boiling point of water. Flavanone is the dihydro derivative of flavone; that is, its molecule contains two additional hydrogen atoms ($C_{15}H_{12}O_2$).

FLAVONOLS (*flay*-von-olls) A class of organic chemical compounds derived from a 3-hydroxyl derivative of flavone and occurring in plant pigments. They may be simple, like quercetin, which is a pentahydroxy flavone, or combined with sugars to form glycosides like rutin, quercitrin, and isoquercitrin. They are usually nontoxic to animals and formerly were important as yellow vegetable dyes.

FLAVOPROTEIN (flay-vo-*pro*-tee-in) A combination of a protein, a material that yields only amino acids on hydrolysis, with a yellow-green fluorescent pigment, riboflavin.

FLOCCULATING (flock-you-*late*-ing) Coagulating or coalescing finely divided suspended matter. Flocculation is widely used in clarification of liquid products.

FOLIC ACID (*foe*-lik) Several acids that come under this heading are organic compounds occurring mainly in leafy plant material. They are important to animal life and are classed as vitamins. Medicinally, folic acids are used to combat certain types of anemia.

FOOTS, or SOAP STOCK The product that is separated by alkali neutralization of the fatty acids in crude vegetable oils. It consists mainly of soap, entrained neutral oil, nonfatty organic substances, and moisture. It is used in the manufacture of soap and for the recovery of fatty acids.

FORMULA In the chemical sense, a representation of the kinds and proportions of atoms in the molecule of a chemical compound by a combination of symbols for the chemical elements present and the use of subscript numerals after the symbols to indicate the number of such atoms when greater than 1. The simplest chemical formula shows the kind and number of atoms in a molecule. It is known as the empirical formula. Other chemical formulas employ various signs or diagrams to give additional information, such as the grouping of atoms within the molecule, the electric charge carried by different atoms, the spatial structure of a compound, the valence bonds between radicals and atoms, and the arrangement of atoms in an optically active compound.

FRACTIONAL DISTILLATION A physical method for separating liquid mixtures of chemical compounds by distilling them at gradually increasing temperatures and collecting any uncondensed gas and the condensed liquid and residue as a number of fractions, each one of which represents a definite range of boiling points. The process is repeated with individual fractions, the purpose being to narrow the boiling ranges of the final fractions as much as possible, and eventually to obtain fractions having fixed boiling points (characteristic of pure compounds). Petroleum refining is an example of fractional distillation. The products of the initial distillation of paraffin-base petroleum are gas, mineral naphthas, gas oils, lubricant stock, and residues. From these are obtained the hydrocarbon mixtures known as rhigoline, petroleum ether, benzine, ligroin, cleaners' naphtha, gasoline, kerosene, fuel oils, gas oils, lubricating oils, Diesel fuels, petrolatum, and paraffin.

FREE FATTY ACIDS A group of organic, aliphatic-type, monobasic acids occurring in the uncombined state in fats and oils or their derivatives. Fats generally are compounds of fatty acids and glycerol. Under certain conditions reaction with water decomposes these compounds into free fatty acids and free glycerol. The content of free fatty acids can be measured easily and is a criterion of fat quality.

FROTH FLOTATION A method of floating particles or bodies on a given liquid according to their wettability rather than their density. Bubbles formed in the liquid by vigorous stirring become attached to particles or bodies not easily wetted by the liquid and cause them to float.

FULLING A process of imparting a felt-like character to wool cloth, or of producing felt. The effect is obtained by repeatedly squeezing the cloth while it is in folds and is wet with a hot soap solution.

FUNGI (fun-jye) (A primary botanical division of primitive plants, including those destitute of chlorophyll (green coloring substance) and typically parasitic. Fungi reproduce by means of asexual spores developed in various ways. Popularly they are mushrooms, toadstools, and molds.

FURFURAL or FURFURALDEHYDE One of a class of organic compounds known as aldehydes. Furfural is a high-boiling, amber-colored, limpid liquid having a faint odor of bitter almonds.

GALLATES (gal-lates) Salts of gallic acid, an organic acid that occurs in many plants, particularly tea. The acid is used commercially in making dyes and ink, and medicinally as an astringent since it acts similarly to alum. Some gallates can reduce the rate of spoilage of edible fats.

GAMMA RAYS A type of ray similar to X-rays but of shorter wave length, emitted by certain radioactive substances, for example, radium.

GEL A gelatinous colloid. A gel containing fruit juices and 65 percent or more of sugar is defined as a jelly.

GELATION Partial coagulation of an aqueous colloid which results in the formation of a gel.

GENES The basic units within the chromosomes in the nucleus of the living cell which are responsible for the transmission of hereditary traits, including chemical reactions, of living organisms.

GERM That part of the grain kernel, also called the embryo, which becomes a seedling in the process of germination. It is embedded in the endosperm and is covered only by the pericarp, or seed-coat layer.

GLASSINE (glass-seen) A thin transparent paper made from sulfite pulp by long-continued beating and supercalendering.

GLIADIN (glye-a-din) The portion of the principal group of proteins (gluten) in wheat flour that is soluble in 60 to 70 percent alcohol. Wet gliadin forms a soft and sticky mass of gluelike consistency.

GLUCONIC ACID (glue-con-ick) An acid derived from glucose and having the formula $C_6H_{12}O_7$. It is made from the sugar glucose by oxidation through the action of a mold, Aspergillus niger. The calcium salt, calcium gluconate, is used medicinally as a source of calcium.

GLUCOSE, DEXTROSE, or GRAPE SUGAR A carbohydrate that is a constituent of many animal and vegetable fluids. It is formed by the hydrolysis of starch, cane sugar, and glucosides. Dextro-glucose, or dextrose, comes in the form of colorless needles, soluble in alcohol and water. It causes polarized light to be rotated to the right.

GLUTELINS (glue-tih-lins) A group of simple vegetable proteins, coagulated by heat, insoluble in water or dilute salt solution, and soluble in very dilute acids or alkalies. An example is glutenin from wheat.

GLUTEN (*glue*-ten) The protein-rich product derived from cereal grains. Gluten is spoken of loosely as the protein constituent obtained in the separation of starch from corn in the wet-milling process. For wheat, the term is more specifically applied to the viscous and semielastic substance that gives adhesiveness to dough and is responsible for the bread-baking quality of wheat flour.

GLYCERIDES (*gliss*-er-ides) Natural fats and oils formed in plants and animals by the chemical union of glycerin and fatty acids.

GLYCERIN (*gliss*-er-in) or GLYCEROL A highly viscous substance used widely as a solvent and lubricant in medicine, perfumery, and antifreeze; also used in the manufacture of explosives (nitroglycerin). It exists in combined form in fats and oils and is a byproduct of the manufacture of soaps.

GLYCOSIDE (*glye*-co-side) A compound which can be split by hydrolysis into a sugar and one or more other substances. The glycosides are generally white or colorless, crystalline compounds. They occur chiefly in plants and are often very bitter. Some are important medicinally, digitalis and rutin, for example. Many occur as plant pigments, such as indican from which indigo was formerly obtained.

GOSSYPOL (*goss*-ih-pole) A bright-yellow pigment found in distinct structures, called pigment glands, in cottonseed. Gossypol exhibits such a variety of reactions that efforts to identify it with any known class of organic compounds have been fruitless. The name gossyp(ium phen)ol indicates both its origin in cottonseed and its chemical nature.

GOSSYPURPURIN (goss-ih-*per*-per-in) A dark-purple pigment found in cottonseed. It is closely related chemically to gossypol, but differs from it in that it contains nitrogen in addition to carbon, hydrogen, and oxygen. Gossypurpurin has been synthesized in the laboratory from gossypol.

GRAM-NEGATIVE A term applied to any bacterium which, when dried on glass, stained, fixed, decolorized, and counterstained by the method of the Danish botanist Gram, does not retain the crystal violet dye and, when seen through a microscope, appears pink because the cell has taken up the red counterstain (safranin).

GRAM-POSITIVE Refers to a bacterium which retains the crystal violet dye and resists decolorizing with alcohol. The cell appears blue when viewed through a microscope.

HALIDES (*hal*-ides) Compounds of a halogen (fluorine, chlorine, bromine, or iodine) with an element or radical, as in calcium fluoride (CaF_2) and allyl chloride ($CH_2:CHCH_2Cl$).

HEAT BODYING The process of heating a drying oil, such as linseed or tung oil, to induce partial polymerization and thereby improve its value for use in paints and varnishes. As the oil polymerizes it becomes more viscous.

HEMICELLULOSE (hem-i-*sell*-yew-lose) A group of gummy carbohydrate substances intermediate between cellulose and sugars. They resemble cellulose proper in certain respects, as being insoluble in water, but are less complex and are easily broken down to simple sugars.

HEMOGLOBIN (hee-mo-*glo*-bin) The respiratory pigment of all vertebrate animals, present as the coloring matter in red blood cells. Hemoglobin is a large complex molecule, composed of a protein, globin, and an iron-containing pigment, hematin. Hemoglobin, along with related compounds, gives meat its characteristic fresh color and, through degradation, develops off-colors on storage.

HEMOSTATIC (hee-mo-*stat*-ik) Serving to arrest the flow of blood.

HEPARIN (*hep*-a-rin) A complex sugar material, found in body tissues, which inhibits coagulation of the blood.

HESPERIDIN (hess-*pear*-i-din) A crystalline substance found in oranges and other fruits. Chemically it is a rhamno-glucoside of hesperetin, a flavanone closely related to flavone. Hesperidin was formerly thought to be "vitamin P" but is now considered inert. A crude hesperidin containing a "vitamin P" substance as an impurity has been used in medicine.

HETEROLOGOUS (het - er - *oll* - o - gus) Characterized by different elements; the lack of correspondence between parts or to their having a different origin; opposed to homologous. In immunology: Obtained from an animal of different species—said of vaccines, serums, and the like.

HEXITOL (*hex*-i-tole) A sugar alcohol containing six carbon atoms with one hydroxyl group attached to each carbon, as in sorbitol, or dulcitol, $C_6H_8(OH)_6$.

HISTAMINE (*hiss*-ta-min) A colorless crystalline organic compound found in ergot and formed by bacterial decomposition of histidine and by at least one enzyme. It has been reported to be formed when tissue injury occurs and when antigen antibody reactions take place, thus accounting for the shock that results from severe injuries and for the symptoms of allergy. Histamine constricts the smooth muscle of the bronchioles, as in asthma. It lowers blood pressure by dilating the blood vessels and decreases the coagulability of the blood, as in shock.

HISTOLOGY (hiss-*tol*-o-gi) The study of the minute structure of animal and vegetable tissues as observed with the microscope.

HOLOCELLULOSE (holl-o-*sell*-yew-lose) Holocellulose consists of the cellulose and the hemicellulose in wood. It is the white fibrous residue that remains after the other components, comprising the extractives, lignin, and ash-forming elements, have been removed from wood by chemical means.

HOMOGENIZE (hoe - *mah* - jen - ize) To pass a fluid product (milk, cream, etc.) through a homogenizer (homogenizing machine), in which the product under high pressure is forced through very small openings at a high rate of speed against a hard surface. The process breaks up the fat globules and makes them smaller. Because of the smallness of the fat globules, the cream will not rise on homogenized milk and the milk itself looks creamier and richer.

HORMONE Any of various organic substances formed in the ductless glands, such as thyroid, pituitary, and adrenal, and secreted in small quantities directly into the blood stream, with strong physiological effect, acting usually as a messenger for stimulation of a specific function.

HUMECTANT (hue-*mek*-tant) A substance that absorbs moisture. It is used to maintain the water content of products like tobacco, glue, inks, films, dentifrices, cosmetics, baking products, leather, soaps, and textiles.

HUMUS Residual organic matter remaining in soil after the action of soil bacteria on plant products; an organic (animal or plant) substance that gives soil its base exchange properties which hold inorganic nutrients and supply them at a rate needed by growing plants.

HYDRATION (hye-*dray*-shun) The act or process of causing a chemical compound to combine with water. Many compounds, both organic and inorganic, react with definite, fixed amounts of water to form new, so-called hydrated compounds. Soaps, the phosphatides found in natural fats and oils, and many other organic compounds react with water in much the same way that cement reacts with water in the hardening of concrete.

HYDROCARBON (*hye*-dro-kar-bon) A compound consisting entirely of carbon and hydrogen. The most common hydrocarbons are those constituting natural gas, gasoline, kerosene, and lubricating oils.

HYDROGENATION (hye-dro-jen-*ay*-shun) The act of combining with hydrogen, one of the chemical elements, as hydrogenation of an oil. Liquid oils or fats of soft consistency are hardened by the addition of hydrogen to yield hydrogenated products of greatly increased consistency and of higher temperature of melting or liquefying. Thus, an oil, such as cottonseed, may be modified to give it margarine, or shortening, characteristics.

HYDROL (*hye*-drole) A brown, sirupy byproduct from the manufacture of corn sugar (dextrose); also called hydrol sirup or corn-sugar molasses. It is used in animal feeds as an additional source of carbohydrate and in the fermentation industries.

HYDROLYSIS (hye-*drol*-i-sis) A chemical process of decomposition involving addition of the elements of water. Water may cause salts of weak acids or weak bases to break down in part into the acid and the hydroxide of the metal with which it was combined. An excess of water under certain conditions can break down an ester into the acid and the alcohol of which it is composed. In these cases hydrolysis is the reverse of neutralization or esterification. In many cases hydrolysis is induced by the presence in small amount of an enzyme, a dilute acid, or other agent. Thus cane sugar boiled with dilute hydrochloric acid yields a mixture of dextrose and levulose.

HYDROLYZATE (hye-*drol*-i-zate) The product resulting from hydrolysis; for example, the mixture of amino acid salts and their decomposition products resulting from the treatment of proteins with alkaline or acid solutions or with enzymes.

HYDROSTATIC PRESSURE The pressure acting at any point in a liquid below its surface is dependent on the weight of the liquid above it—that is, the height of the liquid column times its density. This principle is applied in testing the resistance of fabrics to water leakage by determining either the height of a column of water above a fabric that will cause it to leak or the amount of water that leaks through a fabric during a fixed period of time when the height of the water column is kept constant.

HYDROXYL (hye-*drox*-il) A chemical group consisting of one hydrogen and one oxygen atom. If a hydroxol group is attached to an aliphatic organic radical, the compound formed is an alcohol; if attached to an aromatic organic radical, it is a phenol. Hydroxyls also occur in other types of organic and inorganic compounds.

HYGROSCOPIC (hye-gro-*skopp*-ik) Readily absorbing or retaining moisture. Examples: Caustic potash, calcium chloride, table salt, and sugar.

HYPEREMIA (hye-per-*ee*-mi-a) A super-abundance or congestion of blood in any part of the body. Blushing is a hyperemia of the skin.

HYPERPLASIA (hye-per-*play*-zi-a) The abnormal multiplication or increase in number of tissue elements.

HYPOHALITES (hye-po-*hal*-ites) A class of compounds characterized by a grouping containing one oxygen and one halogen atom.

i- A symbol for the combining form, *iso-*, indicating equality, similarity, uniformity, or identity. It is used to denote a compound isomeric with another; e. g., *i*-cyanic acid is isomeric with cyanic acid. It also denotes a compound having a normal or straight chain of carbon atoms to which is attached one methyl group in the position next to one end in the molecule.

INACTIVATED Used to describe enzymes, serums, or catalysts that do not have their usual effects because their activity has been destroyed by scalding or other chemical or physical means.

INERT (in-*ert*) Not having or showing active properties, especially not having any chemical action.

INORGANIC Designating, or composed of, matter other than animal or vegetable. Pertaining to chemicals that do not contain carbon, carbonates and cyanides excepted.

INVERT SUGAR A mixture of the simple sugars dextrose and levulose produced by the inversion of sucrose (cane sugar). This inversion, or splitting, can be accomplished in the presence of water by invertase (an enzyme occurring in yeast) or by heating with dilute acid. Commercially, invert sugar is usually available only as a concentrated sirup of the two sugars together with a little residual sucrose which was not inverted.

IN VITRO (in-*vye*-tro) Within a glass; observable in a test tube as contrasted with *in vivo*.

IN VIVO (in-*vye*-vo) In life or, specifically, referring to various tests or functions in or on living animals.

IODINE A nonmetallic element of the halogen group. It is found combined, as in the form of iodides, and is distributed widely in nature but sparingly in quantity.

ION (*eye*-on) An electrically charged atom or radical (combining unit). Example: Sodium ions and chlorine ions are formed when sodium chloride ($NaCl$) is dissolved in water. The sodium atom gave up one electron when it combined with the chlorine; hence, it is positively charged. Such ions migrate toward the negative pole, or cathode, when an electric current is passed through their solutions. Hence they are called cations. The chlorine, having acquired an electron, becomes the negatively charged ion which migrates to the positive pole, or anode; hence it is called the anion.

ION EXCHANGE A chemical process involving reversible interchange of ions between a liquid and a solid but no radical change in structure of the solid. This principle has been known for a century and used to soften water for 40 years. During the past decade, its use has been widely diversified to include treatment of fruit juices, sugar solutions, etc. The two types of ion exchange are: (1) Cation exchange, in which the positive ions in solution are exchanged for the positive ions of an insoluble matrix (the ion-exchange material), e. g., removal of metals from apple or grape juice; (2) anion exchange, in which the negative ions in solution are exchanged for negative ions of the ion-exchange material, as in the recovery of tartaric acid from grape juice.

IONIZATION (eye-on-i-*zay*-shun) The process of converting molecules of gases into ions. When an atom or molecule of gas loses one electron it is ionized and bears a positive charge of electricity. The gas is said to be conducting, permitting an electric current to pass from the anode to the cathode, or vice versa.

ISO ACIDS (*eye*-so) Fatty acids which are isomeric, or differently arranged than the naturally occurring acids.

ISOELECTRIC POINT (eye - so - eh - *leck*-trick) The hydrogen-ion concentration at which a protein is neutral and has the greatest tendency to precipitate. Literally, isoelectric point is the point of electric neutrality or zero potential.

ISOMERS (*eye*-so-mers) Molecules which have the same component parts but are arranged differently. The person one sees in a mirror has the same components but they are arranged differently; so if one were a molecule he could speak of his mirror image as his isomer.

ISOPRENE (*eye* - so - preen) A rather simple chemical compound of carbon and hydrogen having the formula C_5H_8. It was first made (1860) by heating natural rubber to a high temperature, but may also be obtained from turpentine or petroleum and by chemical synthesis. Isoprene as such is not known to occur in nature, but isoprene units provide the basic structure for varied classes of substances having widely different physical properties and physiological functions which do occur naturally. Among the simpler natural substances based on the isoprene unit are the terpene essential oils obtained from conifers (turpentine), citrus fruits, and many flowers. More complex combinations of isoprene are found in rosin, in the chlorophyll of the green leaf, in the class of plant pigments known as carotenoids (such as the coloring matter of tomatoes or carrots), and in vitamins, hormones, heart poisons, shark-liver oil, and natural rubber.

ISOPROPANOL (eye-so-*pro*-pa-nole) or ISOPROPYL ALCOHOL A compound composed of three carbon atoms, eight hydrogen atoms, and one oxygen atom. It is a colorless liquid similar, both chemically and physically, to wood alcohol and grain alcohol. It is used widely as a germicide, denaturant, and solvent.

ISOTOPES (*eye*-so-topes) Two or more atomic species of an element having the same atomic number but differing in atomic weight; many of the common elements are mixtures of isotopes.

KERATIN (*kare*-a-tin) The substance of which wool fiber, horns, feathers, claws, and nails are composed. It is a complex protein material consisting, like other proteins, of carbon, hydrogen, oxygen, nitrogen, and sulfur. Keratin protein is distinguished in general by the high insolubility in common solvents, behavior that is related to the presence of relatively large amounts of sulfur which serves to vulcanize the material. Chemically, the vulcanization involves the tying together of the long protein molecular chains into networks. The characteristic inertness toward solvents of the keratins depends on the stability of the network.

KETONES (*kee*-tones) A series of inflammable liquids which are similar in possessing the same functional group (keto group), but differ in other properties such as the boiling points. The ketones are principally used as solvents for other materials.

KOJIC ACID (*ko*-jick) A fermentation product having an unusual ring system; very reactive chemically, but not a true acid.

l- An abbreviation for the combining form *levo*-, indicating that the compound to whose name it is attached is levorotatory.

LABILE (*lay*-bil) Subject to change, as when heated or exposed to conditions that lead to alteration in chemical or physical structure.

LACTIC ACID (*lack*-tik) A fairly strong organic acid that exists in sour milk. When pure it is a colorless liquid, miscible with water, alcohol, or ether in all proportions. It is a metabolic intermediate in many living forms and is produced in quantity by many micro-organisms.

LACTOFLAVIN (lack-to-*flay*-vin) A term sometimes used for riboflavin or vitamin B_2. It is a water-soluble, yellow pigment with a greenish fluorescence and occurs in milk

whey, egg yolk, egg white, leaves of plants, and animal tissues.

LANOLIN Wool wax of greater purity than the ordinary wool grease or common degras; the USP and cosmetic grades of lanolin are highly purified, refined, bleached, and deodorized.

LARD STEARINE (*stee*-a-rin) The solid portion of lard; it may be obtained by pressing out the more liquid portion of the lard as in a hydraulic press.

LATEX A milky, usually white, fluid emulsion found in certain cells in some families of seed plants. The latex contains various gum resins, fats, waxes, and often complex mixtures of other substances, frequently including poisonous compounds. Rubber, gutta-percha, chicle, and balata are the chief commercial products obtained from latices.

LECITHIN (*less*-i-thin) A phospholipid occurring in many biological materials. Lecithin consists of glycerol, phosphoric acid, fatty acids, and a nitrogenous base, choline. It is used as an emulsifier.

LEVOROTATORY (lee-vo-*ro*-ta-to-ree) Descriptive of certain optically active organic compounds, including some sugars, which, when dissolved in water and tested in a polariscope, turn the plane of polarized light to the left (counterclockwise). The opposite of dextro-rotatory. A solution of levulose (fructose) or of invert sugar is levorotatory.

LEVULOSE (*lev*-you-lose) A sugar in fruits, which in solution rotates the plane of polarized light to the left. Also called fructose.

LIMONIN (*lye*-mo-nin) A bitter white substance belonging to the class of compounds known as glycosides. Found especially in navel orange pulp and in the seeds of oranges and lemons.

LINEAR ACCELERATOR A device for speeding up protons and deuterons as projectiles for disintegrating the nucleus of atoms. Superimposed high potential fields cause the projectile to gain speed in a linear path up to about 40 million volts.

LINOLENIC ACID (lin-o-*lee*-nik) A major component of linseed oil. It is responsible for the soft liquid characteristics of the oil and for its drying properties, which are important in paints.

LINTERS The short fibers remaining on cottonseed after ginning. The word is also applied to the machines that remove this short fiber from the seed (also called delinters). Linters are too short for textile use, but they are used in making cotton batting, upholstery, and mattress stuffing, and, after purification, as a raw material for chemical conversion to cellulose derivatives.

LIPASE (*lye*-payz) Any of a class of enzymes that accelerate the hydrolysis of fats to fatty acids and glycerol. In milk processing the lipase that occurs in all milk must be destroyed by heat; otherwise it will cause a rancid or bitter flavor to develop.

LIPIDS (*lip*-ids) Fatlike substances characterized by their insolubility in water and their greasy feel. Lipids readily take oxygen from the air and become rancid. In so doing, they may catalyze (speed up) the destruction of other valuable nutrients with which they are in contact.

LIPOPROTEIN (lip-o-*pro*-te-in) A comparatively stable complex or compound consisting of protein and lipid. The lipid portion is usually phospholipid but may also be one or more other lipids.

LIPOVITELLENIN (lip-o-vye-*tell*-en-in) A lipoprotein of egg yolk. It is poorly characterized chemically, but probably comprises about one-eighth of the total solids of yolk and is one-third to two-fifths lipid. The lipid is apparently mostly lecithin.

LIPOVITELLIN (lip-o-vye-*tell*-in) A lipoprotein of egg yolk. It is inadequately characterized chemically, but probably comprises about a sixth of the total solids of yolk. It is slightly less than one-fifth lipid, which appears to be mostly lecithin.

LIQUID SHEAR A method of breaking up solid particles into smaller components or parts while suspended in a liquid slurry. Disintegration is attained by causing the particles to collide or rub against each other, rather than by impact of a blade against the particles. Cottonseed flakes, for example, are separated into their component parts by the liquid-shear action of a dissolver-type impeller. Equivalent terms are "hydraulic shear," "interfacial shear," and "fluid friction."

LIVETIN (*liv*-ih-tin) The water-soluble protein fraction of egg yolk; that is, the proteins of egg yolk other than the lipoproteins. This fraction contains most of the small amount of enzymes in egg yolk.

LYOPHILIZATION (*lye*-o-fill-ih-*zay*-shun) The process of vacuum-drying substances from the frozen state. The water is sublimed into a trap at low temperature or is absorbed by drying agents. Verb: lyophilize.

LYSINE (*lye*-seen) A basic amino acid present in proteins. It is one of the essential amino acids required by man and animals and is the limiting amino acid in many proteins.

LYSOZYME (*lye*-so-zime) An enzyme that digests certain high-molecular-weight carbohydrates and kills certain micro-organisms which contain this type of carbohydrate. It digests out the carbohydrate from the cells of the micro-organisms, and

the micro-organisms therefore disintegrate, or lyse. Lysozyme activity is found in many biological materials, but egg white is by far the most available source. Egg-white lysozyme is about 2.5 percent of the total solids of egg white and is one of the most easily obtainable crystalline proteins.

LYTIC (*litt*-ick) Pertains to the dissolving of a substance as the result of the action of another substance; e. g., the dissolving of certain bacteria by lysozyme.

MALIC ACID (*may*-lik) An organic acid quite commonly found in fruits, particularly in apples.

MALTING The process of germinating grain, generally barley, to develop the enzyme diastase. The diastase is capable of saccharifying not only the starch of the malt itself but also that of the grain mixed with it. Hence, malt is used in the brewing and distilling industries to convert starch to fermentable sugars.

MERCERIZE (*mur*-sur-ize) To treat cotton fibers, yarns, or fabrics with a solution of concentrated caustic alkali to make them stronger. If kept under tension during the process they acquire a luster.

METABOLISM (meh-*tab*-oh-lism) The sum of the chemical changes proceeding continually in living cells, by which energy is provided for the vital processes and activities and new material is assimilated to repair the waste. These changes are sometimes classed as building up (anabolism) and breaking down (catabolism). Photosynthesis is anabolic; respiration is catabolic.

MICROBE A minute organism, a micro-organism, a germ; generally applied to bacteria, but may include yeasts, molds, algae.

MICROFIBRILS (mye-kro-*fye*-brils) The small fibers which, cemented together as bundles, comprise the spindle cells of wool.

MICRO-ORGANISM A minute animal or plant; usually bacteria, yeasts, molds, or algae.

MICROTOME (*mye*-kro-tome) An instrument for cutting thin sections for microscopical examination.

MICROWAVE An electromagnetic wave with a length of from about one-quarter inch to 6 inches. Its main use is in radar and television.

MISCELLA (miss-*sell*-a) A mixture of a solvent, such as hexane, with an oil.

MOLD BRAN A fungal-amylase preparation that has been made by growing mold on moist wheat bran. The mold bran contains a mixture of enzymes, primarily those that convert starch to dextrins or sugars.

MOLDS The common name applied to various fungi that in nature appear on damp or decaying matter. Certain molds produce the appearance and flavor of such cheeses as Roquefort and Camembert. Others are used for the production of various organic acids, enzymes, and the antibiotic drug penicillin.

MOLECULE A unit of matter, the smallest portion of an element or compound that retains chemical identity with the substance in mass.

MONOSODIUM GLUTAMATE (mon-o-*so*-di-um *gloo*-ta-mate) A crystalline salt of an amino acid. It is added to certain foods, particularly vegetables and meats, to improve or accent the flavor; it does not enhance the flavor of all foods. Glutamate is an active ingredient in soy sauce and similar products. Chief sources of the commercial glutamate on American markets are sugar-beet pulp, wheat gluten, and soybean protein.

MORDANT (*mor*-dant) A substance (usually a salt of aluminum, iron, tin, or chromium) that can be deposited on a fiber to form an insoluble compound with a dyestuff, thereby fixing the color permanently to the fiber.

MORPHOLOGY (more-*foll*-o-jee) The branch of biology dealing with the form and structure of animals and plants.

MUCILAGE (*mew*-si-lij) A sticky substance found in plants, as in flaxseed and quinces. Chemically, mucilages are mixtures of carbohydrates and related compounds. Also, an aqueous solution of a gum, or of a substance allied to it, used in medicine and as an adhesive.

MUCIN (*mew*-sin) A class of naturally occurring complexes or compounds consisting of protein and carbohydrate. They are highly viscous and are poorly soluble in water.

MYCELIUM (mye-*see*-li-um) Collective name for the microscopic threads (hyphae) which form the vegetative part of mushrooms and other molds (fungi). The mycelium reproduces indefinitely by vegetative growth in a suitable environment.

n- In chemical names: An abbreviation for normal, as distinguished from isomeric. It designates aliphatic hydrocarbons or hydrocarbon derivatives having a straight-chain structure; that is, one in which no carbon atom is united with more than two other carbon atoms in the molecule.

NARINGIN (na-*rin*-jin) A white crystalline material belonging to the class of compounds known as glycosides. It is the very bitter substance in the peel of some grapefruits.

NEOMYCIN (*nee*-oh-*mye*-sin) An antibiotically active mixture of two or more chemical fractions produced in the fermentation of a suitable substratum by a selected strain of *Streptomyces fradiae*.

NEPS Small knots of tangled fibers, composed primarily of thin-walled (immature) fibers, and varying in size from a tiny speck to the size of a pinhead. Neps are formed by mechanical handling of the fibers and are not found in unpicked cotton. They occur in all stages from the ginned lint through the woven fabric.

NEUTRALIZATION Adjustment of hydrogen- or hydroxyl-ion concentration toward the point (pH 7.0) at which the number of hydroxyl ions is exactly equal to the number of hydrogen ions. If the number of hydrogen ions is the greater, as at pH values less than 7.0, it is necessary to add a source of hydroxyl ions, a base, e. g., sodium hydroxide. If the number of hydroxyl ions exceeds the number of hydrogen ions, a source of hydrogen ions, an acid, must be added to equalize the numbers of the two ions.

NEUTRON One of the essential parts of the nucleus of an atom, the other being the proton. The neutron bears no electric charge; its mass is nearly the same as the proton, which carries a positive unit charge.

NIACIN (*nye*-a-sin) One of the water-soluble vitamins of the B-complex group. It is also known as nicotinic acid.

NITROGEN A gas which occurs in air to the extent of 78 percent by volume. Compounds of nitrogen, such as ammonium sulfate and potassium nitrate, are used in fertilizer to provide growing plants with nitrogen in a usable form. Plants contain many compounds of nitrogen, especially the proteins which include the enzymes. They cannot use nitrogen gas as such, but certain bacteria which grow on the roots of legumes have the ability to convert atmospheric nitrogen to compounds of nitrogen.

NUTRIENTS A general term used to refer to the ingredients of a food or foods that are necessary for growth, repair, or maintenance of body tissues and their functioning. Nutrients may refer to simple substances, as water, calcium, ascorbic acid, and sugar, or to complex substances, as proteins and fats, which are made up of several nutrients utilized in different ways in the nutrition of the body. Nutrient is not commonly used to refer to a food in its natural state, as milk, or eggs, which is made up of many nutrients, but may describe a prepared mixture of several nutrients, for example nutrient broth. Science has identified some 40 nutrients in their simplest form which are essential to the body. They include 10 or more minerals, a dozen vitamins or vitaminlike substances, some 8 or 10 amino acids, and 3 fatty acids, besides water, sugar, and some others. Certain nutrients can be synthesized from the diet or derived from other substances in the body.

o- An abbreviation for the combining form *ortho-*, indicating that a benzene nucleus is substituted in the 1.2-positions.

OESTROGENIC (*es*-tro-*jen*-ik) Capable of producing in animals the characteristic changes of oestrus (sexual heat). In humans the hormones called oestrogens prepare the uterus for pregnancy. In therapy, the oestrogens are used in correcting functional amenorrhea, scanty menstruation, menopausal disturbances, delayed puberty, sexual frigidity, and functional sterility.

OLEIC ACID (oh-*lee*-ik) A colorless, liquid, unsaturated fatty acid that occurs in combined form in animal fats and vegetable oils. Commercial oleic acid obtained from tallows and greases is impure and varies from pale yellow to red brown. Chemically pure oleic acid is preferably obtained from olive oil.

OLEORESINS (o-lee-o-*rezz*-ins) Natural products consisting of essential oils and resins.

ORGANIC As applied to chemistry: The branch of chemistry that treats of the carbon compounds produced in plants and animals or in the laboratory.

ORGANIC ACIDS Compounds that contain primarily carbon, hydrogen, and oxygen and taste sour. Examples are acetic acid (CH_3COOH) in vinegar and lactic acid ($CH_3CHOHCOOH$) in sour milk.

ORGANIC COMPOUND A substance formed by the union of carbon and hydrogen, carbon, hydrogen, and oxygen, or those elements together with others in definite proportions by weight. Example: Ethyl alcohol (C_2H_5OH).

ORGANISM A living thing that is organized in a definite pattern with a definite function and consists of an individual cell or a complexity of cells which undergoes dynamic changes and contains a colloidal medium, protoplasm, the physical and chemical basis of all life.

ORGANOLEPTIC (or-gan-o-*lep*-tik) Descriptive of any test that is made through the use of one or more of the five senses. Evaluation of oils, for example, is made through odor, taste, sight, and feeling.

OSSEIN (*oss*-ee-in) The chief organic basis of bone tissue, which remains as a residue after removal of the mineral matters from bone by dilute acid. It is considered to be identical chemically with the collagen of connective tissue. It is hydrolyzed by boiling water to glue or gelatin, being an important source of edible gelatin.

OVALBUMIN (ov-al-*bew*-men) Literally, egg albumin. The principal protein of egg white (albumen), comprising approximately 55 percent of the total solids. Ovalbumin is responsible for much of the distinctive character of egg white in cookery and commercial uses.

OVOMUCIN (ov-o-*mew*-sin) The mucin in egg white, probably comprising 1 to 3 percent of the total solids. It is an ill-defined protein-carbohydrate complex in egg white obtainable in higher amounts from thick white than from thin white and probably responsible for the firmness of thick white.

OVOMUCOID (ov-o-*mew*-koid) A protein of egg white, comprising approximately 12 percent of the total solids. It specifically inhibits the action of the digestive enzyme trypsin. It is destroyed by the digestive enzyme pepsin, and apparently for this reason it is not injurious when consumed in the diet.

OXIDATION The act of oxidizing, or an increase in the valency of an element. The substance causing the oxidation is the oxidizing agent.

OXYGEN A gas. One of the most abundant chemical elements, which exists in the earth's atmosphere in free form diluted with nearly four times its volume of nitrogen, a variable and very small quantity of carbon dioxide, about one-twentieth of its volume of argon, and traces of the other inert gases associated with argon. In combined form oxygen is very abundant in water, in minerals, and in the products of plant and animal life. Oxygen is essential to the combustion of fuels and to the existence of animal life. In the respiration of animals oxygen continuously purifies the blood after it absorbs the waste products of metabolism.

p- An abbreviation for the combining form *para-*, indicating that a benzene nucleus is substituted in the 1.4-positions.

PALMITIC ACID (pal-*mit*-ik) A white, crystalline saturated fatty acid having the formula $CH_3(CH_2)_{14}CO_2H$. It occurs in combined form in animal and vegetable oils.

PANCREATIN (*pan*-kree-a-tin) A preparation made from the pancreas of animals, which is used in medicine as an aid in digestion. It contains enzymes that attack proteins, carbohydrates, and fats.

PANTOTHENIC ACID (pan-toe-*then*-ik) A vitamin of the vitamin B complex that occurs in animal tissues, liver, and kidneys. Its absence in the diet or body of rats results in loss of weight and grayness of hair followed by loss of hair. The function and action in man are unknown. It is a pale-yellow oil, soluble in water, slightly soluble in ether, and insoluble in benzene.

PATHOGEN (*path*-oh-jen) A microorganism, bacterium, or protozoon that produces disease.

PECTIN (*peck*-tin) A noncrystalline, colloidal substance naturally occurring in fruits and vegetables, which dissolves in boiling water and forms a jelly upon subsequent cooling when suitable concentrations of acid and sugar are present. It is used commercially to form jellies with fruit juices. It plays an important role in the setting of jam.

PENICILLIN (*pen*-i-*sil*-in) A small group of closely related chemicals obtained from the clear liquid of a culture of the mold *Penicillium notatum*. It is effective in the treatment of a wide variety of infections that are due to certain bacteria.

PENTONIC ACIDS (*pen*-ton-ick) The acids obtained by the oxidation of the 5-carbon aldehyde sugars or aldopentoses.

PENTOSANS (*pen*-to-sans) A class of substances which yield pentoses (simple 5-carbon sugars) on hydrolysis. They are complex carbohydrates widely distributed in plants, as in fruits, wood, corncobs, and oat hulls. On digestion with steam or acid under pressure, pentosans yield furfural.

PEPSIN A protein-digesting enzyme that is secreted in the stomach of man and higher animals. The term is also used for a preparation from the stomachs of pigs, cows, or sheep, which is used in medicine to aid digestion.

PEPTONES Water-soluble substances produced from proteins by the action of proteolytic enzymes, acids, or alkalies. They are used in preparing nutrient media for bacteriology and occasionally in medicine as a nutrient.

PERICARP (*pear*-ih-karp) The outer protective wall that covers the kernels of cereal grains. It consists of several layers, the principal ones being endocarp, mesocarp, epicarp. The pericarp is the major constituent of the bran.

PEROXIDATION The chemical reactions by which atmospheric oxygen is added to fats to form peroxides. These peroxides are chemically related to the well-known hydrogen peroxide.

PEROXIDASE (per-*ox*-ih-dase) An enzyme of vegetable origin that splits hydrogen peroxide in the presence of an acceptor of the oxygen.

PETRI DISH (*pay*-tree) A shallow covered dish of thin glass, used for plate cultures in bacteriology.

pH An abbreviation of potential hydrogen. It is a symbol, suggested by the Danish chemist Sörensen, for use with a numeral from 1 to 14 to denote the negative logarithm of the concentration of the hydrogen ion in gram atoms per liter, which concentration is an expression of true acidity or alkalinity. The atomic weight of hydrogen is 1, so a gram atom is 1 gram. The expression pH 0, seldom used, would mean 1 gram of hydrogen ion (H^+) per liter, a degree of acidity rarely encountered; pH 1 would mean $\frac{1}{10}$ as much; pH 2, $\frac{1}{100}$ as much; pH 3, $\frac{1}{1000}$ as much; and so on. Water (H_2O) containing neither acid nor alkali dissociates very slightly, so that in 1 liter there is one ten-millionth (10^{-7}) gram of hydrogen ions. Since water is neutral in reaction, pH 7 represents the neutral point on the pH scale. Higher concentrations of hydrogen ion, from pH 6 to pH 1, indicate increasing degrees of acidity; lower concentrations of hydrogen ion, from pH 8 to pH 14 indicate increasing degrees of alkalinity.

PHENOLIC (fee-*no*-lik) Pertaining to phenols—organic compounds that contain one or more hydroxyl groups attached to an aromatic or carbon ring.

PHEOPHYTIN (fee-o-*fy*-tin) A product split from chlorophyll when it is decomposed by heat or light.

PHOSPHATIDES (*foss*-fa-tides) Fatty substances that occur in cellular structures of animals and plants and contain esters of phosphoric acid.

PHOSPHOLIPIDS (*foss*-fo-*lip*-ids) Substituted fats containing phosphoric acid and usually a nitrogen compound. Their content of phosphoric acid makes them more water-soluble than other fats. Consequently, they are usually good emulsifiers. Examples: Lecithin, cephalin, sphingomyelin. They are considered to play important roles in life processes.

PHOSPHORYLATION (*foss*-foe-ril-*ay*-shun) The act or process of converting into a compound of phosphorus; e. g., the uniting of the cellulose molecule with the phosphoric acid molecule.

PHOTOCHEMICAL Pertaining to the chemical effects of light.

PHOTOSENSITIZATION (foe-toe-*sen*-sih-tih-*zay*-shun) The process of rendering something sensitive to light. The condition of a living cell, tissue, or organism acted upon by a substance, such as a dyestuff, that renders it sensitive to a particular region of the spectrum to which it was previously insensitive.

PHYTOL (*fye*-tole) A colorless, oily, unsaturated alcohol obtained from chlorophyll, the green coloring matter of plants.

PHYTOSTEROLINES (fye-*tahs*-tur-o-leens) Sterol glycosides derived from plants. "Phyto" is a prefix derived from the Greek, indicating plant or vegetable. Phytosterolines are compounds composed of a sterol (a complex, solid alcohol) and a sugar. The compounds occur as minor constituents in vegetable oils, where they ordinarily are of little importance.

PIGMENT   A coloring matter, or substance that imparts a color (including black or white) to other materials (except by dyeing). Any of various coloring matters in animals or plants, especially solid or opaque coloring matter in a cell or tissue.

PLIOFILM   (*ply*-oh-film)   The trade name of a water- and moisture-resistant transparent sheet material made by chemically combining rubber and hydrochloric acid under controlled conditions.

POISE   The centimeter-gram-second unit used to designate the viscosity (internal resistance to flow) of a liquid as compared to the viscosity of water at 20° C. (68° F.). For the viscosity determination of a solid, the material is first dispersed in a suitable medium, such as a cuprammonium hydroxide solution for cotton. The shorter the molecular chain length, the greater is the dispersion, as indicated by a more rapid rate of flow.

POLARIMETRY   (*po* - ler - *im* - eh - tree) Measurement of the angle of rotation of the plane of polarized light by means of the polariscope.

POLARIZED LIGHT   (*po*-ler-ized)   Light of a single wave length, as that from a sodium vapor lamp, which has passed through a doubly refracting prism of calcite so constructed as to split the light into two rays, one of which is totally reflected and absorbed while the other is transmitted as parallel vibrations in only one plane. Certain media, such as glass under strain or mica, change plane-polarized light to circularly or elliptically polarized light.

POLYAMIDE RESINS   (pol-i-*am*-id)   Synthetic resins produced by the polymerization of aminated derivatives of unsaturated organic acids. The generic trade name for fiber-forming linear polymers prepared by the polymerization of polymethylene amides of such acids as adipic and sebacic is nylon. Fibers prepared from these polymers have a proteinlike structure and take dyes that are adapted to wool or silk.

POLYETHYLENE   (pol-i-*eth*-ih-leen)   A water- and moisture-resistant transparent sheet material made by chemically combining many molecules of ethylene under controlled conditions.

POLYMER   (*pol*-ih-mer)   A chemical compound formed by combining two or more similar smaller molecules. The smaller molecules constitute the monomer. Polymers are called dimers, trimers, tetramers, and so forth, depending on how many molecules combine to form the new substance. The word "polymer" has come to be used chiefly to mean polymers of high molecular weight

formed of many monomer molecules. If the monomers are lined up end to end to form a long chain, they are called linear high polymers and are important industrially and in nature.

POLYMOLECULARITY   (pol-ih-moe-lek-yew-*lar*-ih-tee)   The state of consisting, not of identical molecules as do most simple substances, but of very similar molecules differing only in size. The word was coined because of the fact that it is this property of compounds of high molecular weight, especially of the linear polymers, that is responsible for many of their technically important properties. For instance, polymolecularity hinders crystallization and is thus a contributing factor to the toughness of certain plastics and textiles.

POLYMORPHISM   (pol-ih-*mor*-fism)   The ability of certain substances to crystallize in two or more different forms or systems. For example, the commonly occurring fat tristearin can form three kinds of crystals, and consequently its solid form possesses three sets of physical properties. Tristearin will melt at 130.0°, 149.0°, or 160.5° F., depending on the conditions under which it was solidified.

POLYMYXIN   (pol-ih-*mix*-in)   One of the antibiotically active polypeptides of a chemically related series which specifically inhibits gram-negative bacteria and is produced through fermentation of suitable culture media by a bacterium, *Bacillus polymyxa.*

PRECIPITATE   A substance separated from a solution as a solid in consequence of some chemical or physical change, as by the action of a reagent, or cold, or of heat; usually a solid separated in a noncrystalline or minutely crystalline form. The precipitate may fall to the bottom, may be diffused through the solution, or may float at or near the top. Example: A precipitate of camphor is formed when water is added to spirits of camphor.

PROLAMINES   (pro-*lam*-ins)   A class of proteins. The distinguishing feature of prolamines is their solubility in concentrated alcoholic solutions. They are insoluble in water and in salt solutions. Only a few proteins belong to this class; namely, zein from corn, gliadin from wheat, and hordein from barley.

PRO-OXIDANT   Any substance that accelerates oxidation may be spoken of as a pro-oxidant. Generally, pro-oxidants are traces of highly active catalysts or compounds, such as copper and iron metals, enzymes, hemoglobin, and pigments.

PROPANE   (*pro*-pane)   A simple hydrocarbon found in petroleum and composed of three atoms of carbon and eight of hydrogen. Its chemical and physical properties resemble those of natural gas or methane. When propane is liquefied by compression at ordinary temperatures, it can be used as a solvent for certain constituents in fats and oils.

PROPHYLACTIC (pro - fill - *ack* - tik) A remedy or treatment that tends to ward off disease. Vaccinations against diphtheria, smallpox, typhoid, and the like are examples.

PROPYL GALLATE (*pro*-pil-*gal*-ate) A compound sometimes used as an antioxidant to retard the action of oxygen on fats and oils. It is an ester of propyl alcohol and gallic acid.

PROTEIN   Any of a class of naturally occurring, extremely complex combinations of amino acids, which are essential constituents of all living cells, both animal and vegetable. All contain carbon, hydrogen, oxygen, and nitrogen. More than 50 fairly definite proteins are known.

PROTEINASES (*pro*-tee-in-azes) Enzymes that aid in the digestion of proteins by converting them into smaller fragments which are more soluble in water and more readily absorbed from the intestine. Example: Pepsin in the stomach.

PROTEOLYSIS (*Pro*-tee-*oll*-ih-sis) The conversion of proteins into peptones and amino acids by decomposition or hydrolysis of the protein molecule.

PROTEOLYTIC (pro-tee-o-*lit*-ik) Protein destroying or dissolving. Proteolytic enzymes split or hydrolyze proteins with the formation of simpler and more soluble products, as in digestion.

PROTEOSES (*pro*-tee-ozes) Water-soluble substances produced from proteins by splitting with enzymes, acids, or alkalies. Proteoses may be precipitated by saturating their solutions with ammonium sulfate; under these same conditions peptones remain soluble.

PROTON   See NEUTRON.

PROTOPLASM   The mass of living material found within a single cell cavity. It exists in many different modifications; ordinarily, it is a thick viscous semifluid or almost jellylike, colorless material containing a large percentage of water and holding fine granules in suspension.

PROVITAMIN A   See CAROTENE.

PURE   In chemistry a substance is pure when it consists of only one chemical compound completely free of any foreign material. Practically, purity is defined in terms of the proportions of extraneous materials, which must be so small that they will not interfere with the particular purpose for which the chemical is to be used. Thus water is hygienically pure as it comes from the

water faucet, but for most laboratory purposes only distilled water is considered to be chemically pure.

PYRETHRINS (pye-*ree*-thrins) Insecticidal compounds present in the flowers of the pyrethrum plant. The general term includes four compounds that occur together in the flowers, namely pyrethrin I, pyrethrin II, cinerin I, and cinerin II. The pyrethrins are effective and quick-acting against many insects and have very little toxicity to warm-blooded animals.

PYRHELIOMETER (pyre-*hee*-li-*om*-e-ter) An instrument designed for use in measuring solar radiation. All the wavelengths are transformed by it into heat and measured by a sensitive thermometer. The result is expressed in heat units (calories) per square centimeter per minute of a surface normal to the radiation.

PYRIDINIUM (*pir*-ih-*din*-i-um) The positively charged ion of pyridine, a colorless, liquid nitrogeneous base, of pungent odor, obtained in the distillation of bone oil, coal tar, etc., and by the decomposition of certain alkaloids. It is the parent of such organic compounds as nicotine.

PYROLIGNEOUS (pye - roe - *lig* - nee - us) Obtained by destructive distillation of wood. Pyroligneous alcohol or spirit is wood alcohol (methanol). Pyroligneous acid is a reddish-brown aqueous liquid produced by destructive distillation of hardwoods. It has the characteristic odor given off by organic substances burned in closed vessels and contains 4 to 8 percent of acetic acid and some wood alcohol.

PYROLYSIS (pye-*rol*-ih-sis) The subjection of organic compounds to the action of heat, thereby causing decomposition and interaction.

PYROPHYLLITE   A mineral extensively used as a carrier or diluent for insecticide and fungicide dusts. It is so named because its plate or leaflike structure (*phyllon*) will separate when heated (*pyro*). The mineral is ground to such fineness that 85 percent will pass through a 325-mesh screen. The particles have a flat or platelike structure, so they adhere quickly to plant surfaces dusted with them. The mineral looks, feels, and acts like talc, but it is chemically inert or neutral to most materials used as insecticides and fungicides. It does not absorb moisture from the air.

QUERCETIN (*kwer*-sit-in) A plant pigment of the class known as flavones. A deep-yellow, crystalline substance only slightly soluble in water but soluble in alkalies. It is widely distributed in the vegetable kingdom, sometimes free and also combined with sugars to form the flavonol glycosides, like rutin, quercitrin, and isoquercitrin. The term is derived from the botanical name for the oak, *Quercus,* since it occurs in the bark of some oak species. Not to be confused with another substance, quercitol, also derived from the oak.

RADIOACTIVITY Spontaneous disintegration of elements, accompanied by the emission of rays; occurs usually in elements having higher atomic weights than lead, and is not affected by chemical or physical influences.

RADIO-FREQUENCY RADIATIONS That part of the spectrum of electromagnetic radiations used largely for radio transmission, the frequency ranging from 10,000 to 1,000,000,000 waves per second.

RAFFINATE In the oil trade, a refined product; the oil layer that has been extracted many times with a solvent heavier than itself.

RAFFINOSE (*raff*-ih-nose) A trisaccharide which may be obtained as a by-product in the beet-sugar industry. Its molecule contains one unit each of galactose, glucose, and fructose. The glucose and fructose units are united in the same manner as in sucrose.

REDUCING AGENT A chemical substance having the ability to deoxidize or change an element from a higher to a lower valence, or combining power. Example: Hydrogen reduces red-hot iron oxide to metallic iron.

REFLECTANCE The return of light or sound waves from surfaces; in color measurements it pertains to the visible light reflected from the samples under study.

REFRACTIVE INDEX The ratio of the velocity of light in a certain medium to its velocity in air under the same conditions. The refractive index of a pure organic liquid is constant at any given temperature. Therefore this value, as determined with a refractometer under standard conditions, helps to establish the identity of unknown liquids or the purity of known liquids.

REHYDRATED Recombined with water; usually refers to a dehydrated product to which water has been added to bring it back to its original content.

RENNIN (*renn*-in) An enzyme of the gastric juice from the fourth stomach of a calf. It coagulates milk with the formation of curd and whey and is used in making cheese. Synonyms: Rennet, rennase.

RESIDUE That which remains after a part is taken or separated. Agricultural residues refer specifically to the dry portion of agricultural crops as distinct from the fruit, grain, or other ingredient for which the crop is grown, e. g., stalks, straws, cobs, seed hulls, nutshells, fruit pits. Vegetables wastes, such as green pea vines and bean vines, are sometimes called vegetable residues.

RESIN (*rezz*-in) Any of a variety of solid or semisolid substances, chiefly of vegetable origin, having the appearance of rosin. They are transparent or translucent, and soluble in ether, alcohol, and other organic solvents, but not in water. Many are produced as exudates from plants, either alone or in admixture with essential oils. They are found in fossils after plants have decayed. Resins are used in making varnishes and resin soaps and in medicines. Also any of a large number of artificial products that possess most of the physical properties of natural resins.

RHAMNOSE (*ram*-nose) A sugar ($C_6H_{12}O_5.H_2O$) sometimes found free in plants, but usually combined with other substances to form glycosides like quercitrin and naringin. Chemically it is a methyl derivative of a 5-carbon sugar, or pentose. It is not fermentable by ordinary yeast and finds use in certain culture media used to differentiate between fermenting and nonfermenting bacteria.

RIBOFLAVIN (*rye*-bo-*flay*-vin) The essential vitamin B_2 occurring in many foods, such as meat, fruit, and vegetables.

ROSIN (*rahs*-in) The resin remaining after distilling turpentine from the exudation of various species of pine, e. g., *Pinus palustris* (longleaf).

ROTENONE (*roe*-teh-nohn) A white, crystalline insecticidal compound occurring in many species of *Derris, Lonchocarpus, Tephrosia, Mundulea,* and *Millettia,* especially in the roots. The chief sources of rotenone insecticides are *Derris elliptica* from the East Indies and *Lonchocarpus* species from South America.

RUTIN (*rue*-tin) A new, cheap, non-poisonous drug that is extracted from buckwheat plants. It exists in tobacco leaves, in yellow pansy blossoms, and in at least 35 other plants. It is used to treat various conditions associated with hemorrhage or weak capillaries.

SACCHARATE or SUCRATE A compound of a sugar like sucrose (ordinary cane or beet sugar) with a metallic oxide, such as calcium oxide (lime). An example is mono-calcium saccharate ($CaO.C_{12}H_{22}O_{11}.H_2O$) which is composed of one molecule of calcium oxide, one of sucrose, and one of water. The term also means a salt of saccharic acid, the latter being obtained by oxidizing dextrose or other 6-carbon sugars.

SALOMETER (suh-*lahm*-eh-terr) An instrument (special hydrometer) for measuring the percentage of saturation of a brine solution with respect to salt. Used in pickling and meat-packing industries. Also called a salimeter or salinometer.

SALT Generally refers to common table salt, or sodium chloride, the formula of which is NaCl. A salt results from neutralization of an acid by a base (metal or metallic oxide). Other examples of salts are sodium nitrate ($NaNO_3$), potassium chloride (KCl), and calcium sulfate ($CaSO_4$).

SAPONIN (*sapp*-poh-ninn) Any one of a group of substances occurring in many plants and characterized by the property of producing a soapy lather with water. Commercial saponin is a mixture of saponins extracted from soapbark or soapwort as a white, amorphous powder. It is used as a foam producer in beverages and fire extinguishers, as a detergent, and for emulsifying oils. Saponins are generally bitter and acrid and cause sneezing.

SCALDING A step in the processing of foods which comprises cooking slightly by the action of steam or boiling water, the purpose being the inactivation of certain enzymes that might cause deterioration in the product during storage. In this sense the word is used interchangeably with blanching.

SEPTICEMIA (*sepp*-tih-*see*-mih-ah) A morbid condition due to the presence of a virus or bacterial infection and the associated poisons (toxins and toxalbumins) in the blood. A diseased condition, which has become generalized by virtue of its spread through the animal's body by way of the blood stream. Not a localized condition.

SESAMIN (*sess*-a-min) A white, crystalline compound present in sesame oil, which is obtained from the seeds of *Sesamum indicum*. Sesamin concentrates, obtained from sesame oil in the process of refining it for use as an edible oil, are used in pyrethrum insecticides. The sesamin itself is not insecticidal, but it greatly increases the effectiveness of the pyrethrins. The aerosol bombs used by the Armed Forces during the Second World War contained sesame oil and pyrethrum extract.

SODA ASH A commercial anhydrous sodium carbonate. A relatively mild alkali. Its water solution will not attack fats but will react with the free fatty acids in crude fats. Therefore soda ash is used in refining fats and oils. It is also used in the manufacture of soap, paper, chemicals, paints, drugs, leather, textiles, and many other articles.

SOLUBLE When a substance (solute) such as salt or sugar is placed in water (solvent), it apparently disappears because it is dissolved in the water. The solute is said to be soluble in the solvent. The extent to which the solute dissolves is known as its solubility.

SONIC (*sahn-ick*) Pertaining to sound.

SPECIFIC GRAVITY The relative weight of a given volume of any kind of matter as compared with the weight of an equal volume of a standard substance. In the case of solids and liquids, the standard is usually water. In the case of gases, the standard is oxygen, hydrogen, or air.

SPECTROPHOTOMETER (speck-tro-fo-*tom*-eh-terr) A device for measuring the quantity of light of any particular wave-length range absorbed by solutions, either colored or colorless, or in the infrared region of the spectrum.

SPECTROSCOPE (*speck*-tro-scope) An instrument for analyzing light by separating it into its component rays, consisting essentially of either a prism or a ruled grating and necessary optics.

SPINNERET A small (usually platinum) plate having fine holes through which a fiber-forming solution passes into a solidifying medium, thus forming filaments.

SPINNING DOPE The liquid from which synthetic fiber is formed in the spinning processes. It consists of the fiber-forming material dissolved in a solvent. The dope is forced through the small holes of a spinneret just before being solidified as filaments by cooling, coagulation, or solvent evaporation.

SPIRABILITY The ability of cotton fibers to be twisted, as in the manufacture of a yarn or thread. Under the microscope the spiralled cotton fibers give the appearance of long and irregularly twisted ribbons. This property permits the fibers, when twisted together, to interlock better one with another.

SPORANGIUM (spo-*ran*-jih-um) A fruiting structure found among the lower forms of plant life within which the asexual reproductive cells (spores) are formed. The spores formed inside a sporangium are called sporangiospores, as contrasted with conidium, a spore borne externally on the surface of a fruiting structure.

SPORE A single cell from a fern, fungus, bacterium, or protozoon that has entered the resting state and is capable of growth and reproduction when conditions become favorable. Organisms in spore form are more resistant to destruction by heat and other hazards than when they are in active growth. Both in plants and animal life spore formation often provides the organism with a means of surviving unfavorable seasons or extremes of temperature, the spores then being surrounded with a tough investing wall and possessing great tenacity of life. This is the case with the endospores of many bacteria and often increases the difficulty of sterilization.

STAPLE LENGTH The length factor of a selected group of fibers from a bale or sample as determined by the commercial classer; therefore the length factor of quality assigned to a bale or sample containing fibers of various lengths.

STARCH A white, odorless, tasteless, granular or powdery complex carbohydrate, occurring widely in plants, especially in seeds, bulbs, and tubers. It is an important constituent of food, and is used for making commercial glucose, for stiffening fabrics, and for making pastes.

STARTER A culture of harmless living bacteria, used to inoculate or start growth in milk or other products, for the purpose of producing a desirable fermentation.

STEARIC ACID (ste-*air*-ick) A white, crystalline, saturated fatty acid having the formula $CH_3(CH_2)_{16}CO_2H$. It occurs in combined form in animal and vegetable oils. The commercial grade may contain as much as 60 percent palmitic acid. Commercial stearic acid is used in large quantities in rubber compounding, and in the preparation of soaps, greases, and chemicals.

STERILIZATION The destruction or removal of all living bacteria, micro-organisms, and spores. It is accomplished either physically (by heat or other radiant energy and filtration) or chemically (by germicides).

STEROL (*stair*-ole) Any of a class of solid higher alcohols, such as cholesterol and phytosterol, widely distributed in animals and plants. Sterols in general are colorless crystalline compounds of very complex nature and play important physiological roles not yet fully understood. The sterols are neutral and comparatively stable substances which occur partly in the free condition and partly esterified with higher fatty acids. Sterols of animal origin are called zoösterols; those of plant origin, phytosterols. Sitosterol ($C_{29}H_{50}O$) is the most widely distributed phytosterol. It consists of mixtures of at least three optical isomers and contains appreciable amounts of dihydrositosterols. Stigmasterol is a phytosterol that is found in the soybean, calabar bean, and other legumes. It has the empirical formula $C_{29}H_{48}O$ and serves as the starting material for the synthesis of a number of the sex hormones.

STREPTOMYCIN (strep-toe-*my*-sin) An antibiotically active chemical compound, $C_{21}H_{39}N_7O_{12}$ (N-methyl-l-glucosaminidostreptosideo-streptidine), produced in the fermentation of suitable culture media by selected strains of *Streptomyces griseus* or *S. bikiniensis*.

SUBSTRATE (*sub*-strate) A medium for micro-organisms. It may be liquid or solid and may contain a variety of nutritive materials. The term is also used to indicate the principal substance in a medium which the micro-organisms are using or converting to other substances. Thus glucose is often called the substrate.

SUBTILIN (*sub*-tih-lin) An antibiotic produced during the fermentation of a suitable culture medium by a special strain of the bacterium *Bacillus subtilis*.

SUCROSE (*soo*-kroze) Cane or beet sugar, a disaccharide hydrolyzing to fructose and glucose. A sweet crystalline carbohydrate, colorless when pure, it is used extensively in preserves, jams, confectionery, beverages, and sweetening.

SUGAR Any of a class of sweet, soluble compounds comprising the simpler carbohydrates. The simple sugars are those that are not reduced to simpler or smaller molecular units by hydrolysis. Complex sugars are formed by the union of molecules of two or more of the simple sugars.

SULFATED (*sull*-fate-ed) Treated with sulfuric acid so as to form a salt or ester of the acid. Many types of compounds, including fats and oils, form esters with sulfuric acid. Sulfated oils are the oldest of the nonsoap surface-active agents.

SULFITING The practice of treating certain fruits and vegetables, prior to dehydration, with low concentrations of sulfur dioxide or a salt of sulfurous acid dissolved in water to inactivate enzymes that promote oxidative darkening. In the preparation of dehydrated cabbage, sulfiting makes possible the use of higher drying temperatures and better retention of color and vitamin C. During the Second World War, Government specifications for dehydrated cabbage required the application of 750 to 1,500 parts of sulfite per million parts of dehydrated product.

SULFONATED (sull-fuh-*nate*-ed) Treated so as to introduce the sulfonic acid group, which consists of one atom of sulfur, three of oxygen, and one of hydrogen. When a material like cottonseed oil is sulfated by treatment with sulfuric acid, a small amount of sulfonated product is also formed. In sulfonated compounds, the sulfur is attached directly to a carbon atom, whereas in sulfated compounds the sulfur is connected to a carbon atom through an atom of oxygen.

SUPERNATANT (soo-purr-*nay*-tent) Floating uppermost or above something; said especially in chemistry of the liquid from which a precipitate has been thrown down.

SYMBIOSIS (sim-bih-*oh*-sis) The association of different organisms living together in nature to their mutual advantage. Some regard the relationship as one wherein one type of cell or micro-organism is benefited and its neighbor is neither harmed nor benefited. See ANTIBIOSIS.

SYNDROME (*sin*-drome) A characteristic group of symptoms that indicate a certain physical condition or disease.

SYNERGIST (*sin*-er-jist) A substance that increases the effect of another substance, although its effect is negligible when used alone. Lecithin, citric acid, and phosphoric acid are examples of substances that act synergistically to prolong the keeping time of fats containing natural or added antioxidants. Sesamin is a synergist for pyrethrum in insecticides.

SYNTHESIS In a chemical sense, the processes and operations necessary to build up a compound. In general, synthesis comprises a reaction, or a series of reactions, in which a complex compound is obtained from elements or simple compounds. Thus, the synthesis of ammonia is brought about by mixing the elements nitrogen and hydrogen under proper temperature and pressure conditions and in the presence of a catalyst.

SYNTHETIC Produced by an artificial means. Example: Oil of wintergreen obtained from leaves of the checker berry consists of practically only one constituent—methyl salicylate. This compound can be produced artificially by distilling a mixture of methyl alcohol and salicylic acid in the presence of sulfuric acid.

TACKINESS OR TACK The property of an adhesive which determines the rapidity and strength of its adhesive action. An adhesive is said to have high tackiness or quick tack if it bonds materials quickly and firmly.

TANNINS A group of astringent, aromatic, acidic compounds found in the bark, roots, wood, foliage, or fruit of various trees and other plants which have the ability to convert hide substance (collagen) into leather.

TARTARIC ACID (tahr-*tarr*-ick) An organic acid derived from the tartar deposits in grape wine, used to acidify drinks, in photography, and in medicine.

TERPENE (*turr*-peen) A hydrocarbon having the general formula $C_{10}H_{16}$, found in essential oils, resins, and other vegetable aromatic compounds. Turpentine is an example of a terpene-containing substance.

TERPENE ALCOHOL Any one of a series of isomeric compounds having the formula $C_{10}H_{15}OH$. These are constituents of many volatile oils obtained by the steam distillation of plants.

THERMAL Pertaining to heat or temperature. In physics, thermal capacity is the amount of heat necessary to change the temperature of a unit mass of a body 1° C. In physical chemistry, thermal constant is the heat in calories evolved during a particular reaction. In bacteriology, the thermal death point is that temperature which will kill an organism under certain arbitrarily selected conditions.

THERMAL CRACKING A process in which complex molecules are broken down into simpler ones by the action of heat, usually in the presence of catalysts; e. g., the production of gasoline from petroleum.

THERMODURIC (thurr - mo - *derr* - ick) Applied to various species of bacteria that are heat-resistant to the extent that they can withstand commercial pasteurization. These organisms are usually associated with the environment of milk production; that is, they may be on the coat of the milking animal, in the manure, or in barn dust. Absence or ineffectiveness of cleaning or germicidal treatment favors the selective multiplication of these organisms on milking utensils. Milk coming in contact with such utensils may be so contaminated with these organisms that it becomes impossible to obtain a satisfactory reduction in bacterial content by pasteurization. Usually the thermoduric organisms are not disease producing, but their presence indicates inadequate sanitary procedures in milk production.

THERMOPHILE (*thurr*-mo-file) An organism growing at a high temperature, as certain bacteria which thrive at 122°–131° F., but do not grow well at lower temperatures. By derivation from the Greek, heat-loving.

THERMOPILE (*thurr*-mo-pile) A device used to determine the radiant energy of a light source. It is composed of a number of thermocouples connected in series which multiplies the energy received and so gives a greater sensitivity. Basically, a thermocouple consists of two wires of a similar metal, one end of each joined to the ends of a wire of a dissimilar metal, the other ends attached to a galvanometer. The incident energy raises the temperature, initiating a flow of electricity as shown on the galvanometer directly as voltage or indirectly as temperature.

THERMOPLASTICITY (*thurr* - mo - plass-tiss-ih-tee) The property of becoming plastic when heated. Plastic is derived from a Greek word meaning to form. Thermoplastic materials soften when heated but do not melt and can therefore be formed by pressure into toys, dishes, radio cabinets, etc. When cooled, the molding material solidifies and will hold its shape until again heated to the softening point.

THIAMINE. See B-COMPLEX VITAMINS.

THROMBIN (*throm*-bin) A substance present in blood serum that unites with fibrinogen (a soluble protein existing in the blood) to form an insoluble fibrous protein, fibrin, which clots in wounds and prevents loss of blood.

THYROTROPIC (*thigh*-ro-*trop*-ick) A substance that produces effects in the animal body by means of its action on the thyroid gland. The thyrotropic hormone secreted by the pituitary gland stimulates the thyroid gland, with a resultant increase in body temperature, metabolism, and rate of growth of young.

TITER or TITRE (*tie*-terr, *tee*-terr) (1) The strength of a solution, or the concentration of a substance in solution, as determined by titration or by microbiological assay; (2) the solidifying point of the washed fatty acids separated from a fat. The determination of this point is called the titer test.

TOCOPHEROL (toe-*koff*-err-ole) From the Greek *tokos*—childbirth—and *phero*—to carry. Same as vitamin E or antisterility vitamin. There are four tocopherols known. These are designated by *alpha, beta, gamma,* and *delta,* the four first letters of the Greek alphabet. They are thick oils at room temperatures. Tocopherol (vitamin E) is necessary for normal reproduction in many animal species, but its significance in human nutrition is not definitely established. *Delta*-tocopherol is an active antioxidant, and finds some use in preventing oxidative rancidity of certain edible oils.

TRIGLYCERIDE (try-*gliss*-er-eyed) A tri-acid ester of glycerol, or glycerin. Ordinarily fats are composed almost entirely of triglycerides, each molecule of fat being composed of one molecule of glycerol and three molecules of fatty acid. The fatty acid molecules may be all alike, all different, or two of one kind and one of another kind. The most common fatty acids are palmitic, stearic, oleic, and linoleic. The fatty acids contribute from 94 to 96 percent of the total weight of a molecule of fat and determine to a large extent its chemical and physical properties.

TRYPAN BLUE (*trip*-pan) A blue dye commonly used as a direct dye for cotton. Because of its molecular size it escapes by leakage through walls of blood vessels and true capillaries at a slow rate. The dye is, therefore, useful in man and animals for determinations of blood volume, and for detecting areas of irritation where the capillaries may be open in greater number or may be more permeable.

TRYPSIN (*trip*-sin) An enzyme that aids digestion in the small intestine by breaking down the large protein molecules.

TRYPSINOGEN (trip-*sin*-oh-jenn) A substance produced in the body by the pancreas. It is discharged into the small intestine, where it is converted into the enzyme trypsin on contact with enterokinase, an activator present in the intestine.

ULTRACENTRIFUGE (ull-tra-*sen*-trih-fuge) A centrifuge operating at extremely high speeds. The ultracentrifuge, which operates at hundreds of thousands of revolutions per minute, is used to determine the size and distribution of particles in colloidal dispersion.

ULTRASONIC, ULTRAPHONIC, SUPERSONIC Pertaining to vibrations and waves whose frequencies are greater than those which affect the human ear, that is, greater than 20,000 per second.

UNSATURATED FATTY ACIDS Fatty acids that contain less than the maximum proportion of hydrogen, relative to the amount of carbon present. These hydrogen-deficient fatty acids are very reactive. Their occurrence in fats has a pronounced depressing effect on the melting point and storage life of the fat.

URONIC ACIDS Aldehyde carboxylic acids, fairly abundant in nature, that are related to such sugars as glucose, galactose, and mannose. The one known for the longest time is D-glucuronic acid, which occurs in animal urines combined with phenols and alcohols. Glucuronic acid is utilized by certain animals to render innocuous harmful substances, which combine with the acids and are thus removed from the organism. Free glucuronic acid is sirupy, but it forms a crystalline lactone.

VACUOLE (*vack*-you-ole) A small cavity or space in the tissues of an organism, containing air or fluid.

VACUUM From a Latin word meaning empty. Strictly, a vacuum is space devoid of matter. Ordinarily, a vacuum is understood to mean any space from which air or other gas has been completely or partly removed. The first condition represents an *absolute vacuum,* while the second represents a *partial vacuum.* The degree of vacuum is measured barometrically in relation to air pressure, which under normal conditions equals that of a column of mercury 760 millimeters (nearly 30 inches) high. The absolute vacuum existing in the portion of a barometric tube between the mercury and the closed top is called a *Toricellian vacuum* from the name of an Italian inventor who constructed barometers. With the best air pumps, the gas pressure can be reduced to less than one-millionth of a milliliter of mercury. *High vacuum* means rarefaction of air or other gas to a pressure below that of one hundredth of a millimeter of mercury, such as exists in X-ray tubes. *Low vacuum* means rarefaction to a pressure equal to that of 1 to 50 millimeters of mercury.

VALENCE A chemical term used to indicate the capacity of an atom to combine directly with atoms of other elements in definite proportions. A number of the elements exhibit two or more valences in comparison with that of hydrogen, which is taken as unity. Under favorable conditions compounds containing these elements can undergo changes in the course of which the valence of the element itself alters. For example, in a reduction reaction the active valence of the positive element is decreased or that of the negative element is increased; e. g., the element copper would change from its cupric form, having a valence of 2, to its cuprous form, having a valence of 1. An oxidation reaction would result in the converse.

VAPOR PHASE OXIDATION A process in which the material to be oxidized by air or oxygen is first converted to the gaseous form to facilitate contact with the catalyst, followed by application of heat and pressure and the establishment of a continuous process. It is used extensively in industry, as in the conversion of methanol to formaldehyde, hydrocarbons to alcohols and acids, and naphthalene to phthalic acid.

VERATRINE A mixture of alkaloids obtained from the seeds of several species of lilies of the genus *Schoenocaulon*, commonly known as sabadilla. Dusts and kerosene extracts prepared from sabadilla seeds are used as insecticides.

VIABILITY (vye-a-*bill*-ih-tee) The ability to live, grow, and develop, as the grain of corn that germinates beneath the soil and emerges to grow into a tall stalk bearing ears of corn. The word is derived from the French and Latin words meaning life.

VINYL (*vye*-nil) The chemical grouping $CH_2=CH-$ characterized by its outstanding ability to give compounds a high degree of chemical reactivity, such as the tendency to polymerize.

VISCOSITY (viss-*koss*-ih-tee) Internal fluid friction; the combined effects of cohesion and adhesion manifested by stickiness or some resistance to flow. The antonym of fluidity.

VITAMINS A group of chemical constituents of foods in their natural state, of which very small quantities are essential for the normal nutrition of animals and plants. They are accessory food factors which must be supplied for the nutrition of an organism and which exert an important action in the control and coordination of physiological function by virtue of specific molecular structure.

VITAMIN B_{12} One of the recently discovered vitamins. It is found in liver in small quantities. It is now obtained commercially by fermentation methods. One of its chief uses is as a medicinal in combatting pernicious anemia. It is now being added to animal feeds in order to obtain more rapid growth. This vitamin is unusual in that it contains 4.0 to 4.5 percent of the metal cobalt as well as some phosphorus.

VITAMIN E A vitamin commonly known as the antisterility factor, the presence of which is considered necessary to normal reproduction in many animal species. It is a thick oil at room temperature and, because of its antioxidant properties, is sometimes used to retard rancidity of fats and oils. The vitamin is not a single pure chemical but several related ones called tocopherols. It is obtained largely from wheat-germ oil but is also found in corn, cottonseed, and other oils.

VITAMIN K Commonly known as the antihemorrhagic factor or coagulation vitamin. In pure form it is a yellow crystalline powder, insoluble in water. It is present in green-leaf vegetables such as cabbage, spinach, and cauliflower. This vitamin is essential for normal blood clotting.

"VITAMIN P" A compound or group of compounds found in a variety of foods and plants such as citrus, buckwheat, tobacco, and asparagus and known to be beneficial in certain disease conditions in which the capillaries are more permeable or fragile than normal. The letter P was used to identify the "vitamin" because it was supposed to restore permeability to normal. At the present time most of the scientific evidence indicates that "vitamin P" is not a vitamin in the true sense of the word. There is no specific disease state which can be treated successfully with "vitamin P" and "vitamin P" alone. As now used, "vitamin P" refers to a group of substances, more or less closely related chemically, which produce definite physiological effects even in normal animals. These effects are explained in terms of chemical action on various enzymes, and on at least one hormone and at least one true vitamin.

VOLATILE (*vahl*-a-till) Describing a substance that evaporates rapidly.

WAVE LENGTH The distance between corresponding points on consecutive waves. The distance in the line of advance of a wave from any one point to the next point at which, at the same instant, there is the same phase. The length of light waves is measured in angstrom units, so named in honor of A. J. Ångström, a Swedish physicist, noted for optical research. One angstrom unit (A.) is equal to one ten-millionth of a millimeter, a millimeter being about one twenty-fifth of an inch. Visible light rays vary in length from 3,900 to 7,700 A. The shortest ultraviolet ray has a wave length of 130 A., and the shortest cosmic ray, a wave length of three one-hundred thousandths of one angstrom unit. The shortest Hertzian waves have a wave length of one one-hundredth of a millimeter. Radio broadcast waves are measured in meters and the wave length of the longest electric wave is 5,000 kilometers (3,100 miles).

WAX   One of many natural products, of which beeswax is best known, having some properties similar to those of fats. They contain esters and often free fatty acids, free alcohols, and higher hydrocarbons. They occur as insect secretions and protective coatings on the cuticle of the leaves or fruits of plants, and rarely as constituents of cells. The well-known natural waxes include spermaceti, carnauba wax, and China wax.

WETTABILITY   The ability of a solid to be wet by a liquid, usually understood to be water. The degree of wetting measured by the adhesion tension between a solid and liquid phase.

WHEY   The serum or fluid part of milk that separates from the curd or solid part when milk is curdled in making cheese. It is thin, watery, and light yellow in color.

WINTERIZATION   Removal of a part of the more saturated glycerides from a fatty oil so that the oil will remain bright and clear at low temperatures, such as those likely to be encountered in the home refrigerator. Winterization is brought about by chilling the oil to solidify some of the stearates and palmitates in the oil and removing them from the liquid fraction. The trade considers an oil to be winterized when it will remain clear after being held at the temperature of crushed ice for 5½ hours.

WOOL OLEINE   (oh-leh-inn)   A liquid fraction obtained by pressing (at 65°–70° F.) the first cut of the condensate obtained in the destructive distillation of wool grease; it is a mixture of fatty acids, alcohols, and unsaturated hydrocarbons.

WOOL PITCH   The material left in the still at the conclusion of the destructive distillation of wool grease with steam at 450°–750° F.; it varies widely in composition, but consists mainly of polymerized hydrocarbons, normal fatty acids, and oxidation products.

WOOL STEARINE   The solid fractions from the first and second cuts of the condensate resulting from the destructive distillation of wool grease; it is a mixture of fatty acids, alcohols, and unsaturated hydrocarbons.

WOOL WAX   The part of the greasy conglomeration on the fleece of a sheep that consists of a complex mixture of chemical compounds called esters; the individual esters are compounds in which any one of

the 32 or more different fatty acids may be combined with cholesterol, one of two or more triterpene alcohols, cetyl alcohol, ceryl alcohol, or one of a group of unidentified fatty alcohols. Fats differ from wool wax in being complex mixtures of esters of fatty acids with glycerol.

X-RAY DIFFRACTION ANALYSIS   A means for determining the internal structure of a substance by the diffraction pattern formed when a pin-point beam of X-rays passes through it. When X-rays are diffracted by a crystal or some crystal-powder acting as a grating, and the diffracted rays are photographed, the photograph shows a definite pattern of points. If the X-rays are diffracted by a substance in the gaseous state, a corona or diffuse fog will appear in the photograph. If the sample is a liquid or amorphous substance, the photograph will show a halo, and if it is an amorphous substance under tension, like stretched rubber, the photograph will show a number of concentric rings, indicating a regular space lattice with the molecules in definite positions and oriented to one another.

YARN NUMBER   A relative measure of the fineness of yarns. Yarn number is expressed either as the weight per unit length (for cotton, linen, wool, etc.) or as length per unit weight (for silk, rayon, etc.) to which a yarn is spun. For example, cotton yarn numbers designate the number of 840-yard hanks in a pound. The "denier" of silk or rayon yarn is the number of grams per 9,000 meters. In the newer Grex system—which is applicable to all fibers—the "Grex" is the number of grams per 10,000 meters.

YEAST   Microscopic, one-celled fungi that reproduce vegetatively by budding or fission. Best known are those used in bread making and for converting sugar to alcohol in the brewing and distilling industries.

YOLK   (yoke)   As applied to wool scouring, yolk comprises all the substances present on the fleece of a sheep when it is sheared and which are removed from the fiber by scouring before the conversion to yarn begins. Yolk includes the wool wax, the suint, decomposition products of skin and fiber, and foreign matters such as sand, clay, burs, and dip residues, which vary with the environment in which the animal lived.

ZEIN   (zee-inn)   An alcohol-soluble protein obtained from corn. It is insoluble in water and dilute salt solution, but is soluble in dilute sodium hydroxide and 60 to 70 percent alcohol. It is not a complete protein for nutritional purposes, being deficient in the amino acids tryptophane and lysine.

Index

Compiled by
Laura Louise Crouse,
Catherine F. George